MALVERN COLLEGIATE

DEPT: _____ Textbook # _____

	YEAR	STUDENT NAME	FORM	TEACHER NAME
1)	01/02	Awan C-Goddard	11D	Ms. Kopplin
2)	02/03	Zutaught	11E	MS. Blake
3)	05/06	Dorothy Kane	11D	Ms Blake
4)	06/07	Stephen Tong	11C	Dawson
5)	07/08	Marcus Alexander	#11I	Moss
6)	08/09	Hayley Burgess	11D	Bugelli

09/10 Caitlin Harvey 11F Blake.
10/11 Connor Brooks 11F Ms. Blake
11/12 Talene Francis-Prettie 11D MS. obrian.

Biology 11

McGraw-Hill Ryerson

Authors

Don Galbraith
Ontario Institute for Studies in
Education of the University of Toronto
Toronto, Ontario

Leesa Blake
Malvern Collegiate Institute
Toronto, Ontario

Jean Bullard
Professional Writer
Columbia Beach, British Columbia

Anita Chetty
Dr. E.P. Scarlett High School
Calgary, Alberta

Eric Grace
Professional Writer
Victoria, British Columbia

Donna Matovinovic
Edmonton Public Schools
Edmonton, Alberta

Grace Price
L'Amoreaux Collegiate Institute
Agincourt, Ontario

Adrienne Mason
Professional Writer
Tofino, British Columbia

Contributing Authors

Catherine Little
Toronto District School Board
Toronto, Ontario

D'Arcy Little, M.D.
York Community Services
Toronto, Ontario

Keith Gibbons
Catholic Central High School
London, Ontario

Chris Schramek
John Paul II Catholic Secondary School
London, Ontario

Consultants

Dr. Peter Chin
Associate Professor, Science Education
Queen's University, Faculty of Education
Kingston, Ontario

Nancy Flood
University College of the Cariboo
Kamloops, British Columbia

Malisa Mezenberg
Head of Science
Loyola Catholic Secondary School
Mississauga, Ontario

Probeware Specialist

Dan Braun
Kingsville District High School
Kingsville, Ontario

Technology Consultant

Steve Masson
R.H. King Academy
Scarborough, Ontario

**McGraw-Hill
Ryerson**

Toronto   Montréal   New York   Burr Ridge   Bangkok   Beijing   Bogotá   Caracas   Dubuque
Kuala Lumpur   Lisbon   London   Madison   Madrid   Mexico City   Milan   New Delhi
San Francisco   Santiago   St. Louis   Seoul   Singapore   Sydney   Taipei

McGraw-Hill Ryerson Limited

A Subsidiary of The McGraw·Hill Companies

COPIES OF THIS BOOK MAY BE OBTAINED BY CONTACTING:
McGraw-Hill Ryerson Ltd.

WEB SITE:
http://www.mcgrawhill.ca

E-MAIL:
orders@mcgrawhill.ca

TOLL FREE FAX:
1-800-463-5885

TOLL FREE CALL:
1-800-565-5758

OR BY MAILING YOUR ORDER TO:
McGraw-Hill Ryerson
Order Department
300 Water Street
Whitby ON, L1N 9B6

Please quote the ISBN and title when placing your order.

STUDENT TEXT ISBN
0-07-088708-X

E-BOOK CD-ROM ISBN
0-07-089358-6

McGraw-Hill Ryerson Biology 11

The information and activities in this textbook have been carefully developed and reviewed by professionals to ensure safety and accuracy. However, the publishers shall not be liable for any damages resulting, in whole or in part, from the reader's use of the material. Although appropriate safety procedures are discussed in detail and highlighted throughout the textbook, safety of students remains the responsibility of the classroom teacher, the principal, and the school board/district.

0-07-088708-X

http://www.mcgrawhill.ca

2 3 4 5 6 7 8 9 0 TRI 0 9 8 7 6 5 4 3 2 1

Printed and bound in Canada

Care has been taken to trace ownership of copyright material contained in this text. The publisher will gladly take any information that will enable it to rectify any reference or credit in subsequent printings. Please note that products shown in photographs in this textbook do not reflect an endorsement by the publisher of those specific brand names.

National Library of Canada Cataloguing in Publication Data

Main entry under title:

Galbraith, Donald I., date

McGraw-Hill Ryerson biology 11

Includes index.

ISBN 0-07-088708-X

1. Biology. I. Blake, Leesa. II. Title. III. Title: Biology 11. IV Title: McGraw-Hill Ryerson biology eleven.

QH308.7G37. 2001   570   C2001-930334-3

The Biology 11 Development Team
SCIENCE PUBLISHERS: Trudy Rising, Jane McNulty
PROJECT MANAGER: Dan Kozlovic
SENIOR DEVELOPMENTAL EDITORS: Jenna Dunlop, Dan Kozlovic
DEVELOPMENTAL EDITORS: Darcy Dobell, Anita Drabyk, Mary Knittl, Tom Shields
SENIOR SUPERVISING EDITOR: Linda Allison
PROJECT CO-ORDINATORS: Valerie Janicki, Shannon Leahy
COPY EDITORS: Linda Jenkins, Pam Young
PROOFREADER: Carol Ann Freeman
PERMISSIONS EDITOR: Ann Ludbrook
SPECIAL FEATURES CO-ORDINATOR: Jill Bryant
PRODUCTION CO-ORDINATOR: Jennifer Vassiliou
COVER DESIGN, INTERIOR DESIGN, AND ART DIRECTION: Pronk&Associates Inc.
ELECTRONIC PAGE MAKE-UP: Pronk&Associates Inc.
SET-UP PHOTOGRAPHY: Ian Crysler
SET-UP PHOTOGRAPHY CO-ORDINATOR: Shannon O'Rourke
TECHNICAL ILLUSTRATION: Pronk&Associates Inc., Brett Clayton, Deborah Crowle,
     Imagineering Scientific & Technical Artworks, Inc., Jun Park, Bart Vallecoccia
COVER IMAGE: Will&Deni McIntyre/Photo Researchers, Inc.

Acknowledgements

Producing a textbook of high quality is a true team effort, requiring the input and expertise of a very large number of people. The authors, consultants, and publishers of this book would like to convey our sincere thanks, first and foremost, to Catherine Little and D'Arcy Little, who wrote our Biology Course Challenge, and to the reviewers listed below who provided critical analyses of our draft manuscript, and often provided reviews of designed pages, as well. Their assistance was invaluable in helping us to develop a text that we hope you will find completely appropriate for your teaching and your students' learning. We also thank the following writers who authored the Special Features in *Biology 11*: Meaghan Craven, Linda Cornies, Keith Gibbons, Paul Halpern, Marian Hughes, Natasha Marko, Anne McIlroy, Christopher Rutty, Elma Schemenauer, Chris Schramek, and Erik Spigel. Special thanks go to the following people who wrote additional questions, provided additional activities, or provided last-minute advice: Bruce Evans, Jim Lewko, Heather Highet, and Steve Masson. Finally, we thank the wonderfully co-operative design studio, Pronk&Associates Inc., and its talented staff, who worked with us closely under very difficult timelines. This close teamwork was critical throughout this book's final stages of development.

Pedagogical and Academic Reviewers

Marietta Alibranti
Elia Middle School
North York, Ontario

Alex Annab
Iona Catholic Secondary School
Mississauga, Ontario

Gabriel Roman Ayyavoo
Francis Libermann Catholic High School
Scarborough, Ontario

Real Charette, Ph.D.
Beatrice Desloges
Orleans, Ontario

Bruce Evans
St. Joan of Arc Catholic High School
Maple, Ontario

Derek Featherstone
Educational Consultant
Kanata, Ontario

Keith Gibbons
Catholic Central High School
London, Ontario

Heather Highet
Limestone District School Board
Kingston, Ontario

John Jefferson
Sir Oliver Mowat Collegiate Institute
West Hill, ON

Terry Kilroy
Widdifield Secondary School
North Bay, ON

Rita Kunz
Northern Secondary School
Toronto, Ontario

James Kushny
Lakeshore Collegiate Institute
Etobicoke, Ontario

Jim Lewko
Toronto District School Board
Toronto, Ontario

D'Arcy Little, M.D.
York Community Services
Toronto, Ontario

Donna MacGillis
Tagwi Secondary School
Avonmore, Ontario

Donna Matovinovic
Edmonton Public Schools
Edmonton, Alberta

Mark Medland
Madawaska Valley District High School
Barry's Bay, Ontario

Linda Meulenbroek
St. Patrick's High School
Ottawa, Ontario

Dermot O'Hara
Mother Teresa Catholic Secondary School
Scarborough, Ontario

Dennis Pikulyk
Wexford Collegiate Institute
Scarborough, Ontario

Chris Schramek
John Paul II Catholic Secondary School
London, Ontario

Safety Reviewer

Margaret Redway
Fraser Scientific & Business Services
Delta, British Columbia

Contents

UNIT 1

Cellular Functions 2

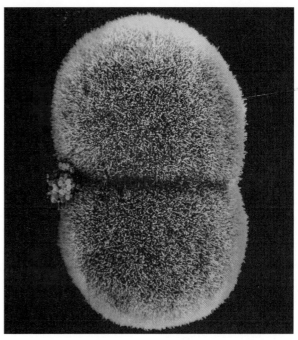

UNIT ③

Internal Systems and Regulation 246

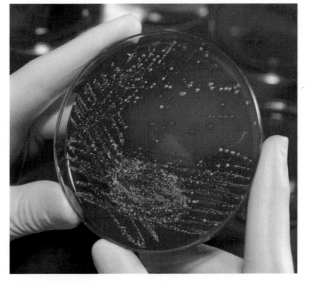

UNIT 5

Plants: Anatomy, Growth, and Functions 518

Safety in Your Biology Laboratory

Active involvement in science enhances learning. Thus, investigations are integrated throughout this textbook. Keep in mind at all times that working in a laboratory can involve some risks. *Therefore, become familiar with all facets of laboratory safety, especially for performing investigations safely.* To make the investigations and activities in *Biology 11* safe and enjoyable for you and others who share a common working environment,

- become familiar with and use the following safety rules and procedures, and

- follow any special instructions from your teacher.

Your teacher will tell you about any additional safety rules that are in place at your school.

General Rules

1. Read through all of the steps in the investigation before beginning. Be sure to read and understand the *Cautions* and safety symbols at the beginning of each Investigation or MiniLab.

2. Listen carefully to any special instructions your teacher provides. Get your teacher's approval before beginning any investigation that you have designed yourself.

3. Inform your teacher if you have any allergies, medical conditions, or physical problems (including a hearing impairment) that could affect your work in the laboratory. Inform your teacher if you wear contact lenses. If possible, wear eyeglasses instead of contact lenses, but remember that eyeglasses are not a substitute for proper eye protection.

4. Know the location and proper use of the nearest fire extinguisher, fire blanket, fire alarm, first-aid kit, and eye-wash station (if available).

5. Never eat, drink, or taste any substances in the lab. Never pipette with your mouth. If you are asked to smell a substance, do not hold it directly under your nose. Keep the object at least 20 cm away, and waft the fumes toward your nostrils with your hand.

6. When you are directed to do so, wear safety goggles and protective equipment in the laboratory. Be sure you understand all safety labels on materials and pieces of equipment. Familiarize yourself with the safety symbols used in this textbook, and with the WHMIS symbols found in *Appendix 5* at the back of the book.

Lab Precautions

7. Make sure your work area is clean, dry, and well-organized.

8. Wear heat-resistant safety gloves, and any other safety equipment that your teacher or the *Cautions* suggest, when heating any item. Be especially careful with a hot plate that may look as though it has cooled down. If you do receive a burn, apply cold water to the burned area immediately. Make sure your teacher is notified.

9. Make sure the work area, the area of the socket, and your hands are dry when touching electrical cords, plugs, sockets, or equipment such as hot plates and microscopes. Ensure the cords on your equipment are placed neatly where they will not cause a tripping hazard. When unplugging electrical equipment, do not pull the cord — grasp the plug firmly at the socket and pull gently.

10. Never use water to fight an electrical equipment fire. Severe electrical shock may result. Use a carbon dioxide or dry chemical fire extinguisher. Report any damaged equipment or frayed cords to your teacher.

11. Cuts, scratches, or any other injuries in the laboratory should receive immediate medical attention, no matter how minor they seem. If any part of your body comes in contact with a potentially dangerous substance, wash the area immediately and thoroughly with water.

12. If you get any material in your eyes, do not touch them. Wash your eyes immediately and continuously for 15 min, and make sure your teacher is informed. If you wear contact lenses, take your lenses out immediately if you get material in your eyes. Failing to do so may result in material being trapped behind the contact lenses. Flush your eyes with water for 15 min, as above.

13. When using a scalpel or knife, cut away from yourself and others. Always keep the pointed end of any sharp objects directed away from yourself and others when carrying such objects.

14. When you are heating a test tube, always slant it so the mouth points away from you and others.

Safety for Animal Dissections

15. Ensure your work area is well ventilated.

16. Always wear appropriate protective equipment for your skin, clothing, and eyes. This will prevent preservatives from harming you in any way.

17. Make sure you are familiar with the proper use of all dissecting equipment. Whenever possible, use a probe or your gloved fingers to explore the specimen. Scalpels are not appropriate for this. They can damage the structures you are examining.

18. If your scalpel blade breaks, do not replace it yourself. Your teacher will do this for you.

Laboratory Clean-up

19. Wipe up all spills immediately, and always inform your teacher. Acid or base spills on clothing or skin should be diluted and rinsed with water. Small spills of acid solutions can be neutralized with sodium hydrogen carbonate (baking soda). Small spills of basic solutions can be neutralized with sodium hydrogen sulfate or citric acid.

20. Never use your hands to pick up broken glass. Use a broom and dustpan. Dispose of broken glass and solid substances in the proper containers, as directed by your teacher.

21. Dispose of all specimens, materials, chemicals, and other wastes as instructed by your teacher. Do not dispose of materials in a sink or drain unless directed to do so.

22. Clean equipment before putting it away, according to your teacher's instructions. Turn off the water and gas. Disconnect electrical devices. Wash your hands thoroughly after all laboratory investigations.

Working with Living Organisms

23. On a field trip, try not to disturb the area any more than is absolutely necessary. If you must move anything, do so carefully. If you are asked to remove plant material, do so gently. Take as little as possible.

24. In the classroom, remember to treat living organisms with respect. Make sure all living organisms receive humane treatment while they are in your care. If it is possible, return living organisms to their natural environment when your work is done.

NOTE: Some schools do not permit labs that involve bacteria. Your teacher will inform you of your school board's policy in this regard.

25. When working with micro-organisms, observe your results through the clear lid of the petri dish. Do *not* open the cover. Make sure that you do not touch your eyes, mouth, or any other part of your face.

26. When handling live bacterial cultures, always wear gloves and eye protection. Be careful not to spill the cultures. Wash your hands thoroughly with soap immediately after handling any bacterial culture.

27. Carefully clean and disinfectant your work area after handling bacterial cultures and other living organisms.

28. Follow your teacher's instructions about disposal of your swabs, petri dishes containing your cultures, and any other disposable materials used in the lab.

29. Your teacher will autoclave cultures before discarding them, if an autoclave is available. If an autoclave is not available, the culture surface should be sprayed with a 10% solution of chlorine bleach. (Your school may have other disposal techniques to follow, as well.)

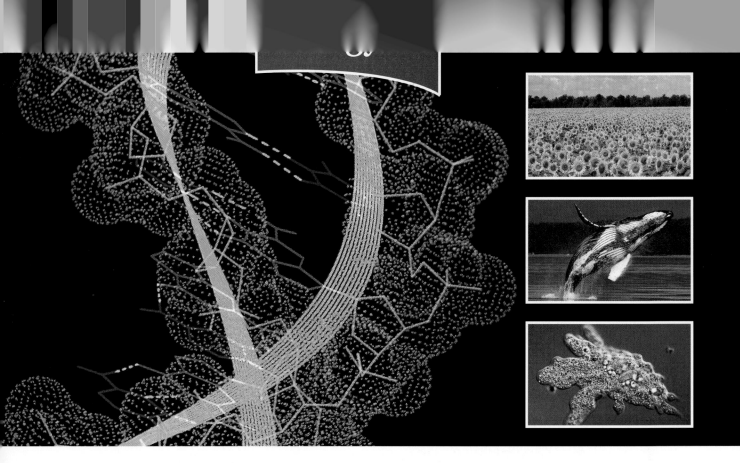

What was the most important discovery in biology in the 20th century? Many biologists would say it is the discovery of the precise molecular structure of DNA: deoxyribonucleic acid. This molecule, shown on the cover of your textbook, is made up of only four types of smaller molecules. Yet, it is the common basis for Earth's millions of diverse forms of life. DNA is responsible for determining the genetic makeup of every organism, including you.

Understanding the structure of DNA has applications beyond the biology laboratory. For instance, many of the medicines you use are linked to this discovery. Through biotechnology, genetic diseases may be treated. Computer programmers apply the discovery of DNA's structure to develop artificial intelligence. In the coming years, applications such as these will continue to influence all of our lives.

Biology means, literally, "the study of life." When you study biology, you study the molecules that are important to life, such as DNA. You study the behaviour and processes of the smallest individual cells to the largest multicellular organisms, as shown in the illustration on the next page. Biology involves technological applications such as those mentioned above, and requires you to consider their impacts on society and on the environment.

This course is designed to help you develop fundamental concepts and skills of biology. You will also relate the ideas and applications of biology to technology, society, and the environment.

In *Unit 1*, you will observe cells and examine the molecules that build and support their function. From this understanding, you will investigate genetics in *Unit 2*. You will learn how organisms pass on their characteristics to new cells and to new organisms from generation to generation. *Unit 3* explores the ways that cells work together to enable multicellular organisms to function and survive. Different environments are home to different types of organisms. *Unit 4* surveys the huge diversity of species found around the world. You will also consider why this diversity is essential to the survival of all organisms. The final unit, *Unit 5*, focuses on green plants. You will study their anatomy and physiology, and consider the numerous ways that people and other organisms depend on plants.

At the end of each unit, you will find a culminating performance task that your teacher may assign. This task involves either an issue to analyze, a project to undertake, or an investigation for you to design and perform.

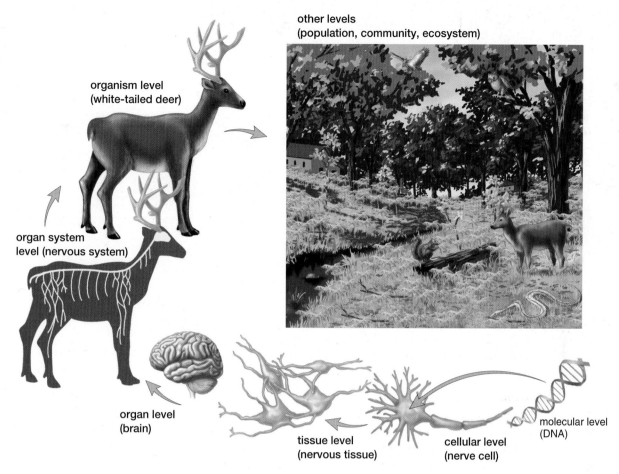

other levels
(population, community, ecosystem)

organism level
(white-tailed deer)

organ system
level (nervous system)

organ level
(brain)

tissue level
(nervous tissue)

cellular level
(nerve cell)

molecular level
(DNA)

This illustration gives you a visual summary of the levels of biological organization.

Throughout the units, one of these logos will remind you of the upcoming assignment. You will also find ideas to help you prepare and plan for it.

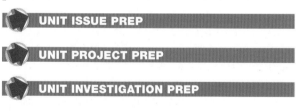

UNIT ISSUE PREP

UNIT PROJECT PREP

UNIT INVESTIGATION PREP

Biology 11 Course Challenge

After Unit 5, you will find the *Biology Course Challenge*. This culminating project is designed as an overall performance assessment task that encourages and supports you in integrating what you have learned during each unit of the course. Throughout the textbook, references to the *Course Challenge* are highlighted with a *Course Challenge* logo. These references include reminders to

think about your upcoming challenge, and hints on how you can prepare for it.

- In the *Biology Course Challenge, Using Forensic Science*, you will develop and solve a forensics mystery.

- The *Course Challenge* offers you an opportunity to demonstrate your understanding of the concepts covered in the entire course, apply the skills of inquiry, communicate ideas, and make meaningful connections among science, technology, society, and the environment.

- Watch for this logo, which appears in every unit of the textbook. It will remind you to think about the upcoming *Course Challenge* and provides hints on how to prepare for it.

COURSE CHALLENGE

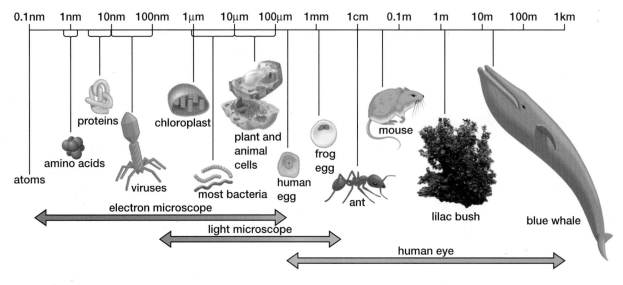

0.1nm 1nm 10nm 100nm 1μm 10μm 100μm 1mm 1cm 0.1m 1m 10m 100m 1km

atoms

amino acids

proteins

viruses

chloroplast

most bacteria

plant and animal cells

human egg

frog egg

ant

mouse

lilac bush

blue whale

electron microscope

light microscope

human eye

How large does an organism have to be before it can be seen by the unaided human eye?

Support for Reviewing Essential Skills

The Appendices at the back of your textbook can help you review skills that are essential to all scientific investigation. For example, in this course you will study large organisms, microscopic organisms, and sub-microscopic molecules and atoms, as shown above, that are vital to all forms of life.

The illustration above surveys the range of sizes, from atoms to whole organisms, that you will encounter in this course. If you would like to review metric measurements or how to use exponents to express large and small numbers, turn to *Appendix 6, Units of Measurement*, and *Appendix 7, Scientific Notation*.

Be sure to explore the other appendices at the back of book. If, for example, you need a reminder on microscope techniques, *Appendix 3, Care and Use of a Microscope*, is there to assist you.

Achieving Excellence

You will find it useful to know how your achievement in this course will be determined. Take some time to read the Achievement Chart at the bottom of the right-hand page. It identifies four main categories that you may use to assess your own learning during the course. Your teacher will use these categories to assess your achievement of curriculum expectations for your biology course.

In consultation with your classmates and your teacher, you may be asked to design or to review rubrics that are based on the Achievement Chart. These rubrics will provide specific criteria for assessing each of the four Achievement Chart categories.

The features outlined below are developed to provide both you and your teacher with a variety of ways to assess your achievement.

Section Review

- Each numbered section in each chapter is followed by a set of section review questions.

- These questions, indicated by the following symbols, are organized according to the categories given in the Achievement Chart.

  K/U Knowledge and Understanding

  I Inquiry   **C** Communication

  MC Making Connections

- Section Review questions appear, in general, in order from least to most challenging.

Chapter Review

- Each chapter ends with a set of features and questions to review and reinforce your understanding of the knowledge, concepts, skills, and issues presented in the chapter.

- Chapter Expectations is a list of the key concepts and ideas presented in the chapter. Each concept includes the section number where it is discussed, for easy reference.

- Language of Biology is a list of key terminology that appeared in boldfaced type in the chapter. Several ways of reviewing your understanding of these terms are provided.
- Review questions for the entire chapter are provided, organized according to the four categories of the Achievement Chart.

Unit Review

- Following each unit, a four-page review allows you to assess your understanding of the entire unit.
- Questions are organized according to the four categories of the Achievement Chart. Within each category, questions are listed in order of increasing difficulty.
- A short feature at the end of the Unit Review presents you with questions and comments to help you prepare for your *Course Challenge*.

Other Features to Assist Your Understanding

A casual flip through the pages of your textbook will show you a wide range of features and items to stimulate your interest, aid your understanding, and practise your skills. The following represent a small sample of these helpful features.

Pause and Record: Draw upon prior knowledge and new concepts and skills to construct your own learning and keep an ongoing record of your progress.

Fast Forward and Rewind: Easily find cross-references to related subject matter in earlier and later chapters.

Play: Access the Biology 11 Electronic Learning Partner for simulations, animations, and 3-dimensional models to enhance you learning.

Probeware: Use electronic probes for certain investigations and projects, if they are available in your school.

Web Link: Investigate the intricate web of life through the Internet's virtual web of information.

Biology at Work: Explore the range of biology careers and opportunities available to you.

Biology Magazine: Reflect on topical issues that touch your life and encourage you to make connections among science, technology, society, and the environment.

Canadians in Biology: Meet Canadian scientists involved in important research and discoveries.

Achievement Chart

Knowledge and Understanding	Inquiry	Communication	Making Connections
- Understanding of concepts, principles, laws and theories - Knowledge of facts and terms - Transfer of concepts to new contexts - Understanding of relationships between concepts	- Application of skills and strategies of scientific inquiry - Application of technical skills and procedures - Use of tools, equipment, and materials	- Communication of information and ideas - Use of scientific terminology, symbols, conventions, and standard (SI) units - Communication for different audiences and purposes - Use of various forms of communication - Use of information technology for scientific purposes	- Understanding of connections among science, technology, society, and the environment - Analysis of social and economic issues involving science and technology - Assessment of impacts of science and technology on the environment - Proposing courses of practical action in relation to science- and-technology-based problems

Cellular Functions

It has been said that we are made of the stuff of stars. What do you think this means? The pine wood cells pictured on the right and all other organisms on Earth are made mostly of only six common chemical elements. These elements originated under the conditions of massive gravity and heat found in stars. Evidence that the molecules of life — compounds containing carbon, hydrogen, and oxygen — exist throughout the universe is found in comets like Hale-Bopp, shown below. Scientists have recently found that such rocks, travelling through space, transport compounds and molecules that form the basis of life on Earth.

Within cells, these molecules are transformed into living organisms with a multitude of complex strategies for survival. The same few molecules are used over and over in different combinations to make literally millions of different structures and to carry out all the different functions needed by living things. The processes involved in sustaining life all begin at the molecular level within the microscopic spaces of the cell. This includes the storage and release of the energy needed to power cellular process — which ultimately comes from the Sun.

Overall Expectations

In this Unit, you will discover

- What molecules make up cells

- How the cell membrane separates cells from their external environment but allows substances into and out of the cell

- What special functions cell structures have and how these contribute to keeping an organism alive

- What processes in cells capture and release the energy needed for survival and how we harness these processes

Unit Contents

◆ UNIT INVESTIGATION

Look ahead to pages 110–111.

- You can start planning your investigation well in advance by knowing what you will need.

- As you work through the unit, watch for ideas and materials that will help you prepare your experimental design.

The image below may look like a single-celled organism, but it is actually a comet called Hale-Bopp. What does a comet have to do with the pine wood cells on the right?

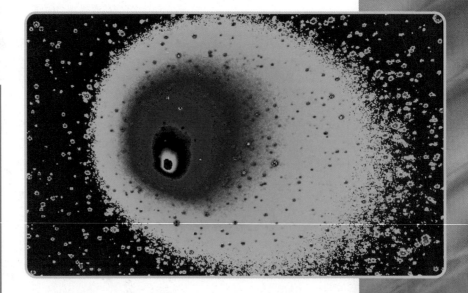

3

CHAPTER 1

Exploring the Micro-universe of the Cell

Reflecting Questions

- What are the key molecules of life?
- How does the cell membrane define the living cell and separate it from its environment?
- How does a cell control the movement of materials that enter and leave it?

The micro-universe of the cell is a world of stunning beauty, high drama, and battles to the death. All of it relies on and revolves around the molecules of life. Why does the didinium in the photograph on the right hunt the paramecium — a larger micro-organism? The didinium cannot make all the molecules it needs, such as proteins, from the substances dissolved in its watery environment. So the didinium must acquire these molecules from its prey. It then uses the molecules to build and repair cellular structures and as a source of energy for cellular processes.

The didinium and paramecium, as well as the vorticella pictured below, separate themselves from the outside world with a cell membrane. How then does the didinium "eat" the paramecium? If the didinium opened a hole in its cell membrane large enough to take in the paramecium, the didinium's own cell contents would leak out into the water surrounding it. Indeed, how do any of these cells take in molecules they need or excrete wastes? Clearly, the cell membrane must do much more than separate the cell contents from the external environment. How does this living edge of the cell function?

Cellular dramas are also taking place in the human body. For example, cells that line your stomach live no longer than four days because the acid produced there eventually destroys them. As the old cells die, replacement cells emerge to face the acidic battleground. If this did not

happen, you would not get the nutrients you need to feed the cells of your body.

Earlier courses introduced you to cells and cell reproduction. In this chapter, you will discover the molecules of life. In particular, you will investigate the large molecules — carbohydrates, lipids, proteins, and nucleic acids — that nourish, build, and direct the living cell. You will also examine the role that the cell membrane plays in transporting substances into and out of the cell.

Beautiful but deadly, the single-celled vorticella pictured below use the coiled spring in their cilia to leap out to grab their prey (bacteria).

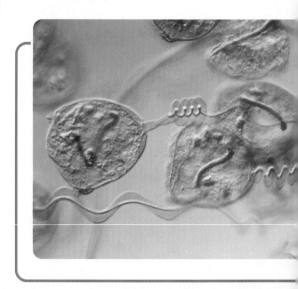

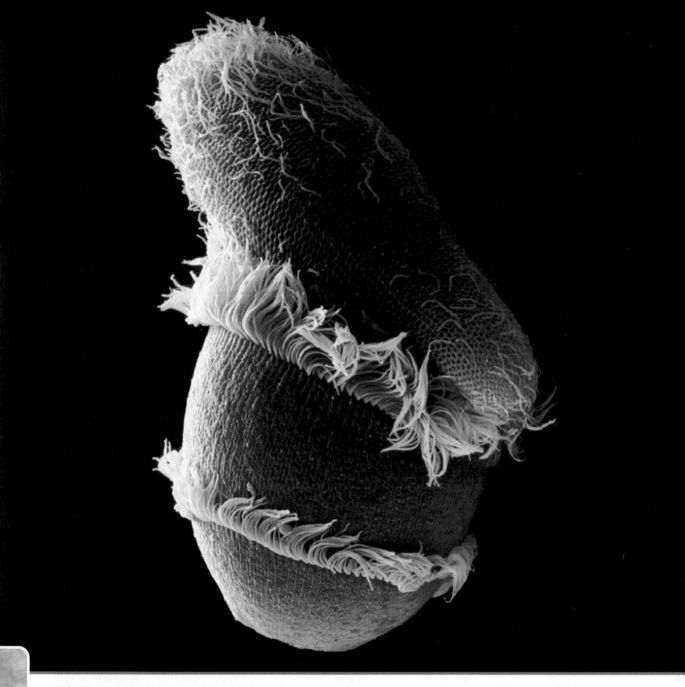

Chapter Contents

The Molecular Basis of Life

EXPECTATIONS

- Describe the structure and function of important biochemical compounds.
- Test for macromolecules found in living organisms.
- Use three-dimensional models of important compounds.

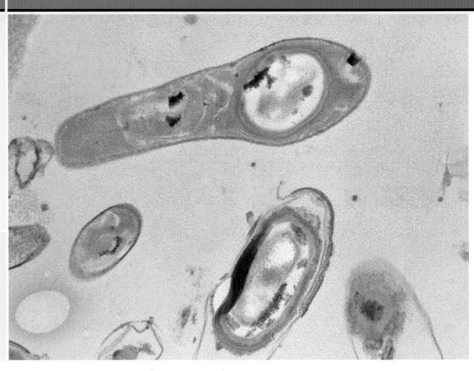

Figure 1.1 These bacteria remained dormant in a salt crystal, probably from before the time of the dinosaurs. In 2000, scientists revived them by giving them water and carbon-containing compounds.

When you think about cells, what first comes to mind? How small they are? How such tiny living things can do so much work? How a single fertilized egg cell can produce all the many specialized cells of a large organism, such as a human being? This chapter, and the other chapters in this unit, will help you answer these questions — and perhaps also help you find new ones to ask.

Less than two hundred years ago, people did not know of the existence of cells. The development of the first microscopes finally gave scientists access to the miniature world of the cell. Early investigators discovered what you now take for granted: that all living things are made up of one or more cells. Other scientists determined that cells are also the fundamental functional units of life. What does this mean?

THINKING LAB

Life: A Winning Experiment

Background

Where do cells come from? Prior to the development and acceptance of the cell theory in 1864, at least one early investigator thought that mice could be generated spontaneously by leaving a dirty shirt in a bucket. In 1860, the Paris Academy of Sciences offered a prize to anyone who could prove or disprove the spontaneous generation of life. The biologist Louis Pasteur took up the challenge. The two Erlenmeyer flasks shown here reproduce the results of Pasteur's winning experiment. Each flask and the stopper were sterilized. Each contains 100 mL of vegetable broth that was boiled for 10 min. Then, the sterilized stopper were placed in one flask, while the second was left unstoppered. This is what the flasks looked like five days after they were filled.

Analyze

1. Describe any differences you observe in the broth of the two flasks.

2. If you see any evidence of life generating life in these photographs, where did the living organisms come from?

>> FAST FORWARD

To review the cell theory, turn to *Appendix 1*.

Word LINK

Look at the ingredients list on a milk package. You will see the word *pasteurized* connected with the ingredients. Find out what this word means. Why does it appear on a milk carton? Explain in your own words where this term came from and how it relates to cells.

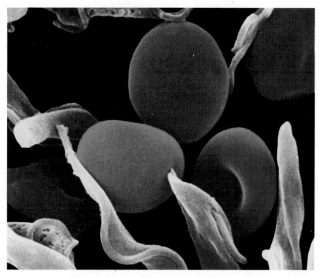

Figure 1.2 The flat, undulating cells (trypanosomes) you see among the red blood cells enter the bloodstream when a tsetse fly bites and cause a disease called African sleeping sickness. The structure of their cell membranes can make them difficult for the human immune system to destroy.

What must the cells pictured in Figure 1.1 do to stay alive? Like you, they have to obtain and ingest food and water, get rid of wastes, grow, and respond to changes in their environment. At some point, they will reproduce, creating more cells. Each one of these cells has to perform key life processes.

How does one cell do all that? Each cell uses energy to fashion the structures it needs out of materials available in its external environment — atoms and molecules. Each cell also maintains a sophisticated barrier between itself and the outside world: the cell membrane. For example, the parasites pictured in Figure 1.2 have cell membranes that help them evade the human immune system.

How have scientists learned so many of the cell's secrets? Technology and scientific inquiry have provided many answers. The technology for examining cells you probably know best is the compound light microscope. However, its glass lenses can only magnify the cell enough to allow you to see some of the larger cell features. Light microscopes cannot resolve — or form distinct images of — objects as close together as are most structures in the cell.

The nature of visible light itself limits the resolving power of a light microscope. When a light wave passes through a specimen with structures less than 0.2 μm apart, the wave bounces back from the two features as if they consisted of a single point. The features are too close together to block the light wave separately, which would reveal them as two points.

Before the invention of the electron microscope, how did biologists gather information about the inner workings of the cell? Living things depend on chemical reactions, which take place at the level of the molecule. So scientists used chemical knowledge and procedures to learn about the world of the cell: the molecules that living cells use, form, excrete, and interact with. This section will introduce you to that world.

|| PAUSE ● RECORD

Explain why biologists describe the cell as the unifying structure that links all life.

 MINI LAB

The Resolving Power of Skin

You may not think of your skin as an exploratory tool that has resolving power, but that is one of its functions. The network of nerves in your skin gives you greater resolving power in some places than in others. What does this mean? Tape two pencils together, and ask a classmate to touch both pencil points *gently* on the following spots while you keep your eyes closed: a fingertip, the palm of your hand, the back of your hand, and the back of your neck.

Ask your classmate to record what you felt each time, two points or one.

Analyze

1. Which part of your skin has the greatest resolving power (lets you clearly distinguish the two pencil points)? Which has the least resolving power?

2. Suggest how differences in sensitivity to touch are related to differences in the number and closeness of nerve endings in your skin.

Living Organisms Rely on Small Molecules

You may not think of your body in terms of chemical reactions, yet you rely on your cells to perform trillions of chemical reactions every second. Without these, you could not remain alive. The study of these reactions and the molecules and processes involved in them is called **biochemistry**. Some of the smallest molecules involved in biochemical reactions are the most important.

Your breath contains three kinds of small molecules critical to life. When you "see your breath" on winter days, what you are seeing? Like clouds, your visible breath consists of condensed water vapour molecules (H_2O) released through your lungs. Your exhaled breath also contains two other kinds of small molecules important to your cells: oxygen (O_2) and carbon dioxide (CO_2). The oxygen is left over from the previous inhalation (your body absorbs only a small fraction of the oxygen you take in with each breath).

Your cells use the oxygen molecules that do pass in through your lungs to help release energy from simple food molecules. This process, called cellular respiration, can be summarized in an equation:

$$C_6H_{12}O_6 + 6O_2 \longrightarrow 6CO_2 + 6H_2O + energy$$

glucose   oxygen   carbon   water
                          dioxide

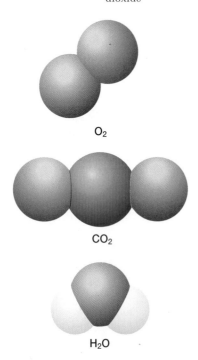

Figure 1.3 Life as we know it would not exist without these small molecules.

Thus, the carbon dioxide and water you exhale are waste products of this reaction, which occurs in your cells. The compounds produced by the process of converting food into energy are small molecules. Figure 1.3 uses models to illustrate how atoms in molecules of water, oxygen, and carbon dioxide are arranged.

Water: The Primary Molecule of Life

Water is the most abundant molecule in any cell. The unique chemical properties of water enable it to act as a carrier for dissolved molecules inside and outside the cell, and as a raw material in essential cell reactions. It also functions as a lubricant between organs, tissues, and individual cells.

These properties of water make possible life as we know it.

- remains liquid over a wide temperature range, including temperatures at which most small molecules are gases (such as room temperature)

- dissolves most substances involved in living processes, such as oxygen, carbon dioxide, glucose, amino acids (components of proteins), and sodium chloride (salt)

- changes temperature gradually when heated or cooled, so it protects cells from rapid temperature changes and provides a stable environment for cell reactions

- is the only pure substance that expands when it becomes a solid, which means that it floats when it freezes (see Figure 1.5)

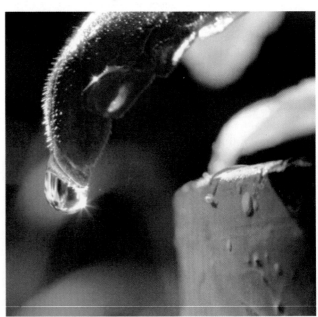

Figure 1.4 Water molecules cling together, which helps water to creep up thin tubes, such as those running from the roots to the tops of plants.

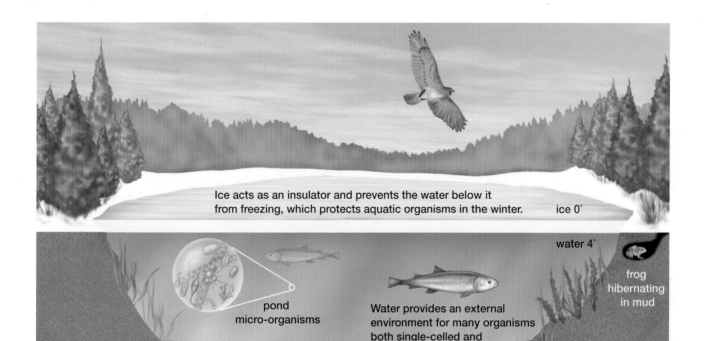

Figure 1.5 All organisms require water to live.

Ice acts as an insulator and prevents the water below it from freezing, which protects aquatic organisms in the winter.   ice 0°

water 4°

frog hibernating in mud

pond micro-organisms

Water provides an external environment for many organisms both single-celled and multicellular.

The special properties of water are determined by its chemical structure. The uneven distribution of electrical charges on a water molecule allows one water molecule to attract another water molecule at room temperature enough to form a liquid. (Larger molecules such as oxygen and carbon dioxide remain gases at room temperature.) Figure 1.4 shows how this property is important to plants. Molecules with uneven charge distribution are said to be **polar** (because they have oppositely charged "poles"). Although carbon dioxide contains oxygen, it has an even distribution of electrical charge. This means that it is **nonpolar**.

>> FAST FORWARD

To review chemical bonding, turn to *Appendix 2*.

Organic Compounds

The term **organic compound** refers to molecules that contain both carbon and hydrogen, which means that molecules such as oxygen, water, and carbon dioxide are *inorganic*. Although living things require water to perform their life functions, and most also require oxygen, these molecules can be generated without the involvement of living things.

The molecules that form a more permanent part of living cells all have a carbon "backbone." This abundance of carbon in organic compounds is why scientists call life on Earth carbon based. Each carbon atom can form up to four bonds with other atoms. Hydrocarbon molecules (organic molecules containing *only* carbon and hydrogen) come in an enormous range of sizes and shapes, including open-ended chains and closed, loop-like "rings," such as those shown in Figure 1.6. From previous studies, you may recognize the lines joining the atoms in this figure as covalent bonds.

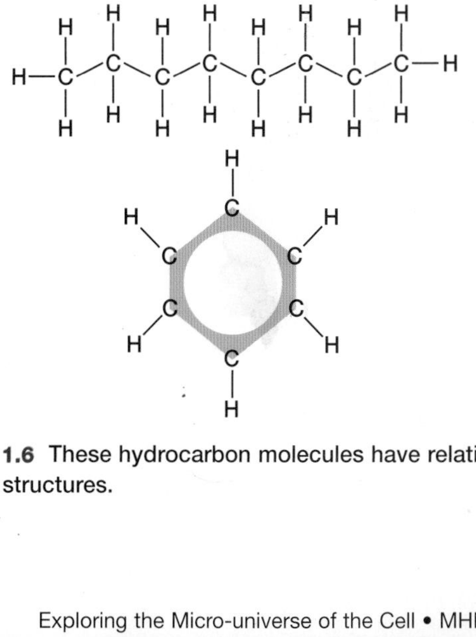

Figure 1.6 These hydrocarbon molecules have relatively simple structures.

In addition to carbon and hydrogen, many organic molecules contain other elements, the most important of which are oxygen, nitrogen, phosphorous, and sulfur. You may recall from earlier studies that normal air is about 20% oxygen and 78% nitrogen, so it is not surprising that many organic molecules contain these two elements.

Living cells make and use a variety of organic molecules, such as glucose (a sugar). The cells of plants and some other organisms manufacture glucose through the process of photosynthesis summarized in this equation:

$$6CO_2 + 6H_2O \xrightarrow{\text{light}} 6O_2 + C_6H_{12}O_6$$

carbon   water   oxygen   glucose
dioxide

Both plants and animals use glucose as a food from which they obtain energy.

In this chapter, you will explore only the principal organic molecules contained in carbohydrates, lipids, and proteins, as well as the nucleic acids. that make up the DNA in chromosomes. Figure 1.7 illustrates foods containing these molecules. All of these organic compounds are very large molecules, or **macromolecules** (*macro* means large), composed of smaller subunits.

≫ FAST FORWARD

To view the periodic table, turn to *Appendix 11.*

Math LINK

This chart gives you the chemical formulas for a number of important biological molecules and the mass of each in atomic mass units. Use this information to determine the mass of a molecule of table sugar (sucrose), which has the chemical formula $C_{12}H_{22}O_{11}$.

Molecule	Chemical formula	Atomic mass units
Water	H_2O	18
Oxygen	O_2	32
Carbon dioxide	CO_2	44
Glucose	$C_6H_{12}O_6$	180

The Structure and Biological Function of Carbohydrates

Very interested in the food produced by plants, early scientists chemically analyzed sugars and starches. They discovered that these compounds always contain carbon, hydrogen, and oxygen — almost always in the same proportion: two atoms of hydrogen and one atom of oxygen for every atom of carbon, or CH_2O. Since the formula for water is H_2O, the scientists concluded that sugars and starches consist of carbons with water attached to them, or **carbohydrates** (*hydro* means water). Carbohydrates provide short- or longer-term energy storage for living organisms.

Figure 1.7 Foods rich in carbohydrates, lipids, and proteins.

A carbohydrate molecule with three to seven carbon atoms (and the corresponding number of hydrogen and oxygen atoms) is called a **monosaccharide**, or simple sugar (*mono* means one; *sakkharon* means sugar). Figure 1.8 shows the single, closed ring-like structures of three common monosaccharides: glucose, fructose, and galactose.

A **disaccharide**, or double sugar, is made up of two simple sugars (*di* means two). Figure 1.9 shows how two glucose units link together to form one molecule of the disaccharide maltose. Malted products such as beer contain maltose. You may be more familiar with another disaccharide, sucrose, which is made by joining glucose with fructose. Sucrose is in many food products, from brownies to barbeque sauce.

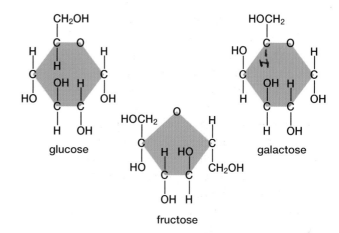

Figure 1.8 Living cells use molecules of glucose or other simple sugars, such as fructose and galactose, as a quick source of energy. Although all three simple sugars have the same composition of atoms, the arrangement of these atoms differs slightly in each molecule.

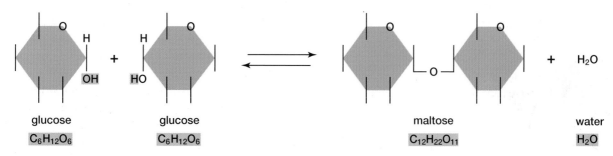

Figure 1.9 Note the role played by water when glucose units are linked to form maltose and when maltose is broken apart to form individual glucose molecules.

Modelling Sugars

In this lab, you will construct models of two glucose molecules and join them together to make a disaccharide molecule. To do this, you will need the following molecular model materials: 12 carbon atoms, 24 hydrogen atoms, 12 oxygen atoms, and 50 bonds.

Use the diagram of glucose in Figure 1.8 above as a guide to building your glucose molecule models. Note that glucose has a ring structure consisting of five carbon atoms and an oxygen atom. A sixth carbon is attached to one of the ring carbons. Keep in mind that each carbon has four bonding sites. Set both of your glucose models side by side so that they match the orientation of the glucose molecules

on the left side of Figure 1.9. Break and re-make bonds to build a model of the disaccharide maltose.

Analyze

1. Which atoms are involved in the breaking and making of bonds when a disaccharide is formed? Suggest a reason for this.

2. Describe how you think the glucose and fructose subunits in sucrose are linked. Build a molecular model to show this.

3. How might a cell use the three-dimensional shape of a glucose molecule to orient the connecting atoms between two glucose "rings"?

A **polysaccharide** is a complex carbohydrate consisting of many simple sugars linked together (*poly* means many). Figure 1.10 shows the structure of the polysaccharides starch, glycogen, and cellulose. **Starch** performs the important function of energy storage in plants. **Glycogen** performs the same function in animals. Compare the structures of the starch and glycogen molecules, and note the many "branches" on the glycogen molecule. The larger amount of branching in glycogen means that glycogen molecules pack more glucose units into a single cell than do starch molecules.

Plants produce an even larger polysaccharide macromolecule called **cellulose**, out of which they build their cell walls. Cellulose is considered a structural molecule because it protects individual cells and provides support for the whole plant. As a polysaccharide made up of glucose units, cellulose also stores a great deal of energy. However, only a few bacterial species produce the digestive chemicals needed to break cellulose down into glucose units and release energy. So — to obtain nourishment from grass, leaves, wood, and other cellulose-rich plant materials — animals such as cattle, rabbits, and termites must host these bacteria in their guts. The human gut does not host these bacteria, so the food energy in cellulose is not directly accessible to us.

The Structure and Biological Function of Lipids

Lipids are a diverse group of macromolecules that have one important feature in common: they do not dissolve in water. Living organisms use lipids for many purposes: long-term nutrient and energy storage, insulation, cushioning of internal organs, and hormones to send messages around the body. Lipids are also the primary structural component of the cell membrane of every cell.

The lipid with which you are likely most familiar is fat. Fats include not only substances such as butter but also oils such as canola oil. Whether in solid or liquid form, one gram of lipid contains 2.25 times as much energy as one gram of carbohydrate.

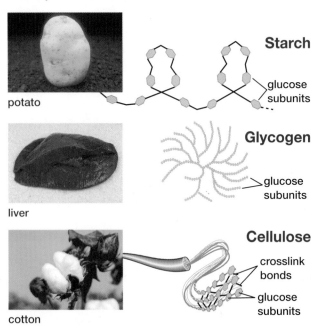

potato

liver

cotton

Starch

glucose subunits

Glycogen

glucose subunits

Cellulose

crosslink bonds

glucose subunits

Figure 1.10 Look at the structural differences among the polysaccharides starch, glycogen, and cellulose. Notice that all three consist of glucose subunits.

Figure 1.11 The white walrus has just returned from an extended swim in extremely cold water. You can see its blubber right through its skin because the blood vessels in its skin have constricted (narrowed) to conserve heat in the cold water. Without normal blood flow, the skin becomes nearly transparent, making the walrus appear white.

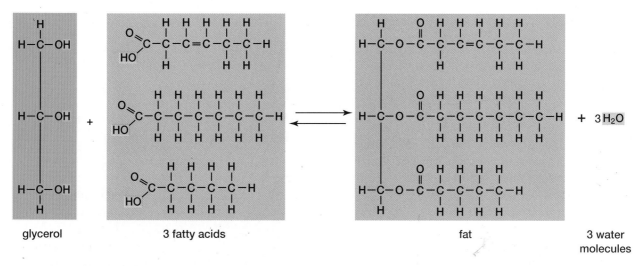

glycerol   3 fatty acids   fat   3 water
                                                                molecules

Figure 1.12 Notice that in each fatty acid chain of a triglyceride molecule only the carbon atom at the glycerol end has oxygen attached to it. All the rest of the carbon atoms on the fatty acid have only hydrogen atoms attached to them.

All fat molecules have the same basic three-branched structure. Figure 1.13 shows how this structure forms in a chemical reaction involving one molecule of an alcohol called glycerol and three molecules of **fatty acid**. Another name for this structure is a triglyceride.

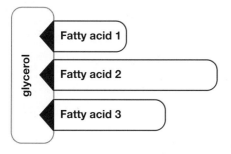

Figure 1.13 On this simple model of a triglyceride (fat) macromolecule, the triangles represent glycerol's three reaction sites.

A fatty acid is a hydrocarbon chain with a difference: at one end, the carbon has an acidic — COOH group instead of hydrogen attached to it. It is this acidic group of a fatty acid that attaches to one of the three main reaction sites on a glycerol molecule, as shown in Figures 1.13 and 1.14. The triglyceride produced is nonpolar. This means that it will not be attracted to (polar) water molecules, which is why fats are insoluble in water.

‖PAUSE   ●RECORD

Compare Figure 1.12 (lipid formation) with Figure 1.9 (carbohydrate formation). What do the two reactions have in common? (Hint: Look at the blue highlighting on each figure.) How do they differ?

Glycerol always has the same composition; not so for the three fatty acids, which may be identical or nonidentical, short or long, saturated or unsaturated. In the hydrocarbon chain of a **saturated** fatty acid, each of the carbon atoms beyond the one bonded to oxygen is bonded to four other atoms. An **unsaturated** fatty acid has bonding sites (double bonds) where additional hydrogen atoms could be attached. Figure 1.14 shows the difference between a saturated and an unsaturated fatty acid.

If unsaturated fatty acids dominate, the resulting fat will likely be liquid at room temperature. If saturated fatty acids dominate, the resulting fat will likely be solid at room temperature.

➤➤ FAST FORWARD

To learn about double bonds, turn to *Appendix 2.*

Ⓐ

H H H H H H
| | | | | |
O   C–C–C–C–C–C–C–H
‖ | | | | | |
HO   H H H H H H

Ⓑ

H H H H H
| | | | |
O   C–C–C=C–C–C–H
‖ | | |
HO   H   H H

Figure 1.14 (A) This fatty acid is saturated with hydrogen. (B) This fatty acid has room for two more hydrogen atoms, one on each of the highlighted carbon atoms. Such a fatty acid is called unsaturated.

The Structure and Biological Function of Proteins

Most cellular structures are made of various types of **protein**. Proteins also serve many other functions in cells. In fact, they display greater structural complexity and functional diversity than either lipids or carbohydrates.

Your hair and fingernails are both made of the same type of protein, keratin, yet each has its own distinctive properties. The bones and muscles inside your hand and the ligaments and tendons connecting them also contain distinctly different proteins. Without these proteins, you would not be able to move your hand.

In addition to their structural functions, proteins also

- function as enzymes to facilitate chemical reactions (the enzyme amylase in your saliva begins the breakdown of starches into simple sugars while you chew)

- help transport substances across cell membranes or to different parts of an organism (the hemoglobin in your blood transports oxygen from your lungs to each cell in your body)

Figure 1.15 Feathers, spider webs, wool, and silk are made up of proteins. In fact, feathers consist mostly of the same protein, keratin, that makes up human nails and hair.

- act as chemical messengers (some hormones are proteins rather than lipids, such as the insulin that helps to regulate the amount of glucose available to cells)

Like other macromolecules, proteins are assembled from small units. In proteins, the building blocks are **amino acid** molecules. Figure 1.16 shows the chemical structure of five representative amino acids. Note the *unhighlighted* part of each amino acid. It contains two carbon atoms, two oxygen atoms, four hydrogen atoms, and one nitrogen atom per molecule. The number and arrangement of these atoms is identical for all but one amino acid (proline). What differs substantially from one amino acid to another is the highlighted remainder group (or R group).

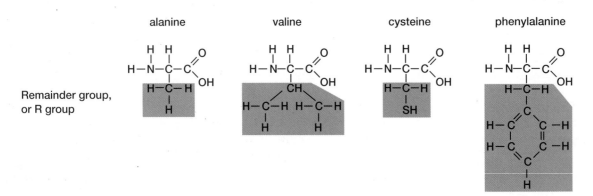

Figure 1.16 Note that these five representative amino acids differ from one another by their R groups.

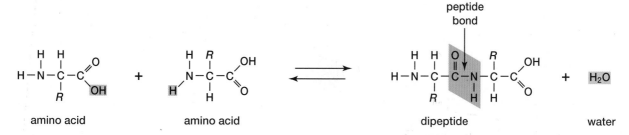

amino acid + amino acid ⇌ peptide bond — dipeptide + H₂O water

Figure 1.17 In the first stage of the formation of a polypeptide, two amino acids are linked together. The R groups appear only as "R" because they do not take part in the reaction that produces or breaks a peptide bond.

A chemical linkage called a **peptide bond** joins individual amino acids together. Figure 1.17 shows how a peptide bond between two amino acids is formed or broken. Regardless of which R group is present, amino acids always bond to each other in the manner shown in Figure 1.17. However, a chain of amino acids is not yet a protein, only a **polypeptide**.

Figure 1.19 on the next page shows the steps between a peptide bond and a finished protein molecule. The final shape of the protein's three-dimensional structure determines what properties it will have and therefore what functions it can perform.

If a protein molecule is exposed to extreme temperatures, extreme pH conditions (very acidic or very basic), or harsh chemicals, it will unfold or change shape. When this happens, the protein is said to have been **denatured**. The protein loses its ability to perform its normal function.

Why can some proteins such as enzymes or hemoglobin function in a water solution while others (such as the keratin in your fingernails) are usually insoluble in water? This depends on how the polypeptide(s) making up a protein are twisted and folded. When the parts of the R groups that can interact with water end up on the outside of the final protein structure, the protein is soluble in water. When the parts of the R groups that do *not* interact with water or react only slightly with it end up on the outside, the protein will not dissolve in water.

> ► PLAY
>
> To enhance your learning about macromolecules, go to your Electronic Learning Partner.

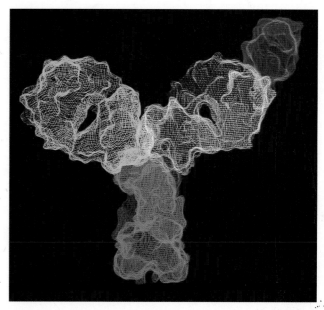

Figure 1.18 This computer-generated image of a protein molecule makes the protein's complex, three-dimensional structure easier to visualize.

Humans need 20 amino acids — known as the common amino acids — to make the protein macromolecules required for healthy body structures and functions. Your body can manufacture 12 of these amino acids from non-protein food sources. The other eight must be present in your food because your body cannot manufacture them for itself. These eight are referred to as **essential amino acids**.

With 20 different amino acids to combine, proteins exist in thousands of distinctly different forms. Each kind of organism manufactures its own characteristic proteins or variations on proteins common to a number of species, such as hemoglobin. Indeed, it is our proteins that make us different from ants, amoebas, or ash trees.

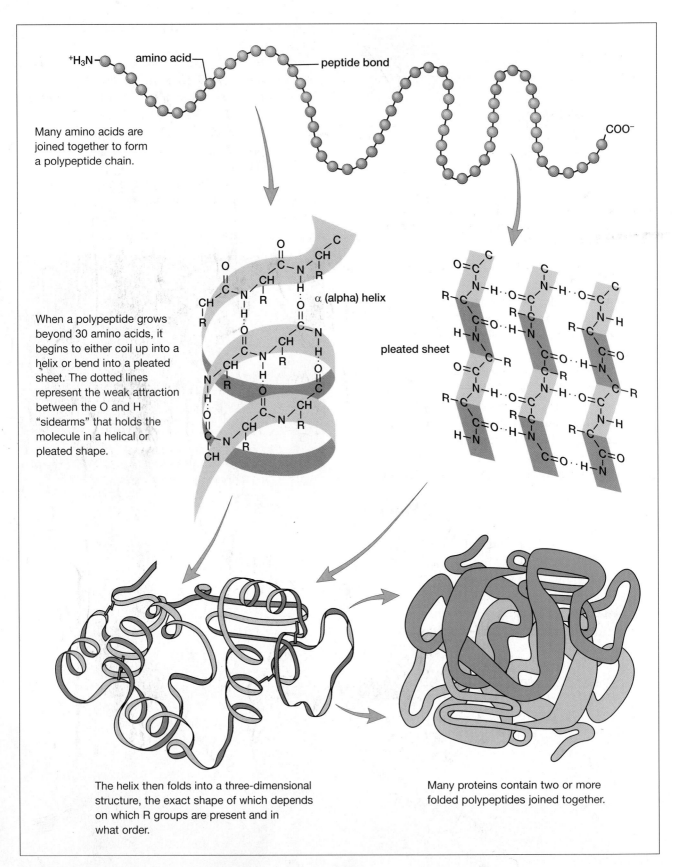

+H₃N— ——amino acid—— ——peptide bond——   COO⁻

Many amino acids are joined together to form a polypeptide chain.

When a polypeptide grows beyond 30 amino acids, it begins to either coil up into a helix or bend into a pleated sheet. The dotted lines represent the weak attraction between the O and H "sidearms" that holds the molecule in a helical or pleated shape.

α (alpha) helix

pleated sheet

The helix then folds into a three-dimensional structure, the exact shape of which depends on which R groups are present and in what order.

Many proteins contain two or more folded polypeptides joined together.

Figure 1.19 The formation of a protein molecule from a polypeptide

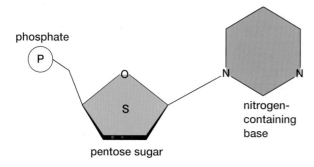

phosphate

P

O

S

N   N

nitrogen-
containing
base

pentose sugar

Figure 1.20 Generalized nucleotide. Nucleotides consist of a five-carbon simple sugar (ribose in the case of RNA and deoxyribose in DNA), a nitrogen base, and a phosphate group, symbolized here by Ⓟ.

Nucleic Acids

Nucleic acids direct the growth and development of every living thing by means of a chemical code. They determine how the cell functions and what characteristics it has.

The cell contains two types of nucleic acid: RNA (ribonucleic acid) and DNA (deoxyribonucleic acid). You may already have learned that DNA is the main component of the genes, or hereditary material, in all cells. Each gene contains instructions for making RNA. RNA, contains the instructions for making proteins. These proteins

make up much of the structure of a cell and control how it functions.

Like proteins and carbohydrates, nucleic acids consist of long chains of linked subunits. These subunits are called **nucleotides**, which are depicted in Figure 1.20. DNA is made up of just four different nucleotides. So is RNA. Each DNA nucleotide has an RNA nucleotide counterpart.

RNA consists of a single, long chain of nucleotides. In DNA, two enormous nucleotide chains are attached in a ladder-like structure, which then coils into a double helix shape. Figure 1.22 illustrates this DNA structure.

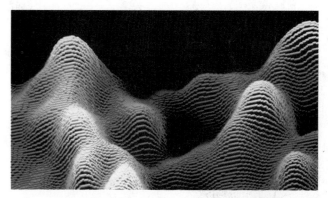

Figure 1.21 This image shows the shape of individual atoms on a section of a DNA molecule. It was mapped using a probe through which a tiny electric current flows.

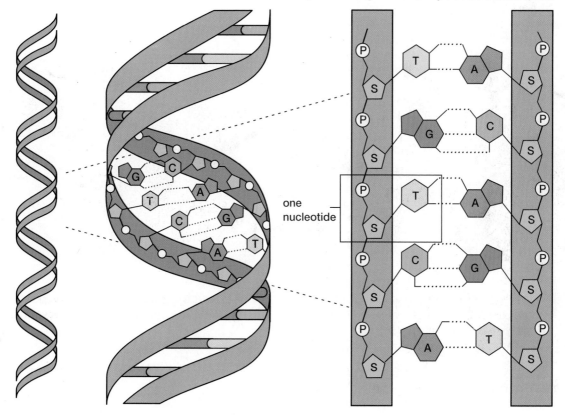

one nucleotide

Figure 1.22 DNA's structure. Each DNA strand contains carbon rings (sugar) and phosphate molecules, while the ladder "rungs" between the strands consist of nitrogen bases.

Investigation   **1 • A**

SKILL FOCUS

Conducting research

Performing and recording

Analyzing and interpreting

Communicating results

What's Here? Testing for Macromolecules

Biochemists have developed standard tests to determine the presence of the most abundant macromolecules made by cells: carbohydrates, lipids, and proteins. In this investigation, you will conduct standard tests to determine the presence of glucose, starch, lipid, and protein in known samples. Each test involves an indicator, which is a chemical that changes colour when it reacts with a specific substance.

Pre-lab Questions

- Glucose is a monosaccharide. What does this mean?
- Proteins are made of amino acids. What atom is present in an amino acid that is not present in a sugar molecule?
- Identify two health hazards related to using a copper sulfate solution.

Problem

How can you determine the presence of glucose, starch, lipid, and protein in various samples?

CAUTION: Be careful when handling iodine, Benedict's solution, Sudan IV, and Biuret reagent as they are toxic. Avoid allowing the hot water bath to boil vigorously because this can cause test tubes to break. Clean up spills immediately, and notify your teacher if a spill occurs.

Materials

safety goggles	40 mL sucrose solution
disposable gloves	40 mL starch solution
apron	40 mL distilled water
marker	Benedict's solution in a
6 graduated cylinders	dropper bottle
12 test tubes	iodine solution in a
test tube rack	dropper bottle
hot water bath	Sudan IV solution
test tube clamp	(0.5% alcohol solution)
test tube brush	in a dropper bottle
40 mL protein solution	Biuret reagent in a
(2% gelatin solution)	dropper bottle
40 mL vegetable oil	glassware soap
40 mL glucose solution	

Procedure

- Follow your teacher's instructions for the disposal of the test solutions and samples.

- Use the same graduated cylinder to measure samples of the same substance for all four parts of this investigation. For example, use the same graduated cylinder to measure out vegetable oil each time.
- Perform parts B, C, and D of this investigation while you heat samples for part A.
- Carefully clean your work area after you finish each test.
- Wash glassware throughly with soap and water.

Part A

1. Set up the hot water bath as shown below. Use a medium setting for the hot plate.

2. Mark the six graduated cylinders with the numbers 1 to 6.

3. Mark six test tubes with the numbers 1 to 6.

4. Measure out 10 mL of protein solution into graduated cylinder 1, 10 mL of vegetable oil into graduated cylinder 2, 10 mL of glucose solution into graduated cylinder 3, 10 mL of sucrose solution into graduated cylinder 4, 10 mL of starch solution into graduated cylinder 5, and 10 mL of distilled water into graduated cylinder 6.

5. Add 10 mL of each sample to the test tube with the same number.

6. Add 5 drops of Benedict's solution to each test tube. Safely mix the contents of each test tube by swirling the test tube as shown below.

7. Heat each test tube in the hot water bath for 5 min. If your hot water bath is large enough, heat two test tubes at a time. After 5 min, use a test tube clamp to move each test tube to the test tube rack.

8. When all the test tubes have been heated and removed, turn off the source of heat and let the water bath cool.

9. Record your observations for each test tube.

10. When the test tubes have cooled, wash them. When the hot water bath has cooled, pour out the water and wash the glassware.

Part B

1. Repeat steps 3, 4, and 5 from Part A.

2. Add 5 drops of iodine solution to each test tube. Carefully mix the contents of each test tube.

3. Record your observations for each test tube. Then wash the test tubes.

Part C

1. Repeat steps 3, 4, and 5 from Part A.

2. Add 5 drops of Sudan IV solution to each test tube. Safely mix the contents of each test tube.

3. Record your observations for each test tube. Then wash the test tubes thoroughly.

Part D

1. Repeat steps 3, 4, and 5 from Part A.

2. Add 5 drops of Biuret reagent to each test tube. Safely mix the contents of each test tube.

3. Record your observations for each test tube. Then wash the test tubes and graduated cylinders.

Sample	A. Benedict's solution + heat	B. Iodine solution	C. Sudan IV solution	D. Biuret reagent
1. protein solution				
2. vegetable oil				

Post-lab Questions

1. Describe a positive test for starch. Explain how you know.

2. Describe a positive test for glucose. Explain how you know.

3. Describe a positive test for lipids. Explain how you know.

4. Describe a positive test for protein. Explain how you know.

Conclude and Apply

5. What was the purpose of testing distilled water for each part of the investigation?

6. Suppose you have a sample of breakfast cereal that may contain one, two, three, or all four of the macromolecules you tested for in this investigation. Write a procedure describing how you would test the sample to determine which macromolecules it contains.

Exploring Further

7. Physicians often want to know the glucose and lipid levels in a patient's blood and whether proteins are present in a patient's urine. Research to find out what this information might show about an individual's health.

Manipulating Macromolecules

The study of biological molecules has been revolutionized by the use of computers. Today, sophisticated software programs allow biochemists to explore, build, and manipulate three-dimensional models of macromolecules. In this lab, you will use the Internet to view and manipulate similar models. (You may need to download free software to run the simulations, such as Chime. Check with your teacher before you download anything onto a school computer.) Your teacher will give you a list of sites that contain three-dimensional models of proteins and other macromolecules. Go to each site, and use the simulations to view and manipulate the molecular models.

Analyze

1. Describe each type of model the site(s) allowed you to view, for example, a ball-and-stick model, space-filling model, and so on.

2. How does rotating a molecule change what you can see about it?

3. Draw structural formulas for two of the three-dimensional models that you viewed.

4. What did the computer simulations of molecules show you that would be more difficult to see using molecular model kits?

SECTION REVIEW

1. **K/U** List the key life processes of cells.

2. **K/U** Identify three inorganic molecules important for cells.

3. **K/U** Describe the unique properties of water. Explain how each property is important to cells.

4. **K/U** Copy and complete this chart:

Macromolecule type	Diagram	Sample Molecule	Function in the cell
monosaccharide			
carbohydrate			
lipid (2 examples)			
protein (2 examples)			
nucleic acid			

5. **K/U** What is a peptide bond?

6. **K/U** Why are some amino acids described as essential amino acids?

7. **I** Some people add cold milk to hot coffee. Others heat milk so that it is hot and steamy. Does heating milk change its chemical make-up? Predict any changes, and design a lab that would test your prediction.

8. **K/U** Some oils, such as olive oil, are liquid at room temperature. How can the structure of the oil molecules be changed so that they are almost solid at room temperature?

9. **MC** Find a Materials Safety Data Sheet, and identify health hazards related to Biuret's reagent.

10. **MC** Explain how computer molecular-model simulations could benefit biomedical research.

UNIT INVESTIGATION PREP

How is whole milk different from skim milk?
- Design a series of tests to identify the macromolecules in whole milk. Which indicators would you use?
- Predict which macromolecules you would find if you performed the tests you designed above. Would you expect different results with skim milk? Explain.

Cell Membrane Structure

- Identify the structure and function of phospholipids.
- Describe the fluid-mosaic structure of the cell membrane.

Figure 1.23 From an altitude of 10 000 m, a city may look quiet and still. From 1000 m, it becomes clear that buses, trucks, and cars are moving. Airplanes fly into its airport. Ships and boats come and go from its harbour. How does this city resemble a cell?

When viewed with even the most powerful light microscope, the cell membrane looks like nothing more than a thin, dark line. Yet if the cell membrane functioned only as a barrier separating the inside of the cell from its external environment, how could the cell survive? How would the cell get the raw materials it needs to build macromolecules? The cell membrane must also regulate the movement of materials from one environment to the other.

Figure 1.24 What was the original purpose of this wall around the old part of Québec City? How did its original function resemble that of a cell membrane?

The efficient operation of a city such as the one pictured in Figure 1.23 would soon grind to a halt without adequate routes for the flow of people and things in and out. Similarly, the activities of a living cell depend on the ability of its membrane to

- transport raw materials into the cell
- transport manufactured products and wastes out of the cell
- prevent the entry of unwanted matter into the cell
- prevent the escape of the matter needed to perform the cellular functions

Getting the Cell Membrane in Focus

The development of the electron microscope gave scientists the information they needed to begin exploring how the cell membrane performs its regulatory functions. An **electron microscope** uses beams of electrons instead of light to produce images. Electron microscopes and other devices separate electrons from their atoms and focus them into a beam. For example, the image on a TV set is formed by electron beams that cause the inner coating on the screen to glow.

Compared to light, an electron beam has a very short wavelength — so short that it can pass between two cell features less than 0.2 μm apart and form an image of them that shows two distinct and separate points.

Figure 1.25 James Hillier was in his early twenties when his professor asked him to help build a practical electron microscope. The microscope that Hiller and Albert Prebus built is now on display at the Ontario Science Centre in Toronto. It has 7000x magnification.

The first really usable electron microscope was built in 1938 at the University of Toronto by two graduate students, James Hillier (1915–) and Albert Prebus (1913–1997). Their microscope revealed that what look like "grains" under the light microscope are complex cellular structures. In Chapter 2, you will learn more about these structures. This section continues the story of research into the cell membrane.

When electron microscopy finally yielded a more detailed view, microscopists saw that the cell membrane is in fact a bilayer, or a structure consisting of two layers of molecules. Chemical analysis revealed that this bilayer is composed mainly of **phospholipid** molecules, a type of lipid.

Phospholipids have two fatty acids bonded to a glycerol "backbone." The third glycerol reaction site is bonded to a chain containing phosphorus, and in some cases nitrogen as well.

This makes the shape and properties of a phospholipid quite different from those of a triglyceride. The phosphate chain forms a "head," while the two fatty acids form two "tails." The electric charge in the molecule is unevenly distributed, as shown in Figure 1.27: the molecule has a polar head and nonpolar tails.

The polar head of a phospholipid molecule is attracted to water molecules, which are also polar. This makes the phosphorus end of a phospholipid water soluble. The hydrocarbon chains in the fatty-acid tails of the phospholipid are not attracted to water molecules. They are, however, compatible with other lipids.

Word LINK

Earlier in this chapter, you learned that *hydro* means water. Many textbooks use the terms *hydrophobic* and *hydrophilic* to describe the way that molecules interact with water. Write a definition for each of these words, including the word *soluble* in one definition and *insoluble* in the other. Which end of a phospholipid is hydrophobic and which is hydrophilic?

Figure 1.28 shows what can happen when a film of phospholipid molecules is spread in a water sample. Through a combination of attraction and repulsion, the phospholipids spontaneously arrange themselves into a spherical, cage-like bilayer. Their water-attracting polar heads face both the inside and the outside of the sphere, while

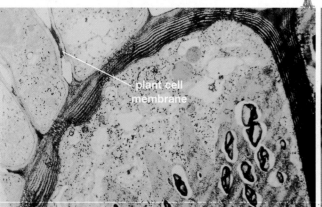

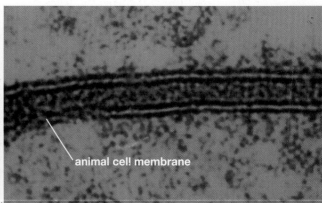

Figure 1.26 Electron microscopy showed that the cell membranes of both plant and animal cells have a two-layered structure. This gave scientists the clue they needed to begin unravelling the mystery of how the cell membrane works.

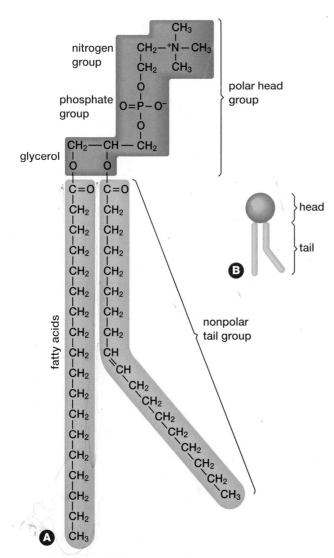

Figure 1.27 Constructed much like a triglyceride (fat), phospholipids contain a phosphate group and sometimes also a nitrogen group.

their water-averse, nonpolar lipid tails face each other. This sandwich-like phospholipid structure, called a **phospholipid bilayer**, forms the basis of the cell membrane.

BIO FACT

The ability of phospholipids to spontaneously form a spherical bilayer in water likely played a key role in the formation of the first cells about 3.8 billion years ago.

The Fluid-Mosaic Membrane Model

The fact that lipids do not dissolve in water creates a border around the cell. The phosphate edges of this border help to define and contain the more fluid lipid centre. However, there is much more to a cell membrane than its phospholipid bilayer.

Figure 1.28 The molecular structure of a phospholipid bilayer. Unlike the cell membrane of a living cell, this bilayer contains only water inside it.

Based on intensive research by biochemists and electron microscopists, biologists have inferred that the cell membrane also contains a mosaic of different components scattered throughout it, much like raisins in a slice of raisin bread. For example, numerous protein molecules stud the phospholipid bilayer. The phospholipid molecules and some of these proteins can drift sideways in the bilayer, a phenomenon which supports the idea that the phospholipid bilayer has a fluid consistency. Thus, this description of the cell membrane is called the **fluid-mosaic membrane model**.

Figure 1.29 on the next page shows how proteins and phospholipids fit together in the continuous mosaic of an animal cell membrane. Note that this cell membrane also contains another type of lipid: cholesterol molecules. Cholesterol allows animal cell membranes to function in a wide range of temperatures. At high temperatures, it helps maintain rigidity in the oily membrane bilayer. At low temperatures, its keeps the membrane fluid, flexible, and functional — preventing cell death from a frozen membrane. Cholesterol also makes the membrane less permeable to most biological molecules. Plants have a different lipid that serves a similar function in their cell membranes.

The shapes of the membrane proteins vary according to their function, and each type of cell has a characteristic arrangement of proteins in its membrane. For example, the membrane of a human red blood cell includes 50 different protein types arranged in a pattern that only other cells from humans with the same blood type can "recognize."

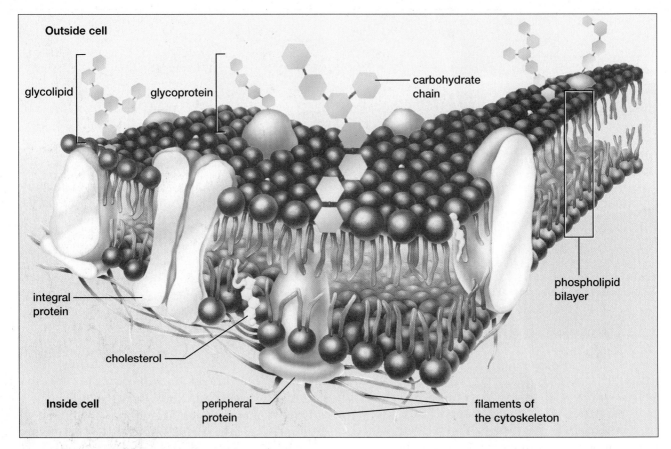

Outside cell

glycolipid

glycoprotein

carbohydrate chain

phospholipid bilayer

integral protein

cholesterol

Inside cell

peripheral protein

filaments of the cytoskeleton

Figure 1.29 Fluid-mosaic model of membrane structure. Notice that many lipids and proteins facing the exterior of the cell have carbohydrate chains attached to them, while on the interior of the cell, parts of the cell's skeleton (called its cytoskeleton) support the membrane. Each type of cell has its own unique "fingerprint" of carbohydrate chains that distinguish it from other kinds of cells.

SECTION REVIEW

1. **K/U** List the functions of the cell membrane.

2. **C** Compare the structures of a phospholipid and a fatty acid using a simple diagram of each type of molecule. Label any differences in polarity.

3. **C** Make a model cell membrane that shows the different components. Include a legend that makes your model easy to understand.

4. **C** Cells are organized differently from the world outside the cell membrane. Draw a diagram of a predator cell, showing how this organization inside the cell is different from the material outside the cell. Then make a second diagram to show the impact that opening a hole in the cell membrane would have on the cell.

5. **K/U** Identify the component(s) of the cell membrane that give it a fluid consistency.

6. **K/U** Why does the cell membrane require a fluid consistency?

7. **K/U** Why does your body manufacture cholesterol even if you do not eat any foods that contain cholesterol?

8. **K/U** Explain why the electron microscope is better than the light microscope for looking at the cell membrane.

9. **K/U** What other cellular structures might the electron microscope provide useful information about that a light microscope could not?

10. **MC** Oil acts as an organic solvent. What kinds of problems would organisms coming into contact with an oil spill have?

Through the Cell Membrane

EXPECTATIONS

- Explain the dynamics of the transport of substances through the cell membrane, including facilitated diffusion.

- Design and carry out an investigation to examine the movement of substances across a membrane.

Figure 1.30 Two different water environments meet when the Thompson River joins the Fraser River, much like the internal environment of a cell and the extracellular fluid meeting at the cell membrane.

The conditions inside every cell must remain nearly constant for it to continue performing its life functions. The steady state that results from maintaining near-constant conditions in the internal environment of a living thing is called **homeostasis**. The structure chiefly responsible for maintaining homeostasis inside a living cell is the cell membrane.

You have seen that the cell membrane's structure is remarkably complex. The cell membrane uses several methods to transport molecules of different sizes and with different properties in and out of the cell. The primary methods it uses rely on the fact that the cell membrane is semi-permeable, allowing some molecules to pass through it while preventing others from doing so. This section will examine those transport methods that involve substances moving through the cell membrane.

On both sides of the cell membrane, water is the solvent, the meeting place for all of the other chemicals. As you learned in Section 1.1, water has special properties that make it a functional medium for living reactions. For example, the external environment of a single-celled life form, such as the amoeba shown in Figure 1.31, consists primarily of water. This external environment also contains other microscopic aquatic organisms, decaying organic matter, and dissolved gases (such as oxygen) and other inorganic substances.

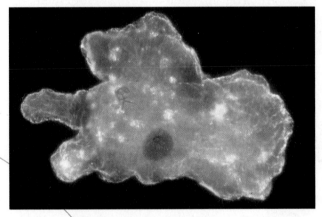

Figure 1.31 This amoeba has little sensory equipment, limited locomotion, and a seemingly fragile membranous covering. Yet it copes with an external environment as complex as yours.

In the case of a multicellular organism, every cell is bathed in a thin layer of **extracellular fluid**. The extracellular fluid consists of a variable mixture of water and dissolved materials. Some are substances that a particular cell type requires; some are substances needed by all cells. Other materials are wastes that the cell has already discarded — and that the organism will eventually get rid of.

Diffusion and the Cell Membrane

One passive method by which small molecules move through the cell membrane is diffusion. **Diffusion** is the movement of molecules from a region where they are more concentrated to one where they are less concentrated. Many molecules — especially small, uncharged ones, such as oxygen — can move easily through the cell membrane as a result of this process.

How does diffusion work? You may remember from earlier studies that molecules are in constant motion — even in a solid. In a liquid, this means that the molecules move about randomly all the time. As they collide with each other and with the walls of their container, they rebound, changing speed and direction. This constant, random movement of molecules in a liquid is called Brownian motion. It drives the process of diffusion.

If molecules of another substance are added to water, they will be bounced around by the motion of the water molecules and each other until the new substance is spread evenly throughout the water. From earlier studies, you will recall that in this case the water is acting as a solvent that dissolves other substances, or solutes.

Diffusion always results in the net movement of particles from a region of high concentration toward a region of low concentration. The difference in concentrations between these regions is called the **concentration gradient**. For example, in the river pictured in Figure 1.30 on the previous page, the concentration of mud particles is very high on one side and very low on the other. What do you think happens to the concentration of the mud particles farther downstream?

Over short distances, diffusion works well to transport small molecules across the cell membrane. For example, oxygen and carbon dioxide cross the cell membrane by diffusion. As a cell uses up dissolved oxygen, more oxygen enters the cell; as a cell generates carbon dioxide, more carbon dioxide leaves the cell.

Diffusion Limits Cell Size

Diffusion also explains how molecules move around once inside the cell. But the concentration gradient within a cell is not nearly as great as that across the cell membrane. Once molecules have diffused through the membrane, their rate of diffusion slows down abruptly. How does this fact limit the maximum size of cells? Figure 1.32 gives some clues.

For the cell, having a large surface area relative to its volume increases the area available for materials to diffuse in and out.

A human – sized amoeba?

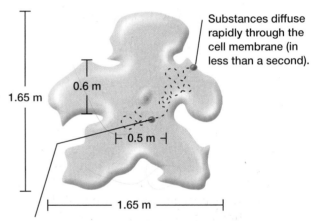

Figure 1.32 This amoeba has two problems: (1) It would take years for molecules critical to survival, such as oxygen, to reach its centre via diffusion. (2) Relative to the volume of the "body" that it has, it does not have much surface area (cell membrane) across which substances can move in and out.

MINI LAB

Random Walking

In this lab, you will measure how long it takes for food-colouring particles to diffuse different distances. Fill a 25 mL graduated cylinder with warm tap water. Gently tap the side of the cylinder to eliminate all air bubbles in the water. Use a long pipette to take a 1 mL sample of undiluted blue or red food colouring, and then rinse the outside of the pipette with running water. Carefully insert the pipette into the cylinder until the tip reaches the bottom of the water. Release the food colouring into the water. Time how long it takes for the colour to move 3 mL up the cylinder. Time how long it takes for the colour to move up 10 mL.

Analyze

1. Make a general statement about the speed of diffusion and distance.

2. Explain why you think this MiniLab is called "Random Walking."

3. Make a prediction about what would happen to the rate of diffusion if you (a) increased the temperature of the water or (b) decreased the temperature of the water. In each case, explain your reasons why.

4. State whether temperature is a dependent or an independent variable in testing rates of diffusion.

Osmosis: The Diffusion of Water

Water from the extracellular fluid and from inside the cell also diffuses freely through the cell membrane in such a way that the concentration of water on either side of the membrane usually remains equal. This diffusion of the *solvent* across a semi-permeable membrane separating two solutions is called **osmosis**. For cells, where the solvent is water, the water molecules move from a region of higher concentration to a region of lower concentration — as in any other form of diffusion.

The direction of osmosis always depends on the relative concentration of water molecules on either side of the cell membrane:

- When the water concentration inside the cell equals the water concentration outside the cell, equal amounts of water move in and out of the cell (isotonic conditions).

- When the water concentration outside the cell is greater than that inside the cell, water moves into the cell (hypotonic conditions).

- When the water concentration inside the cell is greater than that outside the cell, water moves out of the cell (hypertonic conditions).

The cell membrane cannot prevent this movement of water (because it is permeable to water molecules), and the only energy involved is the Brownian motion of the water molecules. Hence, osmosis (like diffusion) is a passive process that does not require energy from the cell. Clearly though, the cell can remain healthy only if the water concentrations inside it and in the extra cellular fluid surrounding it stay in balance.

Blood plasma and the fluid that bathes our cells are usually isotonic. Figure 1.33 illustrates what happens to a red blood cell in an isotonic and a hypotonic environment. The figure also shows how the concentration of solutes on either side of the cell membrane affects the concentration of water. One of the dangers a cell faces under hypotonic conditions is that the cell membrane may burst. The destruction of a cell through this process is called **lysis**.

What would happen to this cell under hypertonic conditions? When water diffuses out of the cell, the process is called **plasmolysis**. A higher concentration of solutes in the extracellular fluid than in the intracellular fluid can cause plasmolysis.

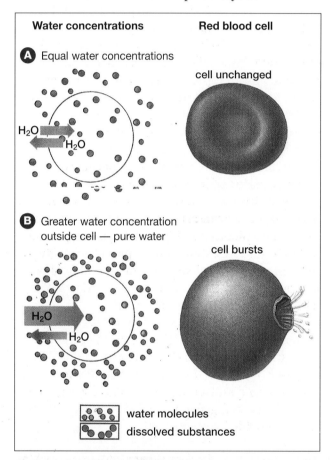

Figure 1.33 If a cell is placed in a hypotonic solution, water enters the cell by osmosis. Under these conditions, cells without cell walls may burst.

Facilitated Diffusion

Although water, oxygen, and carbon dioxide can pass through the cell membrane without assistance, other substances cannot do so without help. This makes the cell membrane a **selectively permeable membrane**. For example, glucose cannot cross the cell membrane by simple diffusion — even if the glucose concentration outside a cell is greater than that within. The glucose molecule is too big to diffuse between the phospholipid molecules of the membrane and is *insoluble* in lipids, so it cannot dissolve in the lipid bilayer.

How then do molecules such as glucose get in and out of the cell? This is where many of the proteins studded in the cell membrane play a role. Specialized transport proteins in the cell membrane help different kinds of substances move in and out of the cell. The structure of these transport proteins enables them to be highly selective. A particular transport protein will recognize and help to move only one type of dissolved molecule or ion based on the particle's shape, size, and electrical charge.

In the case of glucose, a type of membrane protein called a **carrier protein** facilitates the movement of glucose molecules from a region where they are more concentrated to a region where they are less concentrated. Because the relative concentration of glucose still drives its movement through the carrier protein, this **facilitated diffusion** is also an example of passive transport. Figure 1.34 shows how a carrier protein works.

DESIGN YOUR OWN
Investigation

1 • B

SKILL FOCUS

Hypothesizing

Modelling concepts

Initiating and planning

Analyzing and interpreting

Osmosis in a Model Cell

The small size of living cells makes it difficult to observe osmosis actually occurring across their membranes. However, you can make a model of a cell to study the process of osmosis. You can use dialysis tubing, which provides a synthetic membrane permeable to water molecules, as the membrane of a model cell. In this investigation, you will design and conduct an experiment to determine how the composition of the extracellular fluid affects osmosis.

Problem

How does the presence or absence of solutes in the extracellular fluid affect the direction and amount of osmosis through the model cell's membrane?

Hypothesis

Make a hypothesis about the effect of solutes in the extracellular fluid on the flow of water through the cell membrane by osmosis.

CAUTION: Follow your teacher's directions for conducting laboratory experiments safely. Do not consume any food products in the laboratory.

Materials

dialysis tubing	4 mol/L sucrose solution or
string to tie tubing	table syrup
support stand to hang	sodium chloride (table salt)
"cell" in beaker	tap water
large beakers (500 mL)	any other materials
or jars	you require
distilled water, egg white,	
or Ringer's solution	

Experimental Plan

1. Examine the materials provided by your teacher. As a group, list the possible ways

Carrier proteins depend on their three-dimensional shapes to do their jobs. A carrier protein will accept only a non-charged molecule with a specific shape, much as a shape-sorting toy allows a child to insert a triangular piece only in a triangular hole. However, carrier proteins allow molecules to move both in and out of the cell.

> PLAY

To review cell membrane structure and enhance your learning about membrane transport, go to your Electronic Learning Partner.

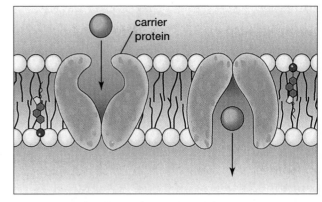

Figure 1.34 Carrier proteins change shape to allow certain molecules to cross the cell membrane.

you might test your hypothesis using these materials.

2. Agree on one way that your group could investigate your hypothesis.

3. Your experimental design should use a control and test only one variable at a time. Plan how you will collect quantitative data.

4. Write a numbered procedure for your experiment that lists each step, and prepare a list of materials that includes the quantities you will need.

Checking the Plan

1. What will be your independent variable? What will be your dependent variable(s)? How will you set up your control?

2. What measurements will you make? How will you determine if the solute content in the extracellular fluid has affected the direction or amount of osmosis? Have you designed a table for collecting data?

3. How many trials will you carry out? How long will you allow each trial to run?

Data and Observations

Conduct your experiment, make your measurements, and complete your data table. Design and complete a graph or other visual presentation of your results.

Analyze

1. How did any changes you observed in your model cell(s) relate to the solute concentrations of the extracellular fluid in which you placed the cell(s)?

2. What evidence do you have that the amount of water inside the cell was or was not changed by osmosis?

3. What evidence do you have that dialysis tubing is permeable to water?

Conclude and Apply

4. How do solutes affect the concentration of water?

5. Based on your results, predict how the use of road salt to melt ice or snow affects the plants bordering the sidewalk, road, or highway. Explain.

Exploring Further

6. Using what you learned in this investigation, design an experiment that would help solve a related problem: How will the presence or absence of solutes in the model cell's *intracellular* fluid affect the direction and extent of osmosis through the model cell's membrane? If time and materials are available, perform the experiment and anlayze your results.

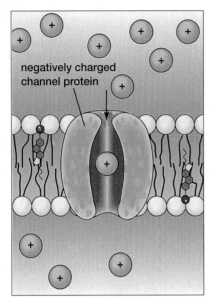

Figure 1.35 Channel proteins provide water-filled passages through which small dissolved ions can diffuse.

Channel Proteins

Since carrier proteins cannot transport charged particles across the cell membrane, a different type of membrane protein called a **channel protein** does this. Channel proteins have a tunnel-like shape that allows charged particles (ions) to pass through the lipid bilayer. Figure 1.35 illustrates how this process works.

To pass through a channel protein, an ion in solution must be small enough to fit through the "tunnel." It must also have the right charge. In much the same way that like poles of two magnets repel each other, a positively charged channel protein repels positively charged ions and a negatively charged channel protein repels negatively charged ions.

BIO FACT

In cystic fibrosis, a genetic disorder, faulty channel proteins cause chloride ions to build up outside the cell and sodium ions to build up inside the cell. This makes water move into the cell (by osmosis). The cells that line the lungs, intestines, and pancreas take water from the mucous layer coating the passageways, leaving the mucous thick and sticky. In the lungs, the thick mucous interferes with breathing. It interferes with the absorption of nutrients in the intestine. Intensive research has led to an increase in the quality and length of life for people living with the disease.

In all of the forms of passive transport you have looked at, any substances crossing the cell membrane travel *along* (or down) their concentration gradient.

No cellular energy is required regardless of whether the substances move in or out of the cell. Facilitated diffusion does require the participation of specialized membrane proteins, but the proteins *do not* require energy from the cell to do their job.

Active Transport

A cell often needs to maintain an intracellular environment vastly different from that outside the cell. For example, it must concentrate nutrients for growth and maintenance inside, and also carry out any specialized functions it may have. In addition, many of the cell's waste products are highly toxic and must be completely removed from the intracellular environment. Passive transport would allow some of these materials to remain in the cell.

How does the cell acquire control over the substances it needs for life? To do this, the cell must expend energy to transport substances (solutes) from an area of lower concentration to one of higher concentration, much like pushing an object up a hill. This process of moving substances *against* (or up) their concentration gradients is called **active transport**.

How much energy does it take to move a substance up a concentration gradient? That depends on how steep the uphill gradient is. Particles move down a concentration gradient with the same ease that you might ride a bike down a hill. A similar analogy can be made for particles being moved up a concentration gradient. Like the cyclist in Figure 1.36, the steeper the hill the harder the you have to pedal to get up it.

Figure 1.36 Like a cyclist pedalling up a steep hill, the cell must expend a great deal of energy to pump molecules and ions in or out of the cell against their concentration gradients.

Dr. Pierre Côté with a sample of ZeeWeed membrane and a glass of water that has passed through the membrane.

Civil Engineer

Traditionally, "membrane" is used to refer to a thin film with microscopic pores that admit only particles small enough to pass through. Membrane filtration technology beyond teabags and coffee filters is nothing new. For example, hospital dialysis machines use membranes to filter the blood of patients whose kidneys no longer function. However, the use of this technology is costly. Until recently, membrane technology for water filtration has been costly, too.

Enter Dr. Pierre Côté, civil engineer, with a new kind of membrane. A book about the potential environmental impact of Earth's rapidly growing human population motivated him to focus on environmental engineering, especially water treatment.

A typical water treatment plant passes water through clean sand as a primary filter and then gel-like coagulants to trap fine sediments, such as clay. After this, chlorine is added to kill remaining bacteria. (A conventional "activated sludge" sewage treatment plant uses bacteria to break down wastes.) Now, Dr. Côté's prize-winning membrane technology offers a new approach.

Designing an Award-Winning Membrane

Dr. Côté received a Manning Innovation Award of $100,000 for his development of ZeeWeed, a unique filtration membrane that represents a revolution in water treatment. It can be used to treat ground or surface water for drinking or to purify municipal and industrial wastewater before discharge to the environment.

ZeeWeed is composed of thin, hollow fibres. The membrane of the fibres has pores small enough to block the passage of viruses and of micro-organisms such as bacteria. These fibres are mounted in an open frame that can be immersed directly in the water to be treated. Like living seaweed, ZeeWeed fibres float freely. ZeeWeed has low energy requirements. A light stream of air bubbles keeps the Zeeweed fibres moving, thereby exposing the fibre membranes to incoming water currents. A slight suction on the clean water side draws water through the pores of the membranes into the hollow interior of the fibres, leaving the micro-organisms and viruses behind.

Dr. James M. Dickson of McMaster University's Membrane Research Group describes such membranes as "not very smart" when compared with the cell membrane. "They're designed to do a very specific job, and that's all they do." The membrane around a living cell must sense and respond to every aspect of the internal and external environment. It must perform dozens of distinctly different sensing, separation, and transportation tasks — some of them thousands of times per minute.

Teamwork Pays Off

As the chief technical officer at Oakville's Zenon Environmental Inc. — a global leader in advanced membrane technologies for water purification, wastewater treatment, and water recycling — Dr. Côté loves his job. "Just coming to work is fun. It's not working," he says. "I'm doing research and development, so it's always something new." When asked what he'd do with the prize money from the Manning Award, he replied "I will share it with my [research] team and the workers at Zenon." Like other researchers in both the pure sciences and the technologies, Dr. Côté recognizes that new developments almost always result from a team effort.

Career Tips

1. Research further to discover how civil engineers are solving other real-world environmental problems.

2. What knowledge of cell biology should a manager at a water-treatment facility have to do the job effectively? How does this person work with the Ministry of the Environment, water-testing facilities, and local landowners to ensure the delivery of safe drinking water?

When a person is resting, his or her cells use up to 40% of their energy on active transport. Many types of specialized cells use much more. For example, the cells in your kidneys that filter your blood use up to 90% of their energy on active transport.

What kind of substances do cells need to pump in or out by active transport? A few examples follow:

- Kidney cells pump glucose and amino acids out of the urine and back into the blood.
- Intestinal cells pump in nutrients from the gut.
- Root cells pump in nutrients from the soil.
- Gill cells in fish pump out sodium ions (their extracellular fluid is less salty than sea water).

Figure 1.37 How does the work done by a refrigerator resemble the work done by active transport in cells?

Math LINK

Specialized cells in your stomach lining secrete acid so that you can digest foods. They maintain the concentration of acid at about 0.000 15 g/mL of fluid. That number may seem low, but the concentration of acid inside the cells is much lower — less than 0.000 000 000 05 g/mL. Compare the acidity of the fluid inside your stomach to the acidity inside these cells: divide the stomach's acid concentration by the cell's acid concentration. Write your answer using scientific notation. What does this ratio tell you about the concentration gradient faced by the cells? Why must the cells consume large amounts of energy to pump acid out across their cell membranes?

It may help to think of the cell as a refrigerator. Although food comes into the kitchen, some food must be actively concentrated in the refrigerator and some items in the refrigerator need to be taken out. The refrigerator has to maintain a special environment inside in order to keep the food fresh. To do this, the refrigerator uses a mechanism to cool the inside air and pump out excess heat. It also removes the water from the air inside and sends it outside (the water comes from the food that enters the refrigerator). Otherwise, the water would condense on surfaces in the cold

THINKING LAB

Relative Concentration Challenge

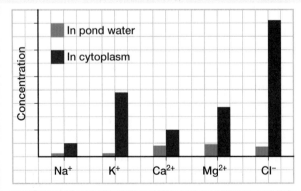

Background

Nitella, a green alga, is a common pond organism that has very long cells and a plantlike structure. If left undisturbed,

Nitella can spread across the bottom of a pond, providing refuge for many pond dwellers. Pond water contains several of the dissolved ions needed by pond organisms, such as sodium (Na^+), potassium (K^+), calcium (Ca^{2+}), magnesium (Mg^{2+}), and chloride (Cl^-). In this lab, you will investigate the concentration of these ions inside and outside of *Nitella*. The vertical blue bars on the graph represent ion concentrations inside the *Nitella* cells. The green bars represent the concentration of ions in the pond water outside *Nitella*'s cell membrane.

You Try It

1. If ions simply diffuse through *Nitella*'s cell membrane, how would the blue and green bars for each ion compare? Suggest why simple diffusion cannot account for the data presented in the graph.

2. What evidence is there that *Nitella* must somehow be forcing ions inward against a concentration gradient?

environment. Every time you open the refrigerator, warm air flows in and cold air flows out, both along their concentration gradients. Even with the door closed, the refrigerator pump must still come on frequently and use energy to maintain the special internal environment.

Active Transport Pump

The cell uses an elegant system to actively transport substances in and out against their concentration gradients. The engine that drives this system is a pump, which runs on energy from cell metabolism. The pump is a cell membrane protein. This transporter protein actively pumps ions across the membrane against their concentration gradients. Cells have several different transporter pumps.

The best-understood example of an active transport pump is the sodium-potassium pump in animal cells. The cell membrane of every cell in your body uses these pumps. As Figure 1.38 shows, this transporter pumps sodium and potassium ions.

When three (positive) sodium ions inside the cell and two (positive) potassium ions from the extracellular fluid bind to the transporter's protein complex, the transporter taps a form of cellular energy (ATP). This allows the protein to change shape. In its new shape, the three sodium ions move to the outside of the cell and the two potassium ions move inside — the transporter has flipped the ions. Then it releases all of the ions and returns to its original shape.

> **>> FAST FORWARD**
>
> To learn more about cellular respiration and ATP, turn to Chapter 3, Section 3.3.

> **> PLAY**
>
> To view an animation of and explore active transport, go to your Electronic Learning Partner.

Tapping the Energy Stored by Active Transport

The cell uses the artificial concentration gradient it has created for sodium ions to push molecules it needs, such as glucose and amino acids, into the cell. The cell cannot function if it only gets as many of these molecules as diffusion will allow into the cell, so the cell must move extra glucose and amino acids in *against* a concentration gradient.

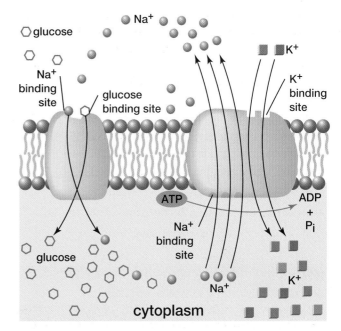

Figure 1.38 The primary components of the active-transport system driven by the sodium-potassium pump

How can a sodium ion exert a pushing force on a molecule? Think of the sodium ions as skiers at the top of a ski hill with nowhere to go but down. The cell pushed them up the chair lift. Now it makes them take a molecule down the hill with them. A type of carrier membrane protein helps the sodium ion and a molecule (such as glucose) enter the cell. When one sodium ion and one glucose molecule bind to this carrier protein, it changes shape. It now allows the sodium ion to ride down its concentration gradient into the cell — providing the energy to move the glucose molecule as well. Plant and bacterial cells use hydrogen instead of sodium ions to do this.

Another protein in the cell membrane also taps the energy stored in the sodium-ion concentration gradient — this time to push another positive ion *out* of the cell. A common use for this exchange of one ion for another is pumping unwanted hydrogen ions (H^+) out of the cell *against* their concentration gradient. This keeps the cell interior from becoming too acidic.

The artificial concentration gradients that active transport creates for sodium and potassium ions result in a constant tendency for potassium ions to diffuse out of the cell and for sodium ions to diffuse back into it. So the sodium-potassium pump must work constantly. In fact, even when you are resting it consumes nearly one third of the energy generated by your cells. This high-energy requirement is thought to be caused by the need for rapid, repeated changes of shape in the transporter protein complex.

Through its active transport system, the cell stockpiles nutrients it needs for maintenance and growth and pumps out unwanted particles. In addition, it creates an electrical potential across the cell membrane that allows nerves and muscles to work. The higher concentration of positive ions outside the cell creates an electrical charge across the cell membrane.

BIO FACT

For a nerve impulse to travel the length of a nerve cell, it must keep changing the electrical charge across the cell membrane as it goes. The change in charge in one part of the nerve cell membrane causes special ion channels to open in the next part. During the millisecond that each of these sodium ion channels remains open, some 7000 sodium ions pass into the cell through each one. To allow for a new nerve impulse, the cell must pump out all of these sodium ions.

SECTION REVIEW

1. **K/U** Define diffusion using one specific example.

2. **K/U** Explain the concept of a concentration gradient, and use diagrams to clarify your explanation.

3. **K/U** Identify three different molecules that diffuse into cells.

4. **K/U** Distinguish between osmosis and diffusion.

5. **K/U** What is homeostasis? Why is homeostasis important to cells?

6. **K/U** Diffusion allows for the effective movement of substances over short distances. How is this important for the cell?

7. **C** Some potato cells are immersed in tap water. Make diagrams showing the relative concentration of water in both the cells and in the water.

8. **K/U** Describe the movement of water inside a cell in a hypertonic environment.

9. **K/U** How is facilitated diffusion different from diffusion?

10. **K/U** Identify two situations where cells need to use active transport. Describe an additional possible situation where active transport might make sense.

11. **K/U** Make a diagram of the sodium-potassium pump, and briefly explain how it works.

12. **K/U** What would happen to a cell if its cell membrane were permeable rather than semi-permeable?

13. **K/U** Why does oxygen continue to diffuse into cells on an ongoing basis?

14. **MC** Explain why water pollution has such a profound effect on living organisms.

15. **I** Cystic fibrosis is the result of genetic mutations within a gene identified as cystic fibrosis transmembrane conductance regulator (CFTR), which codes for a channel protein. An experiment was conducted to identify the specific ion being transported by CFTR. The candidate ions were chloride (Cl^-), magnesium (Mg^{2+}), and sodium (Na^+). The experiment involved comparing cytoplasmic levels of these ions between normal cells and cystic fibrosis cells. Interpret the results below, and give a possible explanation for them.

Ions	Cytoplasmic ion concentration (mmol/dL)	
	Normal CFTR	**Abnormal CFTR**
Mg^{2+}	0.02	0.02
Na^{1+}	0.05	1.55
Cl^{1-}	1.2	0.001

16. **C** Plan a dramatic presentation involving students in the class to show the difference between passive transport and active transport in the cell.

UNIT INVESTIGATION PREP

Cells need to bring in (absorb) nutrients.
- What method(s) of transport do cells in the intestine use to absorb nutrients? Explain why.

- Draw a picture showing how glucose and galactose enter a cell. Use a different shape for each simple sugar.

- If a cell has adequate glucose in its extracellular environment, explain why a cell might not have enough glucose inside. Give several possible reasons.

- Explain the processes of endocytosis and exocytosis.

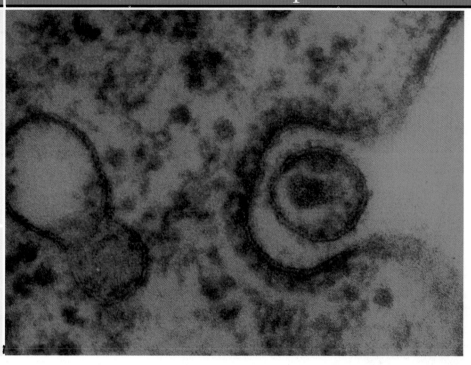

Figure 1.39 By binding to two cell membrane receptors, a human immunodeficiency virus (HIV) tricks a cell into transporting it inside (through a process called receptor-assisted endocytosis).

Very few materials that the cell must take in or expel are too big or too polar to cross through the cell membrane via passive transport (diffusion, osmosis, and facilitated diffusion) or active transport. The cell uses a specialized method of moving these substances in and out so that they do not have to pass through the lipid bilayer. The cell membrane can fold in on itself to create a membrane-enclosed, bubble-like sac, or **vesicle**. The cell uses these vesicles to "swallow" or expel various materials.

Endocytosis

When the cell membrane folds inward, trapping and enclosing a small amount of matter from the extracellular fluid, the process is called **endocytosis** (*endo* means within). There are three main forms of endocytosis: pinocytosis, phagocytosis, and receptor-assisted endocytosis.

Pinocytosis, or cell "drinking," involves the intake of a small droplet of extracellular fluid, together with any dissolved substances or very small particles that it may contain. This process occurs in nearly all cell types nearly all of the time.

Phagocytosis, or cell "eating," involves the intake of a large droplet of extracellular fluid, often including particulate matter such as bacteria or bits of organic matter. This process occurs only in specialized cells, such as a single-celled amoeba or the bacteria-eating cells of our own immune system (macrophages) — and only when they encounter something "suitable for engulfing."

Receptor-assisted endocytosis involves the intake of specific molecules that attach to special proteins in the cell membrane that serve as receptors. These **membrane receptors** possess a uniquely shaped projection or cavity that fits the shape of only one specific molecule.

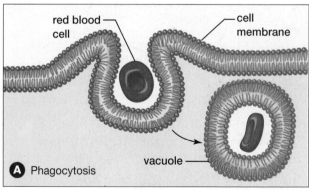

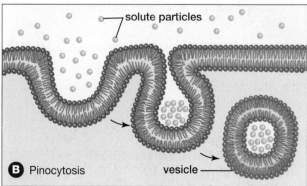

Figure 1.40 (A) Animal macrophages take in worn-out red blood cells as well as bacteria by phagocytosis. (B) In pinocytosis, the cell takes in solute particles along with fluids.

The Mystery of the Frozen Frogs

Dr. Kenneth Storey with a graduate student

Humans die if they are frozen. Ice crystals form inside our cells, irreparably damaging the cell membrane. But some species of frogs freeze solid every winter in Canada. Frozen frogs have no heartbeat. They stop breathing. They appear to be dead, but come spring, they thaw out and hop away. Award-winning cryobiologist Kenneth Storey has spent much of his career trying to understand this survival mechanism. At his lab at Carleton University in Ottawa, he began freezing thumbnail-sized wood frogs and spring peepers in cozy moss-filled boxes, carrying out experiments to try to discover the molecular secrets that allow them to survive being frozen.

A Natural Cryoprotectant

Dr. Storey suspected that the frogs have a mystery molecule that allows their cells to withstand the rigours of freezing. He soon discovered that the molecule was glucose, the same blood sugar that your cells use for fuel. As soon as ice starts forming on their smooth, green skin, frogs start packing their cells with glucose (released from glycogen stored in the liver). This prevents ice crystals from forming within the cells. If humans had the same glucose levels in their blood as freezing frogs, they would be diabetic and extremely sick. So Dr. Storey's next challenge is to find out what makes frog cells pull the glucose out of the blood.

But Would It Work for Individual Human Organs?

From the beginning of his frog research, Dr. Storey believed that the secret of the icy frogs might one day

help save human lives by allowing organs that have been donated for transplant to be frozen. Doctors now have to race against time once a heart or a liver has been taken from a donor. Human livers taken from donors for transplant generally last only six to eight hours after death, a heart and lung only four to five. Freezing would give doctors time to wait for the perfect match. During the Second World War, scientists did experiments to learn how to freeze blood. After the war, they tried to same approach with organs, but failed to freeze them without destroying them. That is when they began looking for a model in the natural world. When a scientist in Minnesota accidentally left frogs in his car trunk overnight and found they survived freezing, Dr. Storey was intrigued.

One Mystery at a Time

Dr. Storey was recognized in 1984 with a Steacie Award as one of Canada's most promising young scientists. Discovering that glucose was the cryoprotectant in frogs was only the first step. He has found more than 20 genes (out of the 2 000 that make up a frog's chromosomes) that are turned on when the animal starts to freeze. It appears that these genes shut down the frog's metabolism and then pack its cells with sugar. Dr. Storey explains that once he and other scientists have identified all the genes that are involved in cryoprotection, they then have to discover how to turn the genes on and off.

Not Only Frogs Are Cool

Researchers in his lab now study ground squirrels, bats, snails, and turtles. Some turtles can hibernate for three or four months under water without breathing. A hibernating ground squirrel does not freeze solid, but it does turn off its metabolism and lives in a state of suspended animation. Are the same genes involved in freeze-tolerant frogs, turtles, and squirrels? No, says Dr. Storey, but the processes and mechanisms seem to be similar. For example, in both squirrels and frogs, enzymes known as "stress-activated kinases" are turned on when an animal starts to freeze, and these act to shut its metabolism down. Dr. Storey says it will take years to figure out exactly how it all works. If he cannot get organs to freeze without damage (like those of a frog), the next best thing would be to get them to stay in a squirrel-like state of hibernation.

"These animals are living in a state of suspended animation. If you think about suspended animation, that is exactly what you want for organs for transplant. Squirrels aren't dead at five degrees. We want mammalian organs to act like that in fridges everywhere."

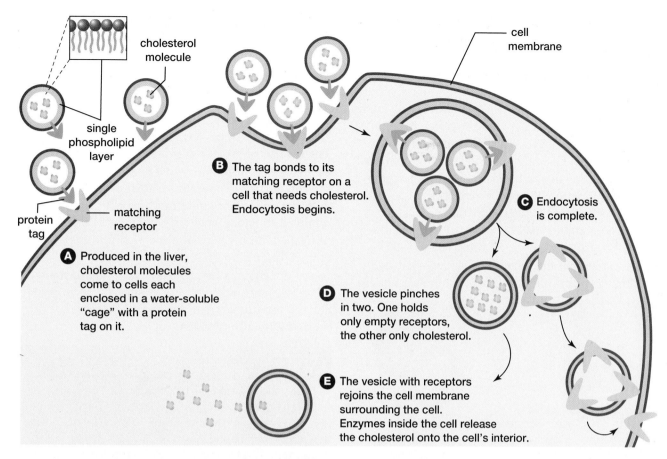

cell membrane

cholesterol molecule

single phospholipid layer

protein tag

matching receptor

B The tag bonds to its matching receptor on a cell that needs cholesterol. Endocytosis begins.

A Produced in the liver, cholesterol molecules come to cells each enclosed in a water-soluble "cage" with a protein tag on it.

C Endocytosis is complete.

D The vesicle pinches in two. One holds only empty receptors, the other only cholesterol.

E The vesicle with receptors rejoins the cell membrane surrounding the cell. Enzymes inside the cell release the cholesterol onto the cell's interior.

Figure 1.41 The transport of cholesterol molecules from the extracellular fluid into the cell interior is an example of receptor-mediated endocytosis.

Animal cells bring in cholesterol using receptor-assisted endocytosis. To ensure that the membranes of cells and of structures within cells have enough cholesterol, your liver manufactures the cholesterol that your cells need from natural lipids in your diet — even if you eat only "cholesterol-free" foods.

However, being a lipid, cholesterol cannot dissolve directly in your blood or extracellular fluid (which are water based). Thus, cholesterol cannot cross the cell membrane by pinocytosis. Figure 1.41 shows the method by which your cells take up cholesterol.

 **MINI LAB**

Freezing Cells

Many Canadian plants and animals must be able to survive −40°C temperatures for extended periods. What happens to the cell membrane and the contents of the cell at these temperatures? Freezing models of the cell will help you appreciate the nature of the challenge organisms face in cold climates.

Collect three small pill vials or film canisters. (A pharmacy or photo shop may be able to provide containers.) These containers will represent the cell membranes of three individual cells. Use a permanent marker to label one "A," one "B," and the third "C." Because cells contain more water than any other substance, fill model cell A with water to represent the cell's contents. Living cells run on sugar, so fill model cell B with a dilute sugar solution (5 mL glucose

or honey in 50 mL water). For comparison, fill model cell C with a more concentrated sugar solution, such as undiluted corn syrup, molasses, or table syrup. Make sure all three containers are filled to the very top. Place them in a sealed plastic bag, and leave them in a freezer overnight. Examine each container the next day.

Analyze

1. What happened to model cell A? Suggest why this happened.

2. What happened to model cells B and C? Suggest why.

3. Based on the behaviour of these models, what do you think would happen if a real cell were frozen?

4. Explain how your own cells could survive in below-freezing temperatures. What about plant cells?

Cholesterol molecules are transported in the blood and extracellular fluid inside droplets covered with a single layer of phospholipids. These phospholipids have their lipid-soluble tails pointed inward (at the cholesterol) and their water-soluble heads pointed outward (at the blood or fluid). Each droplet has a protein "tag" on its surface that can be recognized only by a matching receptor on the cell membrane. Once the tag and receptor connect, the surrounding membrane folds inward, forming a vesicle filled with cholesterol molecules attached to receptors. Figure 1.42 depicts this process. The vesicle empties its contents inside the cell and then returns to the cell membrane, where it turns *inside out* so that the receptors face outward again. This recycles both the receptors and the membrane.

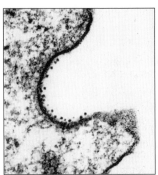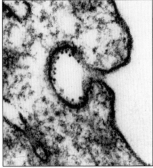

Figure 1.42 How do these photographs of receptor-assisted endocytosis provide clues to the way that the cell membrane works?

Web LINK

To find out more about endocytosis, visit the web site shown below. Go to **Science Resources**, then to **BIOLOGY 11** to find out where to visit next. Compare the images and describe what you see.

www.school.mcgrawhill.ca/resources/

⏸ PAUSE ⏺ RECORD

List the three main forms of endocytosis and state what they have in common. Develop a chart or set of diagrams to show how they differ.

Exocytosis

The reverse of endocytosis is **exocytosis**. In exocytosis, a vesicle from inside the cell moves to the cell surface. There, the vesicle membrane fuses with the cell membrane (thus restoring membrane removed in endocytosis). The contents of the outward-bound vesicle are secreted into the extracellular fluid. Exocytosis is especially important in cells that specialize in the secretion of various cell products. For example, specialized cells in the human pancreas below secrete the hormone insulin by means of exocytosis.

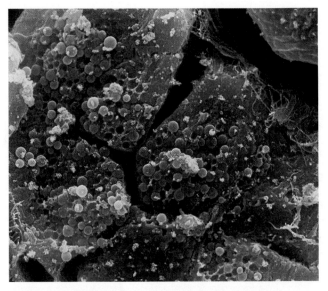

Figure 1.43 Exocytosis in pancreatic cells appears as vesicles releasing their contents on the surface of the cells.

SECTION REVIEW

1. **K/U** Identify two examples of exocytosis in your body.

2. **K/U** White blood cells move throughout the body to engulf matter, including parts of dead cells. Use labelled diagrams and words to explain this process.

3. **K/U** How does the structure of the cell membrane facilitate endocytosis and exocytosis?

4. **K/U** Endocytosis involves the formation of vesicles to bring matter into the cell. Once inside, what happens to this matter?

5. **K/U** What do membrane receptors and carrier proteins have in common? How are they different?

6. **C** Compare and contrast endocytosis and active transport, using a chart to organize your information.

7. **K/U** Suggest one way that specialized cells using phagocytosis to bring in materials may replace the pieces of cell membrane used to form vesicles.

8. **MC** Explain how the development of the electron microscope and research into cell membrane function have helped scientists understand how a virus can get into cells. How might this technology and its applications have affected the field of medicine?

Chapter Expectations

Briefly explain each of the following points.

- The subunits of every organic macromolecule contain carbon. (1.1)
- Carbohydrates provide energy storage. (1.1)
- The structure of proteins allows them to play important roles in an organism. (1.1)
- Indicators form the basis of standard tests for biochemical compounds. (1.1)
- The nucleic acids in DNA have a different monosaccharide base than the ones in RNA. (1.1)
- Three-dimensional models of molecules allow scientists to better understand the structure of and interactions between molecules. (1.1)
- The fact that phospholipids do not dissolve in water and have a polar and a nonpolar component makes them a useful material from which to make cell membranes. (1.2)
- Without the proteins, cholesterol, and other molecules in its fluid-mosaic structure, the cell membrane could not perform its functions. (1.2)
- As a form of passive transport, osmosis relies on a concentration gradient. (1.3)
- In facilitated diffusion, the cell membrane transports specific molecules in or out without expending energy. (1.3)
- Endocytosis and exocytosis allow cells to move large or very polar materials in and out. (1.4)

Language of Biology

Write a sentence using each of the following words or terms. Use any six terms in a concept map to show your understanding of how they are related.

- biochemistry
- polar
- nonpolar
- organic compound
- macromolecule
- carbohydrate
- monosaccharide
- disaccharide
- polysaccharide
- starch
- glycogen
- cellulose
- lipid
- fatty acid
- saturated
- unsaturated
- protein
- amino acid
- peptide bond
- polypeptide
- denatured
- essential amino acids
- nucleic acids
- nucleotides
- electron microscope
- phospholipid
- phospholipid bilayer
- fluid-mosaic membrane model
- selectively permeable membrane
- homeostasis
- extracellular fluid
- diffusion
- concentration gradient
- osmosis
- lysis
- plasmolysis
- carrier protein
- facilitated diffusion
- channel protein
- active transport
- endocytosis
- vesicle
- phagocytosis
- pinocytosis
- receptor-assisted endocytosis
- membrane receptor
- exocytosis

UNDERSTANDING CONCEPTS

1. List the cell processes necessary for life.
2. Describe the unique properties of water that allow life to exist.
3. Identify examples of a monosaccharide, a disaccharide, and a polysaccharide.
4. Identify the three main types of lipids. Explain the importance of each type.
5. Draw a diagram of a phospholipid. Label the polar and non-polar ends.
6. What is a positive test to detect the presence of a protein?
7. Use a sketch to show how a single strand of nucleic acids looks.
8. Many biological molecules are polymers, or long chains made with repeating subunits. List three types of polymers commonly found in cells. Identify the subunit for each molecule.
9. (a) Draw a diagram of a water molecule. Show how this molecule is polar.
   (b) Draw a diagram of a carbon dioxide molecule.
   (c) Explain why carbon dioxide is not polar but water is.
10. Explain how the polarity of water organizes phospholipids into a bilayer.

11. List three molecules that are found on or in the cell membrane other than phospholipds.

12. Cholesterol acts to maintain the cell membrane's fluid consistency in extreme environments. Suggest reasons why this is important to the cell.

13. How is homeostasis important for the cell?

14. Explain the process of diffusion across a membrane.

15. The cells in your body live in an environment with an almost constant temperature. How does this affect diffusion?

16. Define osmosis as a special case of diffusion.

17. **(a)** Explain what happens to a cell placed in a hypotonic solution.
    (b) Will this be the same for a plant cell as an animal cell? Explain.

18. What is a channel protein? Why are channel proteins important to cells?

19. Use examples to explain how facilitated diffusion is different from diffusion.

20. Describe the three types of endocytosis.

21. How is bulk transport different from either passive transport or active transport?

INQUIRY

22. You are interested in identifying the macromolecules present in a popular energy drink used by athletes. Prepare an observation chart that lists the indicators you need to carry out this test. Justify your choices.

23. The effects of different solvents and of varying solvent concentrations on membrane permeability can be studied using beet root. Slices of beet root were placed into one of three solvent solutions for 10 minutes. Then a colorimeter was used to measure the concentration (absorbency) of each solution by comparing its colour to that of a standard beet solution. The tabulated data from the experiment appear below.
    (a) Which alcohol damaged the beet the most at the lowest concentrations?
    (b) Which of the three alcohols seems to affect the beet cell membranes the most? How did you come to this conclusion?
    (c) Make a line graph for this data that would properly identify the independent and dependent variables.

24. A scientist conducted an experiment that investigated the nature of a nerve impulse within a giant squid axon (an extension of a nerve cell). Key to the nerve impulse is the maintenance of sodium and potassium ion concentrations on either side of the cell membrane. Under normal conditions, there is about 30 times more potassium outside of the cell than inside and about 10 times more sodium inside the cell than outside. The result is that a nerve cell has an electric potential (known as the resting potential) of about −0 mV (millivolts) across its cell membrane. In this experiment, dinitrophenol (DNP) was added incrementally to a squid axon and the resting potential was monitored. The results of the experiment are illustrated in the graph below.
    (a) Interpret the results.
    (b) Propose a hypothesis and develop an experiment that would investigate the mechanism of DNP action within the axon.

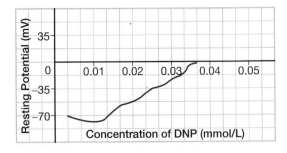

Trial	Concentration (%)	Absorbency (nm)		
		Methanol	Ethanol	Propanol
1	0	250	250	250
2	20	300	270	262
3	40	500	350	299
4	60	625	453	366
5	80	625	630	500
6	100	628	628	600

25. You studied osmosis with an artificial membrane. How would the results change with a living membrane? If a shell is carefully removed from an egg, the membrane underneath is left intact. Design a lab to explore osmosis with this living membrane. Clearly identify your predictions.

26. Three cubes of potato are placed in beakers with different types of solution: hypertonic, hypotonic, and isotonic. Make diagrams to show the movement of water across the cell membranes of the potato cells. Predict any changes that will happen to the potato cubes over a period of two days.

COMMUNICATING

27. Figure 1.5 depicts the consequences of the fact that water is less dense in its solid than in its liquid state. Find out how the polarity of water molecules accounts for this special property of water. Then create a computer-generated diagram to explain this.

28. Make a chart to compare and contrast active transport with passive transport. Include a column for sample molecules.

29. Draw a concept map to describe how material from outside the cell can get inside the cell.

30. Design a poster of a cell membrane. Include information about the function of different parts of the cell membrane.

31. Construct a model of a protein using several different forms for the amino acids. Explain how your model works to a few classmates. As a small group, decide which of the models worked best. Justify your choice. Keep your own model for the end-of-unit review.

32. Suppose that you are a non-phospholipid in a cell membrane. The cell is restructuring and needs to downsize. Write a short promotional speech to save your position.

33. The condition of the cell pictured on the right below is called plasmolysis.

(a) Illustrate what happened to this cell using circles of one colour to represent water molecules, triangles of another colour for solute molecules, and arrows to show the direction of molecule movement.

(b) Explain why plasmolysis kills cells.

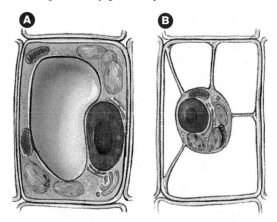

(A) Healthy plant cell (B) Plasmolysis has occurred.

MAKING CONNECTIONS

34. Bacteria and moulds do not grow in honey or pickle jars, even after their containers have been opened. Explain why.

35. Bananas are a good source of potassium ions. Potassium is common in other foods too. What processes would be affected by limited amounts of potassium in the body? Use one or more sources to find health problems connected to such a situation.

36. Find the nutrition chart for several breakfast cereals. Rank the cereals in order of the highest level of carbohydrates to lowest. Look at the marketing approach used on the cereal box. Decide which age group is the target market for each cereal. Suggest reasons for this.

37. Some organisms live in shallow ponds that dry up after a few weeks of hot, dry weather. This means that the concentration of solutes in the water will change. How will this create problems for the cells of organisms for whom the pond water is their extracellular fluid?

38. All cells use combinations of the same fundamental macromolecules. This means that cells share common building blocks. The molecules in your cells are much like the molecules in a pine tree. How might this fact be of benefit to the environment?

Organizing Life

Reflecting Questions

- What structures does the cell contain?
- How do cell structures contribute to life processes?
- How does research into cellular processes help scientists develop new technology?

Without teamwork and organization, the travelling fair pictured on the right could not function. It requires people with different skills contributing different kinds of work to make the whole thing run smoothly. It also requires a lot of organization. Some aspects of running a successful fair are obvious at a glance — the need for a variety of different activities, power, and food concessions, for example. Other important things the fair needs may not be so noticeable, such as restrooms, garbage disposal, and maintenance.

Like the fair, a cell relies on teamwork and organization to function. As a team, the many parts of the cell work together to keep the cell alive. In the photograph of the leaf cell below, you can see some aspects of the internal organization of a cell — some of the members of the cell's team. Also like the fair, many aspects of maintaining a healthy cell are not obvious at a glance. What must a healthy cell do to function? Which parts of a cell take care of each job?

In Chapter 1, you examined one important cellular structure: the cell membrane. This chapter will introduce you to the other important cell structures and explain how they work individually and together, each one depending on the others. You will explore how cell structures process materials brought inside, such as amino acids. You will also examine how the work performed by individual cells in a multicellular

organism relates to the functioning of its organs. Finally, you will learn about how some diseases affect cells and explore how researchers use and develop technologies to treat diseases based on what they discover about the way cells work.

How is the work necessary for life organized and co-ordinated within the tiny space of a cell?

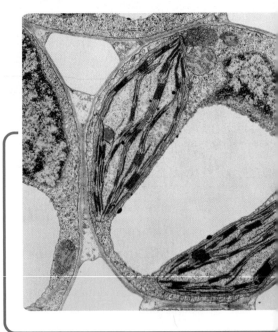

Chapter Contents

Structuring Cell Processes

- Identify the basic features of eukaryotic and prokaryotic cells.

- Describe the structure and function of organelles and other cell structures.

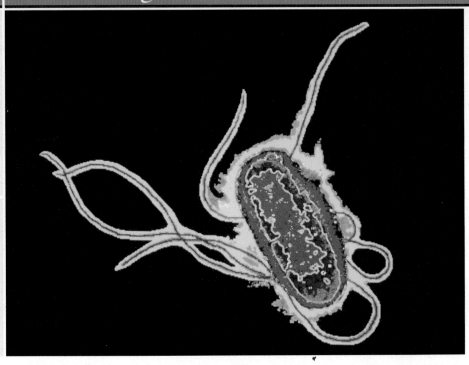

Figure 2.1 Cells with simple internal organization such as this *Escherichia coli* are called prokaryotes. The most abundant cells on Earth, prokaryotes survive in diverse habitats, such as the salt-laden water of the Dead Sea and hot sulfur springs.

Each cell starts out as a fully functional living thing. To sustain life, the cell must create and maintain molecules and structures that then perform the essential tasks necessary for the functioning of the cell. What are these essential tasks? Living cells must

- obtain food and energy

- convert energy from an external source into a form that works within the cell

- construct and maintain the molecules that make up cell structures

- carry out chemical reactions

- eliminate wastes

- reproduce

- keep records of how to build structures

The seemingly endless variety of cells in the world fits one of two basic cell types known as eukaryotic and prokaryotic cells.

Prokaryotes and Eukaryotes

The smallest cells with the simplest type of internal organization lack a nucleus — an enclosed region inside the cell where the DNA is separated from the rest of the cell by a double membrane. Instead, the DNA in these cells is concentrated in an area inside the cell called the nucleoid. Such cells are named **prokaryotes** ("pro" means before, "karyon" means nucleus).

Bacteria, such as the *Escherichia coli* pictured in Figure 2.1, are prokaryotes.

>> FAST FORWARD

To find more detailed information about prokaryotes, turn to Chapter 12, Sections 12.1 and 12.2.

The cells of all other organisms are larger and have a more complex internal structure that includes a nucleus. Such cells are called **eukaryotes** ("eu" means good or true, for true nucleus). Examples of eukaryotes include plants, animals, fungi, and protists.

In addition to the nucleus, eukaryotes have a number of other specialized structures called **organelles**. Each organelle has a highly organized structure and a specific function within the cell. Many organelles are surrounded by their own membranes. The various organelles work together as a team to effectively carry out cell processes — the essential tasks of the cell.

Identifying the different structures of the cell and how they function helps us understand the complex interactions within the cell and between the cell and its external environment. Piecing together the puzzle of how cells function has fascinated people for centuries. With each discovery we come closer to understanding how life works.

Eukaryotic Cells

A great deal of diversity exists among eukaryotic cells. For example, a mature human red blood cell has no nucleus, and the longest cell in your body is a nerve cell that runs from your lower spine to your big toe. To appreciate the specializations of such cells, you need first to understand all the major features of a typical cell.

The organelles in a eukaryotic cell divide its interior into compartments. This allows the many different chemical reactions constantly taking place within the cell to proceed at the same time without interfering with each other. Many organelles contain highly folded membranes that increase the surface area on which chemical reactions can be co-ordinated. This also increases the overall rate of reaction within the cell. The photomicrograph in Figure 2.2 shows such folded structures. Like the cell membrane, organelle membranes have a fluid-mosaic structure. Turn to Figure 2.3 on the next page to learn about the major organelles of a typical animal cell.

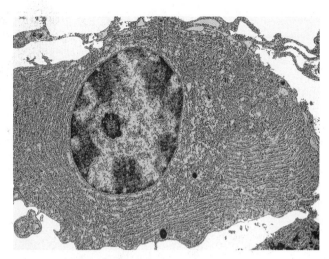

Figure 2.2 This eukaryotic animal cell contains many organelles in addition to its nucleus.

>> FAST FORWARD

To review using a microscope and calculating the magnification and size of a specimen, turn to *Appendix 3*.

Math LINK

The size of cells, cellular structures, and cellular products is measured in micrometres and nanometres. How small is a nanometre? Copy and complete this chart to review the units useful for understanding the size of the cellular world. Then write the equivalent for 1 μm and 1 nm in millimetres.

Unit name	Notation	Equivalent in metres	Example
millimetre		$= 1 \times 10^{-3}$ m	frog egg
micrometre	1 μm		chloroplast
	1 nm	$= 1 \times 10^{-9}$ m	amino acid

MINI LAB

Contrasting Cells

Stains or dyes mark specific macromolecules in the cell and provide a clearer picture of these structures. Traditional stains change colour to indicate the presence of particular macromolecules. In this lab, you will compare unstained and stained cells using a light microscope. Note: Wash your hands thoroughly before and after this activity, and avoid getting methylene blue stain on your skin or in your eyes. To view onion-skin cells, first remove the outer, papery, layer(s) of an onion. Then remove a section of the first ring of the bulb. Using a fingernail, peel a small piece of the inner, transparent, layer off the inside of your onion section. Lay this transparent piece on a glass slide, taking care to ensure that it is not folded. Make a wet mount of this onion skin. Observe the onion cells under low- and high-power magnification. Draw a diagram of one of the onion cells, showing its size in the field of view. Next, use a dropper to add a drop of methylene blue to one edge of the cover slip.

Place a piece of filter paper at the opposite edge of the cover slip to draw the stain through your specimen. Find a well-stained area of your specimen using low-power magnification. Move to high power, and find one clearly stained cell (with blue edges). Draw a diagram of the cell, indicating the colours of the cell features.

Analyze

1. How are stains useful for observing cells?

2. Compare your observations to the photograph of a eukaryotic cell on this page. What part(s) of the cell absorb methylene blue stain?

3. From your investigation to test for macromolecules on pages 16 and 17, what other stain(s) might be useful for viewing cell features?

4. Estimate the size of a plant cell and its nucleus.

5. If a cell part measured 100 μm in diameter, what magnification would you select to see it?

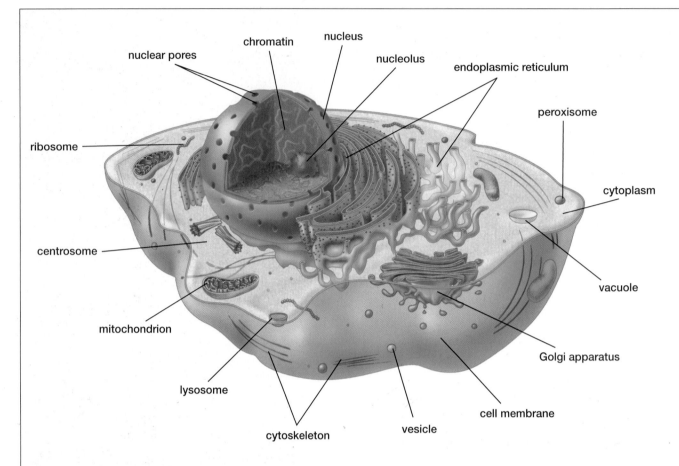

Figure 2.3 Structures of animal cells

- **cell membrane** a fluid-mosaic membrane that separates the cell interior from the outside world and controls the movement of materials into and out of the cell

- **cytoplasm** a gel-like material consisting mostly of water that contains dissolved materials and creates the chemical environment in which the other cell structures work

- **nucleus** the command centre of the cell that contains the DNA blueprints for making proteins and is surrounded by a double membrane to protect the DNA from potentially damaging byproducts of biochemical reactions

- **nuclear pores** pores in the nuclear membrane large enough to allow macromolecules to enter and ribosomes to leave the nucleus

- **chromatin** uncoiled chromosomes (DNA)

- **nucleolus** a specialized area of chromatin inside the nucleus responsible for producing ribosomes

- **ribosome** tiny two-part structures found throughout the cytoplasm that help put together proteins

Electron microscope studies have revealed the major organelles of animal cells shown in Figure 2.3. Experiments, over the past 50 years, have also led to a good understanding of the functions of each of these cell organelles. Use this figure as your quick guide to each organelle and its function. A more complete description of how cells "work" can be found on the pages that follow. The above figure, however, should serve as a useful guide to flip to when you need a reminder about cell structures and their functions. Figure 2.4 is provided to show you one technique scientists have used to view cells at high magnifications in order to establish their detailed structure. It also shows you how technical artists then produce drawings from the images, such as the one you see here, and the ones you will see throughout this textbook. Figure 2.4 shows the freeze fracture technique that involves rapidly freezing a specimen to −100°C and sectioning it in a vacuum. Carbon-and-platinum replicas of sections provide three-dimensional casts that can be examined with a scanning electron microscope.

- **endoplasmic reticulum (ER)** a system of flattened membrane-bound sacs and tubes continuous with the outer membrane of the nuclear envelope that has two types of membrane: rough ER, which is studded with ribosomes and synthesizes proteins, and smooth ER, which synthesizes phospholipids and packages macromolecules in vesicles for transport to other parts of the cell

- **Golgi apparatus** a stack of flattened membrane-bound sacs that receive vesicles from the ER, contain enzymes for modifying proteins and lipids, package finished products into vesicles for transport to the cell membrane (for secretion through exocytosis) and within the cell as lysosomes

- **mitochondrion** the powerhouse of the cell where organic molecules, usually carbohydrates, are broken down inside a double membrane to release energy and transfer it to ATP

- **lysosome** a membrane-bound vesicle filled with digestive enzymes that can break down worn-out cell components or materials brought into the cell through endocytosis

- **peroxisome** a membrane-bound vesicle containing enzymes that break down lipids and toxic waste products, such as alcohol

- **centrosome** an organelle located near the nucleus that organizes the cell's microtubules, contains a pair of centrioles (made up of microtubules), and helps to organize the even distribution of cell components when cells divide

- **vesicle** a small membrane-bound transport sac

- **vacuole** a large membrane-bound, fluid-filled sac for the temporary storage of food, water, or waste products

- **cytoskeleton** a network of three kinds of interconnected fibres that maintain cell shape and allow for movement of cell parts: actin filaments, intermediate filaments, and microtubules

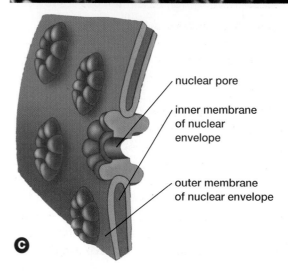

Figure 2.4 (A) The freeze fracture technique used to expose the nucleus for study provides valuable details about organelle and membrane structure. For example, you can see the two layers of the double membrane around the nucleus, or nuclear envelope. (B) A close-up scanning electron micrograph of the nuclear pores reveals their flower-like structure. (C) An artist has rendered the information from electron microscope studies of the nuclear envelope as a three-dimensional drawing.

nuclear pore

inner membrane of nuclear envelope

outer membrane of nuclear envelope

Cell Organelles

Nucleus The genetic information stored in the **nucleus** determines the structural characteristics of the cell and how the cell functions. Unless a cell is in the process of dividing or preparing to divide, the DNA strands remain in an uncoiled state (chromatin). Each nucleus has at least one area of chromatin, called a **nucleolus**, dedicated to producing the special RNA used to construct the many ribosomes required by the cell.

>> **FAST FORWARD**

To find out what happens to the nucleus when a cell divides, turn to Chapter 5, Section 5.1.

Ribosomes Every cell contains thousands of **ribosomes**, tiny organelles that lack a membrane envelope. Assembled in the nucleus, a ribosome consists of a large and a small subunit, both composed of ribosomal RNA and proteins. Cytoplasmic ribosomes, sometimes called free ribosomes, help to produce proteins (mostly enzymes) used within the cell. These ribosomes are attached to a cytoskeleton element in the cytoplasm. Ribosomes attached to the endoplasmic reticulum (ER) produce proteins that are processed in the ER and sent to the Golgi apparatus. Section 2.2 will cover protein synthesis in more detail.

Endoplasmic reticulum The numerous folded membranes of the **endoplasmic reticulum (ER)** provide a huge surface area for chemical reactions to take place. Materials synthesized inside the ER are kept separate from the rest of the cell. It would be harmful for a cell to have large quantities of the digestive enzymes or proteins such as insulin produced in the ER floating through the cytoplasm. As illustrated in Figure 2.5, the outer surface of the rough ER is covered with ribosomes. The proteins produced on these ribosomes are processed and modified with the help of enzymes embedded on the inner surface of the rough ER. Lysosomal enzymes (for cellular digestion) are produced this way.

The tubules of smooth ER also have enzymes embedded on the inner surface for processing macromolecules such as lipids. In addition to synthesizing phospholipids, smooth ER can have specialized functions in different cells. For example, the smooth ER produces testosterone (a lipid) in testicular cells. Sections of smooth ER can pinch off to form vesicles, which transport macromolecules to the cell membrane or Golgi apparatus.

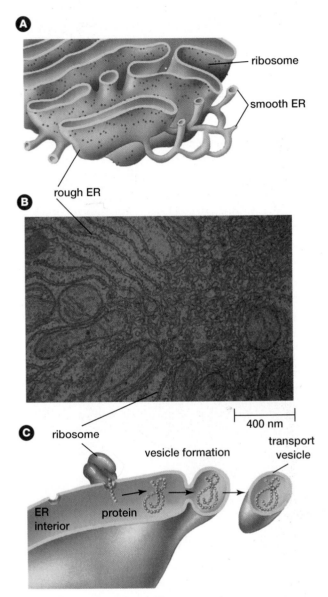

Figure 2.5 (A) Rough endoplasmic reticulum (ER) has attached ribosomes, but smooth ER does not. (B) A transmission electron micrograph of the ER shows the flattened saccules of rough ER and the tubules of smooth ER. (C) Proteins produced on the ribosomes then move into the interior of the rough endoplasmic reticulum (ER).

II PAUSE • **RECORD**

In Chapter 1, you learned about exocytosis. Why can the endoplasmic reticulum (ER) use this process to create transport vesicles for large molecules? What kind of structural maintenance do you think the ER requires? Briefly explain your ideas.

Golgi apparatus When a vesicle from the endoplasmic reticulum (ER) arrives at the **Golgi apparatus**, the vesicle membrane fuses with the membrane of a saucer-shaped sac of the Golgi apparatus. The Golgi apparatus completes the processing of macromolecules synthesized in the ER, making them fully functional (while continuing to keep them separate from the cytoplasm). It then sorts them into packages for transport to appropriate locations. The whole process of protein synthesis in the ER through to packaging the final product in the Golgi apparatus can occur in about 12 min.

Vesicles containing materials intended for use outside the cell pinch off from the Golgi apparatus, travel to the cell membrane, and secrete their contents into the extracellular fluid by exocytosis. You can see such vesicles surrounding the Golgi apparatus in Figure 2.6. The Golgi apparatus forms a special vesicle, the lysosome, to transport cellular digestive enzymes safely through the cytoplasm.

Incoming vesicles provide membrane to replace the membrane lost in outgoing vesicles. This cycling of membrane is possible because the ER, Golgi apparatus, and cell membrane all have the same basic fluid-mosaic structure.

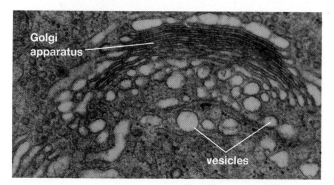

Figure 2.6 To reveal the structural details of the Golgi apparatus shown in the transmission electron micrograph here, heavy metals are used to stain the specimen. An extremely thin section must be taken from the specimen so that electrons can pass through the unstained portions.

Mitochondria Much as we use electricity to run most appliances in our homes, the cell also uses a universal form of energy to run the processes within it. Inside the **mitochondria**, the energy stored in different macromolecules is transformed into a form that can be used throughout the cell (called ATP).

> **≫ FAST FORWARD**
>
> To find out more about how mitochondria provide a form of energy the cell can use, turn to Chapter 3, Section 3.3.

The outer mitochondrial membrane separates the chemical reactions occurring inside the mitochondrion from the rest of the cytoplasm. The folds of the inner membrane, or **cristae**, provide a large surface area for the enzyme complexes involved in forming ATP. Figure 2.7 shows the distinctive membrane structure of a mitochondrion. Cells that use large amounts of energy have a high concentration of mitochondria. For example, a liver cell may contain up to 1000 mitochondria. Mitochondria contain their own ribosomes and a loop of their own DNA. They duplicate themselves by dividing in the middle to produce two daughter mitochondria, much as a prokaryotic bacterium does.

> **≫ FAST FORWARD**
>
> To learn more about how bacterial cells divide, turn to Chapter 12, Section 12.2.

Web LINK

To view three-dimensional animations of mitochondria, go to the web site shown below. Go to **Science Resources** and then to **BIOLOGY 11** to find out where to go next. Can a slice through a mitochondrion make a view of it look like a circular structure? Compare the texture of the outer and inner membranes, and describe the three-dimensional shape of a mitochondrion. **www.school.mcgrawhill.ca/resources/**

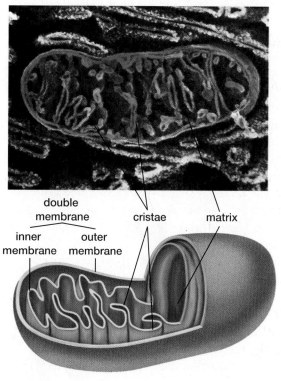

Figure 2.7 The outer portions of a mitochondrion have been cut away to reveal the cristae.

Lysosomes You can think of **lysosomes** as the composters of the cell. Their digestive enzymes break down macromolecules or larger structures, such as a whole bacterium engulfed through phagocytosis or a worn-out organelle. This provides raw materials for use as components of new macromolecules within the cell. Recycling organelles such as mitochondria (mitochondria function for about 10 days in your liver) ensures a constant supply of working organelles. Some of the details of lysosomal digestion will be explained in Section 2.2.

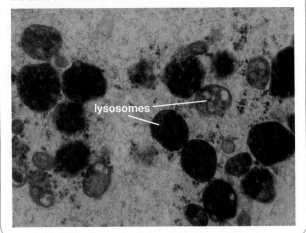

BIO **FACT**

When a tadpole develops into a frog, lysosomes break down the cells of the tail.

lysosomes

Peroxisomes Although **peroxisomes** have a similar vesicle structure to lysosomes and contain strong enzymes, they are formed in the cytoplasm. Most common in liver, kidney, and brain cells, peroxisomes have many functions. One of their main jobs is to break down long fatty acid chains. Peroxisomes also detoxify alcohol (ethanol).

Cytoskeleton Extending from the nucleus to the cell membrane, the **cytoskelton** organizes the location of organelles within the cytoplasm, gives shape to the cell, and allows for movement of parts of the cell. Unlike bones and muscles, the three components of the cytoskeleton — actin filaments, intermediate filaments, and microtubules — can be assembled and disassembled within seconds or minutes. Each component consists of repeated protein subunits that can be added or removed. So when a cell divides, the cytoskeleton disassembles and then reassembles into a structure called a spindle (which evenly distributes the genetic material and other cell contents into two daughter cells). Figure 2.8 (A) gives you a view of microtubules before mitosis and also shows the arrangement of microtubules during mitosis (B).

To reveal the details of faintly visible structures such as the microtubules shown in Figure 2.8, researchers use a technique called fluorescence microscopy. This involves dyes that can temporarily absorb ultraviolet (UV) light energy and emit it at a lower (visible) energy level. A stained specimen is viewed under a fluorescence microscope through UV filters.

 MINI **LAB**

What Do You See?

To prepare a multicellular specimen for viewing with a transmission electron or light microscope, a researcher must slice off a section thin enough for electrons or light to pass through. This means that cellular structures may be cut along many different planes. This often makes their three-dimensional structures difficult to interpret in the two-dimensional view produced. In this lab, you will section various objects and represent the information your sections give you about the specimens. Hard boil three eggs; cook about 10 elbow noodles and straight, tubular noodles; and obtain three oranges. Think about all the different ways that a section might slice through each of these specimens. (Hint: Sometimes a section cuts off only the outside surface of a structure.) Choose five different section planes for each

specimen. Use a sharp knife to slice each of these sections carefully out of the original objects. For each type of specimen, draw the original three-dimensional object and each of the five sections you made of it.

Analyze

1. For someone who had never before seen the original objects, which of the five sections of each would give that person the most complete information about the object's appearance?

2. Suggest a method by which you could use sections to gather enough information about a specimen to identify its three-dimensional shape.

3. Fluorescence microscopy is one of the fastest-growing microscope techniques. Examine the photographs of the microtubules on page 51, and use your experience from this lab to explain why this technique is useful.

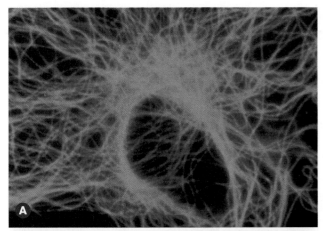

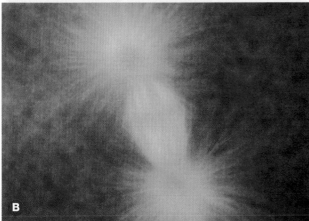

Figure 2.8 Microtubules before mitosis (A), and during mitosis (B).

Long, thin, flexible cables of **actin filaments** form a dense web under the cell membrane. This allows for movement of the membrane. Actin is a protein that can contract and that forms a key component of muscle cells. **Intermediate filaments** anchor organelles into regions in the cell, as well as support the nuclear envelope and cell membrane. The rod-like tubes of **microtubules** act like tracks

along which organelles, such as vesicles and mitochondria, can move and stabilize the shape of cells with irregular contours, such as nerve cells. Microtubules also form the main structural component of spindle fibres and of centrioles, cilia, and flagella.

Web LINK

To view images of centrosomes releasing microtubules, visit the web site shown below. Go to **Science Resources** and then to **BIOLOGY 11** to find out where to go next. Describe a microtubule, how microtubules move as they are released, and the centrosome.
www.school.mcgrawhill.ca/resources/

Centrosome The **centrosome** assembles and co-ordinates the activity of spindle fibres when the cell divides. Since the centrosome lacks a membrane, its most distinctive feature (in an animal cell) is a pair of short, cylindrical **centrioles**. Figure 2.9 illustrates the characteristic pattern of microtubules in the walls of a centriole: a ring of nine sets of microtubule triplets, with no microtubules in the middle (called a 9 + 0 pattern). The centrioles may be involved in the formation of cilia and flagella.

BIO FACT

Plant cells have centrosomes; however, because plant cells lack centrioles, their centrosomes are more difficult to see.

PLAY

To review and learn more about the organelles within the cells of your body, go to your Electronic Learning Partner.

one microtubule triplet

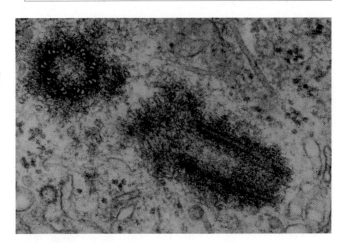

Figure 2.9 Near its nucleus, a nondividing animal cell has a pair of centrioles in its centrosome.

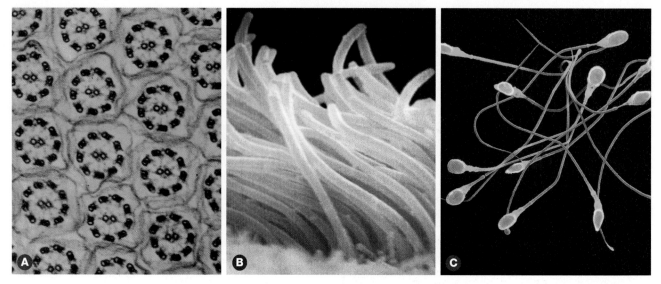

Figure 2.10 (A) This electron micrograph reveals the internal structure of cilia and flagella, and shows their characteristic pattern of microtubule pairs (called a 9 + 2 pattern). (B) Cilia in the tubes to your lungs prevent dirt from entering them. (C) The flagella of sperm propel them toward their ultimate goal, fertilizing an egg.

Cilia and flagella How can some cells move or move the fluid in their external environment? Such cells have flexible projections enclosed in cell membrane that extend outward from the cell. The short cylindrical projections shown in Figure 2.10 (B) are called **cilia** (singular, cilium) and produce a wave-like motion. The long projections shown in Figure 2.10 (C) are called **flagella** (singular, flagellum) and produce an undulating, whip-like motion. Both have the same internal construction and can move a cell through its environment. Cilia have other uses as well. Organisms such as a single-celled paramecium use the co-ordinated movement of many cilia to propel food toward a special feeding groove. The cells lining your trachea use cilia to move particles out of your lungs on a mucus blanket. The movement of cilia and flagella requires energy from the cell.

Structures of Plant Cells

To carry on its life processes, a plant cell requires some specialized structures, such as a cell wall and choloroplasts. It also uses some organelles common to plant and animal cells in a unique way, such as vacuoles and peroxisomes. Figure 2.12 depicts the cellular structures in a generalized plant cell.

Cell wall The **cell wall** around plant and fungal cells, and some single-celled eukaryotes, consists mostly of cellulose fibres and adds strength and rigidity to the cell. Spaces between the cellulose fibres allow molecules to pass to and from the cell. You can see the arrangement of these fibres in Figure 2.11. Plant cells that form part of a supporting structure in a plant have a secondary, stronger, cell wall (which usually contains a substance called lignin) inside the primary cell wall) Unlike the cell membrane, the cell wall does not control the materials that can pass through it. However, the cell wall does help the cell deal with hypotonic or hypertonic environments. It prevents the cell from bursting in hypotonic environments. In hypertonic environments, it provides structural support when the rest of the cell contents shrink.

Figure 2.11 Interwoven cellulose fibres make up eukaryotic cell walls.

Central Vacuole Plant cells usually have a large, fluid-filled **central vacuole**. This presses outwards on the cell wall to help support it. It also provides storage space for water and other substances. These may include toxins that make the cell, and thus the plant, taste bad to animals.

Plastids The green **chloroplast** is one of a group of organelles in plant cells called plastids. All **plastids** contain stacked internal membrane sacs.

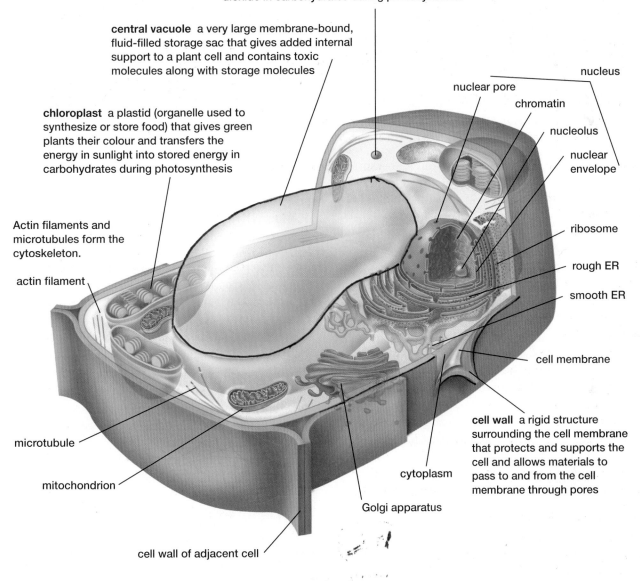

peroxisome a membrane-bound vesicle containing enzymes that convert fatty acids in seeds to sugars (providing a useable food source for a germinating plant) and help fix carbon dioxide in carbohydrates during photosynthesis

central vacuole a very large membrane-bound, fluid-filled storage sac that gives added internal support to a plant cell and contains toxic molecules along with storage molecules

chloroplast a plastid (organelle used to synthesize or store food) that gives green plants their colour and transfers the energy in sunlight into stored energy in carbohydrates during photosynthesis

Actin filaments and microtubules form the cytoskeleton.

actin filament

microtubule

mitochondrion

cell wall of adjacent cell

nucleus

nuclear pore

chromatin

nucleolus

nuclear envelope

ribosome

rough ER

smooth ER

cell membrane

cell wall a rigid structure surrounding the cell membrane that protects and supports the cell and allows materials to pass to and from the cell membrane through pores

cytoplasm

Golgi apparatus

Figure 2.12 In general, plant cells are larger than animal cells. The most distinctive features of plant cells are their cell wall and chloroplasts. Would the cells in a plant root contain chloroplasts?

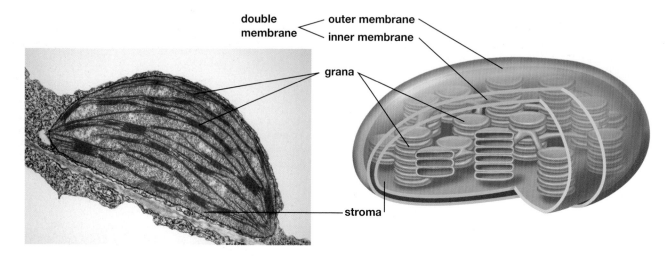

double membrane — outer membrane, inner membrane

grana

stroma

Figure 2.13 Although usually disc-shaped, chloroplasts can alter their shape and move along cytoskeleton elements to change their location in the cell in order to maximize the amount of light they capture.

These sacs are enclosed within a double membrane and have the ability to perform photosynthesis. Only plastids exposed to light develop pigments and participate in collecting energy from light. Plastids also act as storage containers for starches, lipids, and proteins. These organelles contain their own DNA and ribosomes, and new plastids are produced through the division of existing plastids.

The green pigment chlorophyll gives chloroplasts their colour and also absorbs solar energy, allowing photosynthesis to occur. The chlorophyll, other pigments, and enzymes necessary for photosynthesis are contained within a special membrane system. Figure 2.13 shows how this membrane system (the thylakoids) consists of interconnected flattened sacs.

>> FAST FORWARD

To find out more about how chloroplasts transform solar energy into chemical energy during photosynthesis, turn to Chapter 3, Section 3.2.

BIO FACT

Did you know that all of your mitochondria came from your mother? In sexual reproduction, new eukaryotic cells inherit their mitochondria, peroxisomes, and chloroplasts from the cytoplasm of the maternal gamete (egg). In asexual reproduction, new cells receive these organelles from the cytoplasm of an existing cell.

Prokaryotic Cells

About the size of mitochondria, prokaryotic cells such as those shown in Figure 2.14 lack any membrane-bound organelles. They do contain thousands of ribosomes. The **nucleoid** of a prokaryote contains a single loop of double-stranded DNA. However, some prokaryotes also contain self-replicating, circular DNA molecules called **plasmids**. Plasmids often carry information that gives the cell resistance to certain antibiotics and heavy metals or the ability to synthesize or break down unusual compounds.

Almost all prokaryotes have a cell wall consisting of a unique macromolecule called peptidoglycan. Some prokaryotes have a **capsule** or slime layer around the cell wall. Bacteria that can carry out photosynthesis have **thylakoids** that develop from invaginations of the cell membrane. Prokaryotic thylakoids function the same way that those in choroplasts do.

Some prokaryotes have flagella. Unlike eukaryotic flagella, these rotate like propellers. A prokaryotic cell may also have hollow appendages called **pili**. These allow the cells to stick to other cells or surfaces and to exchange plasmids with other prokaryotic cells.

Without the many folded membranes of eukaryotic organelles, prokaryotic cells have limited surface area available for reaction sites — although some species have areas of folded cell membrane. Still, prokaryotes work efficiently to meet their needs using a smaller number of reactions than eukaryotes do. Small prokaryotic cells benefit from rapid internal diffusion of materials. Prokaryotic intracellular fluid contains areas of different concentrations of materials, which provide some segregation of chemicals and reactions.

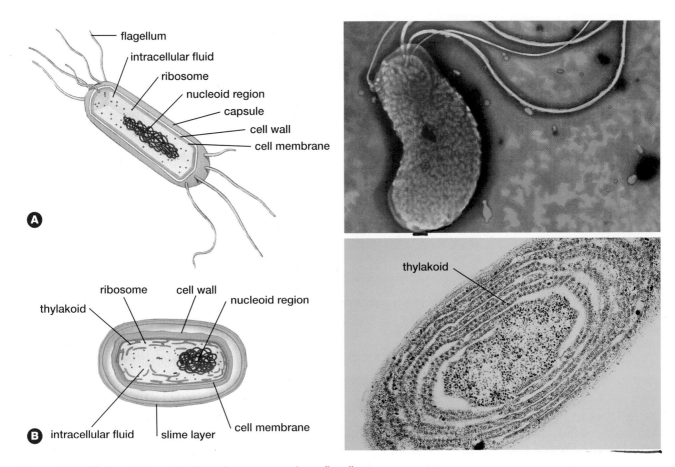

Figure 2.14 (A) Non-photosynthetic prokaryotes may have flagella.
(B) Photosynthetic prokaryotes have thylakoids.

SECTION REVIEW

1. **K/U** List the essential tasks of life.

2. **K/U** A cell is like a small community or a fair. Identify five cell parts that have a similar function to parts of your local community. Explain your choices.

3. **K/U** Complete a chart for eukaryotic cells using the headings shown below:

Organelle name	Description of structure	Description of function	Plant or animal?

4. **K/U** Identify structures that are unique to or perform unique functions in plant cells.

5. **K/U** Organelles divide a eukaryotic cell into different compartments. Explain how this is helpful to the cell.

6. **K/U** List three cell structures that have folded membranes. Explain how the folded membranes help each structure function.

7. **K/U** Prokaryotic and eukaryotic cells have many fundamental differences. List cell structures common to both of these cell types.

8. **K/U** Which cells in your body have large numbers of peroxisomes? Explain why this makes sense.

9. **C** A liver cell can have over 1000 mitochondria. Explain how a liver cell can pack so many specialized organelles inside. If a mitochondrion is 1 μm long, how large would the liver cell need to be? Express your answer in standard (SI) units.

10. **I** In Chapter 1, you tested for the presence of certain macromolecules.

    (a) Describe how you could find proteins in endoplasmic reticulum.

    (b) What other cell components could you find using other indicators?

11. **MC** Some antibiotics interfere with the ability of bacteria to form cell walls.

    (a) Describe how such an antibiotic will stop the bacteria from growing in your body.

    (b) Explain whether this drug would harm human cells and why.

Organelles at Work

- Describe how cell structures work together to carry out protein synthesis and lysosomal digestion.

- Illustrate and explain the function of, and relationship between, protein synthesis and lysosomal digestion.

Figure 2.15 To make silk, a spider's spinnerets draw out a fluid containing protein subunits. How does this process resemble the protein synthesis going on inside the spider's cells?

The processes of protein synthesis and lysosomal digestion illustrate the dynamic nature of the way that the cell's organelles work together. The ability of lysosomes to digest materials within the cell depends on the correct production of enzymes (proteins). Protein production relies on complex interactions among organelles.

Protein Synthesis

Almost all cell processes require proteins, so the production of many different kinds of proteins is a fundamental activity of living cells. In fact, proteins make up about half of the dry mass of cellular material. Many proteins function as enzymes. An important protein is the blood protein hemoglobin, which carries oxygen and carbon dioxide. An organism such as the spider in Figure 2.15 depends on the production of proteins (in the form of the silk threads of its web) to obtain food.

Cells produce proteins only in the amounts and at the times required, and all cells use a similar process for **protein synthesis**. Follow the numbered steps in Figure 2.17 on the next page as you read about how protein synthesis occurs in eukaryotes.

◀◀ REWIND

To review protein structure, turn to Chapter 1, Section 1.1.

1. **Transcription occurs in the nucleus.** As you learned in Chapter 1, DNA codes for cellular proteins. It does this using a code of three nucleotide bases (triplets) for each amino acid. The cell transcribes (copies) the coded information from a section of DNA called a gene. To do this, the cell must unwind and unzip that section of DNA and make an RNA copy of it, as shown in Figure 2.16. During this process of **transcription**, the information along only one of the DNA strands is copied, producing a strand of RNA nucleotides.

Figure 2.16 Many copies of RNA are being transcribed simultaneously from a single strand of DNA (centre).

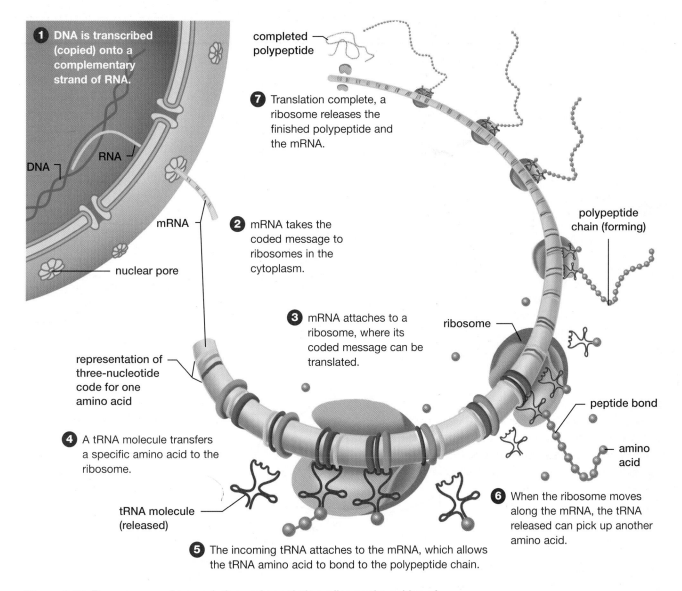

1 DNA is transcribed (copied) onto a complementary strand of RNA.

completed polypeptide

7 Translation complete, a ribosome releases the finished polypeptide and the mRNA.

DNA

RNA

mRNA

nuclear pore

2 mRNA takes the coded message to ribosomes in the cytoplasm.

3 mRNA attaches to a ribosome, where its coded message can be translated.

ribosome

polypeptide chain (forming)

peptide bond

representation of three-nucleotide code for one amino acid

amino acid

4 A tRNA molecule transfers a specific amino acid to the ribosome.

tRNA molecule (released)

6 When the ribosome moves along the mRNA, the tRNA released can pick up another amino acid.

5 The incoming tRNA attaches to the mRNA, which allows the tRNA amino acid to bond to the polypeptide chain.

Figure 2.17 The accuracy of transcription and translation relies on the pairing of nucleotide bases in DNA and RNA. Enzymes direct both processes.

2. **mRNA moves into the cytoplasm.** The completed RNA — called messenger RNA, or **mRNA** — carries the coded message from the DNA in the nucleus, to ribosomes in the cytoplasm.

3. **Translation starts when mRNA attaches to a ribosome.** The **translation** of the coded mRNA message from a sequence of nucleotide bases into a sequence of amino acids takes place on a ribosome. A ribosome can translate any mRNA strand. To begin the translation process, mRNA attaches either to a cytoplasmic ribosome or to a ribosome attached to the endoplasmic reticulum (as shown in Figure 2.5 on page 48).

BIO FACT

To confirm the path that mRNA takes during protein synthesis, researchers stained its nucleic acids with a fluorescing dye and then traced its progress with a fluorescence microscope.

4. **tRNA brings amino acids to the ribosome.** Dissolved amino acids in the cytoplasm must be transferred to the ribosome for assembly into a polypeptide. Another type of RNA called transfer RNA, or **tRNA**, does this. Each tRNA molecule recognizes only one amino acid. It attaches this amino acid to one side of its structure. On the other side of the tRNA molecule, three nucleotide bases match one of the triplet codes on the mRNA.

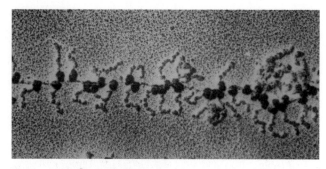

Figure 2.18 Several ribosomes can move along the same strand of mRNA at the same time, creating multiple copies of the same polypeptide. This arrangement is called a polyribosome.

5. **An incoming tRNA positions its amino acid to join the polypeptide chain.** The tRNA carrying the next amino acid in the mRNA code forms a temporary bond with the mRNA at the ribosome. This places the amino acid in the correct position to form a peptide bond with the amino acid on the tRNA molecule already at the ribosome. In this way, about 15 amino acids are added to the polypeptide chain every second.

6. **An outgoing tRNA releases its amino acid and detaches from the mRNA.** A ribosome has room for only two tRNA molecules at a time. When the ribosome moves along the mRNA to the next coding unit, the outgoing tRNA transfers the polypeptide chain to the other tRNA. This frees up space for a new tRNA molecule at the ribosome. The outgoing tRNA molecule can now collect another amino acid.

7. **Translation ends when a ribosome reaches a "stop" instruction.** When a ribosome reaches the "stop" codes at the end of an mRNA strand, it releases the completed polypeptide. Then the ribosome separates into its subunits, which detaches it from the mRNA. The polypeptide must still complete its folding process before becoming a finished protein.

⏸ PAUSE ⏺ RECORD

In Section 2.1, you learned how the endoplasmic reticulum and Golgi apparatus prepare proteins for use by the cell (or by other cells). Use this information and what you know about protein synthesis to draw a simple flowchart that shows how a protein destined for use in a lysosome is produced and transported within the cell.

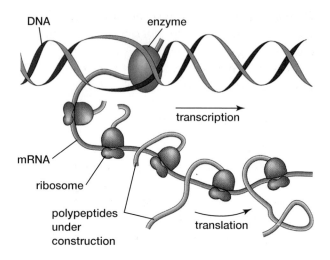

Figure 2.19 Without a nucleus, a prokaryotic cell can carry out transcription and translation at the same time. Although not pictured, tRNA molecules bring amino acids to prokaryotic ribosomes to be added to a polypeptide.

Protein Synthesis in Prokaryotes

Although the processes of transcription and translation in prokaryotes and eukaryotes follow very similar basic steps, you can see from the illustration in Figure 2.19 that protein synthesis in prokaryotes is simpler. The prokaryotic ribosomes (which are smaller than eukaryotic ones) lie close to the DNA, so the beginning of an mRNA strand can attach directly to a ribosome while the rest of the strand is still being transcribed. This allows prokaryotes to produce proteins very rapidly.

> **BIO FACT**
>
> Like prokaryotic cells, mitochondria and chloroplasts of eukaryotes use their own DNA and ribosomes to produce some of the proteins they need. However, most of the proteins needed by mitochondria and chloroplasts are coded for on genes in the cell nucleus, synthesized on cytoplasmic ribosomes, and then transported into the organelles.

Lysosomal Digestion

Only eukaryotic cells contain lysosomes. In plant cells, the specialized vesicles that recycle cellular material (the way that a lysosome does) are often called vacuoles. Each lysosome (or vacuole) contains over 40 different digestive enzymes. After the lysosome leaves the Golgi apparatus, its membrane actively pumps in hydrogen ions to make its interior environment more acidic. This acidic environment activates the lysosomal enzymes.

When active, these enzymes can break apart macromolecules in a step-by-step process. This **lysosomal digestion** can occur in two ways: by breaking down material ingested through endocytosis and by recycling the cell's own organic material. Figure 2.21 illustrates the two pathways of lysosomal digestion.

Endocytosis

After a cell engulfs material by endocytosis, a lysosome fuses with the food vacuole formed to fill the vacuole with digestive enzymes and break down the captured material. You can follow the steps involved in this process in Figure 2.21.

◀◀ REWIND

To review endocytosis, turn to Chapter 1, Section 1.4.

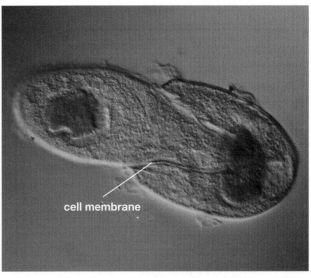

Figure 2.20 You can see what happens to the cell membrane of a didinium as it engulfs a paramecium.

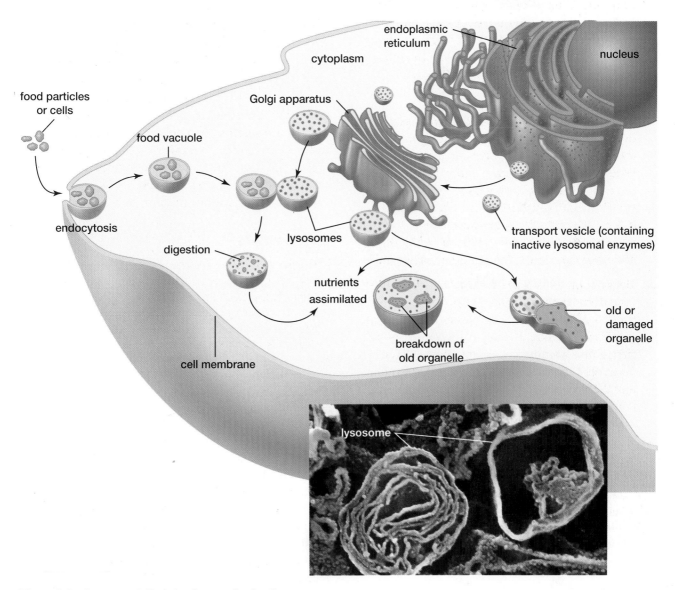

Figure 2.21 Lysosomal digestion in an animal cell

Recycling

A lysosome fuses with and digests organelles no longer useful to the cell. It then recycles their components back to the cytoplasm. You can follow the steps involved in this process in Figure 2.21.

>> **FAST FORWARD**

To learn more about Tay-Sachs disease, turn to Chapter 7, Section 7.1.

BIO FACT

Errors in enzyme production can mean that a particular lysosomal enzyme may not work. This interrupts the orderly sequence of steps for breaking apart large molecules. As a result, the cell accumulates useless molecule fragments. Over long periods of time, the build-up of these fragments inside cells can negatively affect the growth and development of the individual. A number of serious genetic diseases such as Tay-Sachs and Hunter syndrome are linked to faulty lysosomal enzymes.

Investigation 2 • A

Exploring Organelle Function

Lysosomal digestion can be difficult to demonstrate, but you can easily observe the process of peroxisome enzymes breaking down molecules. One of these, catalase, breaks hydrogen peroxide (H_2O_2) down to water and oxygen. To function, lysosomal enzymes need an acidic environment. Does catalase also need an acidic environment?

SKILL FOCUS

Predicting

Performing and recording

Analyzing and interpreting

Identifying variables

Pre-lab Questions

- What is the pH value of an acid solution, a neutral solution, and a dilute acid solution?
- What function(s) do peroxisome enzymes serve?
- Adding hydrogen peroxide to cut potatoes causes foam to be produced. Why?

Problem

How can you demonstrate the effect of pH on the catalase enzyme found in potato peroxisomes?

Prediction

Predict what pH condition will best support enzyme function in peroxisomes.

CAUTION: Acids are corrosive; avoid contact with skin and use water to flood spills. If you are using a computer pH probe, ensure that the probe remains stable so that it does not fall and cause a spill.

Materials

3 graduated cylinders	60 mL 3% hydrogen
2 droppers	peroxide
knife	0.1 mol/L hydrochloric
dissecting probe	acid solution
pH probe or indicator	distilled water
paper	potato

Procedure

1. Prepare 3 hydrogen peroxide solutions of different pH as follows:

   (a) Measure 50 mL of 3% hydrogen peroxide into each of the 3 graduated cylinders.

   (b) Label the cylinders 1, 2, and 3.

   (c) Use one dropper to add 10 drops of 0.5 mol/L hydrochloric acid solution to cylinder 1 and 5 drops of 0.5 mol/L hydrochloric acid solution to cylinder 2.

   (d) Use the other dropper to add 5 drops of distilled water to cylinder 2 and 10 drops of distilled water to cylinder 3.

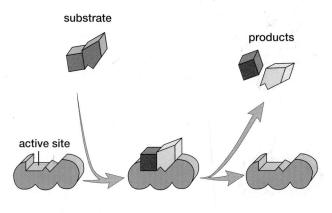

substrate

products

active site

enzyme   enzyme-substrate complex   enzyme

Figure 2.22 The union of the enzyme with its substrate (the molecule) weakens certain chemical bonds within the substrate. This causes the substrate to break apart.

Enzyme Function

Enzymes make possible reactions that would otherwise not proceed at temperatures low enough for life to be possible. An **enzyme** is a protein that functions as an organic catalyst. A catalyst helps a particular reaction go forward without being used up in the process. The cell makes a different enzyme for each reaction it requires.

An enzymatic reaction may either combine molecules to produce a new product or break a molecule into smaller parts. Figure 2.22 illustrates a model of the way an enzyme breaks apart a molecule.

In Chapter 1, you learned that proteins have three-dimensional shapes. An enzyme's shape allows its substrate(s) to attach at a spot called the

(e) Record the contents of each cylinder.

2. Check and record the pH of each cylinder. If you are using a pH probe, keep a running record of the pH.

3. Peel the potato, and cut it into 3 equal cubes. Mince each cube (sample) to an equal fineness.

4. Add one potato sample to each graduated cylinder. Use the dissecting probe to push all of the potato into each hydrogen peroxide solution, rinsing the probe between each use.

5. Observe the contents of each cylinder, and record your observations once a minute for 5 min. Then test and record the final pH for each cylinder. Use a chart to organize your observations. Make a graph to compare the reaction of each sample.

Post-lab Questions

1. In terms of their initial reactions, order the hydrogen peroxide solutions from strongest to weakest.

2. Which solution had the strongest final reaction?

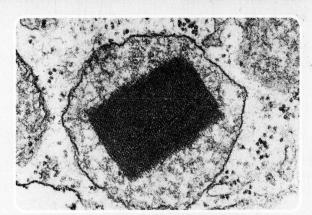

The catalase crystal inside a plant peroxisome allows the organelle to break down hydrogen peroxide.

Conclude and Apply

3. How does pH affect the rate of the catalase reaction?

4. In terms of pH, what kind of internal environment would allow peroxisomes to function most efficiently?

5. Identify the dependent and independent variables in this experiment.

Exploring Further

6. What do you predict the natural pH of a potato to be? How could you test this?

7. Conduct research to find out what other factors can affect the rate of an enzyme reaction.

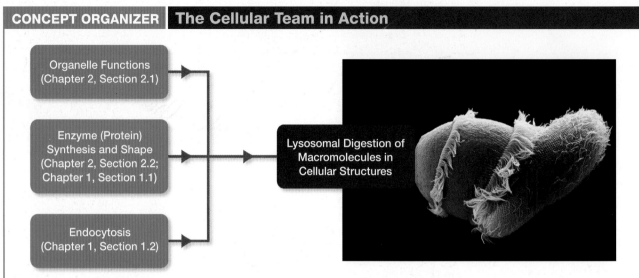

Organelle Functions
(Chapter 2, Section 2.1)

Enzyme (Protein)
Synthesis and Shape
(Chapter 2, Section 2.2;
Chapter 1, Section 1.1)

Endocytosis
(Chapter 1, Section 1.2)

Lysosomal Digestion of
Macromolecules in
Cellular Structures

To understand how a lysosome carries out intracellular digestion, you need to know how a lysosome functions, how its enzymes are formed, and how it connects with the materials it must break down. Which cellular structures are involved in lysosmal digestion?

The process of forming a lysosome begins in the nucleus with the transcription of mRNA for the lysosomal enzymes. In the cytoplasm, ribosomes attached to the endoplasmic reticulum translate this mRNA. The enzymes are transported to the Golgi apparatus, which modifies the enzymes and packages the correct ones together into a lysosome. The three-dimensional shape of the enzymes allows them to do their job. Some materials on which the lysosome works enter the cell in vesicles (food vacuoles) formed by the cell membrane through endocytosis. Once the lysosome has digested the macromolecules, the lysosomal membrane transports nutrients useful to the cell into the cytoplasm. Mitochondria supply the energy required to drive many of these processes.

Figure 2.23 What did happen to the paramecium captured by the didinium?

active site. Here, chemical bonds within a substrate can be broken or bonds between substrates can be formed. Then the enzyme releases the product(s) and can start the process again.

SECTION REVIEW

1. **K/U** List the key steps involved in protein synthesis.

2. **K/U** Why do *all* cells need to perform protein synthesis?

3. **K/U** What is transcription and where does it take place?

4. **K/U** What is translation and where does it take place?

5. **K/U** Eukaryotic cells have a double membrane surrounding their DNA, separating it from the cytoplasm. Identify a reason for this.

6. **K/U** Make a flow chart for the lysosomal digestion of a mitochondrion.

7. **K/U** What is an enzyme and how does it function?

8. **I** Make a prediction about what the optimum pH for catalase could be. Then design a lab that

determines the optimum pH for the catalase enzyme, outlining the procedures you would use.

9. **C** A good analogy for protein synthesis is the manufacturing process. Ribosomes are the factories that produce proteins. Complete this analogy by describing the role of DNA, mRNA, and tRNA. In a small group, prepare a dramatic presentation of this process.

UNIT INVESTIGATION PREP

Food coming from the stomach contains many molecules, such as disaccharides, too large to diffuse or be transported into cells lining the small intestine. How could the intestinal cells break down these molecules? Draw a diagram of this process. For the most economical use of an intestinal cell's resources, where could this process take place?

Specialists at Work

EXPECTATIONS

■ Explain how the cell processes carried out by organelles relate to the function of organs.

■ Present informed opinions on stem cells and technological applications of stem cell research.

Figure 2.24 Groups of specialized cells work together to allow a person to see, hear, taste, smell, smile, think, and talk — and these are only some of the many specialized cells in the body.

A marvel of seemingly endless adaptation, a multicellular organism contains a large number of different kinds of specialized cells. For example, nerve cells connected to muscles carry information to and from your brain to control how much your muscles contract or relax. What structures do each of these cellular specialists (motor neurons and skeletal muscle cells) have that allow them to perform their unique functions? How are these cells created? In this section, you will begin to explore the world of the cellular specialists within your own body.

Organization of Cells

A group of specialized cells that have the same structure and perform the same function is called a **tissue**. Examples of tissues include muscles in animals and bark in plants. A group of different tissues working together form an **organ**. For example, the leaf of a plant is an organ made up of protective tissues on the outside and photosynthetic and other tissues on the inside.

You have already seen how organelles work together to accomplish tasks. Later in this book, you will look at ways in which groups of organs work together as a system, such as the circulatory system. Any large multicellular organism relies on groups of such systems in order to function.

Specialized Cells

How do the specialized cells in a tissue contribute to the function of an organ? A few examples will help provide an answer.

Heart muscle cells To pump blood throughout the body, your heart needs highly efficient muscle cells. The small size of heart muscle cells gives them a large surface area, which increases their access to critical materials, such as oxygen. They have a branched shape that allows them to form an interconnected network of cells. This network can conduct electric impulses and contract in unison — even without a signal from the nervous system.

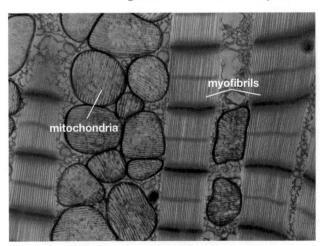

Figure 2.25 Heart muscle cells contain many large mitochondria to power their action. Like all other muscle cells, they contain the actin and myosin filaments (in structures called myofibrils) that allow them to contract.

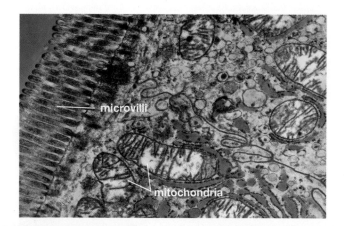

microvilli

mitochondria

Parietal cells Within indentations in the lining of your stomach called gastric pits, cells secrete the juices necessary for digestion. Parietal cells there produce hydrochloric acid. This activates an enzyme secreted by other cells lining the gastric pit and allows digestion to proceed. Parietal cells contain tiny canals that run from the cell membrane facing the gastric pit deep into the cytoplasm. Each canal

Figure 2.26 As well as microvilli, a parietal cell requires large numbers of mitochondria. These power the active transport required to pump hydrogen ions out to the stomach (against the concentration gradient for these ions).

DESIGN YOUR OWN
Investigation

2 • B

Modelling a Specialized Cell

What characteristics does a specialized cell need in order to perform its unique functions? How does its function affect the organelles or other internal structures it contains? In this investigation, you will work in a group to research and create a scale model of a particular eukaryotic cell type. Then you will present your model to the class.

Problem

How does the function of a eukaryotic cell affect its internal structures, size, and shape?

Prediction

Based on your existing knowledge of cell structures and what your cell type does, make a prediction about what internal structures, size, and shape it should have.

Materials

Select your own materials.

Plan

1. Choose a eukaryotic cell type that makes up one kind of tissue, and find out its correct scientific name.

2. Identify research resources such as books, videos, CD-ROMs, and the Internet. If your school has microscope slides of different cell types, you may want to view your cell type under a microscope and record your observations.

3. Discuss what kind of specific information you need to gather about your cell type. Remember that you will need information about its dimensions and internal structures.

4. Identify what limitations, if any, creating a scale model places on your choice of materials.

5. Decide on the materials you will use to make the scale model of your cell, and prepare a list of all the materials you will require.

6. Outline a strategy for completing the model and ensuring that it is to scale.

Computer LINK

You may want to use a computer drawing program to create a scale model or simulation of your cell type. Use the graphics tools you have available to give cell structures a three-dimensional appearance. What advantages does using a computer give you in making your model to scale?

Checking the Plan

1. Have you identified a variety of resource materials? How can you ensure that the information you gather is accurate?

2. Will the type of information you plan to gather help you identify your cell's special function(s)? Will it help you relate the structure of your cell to its function(s)?

is lined with very small extensions of cell membrane called **microvilli**. With little increase to individual cell size, this highly folded fringe of membrane maximizes the surface area for pumping hydrogen ions out into the canals that lead into the stomach.

◄◄ REWIND

To review active transport and how cells pump hydrogen ions out against a gradient, turn to Chapter 1, Section 1.3.

Podocytes Cells excrete toxic nitrogen-containing waste in the form of ammonia, which the liver converts to less toxic substances: uric acid or urea. An important function of your kidneys is to cleanse the blood of this nitrogen waste. Cells called podocytes act as the main filtration barrier in the nephron of the kidneys. A podocyte has long, thin processes that interlock with the processes of another podocyte around the capillaries entering the kidneys.

3. What kind of materials might make it easier to create your model? For example, would creating a poster work well?

4. Do your materials allow you to easily control the size of different cell components in the final model? How will you show the scale on your cell model?

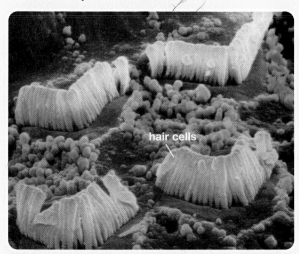

These hair cells in the inner ear transmit information about sound to the brain.

Data and Observations

Conduct your research and gather your data. Record any observations you make both in writing and as labelled drawings. You may find it useful to record information on the size of different cell components in chart form. Collect copies of photographs and illustrations of your cell type for reference when making your model.

Analyze

1. How do the structural characteristics of the cell type you modelled compare to those of the generalized cells you studied in Section 2.1? For example, does your cell type have more of, or lack, a particular organelle?

2. What dimensions does your cell type have (in µm or mm)? How do these compare with the dimensions of other cell types?

Conclude and Apply

3. How does the shape of the cell type you modelled contribute to its special function(s)?

4. What advantage(s) does its size give it in carrying out its special function(s)?

5. How do the composition and arrangement of its internal structures help it carry out its special function(s)?

6. How does it interact with or support the function of other cell types?

Exploring Further

7. All specialized eukaryotic cells arise from undifferentiated cells called stem cells. In order to become part of a specialized cell line, many cells have very interesting developmental paths. Carry out research to trace the development of the cell type that you modelled.

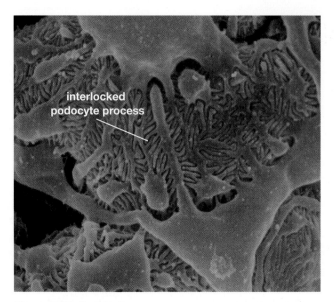

interlocked
podocyte process

Figure 2.27 Podocytes

Arterial blood pressure pushes small molecules such as water, salts, glucose, amino acids, urea, and uric acid from the capillaries into the kidney through thin membranes between prodocyte processes. However, podocytes keep blood cells, platelets, and proteins from leaving the blood. Before urine leaves the kidneys, other specialized

kidney cells extract amino acids, glucose, and required salts from the liquid while some actively transport wastes such as drugs into the urine.

Squamous epithelial cells Deep in your lungs, extremely thin, flat cells line the tiny sacs (alveoli) where gas exchange takes place. Lying directly against the equally thin cells forming capillary walls, these squamous epithelial cells provide the shortest distance possible (about 1 µm) for oxygen to diffuse into and carbon dioxide to diffuse out of your body.

> **≫ FAST FORWARD**
>
> To learn more about how red blood cells transport carbon dioxide to and oxygen from the lungs, turn to Chapter 9, Section 9.2.

COURSE CHALLENGE

You may find what you learn in the Thinking Lab below useful in preparing your Biology Course Challenge. Can you think of a way that you could use this kind of pathology evidence to develop your crime scenario?

THINKING LAB

Cell Detective at Work

Background

Pathologists specialize in identifying signs of disease. Armed with only a light microscope and methylene blue stain, a pathologist can identify the signs of nuclear deterioration that indicate abnormal cell death (necrosis) in a specimen. In an autopsy, the question of whether certain cells died before the organism did helps a pathologist determine the cause of death. In this lab, you will examine liver tissue samples and, like a pathologist, identify signs of necrosis.

> **≫ FAST FORWARD**
>
> For information about mitosis, turn to Chapter 5, Section 5.1.

You Try It

1. Each of the four photographs below was made through a light microscope. Find the cell nuclei in each photograph, and identify any signs of necrosis. Describe what these signs look like. If any of the photographs shows healthy cells, explain how you know this.

2. If starved for oxygen long enough, a cell will shut down and then die. How could you arrange the photographs below to show what this process looks like? Explain your reasons for choosing this order.

3. Contrast what happens to the nucleus in necrosis to what happens to the nucleus in mitosis.

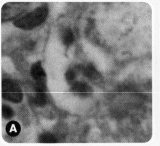

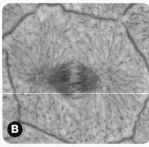

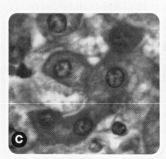

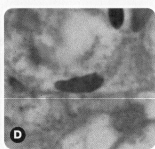

Stem Cells: A Medical Miracle?

Imagine doctors being able to grow new hearts and kidneys or new nerves for patients paralyzed by spinal cord injury. Stem cells could be the key to these kind of dramatic medical advances in the years to come.

What Are Stem Cells?

Stem cells have been described as the blank slate of the human body — undifferentiated (nonspecialized) cells that can give rise to any type of cell, from a nerve cell to a white blood cell. Until they differentiate, stem cells have the unique ability to reproduce themselves indefinitely.

Most of the rapidly dividing cells of a week-old embryo are stem cells. These differentiate to become all of the multitude of cell types in the body. People retain a limited number of stem cells — one for every five million other cells. To replace worn-out or damaged cells, the body uses reserves of stem cells. These are found primarily in bone marrow but also in the blood, muscle tissue, lining of the digestive tract, brain, and retina of the eye.

Where Do Researchers Get Stem Cells?

Doctors already take advantage of the rejuvenating power of stem cells to treat patients with some kinds of leukemia through bone marrow transplants. However, these transplants are extremely painful and must be done under general anesthetic, which entails its own risks. Through the use of drugs or growth factors, adult stem cells can also be encouraged to increase in the bone marrow and can then be collected directly from the blood.

Other sources of stem cells include aborted fetuses, unused embryos from in-vitro fertilization treatments, and cord blood. Cord blood is the blood left in the placenta and umbilical cord following a birth. Canada now has a well-established private cord blood bank in Toronto and a public one in Alberta, which accept donations.

What Issues Surround Stem Cell Research?

- The nature of the sources of stem cells has made it difficult to get enough human stem cells for research.
- Cloning of human embryos could provide a large supply of stem cells.
- A sick person's DNA could be transferred into a human egg. Stem cells from an embryo developed from the egg could be used to treat the sick person.
- A particular human being could be cloned.
- Harvesting the stem cells from an embryo destroys it.
- Moral, ethical, and legal questions arise around using human embryos.
- Potential uses for stem-cell therapies include treating cancers, strokes, hepatitis, spinal cord injuries, Alzheimer's disease, diabetes, heart disease, muscular dystrophy, AIDS, and other disorders.
- It once seemed that adult stem cells could only develop into a few types of tissue, but recent findings have shown that scientists may be able to program adult stem cells to act like embryonic stem cells.

What Discoveries Have Canadians Made?

- At least two types of adult stem cell exist: one that initiates the short-term replacement of tissue and the other that initiates the long-term replacement of tissue. (Hospital for Sick Children, Toronto, Ontario)
- In rats, stem cells from bone marrow injected into damaged heart muscle took on the appearance and function of heart muscle cells, replacing the damaged cells in 20 out of 22 trials. (McGill University Health Centre, Montréal, Québec)
- In the presence of an embryo protein (called sonic hedgehog), adult stem cells from bone marrow rapidly reproduce, much as stem cells do in a human embryo. (J.P. Robarts Research Institute, London, Ontario)

Stem cells hold the promise of releasing millions of people from pain and suffering or death. Stem cells also raise disturbing questions about how we view life.

Stem cells are stored in liquid nitrogen.

Follow-up

Debate with classmates the pro or con aspects of stem cell research. You may want to use the following real-life situation to help focus your discussion:

In the U.S., parents of a six-year-old girl with a rare inherited blood disease asked doctors for help in conceiving a baby that could provide donor stem cells for their daughter. They selected the most suitable embryo from among 15 created through in vitro fertilization. They had a little boy, and their daughter received stem cells from his cord blood in the hope that she will now produce healthy bone marrow.

Apoptosis

The proper development and maintenance of all tissues requires that some cells be removed or replaced. To allow for this, some cells turn on an orderly self-destruct process called **apoptosis** (programmed cell death). For example, as the fingers and toes develop, web-like fetal tissue between the digits goes through apoptosis. These cells are programmed to die at a particular time. Most cells with DNA damage and many infected with viruses die by apoptosis.

When a cell dies from injury, the cell contents scatter into its environment. In your body, this leads to inflammation of the area. In apoptosis, a series of enzyme reactions degrade the contents of a cell. The cell shrinks, and small bulges appear along the cell membrane. Figure 2.35 shows how the cell then breaks into pieces, each bound by a membrane. Finally, special phagocytotic cells engulf and digest these cell fragments. The phagocytotic cells also release chemicals that inhibit inflammation.

Some cells with damaged or defective DNA do not make the correct chemicals to induce apoptosis. Failure of apoptosis can result in some forms of cancer, such as leukemia, and in autoimmune diseases, such as rheumatoid arthritis. Too much apoptosis can lead to degenerative diseases, such as muscular dystrophy.

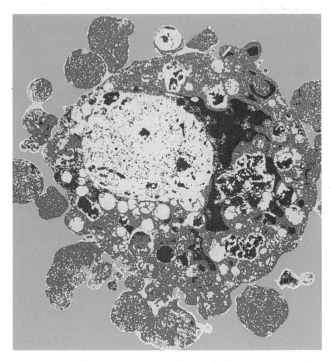

Figure 2.28 Outside the nucleus (yellow) of a cell undergoing apoptosis, the cytoplasm (green/red) is fragmenting.

Web LINK

To view an animation of apoptosis, visit the web site shown below. Go to **Science Resources** and then to **BIOLOGY 11** to find out where to go next. Compare the web animation to Figure 2.28. Identify any similarities and differences.
www.school.mcgrawhill.ca/resources/

SECTION REVIEW

1. **K/U** Explain how tissues relate to organ systems.

2. **K/U** Why are some cells in your body highly specialized?

3. **K/U** Complete this chart in your notebook:

Cell type	Organ	Organ system
heart muscle		
parietal		
podocyte (nephron)		
squamous epithelial		

4. **K/U** Mature red blood cells have no mitochondria. Explain how this reflects the function of these cells.

5. **C** Make a flip book to show the process of apoptosis.

6. **K/U** Apoptosis is often called "programmed cell death." What does this phrase mean?

7. **K/U** How is a stem cell different from a regular cell?

8. **MC** Canadian researchers discovered a gene responsible for programmed cell death. It codes for a protein that intiates apoptosis in embryo cells.

   (a) The scientists cloned mice lacking this gene. None of the mice survived to be born. When the scientists studied the mouse embryos, describe what you think they found.

   (b) Some cancer cells may grow out of control. How could this new research help scientists fight cancer?

UNIT INVESTIGATION PREP

Specialized cells lining the small intestine absorb and help to break down food. What structural features are typical of such a cell? What would happen if these cells could not break down large molecules into subunits, such as monosaccharides?

- Present informed opinions on advances in cellular biology related to new treatments for cancer.

- Analyze ways in which societal needs have led to technological advances related to cellular processes.

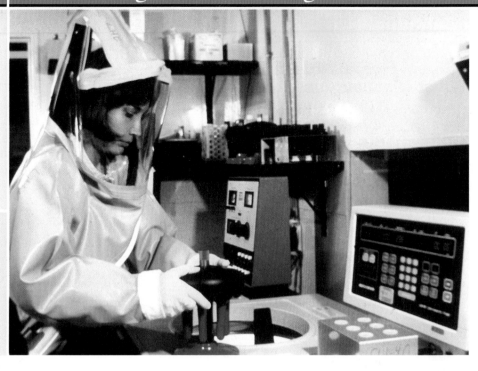

Figure 2.29 Special biohazard equipment has been developed to protect researchers and technicians who work with samples containing extremely dangerous disease-causing agents such as ebola and anthrax.

Research in cell biology involves a cross-section of scientific disciplines and makes use of many different types of technology. Even seemingly unrelated technologies such as the Internet and microcomputers help accelerate the already rapid pace of discoveries related to cells. Figure 2.29 illustrates how researchers need technology far beyond the microscope and petri dish to even look at some kinds of biological processes.

What kind of impact might recent research into cell biology have? What types of technology does it use or apply? This section gives a few examples to help you explore these questions.

Finding New Cancer Treatments

Even as investigators map the process by which apoptosis works, they are looking for ways to activate the apoptotic mechanism in tumour cells. The possibility that cancer cells could be induced to self-destruct may provide the basis for various treatments. To start, researchers look at how treated cells in a culture die. (A culture consists of a few cells placed on a growing medium in a petri dish to multiply.) They track this by tagging cellular structures sensitive to the changes that take place during apoptosis with fluorescing dyes. This allows them to literally see how a particular treatment is working. For example, one fluorescing marker used is sensitive to chemical changes in mitochondria as they degrade in a dying cell. While the

mitochondria remain intact, the marker fluoresces red. When the mitochondrial membrane breaks, it fluoresces green — indicating that apoptosis is underway.

Following another line of investigation, Canadian researchers at the University of Alberta recently discovered that some cancer cells do not produce an important cell membrane receptor. This membrane protein allows the killer cells of the immune system to signal a damaged cell to begin the process of apoptosis. This finding opens the door to research on ways to get these tumour cells to accept or produce the membrane receptor that would then allow killer cells to destroy them.

BIO FACT

A PAP test allows for early detection of cancer of the cervix, a common form of cancer in women. This test involves removing a few cervical cells and checking them under a microscope for signs of cancer.

How Societal Needs Drive Technological Advances

Much modern technology has been developed to meet the needs (or satisfy the wants) of society. As an example, this section reviews the evolution of treatment for diabetes to illustrate ways in which technological advances can be driven by societal needs.

Global Heroes: Banting and Best Discover Insulin

Frederick Banting, right, and Charles Best, left, discovered a life-saving treatment for diabetes: insulin.

A diagnosis of diabetes meant almost certain death until 1922, when the discovery of its cause and treatment thrust two young Canadian researchers into the international spotlight. Frederick Banting and Charles Best seemed unlikely heroes, and neither had any special research qualifications. Though a diabetic's blood contains high levels of glucose, very little of it enters the cells. This means that an untreated patient can literally starve to death while eating what should be adequate meals.

Unexpected Insight

Banting had obtained a medical degree at the University of Toronto and trained in orthopedic surgery. On October 30, 1920, he read a medical journal article about an apparent link between the pancreas and diabetes. He learned that (1) depancreatized dogs developed symptoms of diabetes; (2) a healthy pancreas contains background cells and a small scattering of distinctive cell clusters called the islets of Langerhans; (3) if the main duct of the pancreas is deliberately blocked, the background tissue usually shrivels up but the islets often persist; (4) if the islet cells remain healthy, diabetes does not develop. Apparently, the islets held the key that allowed glucose to enter the body's cells.

At about two the next morning, Banting suddenly awoke with an exciting research idea that would eventually save the lives of millions of diabetics around the world and dramatically change his own.

Banting's Bold Idea

Banting's idea was this: block the pancreatic duct to isolate islets cells from the pancreas of a dog, chemically extract the islet secretions, and administer the purified extract to another dog made diabetic by removing its

pancreas. He hypothesized that the islets extract would normalize the second dog's blood sugar levels.

Banting presented his hypothesis to Dr. J.J.R. Macleod, a diabetes expert at the University of Toronto. Intrigued, Macleod offered Banting a small lab, a supply of dogs, and a 21-year-old assistant, Charles Best. Best was in medical school, and his excellent laboratory skills in biochemistry complemented Banting's surgical experience.

The first exhilarating results supporting their hypothesis came on July 30, 1921, when a diabetic dog's blood sugar did normalize as expected. By November, they had duplicated this result many times over.

Breakthrough

Banting and Best's extract was given to a human diabetic patient for the first time on January 11, 1922, but with disappointing results. Fortunately, J.B. Collip, a biochemist from the University of Alberta, had joined the team late in December. After much "bathtub chemistry," as he later described it, Collip discovered that alcohol in a 90% concentration precipitated the active ingredient out of the raw extract. On January 23, Collip's purer extract was given to the same patient with much greater success.

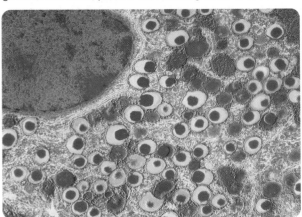

The membrane-bound secretory granules (vesicles) in this islets cell contain insulin (red dots).

Macleod named the extract insulin, after the Latin word for "island." The University of Toronto's Connaught Laboratories immediately began developing large-scale production methods. The outcome was dramatic: within months, insulin was saving lives all around the world.

The media spotlight shone with its brightest intensity in 1923 when Banting and Macleod were awarded the Nobel Prize for medicine. Shocked that Macleod was named and not Best, Banting immediately split his award with his young assistant. Macleod followed suit by sharing his award with Collip. Surely, in this great moment, there was glory enough for all.

Needs of Diabetics Still Drive Research

What makes insulin so important? Diabetes is caused either by a deficiency of insulin, because the islet cells in the pancreas have been damaged or destroyed, or by the inability of cells to respond to insulin. When you eat, the cells in your intestines transfer nutrients into the blood stream. Within minutes of a rise in blood glucose levels, healthy islets cells synthesize quantities of insulin and secrete it into the blood stream. Insulin is a hormone that binds to cell membrane receptors, primarily on muscle and liver cells. This signals the cells to take up glucose and amino acids. By a mechanism not yet understood, it also causes protein synthesis to start. As soon as blood glucose levels fall, insulin production rapidly shuts down. However, your cells have now stored the nutrients they need until the next meal.

Without insulin, or when cells fail to receive its signal, glucose and amino acid transport into cells and protein synthesis within cells shut down. The body uses lipids as an alternative energy source to glucose, and large quantities of lipid products start circulating in the blood. Some of these form deposits in blood vessels, impeding circulation; others are acidic and damage tissues. The blood contains so much glucose that kidney cells cannot filter it back into blood. Glucose in the urine draws water with it by osmosis, causing cells to become dehydrated and circulation to collapse.

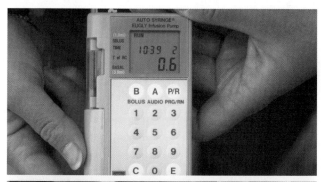
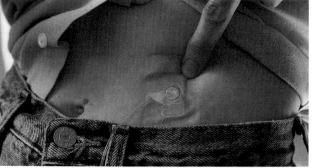

Figure 2.30 A computerized smart insulin pump is still very expensive.

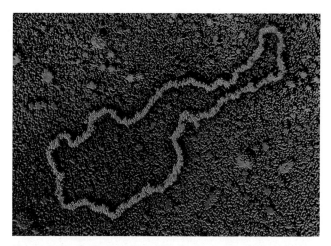

Figure 2.31 Scientists insert the human gene for insulin into a bacterial plasmid such as this one. Other bacteria exposed to the new, recombinant, plasmids take them up and begin transcribing and translating insulin.

Biotechnology and human insulin. The millions of diabetics around the world create a huge demand for insulin. Until 1982, all insulin was extracted from the islet cells of beef cattle or pigs. Animal insulin is similar enough to human insulin that it can work in the human body. However, most diabetes patients eventually developed a sensitivity or even an allergic reaction to it.

The mass production of truly human insulin was one of the first applications of biotechnology. This aspect of **biotechnology** involves the use of living organisms to manufacture products for humans. The pharmaceutical industry now genetically engineers bacteria to manufacture human insulin. The bacteria are given the DNA instructions for making human insulin molecules and then manufacture insulin along with the other proteins they need for their own life functions.

> **≫ FAST FORWARD**
>
> To view how the gene for human insulin is spliced into bacterial plasmids, turn to Chapter 12, Section 12.2.

On-time insulin delivery. Another aspect of biotechnology involves applying knowledge and techniques from engineering to solve biological problems. Regardless of their source of injected insulin, diabetics have to deal with swings in blood sugar levels. Thanks to computerized "smart" pumps, some diabetics now have access to the type of insulin pump pictured in Figure 2.30. This tests a diabetic's blood several times a day and automatically dispenses the correct amount of insulin.

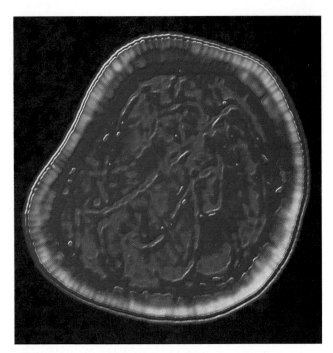

Figure 2.32 Viruses like this rubella virus, which you were probably vaccinated against, infect animal cells.

Viral vector technology. When you hear the word "virus," you may think of flu "bugs" or perhaps something like the more severe ebola virus. A virus is not much more than a small collection of nucleic acids tightly wrapped in a protective protein coat. The nucleic acids contain instructions for manufacturing more viruses, but a virus cannot manufacture anything until it gains access to the organelles of a living cell. Inside a cell, the viral nucleic acids take over cellular operations from the nucleus.

Biologists are now exploiting the ability of viruses to enter cells. University of Calgary researchers are using a virus as a vector (or tiny vehicle) to carry specific pieces of DNA into the livers of diabetic mice. They splice DNA instructions for making a molecule similar to mouse insulin into the DNA of a harmless virus. When the virus enters (infects) mouse liver cells, the cells begin to make the desired insulin-like molecules. Although the engineered insulin is only 40% as potent as natural insulin, this is sufficient to control blood glucose levels. This research may lead to the use of viral vector technology to treat human diabetics, allowing their liver cells to produce insulin-like molecules in a natural way.

> **»» FAST FORWARD**
> To learn more about viral replication and viral vectors, turn to Chapter 11, Section 11.2.

Diabetes and cancer represent just two of many diseases for which researchers continue to search for better treatments. From the examples given, you can see how their work has led to or used technological advances related to cellular processes. This work and other research into cell biology has provided investigators with an arsenal of information and tools that can be applied to finding ways to alleviate human suffering and disease.

Newer Forces Driving Research

Two examples of recently identified diseases that ravage people's health are AIDS (acquired immunodeficiency syndrome) and hepatitis C. AIDS is caused by the human immunodeficiency virus (HIV); hepatitis C is caused by the hepatitis C virus (HCV). Millions of people worldwide are infected with these diseases, and treatments for both are rapidly being developed.

Isolated as a separate disease in 1987, HCV is transmitted through direct contact with infected blood. It spreads quickly among people who share injection needles. Tattooing and body piercing may also put people at risk of acquiring HCV.

The virus damages liver cells. An infected person may not manifest symptoms for 20 years. Symptoms include fatigue, jaundice (yellowing of the skin or eyes), nausea, hair loss, and a build-up of toxins in the blood. Infection can lead to chronic inflammation of the liver, liver cancer, and death. Many people with HCV need liver transplants.

Only in 1990 did a reliable HCV test become available. Many people with hepatitis C got it through blood transfusions received before testing for HCV became established. Scientists in Québec recently developed a combination of drugs that has been shown to be effective in eliminating HCV from the blood.

> **Web LINK**
> To see an animation of the HCV life cycle, visit the web site shown below. Go to **Science Resources** and then to **BIOLOGY 11** to find out where to go next. How does HCV enter liver cells? Which cell structures and processes does HCV use to replicate itself?
> **www.school.mcgrawhill.ca/resources/**

Tracking Treatment Technology

Background

HIV and HCV present special challenges for the immune system and researchers alike. Much like the trypanosomes pictured on page 7, both of these viruses mutate rapidly. This changes the surface proteins of their protein coats and tricks the immune system so that it does not recognize the viruses as invaders. In order to develop successful treatments, researchers must keep abreast of the latest developments in their field and know its history. In this lab, you will help to create and complete a class tracking sheet to capture relevant treatment, technology, and research information about at least two diseases, AIDS and hepatitis C.

Recent Research Finding I: AIDS

People who show evidence of having HIV are constantly tested for viral load (the number of viruses in the blood) and a count of the CD4+T cells in their blood. These cells are the part of the immune system that coordinates the activity of cytotoxic T cells (killer cells) to eliminate a virus. HIV infects CD4+T cells. As the infection develops, the count of CD4+T cells in the blood drops. This diminishes the ability of the immune system to respond to all kinds of infection. Does the HIV virus actually kill all these CD4+T cells? Many uninfected CD4+T cells die by apoptosis. During HIV infection, killer cells appear to bind with CD4+T cells and start the apoptotic cascade. Also, the antibodies formed as part of the immune response to HIV seem to initiate apoptosis in these CD4+T cells.

Recent Research Finding II: AIDS

Typically, HIV enters a CD4-T cell by binding to two different receptors on the cell membrane. First, the virus binds with the CD-4 receptor and then with a nearby CCR-5 receptor. Once attached to both receptors, the virus can enter the cell. A small number of people exposed to HIV never develop AIDS and show no antibody response to it. These people have a natural immunity to HIV. They also have a defective gene that affects the amino acid sequence of the CCR-5 receptor protein. In these people, HIV binds with the CD-4 receptor but cannot bind with the modified CCR-5 receptor. So the virus is unable to enter the cell. The modified CCR-5 receptor does not appear to impair the health or function of the individuals who have it. A new line of research arising from this is exploring ways to make a vaccine that targets and disables CCR-5 membrane receptors.

Web LINK

To see animations and explanations of HIV topics, visit the web site shown below. Go to **Science Resources** and then to **BIOLOGY 11** to find out where to go next. Describe how HIV enters a T-lymphocyte. How does the drug AZT help people with AIDS?

www.school.mcgrawhill.ca/resources/

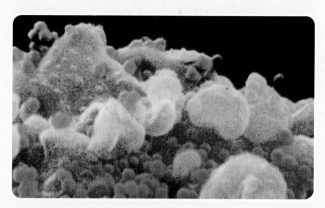

HIV viruses (green particles) are budding from the surface of this T-lymphocyte (a CD4+T cell).

You Try It

1. Use the sample tracking sheet below to develop a class tracking sheet. Decide if any columns should be added to it. For example, would dividing the Treatment(s) column into an Early Treatment(s) and a Current Treatment(s) column make it easier for you to track the evolution of related technologies? Decide if you would like to add additional rows to the tracking sheet. For example, you might include ebola, influenza, or mad cow disease. Add any relevant information to the tracking sheet from this section of the book. Then research the current status of treatment for each disease by searching for information from newspaper articles and current web sites.

2. In the research described above, investigators started by asking themselves a question that led them to examine a specific aspect of HIV infection. Find this question in Recent Research Finding I. Then extrapolate what this question must have been for Recent Research Finding II. Explain how these questions helped to focus the research in each case.

Disease	Causative agent	Method(s) transmission	Method(s) protection	Treatment(s)	Technology involved	Current research	Funding source(s)
AIDS							
hepatitis C							

Disease and Cells

All diseases work at the level of the cell and affect the function of cells in different ways. In this section, you have seen examples of diseases resulting from damage to cells (diabetes and cancer) and caused by viral infections (AIDS and hepatitis C). Other infectious agents include bacteria, mycoplasmas, and prions. In Section 2.2, you read about Tay-Sachs disease, an example of a disease caused by a genetic defect. Environmental factors or ingested toxins can also cause disease.

Whatever the cause of the disease, you have seen how the loss in function of one type of specialized tissue — even the loss of one protein — can have a profound effect on the health of an individual. The interdependent nature of cellular interactions can initiate a cascade of damaging effects in many parts of the body.

Research to understand how cellular structures contribute to life processes helps scientists unravel the mechanisms of disease. This often leads to the development of new technology and treatments.

In medicine as elsewhere, one technology builds on another. The insulin pump could not have been developed until the miniaturization of computers (for military and other purposes) became quite advanced. The technology to manufacture human insulin could not have been developed without the techniques for cloning particular DNA sequences. Techniques developed for apoptosis research may lead to new treatments for cancer. Fantastic new discoveries and technologies are just around the corner.

Word LINK

Choose a disease in which you are interested or that you have read about in this section. In the role of a member of a foundation raising money for research, write a brochure to raise public awareness about the disease. Include information about some of the latest research your foundation funded and any new discoveries or technologies that people's contributions supported. In what ways can raising public awareness benefit researchers or those afflicted with this disease?

SECTION REVIEW

1. **K/U** What do HIV and HCV stand for?

2. **I** Refer to Figure 2.29 at the beginning of this section. Explain how the researcher is protected from biohazards in the workplace.

3. **K/U** Explain how fluorescent dyes can be useful when learning about how cancer cells work.

4. **K/U** How does a faulty membrane receptor help certain cancer cells survive?

5. **K/U** Copy and complete the consequences map on the right in your notebook.

   (a) Why is the diagram called a cascade?

   (b) Identify three technologies used to help prevent the negative consequences of the diabetes cascade.

   (c) Explain how one of these technologies could be used help diabetics with healthy islets cells.

6. **MC** Describe the environmental benefits of using biotechnology to produce insulin instead of earlier insulin production methods.

7. **C** Use labelled diagrams to compare the way that HIV and HCV infect and affect their target cells.

8. **C** Write an article about what impact you think public awareness has on research to detect and treat diseases such as AIDS and hepatitis C.

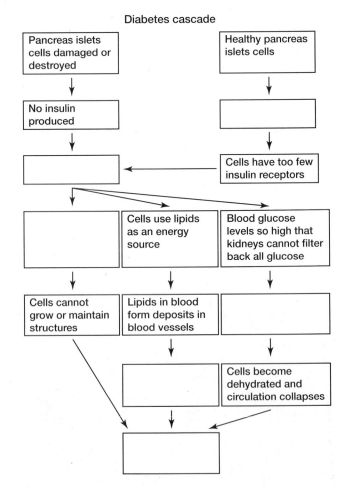

Diabetes cascade

| Pancreas islets cells damaged or destroyed | Healthy pancreas islets cells |

No insulin produced

Cells have too few insulin receptors

Cells use lipids as an energy source

Blood glucose levels so high that kidneys cannot filter back all glucose

Cells cannot grow or maintain structures

Lipids in blood form deposits in blood vessels

Cells become dehydrated and circulation collapses

Chapter Expectations

Briefly explain each of the following points.

- Eukaryotic cells contain membrane-bound organelles, such as the nucleus. (2.1)
- A plant cell has unique structures that allow it to make food and deal with different osmotic conditions. (2.1)
- Cells must make proteins to create structural components, enzymes, and hormones. (2.2)
- In all cells, protein synthesis starts with transcription of the DNA instructions for making a polypeptide. (2.2)
- Lysosomal digestion allows a eukaryotic cell to break down organic compounds and re-use their components, such as the amino acids required for protein synthesis. (2.2)
- A parietal cell pumps hydrogen ions into the stomach, so the cell needs many mitochondria. (2.3)
- Cells in the lungs have a very thin layer of cytoplasm to allow for rapid diffusion of oxygen and carbon dioxide. (2.3)
- Some cancer research is investigating the possibility of triggering cancer cells to undergo apoptosis. (2.4)
- People's need to fight disease leads to research and technological advances. (2.4)

Language of Biology

Write a sentence using each of the following words or terms. Use any six terms in a concept map to show your understanding of how they are related.

- prokaryote
- eukaryote
- organelles
- nucleus
- nucleolus
- ribosomes
- endoplasmic reticulum
- Golgi apparatus
- mitochondria
- cristae
- lysosomes
- peroxisomes
- cytoskeleton
- actin filaments
- intermediate filaments
- microtubules
- centrosome
- centrioles
- cilia
- flagella
- cell wall
- central vacuole
- plastids
- chloroplasts
- nucleoid
- plasmids
- capsule
- thylakoids
- pili
- protein synthesis
- transcription
- mRNA
- translation
- tRNA
- lysosomal digestion
- enzyme
- tissue
- organ
- microvilli
- apoptosis
- biotechnology

UNDERSTANDING CONCEPTS

1. Diffusion works quickly over a short distance, but it is very slow over a long distance. Eukaryotic cells can be very large. Which cell structures compensate for this problem? How?

2. Identify the organelle in the photomicrograph below. Explain how organelle orientation can affect what you see in a photomicrograph of a cell.

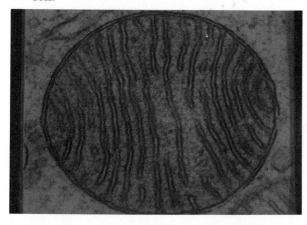

3. Only eukaryotic cells have a cytoskeleton.
   - (a) How has new technology changed cytoskeleton study?
   - (b) Explain how the cytoskeleton is important to the eukaryotic cell.
   - (c) What functions *must* be different in a prokaryotic cell?

4. How does the cell wall prevent lysis?

5. What organelles would be larger or more numerous in a cell that produces large amounts of a protein product?

6. Which cell type is likely to have many peroxisomes: liver cells, red blood cells, and/or parietal cells? Explain your answer.

7. Outline the process of creating a lysosome.

8. Explain how cells recycle matter efficiently.

9. Identify three cell processes that use energy.

10. Some organelles have one membrane layer and others have two. Take an example of each kind of organelle, and explain how the membranes have similar or different functions.

11. White blood cells have lysosomes, but mature red blood cells do not. Explain one reason for this difference.

12. The pancreas has excretory cells. Explain the production and release of insulin in terms of cell processes.

13. How are mitochondria and chloroplasts distinct from other organelles?

14. Testosterone is a lipid molecule. Why is lipid produced in the smooth endoplasmsic reticulum (ER) and not the rough ER?

15. Outline the consequences for a cell if it had no nucleolus.

16. The generalized plant cell below shows all of its key cellular structures.

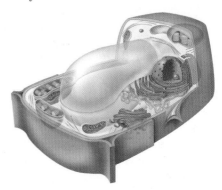

(a) Identify three structures that are critical to the cell's survival.

(b) Justify your selection.

(c) Share your response with other students. Make additional comments after listening to their thoughts.

INQUIRY

17. Refer to these photographs.

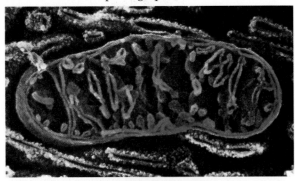

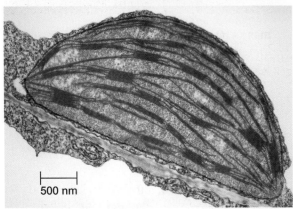

500 nm

(a) If 2 cm represents 265 nm on the mitochondrion electron micrograph, determine the approximate length of this organelle.

(b) Use the scale with the chloroplast electron micrograph to determine the approximate size of this organelle.

(c) Make a diagram showing the relative size of each structure. Include the scale.

18. Some chemicals prevent the organization of microtubules into spindle fibres.

(a) Predict the effect of one of these chemicals on cells.

(b) Design a lab to test your prediction.

19. As a researcher, you are studying a particular genetic disorder that slowly destroys cells through the accumulation of amino acid chains.

(a) Suggest a cell process that is not functioning properly.

(b) What are your reasons for thinking this?

(c) What kind of research could you explore to discover if your ideas are correct?

20. B-cell leukemia is a cancer of the B-cells of the immune system. A researcher has hypothesized that this cancer is due to a failure of the apoptosis of B-cells after they have performed their part in an immune response. From the studies of apoptosis in other cells, a protein known as Bcl-2 has been observed to play a role in the apoptotic process. In a study to investigate whether or not Bcl-2 is involved in B-cell apoptosis, mice were infected with the

Epstein-Barr virus to initiate B-cell production. The mice were then divided into two groups. One group was given injections of Bcl-2; the other was not. Ten days after viral infection, another B-cell count was performed on both groups. The results are illustrated on the right.

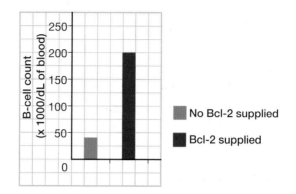

(a) From the results, draw conclusions about what kind of role Bcl-2 may play in apoptosis.

(b) During this experiment, the mice were kept in a sterile environment. Why would this be essential to ensure the validity of the experiment?

COMMUNICATING

21. Create a poster to show how protein synthesis and lysosomal digestion are both parts of a cycle of matter within the cell.

22. Make a five-panel cartoon of apoptosis. Add text in a caption or text bubbles to explain how apoptosis helps recycle matter in the body.

23. Many cellular processes are still poorly understood. Further research and new technology could change this situation. Write a persuasive letter to your MP asking for the government to continue providing grants to fund basic research into cell function.

24. A change in the DNA of a specialized cell can cause a protein error. Use your knowledge of how some diseases affect cells to make a consequences map showing the cascade of steps that could result from this. Choose one of the possible paths from the partial cascade shown below. Keep in mind that the result of some cascades may be something other than cell death. Label points in the cascade where technological interventions can help people deal with the disease.

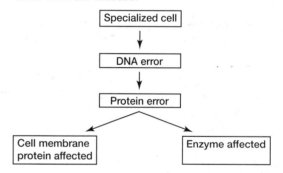

MAKING CONNECTIONS

25. Cells use matter efficiently. Suggest how people could learn from the cell to produce less waste for landfill.

26. A virus consists of only a protein coat and a small piece of nucleic acid.
    (a) What information is coded on the nucleic acid?
    (b) A virus must use a living cell to make new virus copies. Explain why.
    (c) The immune system can attack a virus that it recognizes. This is the basis of vaccine protection from a virus. Which part of the virus should be used for a vaccine? Explain your answer.

27. HIV and HCV are global diseases that kill millions of people each year. However, few Canadians die of these diseases. Explain why many Canadian research teams are trying to find new technologies to fight these diseases.

28. Although many diseases can cause tissue damage or kill people, there are limits to the financial support and teams of trained researchers available to find treatments. Who sets the priorities for research? Identify four criteria that should help people prioritize research funding.

29. A specialized cell in a multicellular animal cannot do the work required by the entire body, but collectively the animal's cells can. Also, the animal's body has the flexibility and resources to be able to deal with problems that arise with individual cells. Explain how these complex interactions are mirrored in the workings of society.

Cells, Energy, and Technology

Reflecting Questions

- How do cells transfer and use energy?
- What are key energy processes in cells?
- How can metabolic processes in cells offer solutions to difficult problems?

The runner in the photograph would come to a complete standstill without energy. Every muscle cell in the runner's body, every cell in her brain, eyes, intestines, and skin, must have energy to function and to stay alive. The cells of her body obtain their energy from the food she eats.

A living plant's need for energy is much like the runner's. Every cell making up a plant's roots, stems, and leaves must have energy to function. Where do the cells of the plant obtain their energy from? The inset photograph shows a fossilized plant. Forests of plants from ancient times stored great amounts of solar energy as organic matter. Buried beneath layer upon layer of sediment, great pressure over many years changed the plant matter into the coal and oil we use today.

The processes that stored this energy long ago continue today in the plants around us. We rely on plants for food, fuel, and other products. Cells continue to use the same processes that store and release energy. How do the cells of living things make use of the molecules you investigated in Chapter 1? How do they obtain the energy needed to run all the chemical processes that you investigated in Chapter 2? So far, this unit has focussed on the matter that makes life possible: organelles and the molecules they require. This chapter rounds out your study of cells and cell processes by concentrating on energy — the other necessity that makes life possible.

You will investigate how organisms obtain energy, and you will be introduced to the mechanisms that allow cells to make use of energy. You will also explore some technologies that humans have developed to make use of biological processes.

Trees of the distant past, buried in swamps and covered with mud and silt over thousands of years, were transformed by the resulting heat and pressure into one of today's principal fuels: carbon-rich coal. What processes allowed them to obtain, then to store, the energy we now use?

Chapter Contents

Cells, Matter, and Energy

■ Explain the molecular principles and mechanisms that govern energy-transforming activities in all organisms.

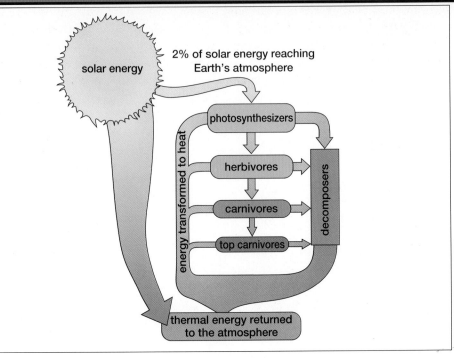

Figure 3.1 Although only a small fraction of the total energy emitted by the Sun reaches Earth's surface to be used by plants and algae to produce food, that small share is enough to sustain life on our planet.

You have learned that all organisms are composed of cells, whether they are plants, animals, algae, fungi, or micro-organisms. They all need food to provide the energy and matter they need for growth and reproduction. As the above flowchart shows, the organisms that photosynthesize obtain their energy directly from the Sun. What about other organisms? What is the source of their energy? The herbivores (plant eaters) obtain it directly from the plants they eat. The carnivores (meat eaters) obtain it from the herbivores they eat, and the top carnivores obtain energy from the herbivores and other carnivores they eat. Notice that the boxes

containing the names of organisms (e.g. carnivores) become smaller and smaller. This is done to illustrate an important point — not all of the energy the photosynthesizers obtain from the Sun is passed on to the herbivores that eat them, and so on. Why not? Think about it. Some of the energy that a dog, for example, obtains from its food is used for everyday processes — walking, running, catching a stick, even blinking its eyes. Some is transformed to other forms of energy, such as sound (as it barks) and thermal energy (heat that keeps its body warm). Thus, some energy escapes

 MINI LAB

Matter and Energy Carousel

Living things use energy to organize matter. How are energy and matter related to the processes of life? Do this activity to find out about this question.

Your class will divide into small groups. Each group will be assigned one coloured marker. The black marker will be used to show the paths of carbon atoms. The red marker will show the paths of oxygen atoms. The blue marker will show the paths of hydrogen atoms, and the green marker will represent the transfer of energy.

There will be six stations set up around the room, each with a different scene. One station will have a picture showing a picnic scene, another will have a forest scene, yet another

will have an underwater scene, etc. At each station your group will use the marker assigned to you to mark coloured arrows on the diagram or photograph, showing the path of the type of atom, or energy, for which your group is responsible. A sheet of lined paper is available at each station for your group to write additional comments. You will remain at the last station, and your group will be responsible for reporting all the results of that station.

Analyze

1. One member of your group will report on the collective findings of all the groups for the station.

2. Was there agreement on what happens to each kind of atom and to energy? If not, what are some questions to which you still need to find answers?

from the food chain at each of the feeding or so-called trophic levels (see Figure 3.1).

What about the matter? Does matter escape from the food chain as energy does, or is it simply cycled over and over and over again?

Figure 3.2 What activities use the energy supplied by the food the fox eats? That energy will no longer be available to the eagle or bear that attacks the fox, or to the decomposers if it dies a natural death.

Thinking About Energy

The following brief review of energy concepts will ensure you understand the nature of energy before you proceed with this chapter. You will probably recall from your previous studies that **energy** is the capacity to do work. You are already familiar with some everyday forms of energy — light energy, sound energy, electrical energy, etc. **Potential energy** is stored energy. An apple hanging from a stem on a tree has potential energy as does the water stored behind a dam, but that energy must be released before it can actually do any work. **Kinetic energy** is the energy of motion, such as the energy of an apple falling to the ground from the tree or water flowing over a dam (its energy can then be harnessed to run turbines to generate electricity, for example). **Chemical energy** is the energy stored in the bonds between atoms in molecules. Thus, chemical energy is potential energy. Once the chemical bonds are broken, the atoms have extra kinetic energy. They have the ability to move, to do work, to make things happen. By 1859, strong evidence persuaded scientists to accept the Law of Conservation of Energy, which states the idea that energy can neither be created nor destroyed, but simply converted to another form of energy. So far, no exceptions have been found to this enormously important idea.

Consider this chain of transformations. A baseball is thrown into a mitt on your hand. You hear a thud as it hits your mitt. You have just observed evidence of energy transformation. The energy of the incoming ball was in the form of kinetic energy (of motion). As the ball hits your mitt, some kinetic energy was transformed into sound energy. A sensitive thermometer would also detect an increase in the mitt's temperature where the ball struck it. In this transformation, kinetic energy was converted to thermal energy. Note that none of the ball's energy has been "lost," it is simply transformed.

Figure 3.3 What energy transformations occur when the ball hits your baseball mitt?

Chemical reactions also involve energy transformations: that is, a change of energy from one form to another. As long as a cell remains alive it retains the ability to control the chemical reactions occurring within it. If too little energy is transformed during certain reactions, the cell dies. The intricate chemical balance that cells are capable of maintaining is difficult to imagine. Taken together, the total of all of the chemical reactions that occur within a cell are known as its **metabolism**. Metabolism includes all of the building up and breaking down of substances in a cell as well as the energy changes that occur simultaneously. A cell's metabolism relies on chemical energy. The next section will reveal where that chemical energy comes from.

1. **K/U** Look at the two photographs shown here to check your understanding of energy. Identify areas in the photographs where an energy transformation is taking place. Some will be useful, ensuring that work is done. Others will be conversions to energy forms that cannot be (or, at least, are not being) used to do work. Identify, as well, where potential energy may be used to do work in the future.

2. **K/U** Why do cells need energy?

3. **K/U** Identify five ways your body uses energy during an average day.

4. **K/U** Glucose is a common source of energy in cells. Where is the energy in glucose?

5. **C** Energy can not be created or destroyed. The flow diagram in Figure 3.1 seems to show a loss of energy.

   (a) Explain this apparent loss of energy.

   (b) Assume that the atmosphere of the Earth changed so that energy from the Sun could reach the surface of Earth but visible light could not. How would the flow diagram change?

6. **C** Make a flow diagram showing the chain of energy transformations for each of the following situations:

   (a) This book falls off a table.

   (b) You walk home after eating a meal.

7. **K/U** Define the term metabolism. Then, do the following:

   (a) List three metabolic processes you have studied in previous chapters.

   (b) For one of these processes, identify how energy is used.

8. **I** Amylose and cellulose are carbohydrates. We can eat both, but can only use amylose as a source of energy. Some animals can digest cellulose and use the energy stored in this carbohydrate. Which molecule has the greatest potential energy? Propose one way to answer this question.

9. **C** The flow diagram in Figure 3.1 shows the Sun as the source of energy for life on Earth. Design a diagram to show the path followed by oxygen among living things on Earth.

10. **MC** Constant solar energy supports the processes of life on Earth. How, then, can we have energy shortages?

UNIT INVESTIGATION PREP

How does energy flow through communities of organisms? How much energy is transferred from herbivores to carnivores, for instance? Energy is also stored in various molecules, including the fat, protein, and carbohydrate in milk. Which of these molecules is your body most likely to use? What is the ultimate source of this energy? Write your thoughts in preparation for your Unit 1 Design Your Own Investigation.

The Process of Photosynthesis

- Explain how plant cells transfer the energy from light into energy stored in chemical bonds.

- Identify the raw materials and end products of photosynthesis.

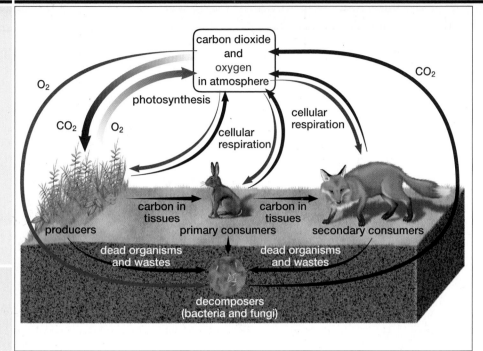

Figure 3.4 Photosynthesis stores energy and cellular respiration releases energy, helping to drive the carbon cycle.

The illustration above depicts the carbon cycle. As well as recycling the element carbon, this cycle also involves two energy transformations that are essential for life. The first of these transformations is photosynthesis, in which light energy from the Sun is used to transform carbon dioxide and water into energy-rich food molecules. You have already learned the chemical equation for this process:

$$6CO_2 + 6H_2O \xrightarrow{\text{light energy}} C_6H_{12}O_6 + 6O_2$$

carbon   water   glucose   oxygen
dioxide

The energy in the food made by this process is used by organisms to grow and carry out all their other life functions. For example, where does your energy come from? It comes from the food you eat. If you eat cheese, the energy comes from a cow, which in turn obtained its energy from the grass it ate. The grass obtained its energy from the sunlight. In other words, the energy in your food also came originally from the light energy, converted to stored energy in the chemical bonds of carbohydrate molecules.

How is the stored chemical energy in food made available for your cells to use? The energy is released by the second important transformation process seen in the carbon cycle — cellular respiration:

$$C_6H_{12}O_6 + 6O_2 \longrightarrow 6H_2O + 6CO_2 + \text{energy}$$

glucose   oxygen   water   carbon   ATP (energy
                                        dioxide   storage
                                                  molecule)

(Note: $C_6H_{12}O_6$ represents a simple carbohydrate, but green plants produce other energy-rich food molecules as well.)

The process of respiration releases energy for use by the cell. Both cellular respiration and photosynthesis are actually a series of many different chemical reactions. All chemical reactions involve the absorption or release of energy. You will explore the major reactions of both photosynthesis and cellular respiration in more detail in this chapter.

What Is Photosynthesis?

The equation for photosynthesis shown on this page shows what photosynthesis does, but not how it works. In fact, the process of photosynthesis involves over 100 different chemical reactions. These reactions proceed in two main stages called the *photo* stage and the *synthesis* stage. Each stage, in turn, involves a set of reactions. The reactions of the *photo* stage supply the chemical energy needed to drive the synthesis reactions forward. The reactions of the *synthesis* stage store chemical energy in the bonds of glucose, a simple carbohydrate molecule. The *photo* stage is also known as the light dependent reactions. The *synthesis* stage is also called the light independent reactions.

Knowledge about exactly how photosynthesis occurs has come from many different sources. Physicists have made some discoveries, chemists others, and biologists still others. Because each specialty has its own preferred terminology, there is often more than one name for the same part or process. To keep your study of photosynthesis straightforward, this book uses only the simpler terms, but other resources or reference books may use different or more advanced terminology.

What Is Light?

Since the first stage of photosynthesis involves light, we begin with a review of the nature of light. As you may know, we are surrounded by both visible and invisible radiation from our Sun and other sources. Examples of invisible radiation include TV signals, microwaves, and X-rays. Visible radiation is usually simply called light.

In earlier studies you learned about the **wave model of light**, whose main ideas are listed below.

- Radiation such as light consists of energy waves with both electrical and magnetic properties. This electromagnetic radiation travels outward from its source in regular waves or pulses of energy, rather than in a constant unchanging flow.

- The entire range of radiation produced by natural or human-made sources is called the **electromagnetic spectrum** (see Figure 3.5).

- All forms of electromagnetic radiation travel at the same astonishing speed, 300 000 000 m/s, but properties vary according to the frequency with which the waves of that type pulse, or vibrate.

- We perceive different frequencies of visible radiation (light) as different colours. Light with the greatest frequency is perceived as violet, while light with the lowest frequency is perceived as red. A combination of all frequencies is seen as white (see Figure 3.6).

The wave model of light is very useful for explaining everyday properties of light, such as the reflection by a mirror or the refraction of a beam of light by a prism (see Figure 3.7).

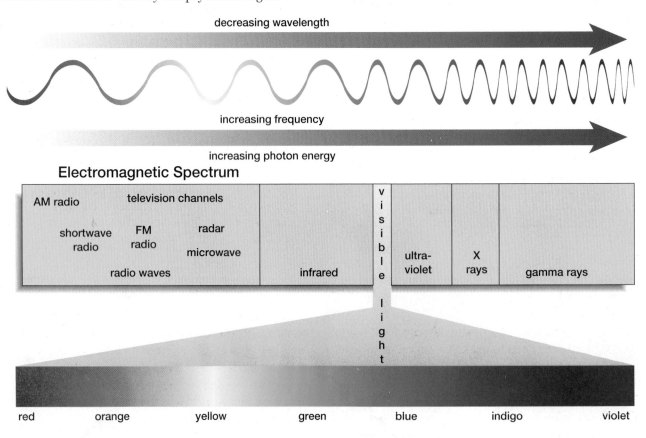

Figure 3.5 This vast range of electromagnetic radiation is emitted naturally in the universe.

Figure 3.6 The sunlight reflected from a snowy mountain peak looks white, but it is actually a mixture of colours that range from red to violet.

BIO FACT

Human eyes cannot detect wavelengths longer than 770 nm. We cannot see infrared radiation, but heat receptors in our skin detect it readily as "heat rays." Similarly, we cannot see wavelengths shorter than 400 nm, nor can we feel this ultraviolet radiation on our skin — at least, not at first. We may, however, feel its effects later. Ultraviolet waves are energetic enough to enter cells and cause increased production of melanin pigment (suntan) or even cause cell damage (sunburn) that may disrupt DNA and lead to skin cancer decades later.

Figure 3.7 A prism can separate the different frequencies of light into distinctly different coloured bands. Our eyes respond differently to the different frequencies.

The Photon Model of Light

To understand photosynthesis, you need to know about another model of light, the **photon model of light**, whose main ideas are listed below.

- Light travels through space in the form of individual energy "packets," which are called **photons**. Like electromagnetic waves, photons travel at 300 000 000 m/s.

- The amount of energy in a photon depends on the frequency of the light. The higher the frequency, the more energy the photon delivers.

- Violet light has a higher frequency than red light. This means that there is more energy in a photon of violet light than there is in a photon of red light.

At first glance, the wave model and the photon model may seem to contradict each other. In fact, the photon model of light caused an uproar in the scientific world when Albert Einstein (1879–1955), first proposed it in 1905. Most physicists accepted the wave model, and did not see how light could be both a wave and a photon. Now we know that a single model is not enough to explain everything we can observe about light. The two models complement each other. Each model fills in the other's gaps or weaknesses. However, the photon model is better suited for explaining photosynthesis.

>> FAST FORWARD

You can find definitions for both wavelength and frequency in the *Glossary* at the back of this book.

BIO FACT

Most of our Sun's radiant energy is given off in three general forms: infrared (IR), visible, and ultraviolet (UV). However, much of the UV and IR radiation that travels toward us never reaches Earth's surface because it is absorbed or reflected by the upper atmosphere.

The Chemistry of Pigments

To use the energy of light for photosynthesis, a plant must first absorb photons of light. Absorption is only one of three possible outcomes when light strikes a surface. Which of the three outcomes (absorption, reflection, and transmission) actually occurs depends on the nature of the surface, as shown in Figure 3.8 on the next page.

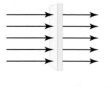
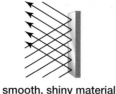

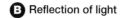
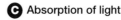

transparent material   **smooth, shiny material**   **opaque material**

A Transmission of light   **B** Reflection of light   **C** Absorption of light

Figure 3.8 What becomes of light energy that is (A) transmitted, (B) reflected, and (C) absorbed?

Investigation   3 • A

Light Colour and Photosynthesis

The oxygen produced during photosynthesis in aquatic plants can be easily seen as bubbles rising to the surface of the water. Counting the bubbles of oxygen that are produced in a given time can be used as a measure of the rate of photosynthesis occurring. Some colours of light promote photosynthesis more than others. You will be using cellophane or filters of different colours to investigate under which colour(s) of light an aquatic plant has the highest rate of photosynthesis.

Pre-lab Questions

1. Which wavelength does chlorophyll *a* most readily absorb? Chlorophyll *b*?

2. What variable(s) must you control in order to establish the effect of light colour on the rate of photosynthesis?

Problem

What colour(s) of light will promote the highest rate of photosynthesis?

Prediction

Predict which colour filter over a light bulb will result in the highest rate of photosynthesis by an aquatic plant.

CAUTION:

Materials

large beaker or jar (about 1 L)
an aquatic plant such as *Rotela*
coloured cellophane or filters (several different colours)
desk lamp with a reflector and 100-W bulb
sodium hydrogen carbonate solution (0.25%)
small graduated cylinder (10-25 mL)
adhesive tape   stop watch

Procedure

1. Prepare the lamp by taping coloured cellophane over its reflector.

2. Make a table to record your results. Include a column for a control and a column for each colour of cellophane tested.

3. Place the plant in the beaker or jar, and cover with water. Add about 5 mL of the sodium hydrogen carbonate solution to the beaker. This will supply the CO that would ordinarily be found in pond water where this plant lives in nature. (Note: Make sure you add the same amount of water and same amount of sodium hydrogen carbonate

Molecules that absorb specific colours (wavelengths) of light are called **pigments**. For example, most plant leaves contain **chlorophyll** pigments which give leaves their green colour. When struck by white light such as that from the Sun, chlorophyll pigments absorb red light from one end of the visible spectrum, and violet and certain shades of blue from the other end. However, chlorophyll pigments transmit or reflect green light from the middle of the spectrum, which is why the leaves of grass appear green to our eyes. Figure 3.9 on the next page explains how this works.

Word LINK

The name "chlorophyll" comes from the Greek *khloros* meaning green, and *phullon* meaning leaf.

solution when you test each light colour as separate trials.)

4. Place the lamp above the beaker, as shown. As soon as you observe bubbles being produced, start timing for 5 min, counting the bubbles produced in that time period. Record the results in your table.

5. Repeat steps 3-5 using a new plant and a different colour of cellophane.

Post-lab Questions

1. Was your prediction correct? If not, why do you think it was not?

2. How could you do a similar experiment using a terrestrial plant? For example, how could you collect the oxygen produced?

Conclude and Apply

3. Make a graph using the data in your table, and write an explanation of the results it shows.

4. Compare your results with those of other classmates. Were there differences in your observations? If so, explain why you think those might have occurred.

Exploring Further

5. If you have access to a spectroscope, use it to find out more about the absorption of light by chlorophyll. A spectroscope is an instrument that displays the visible spectrum when a white light source is shined through its light port. If a coloured, transparent solution or material is placed between the light source and the spectroscope, some of the light is eliminated from the spectrum (because the light is absorbed by the substance).

Use a small test tube containing a solution of chlorophyll, supplied by your teacher, to determine the colours of the spectrum that it absorbs. Use solutions of food colouring for comparison. Make a hypothesis about what colour of light you think your chlorophyll sample will absorb.

Shine a light source through the light port in the back of the spectroscope and observe the spectrum. Using coloured pencils, record your observations of the wavelengths (in nanometres) for each colour visible in the spectrum. Place a small test tube containing clear water in front of the light port to see if any light is absorbed. You can account for this in the observations that follow.

Place each of the test tubes containing different food colouring solutions in front of the light port of the spectroscope. Observe the spectrum for each, and record your results. Then use the spectroscope to test the absorption spectrum for chlorophyll by placing that test tube in front of the light port. Observe the light spectrum, and record your results. Did your results support your hypothesis? Why or why not? How would you improve this experiment?

⊳ PLAY

Use the Light Colour and Photosynthesis activity on your Electronic Learning Partner to examine further the effect of light colour on the rate of photosynthesis.

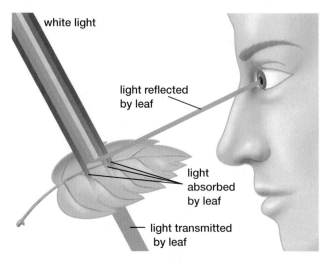

Figure 3.9 Which colours reflect off the leaf and return to the eye? Which colours are absorbed by the leaf, and can no longer be seen?

The term chlorophyll refers to a group of related, but not identical, pigment molecules. Two chlorophylls play an important role in plant photosynthesis. One chlorophyll is yellow-green: that is, it reflects yellow and green light to our eyes. The other is blue-green in colour because it reflects green and some shades of blue. Because they are reflected, these colours do not provide energy for photosynthesis. That is, they never enter the leaf.

> **▐▐ PAUSE** **● RECORD**
>
> The energy for photosynthesis comes from the light that is absorbed. Compare Figure 3.9 with Figure 3.10. What do the peaks on the graph represent? What do the valleys represent?

Chlorophyll's Role

Chlorophyll's role in photosynthesis is twofold: (1) it absorbs red light, violet light, and certain shades of blue, and (2) it converts the absorbed energy into a form that the synthesis reactions can use.

However, chlorophyll can only perform this conversion in a particular environment. The pigment molecules must be embedded on an enzyme-studded membrane. The cell organelle that provides this ideal environment is the chloroplast, as you learned in Chapter 2.

The Structure of the Chloroplast

A typical chloroplast from a plant cell is small. It would require 38-40 chloroplasts to make a line

1 mm long. Yet a single chloroplast can perform hundreds or thousands of reactions in just one second. The key to this remarkable level of activity is the many-folded thylakoid membrane inside the chloroplast.

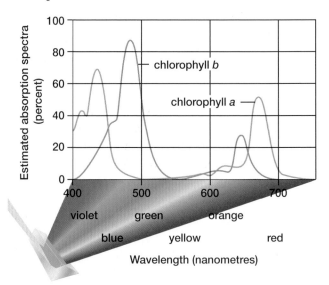

Figure 3.10 Note the labels on each axis. What does the vertical axis measure? What does the horizontal axis measure?

Recall that enzymes promote or catalyze chemical reactions without being used up. Although chlorophyll is not an enzyme, it can also be reused repeatedly. A chlorophyll molecule absorbs light (photons) and then passes the energy on to another molecule.

Both enzymes and chlorophyll are needed to make photosynthesis occur, but they are not raw materials of the process. The materials (CO_2 and H_2O) plus light energy pass into the chloroplast through its outer membrane. Oxygen molecules (O_2) produced by photosynthesis pass out through the same membrane into the cell cytoplasm. Most of this oxygen is a waste product, but the plant's own cells use some of the "waste" oxygen to carry out cellular respiration to release the energy they require from the glucose.

> **▸▸ FAST FORWARD**
>
> Most of the oxygen molecules produced by photosynthesis are released from the cell and pass out through small openings in the plant's leaves into the atmosphere. Eventually this O_2 is used by other organisms to drive cellular respiration. Go to Chapter 14, Section 14.2, to see where this occurs in the leaves.

Photosystems and Energy

Researchers have found that the chlorophyll pigments within the thylakoid membrane are packed into clusters called **photosystems**. Each photosystem is composed of a few hundred pigment molecules (mostly chlorophylls) that act together. Their combined function can be compared to that of a funnel, but instead of funnelling liquid, the photosystems funnel energy. Figure 3.11 illustrates the funnel model of a photosystem. Read the labels and numbered captions carefully.

As light enters a photosystem, the pigments in the "funnel" act like a bucket brigade. Energy resulting from the excitation of electrons by light is relayed from one pigment molecule to another until the energy reaches its target, a special pair of chlorophylls that function as a **reaction centre**.

The reaction centre of a photosystem uses the incoming energy to split water molecules into oxygen atoms and hydrogen atoms to form **ATP** — an energy carrier molecule.

Synthesis Reactions

The synthesis reactions take place in the stroma of the chloroplast. The stroma is a solution containing water and nearly everything else needed to run the synthesis reactions — but the reactions cannot begin without chemical energy. For that, they need energy carrier molecules produced by the photosystems.

Notice that the photosystem reactions need light energy in order to proceed. However, the synthesis reactions also need chemical energy; they get this energy from the energy carrier molecules produced by the photosystems. The synthesis reactions can

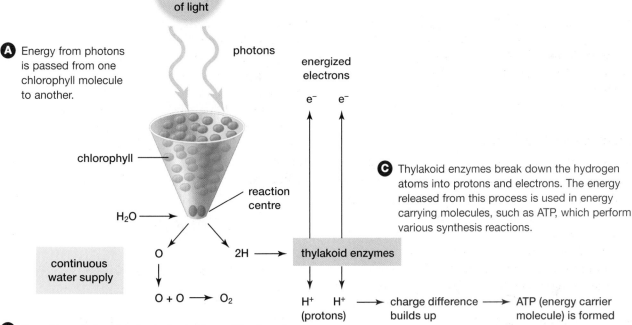

Figure 3.11 The funnel model of a photosystem. Light is transformed into potential energy, or energized electrons.

run for a while in the dark, but only until all of the energy-carrier molecules have been used up. Taken together, the synthesis reactions are called the **Calvin cycle**, after the American chemist Melvin Calvin (1911–1997), who won a Nobel prize for explaining them (Figure 3.12). The product of the Calvin cycle is glyceraldehyde phosphate (PGAL). Molecules of glyceraldehyde phosphate can be bonded together to form glucose, which the plant can use as food. PGAL can also be used to form other compounds, such as sucrose, lipids, and proteins.

Energy for Life

Deciphering the Calvin cycle was an enormous step forward for biologists. It showed them just how complex organic reactions could be, and how chemistry could be a major help in determining the details of biological processes.

The Calvin cycle in photosynthesis is critical to almost all life on Earth. Without the Calvin cycle, photosystems could still release oxygen gas, but there would be no means of manufacturing the glucose that nearly all organisms depend on for stored chemical energy — organisms including animals (such as humans) as well as the green plants and algae that carry out photosynthesis.

>> **FAST FORWARD**

Deciphering the Calvin cycle launched a new era in the scientific discipline of biochemistry, which led eventually to major advances in technologies such as those described in Chapter 3, Section 3.5.

Web LINK

To learn more about the Calvin cycle and how a photosystem operates, visit the web site below. Go to **Science Resources** then to **BIOLOGY 11** to find out where to go next. How are these two systems related? What part of the chloroplast produces O_2? What part of the chloroplast uses CO_2? What types of research led up to the discovery of these processes? Prepare a brief report of your findings.
www.school.mcgrawhill.ca/resources/

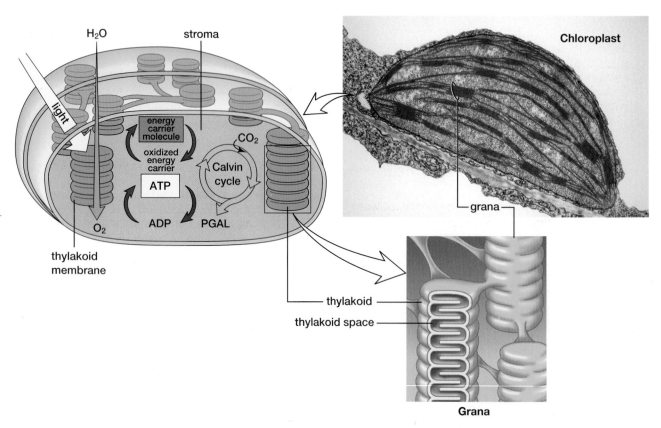

Figure 3.12 A summary of photosynthesis in the chloroplast.

1. **C** The reactions of photosynthesis proceed in two main stages. Name these in order and briefly describe the principal outcome of each.

2. **K/U** What is the principal difference between the photon model of light and the wave model of light?

3. **C** Which model is more useful when discussing photosynthesis? Explain why.

4. **K/U** Define the terms pigment and chlorophyll. Explain how the two are connected.

5. **C** Describe the role that chlorophyll plays in photosynthesis.

   (a) What other substances must be present for chlorophyll to play its role?

   (b) Where in the chloroplast are these substances found?

6. **C** Explain why the enzymes needed for photosynthesis are not regarded as raw materials.

   (a) Explain why chlorophyll is not regarded as a raw material.

   (b) Explain why water and carbon dioxide are regarded as raw materials.

7. **K/U** What is a photosystem made of? Describe what it does.

8. **K/U** Where are the photosystems of a green plant located?

9. **C** Briefly explain the funnel model of a photosystem.

10. **C** In twenty five words or less, describe the Calvin cycle's role in the biosphere.

11. **K/U** Describe the process of photosynthesis and the process of respiration in terms of glucose.

12. **K/U** The carbon cycle shows how carbon atoms are reused as molecules transform.

   (a) Show the recycling of hydrogen atoms between photosynthesis and respiration.

   (b) In a different colour than you used for part (a), show how energy flows as this recycling of hydrogen proceeds.

13. **K/U** Write the simple equation for cellular respiration.

   (a) Which molecule in the equation has the greatest potential energy?

   (b) Where is the kinetic energy?

14. **K/U** Cellular respiration transforms the chemical energy in glucose. Where does the energy go?

15. **K/U** Give three examples of invisible electromagnetic radiation. What is meant by visible radiation?

16. **I** The photosynthetic activity of algae at various temperatures is shown in the table. A chemical indicator added to the test tubes containing the algae changed colour to show how much CO_2 was being used when the algae were photosynthesizing.

Test Tube Number	Temperature of the algae suspension	Time elapsed until colour changed
1	2°C	no colour change
2	10°C	44 min
3	15°C	22 min
4	25°C	30 min
5	30°C	35 min
6	35°C	44 min

Based on the data in the table, answer the following questions:

   (a) At what temperature was the algae most active?

   (b) What can be inferred from the fact that there was no change in colour in the algae at 2°C?

   (c) How was the temperature related to the rate of photosynthesis in these algae?

17. **MC** (a) List two limitations to energy production by plants.

   (b) How could people improve the process?

   (c) Describe the impact of such a change.

The Process of Cellular Respiration

- Explain and illustrate the process of cellular respiration.
- Investigate the process of fermentation.
- Examine the use of micro-organisms in producing ethanol as a fuel.

Figure 3.13 Oxygen from the air helps to release energy from this skier's food fast enough to keep him moving. The water vapour and carbon dioxide that he exhales are end-products of processes occurring within his cells.

As a result of photosynthesis, the skier in Figure 3.13 has the oxygen he needs to breathe. Into his lungs it moves, diffusing through thin blood vessel walls to travel in his blood to every cell in his body. The food he ate earlier in the day has, by now, been digested — broken down into tiny molecules, such as glucose, which have diffused through the lining of his small intestine into thin-walled blood vessels. From there it has travelled to cells throughout his body. Here the oxygen and molecules such as glucose recombine in a series of reactions to complete the process of cellular respiration. **Cellular respiration** includes the series of chemical reactions needed to break down (metabolize) carbohydrates and other molecules in order to release the energy they contain.

Energy in Living Organisms

The energy released by cellular respiration is stored in the form of the energy carrier molecule, adenosine triphosphate (ATP). This important molecule provides the energy for muscles to contract, nerves to conduct impulses, and all that cells require to build protein, pump in substances they need, permit enzymes to act, and so on. Energy is released one ATP molecule at a time, as the cell requires it.

You have learned that photosynthesis occurs in chloroplasts and uses solar energy to produce glucose and other carbohydrates. Glucose and other

molecules are broken down mainly in the mitochondria of cells, producing ATP molecules. All organisms perform cellular respiration, and almost all organisms carry out the process of aerobic cellular respiration in their mitochondria. **Aerobic** means that the process requires oxygen. Aerobic cellular respiration consists of four main phases, as summarized in Figure 3.14.

Through the whole four-phase process, cellular respiration of one glucose molecule produces 38 molecules of ATP in bacterial cells and 36 molecules of ATP in cells with mitochondria. In eukaryotic cells, two ATPs of energy are lost to intermediate energy carrier molecules. The usable energy of ATP is stored when the energy from cellular respiration chemically bonds a third phosphate group to a molecule that is already present, called adenosine diphosphate (ADP). The bonding of a third phosphate (P) to the two-phosphate ADP molecule is what produces the three-phosphate ATP molecule.

This ATP can now release energy for cell activities, when its third phosphate group breaks off. Perhaps surprisingly, the phosphate-to-phosphate bond in ATP, between the second and third phosphate groups is relatively weak — less than 10% as strong as a carbon-to-hydrogen covalent bond, for example. Nevertheless, the amount of energy released by breaking the phosphate-to-phosphate bonds is enough to drive essential cell reactions. In fact, the low energy phosphate-to-

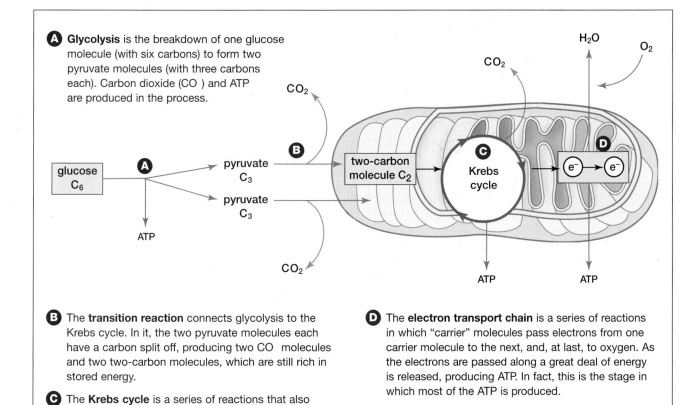

A **Glycolysis** is the breakdown of one glucose molecule (with six carbons) to form two pyruvate molecules (with three carbons each). Carbon dioxide (CO_2) and ATP are produced in the process.

B The **transition reaction** connects glycolysis to the Krebs cycle. In it, the two pyruvate molecules each have a carbon split off, producing two CO_2 molecules and two two-carbon molecules, which are still rich in stored energy.

C The **Krebs cycle** is a series of reactions that also release CO_2, and produce ATP. For every one glucose molecule broken down, two pyruvate molecules are produced and sent through the cycle, so the cycle occurs twice. Other "carrier" molecules attach to electrons from the Krebs cycle.

D The **electron transport chain** is a series of reactions in which "carrier" molecules pass electrons from one carrier molecule to the next, and, at last, to oxygen. As the electrons are passed along a great deal of energy is released, producing ATP. In fact, this is the stage in which most of the ATP is produced.

Figure 3.14 As cellular respiration occurs, energy is released step by step and stored in ATP. Its energy is then transferred to molecules in other chemical reactions, such as those that permit our muscles to contract. The ADP left behind is then available to receive another phosphate group.

phosphate bond is extremely valuable precisely because it is easily broken and the release of energy within a cell can be adjusted to suit the cell's exact requirements. After the third phosphate group breaks off, the ATP molecule reverts to the lower energy ADP molecule, available to accept another phosphate group, producing the ATP molecule, once again. This process continues over and over in every cell, so long as oxygen and molecules of foods are available for the process of cellular respiration to continue.

> PLAY

For more information about energy carrier molecules, refer to your Electronic Learning Partner.

BIO FACT

In an average adult human at rest, it is estimated that this cycle of ADP $\rightleftharpoons$ ATP occurs so often that about 40 kg of ATP are processed per day. Imagine the amount that is processed if a person is running, swimming, or being otherwise very active. Yet, consider that you do not gain 40 kg in mass each day.

Where Cellular Respiration Occurs

Glycolysis (Figure 3.14 A) takes place in the cytoplasm of the cell, not in the mitochondria. **Glycolysis** is the breakdown of glucose into two pyruvate molecules, and it does not use oxygen. All organisms perform glycolysis, but only a small fraction of the available chemical energy is released by this phase (just two ATP molecules from one glucose molecule). What happens next will depend on two factors:

1. The type of organism. Some micro-organisms lack the cell parts and enzymes to perform the aerobic phases of cellular respiration. The Krebs cycle (Figure 3.14 C) and electron transport (Figure 3.14 D) do not occur in these organisms.

2. The availability of oxygen. Even in cells with many mitochondria, a continuous supply of oxygen is needed to sustain a continuous release of energy. If the oxygen supply is deficient, such cells cannot carry out the Krebs cycle; hence electron transport cannot occur.

In either of these cases, the cell may use an alternative process to release further chemical energy from its food molecules.

The Process of Fermentation

Some types of cells can also release energy through the process of **fermentation**. Fermentation includes glycolysis, but not the other parts of aerobic cellular respiration. In fermentation, glycolysis is followed by one of two pathways: the pyruvate formed breaks down to become either lactate or alcohol, depending on the organism. First, look at how fermentation happens in your own body. When muscles work hard, they need more oxygen than the body can deliver. As the oxygen runs out, mitochondrial action shuts down. In the cytoplasm, however, glycolysis continues to break down glucose into pyruvate molecules. In the absence of oxygen, the pyruvate molecules break down to form lactate. Fermentation produces just two ATP molecules, so its energy yield is low, but fermentation is important because it can provide a rapid burst of energy in the absence of oxygen. However, fermentation cannot sustain the release of energy in muscle cells for a prolonged period. After a while, you simply have to stop and rest.

You probably find yourself breathing heavily after you have been running or exercising in some other way. You have a so-called **oxygen debt**; that is, you need oxygen to break down the lactate that has accumulated. Both glycolysis and fermentation

SKILL FOCUS

Initiating and planning

Hypothesizing

Identifying variables

Performing and recording

Conducting research

Seeds and Respiration

Soaking seeds for a short period will lead to their germination. In this investigation, you will determine if germinating seeds respire and, if so, what factor(s) affect the rate of their cellular respiration.

Problem

What factor(s) affect the rate of cellular respiration in germinating seeds?

Hypothesis

Make a hypothesis about one factor that you think will affect the rate of cellular respiration in the germinating seeds supplied by your teacher.

Materials

Rubber or plastic tubing	Glass tubing
E-flask	Bromothymol blue
1- and 2-holed rubber stoppers	any other material your teacher approves

Experimental Plan

1. Decide which variable you will investigate to determine its influence on the rate of cellular respiration.

2. Determine what variable you will measure, for example, oxygen use or carbon dioxide production, etc. If probeware is available, consider using it. (Note: Your teacher will review the tests for oxygen, carbon dioxide, etc., with you, as needed.)

3. Outline your procedural steps for approval by your teacher.

are **anaerobic** processes: they occur in the absence of oxygen. Have you ever noticed that after you've rested for a few moments, you are ready to run again? Here is what happens. As lactate builds up in the muscle cells, it changes their acidity and prevents muscles from contracting. When you stop running, you breathe in more oxygen. When it reaches the cells, they are again able to perform aerobic cellular respiration instead of fermentation, and the lactate molecules leave the muscle cells to go to the liver where they are converted back to pyruvate.

COURSE CHALLENGE

Aerobic respiration stops when oxygen levels are low. Under these conditions, mitochondria start to break down and then the cell prepares to die by way of necrosis. Can a microscopic view of cells indicate that a person died from suffocation? Start making a file of information in preparation for your Biology Course Challenge.

Fermentation in Micro-organisms

Many foods are available because of the process of fermentation, as shown in Figure 3.15 on the next pages. Many different bacteria are responsible for the flavours of different cheeses, in which their fermentation produces lactate. Yeasts also break down sugars by fermentation, but the end-products are carbon dioxide (which we use to make bread rise), and ethanol. This type of fermentation allows us to produce wine from grapes, for example. The fermentation of grains has traditionally been used to make beer. More recently, it is also giving us new fuels for our internal combustion engines, replacing the need for gasoline from fossil fuels.

≫ FAST FORWARD

To learn more about the biology of bacteria and yeast, turn to Chapter 12, Sections 12.2 and 12.4.

Checking the Plan

1. Revise your experimental plan, based on discussions with your classmates and teacher.

2. Be ready to perform your revised procedure, ensuring you take all appropriate safety precautions.

Data and Observations

1. Make sure you produce a table of your observations.

2. Explain the results of your experiment, based on observations you have made.

Analyze

1. Make a graph using the data in your table.

2. Does the variable you investigated influence the rate of cellular respiration? What evidence do you have?

Conclude and Apply

3. Explain how the variable you investigated influences the rate of cellular respiration.

4. How would you make use of this information to provide a greenhouse, or other facility where plants are grown commercially from seeds, with information they need about the variables that are most important for the growth of seeds.

Exploring Further

5. Consider an independent project that might take you beyond this investigation. What other factors might you investigate? What other species would you be interested in investigating? Outline an original experiment that you would like to do based on the information and activities on photosynthesis and cellular respiration you have conducted in this chapter. This outline could, for example, become a science fair project for you to pursue.

Figure 3.15 (a) Bacterial fermentation gives this cheese its distinctive, "sharp" flavour.

(b) Yeast has been added to the dough for this bread, and it is being left in a warm place to ferment.

Investigation   3 • C

Fermentation, a Form of Sugar Metabolism

Glucose is the main source of chemical energy for cells. Yeasts use the process of fermentation to release energy from glucose without using oxygen. This experiment will provide evidence for the chemical breakdown of sugar by yeast cells.

Pre-lab Questions

- What are the products of fermentation with baker's yeast?

- Describe a positive test for glucose using Benedict's solution.

Problem

How can you determine that yeast cells break down sugar?

Prediction

Predict how yeast cells use glucose as food.

CAUTION: Benedict's solution is poisonous. Lift hot test tubes from a hot water bath using a test tube holder.

Materials

hot plate	test tube rack
test tube holder	4 test tubes
electronic or triple	600 mL beaker
beam balance	100 mL graduated cylinder
400 mL beaker	thermometer or
glucose solution or	temperature probe
apple juice (prepared	Benedict's solution
by teacher)	baker's yeast
	distilled water

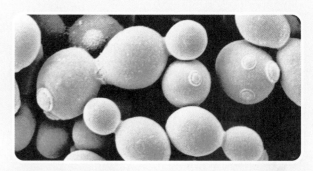

Yeast cells reproducing.

Procedure

1. Fill a large beaker about half full of water, and begin heating it on a hot plate. When the temperature reaches about 35-40°C, it will serve as your hot water bath.

2. Label the test tubes #1, #2, #3, and #4 near their upper rims with a marker that is resistant to heat.

3. Measure about 25 mL of distilled water and pour this into test tube #1.

4. Collect about 100 mL of dilute apple juice.

5. Measure and pour 25 mL of dilute apple juice for each of the other 3 test tubes.

6. Carefully add 7 drops of Benedict's solution to each test tube.

7. Observe and record the colour and appearance of the material in each test tube.

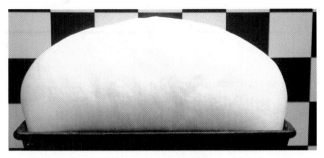

(c) After a few hours, the bread you saw in b has now risen, due to the carbon dioxide bubbles produced by fermentation.

(d) These grapes will be harvested and left in vats to ferment, producing a solution containing alcohol, as well as water, sugar, and flavour molecules.

8. Use the electronic or triple-beam balance to measure one 3 g sample of dry yeast.

9. Add this to test tube #4. Wait 15 min.

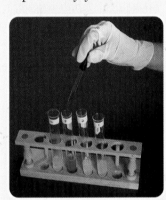

10. Use the balance to measure one 3 g sample of dry yeast.

11. Add this to test tube #2.

12. Test the temperature of the hot water bath with a thermometer. Place all the test tubes in the hot water bath (about 35-40°C). Note: Do not add the test tubes if the temperature is higher than this.

13. After adding all the test tubes to the hot water bath, wait 7 min.

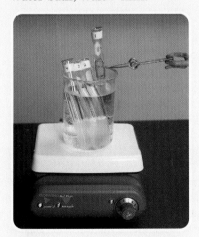

14. Using a test tube holder, remove the test tubes and place them in the test tube rack.

15. Record your observations as quickly as possible.

Post-lab Questions

1. Why did you use glucose and not sucrose for this experiment?

2. What is the purpose of test tube #1?

3. What is the purpose of test tube #3?

4. Which test tube showed the strongest concentration of glucose?

5. Explain why test tube #2 and test tube #3 did not have the same results.

Conclude and Apply

6. Did yeast consume glucose? Explain how you reached your conclusion.

Extend Your Knowledge

7. Predict what would happen if you allowed the yeast in test tube #4 to ferment for one day before being tested with Benedict's.

8. Design an experiment to see if yeast can ferment a larger sugar molecule (a disaccharide) like sucrose or lactose.

9. Repeat the experiment using test tube number 4 only. First use an electronic probe to measure the concentration of CO_2 in the test tubes following step 8. Then complete steps 9, 12, and 13. While the test tube is still in the hot water bath use the probe again to measure the concentration of CO_2 in the test tube. Is there a change? Explain your results.

From the Cornfield to the Carburetor — Using the Products of Fermentation

Ethanol is one of the oldest products of biotechnology. It is grain alcohol, which we have long produced in beer, wine, and spirits. Today "fuel ethanol," or denatured grain alcohol, shows promise as an alternative to petroleum-based fuels, and could help meet some pressing environmental problems.

Ethanol-based fuel is not a new idea — Henry Ford's famous Model T of the early 1900s could run on either ethanol or gasoline. High-performance "top fuel" racing cars use ethanol-based fuels, which have a higher "octane rating" (resistance to engine knock or "pinging") than gasoline and burn at lower temperatures. But because ethanol costs more to produce than gasoline, its use was generally limited to this kind of specialized application.

The Need for Alternative Fuels

Beginning in the late 1970s, however, environmental concerns, rising oil prices, and dwindling petroleum reserves led some governments to take another look at ethanol fuels. Since then, ethanol has come into use in a variety of forms.

In North America, ethanol commonly appears in an unleaded gasoline blend ("gasohol"), as E5 (5% ethanol/95% gasoline by volume) or E10 (10% ethanol/90% gasoline). In gasohol blends, ethanol is a non-toxic octane booster, replacing toxic lead or benzene additives. Because ethanol contains oxygen in its molecular structure, it is also an "oxygenator" that allows gasoline to burn more completely, improving performance and reducing exhaust emissions.

Cars manufactured since 1980 can use gasohol without engine modification, and it has become especially popular in large urban areas where air pollution from automotive emissions is a special concern. Gasohol is currently marketed in Canada from British Columbia to Québec.

A more radical ethanol formula, E85 (85% ethanol/15% gasoline), was introduced in the late 1990s. E85 is used in "flexible fuel vehicles" (FFVs), mainly small trucks, minivans, and sports utility vehicles that can also use unleaded gasoline or any ethanol/gasoline blend.

Where Does Ethanol Come From?

In North America, starch-rich grain "feedstocks" provide the basis for ethanol production. The commonest feedstock is corn, although some Canadian ethanol plants use wheat. (The grain plants used are generally unfit for human consumption.)

 THINKING LAB

Solve an Industrial Problem

Imagine that you work for a company that is about to embark on a large-scale, industrial fermentation project to make a fuel additive. The company needs to produce as much ethanol as possible as quickly as possible for this purpose. Your task is to help decide on the optimal conditions for fermentation.

What variable will you investigate, how will you design your experiment, and how will you present your plan to the Research and Development (R & D) Advisory Group for approval? With a partner, develop a plan for your presentation. Make a hypothesis about how the variable you have selected will affect fermentation. Together, design an experiment to test your hypothesis.

Lay out your plan. Consider that you must be able to convince the advisory group that your experiment is one that will likely provide good information on optimal conditions for fermentation.

Present your plan to your teacher and/or other students as if they are the Research and Development Advisory Board. (Note: ethanol is highly flammable and poisonous. Do not carry out the plan; this activity is to present your experimental plan only.)

Analyze

Could the experiment you designed be used by the company for the large-scale production of ethanol? If yes, suggest other questions the company would need to ask as well. If no, explain why you think such an operation would not be feasible, or should not be undertaken.

Web LINK

To learn more about how companies produce ethanol on a large scale, visit the web site below. Go to **Science Resources**, then to **BIOLOGY 11** to find out where to go next. What processes are involved and what is the ethanol used for? Prepare a brief report on your findings.
www.school.mcgrawhill.ca/resources/

Figure 3.16 Canada's largest ethanol production plant is located in Chatham, Ontario.

Ethanol is produced through the process of fermentation. To prepare for fermentation, the feedstock is ground into meal, then mixed with water to form a slurry called "mash." Enzymes added to the mash convert the feedstock's starches into a simple sugar called *dextrose*. The mash is heated to destroy any stray bacteria, then cooled and placed in fermenters.

In the fermenters, yeast is added to the mash. The single-celled yeast organisms (*Saccharomyces cerevisiae*) consume the dextrose and reproduce, producing ethanol and carbon dioxide gas (CO_2) as by-products. When fermentation is complete, the resulting product, called "beer," is approximately 10% ethanol and 90% water. Figure 3.17 illustrates this complete process.

Distilling the beer to eliminate as much as possible yields nearly pure ethanol; this is then made unfit for human consumption ("denatured") by blending it with about 5% by volume of gasoline. The grain and yeast residues are dried to produce a vitamin- and protein-rich product called Distiller's Dried Grains and Solubles (DDGS), used in poultry and cattle feeds.

Clearing the Air and Cooling the Greenhouse

Because the ethanol molecule contains oxygen, it burns more completely in a vehicle engine than pure gasoline, which contains no oxygen. This improved fuel combustion can reduce tailpipe emissions of carbon monoxide (CO); burning ethanol instead of straight gasoline can reduce emissions by as much as 30% (Figure 3.18). CO is one of the main reactants responsible for the production of ground-level ("bad") ozone, and a primary ingredient in "smog," a form of air pollution that harms plant life and contributes to human respiratory disease.

Emissions of unburned hydrocarbons from petroleum-based fuels, including volatile organic compounds (VOCs) released when gasoline evaporates, also contribute to smog formation. Ethanol is not petroleum-based, and it releases no hydrocarbons through combustion or evaporation. Public health concerns over the effects of CO and hydrocarbon emissions have been a major factor in fuel ethanol's acceptance. The combustion of ethanol does produce carbon dioxide (CO_2), a powerful "greenhouse gas" thought to be one of the main contributors to global warming. However, ethanol, unlike gasoline, is produced from a renewable resource (grain) rather than a non-renewable fossil source (crude oil). This "balances the budget" on greenhouse gas emissions: the growing of ethanol feedstock plants such as corn or wheat absorbs more atmospheric carbon dioxide through

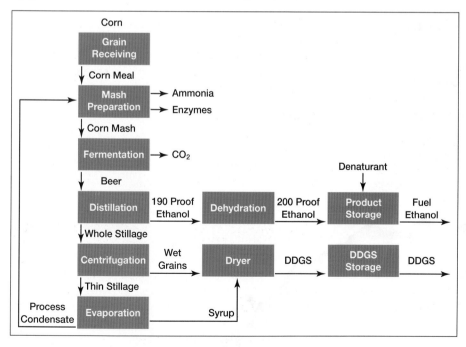

Figure 3.17 The ethanol production process.

photosynthesis than is released during production and use of ethanol fuels. By contrast, all of the CO_2 produced by burning fossil fuel is excess greenhouse gas with no balancing factors. Current estimates indicate that E10 ethanol-blend fuel reduces greenhouse gas emissions by about 3.9%; E85 fuels can achieve a 37% reduction.

Of course, the best way to reduce environmental harm from vehicle emissions is simply to drive less and use alternative transportation whenever possible. If we continue to use our fuel-burning cars for some decades yet, ethanol as an alternative fuel offers a workable way to reduce our impact on the environment.

Figure 3.18 This ethanol-powered truck produces no hydrocarbons during combustion of fuel.

SECTION REVIEW

1. **K/U** List three cellular activities that rely on ATP.

2. **K/U** Make a diagram of ATP and show how energy is released from this molecule.

3. **K/U** What is glycolysis? Where does it occur?

4. **K/U** Identify the three main stages of cellular respiration. Which step produces the most ATP?

5. **C** How is oxygen important to the release of energy in cellular respiration?

6. **C** What strategies can some cells use if oxygen is not available?

7. **I** Some bacteria can only perform glycolysis and fermentation. These bacteria cannot use oxygen. Review the structure of prokaryotic cells (Chapter 2) to explain this. Suggest an experimental procedure you could use to investigate this.

8. **C** **a)** Describe the process used by muscle cells to release energy without oxygen.

   b) Brain cells do not do this process. Suggest reasons for this.

   c) Consider a traumatic situation, like drowning, when oxygen levels drop. Suggest strategies that the body could use to make the most of the oxygen resources left.

9. **K/U** Write a chemical reaction for fermentation.

10. **MC** List the advantages and disadvantages of ethanol as a fuel for automobiles.

11. **I** An experiment was conducted to compare the rate of aerobic respiration to the rate of anaerobic respiration of yeast cells over a period of time. An indirect measurement was made by monitoring the amount of carbon dioxide released from the yeast cells. Supplied with glucose, the yeast cells were incubated within an air-tight vat for several hours. The results are shown in the table below.

Time (hours)	Volume of CO_2 released (mL)
1	5
2	9
3	30
4	48
5	5

(a) At what time period(s) was the yeast metabolizing aerobically?

(b) During what time interval was glucose consumption the greatest?

(c) At what time interval were the yeast cells producing the greatest number of ATP molecules per glucose molecule consumed?

(d) Account for the sudden decrease in CO_2 consumption after the fourth hour.

UNIT INVESTIGATION PREP

What kind of cellular respiration would bacteria use in an anaerobic environment? What kind of waste products might the bacteria produce using this kind of cellular respiration? Write your thoughts in preparation for your Unit 1 Design Your Own Investigation.

Cell Organelles and Biotechnology

EXPECTATIONS

- Explain the flow of energy between photosynthesis and respiration.

- Examine the origins of chloroplasts and mitochondria.

- Identify industrial applications of cellular metabolism.

- Explain the value of the radioactive labelling of carbon compounds in tracking cellular metabolism.

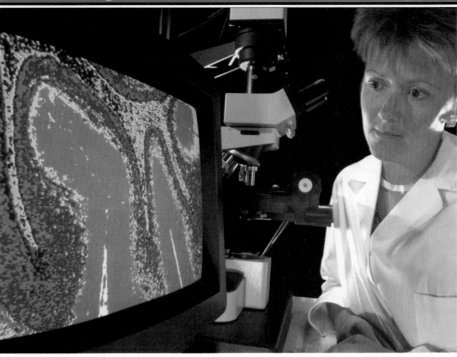

Figure 3.19 This technician is studying a magnified, colour-enhanced image of brain cells.

Much is now known about cell organelles because of the advent of electron microscopy in the last century, and more and better microscopic techniques. As well, the work of chemists on the biochemical pathways occurring within each organelle has led to interesting observations about chloroplasts and mitochondria.

How are they alike and how are they different? As you can see from Figure 3.20 both the chloroplast and the mitochondrion are responsible for a series of critical energetic reactions. The chloroplast is responsible for photosynthesis, the mitochondria for aerobic cellular respiration. The structure of each, with their double inner membranes, and fluid-filled spaces permits many reactions to occur simultaneously. Both contain enzymes that permit all the reactions for which they are responsible to take place continously. Carbohydrates produced by photosynthesis provide the raw material for cellular respiration.

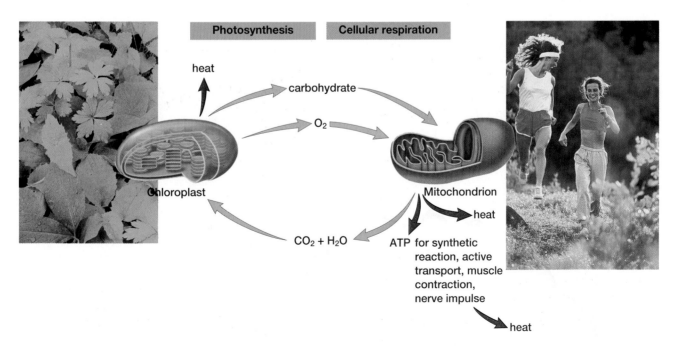

Figure 3.20 Metabolic processes in the chloroplast and mitochondrion.

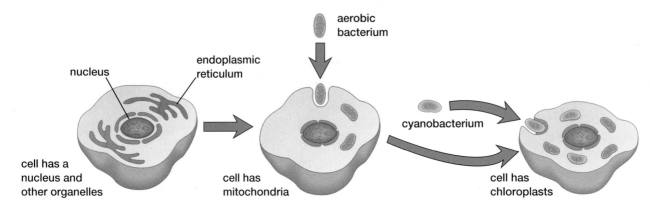

Figure 3.21 Hypothesis on the origin of chloroplasts and mitochondria in eukaryotic cells. Cyanobacteria can produce food using photosynthesis.

An Origin Hypothesis

Most researchers think that eukaryotic cells (such as those in your body) arose from prokaryotic ones (such as bacterial cells). How this happened is a much-discussed topic of interest among biologists. The similarities between the two energy-related organelles of cells, the chloroplast and the mitochondrion, have led to an interesting hypothesis about their origin. This hypothesis is shown visually in Figure 3.21. What if mitochondria were originally aerobic bacteria? And what if chloroplasts were originally cyanobacteria? Perhaps these prokaryotic cells were engulfed by a larger cell at some time in the distant past. The larger cell would have gained the ability to make its own food, and have a greater ability to break down foods by cellular respiration. The smaller bacterial cells would have gained the food-gathering ability of the larger cells. We have some evidence for this hypothesis since both chloroplasts and mitochondria contain a small amount of DNA, and their DNA is in the form of a loop, like bacterial DNA, instead of being like the DNA in eukaryotic cells.

Metabolism and Technology

The cellular processes of bacteria and fungi have been put to widespread use by human beings for thousands of years. For example, people have been eating raised breads for 6000 years (before that they ate only flat breads similar to pitas, chapatis, or tortillas). It is thought that the first alcoholic beverage was a wine, produced about 8000 years ago from fermented grapes domesticated for wine-making. Starchy grains like barley and wheat were purposely left to ferment to produce early beers in the Middle East; then the knowledge was transferred elsewhere.

This section will concentrate on recent human exploitation of cellular processes, and provide you with ideas for further research of your own.

Cellular Processes and Improving the Environment

As you have read in the previous section, the production of ethanol relies upon an anaerobic process — fermentation by yeast — to turn starch-rich grains into fuel. Manure digestors use fermentation by bacteria. Bacteria and animal wastes, such as hog manure, are warmed and mixed in a sealed, airless tank. The resulting biogas is a mixture of methane, carbon dioxide, and small amounts of other gases. This biogas is burned to generate electricity. The residual, nutrient-rich fibres are used as soil conditioners and the remaining liquid is an effective fertilizer.

Figure 3.22 Interest in manure digestors is increasing in North America, especially with the development of huge hog-farming operations and the rise in natural gas prices. Manure digestors have been used successfully in European countries, such as Germany and Denmark.

Another new technology that will help improve our environment is **bioremediation** — the use of micro-organisms to break complex toxic compounds down into simpler, non-toxic substances. Bioremediation has been the focus of intense study and biotechnical development for several decades. Biologists have investigated both soil and water sites contaminated with industrial waste. In these polluted environments, they have identified communities of heterotrophic bacteria and other micro-organisms that were able to survive by consuming toxic substances and metabolizing them through fermentation. Investigating how these communities (called consortia) survived led to the development of biotreatment systems, such as activated sludge bioreactors. They are used to detoxify effluent from industries such as pulp and paper mills. Activated sludge biomass is composed of about 95% bacteria and 5% other micro-organisms, such as amoebas, ciliates, flagellates, and rotifers.

>> **FAST FORWARD**

To learn more about the diversity of bacteria and other micro-organisms, turn to Chapter 12, Section 12.2.

You have learned that heterotrophic bacteria derive energy by breaking down the complex organic compounds they take in from their environment into simpler compounds such as water and carbon dioxide. This makes them important and beneficial decomposers. In a bioreactor, heterotrophic bacteria derive energy from organic waste — such as tree bark and fertilizer — that is dumped into the sludge tank (Figure 3.24). Certain species of bacteria, such as *Pseudomonas*, are maintained along with the other micro-organisms in the tank. Air is bubbled through the tank, keeping the bacteria, sludge, and water in motion. This "activated" environment brings cells together with oxygen and the nutrient-containing waste. In this aerobic process, the bacteria produce enzymes that break down the organic molecules in the toxic compounds. Although the enzymes speed up the process of decomposition, they also produce heat, which is the result of the chemical reactions taking place during metabolism. For this reason, the temperature of the tank is regulated to keep the bacterial reactions efficient and to ensure that the liquid released with the treated effluent is not too warm when it enters the water body.

Figure 3.23 Pulp and paper mills often discharge effluent into water bodies that provide the habitats for fish, such as salmon and sturgeon. Because the effluent can reduce the amount of dissolved oxygen available to aquatic species, its effects are monitored. How might low levels of dissolved oxygen affect the life processes of aquatic species?

The by-product the bacteria produce, which trickles out with the effluent, does not contain living cells that require oxygen. The bacteria are kept in the tank either by using coagulant (flocculant) chemicals or by allowing the sludge to settle. The sludge is then "dewatered," and the solid cake is combined with other wastes and burned to produce energy. Because the solid sludge is often high in nitrogen and phosphorus, it has been used as fertilizer in large-scale growing operations, such as tree farms. However, in some cases, the public has opposed the use of mill waste as fertilizer. Can you suggest reasons for this opposition?

Figure 3.24 Activated sludge bioreactors are part of waste treatment systems that often include primary and secondary effluent clarifiers and dewatering facilities. Not all activated sludge systems operate in the same way. For example, some systems use oxygen from the air in addition to some pure oxygen. Other systems use a high percentage of pure oxygen.

Bioremediation research continues on many fronts in the pulp and paper industry. In the 1990s, increased public concern over chlorine levels in effluent led to numerous studies on reducing or removing chlorine from the pulp "bleaching" process. Chlorine or chlorine-containing compounds are used because they are very effective at breaking down lignin (a glue-like substance that stiffens certain cell walls in woody plants). If not removed, lignin makes the pulp dark and the resulting paper brown - like brown paper bags. Research on lignin removal has resulted in the development of new bleaching technologies that use other less harmful chemicals, such as hydrogen peroxide. Recently, however, researchers have been studying the possibility of using enzymes, such as xylanase, to help break down lignin, thereby dramatically reducing the need for bleaching chemicals.

The Next Step in Bioremediation

The first patent for a genetically engineered organism was issued in 1980. Samples from sites polluted with oil were analyzed. The bacteria found living in the samples were then cultured and tested in the lab. Once scientists located the actual genes used by the bacteria to allow them to metabolize oil, the scientists spliced these genes into plasmids, which could then be taken up by other bacteria. The organism was a greatly enhanced oil-eating bacterium, and was used to clean up oil spills. These bacteria are able to break down the large, complex molecules of oil into simpler molecules, using the energy released by the chemical change. Various naturally occurring bacteria are able to use a wide range of chemicals as a source of energy, including chemicals that are toxic to most other organisms. For example, there

Canadians in Biology

Fighting Foodborne Illnesses

Every year an estimated one to two million Canadians suffer from a foodborne illness. Also known as food poisoning, a foodborne illness occurs when a person eats something that is contaminated with micro-organisms such as bacteria, other micro-organisms, and viruses. These harmful micro-organisms, called "pathogens," have the ability to make us sick, and in some cases can even kill us. But despite the number of foodborne illness cases, Canada has some of the safest food in the world. Scientists and regulators, such as Joseph Odumeru, in Guelph, Ontario work to protect us from foodborne illness. They use their skills, expertise, and the most up-to-date techniques to help keep our food free from contamination and safe to eat.

Dr. Joseph Odumeru

Microbiologist and Food Detective

Odumeru is a senior research microbiologist at the University of Guelph and a regulatory scientist at the Laboratory Services Division. This is an extension of the university that provides services to industry and the government. The Ontario Ministry of Agriculture, Food and Rural Affairs and food companies send samples to the laboratory for testing to determine *potential* sources of outbreaks of foodborne illnesses or to ensure that their food product is safe.

As a microbiologist with 19 years of experience, Odumeru uses his expertise to develop techniques to identify and quantify bacteria in food. This helps the government and food companies identify the type and source of contamination more rapidly and prevents further illnesses.

Bacteria, such as certain *Escherichia coli* in hamburger meat and *Salmonella enteritis* in eggs and chicken, are major causes of foodborne illness. Bacteria can contaminate food in different ways. For example, certain strains of *E. coli* produce a toxin, a poisonous waste product. These toxins can produce severe and sometimes fatal illness. Not all *E. coli* makes us sick, however. Most strains, such as the benign strain of *E. coli*, live in healthy human intestines. However, *E. coli* O157:H7 is different. It actually produces a toxin that breaks down the lining of the intestines and causes symptoms such as bloody diarrhea.

are bacteria that feed on such materials as methylene chloride, detergents, creosote, pentachlorophenol, sulfur, and polychlorinated biphenols (PCBs).

As you have read, in order to find organisms to use in bioremediation, microbiologists take samples from polluted sites and analyze them for signs of life. Any organisms found living in such hazardous conditions are at least resistant to deadly chemicals and may actually use the chemicals. Samples are grown and tested in the lab. If scientists can locate the actual genes used by the organisms to help them metabolize toxic chemicals, they may be able to transfer the genes to other organisms or modify them to improve their effectiveness.

>> FAST FORWARD

To find out more about splicing genes into bacterial plasmids, turn to Chapter 12, Section 12.2.

Cellular Processes and Medical Technologies

In order for scientists to learn how cells function, they must be able to follow metabolic pathways. For example, it was unclear to the scientific community how carbon dioxide entered the metabolic pathway in the chloroplast. Melvin Calvin studied the role of carbon dioxide in photosynthesis. Using a radioactive form of carbon to make carbon dioxide, he traced the sequence of molecules formed.

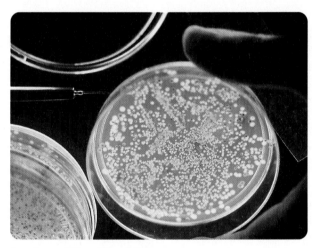

A culture of *E. coli* bacteria.

Bacteria of different species vary in a number of ways that are used in their identification. For example, different bacterial species have different staining characteristics and they use sugar as an energy source in different ways, says Odumeru. Bacteria that turn purple when stained with crystal violet and safranin dyes are called Gram positive bacteria. Those that turn pink are called Gram negative bacteria. These basic techniques are used at Laboratory Services to determine the type of bacteria present in food samples. The abundance of bacteria in a food is another important indicator of whether a food may have caused illness or has the potential to cause illness. Odumeru develops and tests different rapid methods for the detection of pathogens in food. A new system Odumeru is currently using counts the total

organisms in a food within 14 h of testing. Older systems take days to count bacteria. Another method developed by Odumeru and Laboratory Services scientists can detect low levels of *Salmonella* within 24–48 h. The current testing takes five to seven days. The new system means scientists can determine the cause of foodborne illness more rapidly. Quicker identification of the cause of an illness means quicker elimination of the disease source and better treatment for those affected. Each time Odumeru helps to improve methods for detection of bacteria, he helps to improve safety of food in Canada. He says he enjoys the challenge of developing new techniques.

"I love working with lab instruments used for bacterial growth and detection of pathogenic micro-organisms," says Odumeru. "I also enjoy the detective work and challenge of discovering new methods for testing pathogens in food products."

When Odumeru is not researching new ways of ensuring our food is safe, he is supervising the food microbiology staff at Laboratory Services. The staff performs safety tests on different food products. He also coordinates all the research that takes place at Laboratory Services and shares his expertise with graduate students.

Odumeru obtained a certificate in Medical Laboratory Technology before deciding to study Microbiology and Immunology at the University of Western Ontario, in London, Ontario. He went on to obtain his M.Sc. and Ph.D. in Medical Microbiology from the University of Manitoba, Winnipeg.

Radioactive carbon is heavier than regular carbon because there are two extra neutrons in the nucleus. This small difference in mass allowed him to separate the tiny amounts of newly synthesized compounds. What he found was that carbon dioxide was captured to create a molecule already familiar to scientists who studied cellular respiration.

We now have many technologies that assist us in diagnosing diseases without having to perform surgery. X-ray technology has been used effectively for many years, and more recently magnetic resonance imaging (MRI) is also available. (You will learn more about these technologies in Unit 3.) A very interesting new technology that makes use of our knowledge of cell metabolism is an instrument known as PET (positron emission tomography). With it, a radiologist can scan an organ of the body while it is functioning. First the patient is injected with a substance that contains radioactive atoms. These atoms emit radiation that can be followed by the PET scanner as it moves to various parts of the body. Blood flow to the brain or another area can be "watched" and the amount of glucose being metabolized by different parts of an organ can be determined (see Figure 3.25). If there has been brain damage, for example, this is an excellent method for pinpointing the location of the damage. Observation of the activity occurs on a computer screen. Energy given off by the radioactive atoms is converted to the image on the screen.

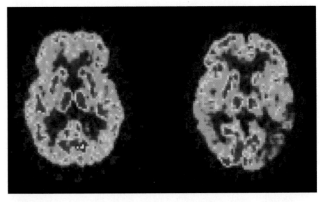

Figure 3.25 This PET scan shows variation in metabolic activity in different parts of a human brain.

SECTION REVIEW

1. **K/U** Mitochondria may have once existed as free-living aerobic bacteria. What is an aerobic bacterium?

2. **C** Draw a diagram of a chloroplast and a diagram of a mitochondrion. Compare these diagrams. How are these structures similar? How are they different?

3. **C** Consider the theory that a large eukaryotic cell captured aerobic bacteria and kept them as organelles, the mitochondria.

   (a) What advantage would this bacterium be to a eukaryotic cell?

   (b) Draw diagrams showing the process of phagocytosis.

   (c) Suggest a reason why the chloroplast was captured after the mitochondrion?

4. **K/U** Manure digestion takes place in sealed airless tanks. Why are the tanks airless?

5. **K/U** Define the term bioremediation.

6. **K/U** How do heterotrophic bacteria contribute to bioremediation?

7. **MC** Oil spills can be an environmental disaster. Some spill sites involve the use of oil-eating bacteria. Often, these bacteria work very slowly. Suggest one strategy to improve this situation.

8. **I** The graph below shows the relationship between yeast population and alcohol concentration.

   (a) Describe the relationship shown.

   (b) Which concentration of alcohol is most lethal for a yeast cell?

   (c) At what percentage alcohol did the yeast cells produce the greatest amount of CO_2?

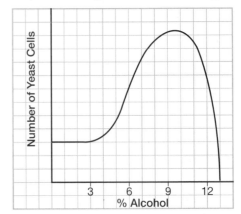

Chapter Expectations

Briefly explain each of the following points.

- Metabolism involves the use of chemical energy. (3.1)
- Through a series of reactions, photosynthesis transfers the energy in light to energy in chemical bonds. (3.2)
- The chemical energy stored through photosynthesis is transferred to a form usable anywhere in the cell during cellular respiration. (3.2)
- All eukaryotic and most prokaryotic cells use glycolysis to form ATP. (3.3)
- Aerobic respiration efficiently produces 36 or 38 molecules of ATP from one molecule of glucose, but it requires that a cell have access to oxygen. (3.3)
- Anaerobic respiration quickly forms two molecules of ATP per molecule of glucose, but produces toxic waste products. (3.3)
- The structure of chloroplasts and mitochondria provides evidence that these organelles may once have been free-living micro-organisms. (3.4)
- Research into cellular biology has led to practical applications. (3.4)
- Some industries harness the ability of bacteria to metabolize organic materials toxic to most organisms. (3.4)

Language of Biology

Write a sentence using each of the following words or terms. Use any six terms in a concept map to show your understanding of how they are related.

- energy
- potential energy
- kinetic energy
- chemical energy
- metabolism
- wave model of light
- electromagnetic spectrum
- photon model of light
- photons
- pigments
- chlorophyll
- photosystems
- reaction centre
- ATP
- Calvin cycle
- cellular respiration
- aerobic
- glycolysis
- fermentation
- oxygen debt
- anaerobic
- bioremediation
- radioactive

UNDERSTANDING CONCEPTS

1. What is the source of energy in your body?

2. Explain the terms "potential energy" and "kinetic energy" with respect to a cell.

3. (a) How do your muscle cells use energy?
   (b) Describe conditions where muscles use an alternative process.
   (c) Explain one possible reason that muscle cells are the best cells to switch to the alternative process.

4. Describe three metabolic processes in your body powered by energy in your food.

5. "Energy is used to keep the cell organized."
   (a) What does this statement mean?
   (b) What would happen to a cell that has no energy?

6. Refer to Chapter 1 to find the structural formula of glucose. Glucose is made of carbon, oxygen and hydrogen atoms. Identify the source of each type of atom in the process of photosynthesis.

7. Write the simple reaction for photosynthesis.
   (a) Which molecule listed has the highest potential energy? Justify your response.
   (b) Which molecule has the lowest potential energy? Justify your response.

8. Describe the features of light energy that are important to the process of photosynthesis.

9. Identify one pigment used by a chloroplast to help with photosynthesis.

10. What colour or colours of light are absorbed by a green leaf? Explain your response.

11. Where in the chloroplast are the photosystems found? Draw a diagram and indicate the location of the photosystems.

12. Briefly describe the role played by each photosystem in the chloroplast.

13. Where do the synthesis reactions of photosynthesis take place?

14. (a) List the three stages of photosynthesis.
    (b) Identify how the energy captured in one step is used to power changes in another step.

15. What is the role of cellular respiration in your cells?

16. Draw a diagram of a cell and show where each stage of cellular respiration takes place.

17. How is oxygen important to cellular respiration?

18. Identify three different organisms that use fermentation regularly.

19. How are radioactive molecules used to study metabolic processes?

INQUIRY

20. Lactose is a sugar that most bacteria can use as a source of glucose. They can do so because they manufacture an enzyme called betagalactosidase (β-gal). This enzyme will break down a molecule of lactose into a molecule of glucose and a molecule of galactose. In an experiment, bacteria were supplied with lactose, and the amount of β-gal was monitored. The results are illustrated in the graph below.
    (a) What can be interpreted from the graph?
    (b) Why would it be incorrect to conclude from these results that lactose is acting directly on the transcription of mRNA to produce the β-gal protein?
    (c) Sketch a graph that would illustrate the relationship between cytoplasmic glucose and β-gal levels after the addition of lactose.

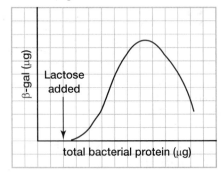

21. Dinitrophenol (DNP) is a chemical that interferes with the production of ATP in both chloroplasts and mitochondria. In an attempt to identify the minimal concentration of DNP required to inhibit ATP production, DNP was applied to separate suspensions of both organelles. Data are presented in the table.
    (a) Which set of data would represent the chloroplast?
    (b) Which organelle would be considered the most active? Explain.
    (c) Which organelle is most susceptible to changing concentrations of DNP? Explain.

Organelle	Concentration of DNP			
	5%	15%	25%	35%
Volume of CO_2 released (mL)	0.50	0.11	0.05	0.01
Volume of O_2 released (mL)	0.88	0.04	0.01	n/a

22. Glycolysis takes place in the cytoplasm of eukaryotic cells. This indicates that the process is very ancient, probably older than the development of eukaryotic cells. Explain briefly.

23. In single-celled organisms, compare the relative need for kinetic energy in a plant-like cell and an animal-like cell.

COMMUNICATING

24. On Earth, matter cycles and energy flows.
    (a) To make this statement clearer, explain how matter is different from energy.
    (b) Draw a diagram to illustrate the given statement.

25. Make a concept map or flowchart that shows what happens to a glucose molecule from the time it enters a plant or animal cell.

26. Make a diagram showing how photosynthesis and aerobic respiration form a cycle of connected reactions.

27. Review the process of phagocytosis from Chapter 1. Describe the structure of the vesicle formed. Compare this to the outer membrane of both the chloroplast and the mitochondrion.

28. Refer to Chapter 2 for information about the chloroplast and the mitochondrion.
    (a) Draw a diagram of a chloroplast. Label your diagram to show the outer membrane, thylakoids, grana, stroma and lamellae.
    (b) Draw a diagram of a mitochondrion. Label your diagram to show the outer membrane, inner membrane, cristae and matrix.
    (c) Compare these two structures. Make a chart to record how the structures are similar and how they are different.

29. A train has derailed 13 km from your home. Some toxic chemicals spilled onto the ground. Develop a bioremediation plan to share with your town council. Who could you contact for support and help?

30. Energy profiles for photosynthesis and cellular respiration are illustrated above.
    (a) With reasons to support your choices, identify which energy profile is for cellular respiration and which is for photosynthesis.
    (b) Compare the energy required to make glucose to the amount of energy required to break it down.

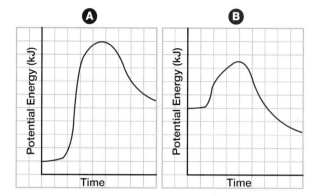

31. Living cells capture a tiny amount of the solar radiation available. This tiny amount supports almost all the life on earth.
    (a) What would be the consequence if twice as much energy were captured? Explain.
    (b) What would be the consequence if half as much energy were captured? Explain.

32. Eukaryotic cells have mitochondria for aerobic respiration. Some eukaryotic cells have chloroplasts to capture solar energy in food molecules. Indicate whether you agree or disagree with the following statements:
    (a) The first cells with chloroplasts were predators. Explain briefly.
    (b) Cells with chloroplasts are still predators. Explain briefly.
    (c) Perhaps the biggest physical difference between a plant cell and an animal cell is the presence of a cell wall. Explain briefly.

MAKING CONNECTIONS

33. Despite many attempts, researchers have been unable to get photosynthesis to proceed outside a chloroplast. Why are researchers still interested in pursuing this goal? What possible practical use could come from attaining the goal?

34. People have made use of fermentation for thousands of years.
    (a) Identify two ancient uses for this cellular process.
    (b) Identify one modern use for this cellular process.

35. People now turn to bacteria for biological solutions of technological problems. Explain this using one example from the text.

36. In Chapter 1, you learned about the experiments conducted by Louis Pasteur to explain how micro-organisms can spoil a broth. This research was funded by the wine industry.

These people wanted to learn more about the biological processes in their industry.
    (a) Today, pasteurization is used in the milk industry, but not in the wine industry. Explain briefly.
    (b) Explain the relationship between the reproducing yeast cells shown here and the process of fermentation.

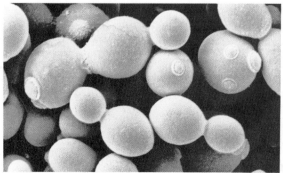

ASSESSMENT

After you complete this investigation,

- assess your procedure by having a classmate try to duplicate your results;
- assess your poster presentation based on how well the representation and analysis of data ties in to your hypothesis or prediction.

Cellular Processes and Lactose Intolerance

Background

During digestion, enzymes on the microvilli of cells lining the small intestine help break down food. One of these enzymes, lactase, breaks the milk sugar lactose down into simple sugars small enough to be transported into the intestinal cells:

$$\text{lactose} \xrightarrow{\text{lactase}} \text{glucose} + \text{galactose}$$

(Galactose is converted to glucose in the liver.)

We all produce lactase as children. However, many people stop synthesizing it as adults. When these people eat foods containing milk, they often experience the symptoms of lactose intolerance: diarrhea, gas, and intestinal cramps. These symptoms result when lactose passes into the large intestine and bacteria there use it as an energy source. The anaerobic conditions in the large intestine require that the bacteria use fermentation to do this.

> ➤➤ **FAST FORWARD**
>
> To learn more about human digestion, turn to Chapter 10, Sections 10.2 and 10.3.

Synthetic lactase is now available to help people with lactose intolerance digest milk. Some brands of milk and other dairy products contain added synthetic lactase. Drugstores also sell synthetic lactase in the form of pills or drops. Synthetic lactase performs the same function as natural lactase.

In this project, you will work in small groups to design and perform an investigation to determine the efficiency of a synthetic lactase product (or products) *or* the conditions under which synthetic lactase works best. Based on your data, you will make a recommendation on how well the product(s) will reduce the symptoms of lactose intolerance *or* on how consumers should use the product(s).

HINT: Remember that a chemical reaction can be affected by time, temperature, and pH.

Pre-lab Focus

- How can you test for simple sugars?
- Does regular milk contain glucose and galactose?

- What product(s) of fermentation might cause the symptoms of lactose intolerance?

Web LINK

To view statistics on lactose intolerance in different populations, visit the web site shown below. Go to **Science Resources** and then to **BIOLOGY 11** to find out where to go next. Which groups of people would be most likely to need lactase products in order to enjoy foods such as ice cream? How many people in your class would you expect to become lactose intolerant later in life?
www.school.mcgrawhill.ca/resources/

Problem

How can people who are lactose intolerant eat foods containing lactose, maximize the sugars absorbed from these foods by cells in the small intestine, and minimize the amount of lactose available to bacteria in the large intestine?

Hypothesis or Prediction

Based on your understanding of cellular processes, formulate a hypothesis or prediction about the effectiveness of a synthetic lactase product *or* the conditions required for it to function best.

Materials

safety goggles	commercial lactase product,
disposable gloves	such as a dairy digestive
apron	supplement or a dairy
hot water bath	product that already
droppers	contains lactase
test tubes	milk products, such as
test tube rack	yogurt or sour cream
test tube holder	(optional)
beaker tong	any other materials
test tube brush	you require
Benedict's solution	

Safety Precautions

- Check WHMIS charts to identify appropriate safety equipment when using chemicals.
- Be careful when handling Benedict's solution.

- Avoid allowing a hot water bath to boil vigorously, since this can cause test tubes to break. Use a moderate heat setting.
- Use test tube holders and beaker tongs to move hot glassware.
- Do not ingest food products in the lab.
- Wash your hands with soap after the lab.

Procedure

1. Design a rubric, an assessment checklist, or some other means of assessing the validity of your experimental design and procedure.

2. Identify a number of testable variables. Select one that you can test and control with the time and materials available.

3. Design an experimental procedure to test your hypothesis or prediction. Your design must identify the control and the dependent and independent variables. The steps must clearly explain how the experiment will be carried out. Where appropriate, use diagrams to help clarify the procedure. Explain what a positive result would be for any indicators. Include a list of materials. Plan how you will collect quantitative data.

4. Develop a flowchart relating the procedure to the hypothesis or prediction. Include lists of materials needed. Explain the purpose of any chemicals you plan to use.

5. Share your plan with one or two other groups for feedback. After making improvements to your experimental design, show it to your teacher for approval.

6. Collect the materials you need.

7. Set up and perform your experiment. If necessary, modify your experimental design. Check the new design with your teacher.

8. Record data and observations. Decide how to present your data in a clear format (for example, using a table, chart, graph, or diagram).

Analysis and Conclusions

1. Prepare a poster presentation of your project that includes:
   - a title
   - your hypothesis or prediction and the reasons behind it

- a flowchart showing your experimental design and indicating positive and negative results for tests
- a diagram showing how lactase breaks down lactose
- a representation of your data
- an analysis of the data
- a conclusion
- next steps
- a recommendation to consumers regarding the lactase product(s) you investigated

2. If cells in the brain use glucose exclusively as an energy source, explain why infants need to produce lactase.

Assess Your Experimental Design

3. Use the rubric or checklist you developed to assess your experimental design.

4. Compare your experimental design and results with those of other groups. Then list ways you could improve your experimental design, and give reasons for any changes you suggest.

5. How did the process of planning your experiment help you think about what you have learned in this unit?

UNDERSTANDING CONCEPTS

True-False

In your notebook, indicate whether each statement is true or false. Correct each false statement.

1. The many kinds of cells have in common many of the same molecules and processes.

2. Water is polar because it is small.

3. Osmosis is the diffusion of sodium chloride across a membrane.

4. Diffusion moves molecules effectively over short distances.

5. The cell membrane is composed mostly of proteins.

6. Passive transport moves materials against a concentration gradient.

7. Pancreatic cells may use exocytosis.

8. DNA contains the instructions for the production of proteins in the cell.

9. The cytoskeleton helps transport material around the cell interior.

10. Lysosomes are important for packaging proteins for the cell membrane.

11. Most organisms rely on the Sun as their ultimate source of energy.

12. Glycolysis takes place in mitochondria.

13. Respiration releases energy with the help of oxygen.

14. Cellular respiration is common to all cells.

15. Mitochondria have their own DNA.

Multiple Choice

In your notebook, write the letter of the best answer for each of the following questions.

16. Glycogen is a
   (a) fat
   (b) hormone
   (c) carbohydrate
   (d) protein
   (e) amino acid

17. Nucleic acids are composed of
   (a) nitrogen bases
   (b) nucleotides
   (c) phosphates
   (d) protein
   (e) all of the above

18. Benedict's solution will show the presence of
   (a) glucose
   (b) sucrose
   (c) maltose
   (d) cellulose
   (e) lactose

19. The cell membrane is described as a fluid mosaic because
   (a) it is made of many different molecules

(b) the phospholipids can change colour

(c) some molecules in the membrane are anchored to the cytoskeleton

(d) the phospholipid heads are attracted to water

(e) it contains cholesterol

20. Which of the following best describes one mechanism of active transport?
   (a) Particles move from an area of high concentration to low concentration.
   (b) Glucose enters the cell through a channel protein.
   (c) Water moves into the cell.
   (d) A membrane protein pumps ions out of the cell.
   (e) The cell membrane folds to form a vesicle.

21. The cytoskeleton allows the following process(es) to proceed:
   (a) protein synthesis
   (b) mitosis
   (c) active transport
   (d) digestion inside the cell
   (e) all of the above

22. Identify the type of cell shown below.

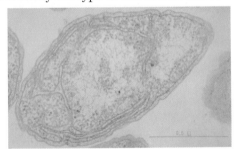

   (a) plant cell
   (b) fungal cell
   (c) animal cell
   (d) prokaryotic cell
   (e) protist cell

23. Proteins are produced
   (a) in the nucleus
   (b) with centrosomes
   (c) on ribosomes
   (d) in special vesicles
   (e) by the nucleolus

24. Energy
   (a) is created by plants
   (b) can be transformed but not destroyed
   (c) is a fundamental component of atoms
   (d) in the form of heat, is the basis of the food chain
   (e) will run out soon

25. Glycolysis describes the process of
   (a) making proteins on ribosomes
   (b) breaking glycogen into glucose
   (c) making glycogen in the liver
   (d) red blood cells bursting as a result of osmosis
   (e) breaking glucose into pyruvate

26. Oxygen is
   (a) produced through the process of respiration
   (b) used during photosynthesis
   (c) moved into the cell by protein channels
   (d) used in aerobic respiration
   (e) made by fermentation

Short Answers

In your notebook, write a sentence or a short paragraph to answer each of the following questions.

27. Describe the characteristics of water that are important for life.

28. Draw a diagram showing the structural formula of a glucose molecule.

29. List four carbohydrates and explain the role of each in the cell.

30. How is the basic structure of a lipid different from the basic structure of a carbohydrate?

31. Using a diagram, explain the molecular structure of a fatty acid.

32. List the functions of proteins in the cell. Identify an example for each.

33. Draw a short polypeptide with four amino acids. Show the peptide bonds.

34. Describe the composition of the extracellular fluid.

35. How does a concentration gradient determine the direction of the flow of molecules?

36. How does diffusion limit cell size? What can cells do to increase their efficiency?

37. Explain how the cell wall affects the response of plant cells to being in a hypotonic solution.

38. Use examples of passive and active transport to explain how the cell membrane is selectively permeable.

39. Current models of cells show more structures than older models do. Explain this in terms of changing technology.

40. List five structures in the cell that have a membrane. In each case, explain the purpose of the membrane.

41. Structures A, B, C, and D in the cell shown here are involved in making a product to be released outside the cell.

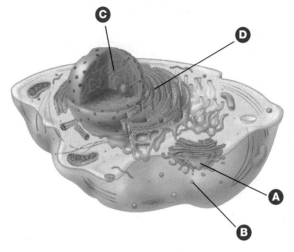

State whether the cell is a plant or animal cell, and list the names of the cellular structures that correspond to labels A, B, C, and D. What product do these structures work together to produce? Give the order in which each of the cellular structures contributes to this process.

42. Explain how the instructions to make a protein end up at ribosomes.

43. Give an example of a specialized (tissue) cell and how its structures contribute to the function of an organ.

44. Lysosomes help cells reuse matter. How is this beneficial to the cell?

45. Current technologies used to fight cancer are based on research into how cells function. Explain this statement.

46. The AIDS virus attaches to T-lymphocytes. Why are some of these cells immune to this virus?

47. Define chemical energy.

48. Briefly describe the process of photosynthesis.

49. Why are leaves green?

50. Both mitochondria and chloroplasts have a double membrane. Identify the similarities and differences between these structures.

51. Yeast have mitochondria, so they can carry out aerobic respiration. They can also use fermentation to release energy. Describe the conditions yeast requires to make dough rise.

52. Explain the flow of energy between photosynthesis and respiration.

53. Glycolysis occurs in the cytoplasm, not the mitochondria. Why does this suggest that glycolysis is a process that developed in early cells?

54. Explain how bacteria are used to solve environmental problems.

INQUIRY

55. Design a lab to determine if a sports drink is isotonic to an animal cell. Include your prediction and your reasons for this prediction.

56. An experiment was conducted to find out whether heat affects osmosis across an egg's membrane (a fluid-mosaic membrane). A portion of shell was removed on each of three eggs to allow observations. One egg was placed in a hot water bath at 40°C for one min and another in a hot water bath at 70°C for one min. The third egg was not heated. The mass of each egg was recorded. Each egg was placed in a beaker of distilled water overnight. The next day, the final mass of each egg was recorded. These observations were made.

Egg	Description of egg next day	Initial mass	Final mass
1. Heated at 40°C	The membrane is somewhat translucent. The interior is thicker and less yellow than for uncooked egg.	35 g	38 g
2. Heated at 70°C	The membrane is opaque and white. The interior (yolk) is not visible at all.	44 g	44 g
3. Uncooked	The membrane is translucent. The yellowy interior is visible.	37 g	42 g

(a) Which egg showed the greatest change in mass? Explain why this happened.

(b) Present the results as a labelled graph.

(c) How does heat affect membrane function?

(d) Predict the temperature at which the function of an egg membrane changes. Design an experiment to find this temperature.

57. Use the protein model kit you designed in Chapter 1 to explain how an error in the nucleotide sequence of DNA can provide some people with immunity to AIDS.

58. The following graph illustrates data on the number of mitochondria in each of three cell types.

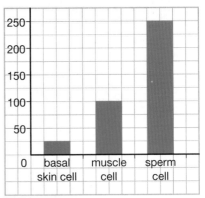

Number of mitochondria

(a) Which cell type would require the most glucose for its functions?

(b) Speculate why a basal skin cell would have the least number of mitochondria of the three types of cells studied.

59. An aquatic plant was immersed in a beaker of water. A pH meter was placed into the water to monitor any changes in the pH over a 24-hour period. The experiment was set up next to a window. The results are illustrated below.

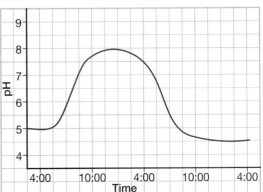

(a) Carbon dioxide will react with water to form carbonic acid. At what time of day did this experiment begin? Support your answer.

(b) Use this graph to support the hypothesis that the rate of photosynthesis is faster than the rate of cellular respiration.

(c) What effect would adding a chemical such as DNP, which inhibits the production of ATP, to the beaker have on the pH over the same time period?

60. Bacteria that metabolize lactose are used to make yogurt. How can you measure their activity indirectly? Identify factors that might affect the work of these bacteria.

COMMUNICATING

61. Apoptosis is the result of a cascade of events that can be triggered by a protein from a killer cell of the immune system attaching to a membrane receptor. Draw a diagram to show the cascade.

62. Make a flowchart showing how a mutation in one chromosome can result in cancer.

63. A research team in Canada has developed a new medical treatment for hepatitis C. Write a newspaper article that outlines how this work will have global significance.

64. Develop a chart to compile evidence that mitochondria and chloroplasts were once bacteria that have become adapted to life inside a larger cell.

65. Make a concept map showing the benefits of research into cellular structure and function.

MAKING CONNECTIONS

66. In remarkable cases, small children have survived exposure to sub-zero temperatures for several hours without winter clothing. A critical factor in the successful resuscitation and subsequent normal functioning of these children involves the activation of the mammalian diving reflex. When the face encounters cold water (or snow), the body responds by slowing down the metabolic processes and conserving the delivery of oxygen to the brain. Other natural reactions to harsh conditions protect the cells so that they can recover. Identify one possible research pathway to explore how cells survive extreme conditions. Justify funding research to discover the cellular mechanisms involved in this pathway.

67. The undulating cells among the red blood cells below survive as a result of mutations. These mutations give successive generations of this organism membrane proteins that make it appear "human" to the host immune system. Explain how different membrane proteins could be produced. Suggest treatments that might help the human body fight this invader.

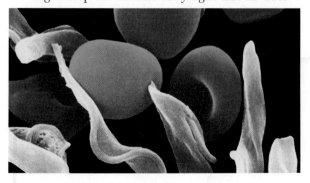

68. List the benefits of new cancer therapies that target apoptosis triggers.

69. Hepatitis C and AIDS affect many people in the developing world. Continued research into effective treatments could help both the global community and economy. Present your opinion about this, and give reasons for it.

70. Before people understood the danger of many industrial chemicals, hazardous materials were simply dumped onto the land next to an industrial complex. Many old industrial sites now have toxic soil. Suggest how the study of bacterial processes could provide new biotechnologies to clean up these sites.

COURSE CHALLENGE

Consider the following as you continue to build your biology research portfolio.

- The most common cause of abnormal cell death (necrosis) is a lack of oxygen. Create a chart to contrast the appearance of cells that have died due to necrosis and apoptosis.

- Adult brain cells usually die after three to five minutes without oxygen. Other body cells begin to go through necrosis within minutes or hours after. How can a pathologist decide on the cause of death based on tissue samples? Think about what kind of cell damage diseases, infections, and old injuries might cause.

2

Genetic Continuity

◆ UNIT ISSUE PREP

Read pages 240–241 before beginning this unit.

- Choose the genetic technology you will be examining.

- Set up files to organize your information on your genetic technology.

- Begin collecting information in preparation for your action plan.

High above the ground, within the coastal forest of Australia, you hear loud chatter and screeches. A flock of brightly coloured rainbow lorikeets gather in a treetop. Of the 58 species of parrots that live in Australia, each has plumage that is unique. No two species of parrot there have the same feather colour and pattern. Why do rainbow lorikeets have red, blue, and yellow feathers? Feather colour is a characteristic, or trait, that is inherited. This trait, along with many other traits, is passed from parents to offspring through reproduction.

Information about traits is found in the nucleus of each cell in your body and determines what kind of traits you will have, such as the colour of your skin, the texture of your hair, as well as your sex. You, like all other organisms that are alive, are each part of an unbroken family line. Each person has or has had parents, grandparents, great grandparents, and so on, which date back many thousands of years. Everyone in your family inherited traits from their parents, and you inherited these traits from your parents.

In this Unit, you will explore how traits are inherited using examples from living organisms. Some traits have a simple inheritance pattern while the inheritance of other traits may be very complex. You will discover how genetic information is transmitted from cell to cell and why this process is important in determining variation among offspring. Finally, medical research has made important discoveries in human genetics. You will consider how this information might be used and who should be responsible for making these decisions.

How do individuals inherit characteristics from their parents?

Heredity

Reflecting Questions

- Why do you share some characteristics, such as eye and skin colour, with your parents?
- Why do you inherit some characteristics and not others?
- Can you predict the types of traits a person will inherit?

For centuries people have realized that certain physical characteristics are passed from one generation to the next. This knowledge was used to produce crops and livestock with desired characteristics. Plants were selectively bred to produce heartier and more nutritious crops — a prime example of this ingenuity is the development of varieties of wheat. Livestock were bred to produce offspring with certain characteristics, such as stronger oxen or cows that could produce larger quantities of milk. How these characteristics were passed from parents to offspring, however, remained a mystery.

Have you ever traced your family history and found that you very closely resemble one of your distant relatives? Members of a family share many similarities in appearance, such as height, eye colour, and hair colour.

People noted that there was variation in how characteristics were inherited by offspring. In other words, offspring did not look exactly like their parents. Why were some characteristics passed on to offspring, but not others? Why did the inheritance of some characteristics skip one or more generations? These questions remained unanswered until the late nineteenth century, when an Austrian monk performed a series of simple experiments and discovered how heredity worked.

In this chapter, you will learn how characteristics are passed from parents to their offspring. For many characteristics, this process follows simple models. You will use these models to predict the genetic make-up and physical appearance of offspring. Does the inheritance of one trait influence the inheritance of others? Also, you will infer the genetic make-up of parents based on data collected about the characteristics of offspring. Finally, you will learn how to construct pedigrees, or family histories, for characteristics that are found in your own or other families. Pedigrees are useful in determining the likelihood of a trait being expressed in a family.

Why do members of a family share similarities in appearance?

Chapter
Contents

Genetics of Inheritance

Figure 4.1 Selective breeding is used to develop special varieties of dog.

Every living organism is made up of many different **traits**, or distinguishing characteristics, that make it a unique individual. Certain traits in plants and animals may have qualities that people want to promote. For example, dog breeders have used the variations in traits of hair colour to produce the yellow, black, and brown colour variations of Labrador retrievers. Such variations are achieved through selective breeding of individuals. That is, only certain individuals that show the desirable trait are permitted to reproduce. People have been selectively breeding plants and animals for thousands of years (see Figure 4.1). They knew from observation and experience that certain physical traits could be transmitted, or **inherited**, by each generation from the preceeding generation. However, the actual mechanisms of how this occurred were unknown.

Early Ideas About Heredity

Genetics is the branch of biology dealing with the principles of variation and inheritance in animals and plants. The study of genetics gives us greater understanding of how we can determine the likelihood of inheriting certain traits and helps explain and predict patterns of inheritance in family lines. For much of human history, people were unaware of the scientific details of how babies were conceived and how heredity worked. Clearly, there was some hereditary connection between

parents and children, but the mechanisms were not readily apparent.

The Greek philosopher, Hippocrates (460–377 B.C.E.) theorized that every part of the body was involved in the production of the "seeds" of the parents. These seeds then fused together to give rise to a new individual. Aristotle (384–322 B.C.E., see Figure 4.2) suggested that male and female semen mixed upon conception.

Figure 4.2 Aristotle suggested that the mother had an essential role in the process of generation.

During the 1500s, English physician William Harvey speculated that new individuals arose through the process of epigenesis. His theory suggested that the embryo formed in stages, and its development was affected by factors both inside and outside of the mother. A Dutch scientist, Anton van Leeuwenhoek (1632–1723), used a microscope to examine the gametes of humans and other animals. Leeuwenhoek discovered what he called "animalcules" in the semen and proposed that they were preformed embryos (see Figure 4.3). Leeuwenhoek and other scientists suggested that the female contribution to the next generation was only the influences of the uterus in which the embryo developed.

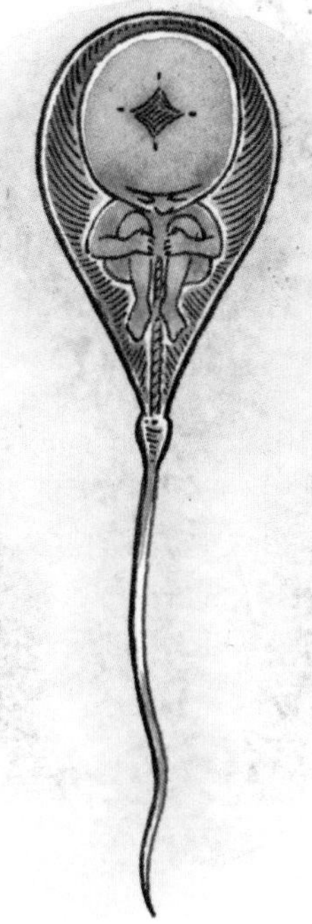

The notion of pangenesis originated with the Greeks. It proposed that males and females formed "genes" in every organ. These "genes" then moved through the blood to the genitals and into the children. This concept influenced biology until little over 100 years ago. Francis Galton, a cousin of Charles Darwin, disproved this theory during the 1870s.

Word LINK

The terms "blood relative," "full-blooded," and "royal blood" are all relics of the concept of pangenesis.

During the nineteenth century, the "blending theory" of inheritance became popular. This theory suggested that sperm and egg mixed together, resulting in offspring that were a blend of the parent's characteristics. Sex cells were collectively known as gametes (*gamos*, Greek for marriage). According to this theory, the offspring of a plant with red flowers and a plant with white flowers were expected to have pink flowers. However, this was not always the case. As well, the theory of blending inheritance could not explain other anomalies in the inheritance of certain characteristics, and it ignored characteristics that skipped a generation.

≫ FAST FORWARD

To learn about variation among different organisms and how organisms are classified, turn to Chapter 11, Section 11.1.

Figure 4.3 Leeuwenhoek believed that the development of offspring was controlled entirely by the male parent. Each sperm cell contained an embryo of the future offspring.

MINI LAB

The History of Your Inheritance

You share many characteristics with your sisters, brothers, parents, and other relatives. Obtain photographs showing the different generations of your family. If you do not have photographs, you can use those of a friend's family. Try to identify one or two physical characteristics that seem to be found in most of your family members. Why do you think these particular characteristics are so common? Try to identify five or six of your physical characteristics in other members of your family. Some examples of characteristics

that can be easily traced include eye colour, detached versus attached ear lobes, and hairline (smooth versus pointed). Trace the pattern of inheritance of each of these characteristics from your great grandparents to you.

Analyze

1. Are there some inherited characteristics that you have that your parents do not? Do you have any characteristics that are unique to you?

2. How could you explain the pattern of inheritance for some of your traits?

Charles Darwin (see Figure 4.4) theorized that offspring had variations of their parents' characteristics, but he was unable to explain the basis of heredity. The answer of how traits were inherited came from his contemporary Gregor Mendel (1822–1884), an Austrian monk. Mendel developed the fundamental principles that became the modern science of genetics. He experimented with pea plants and proposed two generalizations of heredity, later known as Mendel's laws of heredity. In the following sections, you will learn how Mendel performed his experiments and formed his conclusions about heredity. You will also conduct your own experiments on heredity based on genetic principles developed by Mendel.

Figure 4.4 Charles Darwin could not explain the process of heredity. He suggested that current science had not yet discovered its physical basis.

Web LINK

Through the years, many researchers were involved in studying heredity. Select four or five scientists who helped establish fundamental principles in the field of genetics. Using a timeline, document the individuals, their work, and dates when they completed or published material. Begin your own history of genetics timeline by visiting the web address shown below. Go to **Science Resources**, then to **BIOLOGY 11** to find out where to go next. Obtain a photograph of each person for your timeline. How did each researcher advance the study of heredity and genetics? Present your findings to the class in the form of a poster. Note: Include researchers who have not been mentioned thus far.

www.school.mcgrawhill.ca/resources/

SECTION REVIEW

1. **K/U** Define the following terms: genetics, heredity, trait, epigenesis, pangenesis.

2. **K/U** Explain the ideas behind the theory of "blending inheritance." Why was this theory considered incorrect?

3. **MC** What is the importance of studying genetics with respect to agriculture?

4. **C** Create a flowchart to show the different people involved in the development of the scientific details of heredity.

5. **MC** Modern genetics is built on the foundations of various discoveries that have spanned more than 200 years. Gregor Mendel, as you will see, contributed essential knowledge used by geneticists today. How do you think the theory of inheritance would have developed if the different scientists did not reach the conclusions they did? How might this

have affected the development of genetic theory? Explain your answer.

6. **MC** We now know that DNA is responsible for the transmission of genetic characteristics. Using your knowledge of cells and cell organelles, explain how this method of transmission works. You may have to recall your previous studies regarding chromosomes and cell division.

7. **I** Suppose a farmer in the early fourteenth century had a group of sheep that seem to have thicker, warmer wool. In conversation with another farmer, he discovers that another group of sheep produce more edible meat per kilogram. Both farmers decide to mate their sheep together hoping for sheep that have thicker wool and produce more meat. They are successful in their venture. How would Hippocrates have explained the result? How would Leeuwenhoek have explained the result? How would you explain the result?

The Inheritance of One Trait

EXPECTATIONS

- Explain the concepts of dominance and recessiveness.
- Solve basic genetics problems involving crosses.
- Investigate and analyze a typical pedigree.

Figure 4.5 Gregor Mendel (1822–1884), an Austrian monk, studied garden pea plants as a means to explain the inheritance of characteristics.

Knowledge of the mechanisms controlling inheritance came as a result of careful experiments. This work was begun in 1853 by a monk in the monastery of St. Thomas in Brunn (now Brno, in the Czech Republic) named Gregor Mendel (see Figure 4.5). Before his work at the monastery, Mendel attended the University of Vienna, where his studies included mathematics and botany. This training became especially important during Mendel's study of heredity. He conducted a series of experiments on plants over an eight-year period (1853–1861). Following his experiments, Mendel published a paper outlining his conclusions.

Why did Mendel succeed in discovering the basis of inheritance when others before him had failed? There are three key points to any successful experiment in biology:

1. choosing the appropriate organism to study,
2. designing and performing the experiment correctly, and
3. analyzing the data properly.

Mendel conducted his research using the common pea plant (*Pisum sativum*), as shown in Figure 4.6. These plants were an excellent choice for four main reasons. The common pea plant was commercially available throughout Europe. It was easy to grow and matured quickly. Thirdly, the sexual organs of the plant are entirely enclosed in the flower. This means that pea plants self-pollinate, or fertilize eggs with pollen from the same flower, which allowed Mendel to control which plants reproduced. He introduced pollen from one flower to the pistil of another flower, cross-pollinating between plants to perform his experiments (see Figure 4.7 on the next page). Finally, different varieties of the common pea had different traits that could be observed easily from one generation to the next. Mendel examined seven different traits, as shown in Figure 4.8 (see next page). Each trait had only two possible variations. Mendel's decision to look at single traits helped him formulate his conclusions about heredity.

Figure 4.6 Common garden peas provided an excellent research organism for Mendel's experiments. These plants were easy to cultivate and had several traits that could be studied.

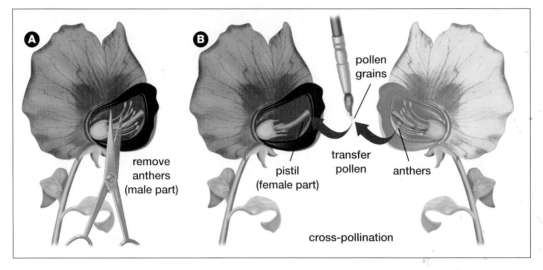

Figure 4.7 Cross-pollination is a method whereby the pollen (male gamete) from one flower is transferred to the pistil (female part) of another flower. In this way, Mendel controlled the breeding patterns in his pea plants.

	Seed shape	Seed colour	Flower colour	Flower position	Pod colour	Pod shape	Plant height
Dominant trait	round	yellow	purple	axial (side)	green	inflated	tall
Recessive trait	wrinkled	green	white	terminal (tips)	yellow	constricted	short

Figure 4.8 Mendel examined seven different characteristics of pea plants. Each trait had only two possible variations.

How did Mendel set up his experiment? The first thing he needed to do was to obtain purebred plants for the trait he wanted to study. A **purebred** organism is descended from ancestors of a distinct type, or breed. Purebred organisms in a given species or variety all share similar traits. For example, a certain variety of day lily may have a particular flower colour. This trait is inherited from previous generations, and results from a long period of selective breeding. Mendel produced purebred

varieties of pea plants through selective breeding. He chose plants that were tall, for instance, and bred them together. These plants produced seeds, which Mendel planted and grew. Some of these plants grew tall and some were short. Mendel selected only the plants that grew tall and bred them together again. He continued to breed only tall plants each generation until only tall offspring were produced. Mendel did the same for short plants, breeding only short plants together. In this way, he produced plants that were **true breeding**. That is, they only produced offspring that grew either tall or short. Mendel also produced true breeding pea plants for each form of the other six traits shown in Figure 4.8. Similar to plant height, the other traits were easily distinguished and could be classified into one of two categories.

Biology At Work

Plant Breeder

There is a pink and burgundy "Angel on My Shoulder." To my right is a salmon pink "Jazz Beat" and beyond that, a lemon yellow "Tuscany Lights." These are all varieties of day lilies that you might see at Henry Lorrain's *We're In The Hayfield Now Day Lily Gardens* near Orono, east of Toronto. Henry specializes in breeding new varieties of day lilies. He displays and sells them at his gardens, as well as supplying them to companies that resell them to gardeners.

Day lilies, a favourite with many gardeners, range in colour from red to pink to yellow to almost white. They are easily grown, tolerating a variety of temperatures, light conditions, and soils. They have a long growing season and, though their blossoms last only one day, a new crop of flowers bursts forth every morning.

Day lily breeders, Henry Lorrain and Douglas Lycett

Lilies of the Field

It was Henry Lorrain's partner, Douglas Lycett, who inspired Henry's interest in day lilies. Douglas Lycett died in 1998, but Henry continues his work. Using the method called hand pollination, Henry takes pollen from the stamen of one variety of day lily and applies it to the pistil of another. His aim might be, for example, to get a gold edge on a purple day lily or to produce a hardier day lily with prettier blossoms. Once Henry has pollinated the flowers, he waits for them to produce seeds. The

following spring, he and his staff plant these seeds in seed trays and, when the ground is warm enough, they plant them outdoors. The plants do not bloom until the following year. "There's lots of variety in how the flowers look," Henry says. "Some are awful but others are spectacular." The plants with the spectacular flowers are the ones Henry chooses to propagate and eventually sell.

The goal of plant breeders like Henry Lorrain is to alter plants genetically to suit human needs and preferences. This can include developing anything from a gold-edged purple day lily, to oats that are more nutritious for horses, to a variety of potatoes that resist diseases (such as potato blight). Some plant breeders, like Henry, have their own companies. Some work for companies that supply seeds and bulbs to farmers and gardeners. Some do research and teach at universities. A number of Canadian plant breeders work for federal and provincial departments of agriculture, where they carry out research. They inform farmers and gardeners of new varieties, telling them which varieties are likely to grow best in certain conditions. They develop and enforce standards for the production and sale of seeds and other plant products. Some plant breeders work for international agencies, where they help to improve living standards in developing countries.

Career Tips

1. Plant breeding draws on many sciences including agriculture, biology, horticulture, botany, genetics, and plant biochemistry. Studying one or more of these sciences could lead you into a career in plant breeding. Some universities also offer programs specifically geared to plant breeding.

2. Find out more about one of the following: (a) Charles Saunders and Marquis wheat; (b) Baldur Stefansson and canola; (c) J. Patricia White and the Silken Laumann Rose.

3. Genetically modified foods have been both promoted and opposed for several years. Research this issue. Use what you learn as the basis for a pro and con chart, class debate, or letter to a company president.

Mendel's First Experiment: A Monohybrid Cross

Once Mendel had his purebred plants, he designated them the parent generation, or **P generation**. Then, he crossed a true-breeding tall pea plant with a true-breeding short pea plant. The offspring from this cross were the first **filial generation**, or **F₁ generation**. Mendel called the F₁ generation **hybrid** plants to indicate they were the result of a cross between two different purebred plants. This is called a **monohybrid** cross, because only one trait, plant height, was involved.

What happened when Mendel planted the seeds of the F₁ generation? According to the theory of blending inheritance, he should have obtained plants of medium height. What Mendel observed, however, was that 100% of the plants in the F₁ generation were tall! (see Figure 4.9). This led Mendel to conclude that the trait for tall plants must be dominant, and the trait for short plants must be recessive. A **dominant** trait is a characteristic that is always expressed, or always appears, in an individual. A **recessive** trait is a characteristic that is latent (present but inactive) and is therefore not usually expressed in an individual. (A recessive trait may be expressed if it is the only trait present, as Mendel observed in his short-growing plants.) Thus, the trait for tall pea plants was dominant over the trait for short plants. All the pea plants grew tall if they possessed the dominant trait for size — tall.

Mendel conducted this experiment many times using true-breeding plants for each of the seven traits he had chosen to study. He obtained the same results every time: one trait was dominant over the other. Mendel concluded that heredity was definitely not just a blending of traits. He also concluded that when plants with two contrasting traits are crossed, one trait is always dominant over the other. This led him to formulate the **principle of dominance**: when individuals with contrasting traits are crossed, the offspring will express only the dominant trait. Return to Figure 4.8 on page 124 to see which traits in pea plants were dominant and which were recessive.

Law of Segregation

The next experiment Mendel conducted involved breeding the F₁ generation. He allowed the hybrid tall plants of the F₁ generation to self-pollinate. This produced the second filial generation, or **F₂ generation**. Figure 4.9 shows the traits that Mendel observed in the F₂ generation.

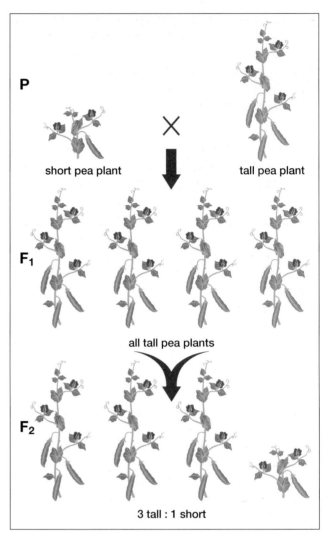

P

short pea plant   tall pea plant

F₁

all tall pea plants

F₂

3 tall : 1 short

Figure 4.9 Mendel crossed a purebred tall pea plant and a purebred short pea plant. The resulting F₁ generation was all tall pea plants. Mendel then allowed plants of the F₁ generation to self-pollinate. In the F₂ generation, three quarters of the pea plants were tall and one quarter were short.

Three out of four plants in the F₂ generation were tall while one was short. Mendel repeated this experiment many times and examined all seven traits. He obtained the same results time after time. The F₂ generation resembled one parent from the P generation 75% of the time and the other parent from the P generation 25% of the time. This ratio of 3 : 1 is known as the **Mendelian ratio**. Why did this happen? Based on his observations of traits in the F₁ and F₂ generations, Mendel drew the following conclusions:

- Each parent in his F₁ generation starts with two hereditary "factors." One factor is dominant and the other is recessive.

- The factors separate in the parent. Only one factor from each parent is contributed to the offspring.

- Each offspring inherits one factor from each parent. If the dominant factor is present it will be expressed even if the recessive factor is also present.

- The recessive factor will be expressed if only recessive factors are present.

Mendel's results from the F_2 generation gave rise to his first law of heredity. The **law of segregation** states that inherited traits are determined by pairs of "factors." These factors segregate (separate) in the gametes, with one in each gamete. You will learn more about how gametes are formed in Chapter 5.

We know today that Mendel's "factors" were **genes**, the part of the chromosome that governs the expression of a particular trait. A gene can occur in alternate forms called **alleles**. When two alleles are present, a dominant allele may prevent the expression of the recessive allele. Even though the dominant allele is expressed and the recessive allele is not, the recessive allele has not been altered physically and will pass unchanged in an individual's gametes to the next generation, where it may or may not be expressed.

Let's examine Mendel's experiments again, from the point of view that each trait is associated with a different allele. In Mendel's first experiment, he started with two purebred plants, as shown in Figure 4.10. Using letters to represent the different alleles, a purebred tall pea plant will have two uppercase letters, TT. In other words, the plant is **homozygous** for tall (the two alleles are the same). The purebred short pea plant has two alleles for short, designated in lowercase letters as tt. It is said to be homozygous for short. What happened when Mendel crossed the two plants? Each parent contributed one allele to each offspring — one T from the tall plant and one t from the short plant. The product of the cross was a tall offspring with alleles T and t. A plant that has a dominant and a recessive allele is said to be **heterozygous** for tall (the two alleles are different). The tall allele is dominant and is therefore expressed. The short allele is recessive and, while present, will not be expressed. Study Figure 4.11 to learn how alleles were distributed among the offspring when plants of the F_1 generation reproduced. Recall that the recessive trait is expressed only when there is no dominant allele.

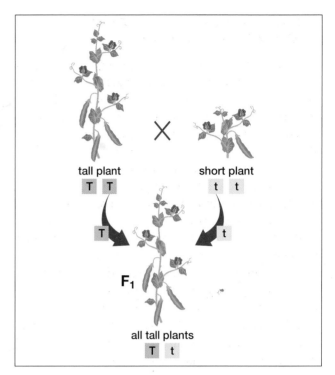

Figure 4.10 A cross of purebred short and tall pea plants illustrates Mendel's principle of dominance. Dominant alleles (T) are expressed in the F_1 generation and recessive alleles (t) are not expressed.

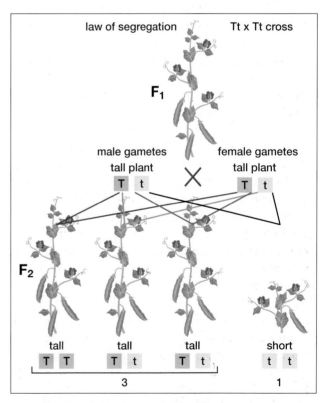

Figure 4.11 Individuals from the F_1 generation of pea plants produced a 3 : 1 ratio of tall plants to short. Mendel concluded that each parent plant had two factors and that these factors segregate during the production of gametes (eggs or sperm).

1. A coin is tossed in the air and allowed to land on the table. What is the probability that the coin will come up heads? Derive a simple formula that expresses the probability of this occurring.

2. Calculate the probability of throwing a pair of sixes when two dice are rolled.

3. What are the chances that a family of four children will have two boys and two girls? All girls? At least three boys?

4. In humans, albinism (lack of skin pigment) is due to a recessive gene. Suppose that two normally pigmented parents produce an albino child. What are the chances of their second child also being albino?

Probability and Genetics

If you flipped a coin into the air, what is the chance that it would land on the ground heads up? The coin could land tails up, too. In fact, there is an equal chance, or **probability**, of getting either a head or a tail. This probability can be expressed as a ratio — one head: one tail, or 50 : 50. This is the ratio you would expect because there is an equal chance for each outcome — heads or tails. What would be the possible outcomes if you flipped two coins at the same time? Complete the next MiniLab to find out.

The probability, or chance, that two or more independent events will occur together is the product of their individual probabilities of occurring alone. For example, what is the probability of flipping two coins and getting two heads at the same time? The chance of getting one head is $\frac{1}{2}$ or 50 : 50. The chance of getting the second head is also $\frac{1}{2}$ or 50 : 50. The chance of getting both heads at the same time is $\frac{1}{2} \times \frac{1}{2} = \frac{1}{4}$. Figure 4.12 shows all possible outcomes of flipping two coins.

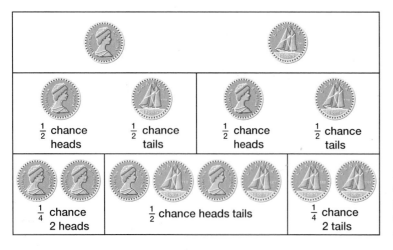

$\frac{1}{2}$ chance heads $\quad$ $\frac{1}{2}$ chance tails $\quad$ $\frac{1}{2}$ chance heads $\quad$ $\frac{1}{2}$ chance tails

$\frac{1}{4}$ chance 2 heads $\quad$ $\frac{1}{2}$ chance heads tails $\quad$ $\frac{1}{4}$ chance 2 tails

Figure 4.12 There are two possible outcomes when tossing a coin in the air. To find the probability of several different combinations of outcome, you need to multiply the individual outcomes.

MINI LAB

Heads or Tails?

In this lab, you will investigate the probability of turning up heads or tails during the toss of two coins. Together with a partner, two coins, paper, and a pencil, flip one coin 20 times and record how many times you get heads and how many times you get tails. Tabulate the class results. Now both of you flip a coin at the same time and record how many times you get two heads, two tails or one of each. Do the toss 20 times. Use H for heads and T for tails. Tabulate the class results.

Analyze

1. What do the results of the first part of the experiment seem to show? How many times did you record heads? How many times did you record tails? What is the probability of either heads or tails being the result of each toss? Do the class results support this?

2. In the second part of the experiment, what are the chances of two heads turning up? Of two tails turning up? What is the chance that you will turn up one of each? Is it greater or less than the chance of turning up both heads or both tails? Do the class results support this?

3. How does this experiment help illustrate ratios and probabilities in inheritance?

The law of probability forms the basis for solving genetics problems. The two alleles for each parent represent probabilities. For example, in a cross of pea plants that are heterozygous for tall (Tt), it is probable that half of the gametes will contain the T allele and half will contain the t allele. A gamete with the T allele may combine with a gamete with either another T allele or a t allele. This happens entirely by chance. The probability of getting a particular combination of alleles in a given zygote depends on the genetic makeup of the parents.

Punnett Squares

What are the possible combinations of alleles in the offspring? The results can be organized easily in a **Punnett square** (see Figure 4.13). A Punnett square is used to calculate the probability of inheriting a particular trait. It is a simple method of illustrating all possible combinations of gametes from a given set of parents. All the possible gametes for one parent are listed across the top and all the possible gametes for the other parent are listed down the side of the square. Then, each box is filled in by copying the row and column-head letters across or down the empty squares. This will give you a prediction of the outcome of a particular cross for a given set of alleles. Using the Punnett square, you can determine both the genotypes and phenotypes of the offspring of different crosses. The **genotype** is the genetic make-up of an organism. The **phenotype** is the appearance of the trait in an organism. For example, the genotype of the F_1 generation of pea plants is Tt but the phenotype is tall.

BIO 🧬 FACT

The use of a Punnett square to determine the outcome of various crosses was first proposed by Reginald C. Punnett, an early twentieth century English geneticist who worked with traits of feather colour in chickens. He discovered certain fundamentals of genetics, including sex determination and traits that are linked, or specific, to each sex.

➤ PLAY

An interactive exploration involving various crosses can be found on your Electronic Learning Partner.

Using the Punnett square, you can examine the genotypes and phenotypes of the $F_1 \times F_1$ cross. Recall that all of the F_1 generation of pea plants had the genotype Tt. The only possible gametes for both the mother and the father then are T and t. The Punnett square shows that this results in one genotype TT, two genotypes Tt, and one genotype tt. Expressed as a **Mendelian ratio for genotype**, this is 1 : 2 : 1. There is one homozygous dominant genotype, two heterozygous genotypes and one homozygous recessive genotype. The Punnett square also indicates the expected phenotype. Three of four offspring have the T allele and will be tall. Only one genotype, homozygous for the recessive characteristic, will result in a short pea plant. Expressed as a Mendelian ratio for phenotype, this is 3 : 1. The concepts of phenotype, genotype, dominant allele and recessive allele are summarized in the concept organizer in Figure 4.14 on page 131.

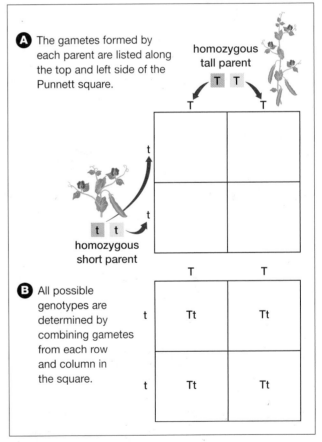

A The gametes formed by each parent are listed along the top and left side of the Punnett square.

homozygous tall parent

homozygous short parent

B All possible genotypes are determined by combining gametes from each row and column in the square.

Figure 4.13 A Punnett square can be used to determine the outcome of crosses. According to Mendel, the alleles separate during gamete formation to produce T gamete and t gamete. Each gamete of one plant has the opportunity to pair with the gametes of the other plant. All possible pairings of alleles produce tall plants (Tt).

Solving a Punnett Square

Tall pea plants are governed by the allele T while short pea plants are governed by the allele t. Suppose a heterozygous tall pea plant was crossed with a short pea plant. What are the genotypes of the parents? Identify the genotypes and phenotypes of the offspring of the F_1 generation.

What is required?

You are asked to find the genotype of each parent as well as the genotypes and phenotypes of the F_1 generation.

What is given?

You know the genotypes and phenotypes of each parent:

T represents the allele for tall plants

t represents the allele for short plants

For the heterozygous tall parent, the genotype is Tt

For the short parent (homozygous short) the genotype is tt (must be tt because of the law of dominance)

Plan your strategy

You are asked to make the following cross: Tt x tt

Act on your strategy

The genotypes of the parents are: Tt (heterozygous tall plant), and tt (homozygous short plant). Place the alleles of each parent along the columns and rows of the Punnett square and complete the possible crosses.

	T	t
t	Tt	tt
t	Tt	tt

The genotypes of the offspring are: two Tt and two tt. This is a genotypic ratio of 1 : 1.

These genotypes correspond to the following phenotypes:

Tt — heterozygous tall plant

tt — homozygous short plant

The corresponding phenotypic ratio is also 1 : 1.

Check your solution

The parent genotypes are Tt and tt representing tall and short plants, respectively. The genotypes of the F_1 generation are Tt and tt, which represent the phenotypes tall and short plants, respectively.

1. In pea plants, round peas are dominant over wrinkled peas. Use a Punnett square to predict the phenotypic and genotypic outcome of a cross between a plant homozygous for round peas (RR) and a plant homozygous for wrinkled peas (rr).

2. In tomatoes, red fruit (R) is dominant over yellow fruit (r). If a heterozygous red fruit is crossed with a yellow fruit,

    (a) What is the appearance of the F_1 generation?

    (b) What are the genotypes of the F_2 generation if two plants from the F_1 generation are crossed?

    (c) What are the phenotypes of the F_2 generation?

3. In cattle, horns (h) are recessive over hornlessness (H). If two homozygous cattle, one hornless and the other horned, are crossed, what are the genotypes and phenotypes of the first generation?

Pedigrees

Crosses can be done easily with plants, such as the common garden pea, in order to determine the inheritance of traits. How is inheritance of traits studied among humans? Because experimental crosses are not possible, human geneticists use medical, historical, and family records to study crosses that have already occurred. Records extending across several generations can be arranged in the form of a family **pedigree**.

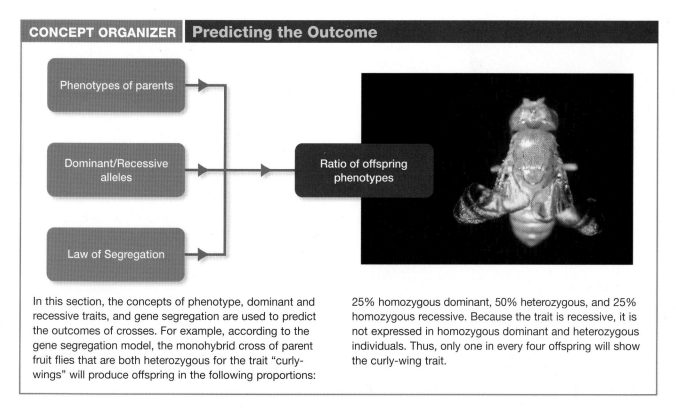

In this section, the concepts of phenotype, dominant and recessive traits, and gene segregation are used to predict the outcomes of crosses. For example, according to the gene segregation model, the monohybrid cross of parent fruit flies that are both heterozygous for the trait "curly-wings" will produce offspring in the following proportions:

25% homozygous dominant, 50% heterozygous, and 25% homozygous recessive. Because the trait is recessive, it is not expressed in homozygous dominant and heterozygous individuals. Thus, only one in every four offspring will show the curly-wing trait.

Figure 4.14 A summary of the major concepts in Mendelian genetics.

This is a diagram that illustrates the genetic relationships among a group of related individuals (see Figure 4.15). Careful analysis of different pedigrees has shown that certain human traits, such as a widow's peak hairline and tongue-rolling ability, are inherited as simple dominant traits. A **simple dominant trait** has only two possible alleles — dominant or recessive. Other inherited traits do not influence the inheritance of simple dominant traits. In other words, a person who inherits a widow's peak hairline has at least one dominant allele present; and this allele is the only factor controlling the inheritance of the trait. Many other common human traits, such as freckles, long eyelashes, and unattached earlobes, are inherited in the same way. That is, they each appear to be controlled by one pair of alleles, one a dominant allele and the other a recessive allele. Other traits, such as albinism, are inherited as recessives.

In order to construct a pedigree, squares are generally used to represent males and circles represent females. Colour represents individuals who are recessive or dominant for a single trait (see Figure 4.15). Generations are indicated by roman numerals to the left of the pedigree. It is important to note that a study of inheritance is usually restricted to either the recessive or the dominant nature of a particular trait. Therefore, only one of the variations uses colour. Some individuals may

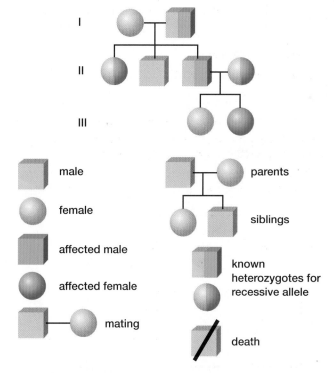

Figure 4.15 This example of a pedigree shows the method of transmission of dominant and recessive alleles from one generation to the next. Standard symbols are used to establish a pedigree.

show only half a square or circle of colour. This indicates that the given individual is a **carrier**, heterozygous for the given trait but does not show it.

For instance, pea plants that are heterozygous for tall (Tt) carry the recessive t allele, although it is not expressed. In human pedigrees, the genotypes are deduced from the phenotypes of individuals, so they cannot always be determined with complete accuracy. In the following investigation, you will construct a family pedigree based on common human traits.

Determining Genotypes

How can you determine if a particular organism is a homozygous dominant or a heterozygous? You cannot deduce this information by looking at the phenotype alone. Recall that tall pea plants may be homozygous dominant (TT) or heterozygous (Tt). In order to determine the genotype of an individual, you must perform a **test cross**. A test cross involves crossing an individual of unknown genotype with a homozygous recessive individual. The offspring will exhibit certain phenotypes that will allow you to determine if your unknown is either homozygous dominant or heterozygous. Study Figure 4.16 on page 134 to learn how results of a test cross are interpreted.

Test crosses are especially valuable for determining whether a particular trait is passed by one, two, or more pairs of alleles. For example, Table 4.1 shows the phenotypic ratios of F_2 offspring produced after mating parents with contrasting traits and then breeding the F_1 individuals. Each ratio gives rise to a particular conclusion about the underlying genetic interactions. Why is it important to know how many pairs of alleles govern a particular trait? Multiple allele inheritance is often influenced by environmental factors, such as diet and climate, while single allele inheritance is not. Plant

Investigation 4 • A

SKILL FOCUS

Predicting

Performing and recording

Analyzing and interpreting

Conducting research

What Traits Can You See in Your Family?

In this investigation, you will prepare four different pedigrees to illustrate the inheritance of common traits in your family. Using the traits of tongue rolling, hitchhiker's thumb, ear lobe attachment, and widow's peak hairline, you will determine the genotype of each family member across three or four generations.

	Tongue	Thumb	Earlobe	Hairline
dominant trait	can roll	straight	detached	pointed
recessive trait	cannot roll	bent back	attached	smooth

Pre-lab Questions

- How many of the traits illustrated in the figure have you noticed among your family members?
- How could you determine whether a trait was dominant or recessive if you were not given that information?

- How can you identify the genotypes of family members if you know their phenotypes?

Problem

If a family member shows a phenotype for a dominant trait, how can you determine whether the individual is homozygous or heterozygous for that trait?

Prediction

Predict how dominant traits are inherited across several generations.

Materials

blank white paper   ruler
pencil   coloured pencils

Procedure

1. Record the phenotypes of different family members from at least three generations

researchers, for example, need to know how much of their plant breeding results are due to genes and how much to the care they give growing plants. You will investigate the inheritance of more than one trait in the next section.

Table 4.1
Results of several test crosses

Phenotypic ratio in F_2 offspring	Conclusion
3 : 1	One pair of alleles at one gene location
9 : 3 : 3 : 1	Two pairs of alleles at two gene locations
No recognizable ratio	Alleles at multiple gene locations

> PLAY

To enhance your learning about pedigrees and crosses, refer to your Electronic Learning Partner.

Web LINK

As you have learned, offspring inherit certain traits from their parents. How traits are expressed, however, may be influenced by other factors. To find out how environmental factors can influence the expression of traits, visit the web site below. Go to **Science Resources** then to **BIOLOGY 11** to find out where to go next. For example, how does ambient temperature affect the growth of plants, hair colour in mammals, or wing patterns in butterflies? How can the sex of a fish change depending on its social environment? How does soil pH affect the colour of flowers? Research an environmental factor and determine how it can influence the expression of a trait in one species. Prepare a 10 min oral presentation for a class symposium.
www.school.mcgrawhill.ca/resources/

including your own. If your relatives do not live nearby, contact them to learn about their traits. In some cases photographs or videos of family members may help you determine certain phenotypic traits. If you cannot contact your family members, select a friend and construct a pedigree with the information from his or her family.

2. Draw four different pedigrees. Use the symbols shown in Figure 4.15 (see page 131) to indicate the sex and genotype status of each individual. Give each pedigree a title to correspond with the trait you are illustrating.

3. Write the name of each person below each symbol in your pedigree.

4. Beside each symbol, indicate what genotype you think the person has.

Post-lab Questions

1. Which of the traits are most common in your family line?

2. Where you unable to determine dominance or recessiveness for one or more of the traits? Explain.

Conclude and Apply

3. Explain how you arrived at the genotypes of at least three members of your family.

4. Which dominant traits do you have? Which recessive traits?

5. Are some traits more or less common in the families of other class members than they are in your family?

Exploring Further

6. Some deleterious, disease-causing recessive traits remain hidden for many generations. Is there any circumstance in which such a recessive allele could be beneficial to individuals who are heterozygous for that allele? Do you know of an example of such an occurrence in the human population? Why do you think these traits continue to exist in the human population?

7. Research a human genetic condition, such as cystic fibrosis, albinism, or sickle cell anemia. Report on the characteristics of the condition and the method of genetic transmission.

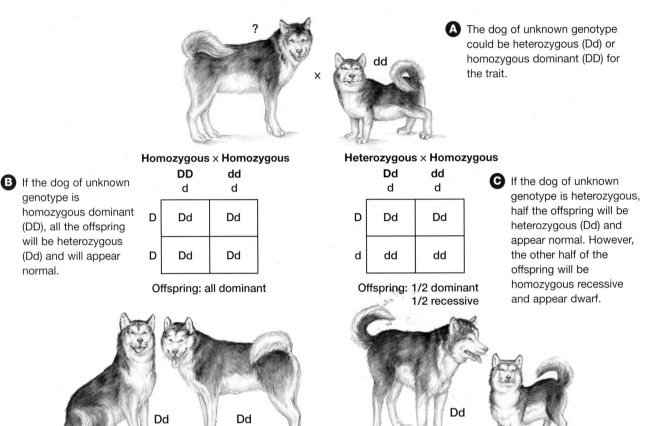

A The dog of unknown genotype could be heterozygous (Dd) or homozygous dominant (DD) for the trait.

Homozygous × Homozygous

B If the dog of unknown genotype is homozygous dominant (DD), all the offspring will be heterozygous (Dd) and will appear normal.

	DD d	**dd** d
D	Dd	Dd
D	Dd	Dd

Offspring: all dominant

Heterozygous × Homozygous

C If the dog of unknown genotype is heterozygous, half the offspring will be heterozygous (Dd) and appear normal. However, the other half of the offspring will be homozygous recessive and appear dwarf.

	Dd d	**dd** d
D	Dd	Dd
d	dd	dd

Offspring: 1/2 dominant 1/2 recessive

Figure 4.16 This test cross of Alaskan malamutes involves a dwarf dog that is homozygous recessive (dd) and a normal-size dog of unknown genotype (D?).

 THINKING LAB

Identify the Genotypes

Background

It is often difficult to determine the exact genotypes of parents of various species when only their phenotypes are known. In this lab, you will deduce probable genotype(s) for parents based on a series of crosses. Carefully read each scenario and the outcome of each cross that is listed in the table, and then complete the questions.

You Try It

1. Suggest probable genotypes for the parents based on the results of each cross.

2. Give a brief explanation of how you determined the genotypes for each of the scenarios described in the table.

3. Identify and explain any evidence that enabled you to be reasonably sure of your answers.

4. Are there any answers of which you are unsure? Why or why not?

5. What additional information would you need in order to positively determine the genotypes of those that you were unsure about?

6. Identify the genetic principle (or principles) that enabled you to solve each scenario.

Scenario	Outcome (offspring)
A watermelon plant with striped fruit is crossed with a plant heterozygous for this characteristic.	All fruit are striped.
A black pig mates with a white pig.	In a litter of 16 piglets, 75% are black and 25% are white.
A yellow-haired female rat is mated with a black-haired male rat.	Of 99 offspring, 46 are black and 53 are yellow.
Two pea plants are crossed.	Plants with green pods and plants with yellow pods are produced in the ratio 3 : 1.
A tall green pea plant is crossed with another of its kind.	Of 18 plants produced, only one is short and yellow.

1. **K/U** State the principle of segregation.

2. **K/U** What important ratio appears in the F$_2$ generation of Mendel's monohybrid crosses? Explain why this ratio appears.

3. **K/U** Differentiate between the following:(a) dominant and recessive; (b) gene and allele.

4. **K/U** Define the "principle of dominance." Briefly describe the experimental results that led Mendel to this principle.

5. **MC** Why might a plant breeder be interested in knowing how certain traits are inherited?

6. **K/U** Why was the pea plant a suitable organism for Mendel to conduct his experiments on heredity?

7. **K/U** What is the purpose of a test cross? Why are test crosses often considered to be unreliable when determining genotypes of animals?

8. **C** Using an illustration, explain the purpose of the Punnett square.

9. **I** In pea plants, yellow peas are dominant over green peas. Use a Punnett square to predict the phenotypes and genotypes of the offspring from a cross between a plant heterozygous for yellow peas (Yy) and a plant homozygous for green peas (yy).

10. **I** As a reward for being a good student, Mr. Singh gives you a rabbit named Bud. Bud has long hair. You introduce Bud to your other rabbit, Sarah, who has short hair. Later that school year, Bud and Sarah produce a litter of one long-haired and seven short-haired bunnies. If short hair is due to the dominant gene (S) and long hair to the recessive allele (s):

    (a) What are the possible genotypes of Bud and Sarah?

    (b) What phenotypic ratio would you expect in the offspring generation of a cross between Bud and Sarah? Create a Punnett square to show the results of the cross.

    (c) How many of the eight bunnies were expected to be long-haired?

    (d) The expected phenotypic ratio would be achieved in every case. Would you agree with this statement? Why?

11. **I** A woman has a father who died of Huntington's disease. What is the probability that she will develop the symptoms of the disease? (Hint: Huntington's disease is caused by a recessive allele.)

12. **I** In humans, albinism (the lack of skin pigmentation) is governed by a recessive allele (a) and normal pigmentation is governed by the dominant allele (A). Given this information, determine the genotypic and phenotypic ratios of the children expected from the following crosses:

    (a) homozygous dominant x heterozygous

    (b) heterozygous x homozygous recessive

    (c) homozygous dominant x homozygous recessive

    (d) heterozygous x heterozygous

    (e) For each of the above crosses, state the percent likelihood of the first child being albino.

    Determine the percent likelihood of having one normal child followed by two albino children in one family.

13. **I** A hornless bull is crossed with three cows, A, B, and C. Cow A is horned and produces calf A' which is also horned. Cow B is hornless and produces calf B', which is horned. Cow C is horned and produces calf C', which is hornless. Give the genotypes and phenotypes of all seven animals.

14. **I** A couple has two children, one of which is a boy. What is the probability that the other child is a girl?

15. **MC** Many characteristics are the result of single gene inheritance. For example, a widow's peak is inherited over a smooth hairline if the allele for the widow's peak is present. How do you think characteristics that are controlled by more than one gene might be expressed?

16. **MC** Can you think of any other organism that would have been a good candidate for Mendel to study the genetics of inheritance? Why did Mendel choose to study plants rather than animals or, indeed, humans?

UNIT ISSUE PREP

If you have decided to investigate breeding technologies in your Unit 2 Issue Analysis, be sure you are familiar with how traits are inherited.

The Inheritance of Two Traits

- Explain the inheritance of more than one trait.

- Predict the outcome of crosses involving two traits.

- Compile quantitative and qualitative data in a laboratory investigation to determine the genotypes of plants.

Figure 4.17 Many varieties of plants, such as this rose, have been hybridized. Each may have a combination of traits including flower shape, colour, and fragrance.

When Mendel performed his monohybrid crosses on pea plants, he was investigating one trait at a time. This method allowed him to determine the inheritance pattern of plant height, for instance, among generations. However, organisms are composed of many traits. The common pea, among other characteristics, has traits for colour, shape, and height. Fragrance in flowers also has a genetic basis and is particularly important in the cultivation of ornamentals, such as roses (see Figure 4.17). How are multiple traits (two or more) inherited? This was the question Mendel sought to answer in his next series of experiments.

Mendel's Second Experiment: A Dihybrid Cross

Mendel wanted to know if the inheritance of one characteristic influenced the inheritance of a different characteristic. For example, did pea shape influence pea colour? Mendel approached this question the same way he had approached the previous ones. First, he produced plants that were purebred for the traits he wanted to examine. Using the combination of the pea's shape and colour, for instance, he selectively bred pea plants until the offspring always had round, yellow seeds. These plants were homozygous dominant for both traits. He then bred plants that were homozygous recessive for both seed shape and colour. These individuals always had wrinkled, green seeds. Mendel then performed a **dihybrid cross**; that is,

he crossed two pea plants that differed in two traits — pea shape and pea colour. The F_1 generation all had round, yellow seeds. Remember that round seed shape and yellow colour are dominant characteristics (see Figure 4.18). The offspring were therefore all heterozygous for the two traits. If R represents the dominant trait for pea shape and Y represents the dominant trait for pea colour, the genotype of the F_1 generation is RrYy. The phenotype is round and yellow seeds. What happens if you cross individuals of the F_1 generation? Figure 4.19 shows all possible genotypes from an F_1 cross.

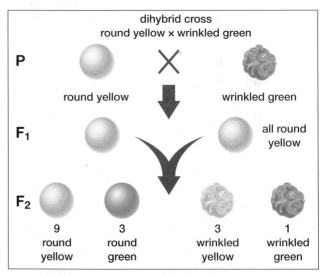

dihybrid cross
round yellow × wrinkled green

P   round yellow   ✕   wrinkled green

F_1 all round yellow

F_2

| 9 | 3 | 3 | 1 |
| round yellow | round green | wrinkled yellow | wrinkled green |

Figure 4.18 Results of Mendel's dihybrid crosses of pea plants. What traits were expressed in the F_1 and F_2 generations?

F₁ cross
RrYy × RrYy

round yellow

round green

wrinkled yellow

wrinkled green

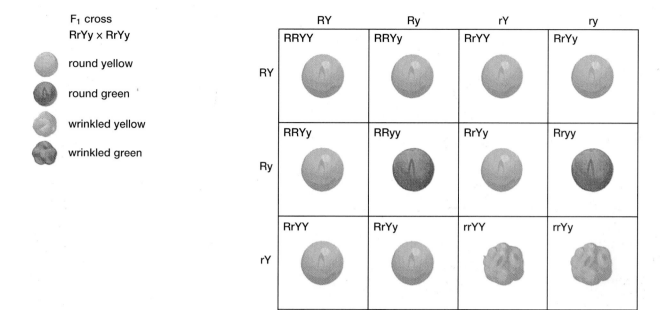

	RY	Ry	rY	ry
RY	RRYY	RRYy	RrYY	RrYy
Ry	RRYy	RRyy	RrYy	Rryy
rY	RrYY	RrYy	rrYY	rrYy
ry	RrYy	Rryy	rrYY	rryy

Figure 4.19 A dihybrid cross of the F₁ generation produced nine different genotypes. How many phenotypes resulted from this cross?

Mendel allowed the F₁ generation of his dihybrid cross to self-pollinate. Of 551 plants in the F₂ generation, Mendel observed the following traits:

- 320 round yellow
- 104 round green
- 101 wrinkled yellow
- 26 wrinkled green

These results represent a phenotypic ratio of 9 : 3 : 3 : 1. The F₂ generations of other dihybrid crosses for other traits showed a similar phenotypic ratio.

Law of Independent Assortment

Mendel realized that a ratio of 9 : 3 : 3 : 1 could be explained if the alleles from one trait were inherited independently of the alleles for another trait. This led Mendel to propose the **law of independent assortment**. This second law of inheritance states that the inheritance of alleles for one trait does not affect the inheritance of alleles for another trait. According to the law of independent assortment, different pairs of alleles are passed to the offspring independently of each other. This means that offspring may have new combinations of alleles that are not present in either parent. A pea plant's ability to produce white flowers instead of purple ones does not influence the same pea plant's ability to produce a round pea shape rather than a wrinkled pea shape.

Web LINK

The common fruit fly, *Drosophila melanogaster*, is often used by researchers to study the inheritance of traits. This fruit fly shows distinct phenotypes, such as eye colour and wing shape, which are inherited as simple dominants. Thus, genotypic and phenotypic ratios can be easily determined from crosses. A virtual computer lab may be used to investigate the inheritance of traits in this fly. To find out how to conduct crosses using virtual flies, visit the web site below. Go to **Science Resources**, then to **BIOLOGY 11** to find out where to go next. The virtual fly lab is recommended over conventional fly labs because there is no need to actually breed flies and wait for offspring to develop. Computer software allows you to create crosses and determine the outcome quickly and easily.
www.school.mcgrawhill.ca/resources/

❚❚PAUSE **●RECORD**

In what step of an experimental design would you use a Punnett square? Explain briefly using an example.

As in the case for a single trait, a test cross may also be used to determine the genotype of an individual for two traits. A two-trait test cross involves crossing an individual that shows the dominant phenotype for two traits with an individual that is homozygous recessive for the same two traits. The individual showing the dominant phenotype for both traits may be either heterozygous or homozygous dominant. A homozygous recessive individual is used in the cross because it provides the best chance of producing an offspring that is homozygous recessive for both traits.

For instance, if a pea plant is homozygous dominant for purple flower colour (PP) and round pea shape (RR), then the F_1 generation will all have the dominant phenotype. This will occur even if the cross involves a homozygous recessive plant, which has white flowers (pp) and a wrinkled pea shape (rr). However, if the pea plant is heterozygous for both traits (PpRr), then there is a 25% chance that the F_1 generation will show the recessive condition for one or both of the traits.

DESIGN YOUR OWN
Investigation 4 • B

Determining Plant Genotypes

In this investigation, you will design and conduct experiments to determine the genotypes of tobacco plant seeds. You will use two batches of seeds that yield slightly different characteristics in the plants. One batch of seeds will produce some seedlings that are green, and some that are white (albino). The other batch will produce some seedlings that are green, some green-yellow, and some yellow. Work in a small group to design your experiments. Then obtain your teacher's approval before completing the investigation.

Problem

How can you determine the genotype of a tobacco seed based on the phenotype of the seedling?

Hypothesis

Each group is responsible for formulating a testable hypothesis of how the plant phenotypes reflect their genotypes. The hypothesis will form the basis of your experimental design.

NOTE: Be careful not to mix seeds from the two batches. Wash your hands following this investigation.

Materials

2 different batches of tobacco seeds
flats, small pots, or plastic cups
growth medium (vermiculite or sterilized potting soil)
magnifying lens or dissecting light microscope
water   labels

Experimental Plan

1. Brainstorm several methods you could use to test your hypothesis, using the materials listed here.

2. As a group, select one method for your experimental design.

3. Your experimental design should include the collection of qualitative and quantitative data.

4. Your plan should consist of a series of easily identifiable and understandable steps that could be duplicated by another group, without the need for additional information or clarification.

Checking the Plan

Review your plan among the members of your group and with your teacher. Possible questions include:

1. What types of data will you collect?

Figure 4.20 shows a Punnett square involving a cross between heterozygous and homozygous recessive individuals. The expected ratio of individuals is one purple flower with round peas, one purple flower with wrinkled peas, one white flower with round peas, and one white flower with wrinkles peas (that is, 1 : 1 : 1 : 1).

Figure 4.20 This two-trait test cross shows a cross between a heterozygous individual and a homozygous recessive individual. The Punnett square shows that there is a 25% chance of producing each of the possible phenotypes.

Parents		Female (pprr)
	Egg	pr
	Sperm	
Male (PpRr)	PR	PpRr
	Pr	Pprr
	pR	ppRr
	pr	prpr

P = purple flower
p = white flower
R = round pea shape
r = wrinkled pea shape

2. What is/are the dependent and independent variable(s)? Does your experiment include any control variables? What variables might you wish to control?

3. What is the duration of the experiment and what data will you collect during this time?

4. Have you prepared a table for collecting your data?

5. Has your plan been approved by your teacher?

6. Have you applied/used all necessary safety precautions?

Data and Observations

Each group is responsible for carrying out their own data collection. Record your observations in your table. Each group is also responsible for analyzing their results. Use a graph or chart to present your results.

Analyze

1. Suggest possible genotypes (combinations of alleles) for the different phenotypes observed (for example, GG might indicate homozygous dominant for green).

2. Why is it not possible for the genotypes of the different batches of tobacco plants to be determined through an investigation of the seeds alone?

3. Identify each of the variables you considered in designing your experiment. Explain how consideration of each variable was necessary in order to obtain valid scientific results.

4. Determine the method of inheritance for the batch of seeds that produced green and/or white tobacco seedlings. Explain.

5. Describe, how you determined the genotypes of the individual seeds using an example from each of the seed batches.

Conclude and Apply

6. Determine the method of inheritance for the batch of seeds that produce green, yellow-green, and/or yellow tobacco plants. How is this method different from the method you described above? Does this method of inheritance follow the principles laid out by Mendel? Explain.

Exploring Further

7. In this investigation, you looked at variations of a single trait — plant colour. How would you modify your experimental design to determine the genotypes of the seeds for two different traits?

The Two-trait Cross

A male and a female guinea pig are both heterozygous for fur colour and fur texture. Both dark fur (D) and rough fur (R) are dominant traits.

(a) What are the recessive traits and what letters do you use for them?

(b) What are the parent phenotypes?

(c) How many different gametes are formed and what are they?

(d) Determine the frequency of offspring that are homozygous for both traits.

(e) Determine the frequency of offspring that have rough, dark fur.

(f) Determine the frequency of offspring that express both recessive traits.

What is required?

You are asked to determine the recessive traits and assign letters to represent them. Further, you are asked to determine the phenotypes of the parents and offspring.

What is given?

You know that both dark fur (D) and rough fur (R) are dominant traits. Therefore, the recessive traits are light fur (d) and soft fur (r). You are told that both parents are heterozygous. This means the genotype of each parent is DdRr. Because of the rule of dominance, each parent would have dark, rough fur.

Plan your strategy

To determine the genotype and phenotype of the offspring, you will need to make the following cross: DdRr × DdRr. A gamete from each parent can include one allele from each trait. Therefore, each parent can produce four possible gametes: DR, Dr, dR, and dr.

Act on your strategy

Place the gametes of each parent along the columns and rows of the Punnett square and complete the possible crosses.

		Female gametes			
		DR	Dr	dR	dr
Male gametes	DR	DDRR	DDRr	DdRR	DdRr
	Dr	DDRr	DDrr	DdRr	Ddrr
	dR	DdRR	DdRr	ddRR	ddRr
	dr	DdRr	Ddrr	ddRr	ddrr

There are only two individuals homozygous for both fur colour and texture. These are DDRR and ddrr. Therefore, the proportion of offspring purebred for these traits is $\frac{2}{16}$ or $\frac{1}{8}$.

The following offspring have rough, dark fur: DDRR, DDRr, DdRR, and DdRr. There are nine individuals with this genotype. Therefore $\frac{9}{16}$ of the offspring have rough, dark fur.

Only one offspring is homozygous recessive (ddrr). Thus $\frac{1}{16}$ of all the offspring will have light, smooth fur.

Check your solution

The genotype of each parent is DdRr. This means that each parent will have dark, rough fur. A cross produces nine possible genotypes in the offspring: DDRR, DDRr, DdRR, DDrr, DdRr, Ddrr, ddRR, ddRr, and ddrr. The phenotypic ratio of the offspring is:

- $\frac{9}{16}$ dark and rough fur
- $\frac{3}{16}$ dark and smooth fur
- $\frac{3}{16}$ light and rough fur
- $\frac{1}{16}$ light and smooth fur

1. In people, curly hair is dominant over straight hair and the ability to curl the tongue is dominant over not being able to curl the tongue. A man with curly hair who has the ability to curl his tongue and a woman with curly hair who cannot curl her tongue have children. What are the possible genotypic and phenotypic ratios of their offspring?

1. **K/U** Define the term "dihybrid cross." State three examples of dihybrid crosses of pea plants that Mendel may have performed.

2. **K/U** State the law of independent assortment. Explain briefly what is meant by independent assortment.

3. **K/U** The Punnett square is often used for solving genetics problems involving monohybrid and dihybrid crosses but rarely for crosses that are more complex (that is 3 or more gene pairs). Explain why this is so.

4. **I** In a dihybrid cross of two pea plants, one homozygous for two dominant traits and the other homozygous for the corresponding recessive traits, what will the phenotypic ratio be for the F_1 generation? for the F_2 generation?

5. **I** Give the possible alleles in the eggs produced by a woman whose genotype is JjKkLl.

6. **I** In *Drosophila melanogaster* (the fruit fly you find hanging around your vegetables and fruits at home) normal wings (W) are dominant over vestigial wings (w); grey body colour (G) is dominant over ebony colour (g); and normal antennae (A) are dominant over antennapedia (a). Bugsy, a male fruit fly who is homozygous dominant for body colour and normal wing shape, mates with Daisy, a female fruit fly who is homozygous recessive for body colour and wing shape.

   (a) Write the genotypes of Bugsy and Daisy for body colour and wing shape. Bugsy and Daisy will be the P generation.

   (b) What are the alleles that Bugsy can provide for body colour? for wing shape?

   (c) What are the alleles that Daisy can provide for body colour? for wing shape?

   (d) Draw a Punnett square and show the possible genotype(s) of the F_1 generation produced by Bugsy and Daisy.

   (e) What are the percentages of each genotype?

   (f) What are the alleles for body colour and wing shape that can be provided by any member of the F_1 generation?

   (g) Now cross two individuals from the F_1 generation (a dihybrid cross). Show this cross. The offspring from this cross will be the F_2 generation.

   (h) What are the genotypic ratios for body colour in the F_1 generation? for wing shape?

7. **I** Dino, another fruit fly, is homozygous recessive for body colour and homozygous dominant for antennae. He mates with Daisy's sister Lulu, who is homozygous dominant for body colour and homozygous recessive for antennae.

   (a) What are the genotypes for the P generation? Be sure to include both traits.

   (b) Draw the Punnett square and show the cross between Dino and Lulu. Their offspring will be the F_1 generation.

   (c) What are the percentages of the genotype(s) found in the F_1 generation?

   (d) List the four possible combinations of alleles that could be produced in the gametes by members of the F_1 generation.

   (e) Cross two individuals of the F_1 generation. Show this cross in a Punnett square.

   (f) What ratio of phenotypes can you expect from this dihybrid cross?

8. **I** In the fruit fly, sepia eye is recessive to red eye, and curved wing is recessive to straight wing. If a pure-breeding sepia-eyed, straight-winged fly is mated with a pure-breeding red-eyed curved-winged fly, what phenotypes will appear in the F_1 generation? If two F_1 flies are allowed to mate, what phenotypes will appear in the F_2 generation and in what ratio?

9. **I** Fruit with seeds are dominant over fruits that are seedless, and blue colour is dominant over purple colour. A homozygous purple fruit with seeds is crossbred with a homozygous blue, seedless fruit. What are the genotypes and phenotypes of the F_2 generation?

Beyond Mendel's Laws

- Explain how incomplete dominance and co-dominance can account for inheritance of intermediate characteristics.

- Solve genetics problem involving multiple alleles.

Figure 4.21 The inheritance pattern of multicoloured corn would have been unknown to Mendel.

In his studies of pea plants, Mendel found that inherited traits were either dominant or recessive. The dominant allele in an individual was always expressed, even if the recessive allele was present. However, some organisms show different patterns of inheritance. For example, the variety of colours of corn shown in Figure 4.21 does not follow the inheritance pattern outlined by Mendel — many colours of kernel are expressed rather than only one. How can we explain the inheritance of traits that do not follow simple Mendelian genetics?

Incomplete Dominance

Not all traits are purely dominant or purely recessive. In some instances neither of the alleles controlling the trait are dominant. When this happens, a blending of the two traits can occur, called **incomplete dominance**. Apparent blending of traits to give an intermediate expression can occur in individuals that are heterozygous. Examples of incomplete dominance can be found in many species of plants, including the snapdragon (see Figure 4.22).

White or red snapdragon flowers are homozygous, while pink flowers are heterozygous. In this example, the letters R and R′ are used (rather than R and r) to indicate alleles that show incomplete dominance (see Figure 4.23). Two red alleles (RR) are necessary to produce a red flower.

Figure 4.22 Snapdragon flowers can be white, red, or pink. Pink flowers result from a cross of individuals with white and red flowers.

Individuals with only one R allele are unable to make enough red pigment to produce red flowers, and they appear pink. Individuals that are white (R′R′) produce no red pigment.

In traits that show incomplete dominance, the alleles segregate the same way as in crosses mentioned earlier in this chapter. However, because neither of the alleles are dominant, only pink flowers (RR′) are produced in the F_1 generation. What happens when two individuals with pink

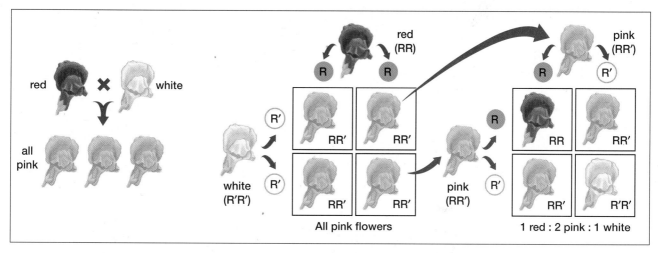

Figure 4.23 Flower colour in the snapdragon is an example of incomplete dominance. Pink flowers are heterozygous (*RR′*), where neither allele is dominant.

flowers are crossed? The phenotypes of the F₂ generation are: 25% red, 50% pink, and 25% white, or a ratio of 1 : 2 : 1. Notice, that the F₂ generation does not show a Mendelian ratio for phenotype of 3 : 1. The ratios for genotype and phenotype are both 1 : 2 : 1 because there is no dominant allele. This supports Mendel's law of independent assortment. Another example of incomplete dominance occurs in the pitch of the human male voice. The lowest and highest pitches occur in men who are homozygous for these alleles. Intermediate pitches occur in men heterozygous for this condition. Fortunately for Mendel, the pea plant traits that he studied were not controlled by incomplete dominance. Otherwise he may not have been able to develop the basic principles of genetics.

Co-dominance

In some cases, both alleles for a trait may be dominant. Such alleles are said to be **co-dominant** because *both* alleles are expressed in the heterozygous individual. For example, feather colour in chickens is governed by two dominant alleles. Black birds are homozygous for the B allele and white birds are homozygous for the W allele.

What happens when a black rooster is crossed with a white hen? If the colours blended, you would expect offsping with grey plumage. If only the B allele was dominant, then only black-feathered young would result. However, the result of the cross is offspring with checkered black-and-white plumage, as shown in Figure 4.24. Some of the feathers are white and some are black.

Figure 4.24 In some varieties of chicken, two alleles for a trait may be expressed equally, such as in this bird with barred plumage.

Multiple Alleles

Many genes have more than two alleles, or **multiple alleles**. An example of multiple alleles occurs in human blood types. In this case, three alleles are involved: A, B, and O. Table 4.2 on page 144 shows the blood types in humans and the possible genotypes for each. Each person has two of the three alleles and each allele determines if the red blood cells do or do not possess certain glycoproteins. People with type A blood have A glycoprotiens on their blood cells. People with type B blood have B glycoprotiens. People with type AB blood have both glycoprotiens. People with blood type O do not have either A or B glycoprotiens. The three alleles for human blood types are I^A, I^B, and i. Alleles I^A and I^B are dominant over i. However, I^A and I^B are co-dominant and are expressed equally.

Table 4.2
Human blood types

Phenotype (blood type)	Genotypes
A	$I^A I^A$ or $I^A i$
B	$I^B I^B$ or $I^B i$
AB	$I^A I^B$
0	ii

There are two possible genotypes for blood types A and B, one homozygous, and one heterozygous. In order to have type AB blood, a person would have to inherit one I^A and one I^B allele. People with type O blood must inherit two ii alleles. You will learn about the inheritance of human blood-related illnesses in Chapter 7.

Human blood type is only one example of a trait that is governed by more than one pair of alleles. Some traits are controlled by far greater numbers of alleles. These types of traits are the result of

Sample Problem

Human Blood Types

If a woman has blood type AB, and a man has blood type A, what possible blood types will their children have?

What is required?

You are asked to determine the possible genotypes of offspring from a cross.

What is given?

You know the genotype of the mother (AB) and father (A). The possible gametes from the mother are $I^A I^B$. The possible gametes from the father are $I^A I^A$ if he is homozygous or $I^A i$ if he is heterozygous.

Plan your strategy

You must make the following crosses:
$I^A I^B \times I^A I^A$
$I^A I^B \times I^A i$

Act on your strategy

Place the alleles of each parent along the columns and rows of the Punnett square and complete the possible crosses. If the father is blood type A homozygous, then:

	Mother I^A	I^B
Father I^A	$I^A I^A$	$I^A I^B$
I^A	$I^A I^A$	$I^A I^B$

If father is blood type A heterozygous, then:

	Mother I^A	I^B
Father I^A	$I^A I^A$	$I^A I^B$
i	$I^A i$	$I^B i$

There are four possible genotypes: $I^A I^A$, $I^A I^B$, $I^A i$, $I^B i$. (Note: the genotypes $I^A I^A$ and $I^A i$ will both produce the same phenotype — type A blood). Thus, the possible blood types of the children are: A, AB, and B.

Check your solution

If the father is homozygous, the possible blood types of the children are A and AB. If the father is heterozygous, the possible blood types of the children are A, AB, and B.

Practice Problems

1. A man has blood type A and his wife has blood type B. A child has blood type O. Could these individuals be the parents of this child? Explain.

2. Suppose a man with blood type B marries a woman with type AB blood. What blood types would you expect to find among their children? What could tell you whether the man was homozygous or heterozygous for the B blood type?

3. In foxes, a pair of alleles, P and p, interact as follows: PP is lethal, usually during the embryonic stage; Pp produces platinum-coloured fur, and pp produces silver foxes. Could a fox breeder establish a true-breeding variety of platinum foxes? Explain.

multiple gene inheritance and are very complex. Skin colour is a good example of this type of inheritance. There are many more than just the two or three phenotypes attributed to skin colour. In fact there may be several phenotypes, or even a continuous variation that cannot be split up into convenient, easily defined categories. The more genes that contribute to a single trait, the greater the number of categories of the trait, with increasingly fine differences between the categories. These complex patterns of inheritance will be addressed in the next chapter.

Since Mendel's time, knowledge of the mechanisms that control the inheritance of traits has developed considerably. It is now understood that the inheritance of one allele can, at times, affect the inheritance of a second allele, or can affect how and when a trait is expressed in an individual. As you have learned not all inheritance follows the simple dominant-recessive pattern. In incomplete dominance, heterozygotes exhibit an intermediate phenotype between the two contrasting phenotypes. Co-dominant alleles, such as those determining blood type, are both present in the phenotype of heterozygous individuals. Many traits are determined by several alleles.

COURSE CHALLENGE

Blood types are often used to help establish the identity of people. How could blood types be used to help determine the presence of disease or as evidence in criminal investigations?

THINKING LAB

Inheritance of Coat Colour in Rabbits

Background

Coat colour in rabbits is governed by four different alleles. Each allele is responsible for producing a different coat colour: dark grey, Chinchilla, Himalayan, and white. Each rabbit has only two alleles. Study the relationship among the alleles in the table and then complete the lab.

Phenotype (coat colour)	Allele	Pattern of inheritance
Dark grey	C	dominant to all other alleles
Chinchilla	c^{ch}	dominant to Himalayan and to white
Himalayan	c^h	dominant to white
White	c	recessive

You Try It

1. List all the possible genotypes for a
   (a) dark grey rabbit
   (b) Chinchilla rabbit
   (c) Himalayan rabbit
   (d) white rabbit

2. Predict the phenotype of a rabbit with the following genotypes. Explain your answers.
   (a) $c^h c^{ch}$ (b) Cc^h

3. Would it be possible to obtain white rabbits if one parent is white and the other is Chinchilla? Explain.

4. Would it be possible to obtain Chinchilla rabbits if one parent is Himalayan and the other is white? Explain.

5. A Chinchilla rabbit is mated with a Himalayan. Some of the offspring are white. What are the parents' genotypes?

SECTION REVIEW

1. **K/U** Define the following terms: carrier, incomplete dominance, co-dominance, multiple allele inheritance, multiple gene inheritance.

2. **K/U** Explain the law of probability as it applies to the inheritance of different traits.

3. **I** Tay Sachs disease is the result of two recessive alleles. Frank's brother died from Tay Sachs disease, but Frank is healthy. Stephanie's brother died from Tay Sachs disease but Stephanie is healthy.

    (a) If Frank and Stephanie have a child, what is the probability that the child will inherit Tay Sachs disease?

    (b) If Frank and Stephanie have a child, what is the probability that the child will not inherit the disorder?

4. **C** Explain how an individual can be a carrier for a particular disease yet not have the disease. Is this explanation true for all people who are carriers?

5. **K/U** Differentiate between co-dominance and multiple allele inheritance.

6. **C** How many different genotypes of the human blood type are possible? Explain. How many different phenotypes are possible? Why are these numbers different? Explain.

7. **MC** A woman sues a man for the support of her child. She has blood type A, her child has type O, and the man has type B. Could the man be the father? Explain your answer.

8. **I** The Punnett square shows a dihybrid cross of F_1 pea plants. Purple flowers (P) are dominant and white flowers are recessive. Tall plants (T) are dominant and short plants are recessive. Determine the phenotype ratios of the F_2 generation. What Mendelian law does this ratio demonstrate?

Female gametes

	PT	Pt	pT	pt
PT	PPTT	PPTt	PpTT	PpTt
Pt	PPTt	PPtt	PPTt	Pptt
pT	PpTT	PpTt	ppTT	ppTt
pt	PpTt	Pptt	ppTt	pptt

Male gametes

9. **I** A mother with blood type AB has a child with the same blood type. What are the possible genotypes of the father?

10. **MC** Mrs. Doe and Mrs. Roe had babies at the same time. Mrs. Doe took home a girl and named her Nancy. Mrs. Roe received a boy and named him Richard. However, Mrs. Roe was sure she had a girl, and sued the hospital. Blood tests showed that Mr. Roe was type O and Mrs. Roe was type AB. Mr. and Mrs. Doe were both type B. Nancy was type A and Richard was type O. Had an exchange occurred? Explain your answer.

11. **I** A rose-combed rooster is mated with two rose-combed hens. Hen A produces 14 chicks, all rose-combed. Hen B produces 9 chicks, 7 of which are rose-combed and 2 single-combed. What are the likely genotypes of the parent birds? Explain.

12. **I** In four o'clock plants, red flowers are incompletely dominant over white flowers. The heterozygous flowers are pink. If a red-flowered four o'clock plant is crossed with a white-flowered four o'clock plant, what will be the flower colour of

    (a) the F_1 generation?

    (b) the F_1 generation crossed with its red parent?

    (c) the F_1 generation crossed with its white parent?

UNIT ISSUE PREP

If you have decided to investigate research into inheritance of complex traits in your Unit 2 Issue Analysis, make sure you are familiar with the different models of inheritance of traits.

Chapter Expectations

Briefly explain each of the following points.

- People before Mendel could not adequately explain how traits were inherited. (4.1)
- A dominant trait is always expressed in an individual. (4.2)
- A homozygous individual is either dominant or recessive for a particular trait. (4.2)
- Punnett squares can be used to determine the outcome of crosses. (4.2)
- In pea plants, Mendel found that the inheritance of one trait was not influenced by the inheritance of another trait. (4.3)
- The law of independent assortment is based on a particular phenotypic ratio in the F_2 generation. (4.3)
- Exceptions to simple Mendelian genetics include incomplete dominance and co-dominance. (4.4)

Language of Biology

Write a sentence using each of the following words or terms. Use any six terms in a concept map to show your understanding of how they are related.

- traits
- inherited
- genetics
- purebred
- true breeding
- P generation
- filial generation
- F_1 generation
- hybrid
- monohybrid
- dominant
- recessive
- principle of dominance
- F_2 generation
- Mendelian ratio
- law of segregation
- genes
- alleles
- homozygous
- heterozygous
- probability
- Punnett square
- genotype
- phenotype
- Mendelian ratio for genotype
- pedigree
- simple dominant trait
- carrier
- test cross
- dihybrid cross
- law of independent assortment
- incomplete dominance
- co-dominant
- multiple alleles

UNDERSTANDING CONCEPTS

1. In your notebook, state whether each of the following statements is true or false. Correct each false statement.
   (a) Heredity is the branch of biology dealing with the principles of variation in plants and animals.
   (b) Gregor Mendel is credited with developing the fundamental principles of genetics.
   (c) The 1 : 2 : 1 ratio is a ratio of phenotypes in a dihybrid cross.
   (d) A hybrid is an organism that is a cross between two different purebred plants.
   (e) The second filial generation is the offspring of the parent generation.
   (f) The Punnett square is a graphical way of illustrating all the possible combinations of gametes.
   (g) The genotype of an organism describes the physical appearance of the particular characteristic under study.

2. Fundamental to our understanding of inheritance is the knowledge of what happens during the process of cell division. What is the genetic significance of meiosis in terms of heredity?

3. Explain the meanings of Mendel's principle of segregation and principle of independent assortment. Under what circumstances does the principle of independent assortment hold true? Give an example in which this law does not apply.

4. What is the difference between a phenotype and a genotype? Does knowledge of an organism's phenotype always lead you to determine the correct genotype? Explain.

5. Explain, using examples, the difference between incomplete dominance and co-dominance.

6. Multiple allele inheritance acknowledges that there are more than two alleles for a given gene. If this is true, why is it not possible to have more than one genotype and phenotype for those characteristics in question?

7. Sometimes we are able to tell the genotype of an organism by knowing the phenotype. In the case of Mendel's pea plants, for example, round seeds (R) are dominant over wrinkled seeds (r).

   (a) For which of the plants carrying various combinations of these traits could you tell the genotype by observation alone? Explain.

   (b) Mendel worked out a method for determining the genotype when he could not tell just by looking at the phenotype alone. What was the system he developed? Explain the genotypes he determined using this system.

8. A pedigree is a diagram that shows how a particular trait is transmitted from generation to generation in a family. Symbols are used to denote males and females with shading to show those who are affected with the trait under study. Complete the pedigree below. Use the defined symbols to determine the genotype (or possible genotypes) of each individual in the pedigree. The couple in the first generation of the pedigree shown below are both carriers of the tongue-rolling trait (they cannot roll their tongues). Assume that each descendent of the couple marries an individual who is not a tongue-roller.

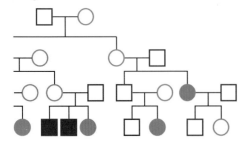

9. Your aunt dies and leaves you her mouse Henry. To obtain some money from your inheritance, you decide to breed the mouse and sell the offspring. In looking over Henry's family history, you discover that Henry's grandfather exhibited a rare genetic disorder, which leads to brittle bones. This disorder is hereditary and is the result of being homozygous for the recessive allele (bb). Based on this information, you realize that there is a possibility that Henry could be heterozygous for the allele. If this is the case, the genetic condition may be passed on to his offspring.

   (a) What method could you use to determine if Henry is heterozygous and carries the recessive allele (b)?

   (b) Using the method you described in question (a), determine which phenotypes and genotypes you would expect to see if Henry is heterozygous or if he is homozygous dominant.

10. The results of monohybrid and dihybrid crosses are fairly easy to predict. We can use the same general principle to find the possible genotypes and phenotypes of offspring from crosses in which three, four, or more traits are involved independently of each other. Show what happens in a cross involving three independent traits at once. Find the ratios of the phenotypes in each case. Black fur (B) is dominant to brown fur (b) in hamsters. Short fur (A) is dominant over long fur (a). Rough coat (R) is dominant over smooth coat (r).

    (a) What happens when a hamster that is homozygous dominant for all three traits is crossed with a hamster that is homozygous recessive for all three traits? Use a Punnett square to determine your answer.

    (b) Determine the genotypes and phenotypes of the offspring of a cross between two organisms from the F_1 generation.

11. Mendel proposed much of his genetic theories based on results he obtained from crossing various pea plants. He crossed a tall pea plant with a short pea plant and observed that all the offspring were tall. From this observation he proposed his law of dominance. How would Mendel's laws have been altered if,

(a) the results of his cross were all short pea plants?

(b) the results of his cross were all plants of medium height?

(c) the results of his cross were plants of many different heights?

COMMUNICATING

12. When we determine genetic ratios that exist among the offspring of different crosses, we are working with probability. Determine the probability of each in the following problems.

(a) A couple are both tested and found to be carriers of the cystic fibrosis gene (cystic fibrosis is a disease caused by the inheritance of two recessive genes). If they have two children, what is the chance that both children will be affected by cystic fibrosis?

(b) What is the chance that both children will be carriers of the trait?

(c) What is the chance that the couple will have two girls who are both affected by cystic fibrosis?

13. The tobacco plant illustrates single gene inheritance. How would you set up an experiment to determine the inheritance of two different characteristics?

14. A wealthy elderly couple dies together in an accident. Soon a man appears to claim their fortune, contending that he is their only child. Other relatives dispute this claim. Hospital records show that the deceased couple had blood types AB and O respectively. The claimant to the fortune is type O. Do you think the claimant is an impostor? Explain your answer.

15. Yellow guinea pigs crossed with white ones always produce cream-coloured offspring. When two cream-coloured guinea pigs are crossed, they produce yellow, cream, and white offspring in the ratio of 1 yellow : 2 cream : 1 white. How are these colours inherited? Explain.

16. The figure shows the results of two crosses. Explain what is being depicted and what genetic principle is illustrated.

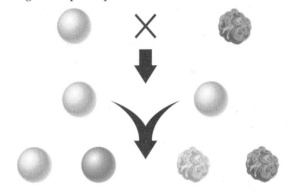

MAKING CONNECTIONS

17. Mendel chose to conduct his research on the commercial pea plant. What do you think would have happened if he had chosen a different specimen on which to conduct his research?

18. People who are heterozygous for a recessive condition do not express the trait, but may pass it on to their children. Do we have a responsibility to inform our children of certain recessive traits they may have inherited? Present your thoughts in a one page essay.

Cellular Reproduction and Chromosomes

Reflecting Questions

- What is the function of mitosis?
- How are eggs and sperm formed?
- What processes contribute to genetic variation?

What is responsible for your eye colour, a crab's hard shell, the scent of a rose, or a cheetah's spotted fur? The answer to this question lies in the cells of each of these organisms. Cells contain genetic information, or genes, which form the basis for the inheritance of traits. Genes are passed from one cell to the next through a process of cell division. However, do all cells contain the same genes? Does a human skin cell contain the same genes as a human brain cell? Do both sperm and egg cells contain the same genes? Where can we find the genes for hair colour?

Research into the mechanisms of cell division has become more and more intricate with the advancement of technology. In less than 150 years, the study of genetics has progressed from Mendel's discovery of genetic "factors" in 1865 to the use of computers to analyze huge amounts of genetic data. Some genetic discoveries have created ethical dilemmas that weigh heavily on the minds of many people. We are faced with two challenges: thinking about the implications of new discoveries, and solving these ethical dilemmas in ways that will help both present and future populations.

New cells are produced throughout your life. This is necessary for growth, maintenance, and repair of your body. In this chapter, you will explore the processes by which cells reproduce and how genetic information is transmitted from cell to cell. In addition, you will discover how sex cells, sperm and eggs, are produced, and the basis for variation among individuals. Finally, you will learn about the theory of inheritance and how certain traits have a pattern of inheritance that is more complex than simple Mendelian genetics.

Chromosomes within the nucleus of a cell contain genetic information. How is this information transmitted from one cell to another?

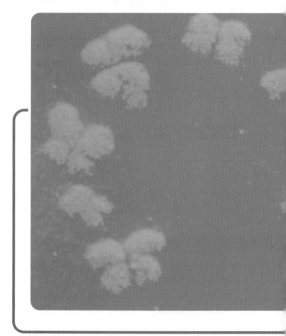

Chapter Contents

How Body Cells Reproduce

- Demonstrate an understanding of the cell cycle and the process and importance of mitosis.

- Perform laboratory investigations to study the processes of mitosis.

- Organize data that illustrate the number of chromosomes in various cells.

Figure 5.1 The number of cells in these frog embryos will double each time cell division takes place.

Recently, researchers in Pennsylvania discovered that a chemical compound in raw garlic can affect how certain body cells reproduce. Preliminary studies show that this compound, diallyl disulfide, can slow the rate at which cancer cells multiply. Somehow diallyl disulfide blocks cancer-causing compounds and thus reduces the growth of a cancerous tumour. The key to understanding how such chemical compounds can affect cells lies in knowing how cells reproduce. Figure 5.1 shows two balls of cells, frog embryos, that are in the early stage of development. How are body cells produced? Do all body cells form the same way?

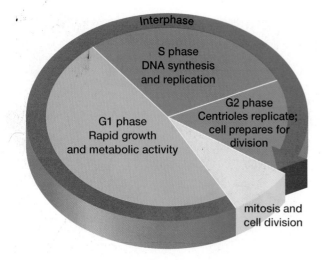

Figure 5.2 The cell cycle. Interphase is the growth stage, and mitosis and cell division are the division stage.

The Cell Cycle

Cells reproduce through a continuous sequence of growth and division known as the **cell cycle**. The cell cycle consists of two main stages, the growth stage and the division stage (as shown in Figure 5.2). In the growth stage, called **interphase**, the cell makes new molecules, which increases the cell's volume and mass. DNA (deoxyribonucleic acid), the molecule that forms the genetic blueprint of the cell, is copied during interphase in a process known as DNA replication. You will learn more about the process of DNA replication in Chapter 6.

During the first part of interphase, called gap 1 (G1), cells are carrying out metabolic activities to prepare for the synthesis phase (S phase). DNA is replicated during the S phase of the cell cycle. Scientists are very interested in what stimulates a cell to progress from G1 to S phase. Once a cell has completed the G1 phase, it can either progress to S phase or enter a rest phase. Cells that enter a rest phase can still function, but they do not progress through the entire cell cycle and therefore no new cells are produced.

Cells that progress through the S phase then enter the last segment of interphase, called gap 2 (G2). During the G2 phase, cells are preparing to undergo division. The division stage involves two processes: **mitosis** (division of the cell's nucleus) and cell division. These two processes are the shortest events in the cycle of a cell. Cell division involves division of the cytoplasm of the cell to form two new cells.

How does the cell cycle vary among different kinds of cells? The timing of the cell cycle and the lengths of the different phases depend on the type of cell and its environment. Study Figure 5.3, which shows the cell cycle for two different types of cells. What can you infer about the roles of each of these cells? Think about the different kinds of cells that make up the body of a bird, for example. Some cells are skin cells while others may be bone, muscle, or organ cells. Why might the cycle of some kinds of cells be faster than the cycle of others?

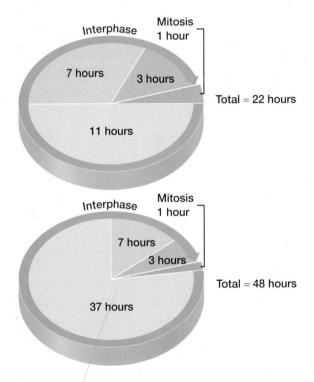

Figure 5.3 Different types of cells spend different relative lengths of time in the phases of the cell cycle.

What is the Function of Mitosis?

The giant pumpkin shown in Figure 5.4 has a mass of several hundred kg. It began life as a single cell and is now made up of billions of cells. How did the pumpkin grow so large? In order for an organism to grow, repair, and maintain its functions, new cells are needed. Each cell that undergoes mitosis will divide to produce two new cells. As mitosis and cell division occur, the pumpkin grows and the

BIO FACT

The life span of a cell in the lining of the stomach wall is only two days. The life span of a brain cell is 30–50 years.

number of cells increases throughout the fruit. Through the process of mitosis and cell division, organisms can also regenerate damaged tissues. Every time you cut your finger, mitosis and cell division form new skin cells over the injured area. In certain cases, some organisms can regenerate entire body parts that have been lost. For example, when a starfish loses an arm as a result of an attack by a predator, a new arm is regenerated through the process of mitosis and cell division (see Figure 5.5). Mitosis and cell division are also necessary for maintenance of the body. Some cells need to be replaced because they cannot function properly. Others are replaced when they die. For instance, in the average person, millions of red blood cells die every day. These are replaced by new blood cells that are formed through mitosis and cell division.

Figure 5.4 This pumpkin required only four months to grow to this enormous size.

Figure 5.5 This starfish lost three arms. It was able to regenerate them through the process of mitosis and cell division.

Mitosis and cell division occur in all somatic (body) cells. New cells that are produced for growth or repair are identical to the previously existing cells. For example, if skin cells are damaged, they are replaced with new skin cells — not cells of a different kind. The instructions to form each new cell are stored in the nucleus of the cell. **Chromosomes** within the nucleus hold the genetic information needed to maintain the cell and to make new copies of the cell. Figure 5.6 shows a typical chromosome in a body cell. Each chromosome is made up of two **sister chromatids**, which are held together by a **centromere**. Sister chromatids are genetic copies of each other; that is, the DNA in one sister chromatid is identical to the DNA in the other. Why is a copy of DNA necessary in a cell? How is this information passed from one cell to the next? You will consider these questions in the next Thinking Lab.

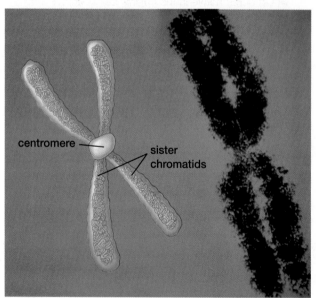

centromere

sister chromatids

Magnification: 97 875x

Figure 5.6 A chromosome is made up of two sister chromatids that are joined by a centromere. This chromosome is ready to undergo mitosis.

The function of mitosis is to maintain the same number of chromosomes from cell to cell. During cell division, the original or **parent cell** divides to produce two new **daughter cells**. Mitosis ensures that each daughter cell contains the same number of chromosomes and the same genetic information as the parent cell. A body cell contains two copies of every chromosome. During mitosis, a parent cell produces two identical daughter cells. For example, your skin cells, like all of your somatic cells, have 46 chromosomes (two copies of each chromosome). Before mitosis, the parent skin cell has 46 chromosomes. After mitosis, the resulting two new daughter skin cells also each have 46 chromosomes. This is important because each new skin cell must have a complete set of genetic instructions to maintain itself and to produce new skin cells.

Word LINK

The word "somatic" comes from the Greek word *soma*, meaning body.

◄◄ REWIND

To review the structure and function of various cell organelles, turn to Chapter 2, Section 2.1.

The Phases of Mitosis

Several events must occur during mitosis to maintain the same number of chromosomes from parent cell to daughter cells. These events, or phases, can be observed most easily in the rapidly growing areas of plant and animal tissues. For example, the root tip is an area of the onion that grows rapidly and therefore contains cells that undergo mitosis frequently. At any given time, many onion root tip cells are in different phases of mitosis. Although these phases are continuous, for convenience they are divided into four main phases ordered according to the sequence in which they occur. The phases are called prophase, metaphase, anaphase, and telophase. Each phase is characterized by a particular arrangement of the chromosomes within the cell and by the appearance or disappearance of other cell structures. Refer to Figure 5.7 on page 156 to help you understand the various phases of mitosis.

Prophase

Mitosis begins with the first of the four stages called **prophase** (Figure 5.7). During prophase, chromatin, which is made up of DNA and proteins, condenses and thickens to form visible duplicated chromosomes. At this stage, each chromosome, having been replicated (copied) during S phase of interphase, is X-shaped. Each half of the X is one copy of the original chromosome. Since the two halves are connected, they are still considered part of a single chromosome. Recall that the chromosome is made up of two chromatids that are held together by a centromere. Because there is a copy of each chromosome (two chromatids), it is possible for each of the daughter cells to receive a full set of the parent cell's genes. If this copying had not occurred, each of the daughter cells would get only half of

the parent cell's genes when the chromosomes divide in mitosis. Other structures in the cell are also changing during prophase. The nuclear membrane and the nucleolus disappear. Centrioles made up of microtubules migrate to opposite poles of the cell. Spindle fibres, also made of microtubules, start to form between the two centrioles.

 THINKING LAB

How Does Mitosis Work to Generate New Cells?

Background

These diagrams show onion root tip cells before and after mitosis. The onion root tip cell at the beginning of mitosis has 16 duplicated chromosomes, each consisting of two chromatids. The two daughter cells at the end of mitosis also have 16 chromosomes each. (Note that a chromatid is half of a duplicated chromosome. After chromatids separate into different cells, they are called chromosomes again.)

You Try It

Study the diagrams of the onion root tip cells shown. Compare the number of chromosomes in cell 1 with the number of chromosomes in cells 2 and 3, and answer the following questions.

1. What do you notice about the number of chromosomes in cells 1, 2, and 3? How is it possible to start with

16 chromosomes in cell 1 and end with 16 chromosomes in each of cell 2 and cell 3? Explain briefly.

2. What do you notice about the characteristics of each chromosome in cells 1, 2, and 3?

3. Do you think there are other cellular structures (that are not visible using the light microscope) involved in the process that takes the chromosomes from cell 1 and divides them between cell 2 and cell 3? If so, hypothesize their role in mitosis.

4. Predict each change in chromosome arrangement that would occur between the original cell 1 and the two new cells 2 and 3. Draw at least five individual cells to illustrate these changes. (Hint: If cell 2 and cell 3 contain the same genetic information, how will the chromosomes have to be arranged to be equally divided between cell 2 and cell 3?)

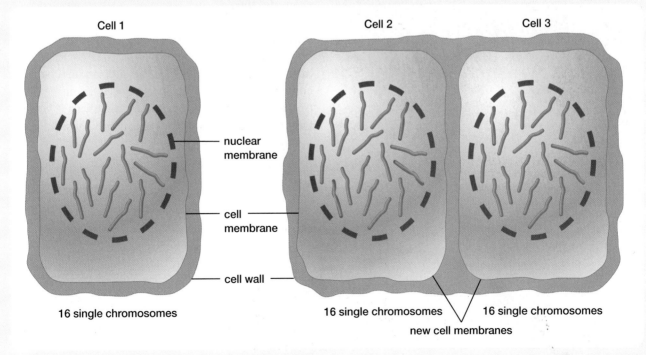

Cell 1 — nuclear membrane — cell membrane — cell wall — 16 single chromosomes

Cell 2 — Cell 3 — 16 single chromosomes — 16 single chromosomes — new cell membranes

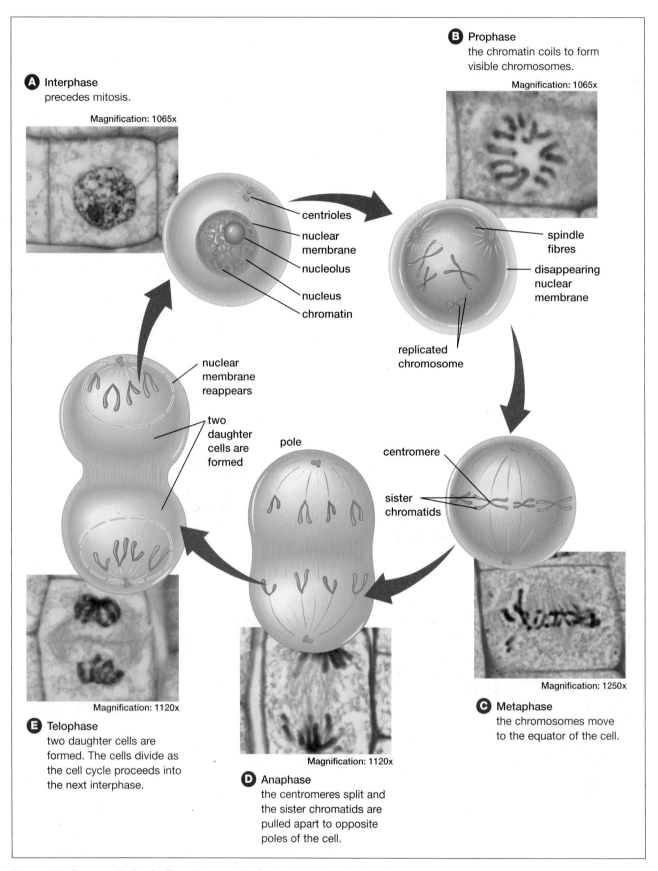

A Interphase
precedes mitosis.

Magnification: 1065x

B Prophase
the chromatin coils to form
visible chromosomes.

Magnification: 1065x

centrioles

nuclear
membrane

nucleolus

nucleus

chromatin

spindle
fibres

disappearing
nuclear
membrane

replicated
chromosome

nuclear
membrane
reappears

two
daughter
cells are
formed

pole

centromere

sister
chromatids

Magnification: 1250x

Magnification: 1120x

E Telophase
two daughter cells are
formed. The cells divide as
the cell cycle proceeds into
the next interphase.

Magnification: 1120x

D Anaphase
the centromeres split and
the sister chromatids are
pulled apart to opposite
poles of the cell.

C Metaphase
the chromosomes move
to the equator of the cell.

Figure 5.7 Phases of mitosis. The diagrams illustrate mitosis in animal cells.
The photographs show mitosis in plant cells.

Metaphase

The second phase of mitosis is called **metaphase** (Figure 5.7). During metaphase, the spindle fibres attach to the centromere of the replicated chromosomes. The chromatids are guided by the spindle fibres to the middle of the cell, also known as the cell's equator. A spindle fibre from one pole is attached to one chromatid and a spindle fibre from the opposite pole is attached to the other chromatid at the centromere. Each chromatid has its own spindle fibre attachment in order to ensure that each new daughter cell will contain one of each of the chromatids (and therefore the same genetic information).

Anaphase

The third phase of mitosis is called **anaphase** (Figure 5.7). During anaphase, the centromere splits apart and the chromatids are pulled to opposite poles of the cell by the spindle fibres. The chromatids are pulled apart as a result of the shortening of the microtubules that make up the spindle fibres.

Telophase

The fourth and last phase of mitosis is called **telophase** (Figure 5.7). Telophase begins when the chromatids have reached the two opposite poles within the cell. At this time, each of the chromatids is called a single, non-replicated chromosome. The chromosomes now begin to unwind and become less visible.

Cytokinesis

Cell division occurs after mitosis. The separation of the cytoplasm and the formation of two new daughter cells is called **cytokinesis**. As part of this process, the spindle fibres are no longer needed, so they break down and disappear. The nucleolus reappears. A nuclear membrane forms around each new set of chromosomes, which are located at the opposite poles of the cell. The cytoplasm (and all of its contents) divides between the two halves of the cell (see Figure 5.8). The final structure to form is the cell membrane. In plant cells, a cell wall forms and separates the two newly formed nuclei, as shown in Figure 5.9. After cytokinesis is complete, two new daughter cells have been formed. In the next MiniLab, you will observe and draw the stages of mitosis in a prepared slide of onion root cells.

> PLAY

To see an animation of the process of mitosis and cell division, refer to the Electronic Learning Partner. This can help you if you are having difficulty visualizing the different stages of mitosis.

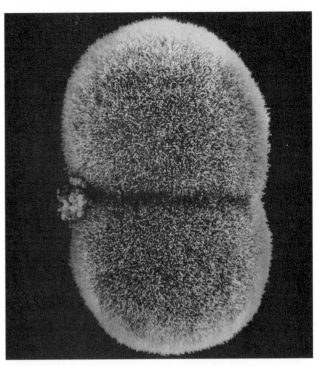

Figure 5.8 This animal cell is undergoing cytokinesis. The cell pinches inward to divide the cytoplasm equally between the two daughter cells.

Figure 5.9 Daughter cells in plants are separated by a cell wall.

Math
LINK

How long does it take to complete each phase of mitosis? From a prepared slide of onion root tip cells, select 30 cells at random and identify the phase in each. Determine the number of cells in each phase and present your findings as a ratio. Which phase requires the most time to complete? Which phase requires the least time to complete? Suggest possible explanations for your answers.

Errors in Mitosis

A serious error can occur if the mitotic process is disrupted by **mutations**. Mutations can be caused by various mutagens, such as toxic compounds, radiation, or viruses. Mutations cause a permanent error, or change, in the normal DNA molecule. For example, certain chemical compounds found in cigarette smoke can alter the structure of chromosomes in an individual parent cell. These mutations are copied during prophase, when DNA replication takes place. When sister chromatids segregate during anaphase, the mutation is passed to the daughter cells. This mutation will only be found in daughter cells produced from the parent cell that contained the mutation. Therefore, the mutation is found in a localized group of cells

rather than in every cell in the body. For example, toxic compounds found in cigarette smoke can cause a change in a gene known as FHIT on chromosome number three in humans. In the lungs, cells containing the mutated form of the FHIT gene undergo mitosis much more frequently than normal lung cells. This results in a mass of cells called a tumour (see Figure 5.10).

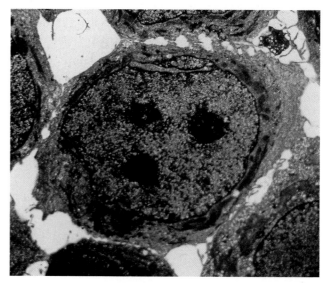

Figure 5.10 This photomicrograph shows uncontrolled mitosis that resulted in a cancerous tumour. What do you notice about this cell that is unusual?

MINI LAB

Observing the Stages of Mitosis in Onion Root Tip Cells

Obtain a prepared slide of onion root tip cells from your teacher. Observe a section of onion root tip cells under the high-power setting of a compound light microscope. For proper care and use of a microscope, turn to *Appendix* 3. Find cells that are similar to each of the phases of mitosis shown in Figure 5.7 on page 156. Make sketches of at least ten onion root tip cells that have different chromosomal arrangements. Organize your drawings into four groups according to where the chromosomes are located in the cell. For example, cells with chromosomes mainly in the centre of the cell should be grouped together.

Analyze

1. List the characteristics that you used to form the four groups of the onion root tip cells.

2. What are the similarities and differences between your grouped drawings of the onion root tip cells and your drawings from the Thinking Lab on page 155? Write a short essay explaining your findings.

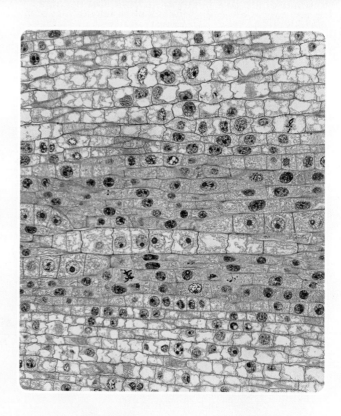

Certain genes work like switches to regulate the rate of mitosis. If these genes are altered by a mutation, the rate of mitosis will also be affected. For example, once a cell has completed its cell cycle, certain genes are "switched on," or activated. These genes produce proteins that stop the process of mitosis. When these genes are "switched off," or inactivated, mitosis can continue and the cell can divide to produce new cells. A mutation could permanently inactivate these genes. As a result, the cell could begin to divide uncontrollably.

The rate of mitosis can also be regulated through genes that start cell division. A mutation could cause these genes to be "switched on" permanently, which would cause uncontrolled cell division. Genes that can be activated by a mutation are called **oncogenes**. For example, retinoblastoma is a retinal cancer that is either inherited or results from a mutation to both copies of the retinoblastoma gene. This mutation results in the formation of a tumour on the retina of the eye.

Wilms tumour is a cancer that can develop as a result of a mutation to the Wilms tumour gene in a kidney cell. Breast cancer is another example of a mutation to both breast cancer 1 (BRCA1) genes. You will learn more about how mutations affect human health in Chapter 7.

SECTION REVIEW

1. **K/U** What is the purpose of mitosis?

2. **K/U** Explain why the DNA that makes up two sister chromatids is identical.

3. **K/U** How can mutations lead to changes in the cell cycle?

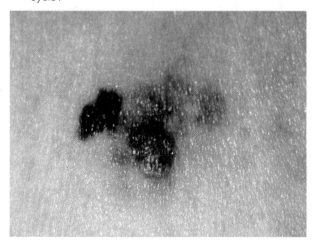

4. **MC** A person notices a dark spot on their skin. This dark spot turns out to be skin cancer. What could have caused the start of the skin cancer tumour and how was mitosis and cell division of these cells affected?

5. **MC** How would a cure for skin cancer possibly work to stop the occurrence of skin tumours?

6. **C** Summarize each phase of mitosis. Use sketches to illustrate your explanations.

7. **K/U** In what areas of a plant would mitosis occur most frequently? Explain why.

8. **K/U** At what time of year would mitosis in a plant occur most frequently? Explain why.

9. **K/U** What would happen to the chromosome number in a cell if that cell does not go through S phase of the cell cycle?

10. **K/U** Why is the process of cytokinesis necessary to ensure the normal functioning of a cell?

11. **K/U** Explain why different kinds of cells in the body might live for different lengths of time.

12. **I** Cancerous cells require less time to complete a cell cycle than do normal cells of the same kind. (The time required to complete interphase and prophase is substantially shortened). What is the importance of these observations? Develop one hypothesis that a scientist might test if they were looking to control cancer.

How Reproductive Cells Are Produced

EXPECTATIONS

- Demonstrate an understanding of the process and importance of meiosis.
- Investigate the processes of meiosis in Easter lilies.
- Investigate the number of chromosomes in cells before, during, and after meiosis.
- Compare the processes of mitosis and meiosis.

Figure 5.11 Every person receives characteristics from both their parents.

Look around you at the diversity of individuals in your neighbourhood, classroom, or home. Other than identical twins, every individual in the world is unique. Diversity exists between sisters, brothers, and even between you and your parents. Diversity is not limited to people, however — all species of organisms show diversity.

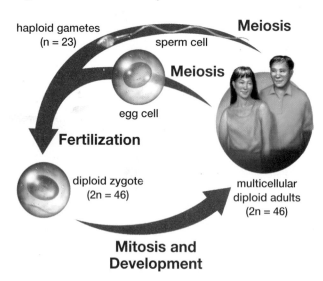

Figure 5.12 The human life cycle

Word LINK

The word "meiosis" comes from the Greek word *meion*, which means to diminish.

What is the Function of Meiosis?

From earlier studies, you learned that reproduction involves the union of two cells to form a zygote (see Figure 5.12). The zygote contains chromosomes from both parents, but it does not contain double the number of chromosomes found in a normal body cell. How is this possible? The answer lies in a process called **meiosis**. Meiosis is a special type of cell division that occurs only in reproductive organs. Meiosis produces reproductive cells called gametes. The gametes, either eggs or sperm, are **haploid** (n), which means they contain only one copy of each type of chromosome that the **diploid** (2n) parent cell contains.

The first part of meiosis reduces the chromosome number from diploid to haploid. This is often referred to as **reduction division**. For example, human sperm cells contain n = 23 chromosomes compared to the 2n = 46 chromosomes found in all somatic cells. Each human sperm or egg cell contains 22 **autosomes** and one **sex chromosome** (either an X or a Y chromosome). Autosomes are chromosomes that are not directly involved in determining the sex of an individual. Females have two X chromosomes and males have one X and one Y chromosome. Table 5.1 shows the number of chromosomes for a variety of organisms. What do you notice about the diploid number of chromosomes for each organism?

Table 5.1
Chromosome numbers of some common organisms

Organism	Diploid body cell (2n)	Haploid gamete (n)
Fruit fly	8	4
Garden pea	14	7
Corn	20	10
Tomato	24	12
Leopard frog	26	13
Apple	34	17
Human	46	23
Chimpanzee	48	24
Dog	78	39
Adder's tongue fern	1260	630

‖ PAUSE ● RECORD

Review the phases of mitosis and predict the changes that must occur in these phases to accomplish reduction division from a diploid parent cell to a haploid gamete cell. Refer to Figure 5.7 on page 156 to help with your predictions.

⟩⟩ FAST FORWARD

To learn more about the evolution of organisms and the importance of genetic variation, turn to Chapter 11, Section 11.4.

Phases of Meiosis

Study Figure 5.13 on the next page, which shows the phases of meiosis. Meiosis involves a sequence of phases that is similar to mitosis: prophase, metaphase, anaphase, and telophase. However, meiosis involves two sequences of these phases, called meiosis I and meiosis II. Select a pair of chromosomes to follow through each phase of meiosis. In your notebook, describe briefly what is happening during each phase. How are the chromosomes arranged in each phase? Use your knowledge of mitosis to describe what events must have occurred to create the different chromosomal arrangements from one phase to the next. How many cells are produced at the end of meiosis II? After you have completed your notes, read the following sections describing the details of each phase of meiosis.

Interphase

Recall that in mitosis, the chromosomes replicate during interphase before cell division begins. This also occurs before meiosis I begins. During replication, the chromosomes are not condensed and are not easily visible. After replication, each chromosome is made up of a pair of identical sister chromatids. The sister chromatids are joined together by a centromere.

Prophase I

In prophase I, similar chromosomes called **homologous chromosomes** pair to form homologous pairs. The homologous pair, which is made up of four chromatids, is called a **tetrad**. The term "tetrad" is from the Greek word *tetra* meaning four. Where does each member of a homologous pair come from? Each diploid cell has two copies of each chromosome. One copy of the chromosome pair was "donated" by the female gamete (egg), and the other copy of the chromosome was "donated" by the male gamete (sperm). During fertilization, the union of gametes forms a diploid zygote. All the cells in your body contain copies of chromosomes of this original diploid zygote. Therefore, each cell has one copy of each of your mother's chromosomes (maternal origin) and one copy of each of your father's chromosomes (paternal origin).

‖ PAUSE ● RECORD

How are homologous chromosomes similar to a pair of shoes? Look at your shoes and those of your classmates. Imagine the classroom now represents a diploid cell populated with shoe "chromosomes." Compare the left and right shoes of one pair. What do you notice about the shape of each shoe, the laces or tying device, markings, and so on?

Like a pair of shoes, homologous chromosomes are similar to each other but they are not identical. The chromosomes are homologous because they are made up of the same genes. However, although homologous chromosomes contain the same genes, they may have different forms of these genes, called alleles. Recall from Chapter 4 that alleles can be recessive or dominant, which can determine whether a trait is expressed or not.

During the pairing process, **crossing over** of chromatids can occur, in which **non-sister chromatids** exchange genes, as shown in Figure 5.14 on page 163. This allows for the recombination of genes in each chromosome and

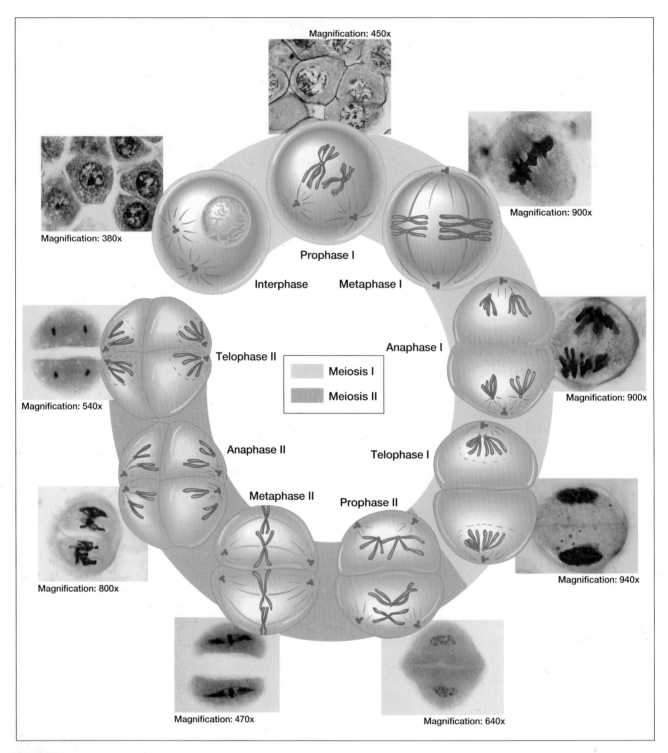

Figure 5.13 Phases of meiosis

Magnification: 450x

Magnification: 900x

Magnification: 380x

Prophase I

Interphase Metaphase I

Anaphase I

Meiosis I

Meiosis II

Telophase II

Magnification: 900x

Magnification: 540x

Anaphase II Telophase I

Metaphase II Prophase II

Magnification: 940x

Magnification: 800x

Magnification: 470x

Magnification: 640x

contributes greatly to genetic variation. As a result of crossing over, individual chromosomes contain some genes from maternal origin and some genes from paternal origin. Without crossing over, every chromosome would either have only a maternal or paternal origin. You will model crossing over in the next Thinking Lab.

> PLAY

To see an animation of the phases of meiosis and crossing over, refer to the Electronic Learning Partner. This can help you if you are having difficulty visualizing the different stages of meiosis.

Metaphase I

Following prophase I, a spindle fibre attaches to the centromere of each chromosome. A spindle fibre from one pole attaches to one pair of sister chromatids, and a spindle fibre from the opposite pole attaches to the other pair of sister chromatids in the tetrad. The spindle fibres pull each tetrad to the equator of the cell. However, the chromosomes do not line up in single file as they do in mitosis. Instead, they line up in their homologous pairs. In each pair, one homologous chromosome is positioned on one side of the cell's equator, and the other homologous chromosome is positioned on the other side of the cell's equator. It is important to note that chromosomes that come from one parent are not all positioned on the same side of the cell's equator. Rather, they are positioned randomly so that some sister chromatids of maternal origin face one pole while other sister chromatids of maternal origin face the other pole of the cell. This random positioning of tetrads along the cell's equator is called **independent assortment**.

Anaphase I

During anaphase I, the homologous chromosomes separate and move to opposite poles of the cell. They are pulled apart by the shortening of the spindle fibres. Notice that the centromere does not split (as it does in mitosis), and that the sister chromatids are held together. Thus, only one chromosome from each pair will move to each pole of the cell.

Telophase I

Telophase I does not occur in all cells. Where telophase I does not occur, cell division goes directly to meiosis II. If telophase does occur, the homologous chromosomes begin to uncoil and the spindle fibres disappear. The cytoplasm is divided, the nuclear membrane forms around each group of homologous chromosomes, and two cells are formed. Each of these new cells contains one copy of each chromosome. Because each chromosome already consists of two chromatids, a second chromosome replication does not take place between telophase I and prophase II of meiosis. In females, meiosis II occurs after the egg is fertilized by a sperm cell.

At the end of telophase I, each cell contains some maternal chromosomes and some paternal chromosomes, due to the independent assortment of chromosomes during metaphase I. Each cell also contains chromosomes that are made up of a combination of maternal and paternal alleles as a result of crossing over during prophase I. You will illustrate these processes and their outcomes in the MiniLab on page 164.

Meiosis II

The phases of meiosis II are identical to mitosis. The two cells from telophase I go through prophase II, metaphase II, anaphase II, and telophase II. Each cell beginning meiosis II is haploid but consists of replicated chromosomes (each consisting of two chromatids). At the end of meiosis II, the daughter cells are still haploid but each cell contains single unreplicated chromosomes (no longer made up of two chromatids attached together). The daughter cells at the end of meiosis II are called gametes in animals and either gametes or spores in plants. In the investigation on page 168, you will study the phases of meiosis and gamete production in Easter lilies.

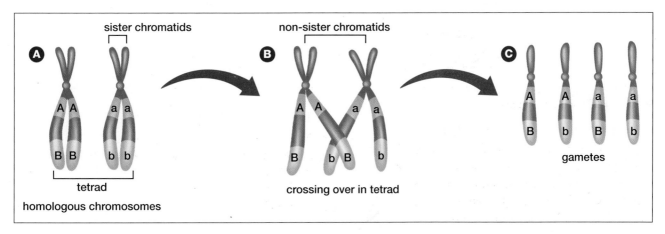

Figure 5.14 During prophase, homologous chromosomes form pairs (A). Non-sister chromatids wind around each other and exchange segments of chromosome (B). As a result, new genetic combinations are produced in gametes (C).

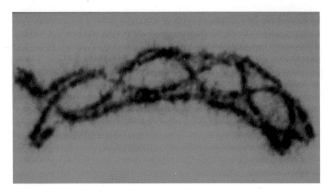

Figure 5.15 Crossing over may occur several times between non-sister chromatids.

Comparison of Meiosis with Mitosis

Now that you are familiar with meiosis and mitosis, what events characterize these two processes? Study Figure 5.16 and prepare a list of events, according to occurrence and process, which distinguish meiosis from mitosis. Which events occur in meiosis that do not occur in mitosis? Why is this so?

| **⏸ PAUSE** | **⏺ RECORD** |

Now that you are familiar with the phases and events in the process of meiosis, draw a consequences map linking the following terms (presented here in no particular order): *independent assortment, homologous chromosomes, crossing over, haploid, reduction division, tetrad, non-sister chromatids, diploid.* Briefly describe what is occurring at each step in your map. You may include sketches to accompany your descriptions.

 THINKING LAB

Modelling Crossing Over

Background

Crossing over occurs during prophase I of meiosis. During tetrad formation, non-sister chromatids cross over and exchange genes. This process creates new combinations of alleles in the resulting gametes. In this lab, you will use a simple model to simulate crossing over and record the possible outcomes.

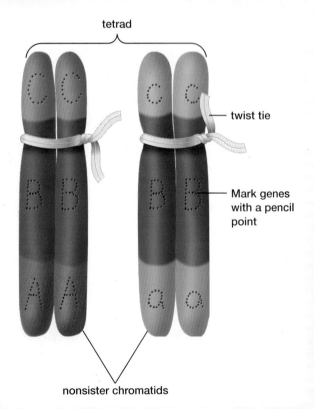

You Try It

1. Make a copy of the data table shown below.

2. Arrange four strips of clay as shown in the illustration. These strips represent a pair of chromosomes after replication. Use different colours of clay to identify the different genes. Using a pencil point, indicate the dominant or recessive allele for each gene as shown.

3. First, assume that no crossing over occurs. Model the appearance of the four gametes that will result at the end of meiosis. Record your model's appearance by drawing the gametes' chromosomes and their genes in your data table.

4. Repeat steps 2 and 3, this time assuming that crossing over occurs between genes B and C.

5. Compare any differences in the appearance of genes on chromosomes in gamete cells when crossing over occurs and when it does not occur. Wash your hands after handling the clay.

6. What would be accomplished if crossing over occurred between sister chromatids? Explain your answer.

7. Define "crossing over." How is this similar to shuffling a deck of cards? Explain your answer.

Appearance of gametes	
No crossing over	Crossing over

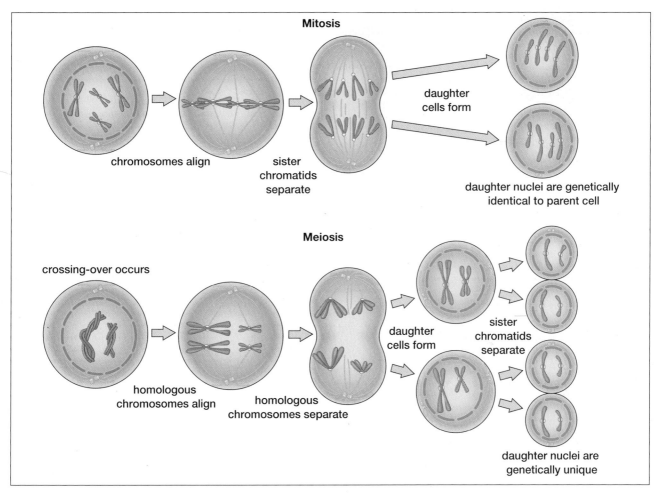

Figure 5.16 Meiosis compared to mitosis. The blue chromosomes were received from one parent and the red chromosomes were received from the other parent. Crossing over is shown in non-sister chromatids that are both red and blue.

MINI LAB

Meiosis I Flip Book

Create a flip-book for each of the steps of meiosis I given in the table shown here. Draw each step on plain 7.5 × 13 mm (3 × 5 in.) index cards. Position your drawing of the cell membrane in the same location on each card. Use different colours to represent chromosomes of maternal and paternal origin and to identify crossing over of non-sister chromatids. When the drawings are complete, tightly bind one end of the cards using an elastic band. Write the name of the phase on the card where that phase begins. By slowly flipping through the book, you can watch the chromosomes appear, double to form sister chromatids, form tetrads of homologous pairs, move to the cell's equator, separate to opposite poles, and become enclosed by nuclear membranes.

Analyze

1. Describe the appearance of the chromosomes in the two cells at the end of telophase I.

2. Are different combinations of chromosomes possible in the daughter cells? Explain your answer.

Steps of Meiosis I	Number of Cards
Original cell	1
Nuclear membrane disappears and sister chromatids form	3
Sister chromatids form homologous pairs (tetrad) and crossing over takes place	4
Centrioles move to the poles of the cell and spindle fibres appear	4
Homologous pairs line up on the cell's equator	2
Homologous pairs are pulled apart, randomly separating non-sister chromatids	3
Spindle fibres disappear and the nuclear membrane forms	3
Cytokinesis occurs forming two cells	3

Web LINK

The technique used to determine the location of genes relative to one another on one chromosome is called chromosome mapping. This is possible, in part, because of crossing over, which affects how genes move together between non-sister chromatids. To find out more about how chromosome mapping is done, go to the web site shown below. Go to **Science Resources**, then to **BIOLOGY 11** to find out where to go next. How do scientists measure the distance between genes? How does the distance between genes affect how they move from one chromatid to another during crossing over? Why is it important to know the position of a gene on a particular chromosome? Present your findings in a brief report.
www.school.mcgrawhill.ca/resources/

COURSE CHALLENGE

You have used a compound light microscope to observe various stages of mitosis and meiosis. What other technology is available to observe cells and cell structures? How has this technology improved our knowledge of cells? How might this be important for your Biology Course Challenge?

➤➤ FAST FORWARD

To find out more about changes in chromosome structure, turn to Chapter 7, Section 7.3.

Biology Magazine   TECHNOLOGY • SOCIETY • ENVIRONMENT

The Origin of Human Sex Chromosomes

Among the characteristics that distinguish women from men, it is only one small chromosome that determines your sex. Of the 46 chromosomes in the human genome, 44 are autosomes and two are sex chromosomes, called X and Y. Women have two X chromosomes and men have one X and one Y chromosome. The Y chromosome is much smaller and contains only about 1% of the genes found in the X chromosome. Why is there such a huge difference in size between the two sex chromosomes?

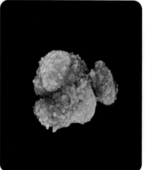

Human female (left) and male sex chromosomes

From X to Y

Genetic scientists have proposed that millions of years ago, the sex chromosomes began as a normal pair of autosomes that were equal in size. However, during the course of human evolution, changes occurred in an X-like ancestor that caused it to become reduced in size. These changes involved mutations that rearranged the chromosome. For example, a small part of the chromosome may have broken away, rotated 180 degrees, and then reattached itself. This type of mutation is called a chromosomal inversion, and it results in a permanent

genetic change. Various other factors can cause chromosomal mutations as well, including radiation, chemical compounds, and viruses. Changes in the structure of the X chromosome were important in determining sex in humans. During meiosis, homologous pairs of chromosomes are able to exchange genetic information through crossing over. This process recombines genes (a source of variation) in each chromosome and keeps the genetic information in both chromosomes similar. Mutations, such as inversions, prevent recombination from taking place because each chromosome no longer has the same genetic sequence. Genetic scientists believe that this process resulted in a reduction in size of one of the X chromosomes to its present Y condition.

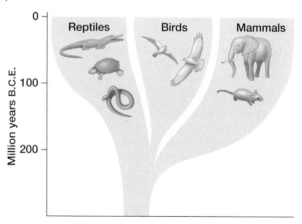

Vertebrate evolution

How many chromosomal inversions were necessary for the Y chromosome to evolve to its present state? Recent work by American geneticists Bruce Lahn and David Page suggests that at least four inversions have taken place in

Gamete Formation

The end result of meiosis is the production of gametes. This process, called **gametogenesis**, results in the production of sperm and eggs, as shown in Figure 5.17. The process of male gamete production in animals is called **spermatogenesis**. The process of female gamete production in animals is called **oogenesis**. These processes are discussed in greater detail on page 170.

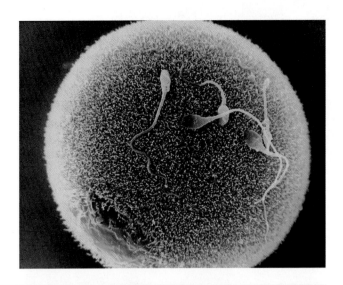

Figure 5.17 Human egg and sperm cells are produced at the end of meiosis.

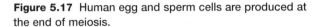

the Y chromosome over the last 300 to 350 million years B.C.E. The researchers used 19 genes to reconstruct the history of changes in the Y chromosome. These are ancient genes that are still common to both the X and Y chromosome, and thus served as "fossils" to help identify past mutation events. The first chromosomal inversion occurred about 240 to 320 million years B.C.E. This marked the origin of the Y sex chromosome and happened at the time when mammals and birds evolved from reptiles. The second and third inversions took place from 80 to 170 million years B.C.E, resulting in greater dissimilarity between the chromosomes. The most recent inversion, about 50 million years B.C.E, occurred during primate evolution when monkeys evolved from their prosimian ancestors.

Are Sex Chromosomes Necessary?

Chromosomes are not always important in determining sex. For instance, many reptiles, including lizards, snakes, and turtles, do not have special sex chromosomes. So, what determines the sex of a snapping turtle? When a female snapping turtle lays her eggs, she buries them in sandy soil. The eggs incubate there until the young turtles hatch. If the temperature of the soil is 23–27°C, all the hatchling turtles will be male. If the temperature is cooler or warmer, they will be female. Temperature of the environment affects genes on certain chromosomes of the embryos. In turn, these genes cause the turtles to develop into either males or females. This systems works because reptiles are cold-blooded and development of the young occurs, in most cases, outside the body of the female.

In contrast, mammals have internal development. Their young develop at a constant temperature. This kind of reproduction requires a different method of determining

sex. The development of a special Y chromosome allows sex to be determined without the effect of temperature. This is believed to be advantageous because species where the young develop inside the female often receive greater care and protection than those species' young that develop outside the body of the parent. This improves the chances of survival of offspring.

Snapping turtle

Follow-up

1. The sex of a person is determined by their chromosomes. Other characteristics, such as personality and intelligence, may be influenced by the environment. How much of a person's behaviour is genetically determined? Debate the issue in class. Provide evidence to support your viewpoint.

2. What other types of mutations cause changes in chromosomes? Provide a brief explanation of each mutation and its effect.

Investigation 5 • A

SKILL FOCUS

Predicting

Performing and recording

Analyzing and interpreting

Communicating results

Meiosis in Easter Lilies

Easter lilies have large anthers (male reproductive structures), which makes them ideal specimens to use when investigating meiosis in plants. The male gametes, or pollen, are produced in the anthers, as shown in the illustration. In this investigation, you will work with a partner to examine cells in the anthers. These cells are undergoing meiosis, which will eventually result in the formation of pollen.

Flower structure

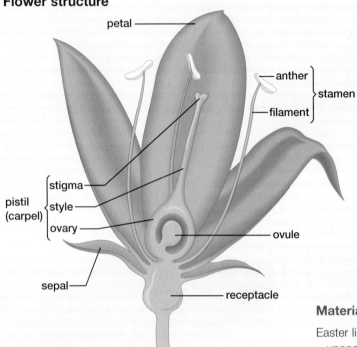

Pre-lab Questions

Study the figure showing flower structure, then answer the following questions.

- Which structures in a flower consist of diploid cells, and which structures produce haploid cells?

- Why does a flower produce haploid cells?

- At what stage(s) in the life cycle of a flowering plant is there opportunity for genetic variation to increase?

- At what stage(s) in the life cycle of a flowering plant does mitosis occur?

- What is the function of mitosis in the life cycle of a flowering plant?

Problem

Where does meiosis occur in a flowering plant?

Prediction

Predict which stage of meiosis will be observed most often? Explain your reasons for making this prediction.

CAUTION: Follow your teacher's instructions on the safe use of a scalpel. When using chromosome stain, avoid contact with eyes or skin. If contact does occur, rinse thoroughly with water and inform your teacher.

Materials

Easter lily with young, unopened flower buds 15 to 20 mm long
compound light microscope
plastic cover slip
tweezers
chromosome stain (for example, Aceto-Orcein)
glass microscope slide
scalpel
filter paper or paper towel

Procedure

1. Working with a partner, select an unopened lily flower bud that is approximately 15 to 20 mm long.

2. Using your scalpel, make a shallow cut along the length of the flower bud. Spread apart the sepals (outer leaf-like structures) and petals with your fingers until you expose the anthers in the middle of the flower.

3. Using the tweezers, remove one of the anthers. Then, with the scalpel, carefully cut off the top section of the anther.

168 • MHR • Genetic Continuity

10. When looking at each groups' slide preparation, take note of the number of cells that you observe in each of the phases of meiosis. Is there a phase that you find more often than other phases?

11. Locate haploid cells that have formed from a diploid nucleus, as well as any tetrads.

12. On completion of this investigation, wash your hands thoroughly.

Post-lab Questions

1. Which phase of meiosis did you find most often? What could you infer from this observation about the length of this phase?

2. What did you notice about the arrangement of the chromosomes in anaphase?

3. What is the diploid and haploid number for the lily, based on your slide observations?

4. Which phase is most useful in determining chromosome number? Explain briefly.

Conclude and Apply

5. What can you infer about the make-up of the chromosomes at the end of telophase II when compared to the make-up of the chromosomes at prophase I?

6. In a flowering plant, what are the four cells at the end of telophase II called, and what is their function?

Extend Your Knowledge

7. Define the term "alternation of generations." Does alternation of generations occur in plants, animals, fungi, and protists? What would be the survival advantage to an organism with a life cycle that included alternation of generations?

>> **FAST FORWARD**

To review the life cycle of a flowering plant and to learn more about the natural history of other organisms, turn to Chapter 13, Sections 13.2 and 13.3.

4. Using your fingers, carefully squeeze the contents of the cut-off section of the anther onto the middle of a microscope slide. These cells are undergoing meiosis.

5. Place two drops of chromosome stain on the sample of cells.

6. Place a cover slip over the specimen and cover it with a piece of filter paper or paper towel.

7. With *very* little pressure, press down on the cover slip with your finger to flatten the cells. (Note: If too much pressure is applied the cells will burst and release their chromosomes. You may have to repeat this step several times before producing a slide where you can see intact cells in the various phases of meiosis.)

8. Using the high-power setting of the compound light microscope, find cells that are in the different stages of meiosis in one field of view. For proper care and use of a microscope, turn to *Appendix* 3. Draw diagrams of the cells that you can see are in various stages of meiosis.

9. You may not find cells in all of the phases of meiosis. Be prepared to share your observations with other groups in the class and to view other groups' slides to observe cells in as many stages of meiosis as possible.

Spermatogenesis

Meiosis in mature males takes place in the testes, the male reproductive organs. Figure 5.18 shows the production of sperm, which starts with a diploid germ cell called a **spermatogonium**. This cell enlarges and undergoes meiosis I and meiosis II. The final product is four haploid sperm cells. Notice that each sperm cell has the same number of chromosomes and the same amount of cytoplasm. Following meiosis II, the sperm cells develop into mature sperm. Each cell loses cytoplasm and the nucleus forms into a head. As well, a long, tail-like flagellum is formed for locomotion. Spermatogenesis can occur throughout the year in some organisms, including humans. In other organisms, sperm production occurs only during a certain time of the year called a breeding season. For example, many species of migratory birds reproduce only during the spring and summer months.

Oogenesis

In females, meiosis takes place in the ovaries, the female reproductive organs. The process starts with a diploid germ cell called an **oogonium** (see Figure 5.18). This cell enlarges and undergoes meiosis I and meiosis II. At the end of meiosis I, the cytoplasm is not equally divided between the two daughter cells. The cell that receives most of the cytoplasm is called the primary oocyte. The other cell is called a polar body and is not a viable sex cell. As the primary oocyte undergoes meiosis II, the cytoplasm is again unequally divided. Only one cell becomes an egg, or ovum, and contains most of the cytoplasm. The other cell, a polar body, is not a viable sex cell. The purpose of the unequal division of the cytoplasm is to provide the ovum with sufficient nutrients to support the developing zygote in the first few days following fertilization.

Meiosis I and meiosis II are not continuous in many organisms. In humans, for example, meiosis I begins in the ovarian tissue of the embryo before

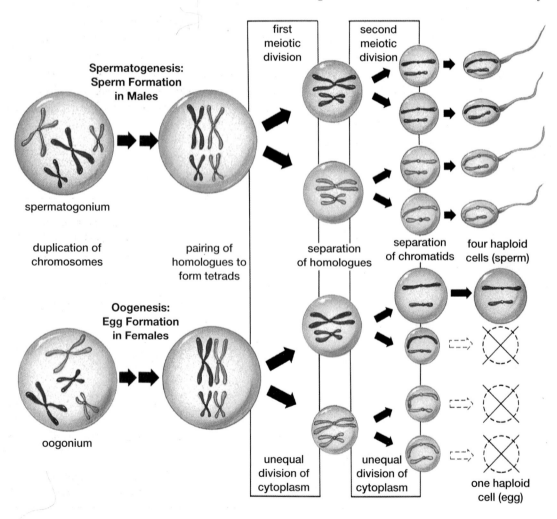

Figure 5.18 Production of sperm and eggs in animals. Which cells are diploid and which are haploid?

birth and does not continue beyond prophase I. The continuation of meiosis I occurs after the female reaches puberty. Normally, only one oogonium undergoes this process each month. Meiosis II takes place after fertilization by a sperm cell. The production of ova (two or more egg cells) in females continues from the start of puberty until menopause, which usually occurs between 40 and 50 years of age.

Meiosis and Genetic Variation

Figure 5.19 shows the variation of fur colour in a litter of kittens. The kittens are different because each has a different genetic make-up. This variation would not have been possible without two important processes of meiosis. First, the combination of genes responsible for fur colour varies because of crossing over between chromosomes during prophase I. (The number of crossovers between non-sister chromatids depends on the size of the chromosomes. Usually two or three crossovers occur per chromosome.) Second, variation depends on how each pair of homologous chromosomes lined up during metaphase I. When the chromosomes separate during anaphase I, some chromosomes of paternal origin move to one pole of the cell while other chromosomes of paternal origin move to the other pole. The same applies for chromosomes of maternal origin. The direction that each chromosome travels is entirely by chance, or random. Both crossing over and random segregation work to shuffle the chromosomes and

the genes they carry. This re-assortment is called **genetic recombination**, and it contributes greatly to variation among organisms. Variation among individuals of a species is important because certain combinations of genes can help an organism survive better than other combinations of genes can.

Figure 5.19 These kittens are from the same litter, yet all have different patterns of fur colour. What events in meiosis can contribute to this variation?

How much genetic variation in sperm or eggs is possible through genetic recombination? Figure 5.20 shows the possible gametes and zygotes for a two-chromosome model. Now consider a fruit fly, which has 2 pairs of chromosomes. Each pair of chromosomes can line up in one of two ways during metaphase I and segregate randomly. This means there are 16 () different kinds of gametes that can be produced. If fertilization is random, as well, 256 () different zygotes are possible. If crossing over is also considered, the possible genetic combinations are almost limitless!

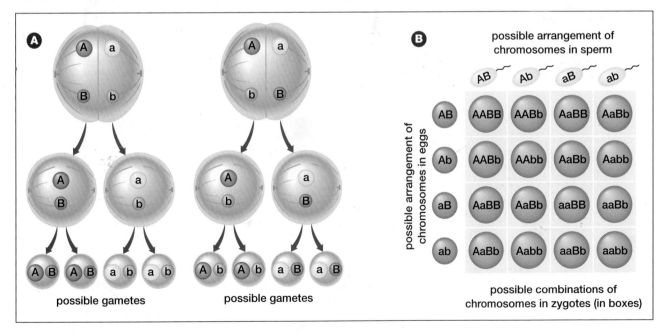

Figure 5.20 Possible gametes and zygotes for a cell with two pairs of chromosomes (). Notice the different ways alleles can segregate to produce gametes (A). A Punnett square shows 16 possible zygotes (B).

In this section, you have learned that genetic information is shuffled between chromosomes during meiosis. This results in the production of genetically unique gametes. During fertilization, gametes unite to form a zygote. Thus, genes from both parents are passed on to their offspring. These sources of genetic variation are summarized in Figure 5.21. What other sources of variation might exist?

Errors in Meiosis

Changes in the structure of a chromosome in gametes can have severe consequences. These changes, or mutations, can be passed from one generation to the next when that gamete combines with another gamete to form a zygote. Because

Biology At Work

Bioinformatics

A new field of research has recently been developed that incorporates biotechnology and computer science. Bioinformatics uses powerful computers to process the vast amounts of information generated by genetic sequencing, such as the Human Genome Project. The results are used to help develop new pharmaceuticals to combat diseases. At Sunnybrook Medical Centre and the Women's College Health Sciences Centre in Toronto, Dr. Corrinne Lobe and her colleagues are applying the new tools of bioinformatics in their research. They are studying how cells develop into different types of tissue and how this relates to cancer growth.

Search for a Cancer Vaccine

Dr. Lobe and her colleagues work extensively with transgenic mice. These mice have been given specific genes that can cause cancer. Using computers to process gigabytes of mouse DNA data, Dr. Lobe has discovered how to turn "on" the cancer-causing genes in mice. In this way, Dr. Lobe studies how cancer cells develop. More importantly, she studies how the immune system of mice can be stimulated through different vaccines to control the growth of cancerous cells. This research may eventually lead to the development of cancer vaccines for people.

In addition to her work as a research scientist, Dr. Lobe is also a marathon runner. The exercise allows her to relax and focus her mind on the scientific challenges she faces. There is a great deal of work to do in her laboratory. The field of bioinformatics offers many new opportunities for exploring, deciphering, and applying the growing volume of data from genetic research.

Dr. Corrinne Lobe

Skills Shortage

In Canada, there are not enough trained people to meet the growing demand for bioinformaticians. To help overcome this shortage, workshops have been set up in Canada for university graduates in the biological and computer sciences, as well those studying mathematics, statistics, or physics. These workshops provide an introduction to the development and use of bioinformatics software.

Career Tips

1. The key to success in this field lies in a broad understanding of the life sciences. A valuable way to learn how bioinformatics is used in research is to spend some time volunteering in genetic research labs.

2. A career in bioinformatics requires good communication skills and experience with computers, software applications, and the Internet.

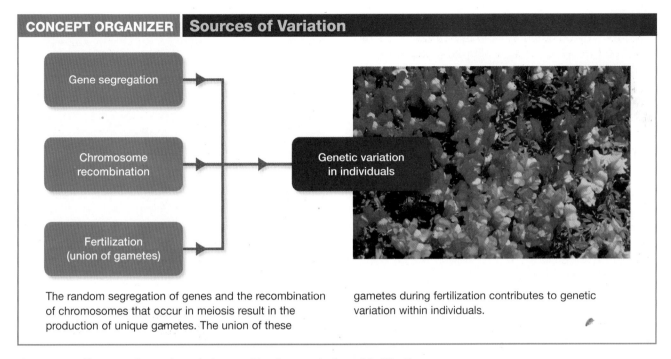

Gene segregation

Chromosome recombination

Fertilization (union of gametes)

Genetic variation in individuals

The random segregation of genes and the recombination of chromosomes that occur in meiosis result in the production of unique gametes. The union of these

gametes during fertilization contributes to genetic variation within individuals.

Figure 5.21 Sources of genetic variation resulting from meiosis and fertilization.

chromosomes are copied during interphase before each mitosis, all the cells that develop from this zygote will also carry the mutation.

The failure of chromosomes to separate properly, called **nondisjunction**, can occur during meiosis. This error results in the addition or deletion of one or more chromosomes from a gamete. Study Figure 5.22 to learn how nondisjunction happens. In what phases of meiosis can nondisjunction occur? If a gamete with an extra chromosome is fertilized by a normal gamete, all the cells that develop from

the zygote will also have an extra chromosome. This is called **trisomy**. An example of trisomy in humans is Down Syndrome, in which there is an extra chromosome number 21. You will learn more about the effects of nondisjunction in human chromosomes in Chapter 7.

What happens if the chromosomes do not segregate during meiosis? This means that the resulting gamete will be diploid rather than haploid. If a diploid gamete unites with a normal haploid gamete, the zygote will contain three sets

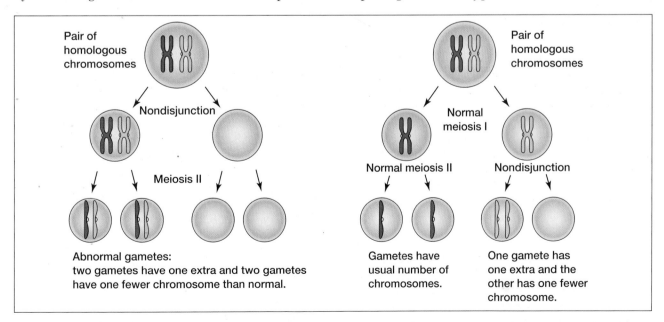

Pair of homologous chromosomes

Nondisjunction

Meiosis II

Abnormal gametes: two gametes have one extra and two gametes have one fewer chromosome than normal.

Pair of homologous chromosomes

Normal meiosis I

Normal meiosis II

Nondisjunction

Gametes have usual number of chromosomes.

One gamete has one extra and the other has one fewer chromosome.

Figure 5.22 Nondisjunction can result in abnormal numbers of chromosomes in gametes. Offspring may inherit an extra chromosome or may be missing a chromosome.

of chromosomes (3n). This condition is called **triploidy**. Organisms that have more than two sets of chromosomes are called **polyploids**. Polyploidy is rare in animals, but is rather common in plants. For example, seedless grapes and watermelon are polyploids. Plant breeders can cross a diploid male plant with a tetraploid (4n chromosomes) female plant to produce the seedless variety of watermelon (see Figure 5.23). The offspring are sterile and therefore do not contain seeds.

Web LINK

Nondisjunction of chromosomes during meiosis can have profound effects. In humans, the results of inheriting a gamete containing either an extra chromosome or lacking a chromosome can vary from mild to fatal. To find out more about the effects of nondisjunction, go to the website shown below. Go to **Science Resources**, then to **BIOLOGY 11** to find out where to go next. Do a survey of four different chromosomal syndromes associated with nondisjunction. Present your findings in a brief report.
www.school.mcgrawhill.ca/resources/

Figure 5.23 Seedless fruits like this watermelon are polyploids.

>> **FAST FORWARD**

To learn more about the frequency of polypoidy in flowering plants, turn to Chapter 13, Section 13.2.

SECTION REVIEW

1. **K/U** What is the purpose of meiosis?

2. **K/U** Where does meiosis occur in organisms?

3. **MC** What characteristics of an egg cell and a sperm cell are critical to their ultimate function of combining to form a zygote?

4. **MC** Given that genes code for the production of proteins, why might an organism that has an abnormal number of chromosomes (either one less or one more than normal) have abnormal physical development or abnormal body function?

5. **MC** What would be the advantage to an organism of having several genes that code for the same protein?

6. **C** Summarize each phase of meiosis. You may use sketches to illustrate your explanation.

7. **C** How can mutations lead to variations in the daughter cells produced through the process of meiosis?

8. **K/U** Why are seeds not good specimens for the microscopic observation of the phases of meiosis?

9. **K/U** Why is the occurrence of mutations in meiosis often more detrimental to an organism than the occurrence of mutations in mitosis?

10. **C** Which division in meiosis, I or II, is most similar to mitosis? Write a brief explanation.

11. **C** Based on your knowledge of meiosis, use diagrams to model the steps that would need to occur to produce triploid gametes from a tetraploid and diploid parental cross. Hint: what happens to the number of chromosomes during meiosis?

12. **I** Hypothesize why triploid offspring are sterile and therefore cannot produce seeds. Design an experiment to test your hypothesis.

UNIT ISSUE PREP

You have probably chosen the genetic issue you will be examining for your Unit 2 Issue Analysis. Decide now how you will use what you have learned about mitosis and meiosis. Will you be able to apply the scientific information you have learned in this section to your Unit 2 Issue Analysis? If so, be sure to collect this information in your files for your Issue.

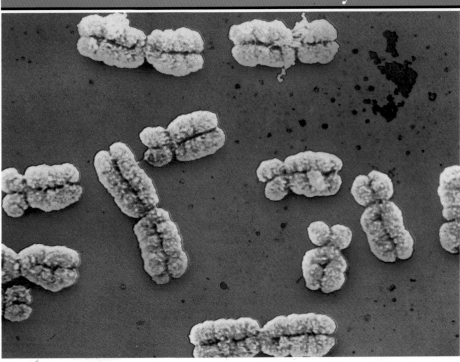

Figure 5.24 How are pairs of chromosomes related to pairs of alleles?

When Gregor Mendel formulated his laws of inheritance of traits, he did not know about meiosis or the existence of chromosomes in cells. Based upon his experiments with pea plants, Mendel concluded that each trait has two factors. During gamete formation, the factors segregate so that each gamete has one factor. Mendel's conclusions were remarkable for his time. However, his findings went largely unnoticed until the early 1900s, when better techniques were developed to investigate cellular processes and chromosomes were actually observed in cells.

In 1902, scientists Walter Sutton and Theodor Boveri made an important discovery while studying the phases of meiosis. They realized that the behaviour of chromosomes during meiosis was related to the behaviour of "factors" in Mendel's experiments with pea plants. Based on their observations, Sutton and Boveri developed a theory about the relationship between Mendel's factors and chromosomes. Figure 5.25, on page 176, compares the behaviour of Mendel's factors and chromosomes. What three observations did these scientists make that helped them to develop their theory? The combined research of Mendel, Sutton, and Boveri formed the basis of the **chromosome theory of inheritance**. This theory states that genes are located on chromosomes, and chromosomes provide the basis for the segregation and independent assortment of genes.

Sex-linked Inheritance

Some traits that are passed from one generation to the next depend on the sex of the parent carrying the trait. This is because the genes for these traits are located on the sex chromosomes. The transmission of genes that are located on one of the sex chromosomes, X or Y, is called **sex-linked inheritance**. A gene that is located on the X chromosome only is called X-linked. A gene that is located on the Y chromosome only is called Y-linked. Most of the known sex-linked traits are X-linked. Very few Y-linked traits are known. This may be because the Y chromosome is much smaller than the X chromosome. Examples of X-linked traits in humans include colour blindness and hemophilia. You will examine the inheritance of these conditions in the human population in more detail in Chapter 7. How do you think people discovered that the inheritance of certain traits was governed by the sex of an individual?

> **BIO FACT**
>
> In humans, colourblindness is rare in females because they must inherit two recessive alleles —— one from each parent —— to be colourblind. Males, however, need to receive only one recessive allele to inherit this condition.

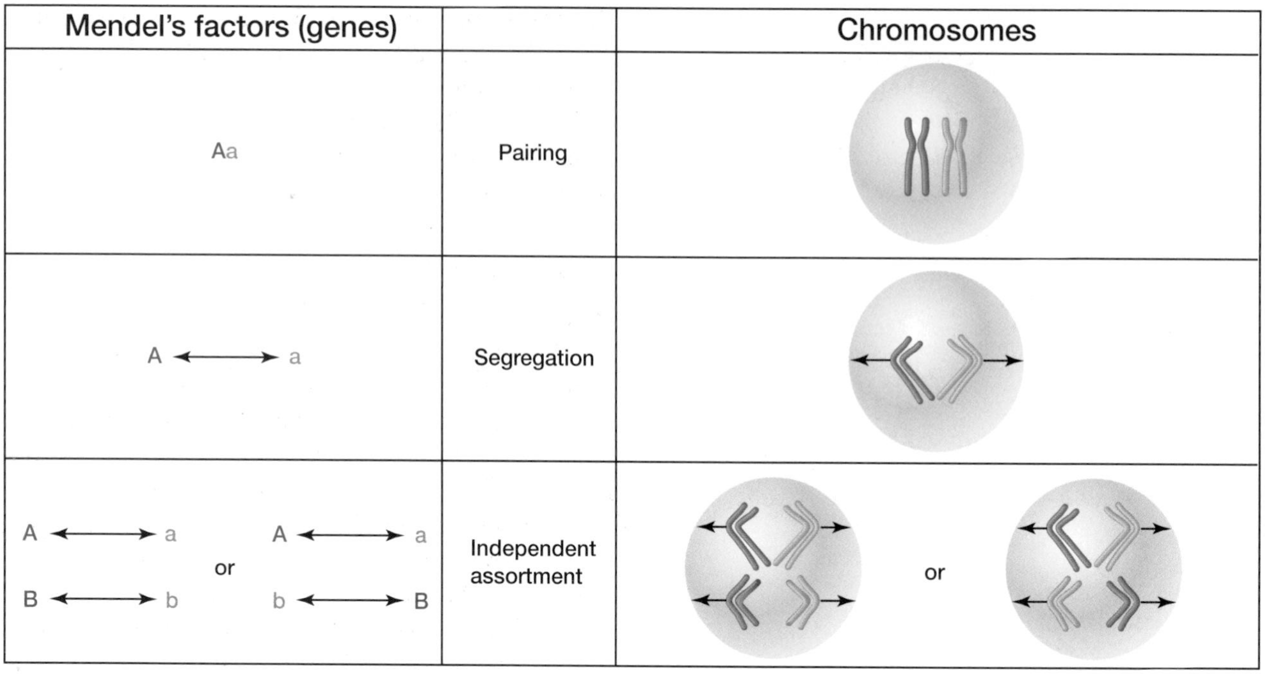

Mendel's factors (genes)		Chromosomes
Aa	Pairing	
A ⟷ a	Segregation	
A ⟷ a A ⟷ a or B ⟷ b b ⟷ B	Independent assortment	or

Figure 5.25 The behaviour of Mendel's factors (genes) and chromosomes during meiosis. Light and dark shades of the same colour show different members of the same homologous pair of chromosomes.

Morgan's Discovery

While investigating eye colour in fruit flies in 1910, American scientist Thomas Morgan produced a white-eyed male fly by crossing two red-eyed parent flies. At first, this did not seem unusual to Morgan. The result could be explained using the law of dominance in a monohybrid cross, which produces a 3:1 ratio of red-eyed fruit flies to white-eyed fruit flies. Red eye colour (allele symbol R) is dominant to white eye colour (allele symbol r) (see Figure 5.26).

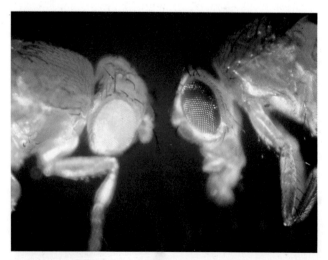

Figure 5.26 In fruit flies, the allele for eye colour is carried on the X chromosome. Red eye colour is dominant to white eye colour.

However, when Morgan crossed the white-eyed male with a red-eyed female he was not able to produce a female fruit fly with white eyes. How could this outcome be explained?

Morgan hypothesized that the gene coding for eye colour in fruit flies was located on the X chromosome, as shown in Figure 5.27. He reasoned that the white-eyed trait was recessive. Therefore, the only way to obtain a female white-eyed fruit fly was if both the male and female parent donated an allele that coded for white-eyes. Figure 5.28 shows a cross between a white-eyed male (genotype X^rY) and a red-eyed female (genotype X^RX^R). The male donates the Y chromosome (which does not carry the eye colour gene) to all male offspring. The female, therefore, donates the X chromosome to the male offspring. The source of the X chromosome in all female offspring from this cross comes from the male, and in this cross both X chromosomes contain the allele that codes for red eyes.

▌▌ PAUSE ▬ ● RECORD

Hypothesize why Morgan was not able to produce white-eyed female fruit flies from a cross between a white-eyed male and a red-eyed female. Is it possible to produce white-eyed female fruit flies? If so, describe the phenotypes and genotypes of the parents.

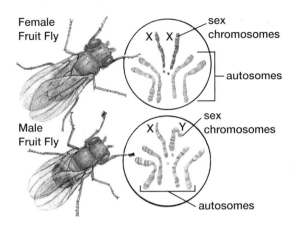

Figure 5.27 In fruit flies (*Drosophila melanogaster*), the gene for eye colour is located on the X chromosome.

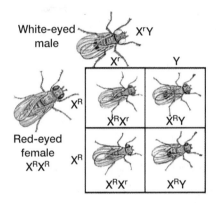

Figure 5.28 Crosses of fruit flies for red eyes (R) and white eyes (r).

Sex-linked Traits and Punnett Squares

Punnett squares can be used to predict the outcome of crosses involving genes that are located on the X or Y chromosome. When creating a Punnett square to determine the outcome of a cross involving a sex-linked trait, assume that the trait is located on the X chromosome unless it is stated that the trait is located on the Y chromosome. As shown in Figure 5.29, the gametes containing the X and Y chromosomes are placed on the outside of the

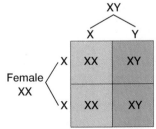

Genotypic ratio = 1/2 XX : 1/2 XY
Phentypic ratio = 1/2 female : 1/2 male

Figure 5.29 In this Punnett square, half of the offspring are female and half are male.

Punnett square in the same manner as autosomal traits. The only differences are that the alleles are written on the X chromosome if the trait is X-linked and no allele is written with the Y chromosome. When the genotype and phenotype ratios are written, the sex is always included in the ratio.

Chromosomes and Gene Expression

Males and females produce the same amounts of proteins coded by genes located on the X chromosome. However, females have two copies of the X chromosome in every cell and males only have one copy of the X chromosome in every cell. Experimental evidence has demonstrated that one of the X chromosomes in each female cell is inactivated. Which one is inactivated is random, and therefore different X chromosomes are active in different cells. The inactivated X chromosome is called a **Barr body**.

The tortoiseshell coat colour in cats is an example of the presence of inactivated X chromosomes. The tortoiseshell pattern can only occur in female cats (see Figure 5.30). Each tortoiseshell cat has a random distribution of orange and black patches. The gene that codes for this orange and black colour is located on the X chromosome. A tortoiseshell cat is heterozygous for the allele that codes for this coat colour. This means that one copy of the X chromosome has an allele that codes for orange pigment and the other copy of the X chromosome has an allele that codes for black pigment. The random inactivation of an X chromosome in every cell of a tortoiseshell cat results in a patchwork orange and black coat colour.

Figure 5.30 Only female cats show the tortoiseshell fur colour pattern. Why is this so?

Polygenic Inheritance

Many traits are controlled by more than one gene. This phenomenon is known as **polygenic inheritance**. The protein products produced by many genes working together results in a range of variation, or **continuous variation**, in a trait. Continuous variation can be defined as the variation among individuals in a population in which there is a gradient of phenotypes for one trait. An example of continuous variation is range of ear length in corn. Figure 5.31 shows that the longest ear length is obtained when both genes controlling corn ear length are homozygous dominant for both alleles. The shortest ear length occurs when both genes controlling corn ear length

are homozygous recessive for both alleles. As indicated by the Punnett square, the longest and shortest phenotypes are the least common because each can only be obtained by one combination of alleles. The medium length is most common because it can be obtained through many different combinations of alleles. In humans, height and skin colour are thought to be polygenic traits. In the following investigation, you will use graphical methods to infer the inheritance pattern of several human traits.

DESIGN YOUR OWN
Investigation

5 • B

SKILL FOCUS

Initiating and planning

Hypothesizing

Identifying variables

Performing and recording

Analyzing and interpreting

Measuring Variation in a Trait

Different traits show different degrees of variation. Some traits are either present or absent, while others show continuous variation. Traits that are either present or absent may be governed by a single gene, whereas traits that show continuous variation may be governed by several or many genes. The graphical representation of a trait can provide information about its inheritance pattern. How can the inheritance pattern of a trait be graphically represented? In this investigation, you will design a method to determine the inheritance pattern of two human traits based on data you will collect.

Problem

How can you infer the inheritance pattern of a trait?

Hypothesis

Make a hypothesis about the inheritance pattern of a trait based on the shape of the trait's graph. The graph should illustrate the variation of the trait on the *x*-axis and the number of students on the *y*-axis.

NOTE: Follow your teacher's directions for conducting this investigation in a manner that is always respectful of others.

Materials

Ruler or measuring tape

Experimental Plan

1. Prepare a list of the possible ways you might test your hypothesis.

2. Decide on one approach for your investigation that could be conducted in the classroom.

3. Your design should test one variable at a time. Plan to collect quantitative data, and prepare a table that will organize the data effectively.

4. Outline a procedure for your experiment listing each step. Provide a list of your materials and the quantities you will require. Get your teacher's approval before conducting your investigation.

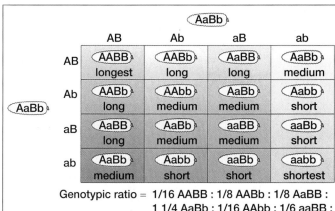

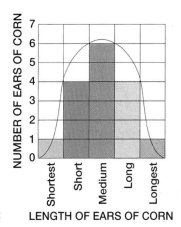

Genotypic ratio = 1/16 AABB : 1/8 AABb : 1/8 AaBB :
1 1/4 AaBb : 1/16 AAbb : 1/6 aaBB :
1/8 Aabb : 1/8 aaBb : 1/16 aabb

Phenotypic ratio = 1/16 longest : 1/4 long : 3/8 medium :
1/4 short : 1/16 shortest

Figure 5.31 Ear length in corn is determined by two pairs of genes. The F$_2$ generation shows continuous variation in this trait, with medium length ears occurring most often.

Checking the Plan

1. What will you measure or count? What kind of graph will you produce using the data?

2. How will you infer the inheritance pattern of a trait from the shape of a graph?

Data and Observations

Conduct your investigation and make your measurements. Enter the data into your table. Make a graph of your results.

Analyze

1. Compare the shape of the graphs for the two human traits you investigated.

2. Suggest reasons for the similarity or difference in the shapes of the two graphs.

3. Compare the shape of the your graphs to the graphs drawn by other students.

4. Suggest reasons for the similarities or differences in the shapes of the graphs.

Conclude and Apply

5. Based on your results, what inferences can be drawn about the inheritance pattern of a trait from the shape of the graph?

Exploring Further

6. What is a normal distribution? How do the results you obtained in this investigation compare with a normal distribution? Explain briefly.

7. The range of variation of the traits you investigated may be the result of many factors. Carry out research to investigate which factors contribute the most, and which factors contribute least, to the variation of the traits that you investigated. From your findings, what could an individual do to influence the development of the traits you investigated?

Computer LINK

Use a spreadsheet program to input the data for the trait being measured. Generate the graphs using the spreadsheet program.

Modifier Genes

Some genes, called **modifier genes**, work together with other genes to control the expression of a trait. The expression of eye colour in humans may involve modifier genes. For example, brown eye colour is the result of the presence of the pigment called melanin that is coded for by the dominant allele for eye colour. Blue eye colour is the result of the absence of the pigment melanin coded for by the recessive allele for eye colour. Various modifier genes help to produce other eye colours, as shown in Figure 5.32.

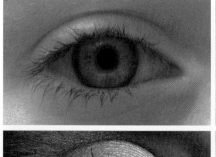
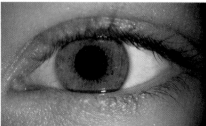
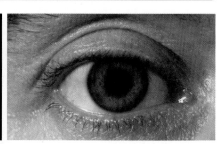

Figure 5.32 The gene for eye colour only codes for the presence or absence of the melanin pigment, which produces either brown or blue eyes. If this is the case, why are there other eye colours in humans?

SECTION REVIEW

1. **K/U** Explain the relationship between Mendel's "factors" and chromosomes.

2. **K/U** What is sex-linked inheritance? Provide an example in your explanation.

3. **K/U** How did the laws of inheritance proposed by Mendel help in the development of the chromosome theory of inheritance?

4. **C** Explain how a range of phenotypes can exist for one trait.

5. **MC** How can variation in a trait be used to produce crops with new genotypes and phenotypes? Use a Punnett square to illustrate your answer.

6. **I** Using a Punnett square predict the genotypic and phenotypic ratios of the F_1 generation from a parental cross between a red-eyed male fruit fly and a white-eyed female fruit fly.

7. **I** Colourblindness in humans is an X-linked recessive trait. What is the probability of a couple having a child that is colourblind if the man is colourblind and the woman is heterozygous for normal colour vision?

8. **I** What is the probability that the child from the cross in question 7 will be a female that is colourblind?

9. **K/U** What type of inheritance could be responsible for the variation in human height? Explain your answer.

10. **I** Fruit flies can have normal wings or stunted wings. In an experiment, you mate several normal-winged females with a male that has stunted wings. In the F_1 generation, only the males have stunted wings. Design an experiment to show that females in the F_1 generation can also have stunted wings. Use a Punnett square to illustrate your reasoning.

UNIT ISSUE PREP

The genetic issue you will be examining for your Unit 2 Issue Analysis may be related to chromosomes and heredity. If it is, consider what some industrial information on this topic would consist of. What types of information on this subject would political leaders discuss? Are there any legal implications that could be applied to this subject? Think about your answers and note your responses in your file for this Issue.

Chapter Expectations

Briefly explain each of the following points.

- Cells reproduce continually through a sequence known as the cell cycle (5.1)
- The growth stage of the cell cycle is called interphase. (5.1)
- The division stage consists of mitosis and cell division. (5.1)
- Mitosis functions to produce new cells, allowing organisms to grow, repair, and maintain regular functions. (5.1)
- Mitosis consists of four stages: prophase, metaphase, anaphase, and telophase. (5.1)
- Meiosis is a type of cell division that occurs in reproductive organs. (5.2)
- Meiosis involves two sequences known as Meiosis I and Meiosis II. (5.2)
- Genetic variation in gametes is a result of the re-assortment of genes on chromosomes by the processes of crossing over and random assortment. (5.2)
- Sex-linked inheritance involves traits carried on genes located on the sex chromosomes. (5.3)
- An inactivated X chromosome is called a Barr body. (5.3)
- Some traits, controlled by more than one gene, are called polygenic inheritance. (5.3)

Language of Biology

Write a sentence using each of the following words or terms. Use any six terms in a concept map to show your understanding of how they are related.

- cell cycle
- interphase
- mitosis
- chromosomes
- sister chromatids
- centromere
- parent cell
- daughter cells
- prophase
- metaphase
- anaphase
- telophase
- cytokinesis
- mutations
- oncogenes
- meiosis
- haploid
- diploid
- reduction division
- autosome
- sex chromosome
- homologous chromosome
- tetrad
- crossing over
- non-sister chromatids
- independent assortment
- gametogenesis
- spermatogenesis
- oogenesis
- spermatogonium
- oogonium
- genetic recombination
- nondisjunction
- trisomy
- triploid
- polyploids
- chromosome theory of inheritance
- sex-linked inheritance
- Barr body
- polygenic inheritance
- continuous variation
- modifier genes

UNDERSTANDING CONCEPTS

1. Which of the chromosomes shown here are homologous? Explain briefly.

2. Explain how mitosis would be affected if DNA were prevented from replicating.

3. What role does mitosis play in the survival of an organism? What plant and animal tissues would be best to use to study the process of mitosis?

4. What role does meiosis play in the survival of an organism? What plant and animal tissues would be best to use to study the process of meiosis?

5. Explain the consequence if no crossing over takes place in meiosis I.

6. Why is meiosis often referred to as reduction division?

7. Draw a series of diagrams illustrating meiosis in a plant cell that has a chromosome number of 2n = 8.

8. A plant can be reproduced using a clipping consisting of a stem and a few leaves. The clipping is placed in water until roots form from the stem. What process, mitosis or meiosis, is responsible for the reproduction of plants through clippings? Explain your answer.

9. How would mitosis differ between a haploid and a diploid organism? How would meiosis differ between a haploid and a diploid organism?

10. What scientific processes were used by Thomas Morgan to construct an understanding of sex-linked inheritance?

11. How does polygenic inheritance differ from single gene inheritance?

12. What information can be determined from a Punnett square involving a sex-linked cross?

13. What are the advantages in plants that can reproduce both sexually and asexually?

14. What are the disadvantages in the ability of plants to reproduce both sexually and asexually?

15. What happens to inheritance information as a zygote divides?

16. What is the relationship between a chromosome and a gene?

17. Explain how an individual can be heterozygous or homozygous for a particular trait.

18. Do both autosomes and sex chromosomes consist of genes and alleles? Explain your answer.

19. Does a human skin cell contain the same genetic information as a human brain cell? Explain your answer.

20. Do both sperm and egg cells contain the same genetic information? Explain your answer.

INQUIRY

21. Using the information provided in Table 5.1 (on page 161), draw a fruit fly cell undergoing mitosis and answer the following questions.
    (a) How many chromatids would be found in a leopard frog body cell in prophase I?
    (b) How many chromosomes would be found in a dog sperm cell?

22. An organism is heterozygous for two genes located on two different chromosomes, as shown in the diagram. Prepare short written answers (including diagrams) to the questions that follow.

    ――――― a ――――― ―― b ――
    ――――― A ――――― ―― B ――

    (a) What happens to the alleles A, a and B, b when they are transmitted through mitosis from a parent cell to two daughter cells?
    (b) What happens to the alleles A, a and B, b when they are transmitted through meiosis from a parent cell to gametes?
    (c) How does the sorting of these alleles during meiosis provide the physical basis for Mendel's law of segregation and independent assortment?
    (d) Predict what would happen if the spindle fibres in a cell undergoing mitosis only formed from one pole of the cell.

23. Is every gene in all cells expressed through the production of proteins all of the time? What evidence supports your answer? Explain your answer.

24. What evidence would you use to indicate that a mushroom contains genes? Outline an experimental procedure you could use to prove the presence of genes.

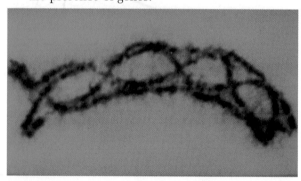

25. Suppose a geneticist wanted to study frequency of crossing over to estimate the amount of variation in a population. Describe a procedure to investigate this idea. What problems might there be with this approach?

26. Hemophilia is a recessive X-linked trait. What is the probability of a couple having a child with hemophilia if the man does not have hemophilia and the woman is a carrier?

27. The F_1 phenotypic ratio for eye colour from a cross between a pair of fruit flies is 1 red eyed female : 1 red eyed male : 1 white eyed male. Determine the genotypes and phenotypes of the parent generation.

28. The F_1 phenotypic ratio for eye colour from a cross between a pair of fruit flies is 2 red eyed females : 2 red eyed males. Determine the genotypes and phenotypes of the parent generation.

COMMUNICATING

29. In which cells in the human body does mitosis occur most frequently? Explain your answer.

30. In which cells in the human body does mitosis occur least frequently? Explain your answer.

31. Create a chart to illustrate the number of chromosomes in the following list of cells before, during, and as a result of mitosis. A human cell with 46 chromosomes, a dog cell with 78 chromosomes, an apple cell with 34 chromosomes, and a corn cell with 20 chromosomes.

32. Create a chart to illustrate the number of chromosomes in the following list of cells before, during, and as a result of meiosis. A human cell with 46 chromosomes, a dog cell with 78 chromosomes, an apple cell with 34 chromosomes, and a corn cell with 20 chromosomes.

33. Would species that have more traits that are determined through polygenic inheritance than single gene inheritance have a survival advantage over species that have very few traits that are determined through polygenic inheritance? Write a short essay to support and explain your reasoning.

34. Compare and contrast the terms gene and allele.

35. Explain the role of autosomal chromosomes and explain the role of sex chromosomes. You may write your answer or use diagrams.

36. What would happen if homologous chromosomes paired with non-homologous chromosomes in meiosis I instead of the matching homolog?

37. What is the purpose of using a Punnett square to predict the outcome of a genetic cross?

38. Can a single Punnett square predict the outcome of several crosses at one time? Explain your answer.

39. In your notebook, complete the following table that compares mitosis and meiosis.

	Mitosis	Meiosis
Occurs in	all body cells	
Number of cells produced per parent cell	two	
Number of chromosomes in parent cell		diploid (2n)
Number of chromosomes in daughter cells	same as parent cell	
Type of cell produced		gametes
Function		transfer of genetic information from generation to generation; increases variation

MAKING CONNECTIONS

40. Does mitosis in humans occur more frequently in a five-year-old or an 85-year-old individual? Explain your answer. Many scientists are working on ways to slow the effects of aging. Given your answer to the first part of the question, suggest an area for further research? List three ways this research could be applied.

41. A scientist produces a new strain of seeds using genetic engineering. What process, mitosis or meiosis, would the seed go through when germinating into a mature plant? Would the seeds produced by the mature plant be identical or different from the original genetically engineered seeds? Explain.

CHAPTER 6

DNA Structure and Replication

Reflecting Questions

- How are traits stored in chromosomes?
- Why is DNA called the "code of life"?
- How do cells copy genetic information?

When a pianist sits down at the piano, he or she can strike the 88 piano keys in millions of different combinations to make music. The number of combinations in which the keys can be played together is as endless as the number of composers who have written, or will write, music. The difference between music and noise, however, depends on striking the keys in a particular sequence. Every keyboard is the same; the difference from one song to the next is how the notes are arranged.

All organisms are formed from the same chemicals, and yet they all look so different. The key is how the chemicals in their cells are arranged. Just as different combinations of piano keys make different tunes, the chemicals in cells can be arranged in a variety of ways to produce the many thousands of characteristics. For example, people share many characteristics. They have a similar body shape and structure. This is because they are made of the same chemical compounds. However, there is considerable variation from person to person. People vary in height, eye colour, hair colour, and other traits. This variation occurs because the chemical compounds can be arranged in different combinations. The organization of these chemical compounds forms the basis for genetic variation.

In this chapter, you will find out what kinds of scientific research led to the discovery of the DNA molecule. You will learn how chemicals in the cells of all organisms can be combined to form molecules of DNA. Although the DNA molecule can hold an enormous amount of genetic information, it is based on a simple code. You will learn how to read this code and then model your own DNA molecules. You will also learn how the DNA molecule is used as a template to form new molecules of DNA. Finally, you will explore recent genetic technologies, such as DNA fingerprinting and cloning, and learn how they are used to identify individuals.

How is genetic information organized in DNA?

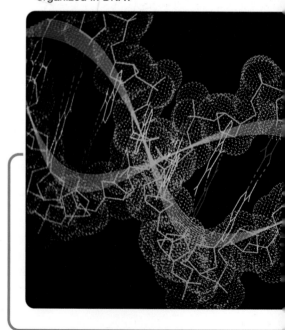

Chapter Contents

The Structure of DNA

- Explain how DNA accounts for the transmission of hereditary characteristics.

- Summarize the main scientific investigations that led to the modern understanding of DNA and genes.

- Research genetic technologies.

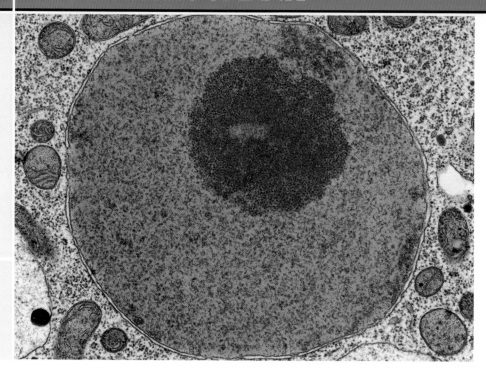

Figure 6.1 This scanning electron micrograph shows the nucleus of an animal cell. The mass of threadlike structures is the cell's DNA.

Earlier in this unit, you learned how genes and chromosomes transmit characteristics from generation to generation. Chromosomes are made of the compound deoxyribonucleic acid, or **DNA**. DNA is like the blueprint or master copy of information used to construct an organism. During mitosis, DNA in the nucleus is copied and passed to the new cells. In this way, new cells receive the same information that was in the original cell. DNA controls the activities of cells by providing instructions for making proteins. Every nucleated cell that has ever been formed in your body or in any other organism contains DNA.

You learned in Chapter 5 how scientists determined that chromosomes carry genetic information. They knew chromosomes were composed of almost equal amounts of two substances, DNA and proteins, but they did not know which substance carried the genetic information.

Scientists knew that chromosomes carried a great deal of information, and they also knew that DNA had a much simpler structure than protein. Because of this, most scientists thought proteins carried the genetic information. A discovery made in the 1950s, however, proved that it was actually DNA that carried genetic information.

In 1952, American scientists Alfred Hershey and Martha Chase performed an experiment using **bacteriophages**, viruses that attack bacteria (see Figure 6.2). Bacteriophages use the bacterial cell's ability to copy DNA in order to quickly produce

new viruses in the host cell. The bacterial cell soon bursts, releasing the viruses, which can then attack other cells. Bacteriophages were ideal for determining whether it was DNA or protein that carried genetic information, because bacteriophages are composed of both of these materials (each of which makes up a different part of the virus).

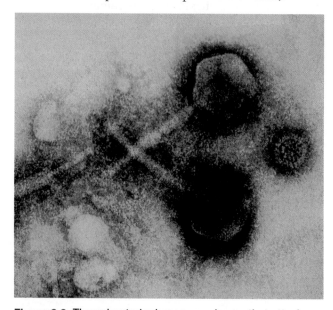

Figure 6.2 These bacteriophages are viruses that attack bacteria.

>> **FAST FORWARD**

To learn more about the life cycle of viruses, turn to Chapter 11, Section 11.2.

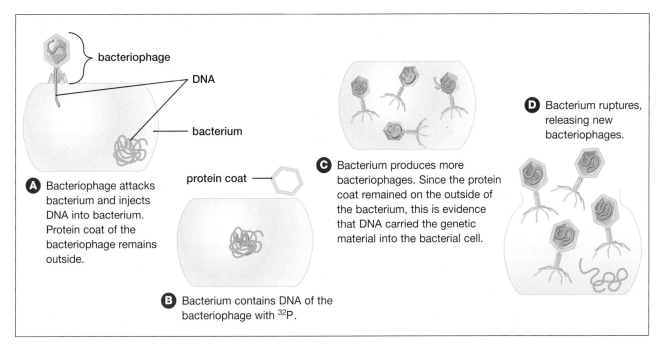

A) Bacteriophage attacks bacterium and injects DNA into bacterium. Protein coat of the bacteriophage remains outside.

B) Bacterium contains DNA of the bacteriophage with ^{32}P.

C) Bacterium produces more bacteriophages. Since the protein coat remained on the outside of the bacterium, this is evidence that DNA carried the genetic material into the bacterial cell.

D) Bacterium ruptures, releasing new bacteriophages.

Figure 6.3 Hershey-Chase experiment

The outer coating of the bacteriophage is made of protein, and the inside of the bacteriophage carries a core of DNA. Hershey and Chase devised a way to mark the protein coat and the DNA using radioactive sulfur (^{35}S) and phosphorus (^{32}P) so they could follow what each component did as the viruses attacked bacteria cells. They found that the protein coat of the bacteriophage remained outside the bacterial cell. However, the bacteriophage's DNA moved into the bacterial cells and directed them to create new bacteriophages (see Figure 6.3). The Hershey-Chase experiment was very important in helping to confirm that it is DNA, not protein, that carries the genetic information.

Nucleotides

While Hershey and Chase's experiment determined the role of DNA in heredity, earlier work by biochemist P.A. Levine had shown that DNA was made up of a series of units called **nucleotides**. Each nucleotide is made of three parts — a sugar called deoxyribose, a phosphate group (also called phosphoric acid), and four nitrogen-containing bases. The nitrogen bases are **adenine, guanine, thymine**, and **cytosine**, which are abbreviated as A, G, T, and C, respectively. Figure 6.4 shows the four nitrogen bases of DNA.

Levine found that each nitrogen base is attached to a sugar, and each sugar is then attached to a phosphate group to form a single nucleotide. Each nucleotide is named for the base it contains.

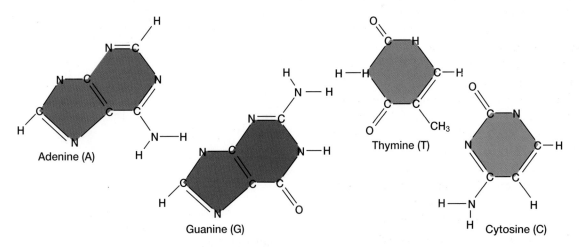

Figure 6.4 The nitrogen bases of DNA are adenine, guanine, thymine, and cytosine.

For example, Figure 6.5 shows an adenine nucleotide. Therefore, in DNA there are four possible nucleotides, each containing one of four bases. Note that adenine and guanine have a double-ring structure. They belong to a group of nucleotides called **purines**. Thymine and cytosine have a single-ring structure. Single-ring nucleotides are called **pyrimidines**.

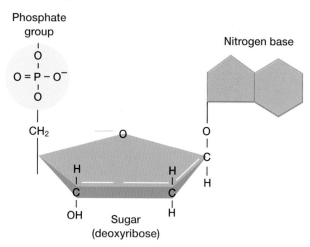

Figure 6.5 One DNA nucleotide, the adenine nucleotide.

Further studies showed that nucleotides are joined together to form long chains, much like beads in a necklace. The phosphate group of one nucleotide is bonded to the deoxyribose sugar of an adjacent nucleotide, as shown in Figure 6.6. The phosphate groups and deoxyribose molecules form the backbone of the chain, and the nitrogen bases stick out like the teeth on a zipper. Erwin Chargaff, another scientist studying the chemical structure of DNA, found that in any given species the amounts of adenine and thymine were virtually the same, as were the amounts of guanine and cytosine. The questions still remained, however, of how DNA was constructed and exactly how DNA carried genetic information.

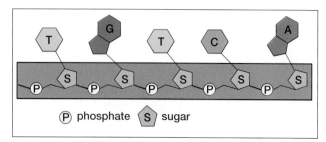

Figure 6.6 Nucleotides are joined together in a long chain.

Word LINK

Now that you know what DNA is made of and where DNA is found, why do you think scientists called this chemical deoxyribonucleic acid?

Discovering the Double Helix

Like athletes, scientists can be very competitive. As the evidence mounted, scientists knew they were very close to determining the structure of DNA. Many people were vying to be the first to make this important discovery. The race was on! Here are the facts the scientists knew at the time.

- DNA is made of nucleotides.

- Nucleotides are linked together in a string. The sugar of one nucleotide is attached to the phosphate group of the next, and the nitrogen bases stick out from one side of this sugar-phosphate "backbone."

- In each DNA molecule, the number of adenine nucleotides equals the number of thymine nucleotides, and the number of cytosine nucleotides equals the number of guanine nucleotides.

- If the nucleotides are strung in a straight line, a typical DNA molecule would be over a metre long. Somehow, the DNA molecule must be compressed.

The work of Rosalind Franklin (see Figure 6.7) provided another crucial piece of evidence needed to solve the mystery of DNA's structure. Franklin, along with Maurice Wilkins, the head of the laboratory where she worked in King's College, London, had perfected a technique that used X rays to photograph molecules. Although it takes an expert eye to interpret these pictures (see Figure 6.8), some of Franklin's photographs of DNA showed patterns that indicated DNA was like a giant spring or coil. Furthermore, the DNA molecule had a constant diameter of 2 nm. It did not get wider in some parts and narrower in others.

Figure 6.7 Rosalind Franklin, a British crystallographer, used X ray diffraction techniques to discover the double helix nature of the DNA molecule.

Watson and Crick also determined that the nitrogen bases were always paired in the same manner: adenine with thymine and guanine with cytosine. (See Figure 6.9) This explained the earlier discovery by Chargaff that adenine and thymine were always present in equal amounts, as were amounts of guanine and cytosine. These paired nitrogen bases are called **complementary base pairs**.

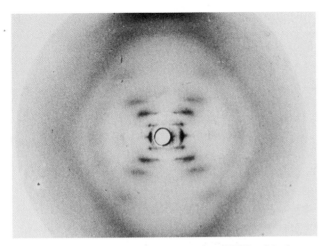

Figure 6.8 X-ray diffraction photograph of DNA taken by Rosalind Franklin.

Armed with this new information, and everything else that had been discovered about DNA, scientists James Watson and Francis Crick at the University of Cambridge, England, set about to propose a structure of DNA that would fit all the known facts. Using Dr. Franklin's photographs, Watson and Crick made scale models to try to fit all of the facts together. Finally, they found a structure that worked. They determined that the structure of DNA was similar to the handrails and steps in a spiral staircase. The "sides" (or handrails) of the DNA molecule were made up of two twisted strands made of alternating deoxyribose and phosphate molecules. In between the two strands were the paired nitrogen bases that were joined by hydrogen bonds. They called this shape the **double helix**.

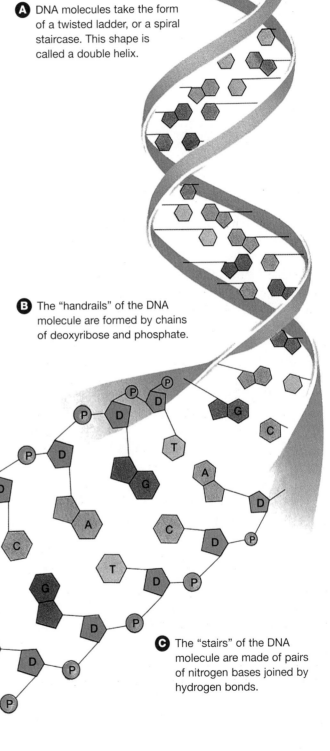

A DNA molecules take the form of a twisted ladder, or a spiral staircase. This shape is called a double helix.

B The "handrails" of the DNA molecule are formed by chains of deoxyribose and phosphate.

C The "stairs" of the DNA molecule are made of pairs of nitrogen bases joined by hydrogen bonds.

Key	
P	= Phosphate
D	= Deoxyribose
A	= Adenine
T	= Thymine
G	= Guanine
C	= Cytosine

Figure 6.9 The structure of DNA

BIO FACT

Watson, Crick, and Wilkins received a Nobel Prize in 1962 for their discovery of the structure of DNA. Why was Rosalind Franklin not recognized for her contribution to the discovery? In 1958, Franklin died of cancer at the age of 37. Because the Nobel Prize cannot be awarded to more than three people and the persons must be living, Wilkins received the honour instead of Franklin.

Word LINK

Francis Crick said, "If you want to understand function, study structure." What do you think he meant by this statement?

Nucleotide Sequences

A fern and a frog are different organisms composed of different proteins. However, if you were to compare the chromosomes of these organisms, you would find that they contain DNA made up of the same types of nucleotides — adenine, thymine, guanine, and cytosine bases. How can organisms be so different if their DNA is composed of the same nucleotides? The answer lies in the *sequence* of the nucleotides along the DNA strands.

Unique genetic information is determined by the sequence of nucleotides. A sequence of A-T-C-G-G-A carries different information from the sequence C-A-G-T-T-A-C. The closer the relationship between two organisms, the greater the similarities in their DNA sequences. For example, the DNA sequence of a wolf would be similar to that of a coyote, but different from that of a cactus.

An interesting feature of DNA is that if you know the sequence of bases on one strand of DNA, you also know the sequence of the bases on the opposite strand because of the way the pairs of bases combine. For example, if the sequence on a section of DNA is A-T-C-G-A-G-T-T, then the opposite strand would have the sequence: T-A-G-C-T-C-A-A.

It may seem hard to believe that all the information needed to build and operate an organism is stored in something as simple as the sequence of four bases along a strand of DNA. To put this in perspective, however, remember that a computer uses only two sources of information — the presence or absence of an electrical impulse — and look at what a computer can do! The Morse code shown in Figure 6.10 on the next page is also very simple. It uses combinations of dots and dashes to represent each letter in the alphabet. The 26 letters can be combined in ways to give all the information that can be conveyed by the English and many other languages.

THINKING LAB

Evidence for Nucleotide Pairs

Background

One of the pieces that helped to solve the DNA puzzle was the discovery of a numerical relationship between the nitrogen bases of DNA. This relationship was revealed by carrying out a chemical analysis of DNA.

You Try It

1. Examine the data in the table. Note the amounts of adenine, guanine, cytosine, and thymine found in the DNA of each of the cells studied.

2. Compare the amounts of A, T, G, and C in each sample of DNA.

3. Why do you think the relative amounts are so similar in human liver and thymus cells?

4. What fact can you state about the overall composition of DNA, regardless of its source?

Proportions of DNA bases in different tissues and organisms

Source of sample	Percent of each base in DNA samples			
	A	G	C	T
Human liver	30.3	19.5	19.9	30.3
Human thymus	30.9	19.9	19.8	29.4
Wheat plant	27.3	22.7	22.8	27.1
Bacterium	24.7	26.0	25.7	23.6

Sign	Signal	Sign	Signal
A	● ▬	S	● ● ●
B	▬ ● ● ●	T	▬
C	▬ ● ▬ ●	U	● ● ▬
D	▬ ● ●	V	● ● ● ▬
E	●	W	● ▬ ▬
F	● ● ▬ ●	X	▬ ● ● ▬
G	▬ ▬ ●	Y	▬ ● ▬ ▬
H	● ● ● ●	Z	▬ ▬ ● ●
I	● ●	1	● ▬ ▬ ▬ ▬
J	● ▬ ▬ ▬	2	● ● ▬ ▬ ▬
K	▬ ● ▬	3	● ● ● ▬ ▬
L	● ▬ ● ●	4	● ● ● ● ▬
M	▬ ▬	5	● ● ● ● ●
N	▬ ●	6	▬ ● ● ● ●
O	▬ ▬ ▬	7	▬ ▬ ● ● ●
P	● ▬ ▬ ●	8	▬ ▬ ▬ ● ●
Q	▬ ▬ ● ▬	9	▬ ▬ ▬ ▬ ●
R	● ▬ ●	0	▬ ▬ ▬ ▬ ▬

Figure 6.10 The Morse code uses a series of short (dot) and long (dash) signals to indicate numbers and letters of the alphabet. When used in the correct sequence, the code can be used to form words and sentences.

BIO FACT

There are about 3 billion nucleotides in each human cell, strung together to make up 46 chromosomes.

PAUSE ● RECORD

If the base sequence on a strand of DNA is T-A-C-C-G-A-G-T-T, what is the base sequence on the opposite strand?

Web LINK

Chromosome 21 was the first human chromosome to be completely sequenced. This means that the genetic information encoded as DNA is known for every gene on chromosome number 21. This milestone was achieved in May 2000. The knowledge of gene sequences and entire chromosomal sequences provides us with the information needed to detect the presence or absence of specific genes in individuals. To find out more about this accomplishment, and to investigate the issues surrounding it, go to the web site shown below. Go to **Science Resources**, then to **BIOLOGY 11** to find out where to go next. Evaluate the risks and benefits of pursuing and then using gene and chromosome sequence information. Should individuals or companies be permitted to patent gene sequences or entire chromosome sequences?
www.school.mcgrawhill.ca/resources/

MINI LAB

Nucleotide Model

Watson and Crick built a model of DNA using wire, string, and tin. They tinkered in their laboratory until they constructed the ladder-like model that helped them understand how DNA was constructed. One of their models is shown here.

With a partner, determine a way to construct a model of two nucleotide pairs in a DNA molecule. You may use materials of your choice. For example, you might use cardboard or wood strips, and small balls of modelling clay for your model.

Analyze

How did making a model of two paired nucleotides help you review and remember the information you have learned so far in this chapter? Why do you think DNA is coiled?

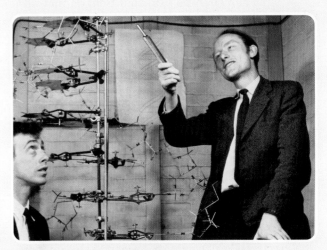

Watson and Crick display their model of the DNA molecule, which shows the characteristic double helix pattern.

Genes and Proteins

Like the Morse code, DNA stores information in a type of code — the **genetic code**. The order of base pairs in a DNA molecule makes up the genetic code of an organism. Before you can decipher the genetic code, however, it is important to understand the type of information that the code carries. For example, what instructions does DNA give to a cell? To answer this, you need to understand the relationship between genes and proteins.

Proteins are made of 20 kinds of amino acids linked together in a certain order in each protein. Linked amino acids form long chains called **polypeptides**, and two or more polypeptides are joined to make a particular protein. A protein may be made of hundreds or thousands of amino acids. Each different type of protein contains different

numbers of the 20 amino acids, arranged in a specific order (see Figure 6.11).

All organisms contain and make proteins. Proteins are important structural components of your cells, and thus of your body as a whole. Certain types of cells are largely made up of protein. For example, your hair and fingernails are made mostly of a protein called keratin. The hemoglobin found in your red blood cells is a protein, as is insulin and other hormones. Other proteins produced by cells, called enzymes, control virtually all of the chemical reactions going on in your body; it is these chemical reactions that provide your body with energy. All of your actions, including running, eating, and even thinking, depend on enzymes. Some enzymes drive the cell cycles of growth and division, while others stop cell cycles.

Investigation 6 • A

DNA Extraction

DNA is always pictured as a double helix. It takes a very high-powered microscope to actually see the double helix, however. In this investigation, you will extract DNA from animal tissue to find out what DNA looks like with the unaided eye.

Pre-lab Question

What two safety precautions must be considered when working with NaCl and ethanol?

Problem

How can DNA be extracted from animal tissue?

Prediction

Predict what must occur to a cell before its DNA can be removed.

CAUTION: When using NaCl, ethanol, and animal tissues, avoid contact with eyes or skin. If contact does occur, rinse thoroughly with water and inform your teacher. Wash your hands thoroughly with soap and water after you have completed this investigation.

Materials

mortar and pestle   cheesecloth

250 mL beaker   50 mL beaker (2)
glass stirring rod   graduated cylinder
small piece of fish muscle tissue (approximately 1 cm^3)
0.9% NaCl (0.9 g of NaCl in 100 mL distilled water)
10% dishwashing detergent (10 mL in 90 mL water)
95% ethanol (ice cold)

Procedure

1. Place the sample of fish tissue in the mortar.

2. Add 10 mL of 0.9% NaCl and grind thoroughly with the pestle for 2 to 5 min.

3. Strain the solution through three layers of cheesecloth and collect the liquid in the 250 mL beaker.

4. Pour the liquid into one 50 mL beaker and add 1.5 mL of 10% dishwashing detergent.

5. Estimate the volume of the extract in the beaker. Then measure approximately twice as much ice-cold 95% ethanol into the other 50 mL beaker.

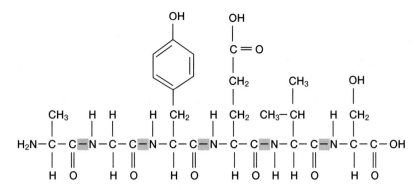

Figure 6.11 This polypeptide is made up of six amino acids. The amino acids are connected with chemical bonds, shown as shaded areas.

DNA determines how amino acids are strung together and how proteins are made. The sequence of amino acids is determined by the sequence of nucleotides in the DNA. In other words, the DNA is a code that specifies how to put amino acids in a particular order. A gene is the segment of DNA that controls the production of a protein. The order of nucleotides in a gene is a type of message — written in genetic code — that provides the information necessary to build a protein.

6. Slightly tilt the beaker holding the fish extract and gently add the ethanol to the suspension by pouring ethanol down the inside of the beaker.

7. Use the glass stirring rod to gently stir the mixture. When you see a precipitate form at the boundary of the two liquids, twirl the rod to spool the DNA sample onto the glass rod.

Post-lab Questions

1. Qualitatively describe DNA.

2. List the components that make up DNA.

Conclude and Apply

3. Draw a labelled diagram of a DNA molecule.

4. Why did you use detergent in step 4? Think about what you normally use detergent for. (Hint: Cell membranes are made of proteins and lipids.)

Exploring Further

5. How is DNA extracted from tissue on a larger scale? Conduct research to find out, and describe the process in a paragraph or flowchart.

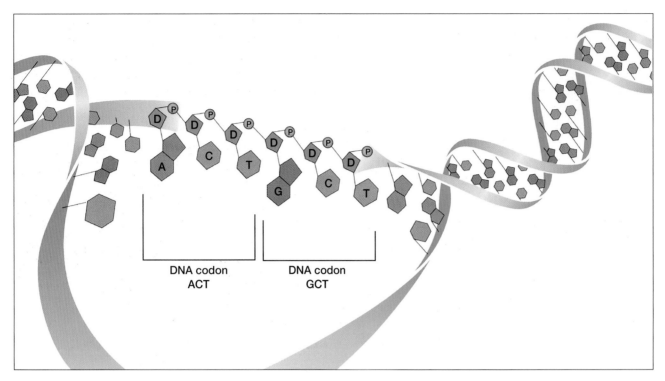

Figure 6.12 Three bases form each codon. Codons define a particular amino acid in a protein.

The Genetic Code

How is the genetic code written? Recall that there are 20 amino acids but that DNA contains only four kinds of bases. If we tried to use nucleotides one at a time to code for amino acids, we would only be able to code for four different amino acids. If we took the nucleotides two at a time (for example, using AT or CG to code for a single amino acid), we still would not be able to come up with enough different combinations to code for all 20 amino acids. It takes combinations of three nucleotides in order to have enough different "code words" to represent 20 amino acids. Using three base sequences at a time (for example, ACT, AAC, CAG), there are 64 possible combinations of the four different nucleotides. This is far more than is needed to code for 20 different amino acids. Each set of three bases is known as a **codon** (see Figure 6.12) Since there are 64 possible codons and only 20 amino acids, in some cases two or more codons code for the same amino acids. In other words, there are codon synonyms.

In order for proteins to be manufactured, genetic information from DNA must be carried to the cell's ribosomes. This task is performed by a molecule similar to DNA, called RNA

Table 6.1 The RNA genetic code

First base in codon	Second base in codon				Third base in codon
	U	C	A	G	
U	phenylalanine	serine	tyrosine	cysteine	U
	phenylalanine	serine	tyrosine	cysteine	C
	leucine	serine	stop	stop	A
	leucine	serine	stop	tryptophan	G
C	leucine	proline	histidine	arginine	U
	leucine	proline	histidine	arginine	C
	leucine	proline	glutamine	arginine	A
	leucine	proline	glutamine	arginine	G
A	isoleucine	threonine	asparagine	serine	U
	isoleucine	threonine	asparagine	serine	C
	isoleucine	threonine	lysine	arginine	A
	methionine	threonine	lysine	arginine	G
G	valine	alanine	aspartate	glycine	U
	valine	alanine	aspartate	glycine	C
	valine	alanine	glutamate	glycine	A
	valine	alanine	glutamate	glycine	G

(ribonucleic acid). RNA also has four bases, however, rather than thymine, RNA contains uracil (U), which forms a base pair with adenine. You will learn more about this process in future studies. Table 6.1 shows the amino acids and their three-letter codes used by RNA.

As you look over the table, notice that 61 triplets correspond to a particular amino acid. The remaining three triplets are stop codons. **Stop codons** indicate that no more amino acids should be added and thus, the production of a particular protein is complete. The amino acid with the base sequence AUG, called methionine, is a start codon, which indicates the first amino acid in a chain that will grow to be a protein.

Math LINK

Four bases cannot make enough pairs to code for 20 amino acids. How many possible code words would pairs of bases provide?

❙❙ PAUSE ● RECORD

Are you clear on the relationship between DNA, genes, nucleotides, codons, and amino acids? Write a description of each. If you need to, review the relevant parts of this chapter before you proceed.

DNA Fingerprinting

You might have heard that courts sometimes use DNA evidence to convict or acquit criminals. To obtain this evidence, scientists isolate DNA from blood or other biological materials, such as hair or skin, found at the crime scene (as shown in Figure 6.13). They also take a DNA sample from a suspect. Tiny quantities of DNA can be copied many times using a special technique so there is enough genetic material to use for tests. The samples are treated with enzymes that cut DNA strands into small fragments at specific locations. These fragments of DNA vary in length from person to person and allow us to identify individuals. The DNA fragments from the scene and those of the suspect are then compared.

Figure 6.13 Forensics investigators study a sample of clothing for DNA analysis.

Figure 6.14 on the next page shows how DNA fragments are analyzed and compared. Each band represents a fragment of DNA. Together, these fragments form distinct patterns that can be used like fingerprints to identify which person, or other organism, the DNA came from. This technique is often called **DNA fingerprinting**. No two individuals (with the exception of identical twins) have the same DNA sequences, and all cells in an individual have the same DNA pattern.

MINI LAB

Reading the Code

Can you read the genetic code? Look at Table 6.1 on the previous page. To find the codon or codons for a particular amino acid, first locate the amino acid in the table. The first base in the codon corresponds to the base in the row to the left of the amino acid. The second base in the codon corresponds to the base in the column in which the amino acid is listed. The third base in the codon corresponds to the base in the row to the right of the amino acid.

Analyze

1. What amino acid is produced by the codon GAG?

2. What is the codon for tryptophan?

3. How many codons code for valine?

4. Codons can only be read in one direction. Why is this so?

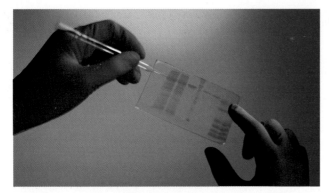

Figure 6.14 The bands on this genetic fingerprint represent different fragments of DNA. The pattern of bands can be used to identify individuals.

Web LINK

DNA has been used to solve many crimes involving people, but wildlife officials can also use this technique. For example, poachers can be traced by comparing DNA found in a carcass at the crime scene with DNA found in antlers, meat, or other parts of an animal, in the possession of the suspected poachers. To learn more about how DNA fingerprinting can be used to solve wildlife crimes, go to the web site below. Go to **Science Resources**, then to **BIOLOGY 11** to find out where to go next. Choose one case where wildlife officials have used DNA to help solve a crime, and prepare a five minute oral presentation about the case.
www.school.mcgrawhill.ca/resources/

ıı PAUSE **● RECORD**

All cells of an individual have the same amount of DNA *except* gametes (sperm and eggs). Based on what you know about reproduction and meiosis, why do you think this is so?

Biology Magazine TECHNOLOGY • SOCIETY • ENVIRONMENT

Is Genetic Testing a Threat?

Vast amounts of information about Canadians are stored on databases in various institutions throughout our country. This information may include your home address, gender, and income. In addition, you may be uniquely identified on various cards you carry, such as a library or debit card, through a magnetic strip, or through a bar code. Is it possible that your genetic identity, too, will be encrypted into a bar code in the near future? As medical research continues to yield more information about the human genome, advanced computer systems can now process these data. How will this information be used? Access to this growing body of genetic information has enormous social, ethical, and economic implications.

ISBN 007088708-X

9 780070 887084

Bar codes such as this could carry a person's genetic information.

The Value of Genetic Testing

Scientists use several mapping techniques to locate different segments of DNA or genes on a particular chromosome. These DNA segments can be cloned (copied), in the laboratory, and stored in freezers for later

use. Cloned segments of genetic material may be sequenced at any future time to determine the exact order of each base in the strand of DNA.

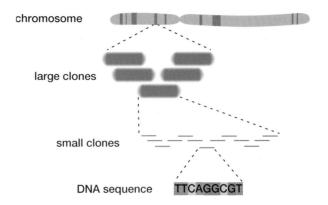

chromosome

large clones

small clones

DNA sequence TTCAGGCGT

DNA mapping can show several levels of detail.

Genetic testing is used to identify genes associated with various inherited diseases, such as cystic fibrosis and Tay-Sachs disease. At present, there are more than 4000 diseases that are known to have a genetic basis. Through genetic testing, we can also identify whether some people may be predisposed to certain diseases, such as Alzheimer's disease or various forms of cancer. Other conditions, including diabetes and heart disease, also have a genetic basis. Knowing that a disease or condition has a genetic basis can save lives because early detection of diseases means that preventive measures (such as medication or therapy) can be prescribed.

Reading a DNA Fingerprint

Background

After samples of DNA have been prepared in the laboratory, segments are stained and prepared in a special gel. These samples can then be compared with other samples to solve a crime or provide answers in other situations, such as a question of paternity (determining the father of a child). You know from your study of heredity earlier in this Unit that a child's DNA is a combination of the DNA of his or her parents. Can you analyze these DNA samples to determine the child's parents?

You Try It

1. Which parental DNA matches the child's? How did you decide this?

2. Try to determine the percentage of the father's DNA that matches the child's. Can you do the same for the mother's DNA? Explain this.

3. Describe other situations where DNA fingerprinting might be useful.

Child	Parents A	B	Parents C	D	Parents E	F	Parents G	H

Individual Privacy

Who should be genetically tested and who should have access to the resulting information? For example, could some individuals be denied employment in the future because of their genetic make-up? Many, employers already conduct employee health assessments for a variety of reasons. These may be necessary in order to:

- meet legal requirements;
- limit employer liability;
- identify employees' work-related needs;
- screen out unsuitable applicants;
- offer advice on health promotion such as diet, exercise, and so on; and/or
- meet company pension and/or insurance scheme requirements.

The results of genetic testing could be used to predict the future health of employees. They could also be used to obtain information about genetic predispositions to occupational diseases. Could a genetic condition place an employee or others at risk in the workplace? Employers are interested in minimizing costs due to absence, sickness, lost time for hospital treatment, or wasted training. How thoroughly should an employer be allowed to investigate the health of a potential employee?

We presently devote much attention to identifying genetic diseases. Although this information can help save lives, we must also consider some of the consequences.

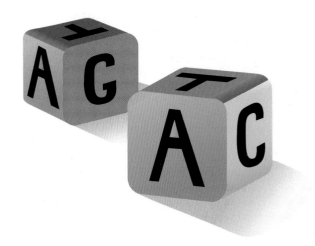

Follow-up

1. What is informed consent?

2. List other possible risks of genetic testing.

3. Should law enforcement agencies promote genetic screening to establish identification data banks to be used in criminal investigations?

4. How can we as a society ensure responsible genetic screening? What role should the provincial and/or federal governments take to regulate genetic testing? Debate this issue in class.

In addition to criminal investigations, DNA fingerprinting has other important applications. For example, it can be used to determine relatedness among people. The DNA of a child can be compared to the DNA of the mother and one or more possible biological fathers. DNA may also be used to establish pedigrees and determine the relationships among people living in different parts of the world. This is important in settling disputes concerning immigration.

DNA fingerprinting is also used by conservation biologists who study endangered wildlife species. For instance, it can be used to determine the species type, maternity, paternity, siblings, and sex of an individual. This allows researchers to answer questions about how individuals move within a population, and the genetic variability within those populations. Such information is important in managing populations of endangered or threatened species. Genetic data from wolves are being used to monitor their movements in the Northwest Territories (see Figure 6.15). Biologists are interested in identifying crucial habitat that wolves are using. Such data will be important in establishing sustainable populations of wolves.

Figure 6.15 Genetic information can be used to study the biology of wildlife, such as this grey wolf.

SECTION REVIEW

1. **K/U** Describe the pattern of pairing of nucleotides.

2. **K/U** Explain why the structure of a DNA molecule is often compared to a zipper.

3. **K/U** What is a codon, and what is its function?

4. **C** Make a sketch showing the structure of a nucleotide.

5. **C** Explain how DNA fingerprinting can be used to solve a crime.

6. **C** Explain the connection between DNA and proteins.

7. **K/U** Why is it important to have a stop codon in DNA?

8. **K/U** Explain how the hair of a suspect and blood found at a crime scene can be used to convict or acquit a suspect.

9. **MC** Explain why many discoveries in science are the result of people working together.

10. **MC** Discuss the following statement: genetic privacy must protect the dignity and integrity of the individual.

11. **MC** If researchers found a gene responsible for alcohol or drug addiction, should employers be informed?

12. **I** The best DNA extractions come from cells that are dividing rapidly. If you were planning to extract DNA from cells other than fish muscle cells (which were used in Investigation 6-A on page 192), what cells might you use? Explain your answer.

13. **I** Determine the possible banding patterns for each child in the DNA fingerprint shown here. Standard markers are used as a control.

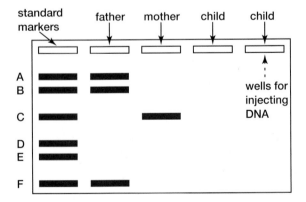

UNIT ISSUE PREP

If you have decided to investigate the field of genetic identification in your Unit 2 Issue Analysis, make sure you have noted how DNA can be used to identify individuals.

DNA Replication

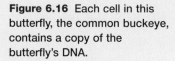

- Describe and explain the process of DNA replication.

- Explain how genetic technologies were developed to copy DNA.

Figure 6.16 Each cell in this butterfly, the common buckeye, contains a copy of the butterfly's DNA.

The butterfly in Figure 6.16 began its development when a sperm cell and an egg cell united to form a fertilized egg. From this one fertilized egg, the process of mitosis eventually formed a butterfly made of millions of cells. As you learned in Chapter 5, before a cell can divide it must first make a copy of each of its chromosomes. This copying process is called **DNA replication**.

During DNA replication, two DNA molecules are made from one. As you can see in Figure 6.17, each new DNA molecule will have one strand of DNA from the original molecule and one new strand. The "parent" DNA molecule and "daughter" molecules are identical — all made up of the same nucleotides arranged in the same order. Figure 6.18 shows an actual strand of bacterial DNA that is replicating.

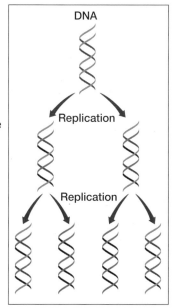

Figure 6.17 DNA replication results in the formation of two DNA molecules from one. Each new molecule contains one original strand of DNA and one newly formed strand, which is shown in red.

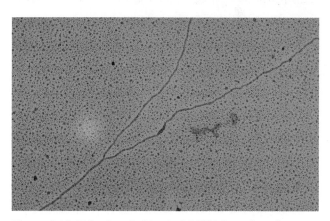

Figure 6.18 This strand of bacterial DNA is undergoing replication. A new strand of DNA is forming at the point where the strands divide.

You know that nucleotides on one strand of DNA always pair with the corresponding nucleotides on the complementary strand. Adenine pairs with thymine, and guanine pairs with cytosine. Therefore, if you know the order of bases on one strand, you can easily determine the order of nucleotides on the complementary strand. This is what happens in the process of DNA replication — one strand acts as a template to make a new strand.

The first step in DNA replication involves an enzyme that breaks the hydrogen bonds between the nitrogen bases that hold the two strands together. When this happens, the double helix structure begins to "unzip." As the DNA unzips, another enzyme moves along each strand attaching

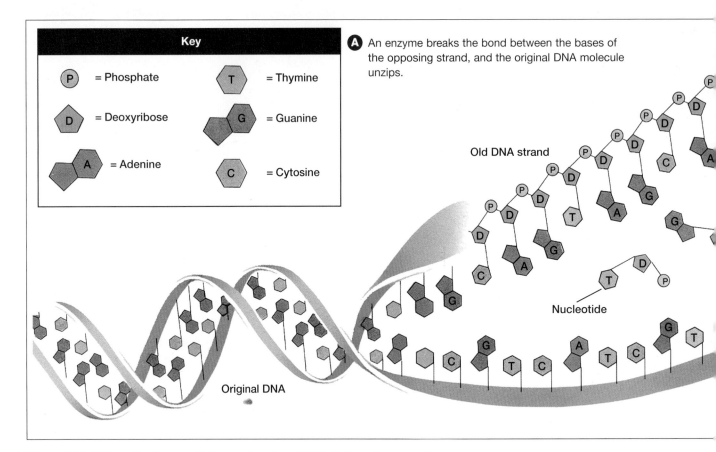

Key

(P) = Phosphate

(D) = Deoxyribose

(A) = Adenine

(T) = Thymine

(G) = Guanine

(C) = Cytosine

A An enzyme breaks the bond between the bases of the opposing strand, and the original DNA molecule unzips.

Old DNA strand

Nucleotide

Original DNA

Figure 6.19 DNA replication results in exact copies of DNA that can be passed on to offspring and to other cells.

free (or unattached) nucleotides to each base (see Figure 6.19). This process continues until the original molecule has been entirely unzipped and two new molecules formed. Each new DNA molecule is identical to the parent molecule.

▶ PLAY

Go to your Electronic Learning Partner to enhance your knowledge about DNA replication.

 MINI LAB

Modelling DNA Replication

Using only different coloured sheets of construction paper, scissors, and tape, model the process of DNA replication. Decide what shapes you will use to represent each of the six molecules in DNA. Work in a small group. Your DNA strand should code for cystine, tryptophan, and lysine, in that order.

Analyze

1. What did you learn about DNA by making a model of its replication?

2. Write a brief summary of how DNA replicates.

BIO FACT

Replication of DNA in a human cell takes about four hours. This occurs during interphase of the cell cycle.

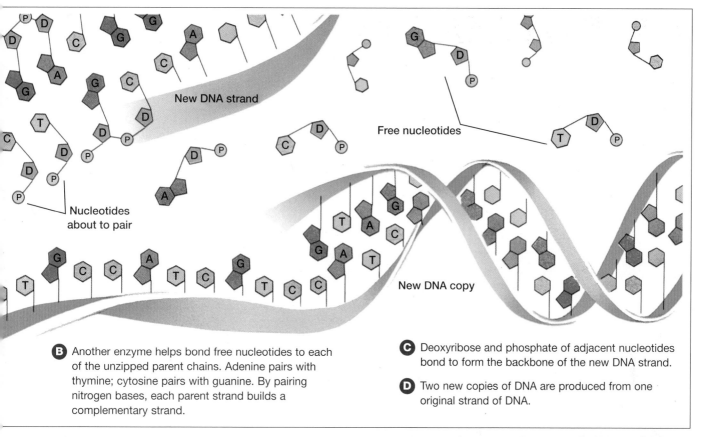

New DNA strand

Free nucleotides

Nucleotides about to pair

New DNA copy

B Another enzyme helps bond free nucleotides to each of the unzipped parent chains. Adenine pairs with thymine; cytosine pairs with guanine. By pairing nitrogen bases, each parent strand builds a complementary strand.

C Deoxyribose and phosphate of adjacent nucleotides bond to form the backbone of the new DNA strand.

D Two new copies of DNA are produced from one original strand of DNA.

Errors in Replication

Mistakes, or mutations, occasionally occur during DNA replication. The number of mutations that are actually passed on to new cells is quite small because special enzymes "proofread" the new strand of DNA for errors after replication occurs. Sometimes these enzymes can remove incorrect nucleotides and insert the correct one. Not every error can be repaired, however.

Mutations occur in all organisms. A mutation may be useful (**positive mutation**), harmful (**negative mutation**), or have no effect on the organism or cell in which it occurs (**neutral mutation**). Albinism, a condition in which pigment is missing from the skin, eyes, and hair, is an example of a genetic mutation (see Figure 6.20). A mutation in the body cell of an organism usually has a much less drastic effect than a mutation in a reproductive cell or in a growing embryo. When mutations occur in a reproductive cell or embryo, the development of the new organism can be affected. A low rate of mutation is present in every population. Each of us carries several mutations in our bodies.

Figure 6.20 This albino white-tailed deer lacks colour because its body cannot convert the amino acid tyrosine into melanin, a natural pigment found in the skin. This condition is caused by a faulty enzyme.

Recall from Chapter 5 that external influences, such as radiation or exposure to chemicals sometimes cause mutations. Such mutagens increase the natural rate of mutation and can alter the DNA and affect its replication. As a result, a different protein or property of that protein may develop, which could adversely affect the cell.

For example, some mutations cause cells to lose control of the cell division process and to grow abnormally. The cells reproduce in an uncontrolled manner and are said to be cancerous. These cells can spread out, crowding out healthy cells and destroying tissues into which they have spread. Since any body cell can behave in this manner, there is not one single type of cancer. The form of cancer depends on which type of body cell has been affected.

Mutagens include gases such as Agent Orange or mustard gas. The most widespread is ultraviolet (UV) radiation from the Sun. When your skin is exposed to UV light, the energy from the light is absorbed by DNA in your skin cells. This causes the hydrogen bonds to break in the base pairs.

Canadians in Biology

Programming Genetic Change

Professor Michael Smith

How do genes work? What part of an organism's genome does what? One way to answer these questions is to compare how a normal gene works with how a mutated version of the same gene works. For a long time, this kind of research was done using radiation to cause random mutations in samples of genetic material. Then, the desired mutations were carefully selected. This process was time-consuming. It would be much more efficient if a researcher could simply select a particular gene and mutate it as desired.

Such a system was first proposed in the 1970s by Canadian scientist Michael Smith. This system, known as site-directed mutagenesis, is now used throughout the world to investigate the structure and function of genes. In site-directed mutagenesis, short segments of DNA, called oligonucleotides, are made in the laboratory. These segments contain an error in the normal sequence of bases. The oligonucleotide is then inserted into a full DNA strand. The DNA, which now contains a mutation, is placed inside an organism, such as a bacterium. Any changes in the function of the bacterium may be attributed to the mutated gene. Although this process is easy to describe, it is very difficult to accomplish in the laboratory.

Professor Smith's technique allows genetic mutations to be, in effect, "programmed" like a computer. His approach is regarded as one of the most important and revolutionary scientific breakthroughs of the twentieth century. It earned Professor Smith the Nobel Prize for chemistry in 1993.

From Humble Beginnings

The path to the Nobel was not easy. Professor Smith had to overcome the initial indifference of his peers before he was recognized as one of the great figures of modern science. Indeed, when he first suggested his idea about site-directed mutagenesis, it was rejected as being of little interest! Despite this setback, Smith continued his research. Eventually, his ingenious method was published and widely accepted as a major achievement.

Michael Smith was born in England in 1932 to a working-class family. He did so well in elementary school that he earned a scholarship to a private secondary school. He was encouraged by his secondary school chemistry teacher, and went on to study chemistry in university. After graduating, he came to Canada and was fortunate to obtain a research position in the laboratory of another future Nobel laureate, University of British Columbia biochemist Gobind Khorana. This led Smith along the path that eventually brought his own Nobel Prize.

Smith carried out scientific research at many places in Canada and the United States before he finally accepted a biochemistry research position at the University of British Columbia in 1966. In addition to being a successful researcher, Michael Smith was also a successful businessman. He helped to establish a biotechnology firm in 1981.

None of Smith's success went to his head, however. He never failed to use his achievements for the good of others. He donated his Nobel Prize money, for example, in support of such organizations as the Society for Canadian Women in Science and Technology. Colleagues, associates, and former students all regard Professor Smith with only the fondest affection. Michael Smith died on October 4, 2000. He leaves behind a rich scientific and personal legacy.

The separated bases then fuse to two adjacent bases. This results in inaccurate replication and abnormal cell division. Eventually, tumours and skin cancer can result.

There are several kinds of mutations. Two of these are base pair substitutions and frameshift mutations. **Base pair substitutions** occur when one base pair is replaced by another base pair in a DNA strand. For example, an A-T pair can be replaced by a G-C pair. This type of change may alter the code and produce a different amino acid, which will result in a different polypeptide chain. This type of mutation can also cause problems if the substitution produces a stop codon. This would halt the formation of a polypeptide chain before it could be completed.

A **frameshift mutation** occurs when one or more base pairs are added or deleted from a DNA strand. This causes the polypeptide chain to be affected from the point at which the new base pair is added or deleted. As you can see in Figure 6.21, all of the codons from that point will code for a different amino acid.

nucleotide	A A T • G C A • T C G • T C A • T T C
amino acid	leucine arginine serine serine lysine

C
↓

mutated nucleotide	A A T • G C A • C T C • G T C • A T T
new amino acid sequence	leucine arginine glutamate glutamine stop

Figure 6.21 Addition of a nitrogen base to a strand of DNA causes a shift in the normal sequence of nucleotides. This is known as a frameshift mutation.

|| PAUSE   ● RECORD

How might a mutation benefit a plant or animal? Discuss this question with a partner.

Cloning

Cloning is the production of identical copies of molecules, genes, cells, or even entire organisms. The sheep in Figure 6.22 is no ordinary sheep. She's Dolly, the first cloned mammal. Dolly was cloned by Scottish scientist Ian Wilmut in 1997. To create Dolly, Wilmut took an egg cell from one adult female sheep and removed its nucleus. He then replaced the nucleus with the nucleus from a mammary gland cell of a different adult female sheep. The egg cell was then implanted into the uterus of a surrogate mother sheep. The cell began to divide and formed an embryo. Five months later, Dolly was born. Dolly was an exact genetic replica of her "mother," the cell that provided the nucleus. It took many failed attempts and experiments before this technique of cloning finally succeded.

Figure 6.22 This sheep, named Dolly, is a genetic copy. She was cloned using the DNA of one cell from another sheep.

 THINKING LAB

Genetic Technologies

Background

Cloning, genetic screening, and organ farming are all new technologies that have emerged in the last few decades. These techniques can be very controversial. While there are many positive aspects to the techniques, serious ethical questions often arise surrounding their appropriate use.

You Try It

1. Using print or electronic media sources, choose a genetic technology to investigate further. It could be a technology you have learned about in this chapter or

earlier in the unit, or it could be a technology you have not studied yet. Suggested ideas include transgenic organisms, the Human Genome Project, use of recombinant bacteria in medicine or agriculture (genetic engineering), organ farming, cloning, and genetic screening.

2. Prepare a short essay that briefly describes this technology and discusses its advantages and disadvantages.

3. Present your findings to the class.

4. Prepare a class debate on one genetic technology.

The possibility of cloning humans concerns many people. Do you think there should be limits on what we can and cannot clone? There are, many ways in which we currently use cloning. For example, cloning is used in agriculture to produce many copies of the same high-quality crop plant. In medicine, cloning is used to produce identical strains of bacteria for research.

More common than the cloning of whole organisms is the cloning of genes. In gene cloning, multiple copies of DNA are produced. Scientists can copy specific sections of DNA and insert them into the chromosomes of bacteria cells. Then, when the bacterial cell divides and its DNA replicates, the new section will be copied as well. Scientists often put DNA they want to replicate in bacteria, because bacteria cells reproduce so rapidly.

One example of a practical application of gene cloning is the production of insulin. (Insulin is a hormone that most people have in their body, but which diabetics lack. As a result, people with diabetes have to take insulin by injection.) Genes that produce insulin are introduced into the DNA of bacterial cells. Insulin is then manufactured by the bacteria.

Gene cloning is one way to create millions of copies of a single gene, but it is not the only way to clone DNA. A **polymerase chain reaction (PCR)** can do a similar thing. However, PCR can copy a DNA sequence that is less than one part in a million of the total DNA sample. This means that a single gene, or an even smaller piece of DNA, can be copied using this technique. PCR can be used to amplify, or generate multiple copies of, DNA from crime scenes. Investigators can thus create a lot of DNA from a small sample, such as a single strand of hair. PCR techniques have been used in a variety of other interesting ways, too. For example, DNA from mummies has been amplified and analyzed to better understand ancient life. As well, the DNA from fossils has been analyzed and used to compare the DNA of extinct species with the DNA of living species.

COURSE CHALLENGE

How can techniques such as the polymerase chain reaction be used to investigate ancient DNA? What specimens or evidence can now reveal new information?

SECTION REVIEW

1. **K/U** One strand of a DNA molecule has the nucleotide sequence A-C-C-T-G. What is the sequence of the nucleotides on the partner strand?

2. **K/U** List the steps that happen in DNA replication.

3. **K/U** What is the codon for serine?

4. **C** Explain some reasons why genes are cloned by scientists.

5. **C** Describe how a frameshift mutation can affect a DNA sequence.

6. **C** When Watson and Crick first started to think about the structure of DNA, they thought DNA had only a single strand of nucleotides. Would this structure have explained successfully how DNA replicated?

7. **MC** Many organisms produce copies of themselves, or clones, through asexual reproduction. However, the idea of cloning humans is controversial. Why do you think this is so?

8. **MC** Should scientists be allowed to pursue certain types of research even if some people consider the research to be controversial? Explain your answer.

9. **I** You examine two different types of cells. One type of cell is part of a gland specialized for producing an enzyme needed for digestion. The other type of cell is part of a tissue specialized for transmitting nerve impulses, a process that does not involve proteins. In which type of cell would you expect to find more DNA replication occurring? Explain your answer.

10. **I** Radiation can cause mutations, which can affect the growth of plants. Design an experiment to show that radiation caused the changes you observed in the experimental plants.

UNIT ISSUE PREP

If you have chosen to investigate cloning for your Unit 2 Issue Analysis, think about the advantages and disadvantages of this technology. Write down your ideas in preparation for your Unit 2 Issue Analysis.

Chapter Expectations

Briefly explain each of the following points.

- DNA is like a blueprint or master copy of an organism's information code. (6.1)
- DNA has three components: deoxyribose (a sugar), a phosphate group, and four nitrogen-containing bases. (6.1)
- Our current understanding of DNA is based on a series of discoveries by a variety of scientists over time. (6.1, 6.2)
- DNA molecules take the form of a spiral staircase (the double helix). (6.1)
- The order of the base pairs in a DNA molecule makes up the genetic code of an organism and provides the information necessary to build proteins. (6.1)
- DNA is copied in a process called DNA replication. (6.2)
- During DNA replication, errors called mutations can occur. (6.2)
- There are a variety of genetic technologies that recombine or use DNA in ways that are manipulated and controlled by people. (6.2)

Language of Biology

Write a sentence using each of the following words or terms. Use any six terms in a concept map to show your understanding of how they are related.

- DNA
- bacteriophages
- nucleotides
- adenine
- guanine
- thymine
- cytosine
- purines
- pyrimidines
- double helix
- complementary base pairs
- genetic code
- polypeptides
- codon
- stop codons
- DNA fingerprinting
- DNA replication
- positive mutation
- negative mutation
- neutral mutation
- base pair substitution
- frameshift mutation
- cloning
- polymerase chain reaction (PCR)

UNDERSTANDING CONCEPTS

1. Draw and label a timeline showing the contributions of different scientists that led to our current understanding of DNA.

2. Describe the structure of a DNA molecule.

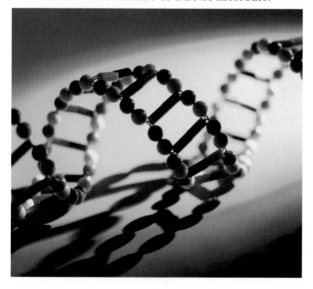

3. Name the two types of nitrogen bases and describe how they differ from one another.

4. Describe the difference between a base pair substitution mutation and a frameshift mutation. Which has the potential to create more harm? Why?

5. Describe two things that can cause mutations.

6. What is a stop codon?

7. What amino acid corresponds to the codons ACG and GCG?

8. If DNA contains 22% adenine, determine the amounts of thymine, cytosine, and guanine.

9. Write the complementary strand for the DNA sequence A-T-C-G-A-T-T-C-A-T-G.

10. Draw and label a series of diagrams showing DNA replication.

11. Explain why DNA is often referred to as the blueprint used to construct an organism.

12. Explain the links between the following pairs of words:
    (a) codon   amino acid
    (b) protein   DNA
    (c) DNA   genes
    (d) purine   pyrimidine

13. Keratin is one type of protein. Name three other proteins in your body.

14. Which type of cell in your body does not have the same amount of DNA as other cells in your body? Explain why this is necessary.

15. In what phase of the cell cycle does DNA replication occur?

16. Why do scientists often use bacteria to help them with DNA replication?

17. Explain how cloning can be used to create human insulin.

18. If the chromosomes of a fish and a frog are made up of the same four nucleotides, explain why these organisms look so different.

19. Explain why mutations can be positive or negative.

20. Why can codons only be read in one direction?

21. What is the codon for methionine?

22. How many codons code for alanine?

23. What is the amino acid produced by the codon UAA?

INQUIRY

24. Use a labelled diagram to describe what is occurring in this photograph.

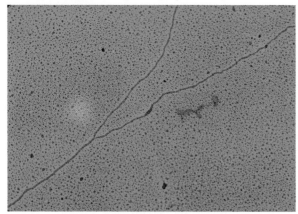

25. If a strand of DNA has the sequence A-T-G-G-C-A-A-C-G-T what is the sequence of nucleotides on the partner strand?

26. Explain what is happening in this illustration.

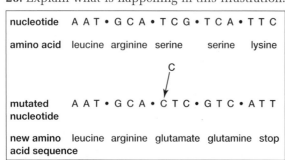

27. Describe the experiment that resolved the question of whether protein or DNA carried genetic information.

28. Explain the technique shown in the illustration here and describe how it can be used.

29. Yeast contains 31.3% adenine, 18.7% guanine, 17.1% cytosine, and 32.9% thymine. What can you deduce about the composition of yeast DNA from this information?

30. Explain how models were used successfully to explain the structure of DNA. What did you learn about DNA when you constructed your model?

31. What is the difference between a qualitative description and a quantitative description?

32. Explain why it would not be possible to code for enough amino acids if there were only two bases.

33. Explain why DNA replication is a necessary step before mitosis or meiosis can occur.

34. Explain why the addition or deletion of three nitrogen base pairs would not have the same effect as the addition or deletion of one nitrogen base pair. Use an illustration to explain your answer.

35. Sickle cell anemia is a type of base pair substitution mutation. Research sickle cell anemia and explain how the mutation occurs and how it affects individuals with this condition.

36. Will the DNA of a rat be similar to that of a mouse? Explain your answer.

37. If there are 64 possible combinations of the four nucleotides, why are there only 20 amino acids? Create a chart or diagram to help explain your answer.

38. Explain why investigators can use DNA from the saliva of a suspect to compare it with the DNA in a blood stain at a crime scene. Create a flowchart showing the steps that the saliva would undergo.

39. Identify the following molecules and describe their relationship in DNA.

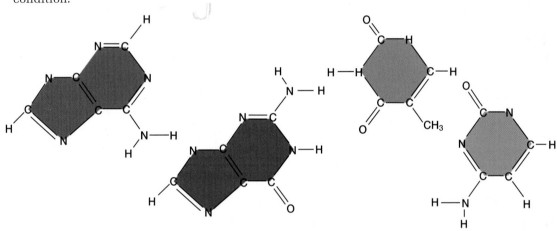

40. Choose one type of genetic engineering and create a table showing the advantages and disadvantages of the technique.

41. At a crime scene, investigators find a hair sample. How can they use this sample to create multiple copies of DNA? How can this be used as evidence to help solve the crime?

42. What would be the outcome if mitosis occurred before replication took place?

43. Make a chart showing the risks and benefits of using gene and chromosome sequence information.

44. Genetic testing can help to identify genes associated with various diseases. What are the positive and negative aspects of this?

45. What can potentially happen to DNA when human skin is exposed to ultraviolet light?

46. Explain why the work of Dr. Michael Smith was so revolutionary that he won the Nobel Prize.

47. Discuss the advantages and disadvantages of cloning technology.

48. How can DNA fingerprinting be used to study the conservation of wolf populations?

CHAPTER 7

Human Genetics

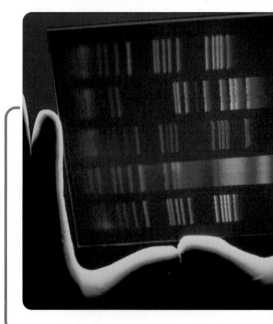

DNA bands, shown here under a green light, are being used to construct human pedigrees.

- What effect can certain genetic conditions and disorders have on people?

- How do changes in chromosome structure and number affect human development?

- How are human genetic conditions diagnosed and treated?

The patterns of inheritance discovered by Mendel in sweet peas and Morgan in fruit flies apply to humans, as well. However, the study of human genetics is not as easy as the study of genetics in other organisms. Sweet peas and fruit flies go through many generations and produce hundreds of offspring in short periods of time. Geneticists can select particular individuals for careful breeding experiments to obtain detailed information about inheritance patterns. Humans, on the other hand, choose their own mates, have long life spans, and produce smaller numbers of offspring. As well, most people do not keep accurate records of their family history. Only in rare cases, such as the British royal family, shown in the large photograph, do we have detailed records spanning four or five generations.

Until recently, most of our understanding about human genetics has come from the study of medical cases involving genetic conditions or genetic disorders. Genetic conditions such as albinism (lack of pigmentation) are rare but not life-threatening, while genetic disorders such as sickle cell anemia cause disease and may lead to death.

Today, molecular geneticists understand genetic disorders and conditions in greater detail. This paves the way for improved methods of diagnosis, prevention, and treatment through techniques such as recombinant DNA technology.

This chapter describes the genetic basis of some human genetic conditions and disorders, and discusses the techniques that have recently enabled some hereditary conditions to be diagnosed and treated. It also provides an example of how the field of biology promises to alter our understanding of human life itself.

Chapter Contents

Patterns of Autosomal Inheritance

- Understand the difference between genetic conditions and genetic disorders.
- Describe genetic disorders involving autosomal and sex-linked inheritance.
- Perform laboratory simulations to explore heterozygous advantage.

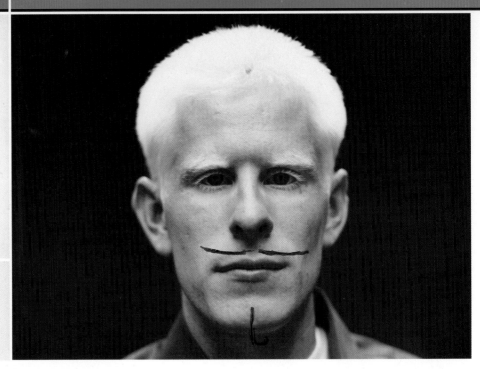

Figure 7.1 Albinism is a rare condition among many organisms. It results from a lack of melanin, a normal skin pigment.

In 1649, an English boy visited his physician, complaining that he was producing black urine. The physician concluded that a fire in the boy's belly was charring and blackening his bile, and that the resulting ashes were then passing into his urine. The physician treated the patient with bleedings, cold baths, a diet of cold liquids, and various drugs. Eventually, the boy grew tired of the therapy (which had no effect) and decided to let nature take its course. He grew into manhood, married, had many children, and lived a long, healthy life — always passing urine as black as ink.

We now know that the boy was suffering from a hereditary condition called **alkaptonuria**. In most individuals, an enzyme converts the inky black urine to its usual colour. In individuals with the condition, the genes that code for the production of this enzyme are not functioning. Enzymes are proteins manufactured from specific instructions carried by specific genes. As you have learned in Chapter 6, genes indicate the exact sequence of amino acids required to make a given protein. The wrong instructions are given when an allele is mutated. This results in an inappropriate sequence of amino acids and creates a defective protein.

BIO FACT

Using special biochemical techniques, scientists discovered the disease alkaptonuria in an Egyptian mummy more than 3500 years old.

PAUSE   RECORD

Enzymes are important chemical catalysts in the body. How do catalysts affect chemical reactions? Are catalysts changed in any way during these reactions? Write your answers in your notebook.

There are many genetic conditions within the human population. For example, albinism (as shown in Figure 7.1) is a rare genetic condition, but it is not life-threatening. Other genetic disorders, however, can cause severe medical problems. Why would harmful alleles that cause disease and early death continue to exist in our population? Recall what you have learned about dominant and recessive alleles and the concept of carriers. In heterozygotes, a normal dominant allele may mask the effects of a harmful recessive one. Thus, the parent is not affected but can pass on the harmful allele to offspring. Also, mutations constantly create new alleles, both harmful and harmless, within a population. Introduction of new alleles creates variation within the population. Variation allows individuals to better adapt to environmental change.

Family pedigrees show us that some traits are inherited according to the principles that Mendel described. Traits can be carried by dominant or recessive alleles, and genes themselves are carried on chromosomes. As you have learned, some genes are carried only on a sex chromosome (usually the

X chromosome) and are called sex-linked traits. Many others are carried on autosomes, which are any of the remaining 22 pairs of chromosomes that make up the human genome. Other genetic traits in the human population are not due to dominant or recessive alleles. Instead, they arise when there are changes in the number of chromosomes or in the actual structure of chromosomes.

Autosomal Recessive Inheritance

There are many autosomal recessive disorders. Such disorders are carried on the autosomes and are not specific to the sex of the person. One example of such a disorder is **Tay-Sachs disease**. Children with Tay-Sachs disease appear normal at birth; however, their brains and spinal cords begin to deteriorate at about eight months of age. By their first birthday, these children are blind, mentally handicapped, and display little muscular activity. Most die before their fifth birthday.

Individuals with Tay-Sachs disease lack an enzyme in the lysosomes of their brain cells. Lysosomes are cell organelles in which large molecules are digested. The recessive allele does not code for the production of the enzyme responsible for breaking down specific lipids inside the lysosomes. As undigested lipids build up inside the affected person, the lysosomes become enlarged and eventually destroy the brain cells that house them (see Figure 7.2).

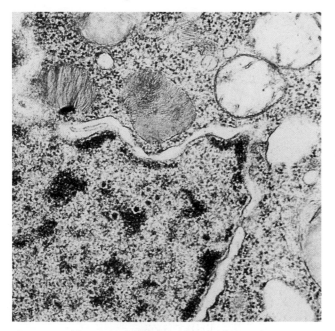

Figure 7.2 Electron micrograph of brain tissue of a person affected with Tay-Sachs disease shows enlarged lysosomes filled with lipid deposits. An enzyme deficiency prevents these deposits from being degraded.

There is no treatment for Tay-Sachs disease. However, a blood test has been developed to identify heterozygous carriers. Carriers have half the enzyme levels of normal individuals, which is enough to function normally. Before the development of this test, the incidence of Tay-Sachs disease was particularly high among Ashkenazic Jews. The origins of Ashkenazic Jews lie in Central and Eastern Europe and today they comprise 90% of the North American Jewish population. It is believed that the long isolation of these people in small European communities led to the increased frequency of the recessive allele within their population. Although Tay-Sachs disease has always been rare in the general North American population (one in 300 000 births), it was far more common among Ashkenazic Jews and their descendants (one in 3600 births). Since the availability of the blood test for carriers, the incidence of Tay-Sachs disease within this Jewish population has dropped dramatically.

Math LINK

You can use simple Mendelian genetics to determine if a condition or disorder is due to an autosomal recessive allele. If both parents are heterozygous carriers of a recessive allele, what proportion of their children will be at risk of inheriting both copies of the allele? What proportion will be at risk if both parents are affected, meaning that they are both homozygous recessive? Construct Punnett squares and present your findings as genotype and phenotype ratios. See Chapter 4, Section 4.2 to review how Punnett squares are constructed.

Another autosomal recessive disorder that affects young children is **phenylketonuria (PKU)**. In individuals with this condition, an enzyme that converts phenylalanine to tyrosine is either absent or defective. Phenylalanine is an amino acid essential for regular growth and development, and for protein metabolism. Tyrosine, another amino acid, is used by the body to make melanin and certain hormones. The phenylalanine in children with PKU is broken down abnormally. In ways that we do not yet understand, the products of this process damage the developing nervous system.

Babies with phenylketonuria appear normal at birth. If their condition is not diagnosed and treated, however, they will become severely mentally handicapped within a few months. Fortunately, newborns today are routinely tested for PKU. Infants who test positive for the disorder are placed on a special diet that prevents the harmful products from accumulating. Once their nervous systems are fully developed, these individuals can go on to lead healthy lives.

Albinism is a genetic condition in which the eyes, skin, and hair have no pigment. The colour of our hair, skin, and eyes is due to varying amounts of a brown pigment called **melanin**, which is produced in special pigment cells. People who are homozygous for this autosomal recessive allele either lack one of the enzymes required to produce melanin or, if the enzyme is present, lack the means to get the enzyme to enter the pigment cells.

Codominant Inheritance

Sickle cell anemia is one of the better-known examples a codominant genetic disorder. Affected individuals have a defect in the hemoglobin in red blood cells. This defect leads to blood clots and reduced blood flow to vital organs. As a result, they have little energy, suffer from various illnesses, and are in constant pain. Many die prematurely.

Hemoglobin is a complex protein that is synthesized and transported in red blood cells. This unique molecule has the ability to pick up oxygen from the lungs, transport it to the tissues, and release it to the body's cells. Like all proteins, hemoglobin is made up of a sequence of amino acids. The sequence in hemoglobin consists of four separate polypeptide chains (two identical alpha

chains and two identical beta chains) of about 150 amino acids each, as shown in Figure 7.3. When individuals inherit the allele for sickle cell anemia, one amino acid (glutamic acid) at a specific location in the beta chain is replaced by another (valine), resulting in abnormal hemoglobin. Figure 7.4 shows the inheritance pattern for sickle cell anemia. The allele Hb^S indicates the abnormal hemoglobin in sickle cell anemia and the allele Hb^A indicates normal hemoglobin.

The abnormal hemoglobin can pick up oxygen at the lungs and transport it to body tissues just as normal hemoglobin does. The oxygen diffuses from the blood across the capillary walls and into the tissue spaces. When the oxygen is released, however, the abnormal hemoglobin changes shape and begins to clump with other hemoglobin molecules in the red blood cell. The red blood cell becomes stiff and deformed, frequently forming a crescent or sickle shape (see Figure 7.5). These deformed cells block capillaries in the joints and vital organs. The condition becomes life-threatening when vessels to vital organs are blocked, because the blockage prevents other red blood cells from reaching these organs with a fresh supply of oxygen. The sickle cells are also very fragile and break down quickly. This results in a condition called **anemia**, where the overall red blood cell count is too low to support the body's oxygen requirements.

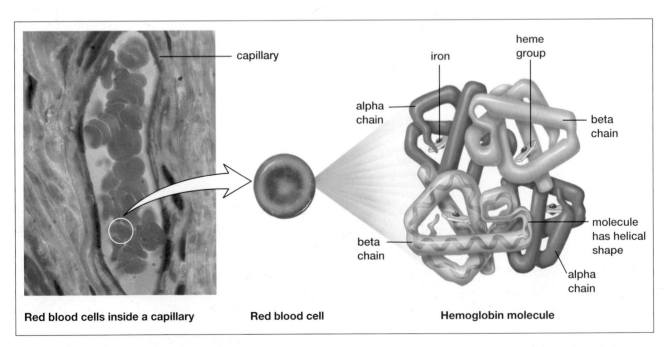

Red blood cells inside a capillary   Red blood cell   Hemoglobin molecule

Figure 7.3 Red blood cells, shown moving through a capillary in the photograph at left, contain many molecules of hemoglobin like the one pictured at right. Each molecule of hemoglobin is composed of two alpha and two beta chains of amino acids.

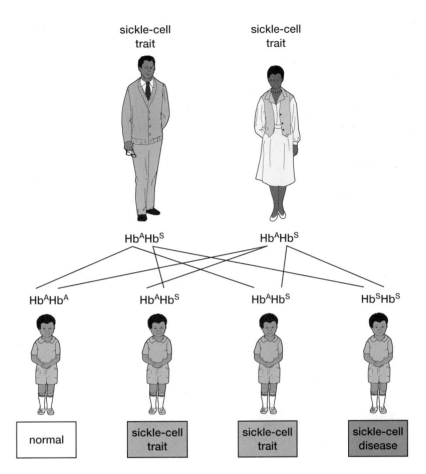

sickle-cell trait   sickle-cell trait

Hb^AHb^S Hb^AHb^S

Hb^AHb^A Hb^AHb^S Hb^AHb^S Hb^SHb^S

normal   sickle-cell trait   sickle-cell trait   sickle-cell disease

Figure 7.4 Inheritance of sickle cell anemia. In this example, each parent is heterozygous for the sickle cell trait. Among the offspring, there is a 50% chance of inheriting the sickle cell trait, a 25% chance of having sickle cell anemia, and a 25% chance of not having the disease.

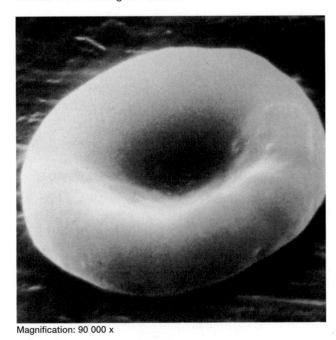

Magnification: 90 000 x

Red blood cells containing normal hemoglobin are round and smooth, allowing them to pass through capillaries easily.

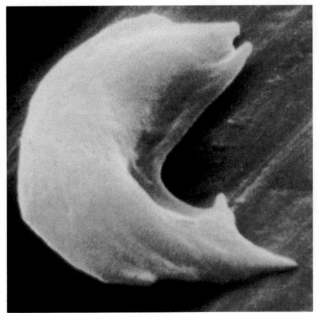

Magnification: 90 000 x

Sickled red blood cells have elongated, blunt shapes that stick easily in capillaries and clog them.

Figure 7.5 Electron micrographs of normal and sickled red blood cells.

Heterozygous Advantage

The recessive allele that causes sickle cell anemia is thought to have originated in Africa. Until recently, homozygous recessive individuals never survived to become parents, indicating that the recessive allele was constantly being removed from the population. Yet in some African regions, almost half the population is heterozygous for sickle cell anemia. Geneticists wondered how this allele could remain at such high levels when it was constantly being removed from the population.

The answer came from studying another serious disease in the regions where sickle cell anemia is most commonly found. In Africa, malaria is a leading cause of illness and death, particularly among the young. Studies revealed that children who were heterozygous for sickle cell anemia were less likely to contract malaria and therefore more likely to survive to parenthood. For reasons yet unknown, heterozygous females are also more fertile than homozygous females.

Word LINK

The word "malaria" comes from the Italian words *mala aria*, meaning bad air, because it was once thought that the disease was caused by inhaling the air around stagnant waters or by drinking from them.

BIO FACT

The association of malaria with stagnant water is at least partly correct, since malaria is caused by an infection of red blood cells by protozoa of the genus *Plasmodium*. These protozoa are carried to their hosts by female mosquitoes of the *Anopheles* genus. Like other mosquitoes, they lay their eggs in slow-moving or stagnant water.

The inheritance of one allele for sickle cell anemia is a classic example of **heterozygous advantage**, in which individuals with two different alleles for the same trait have a better rate of survival. Homozygous dominant individuals do not inherit the allele for sickle cell anemia. However, their normal-shaped red blood cells provide a perfect home for the protozoa that cause malaria. These homozygous dominant individuals are easily infected and, if born in malarial regions, often do not live to reproductive age. Homozygous recessive individuals with sickled cells may not contract malaria, but are likely to die young from the numerous symptoms of sickle cell anemia. In

comparison, heterozygous individuals produce enough normal red blood cells to meet their bodies' oxygen demands and enough sickled cells to reduce their susceptibility to malaria. Clearly, in this case it is an advantage to be a heterozygous carrier of the sickle cell allele.

In 1949, two biochemists, Linus Pauling and Harvey Itano, performed gel electrophoresis on both Hb^S and Hb^A hemoglobin molecules. **Gel electrophoresis** is a procedure in which molecules are placed on a viscous gel that is sandwiched between glass or plastic plates. The procedure is outlined in Figure 7.6.

Pauling and Itano discovered that Hb^S and Hb^A migrated independently of one another and formed two distinct bands on the gel. They knew that the molecule that had the greatest negative charge would migrate faster and farther. This proved to be the normal Hb^A molecule. Can you explain why?

Other scientists later explained that the Hb^S molecule travelled more slowly because it contained the neutral amino acid valine at a site where the more negative amino acid glutamic acid was found in the Hb^A molecule. Therefore, the more negative Hb^A molecule migrated faster across the gel toward the positively charged end, separating itself from the Hb^S molecule. This work paved the way for an important discovery in the field of genetics: the conclusion that genes code for the production of all proteins, not just enzymes. In the next investigation, you will model the inheritance of a recessive allele and heterozygous advantage in a population.

▶ PLAY

To explore gel electrophoresis and DNA testing, refer to your Electronic Learning Partner.

Autosomal Dominant Inheritance

Researchers can use two pieces of evidence from Mendelian genetics to determine if an autosomal dominant allele is responsible for a trait. First, since a dominant allele is expressed in heterozygotes as well as in homozygous dominant individuals, the trait will appear in every generation. Second, if one parent is heterozygous and the other is homozygous recessive for the allele, then 50% of the offspring will have the trait.

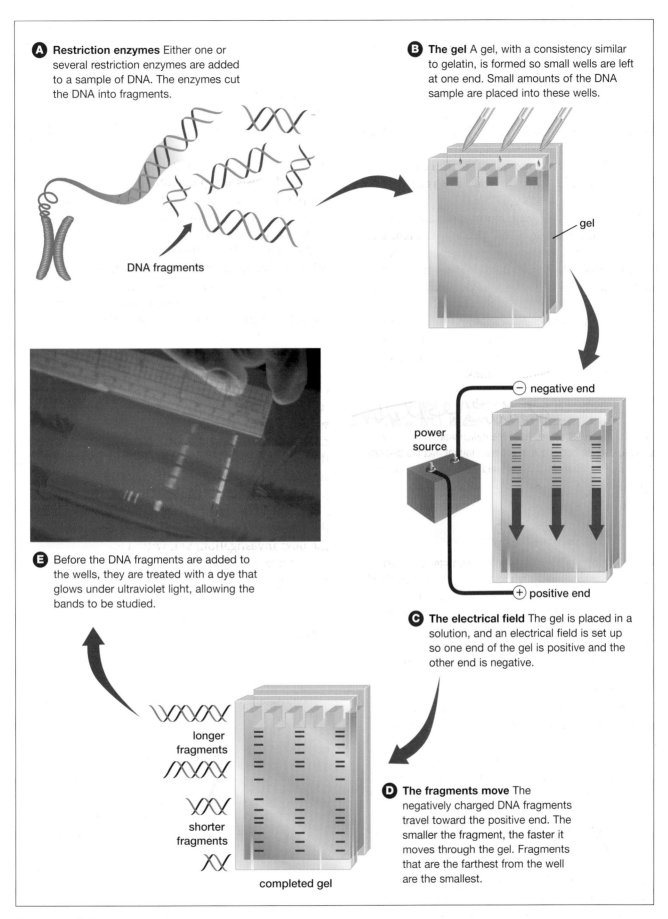

A **Restriction enzymes** Either one or several restriction enzymes are added to a sample of DNA. The enzymes cut the DNA into fragments.

DNA fragments

B **The gel** A gel, with a consistency similar to gelatin, is formed so small wells are left at one end. Small amounts of the DNA sample are placed into these wells.

gel

⊖ **negative end**

power source

⊕ **positive end**

C **The electrical field** The gel is placed in a solution, and an electrical field is set up so one end of the gel is positive and the other end is negative.

E Before the DNA fragments are added to the wells, they are treated with a dye that glows under ultraviolet light, allowing the bands to be studied.

longer fragments

shorter fragments

completed gel

D **The fragments move** The negatively charged DNA fragments travel toward the positive end. The smaller the fragment, the faster it moves through the gel. Fragments that are the farthest from the well are the smallest.

Figure 7.6 Gel electrophoresis

Investigation 7 • A

Genes and Populations

You have learned how certain autosomal recessive traits may affect humans. Such traits are inherited from parents who carry the recessive condition. Other organisms, too, carry recessive traits that may be passed on to offspring. In this investigation, your class will model the inheritance of alleles in a population of randomly mating American coots. The American coot is a large, duck-like bird with a very short, thick, red-tipped bill. It breeds throughout much of southern Canada and is a common summer resident of Lakes Erie and Ontario. Approximately 50% of the starting coots will be heterozygous (Aa), 25% will be dominant (AA) and 25% will be recessive (aa). As a participant, your job will be to record the genotypes of your offspring, compare them with those of others, and interpret the results.

American coot

Pre-lab Questions

- What will happen to the coot population if the recessive allele codes for a serious genetic disorder?
- What will happen to the coot population if the recessive allele also confers partial immunity against some other serious disorder?

Problem

How will you decide which coot genotype is best equipped to survive?

Prediction

Predict the percentage of the total population that each genotype will represent after five generations (steps 1–6 and 7) and 10 generations (step 8).

Materials

2 equal stacks of large index cards (the stock supply), each marked "A" or "a" on one side only

notebook   pencil

eraser

Procedure

1. You will be given your initial genotype on two cards, one with each allele of your genotype. In your notebook, make a chart similar to the one shown here. Record the initial percentages of each genotype and your initial genotype on it.

Data Chart			
Initial percentages	AA	Aa	aa
My initial genotype			
F$_1$			
F$_2$			
F$_3$			
F$_4$			
F$_5$			
Final percentages	AA	Aa	aa

2. Place your two allele cards behind your back and shuffle them. Once mating season begins you may confidently approach another student with that classic line, "Coot, coot?" to which your "mate" will reply, "Coot, coot!" You and your "mate" will then simultaneously present one of your cards to each other. These two cards become the genotype of your first offspring, while the

remaining two cards become the genotype of your second offspring.

3. If the genotype of either offspring is "aa," it will die. Keep trying until you produce two surviving offspring (see Rules of the Game).

4. Now assume that your parent genotypes die and that you and your mate assume the genotypes of your offspring. You may need to get new cards from the stock supply to do this. Record your new genotype as the F_1 generation on the chart.

5. Thank your partner, locate a new "mate," and repeat steps 2 through 4, recording the genotypes of the new offspring as the F_2 generation. Repeat this procedure until you have completed all five generations.

6. Pool the class data, tally the number of students with each genotype, and calculate and record the final percentage of AA, Aa, and aa genotypes.

7. Now begin again with your original genotype and repeat steps 1 through 6 while filling in a second chart. If any offspring is "AA," however, you must flip a coin. If it lands "heads," the offspring lives. If it lands "tails," it dies. Parents must continue to "mate" until two viable offspring are created for each generation.

8. Tally the class data after five generations, then proceed through another five generations using a third chart and tally the data again.

Rules of the Game

The "aa" genotype in offspring is lethal. Offspring with this genotype will not survive to reproductive age. Therefore two "aa" parents cannot successfully mate. If you and your mate are both "aa," one of you will need to obtain a new allele card (and thus genotype) from the stock supply.

Post-lab Questions

1. According to the first chart tally, what happened to the population after five generations?

2. Which genotype did "nature" work to select against?

3. Would it be possible to completely eliminate this genotype from this population?

4. What changed in steps 7 and 8?

5. What happened to the population according to the second and third chart tallies in steps 7 and 8? Compare these results to those of the first chart tally.

6. Can the recessive allele be completely eliminated in steps 7 and 8?

Conclude and Apply

7. Discuss the role of heterozygous advantage in maintaining genetic variation.

8. How can you relate the results you have observed to the pattern of sickle cell anemia inheritance in human populations?

Exploring Further

9. Evidence suggests that Ashkenazic Jews in Europe who carried the allele for Tay-Sachs disease had a survival advantage over those who did not. Research this topic and write a report that identifies the illness the Tay-Sachs allele may protect against. How is this story similar to what you have observed in this investigation?

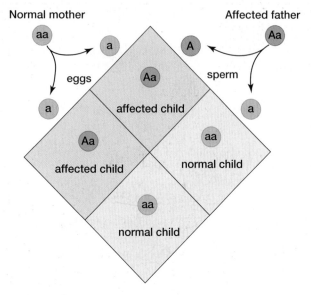

Normal mother

aa

Affected father

Aa

eggs

sperm

affected child

Aa

affected child

Aa

normal child

aa

normal child

aa

Figure 7.7 One example of autosomal dominant inheritance. Carriers of the dominant allele are affected.

Although genetic disorders caused by autosomal dominant alleles are very rare in human populations, they continue to exist. Some of them are caused by rare, chance mutations. In other cases, symptoms arise only after affected individuals have passed the age at which most of them have had children. The Punnett square in Figure 7.7 shows how an autosomal dominant trait can be inherited.

Progeria is a rare disorder that causes an individual to age rapidly. Progeria affects one in eight million newborns and does not run in families. This indicates that this very unusual affliction results from a random and spontaneous mutation of one gene. It also indicates that this mutated gene must be dominant over its normal partner, setting up a cascade of events that accelerates the ageing of the individual.

Huntington disease, an autosomal dominant condition, is a lethal disorder in which the brain progressively deteriorates over a period of about 15 years. Its symptoms typically appear after age 35, which is often after the affected individuals have already had children. Early symptoms include irritability and mild memory loss, followed by involuntary arm and leg movements. As the brain deteriorates, these symptoms become more severe, leading to loss of muscular co-ordination, memory, and the ability to speak. Most people die in their forties or fifties without knowing if their children have inherited the mutant allele.

Incomplete Dominance

The disease familial hypercholesterolemia (FH) is caused by incomplete dominance. That is, the heterozygote exhibits a phenotype somewhere midway between both dominant and recessive traits. Approximately one in 500 people are heterozygous, inheriting a defective allele for a gene that codes for the production of cell surface proteins called LDL receptors. Circulating LDL (low-density lipoproteins) cholesterols must bind to these receptors in order to be taken up and used by cells. With one defective allele, heterozygotes produce only half the required receptors and exhibit twice the normal blood cholesterol level. Homozygous recessives (about one in 1 000 000 people) do not produce any receptors and can have six times the normal blood cholesterol level. Over time, circulating LDLs build up in artery walls and eventually block them. This causes atherosclerosis, which leads to heart attacks and strokes. While heterozygous individuals may have heart attacks by the age of 35, homozygous recessive individuals who have the more serious form of the disease can be stricken by a heart attack at the age of two years.

SECTION REVIEW

1. **K/U** Explain the difference between genetic conditions and genetic disorders, and name one example of each.

2. **C** Explain how a disorder or abnormality can be passed along by autosomal recessive inheritance.

3. **K/U** What is meant by heterozygous advantage?

4. **K/U** Can a recessive allele be eliminated from a population? Explain.

5. **I** Predict why disorders caused by autosomal dominant alleles continue to exist in the human population. What evidence would you need to support your claim?

6. **C** Explain how DNA can be studied using gel electrophoresis.

7. **MC** What steps could you take to start building a list of genetic characteristics for people in your class?

8. **I** Explain some differences between the patterns of inheritance observed in autosomal recessive conditions versus autosomal dominant conditions.

EXPECTATIONS

- Describe the use of technology in detecting genetic disorders.

- Organize data to determine inheritance patterns of recessive human traits.

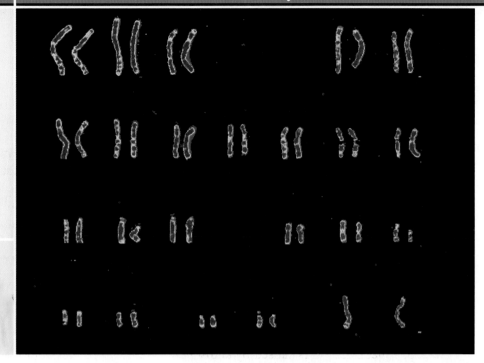

Figure 7.8 This karyotype shows the number of chromosomes found in a normal human body cell. How can karyotypes help to detect genetic disorders?

How do geneticists analyze the pattern of human inheritance? Two techniques that have been used successfully are the examination of karyotypes and the construction of pedigrees.

The Human Karyotype

Humans possess 46 chromosomes in every somatic cell; 44 are autosomes and two are sex chromosomes. A **karyotype**, as shown in Figure 7.8, is an illustration or photograph of the chromosomes in the nucleus of a somatic cell in an organism. To make a karyotype, blood or skin cells, for example, are first grown in a glass container. By adding a special solution, cell division is stopped at metaphase when the chromosomes are clearly visible. Then, the chromosomes are separated from the cells, stained, and photographed. Finally, enlarged images of the chromosomes are cut out and arranged in pairs according to their size, shape, and appearance.

Those chromosomes that are difficult to distinguish based on appearance alone are subjected to special staining techniques that reveal the unique banding pattern of each chromosome. The procedure for making a human karyotype is shown in Figure 7.9 on page 220.

BIO FACT

A karyotype can be prepared using any kind of cell that can be grown in culture, such as bone marrow, skin, white blood cells, or cells from amniotic fluid, for instance.

X-Linked Recessive Inheritance

As stated earlier, genetic conditions and disorders can be carried on the sex chromosomes, especially the X chromosome. For example, hemophilia A is a blood-clotting disorder with an X-linked inheritance pattern. Blood clotting is a multi-step process, and the cascade of reactions that stops bleeding requires the products of many genes. If one of the genes is mutated and its product is defective, then the clotting process is slowed down and a simple cut can become a serious problem. Approximately one in 7000 males inherits the allele for hemophilia A. Female carriers have a clotting time that is almost normal. Like many other sex-linked traits, males are at much greater risk for inheriting the allele than females. A female can only have the condition if her mother is a carrier and her father is a hemophiliac.

≪ REWIND

To review information about sex chromosomes, turn to Chapter 5, Section 5.2. Sex-linked inheritance was introduced in Chapter 5, Section 5.3.

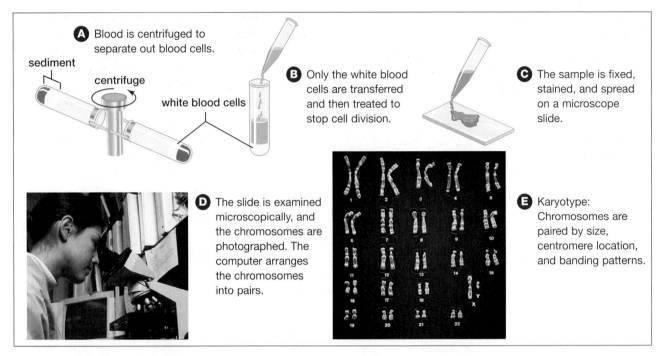

Figure 7.9 The making of a human karyotype. There are 22 pairs of autosomes and one pair of sex chromosomes inside the nucleus of a human somatic cell. To create a karyotype, the chromosomes are sorted by size and appearance into homologous pairs. In females, pair 23 is composed of two homologous X chromosomes, whereas in males there is an X and a Y chromosome.

MINI LAB

What Can a Karyotype Tell Us?

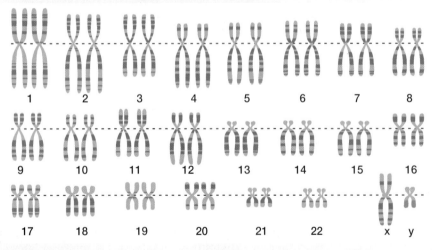

A human karyotype. The chromosomes have been stained to show their bands.

Examine the human karyotype carefully. Count and record the total number of chromosomes in this individual's karyotype, and the number of chromosome pairs. Look at the similarities and differences between the chromosome pairs.

Analyze

1. What characteristics are used to give a chromosome pair a number?

2. Which pair does not have a number? Explain why.

3. What is the sex of the individual? Explain how you know.

4. What stage in the cell cycle would be the best to use for chromosomes for preparing a karyotype? Give reasons why.

Constructing Pedigrees

As you have learned in Chapter 4, a pedigree is a chart that shows the genetic relationships between individuals in a family. After careful data collection involving interviews and direct observations, the pedigree chart is constructed using a standard procedure with specific symbols and definitions. Using a pedigree chart and Mendelian genetics, scientists can determine whether the allele responsible for a given condition is dominant, recessive, autosomal, or sex-linked.

Hemophilia afflicted some members of Queen Victoria's large family. Examine the pedigree of Queen Victoria and her descendants (see Figure 7.10). How quickly can you detect that males are the ones at risk and that females are the carriers? For female carriers, there is a 50% chance they will pass on the X chromosome that carries the recessive allele to their sons. Since fathers always donate their Y chromosome and not their X chromosome to their sons, a son can only inherit the allele for hemophilia from his mother.

⏸ PAUSE ● RECORD

What are the clues we look for when determining whether a trait is X-linked recessive? Suppose a carrier mother ($X^N X^n$) married a normal father ($X^N Y$). Construct a Punnett square and determine who is more at risk, sons or daughters. Can a son inherit the recessive allele from his father? If a daughter is heterozygous, what is the chance that her sons will inherit the allele? Record your conclusions and explain briefly.

BIO ● FACT

The Russian royal family of Czar Nicholas II, the last of the Romanovs, was executed by the Bolsheviks during the Russian Revolution of 1918. The location of their graves was concealed to discourage people from thinking of the Romanovs as martyrs. The grave site remained a mystery for decades, until skeletal remains were recently exhumed from a suspect site. The mystery was only laid to rest when DNA fingerprinting conclusively identified the remains as the Romanovs'.

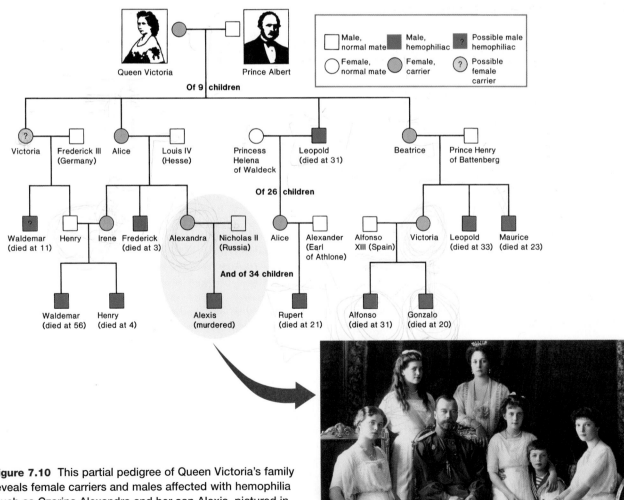

Figure 7.10 This partial pedigree of Queen Victoria's family reveals female carriers and males affected with hemophilia (such as Czarina Alexandra and her son Alexis, pictured in the photograph).

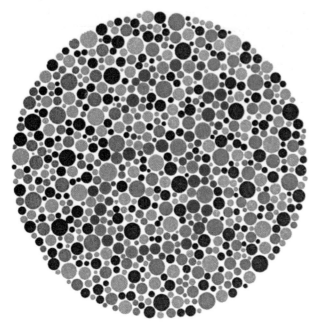

Figure 7.11 People with normal colour vision can determine the number hidden in the dots. Persons with colour blindness cannot distinguish the number.

Colour Blindness

Can you see a number in Figure 7.11? About 8% of men and 0.04% of women cannot identify the number as a result of colour blindness. Why is there such a large difference between the sexes? To perceive colour we require three separate alleles, each coding for three separate light-sensitive pigments. These pigments (red, blue, and green) are called opsins. Opsins are large protein molecules found in specialized cells called cones located in the centre of the retina. Each cone carries only one type of pigment, and colour is seen when different combinations of the three types of cones are stimulated.

The allele for blue pigment is found on an autosome, but the alleles for red and green are found on the X chromosome. Males inherit a single X chromosome from their mother (see Figure 7.12). If the allele for red is defective but the allele for green is normal, then the individual cannot distinguish between red and green. Of course, if the

---

Investigation 7 • B

Predicting
Performing and recording
Analyzing and interpreting
Conducting research

How is Eye Colour Inherited?

Human eyes show great variation in colour. Why is this so? You have your chance to explore this mystery in this investigation.

Pre-lab Questions

- Name and describe the coloured part of the eye.
- What gene product is responsible for eye colour?

Problem

How can you use population studies to develop a theory that will describe the eye colour variation in the human population?

Prediction

Develop one or more ideas for how eye colour is inherited. Choose one idea to investigate.

Materials

magazines
glue
paper for questionnaires

index cards
scissors
computer and printer

Procedure

1. Form groups of eight individuals. Using magazines, cut out pictures of various eyes and glue them onto index cards. As a group, agree on the eye colour that each picture represents and write it on the card for that picture.

2. Using a word processor, construct a questionnaire to ask participants questions such as the following:

   (a) subject's sex

   (b) subject's eye colour

   (c) eye colour of spouse

   (d) eye colour of *biological* family members only. (Note: In Caucasians, eye colour does not fully develop until the age of four. Therefore, you need to note the age of all Caucasian children for whom data are given).

allele for red is normal but the allele for green is defective, the results are the same. In heterozygous females, the dominant allele is normal, which usually results in normal vision. However, there are some cases of heterozygous females having normal vision in one eye and colourblindness in the other eye. Why would it be very rare to find a female who is colour-blind in both eyes?

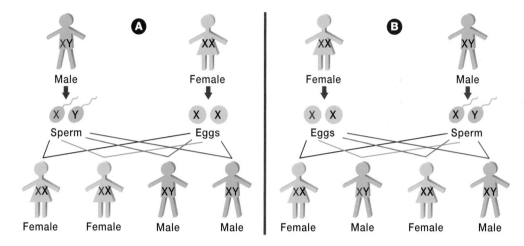

Figure 7.12 In colour blindness, males pass the X-linked allele only to their daughters (A). Females who are heterozygous for the condition have a 50% chance of passing the recessive allele to each child (B).

3. Select a location, such as a church, school, store, etc., at which to gather data. Each group member should select a separate location.

4. Obtain a letter from your teacher that you can show to participants, indicating the nature of your investigation.

5. For each person you interview, complete the questionnaire using the index cards to match and name the eye colour of the subject.

Post-lab Questions

1. Construct an "eye" pedigree for each family for which you have gathered information.

2. Consider your prediction of how eye colour is inherited. If your prediction is correct, what would be the calculated percentages for each eye colour? Use Punnett squares in your calculation.

3. Examine the data you have obtained for the family you studied. Using Punnett squares, calculate the percentage for each eye colour.

4. Construct bar graphs showing the predicted and observed percentages of eye colour on the vertical axis.

5. Compare the information on the pedigrees and graphs constructed by all group members.

Conclude and Apply

6. Can you explain the differences between your theoretical and observed percentages?

7. Is your prediction a plausible explanation for the inheritance pattern of eye colour?

8. What variables were controlled in this investigation?

9. What are some unavoidable sources of error? How could the investigation be improved?

Exploring Further

10. Eye colour among people varies in different parts of the world. Conduct research to determine if there is a relationship between human eye colour and a geographic variable (such as latitude).

The Case of the Caped Murderer

Background

They found Lord William's body in the library, sprawled on the floor with a dagger in his chest. A copy of his new will, leaving all his money to charity, was found unsigned on his desk. The wealthy Lord William was a bachelor who had no family other than his twelve nephews and nieces. His parents and siblings were all dead.

Inspectors Crick and Watson were the first officers to arrive on the scene. Before becoming a detective, Crick had dabbled in genetics. Glancing at the portrait of Lord William's parents above the fireplace, Inspector Crick explained to those assembled that Lord Edward (William's father) had bright red hair, caused by a recessive pair of alleles, while Lady Iris (his mother) had brunette hair, caused by a dominant allele. Crick further noted that Iris must have been heterozygous, because half of her children had been redheads.

Crick and Watson questioned the family and servants and discovered that there was a witness to the murder. On the fateful evening a maid, upon hearing sounds coming from the library, had spied through the keyhole and seen someone wearing a long, hooded black cape. "I could not tell if it was a man or a woman, sir," she explained, "but I did see red hair sticking out from under the hood. The

person was holding a dagger behind his or her back and I noticed that the little finger of that hand was crooked. It was bent inward toward the fourth finger."

"Aha! It's elementary, Inspector Watson!" cried Crick. "A bent little finger is due to a single pair of alleles. If a person carries just one copy of the dominant allele, they will have a bent little finger." Inspector Crick quickly become convinced that the culprit was a niece or nephew who stood to lose an enormous fortune if the new will was signed. To confirm his suspicions, Crick examined old family photographs and portraits, and assembled the following pedigree chart.

You Try It

Study the chart carefully. Determine who has inherited what alleles, and then answer the following questions.

1. Who murdered Lord William?

2. Why didn't Inspector Crick suspect any of Lord William's brothers or sisters?

3. What role did the dominant allele play in unmasking the perpetrator?

4. Why is David not a suspect?

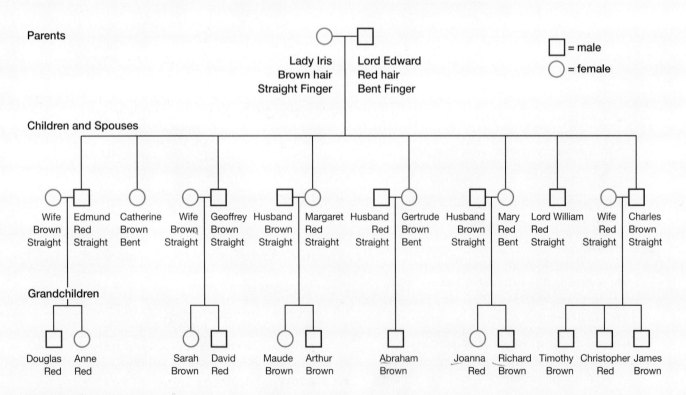

Pedigree of Lord William's family

Duchenne Muscular Dystrophy

There are several forms of muscular dystrophy, but they all involve the wasting away of muscle tissue. The most common and severe type is **Duchenne muscular dystrophy**, another disease caused by X-linked recessive inheritance. The muscle cells of individuals who have this condition become engorged with fat and connective tissue deposits, and they eventually waste away. About one in 3500 boys inherits the gene from his mother. Appearing normal at birth, they first develop symptoms between the ages of two and six. At about age 12, these individuals can no longer walk. Their head and chest muscles weaken, and most individuals suffer respiratory failure in their early twenties. Despite ongoing research, there is still no cure for this and many other genetic disorders.

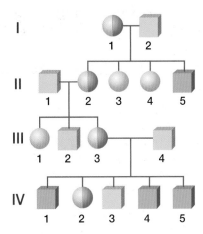

Figure 7.13 This pedigree shows a typical inheritance pattern for Duchenne muscular dystrophy. How does the pedigree indicate that this condition is a sex-linked disorder?

SECTION REVIEW

1. **K/U** What is a karyotype? What type of information can be obtained from it?

2. **K/U** What evidence indicates that the hemophilia allele that spread throughout many European royal families was inherited from Queen Victoria?

3. **MC** Construct a table with the following headings: Disease, Symptoms, Genotype. Summarize the diseases discussed in this section, indicating the symptoms that characterize them and the pattern of inheritance that causes each one.

4. **MC** Indicate how a female could inherit complete red-green colour blindness.

5. **C** Provide two explanations why hemophilia A is considered a life-threatening disease.

6. **I** Albinism is an autosomal recessive condition. Suppose that George with albinism marries Mary who is not affected. They have a daughter, Frances, who has albinism. Frances marries Jack, whose mother and sister both have albinism. Frances and Jack have a daughter, Anne, who is not affected.

   (a) Construct a pedigree of the family.

   (b) Identify the genotype of each person in the family.

7. **I** Construct a data table like the one shown here. Allow enough rows to collect data for all your family members.

   Obtain either PTC (phenylthiocarbamide) paper or sodium benzoate paper from your teacher. Place the paper on your tongue and allow a few seconds for the crystals to dissolve so you can judge the taste.

Do not allow the paper to rest on your tongue longer than 10 seconds. If you only taste paper, then you are taste-blind. Do not taste the paper a second time. The ability to detect the bitter taste of the chemical is determined by a dominant autosomal allele (T). Obtain sufficient paper to test as many members of your family as possible. Try to obtain data for three generations. Wash your hands after handling the paper. Construct a pedigree of your family indicating both genotype and phenotype.

Data Table

Trait	Phenotype	Possible genotype

8. **I** The pedigree shown here is of a family carrying the gene for phenylketonuria. Individuals with shaded symbols have the condition.

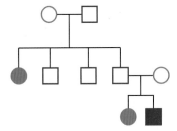

   (a) How is the disease carried to successive generations?

   (b) In the two generations with PKU, evaluate the parents' roles as carriers. (Are none, one, or both parents carriers?) Explain your answer.

Changes in Chromosomes

- Explain the causes of genetic disorders.
- Describe how the structure of chromosomes can change.
- Research diagnoses and symptoms of genetic disorders.

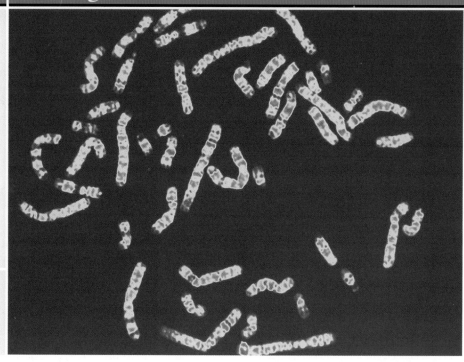

Figure 7.14 Differences in the number and structure of chromosomes can cause genetic diseases.

Nondisjunction

Some genetic conditions and disorders are caused when chromosomes or chromatids do not separate as they should during meiosis. You will recall from Chapter 5 that this phenomenon is called nondisjunction. If nondisjunction occurs in meiosis, the gametes will have either too many or too few chromosomes. If one of these gametes is involved in fertilization, the result will be an embryo with extra or fewer chromosomes than normal. Inheriting an extra chromosome is called trisomy. Human embryos with too many or too few autosomes rarely survive. Embryos that were miscarried (spontaneously aborted) often have one extra or one fewer autosomes than normal.

 THINKING **LAB**

Modelling Nondisjunction

Background

Nondisjunction during meiosis can occur during either anaphase I or anaphase II. During these stages, the centromere splits and the spindle fibres shorten to pull the chromatids to opposite poles of the dividing cell. In this lab, you will apply what you have learned to explore the various types of gametes that can result from nondisjunction and how they relate to certain genetic disorders.

You Try it

1. The diagram on the right shows the gametes that would result if nondisjunction occured at meiosis II. Copy the diagram on the left into your notebook, and complete it to show what would happen if nondisjunction occured at meiosis I.

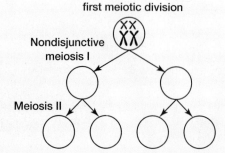

Nondisjunction in the first meiotic division

Nondisjunctive meiosis I

Meiosis II

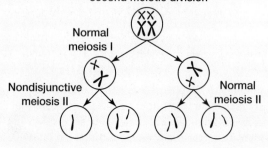

Nondisjunction in the second meiotic division

Normal meiosis I

Nondisjunctive meiosis II

Normal meiosis II

Down Syndrome

One of the most common genetic disorders resulting from nondisjunction during gamete formation is **Down syndrome**, or trisomy 21. Down syndrome arises when an individual receives three rather than two copies of chromosome 21. It is called a **syndrome** because it involves a group of disorders that occur together. Although symptoms can vary from one person to another, most individuals have mild to moderate mental impairment and a large, thick tongue that can create speech defects. In addition, the skeleton may not develop properly, resulting in a short, stocky body type with a thick neck.

BIO FACT

Other trisomies that occur in addition to Down syndrome include trisomy 8, trisomy 13 or Patau syndrome, trisomy 18 or Edward syndrome, and trisomy 22. Infants born with these trisomies have a host of serious physical conditions. Those born with trisomy 13 or 18 seldom live more than a few months.

Individuals with Down syndrome are more susceptible to infections and usually have abnormalities in one or more vital organs. About 40% have heart defects. Surgery early in life has proven to be effective in correcting tongue and facial defects. Individuals can also participate in many everyday activities (see Figure 7.15). They may survive into their thirties or forties and beyond, but have a greater chance of developing a form of senility similar to Alzheimer's.

Although the actual cause of the nondisjunction that leads to Down syndrome is not known, population studies have revealed an interesting relationship. Figure 7.16 is a graph of results obtained from a study of 1119 children born in Victoria, Australia between 1942 and 1957. Can you determine the relationship?

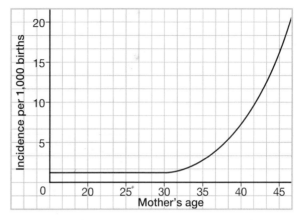

Figure 7.16 Maternal age versus incidence of Down syndrome per 1000 births.

Today's parents have the option of finding out if their developing fetuses will be born with Down. The choice of whether to give birth to such a child often depends on the parents' ethical, moral, and religious decisions. Nevertheless, prenatal diagnosis has played a role in reducing the incidence of Down syndrome in the general population. Historically, the incidence of Down syndrome has been one in every 700 newborns; currently, the incidence is one in every 1100.

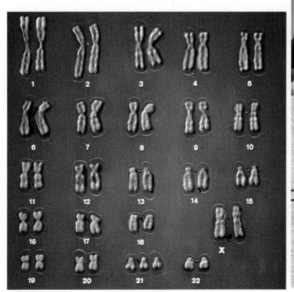

Figure 7.15 A child with Down syndrome at the Special Olympics. Can you spot the additional chromosome in the karyotype?

Pioneer Cytogeneticist

Random chance lies at the heart of genetics. Chance unions of gametes result in genetically unique children. Chance is also at the heart of the life and scientific career of Dr. Irene Ayako Uchida, a Canadian pioneer in cytogenetics, or the study of the chromosomes in cells.

Dr. Irene Uchida working in the laboratory.

Empathy and Science

Irene Uchida was born in Vancouver in 1917 as one of four daughters of Japanese immigrant parents. Her path into genetic science was quite unusual, especially for a woman of Japanese ancestry in the British Columbia of her day.

In 1942, with Canada and Japan at war, Uchida had almost finished her Bachelor of Arts degree at the University of British Columbia when she was suddenly evacuated from her Vancouver home to "Ghost Town" in the B.C. interior, near Lemon Creek. She acted as principal of the largest Japanese internment camp school in the Kootenays. This challenging experience nudged

Uchida toward a career in social work when she resumed her studies at the University of Toronto after the war.

Shortly before she graduated, one of her professors suggested she pursue genetics. A Ph.D. in Zoology followed in 1951, after which Dr. Uchida began work at Toronto's Hospital for Sick Children as a Research Associate.

In 1959, Dr. Uchida moved to the University of Wisconsin and began laboratory studies of human chromosomes and their abnormalities. She wanted to know why Down syndrome children had an extra chromosome. She discovered that there appeared to be a link between maternal radiation received before conception and the extra chromosome 21 found in Down syndrome children. She then started to focus on chromosome 18 trisomy, which usually results in miscarriages.

Building Canada's Genetics Foundation

Today, Dr. Uchida's cytogenetic research is seen as an important forerunner of the ongoing Human Genome Project, to which her Canadian successors have made significant contributions. Her many honours include being named a Woman of the Century in 1967, one of 25 Outstanding Women by the Ontario Government during International Women's Year in 1975, and an Officer of the Order of Canada in 1993.

Dr. Uchida suggests that students approach a career in science with the sort of feistiness and joviality that served her so well. As genetics does, she believes in letting the creative power of random chance help shape the course of your life.

MINI LAB

Genetic Disorders

Most genetic disorders (syndromes) involving nondisjunction are rare in the human population. This table shows the chromosomal basis for various syndromes. Choose a disorder that you have not read about and conduct research about it using your local library or the Internet. Present your findings in an information pamphlet. Use diagrams and graphs to illustrate your pamphlet.

Analyze

1. What is the frequency of the genetic disorder you studied?

2. How does the disorder occur? Use illustrations to describe the process that results in the nondisjunction of chromosomes.

3. Describe the technologies used to diagnose the disorder. Is there a treatment for the disorder? If so, what is involved in the treatment?

Syndrome	Sex	Chromosomes
Down	M or F	Trisomy 21
Patau	M or F	Trisomy 13
Edward	M or F	Trisomy 18
Turner	F	XO
Triplo-X	F	XXX (or XXXX)
Klinefelter	M	XXY (or XXXY)
Jacobs	M	XYY

Changes in Chromosome Structure

Significant changes in the physical structure of chromosomes can occur either spontaneously or when cells are irradiated or exposed to certain chemicals. Essentially, there are four means by which these changes can happen: deletion, duplication, inversion, and translocation, as shown in Figure 7.17.

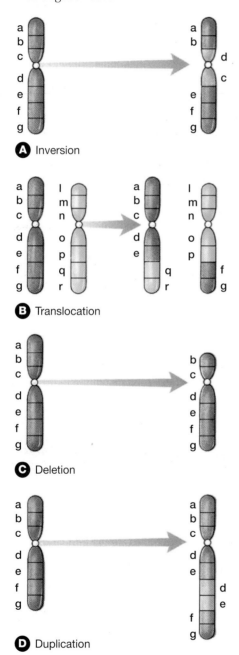

Figure 7.17 Means by which chromosome structures can change

Deletion

In a **deletion**, a portion of the chromosome is actually lost. There are several factors that can trigger a deletion. Viruses, irradiation, and chemicals can cause pieces of a chromosome to be broken off. These pieces are actually genes, and with them go the information required to make vital proteins. For example, when a piece of chromosome 5 is lost, a child is born mentally handicapped and with differences in facial appearance. Because an abnormally developed larynx makes the affected infant's cries sound like the mewing of a cat, this disorder is called *cri-du-chat* (French for cat's cry) (see Figure 7.18).

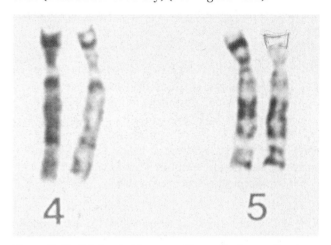

Figure 7.18 Cri-du-chat is caused by a missing portion in chromosome 5 in humans. The tip of the short arm in one of the homologous chromosomes is absent.

Duplication

A **duplication** occurs when a gene sequence is repeated one or more times within one or several chromosomes. Even though certain gene sequences can be repeated thousands of times in normal chromosomes, there appears to be a point at which too many repeats affect the functioning of the gene. For example, in a condition called **fragile X syndrome** (which affects approximately one in 1500 males and one in 2500 females), a duplication occurs in chromosome X (see Figure 7.19, next page). A specific sequence in a specific gene has been studied in affected persons. Most people have about 29 repeats of this specific sequence; people with fragile X syndrome have about 700 repeats of the same sequence.

◄◄ REWIND

To see how new chromosomes can form through changes in structure, turn to Chapter 5, Section 5.2.

Figure 7.19 The arrow indicates the fragile site on this fragile X chromosome.

Inversion

When an **inversion** occurs, a certain gene segment becomes free from its chromosome momentarily before being reinserted in the reverse order. This completely changes the position and order of the chromosome's genes, and can alter gene activity.

Translocation

In **translocation**, part of one chromosome changes places with another part of the same chromosome or with part of another, nonhomologous chromosome. If a part of chromosome 14 exchanges places with a part of chromosome 8, cancer can occur in the affected individual. Similarly, some occurrences of Down syndrome are related to translocation between chromosomes 14 and 21, while one kind of leukemia can be traced to translocation between chromosomes 22 and 9.

SECTION REVIEW

1. **K/U** Indicate the differences between a chromosomal deletion, duplication, inversion, and translocation.

2. **K/U** Identify five conditions that characterize Down syndrome.

3. **MC** Using a concept map, summarize the types of chromosomal defects and the genetic diseases they cause.

4. **C** If a couple has already had a child with Down syndrome, should their medical professional recommend preparing a karyotype during the second pregnancy? Explain.

5. **C** Using diagrams, illustrate some examples of nondisjunction.

6. **I** Which of the following could *not* be determined by observing a human karyotype? Explain.

   (a) The sex of the individual

   (b) The number of homologous pairs

   (c) The presence of Tay-Sachs disease

   (d) The presence of Down Syndrome

The Future of Human Genetics

EXPECTATIONS

- Investigate the advantages and disadvantages of reproductive technologies.
- Analyze genetic technologies to map the human genome.
- Address bio-ethical issues raised by genetic disorders.

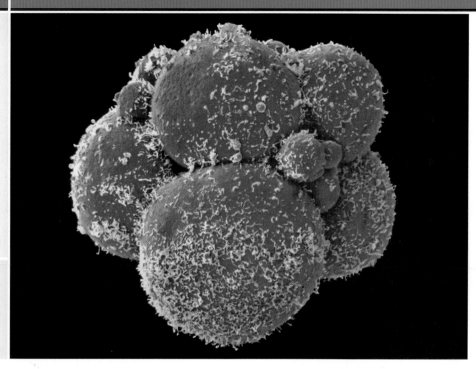

Figure 7.20 The ball of dividing cells shown in this micrograph can be implanted in the uterus to become a healthy full-term baby.

Throughout history, regardless of culture or country, expectant parents have eagerly anticipated the arrival of a new human being. For the nine months a fetus develops within the womb, its parents wondered how it would look and behave. Yet at the moment of birth, concerns about appearance and personality quickly became secondary to concerns about general health and well-being.

Until recently, details about the health of a developing baby could not be known. Today, with new research and technology, the health of the child in the womb need not be a mystery. Information can be gathered not only during development of the fetus — it can even be predicted before conception.

Genetic Counselling

Couples who have a family history of a genetic disorder or have a child with a heritable disorder may want to consult a genetic counsellor before the conception of their next child. A genetic counsellor is a medical professional who gathers detailed information through interviews, blood tests, and discussions with geneticists. The counsellor then constructs family pedigrees. Using these, together with evidence of biochemical disorders and simple Mendelian genetics, the counsellor can predict the probability of the next child having a genetic disorder. A genetic counsellor communicates the

level of risk to the parents so they can make their own decision about whether to conceive another child.

Diagnosis
Preimplantation Diagnosis

Preimplantation diagnosis is available to parents who have a high risk of conceiving a child with a heritable disorder. Sperm and eggs of prospective parents are brought together in a growth medium inside a glass dish. Several eggs are fertilized and begin to divide by mitosis. After two days, each fertilized egg has developed into a ball of eight identical cells, as shown in Figure 7.20.

Because all the cells in the ball have the same genes, one cell can be removed and a karyotype produced while the remaining cells continue to divide. Couples who have a family history of genetic disorders such as cystic fibrosis and Duchenne muscular dystrophy have used this technique to determine whether a disorder has been inherited. If it has not, the ball of cells can be placed inside the uterus so the "test tube baby" can continue its development.

Word LINK

Bringing sperm and eggs together in a glass dish is called in vitro fertilization. *In vitro* is Latin for "in glass."

Prenatal Diagnosis

If a woman has already conceived, several tests can be done to diagnose for heritable disorders. As already noted, a woman over the age of 40 is at a greater risk of having a baby with Down syndrome (see Figure 7.16 on page 227). To determine whether her developing fetus is affected or not, she may choose to have an **amniocentesis**. Throughout its development, the growing fetus is suspended in a fluid-filled membrane inside the uterus called the **amniotic sac**. As the fetus moves and grows inside this amniotic sac, some of its cells are sloughed off and become suspended in the **amniotic fluid**. A sample of this fluid will yield enough cells to create a karyotype that can be used to search for trisomies such as Down syndrome.

After a woman decides on amniocentesis, an **ultrasound** is used to determine the exact location of the fetus in the uterus. During an ultrasound, sound waves beyond the limit of human hearing are sent through the amniotic fluid. The waves bounce off the developing fetus and are used to create a black and white, three-dimensional image of the fetus (see Figure 7.21). When the position of the fetus has been determined, a long thin needle is used to withdraw a small sample of the amniotic fluid. The extracted fluid is placed in a special nutrient-rich medium and the cells are allowed to multiply for several weeks, until there are enough fetal cells to get a good picture of all the chromosomes and create a karyotype.

Due to the potential risk of injury to the fetus, an amniocentesis cannot be done before the fourteenth week of pregnancy. After that, it may take weeks to obtain the results. A woman interested in obtaining results sooner may opt for a procedure called **chorionic villi sampling (CVS)**. Around the ninth week of pregnancy, cells can be removed from a membranous sac called the chorion. The **chorion** is a tissue that surrounds the amniotic sac housing the fetus. It is one of the tissues that make up the **placenta**, an intricately branched structure that connects the mother's blood with the fetal blood. Because the chorion is made of fetal cells, it also contains genetic information about the fetus. The removed cells are grown in a special medium, after which a karyotype allows a diagnosis to be made.

Fetoscopy enables direct observation of the fetus, as shown in Figure 7.22. An **endoscope**, essentially a long tube with a camera on one end, is inserted into a small incision made in the mother's abdomen. The clear view of the fetus it provides lets medical professionals safely perform various procedures directly inside the womb. For example, fetal blood can be collected for karyotyping, excess fluid surrounding the brain can be removed, and fetal blood transfusions can be performed.

Figure 7.22 Fetoscopy provided this actual view of an 18-week-old fetus inside the womb.

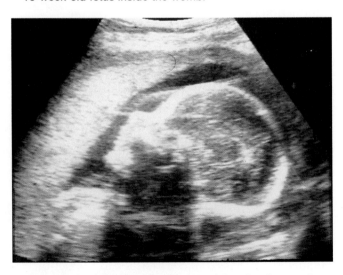

Figure 7.21 In amniocentesis, amniotic fluid is withdrawn from the amniotic sac, after which the fetal cells are cultured and studied. An ultrasound is obtained first, as shown in the photograph of the 25-week fetus, to determine the exact position of the fetus in the womb.

Web LINK

Use the web site below to learn more about genetic testing. Go to **Science Resources**, then to **BIOLOGY 11** to find out where to go next. Use the information you have gathered to answer these questions: What types of tissues are required for a genetic test? Which disorders can be diagnosed through genetic testing? How accurate are the results of the tests? Should insurance companies have access to this type of information?
www.school.mcgrawhill.ca/resources/

Treatment

Genetic Screening and Prevention

If no previous diagnosis has been made, a genetic disorder can be detected at birth. Through routine blood tests using special biochemical procedures, disorders such as phenylketonuria can be detected early enough for parents and medical professionals to carry out preventive measures. With a special diet, for instance, children with phenylketonuria can grow to lead normal lives. Genetic screening and prevention has lowered the incidence of phenylketonuria in the North American population dramatically in recent years.

Surgery

Some genetic conditions can be treated through surgery. Babies born with **cleft palates** have a vertical groove in their upper lips and into the roofs of their mouths. Reconstructive surgery can solve this condition.

Environmental Control

Sometimes the only treatment is to minimize the effects of the symptoms. For example, individuals affected with albinism lack the pigment melanin, which helps protect us from the harmful effects of direct sunlight. Since there is no medical treatment for albinism, these individuals must limit their exposure to direct sunlight.

Gene Therapy

To those who love bacon, eggs, and ice cream, the word "cholesterol" may threaten appetites. **Cholesterol** is a waxy kind of fat found only in animal tissues. Once it enters the blood stream, it is transported either to body cells (where it is stored or used) or to the liver (where it is broken down and removed from the blood). If the cholesterol cannot enter the cells, it will circulate in the blood and eventually collect inside the walls of arteries, causing them to thicken and possibly clog. A clogged artery can lead to a heart attack because the heart cannot get enough oxygen to function properly (see Figure 7.23).

Whether our cells are capable of picking up the cholesterol from our blood or not depends on the genes we inherit. If you inherit one or two copies of the dominant allele for cholesterol reception, your cells will be able to pick up the cholesterol, thus helping to keep your blood cholesterol level low. Individuals who inherit two copies of the recessive allele are not able to properly pick up the cholesterol, and may die of a heart attack when they are as young as two years old. Most do not survive past their teenage years.

Word LINK

The medical term for people who have high blood cholesterol is hypercholesterolemia. It comes from the Greek *hyper-*, meaning excessive or above, cholesterol, and the Greek *haima*, meaning blood.

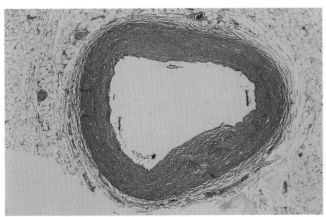
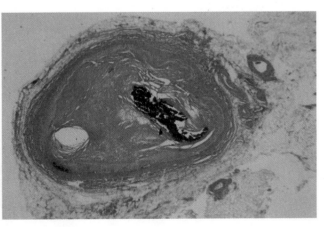

Figure 7.23 Compare the scanning electron micrograph of a healthy artery (left) with the one of an artery clogged with cholesterol (right). What risks does a person with arteries like those on the right face?

Gene therapy is a medical procedure in which normal or modified genes are transferred into the defective cells of an individual. In theory, the transferred genes will allow the recipient's cells to begin functioning normally by giving them the instructions for producing the missing molecules, thus reversing the symptoms of the genetic disorder. In 1992, for example, a 30-year-old Québec woman made genetic history. She had already had a heart attack by age 16 and a bypass operation at age 26. Both of her brothers had died of heart attacks in their early twenties. Amid controversy about the risks and benefits of gene therapy, the woman agreed to participate in a painful and unproven procedure.

The procedure involved removing about 15% of the woman's liver. The liver cells were allowed to multiply in a special medium until a sufficient number of cells had been created. In the meantime, the healthy human gene that she lacked was inserted into the genome of a harmless virus. The modified virus was added to the multiplying liver cells, where it injected its own genetic material into her cells. The harmless virus followed its normal infection cycle and injected its genetic material into the liver cells along with the healthy human gene (see Figure 7.24).

Billions of infected liver cells were then injected into the woman's large hepatic portal vein, which transports blood directly to the liver. Some of the cells became a part of the woman's liver and began behaving as healthy cells by breaking down excess cholesterol. After two years, about 5% of the woman's liver cells were functioning normally. Her blood cholesterol level had dropped about 20% and her arteries were not clogged. At a press conference later, the woman announced that she was enjoying good health and an active lifestyle. Although her cholesterol level remained twice as high as normal, it was significantly lower than it would have been without the gene therapy.

Mapping the Human Genome

The Human Genome Project is unlike any scientific endeavour previously attempted. Originally begun in the United States in 1990, hundreds of scientists in 18 different countries joined the quest to locate all of the estimated 30 000 to 50 000 human genes on our 46 chromosomes and read our entire genome. This was an ambitious undertaking because the human genome is so large that it would fill a thousand 1000-page telephone books if it were printed! Now completed, the project promises to not only expose how each of us is unique, but also how much we are the same. Biology and medicine will enter a new era.

How is it possible to locate each of the genes that code for a human being? The first step is to make a genetic map of each chromosome. The goal is to show all the genes, in their correct sequence, as they would be found on that chromosome. Because each chromosome carries an average of over 1000 genes, this is a daunting task. However, by the year 2000, chromosomes 22, 21, 5, 16, and 19 had already been completely sequenced — that is, the specific sequence of base pairs was known for each.

The next step after determining the position of the genes is to find the specific sequence of base pairs for the remaining chromosomes in the human genome. This would be like trying to put your

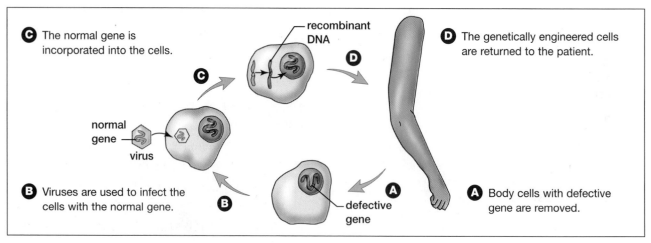

Figure 7.24 In gene therapy, body cells with the defective gene are removed and infected with a harmless virus carrying the normal gene. The virus injects the normal gene into the cells, after which they are returned to the body.

favourite book back together after finding it ripped into letter-sized bits! In order to accomplish this goal, scientists first slice the genome into small manageable pieces using special enzymes. The small pieces of about 1000 to 2000 base pairs are then placed in a special polymerase chain reaction instrument that copies them so there is enough material to work with. Then, another instrument called a DNA sequencer reads the actual sequence of each piece. Finally, a computer program takes the information supplied by the sequencer and determines how the pieces link together. As you can see, this effort requires a tremendous amount of expertise and technology, including scientists in the fields of computer science, physics, chemistry, and engineering, as well as biology.

BIO FACT

It is estimated that 3000 to 4000 disorders are directly caused by defective genes that we inherit. We now know that these mutated genes influence how we respond to common diseases such as cancer, heart disease, and diabetes. These common diseases are believed to be caused by complex interactions between these altered genes and unhealthy lifestyle and environmental factors.

Revolution in the Making

The Human Genome Project promises to revolutionize medical science and the pharmaceutical industry by providing methods for the early diagnosis, treatment, and prevention of hereditary disorders. If the cause of a genetic disorder is known, it may be possible to develop drugs to treat its cause rather than just its symptoms. In addition, certain drugs may only be effective in individuals with certain genotypes. Imagine your pharmacist someday providing you with a drug labelled, "To be taken only by persons with a recessive allele #860"!

Besides drugs, gene therapy may be used to replace the faulty gene. For example, the gene that causes cystic fibrosis has been identified through the efforts of the Human Genome Project, and a diagnostic test has been developed to determine which individuals are carriers. Individuals with cystic fibrosis are now participating in experimental gene therapy procedures.

Prevention is another intriguing possibility. Once we know which genes cause which diseases, individuals can be tested to determine whether they have a predisposition to these illnesses.

THINKING LAB

How Will We Deal with Bio-ethical Dilemmas?

Background

Gardner syndrome is a genetic disorder caused by a mutated gene on chromosome 5 that makes affected individuals more susceptible to colon cancer. It is an autosomal dominant condition in which hundreds of abnormal growths (polyps) form within the colon. Some of these polyps can become malignant, leading to cancer of the colon. Children of affected individuals have a 50% chance of carrying the disorder. Cancer can occur in adolescence or as late as in the person's seventies.

When a 38-year-old father of three sons became extremely ill, his doctor diagnosed him as having Gardner syndrome. Malignant polyps indicated that removal of the entire colon was necessary. Twenty years earlier, the man's mother had died from colon cancer. To help his sons avoid such a fate, the father requested that they be genetically tested. The tests, which the doctor indicated were 99% accurate, revealed that the eldest son had inherited the defective gene. The son graduated from college and found employment. The employer requested a physical examination for health insurance purposes, following which the son's medical

history became available to the health insurance company. The employer, who would pay the health care premiums, was told by the health insurance company that the son's overall premium rate would have to be greatly increased because he was a "high risk" employee.

You Try It

In small groups, discuss and complete the following:

1. Identify the bio-ethical dilemma and write it as a question.

2. What information is required to make this decision?

3. Who will be affected by this decision?

4. What values (yours as well as others') are involved in the decision-making process?

5. Give at least three solutions to the problem that members of your group suggested.

6. Which of these solutions would you choose? Indicate the values that led you to this solution.

7. How will this solution affect the people involved in this problem?

8. Would you be willing to have the consequences of this decision applied to you? Why or why not?

Then, by taking appropriate precautions, they may be able to reduce or even prevent their likelihood of contracting a disease. In 1994, for instance, scientists discovered two genes that cause a form of colon cancer. One million North Americans are believed to carry the alleles that produce this type of cancer. Individuals with these alleles have a 70–80% chance of developing the disease. With the genes identified, scientists are now working on a diagnostic blood test that will enable individuals with a family history of colon cancer to learn if they are at risk.

Figure 7.25 Dr. Lap-Chee Tsui of The Hospital for Sick Children in Toronto is credited with finding the gene responsible for cystic fibrosis.

New Knowledge, New Problems

New knowledge often creates new dilemmas. Just because we locate a defective gene that causes a disease does not mean we have the ability to treat it. For example, we have known for years which defective gene causes Huntington disease. We also have the ability to predict whether an individual has inherited this gene. Yet only a few people have had themselves tested for it.

Put yourself in the shoes of someone who has a family history of Huntington disease, for which there is currently no treatment or cure. Would you want to know that you will be struck with this lethal disease sometime in mid-life, or would you rather live your life without knowing? Would you want others, like your insurance company or future employers, to know? If they did, could they deny you coverage or refuse to employ you? We must consider how much about ourselves we really want to know.

SECTION REVIEW

1. **K/U** Describe how an amniocentesis is done and the circumstances under which it would be recommended.

2. **K/U** What is the advantage of sampling cells from the chorion?

3. **C** Using a flowchart, describe the steps involved in gene therapy.

4. **I** If an Rh⁻ woman is expecting a child who is Rh⁺, the mother's antibodies will destroy the blood cells of the fetus. The developing child will therefore be in danger of developing anemia. Which prenatal procedure could be used to treat the fetus?

5. **C** In groups of three, discuss the qualities you would expect to find in a genetics counsellor if your child was diagnosed with a genetic disorder.

6. **K/U** Explain how the human genome is mapped.

7. **K/U** Explain the role of the polymerase chain reaction instrument and DNA sequencer.

8. **K/U** Defective genes, unhealthy lifestyle, and environmental factors may play a role in causing what?

9. **C** Construct a chart with two columns, one labelled "Advantages" and the other "Disadvantages." Indicate the advantages and disadvantages of mapping the human genome in the appropriate column.

10. **MC** If you were part of a government task force that set policy relating to the findings of the human genome project, what are some of the guidelines you would propose?

11. **MC** Identify two ethical dilemmas that arise from our ability to detect genetic diseases.

UNIT ISSUE PREP

If you have decided to investigate gene therapy for your Unit 2 Issue Analysis, think about what is involved in this procedure. Is gene therapy a generally successful procedure? If not, should it be employed? Write down your ideas in preparation for your Unit 2 Issue Analysis.

Chapter Expectations

Briefly explain each of the following points.

- There are many inherited conditions that can be explained by simple Mendelian genetics. (7.1)
- Diseases such as sickle cell anemia illustrate the interactions between genes within a population and local environmental conditions. (7.1)
- Patterns of human inheritance can be determined through the use of karyotypes and pedigree analysis. (7.2)
- Genetic diseases and disorders can arise from changes in chromosome structure and chromosome number. (7.3)
- Prenatal diagnoses can be used to determine some genetic conditions and disorders. (7.4)
- Certain inherited disorders can be treated and their effects lessened to improve the quality of life of affected individuals. (7.4)
- Gene therapy, a new and controversial medical procedure, can be used to reverse some of the effects of defective genes. (7.4)
- The Human Genome Project heralds a new frontier in diagnosis and treatment of inherited disorders. (7.4)

Language of Biology

Write a sentence using each of the following words or terms. Use any six terms in a concept map to show your understanding of how they are related.

- alkaptonuria
- Tay-Sachs disease
- phenylketonuria (PKU)
- albinism
- melanin
- sickle cell anemia
- hemoglobin
- anemia
- heterozygous advantage
- gel electrophoresis
- progeria
- Huntington disease
- karyotype
- Duchenne muscular dystrophy
- Down syndrome
- syndrome
- deletion
- duplication
- fragile X syndrome
- inversion
- translocation
- amniocentesis
- amniotic sac
- amniotic fluid
- ultrasound
- chorionic villi sampling (CVS)
- chorion
- placenta
- fetoscopy
- endoscope
- cleft palate
- cholesterol
- gene therapy

UNDERSTANDING CONCEPTS

1. Give two reasons why geneticists use fruit flies rather than humans to study genetics.

2. If Huntington disease is lethal, why does it continue to exist in the population?

3. In your notebook, state whether the following statements are true or false. If the statement is false, rewrite the statement to make it true.
   (a) A karyotype can be used to detect deletions, translocations, and nondisjunctions.
   (b) PKU, an inherited disease of the nervous system, has no effective treatment.
   (c) The alleles that code for red and green colour vision are found on the X chromosome, and the allele that codes for blue colour vision is found on the Y chromosome.
   (d) If a couple already has one child with Duchenne muscular dystrophy, then the only prenatal test that can be used on the second child is one to determine its sex.

4. What genetic event is illustrated below?

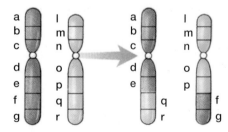

5. Why are heterozygous individuals generally healthy?

6. Describe four diseases that can be treated if they are detected at birth.

7. In disorders where two recessive alleles are present, how does the defective gene cause the disease?

8. What would be the advantage of using chorionic sampling over amniocentesis for prenatal diagnosis of chromosomal abnormalities?

9. Imagine you are a genetics counsellor working with two healthy couples. The first couple has a child who has cystic fibrosis. Cystic fibrosis is caused by a recessive allele carried on chromosome 7.
   (a) What is the probability that their second child will also have cystic fibrosis?
   (b) The second couple has a child with Down syndrome. What is the probability that their second child will have Down syndrome?
   (c) Would you consider the age of the couples? Why?

10. Females with muscular dystrophy are rare in our population because their fathers must have the disease and their mothers must be carriers. Explain the inheritance pattern.

11. Given that the majority of the mutations that occur in the human population have undesirable effects and a mutation is rarely beneficial, why do we say that mutations have an important role to play?

12. Using your library and/or the Internet, research X-chromosome inactivation or Lyonization. Use the information you gathered to explain the following:
   (a) Women who carry one copy of a colourblindness allele can still exhibit normal colour vision
   (b) Anhidriotic dysplasia is a disease in which sweat glands do not form. Males who carry the allele do not have sweat glands, but heterozygous females have some patches of skin with normal sweat glands and some patches without.

13. Suppose that a colour-blind man has parents with normal vision. Would all his sons be colour-blind? Was his mother a carrier? Would all of his daughters be carriers? Explain your answers.

14. Identify the therapy shown in the illustration and describe the events indicated by each letter.

15. This partial pedigree of a large Virginia family shows the inheritance pattern for a condition called syndactyly (where two fingers are joined by a web of muscle or skin). Examine the pedigree and indicate what the inheritance pattern appears to be. Is it dominant or recessive? Is it sex-linked or autosomal? Do individuals who have the condition also have a parent with the condition? How do you explain the inheritance in the male in the seventh generation (the black square)?

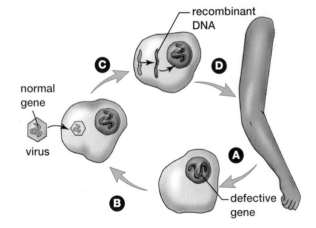

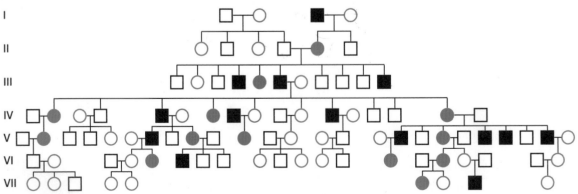

16. Observe the graph shown here and describe the correlation that is being depicted.

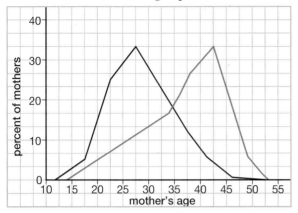

— age distribution of all mothers
— age distribution of mothers of children with Down syndrome

17. This table shows the frequencies of A-B-O blood groups in selected populations of the world. Study the table and answer the following questions.

(a) Which appears to be the most frequent phenotype in most human populations? To what genotype does it correspond?

(b) Does the word "dominant" or "recessive" determine whether an allele is rare or common in a population?

(c) Do the words "dominant" and "recessive" indicate which is the more advantageous phenotype?

(d) Can you explain the population frequency for the pure Peruvian Indians?

Population	Percentage of population exhibiting blood type			
	O	A	B	AB
American Caucasians	45	41	10	4
African Americans	47	28	20	5
African Pygmies	31	30	29	10
African Bushmen	56	34	8	2
Australian Aborigines	34	66	0	0
Pure Peruvian Indians	100	0	0	0
Tuamotuans of Polynesia	48	52	0	0

MAKING CONNECTIONS

18. Using a flowchart, describe the sequence of events used in gene therapy.

19. Outline the procedure for amniocentesis.

20. Examine the pedigree of the British royal family (Figure 7.10 on page 221). How do we determine that it was Queen Victoria and not her husband, Prince Albert, who carried the gene for hemophilia?

21. The IQ (Intelligence Quotient) test was developed in 1903 by Alfred Binet. He believed that IQ can be calculated by taking our mental age, dividing it by our physical age and multiplying by 100. For example, a 10 year old with a mental age of 9 should have an IQ test score of 90. Since it was developed, the concept of IQ has been hotly debated. The central question is whether there are alleles for IQ. Describe the problems associated with trying to find a scientific explanation for differences in IQ scores.

22. Consider the recessive allele that causes sickle cell anemia. How does the fact that we are diploid organisms maintain this allele at lower frequencies in the population? Would you say that haploid organisms are much more sensitive to mutation? Can you explain why diploidy is more predominant in higher organisms?

23. Tristan de Cunha is a small group of islands in the Atlantic Ocean between Africa and South America. In 1814, a group of 15 British settlers arrived on the islands; they are the ancestors of the 300 people who presently inhabit the archipelago. This small population has the highest incidence in the world of an otherwise rare disease called retinitis pigmentosa. Affecting primarily young men on the island, the disease begins when patches of pigmented tissue start growing on the retina. At first, individuals turn their heads to see better. Eventually, as the retina becomes covered with the tissue, they become completely blind. Explain the inheritance pattern beginning with its arrival on the island.

24. Hypophosphatemia causes a deficiency of phosphates in the blood. Males pass on the disease to all their daughters but not to their sons. Females with the disorder pass it on to approximately half their children. Explain the inheritance pattern of the disorder.

A Simulation: Group Action Plan on Genetic Technologies

Background

Every day in the media, whether it is through newspapers, magazines, television, or Internet chat rooms, the topic of genetics is featured. Both technological issues and ethical issues abound when it comes to genetics. In 1989, the federal government's Royal Commission on New Reproductive Technologies formed a mandate. It established an ethical framework and guiding principles to assess how the use of a technology should be viewed and what conclusions should be reached. Examples of technologies defined by this mandate include gene therapy, genetic screening, and in vitro fertilization.

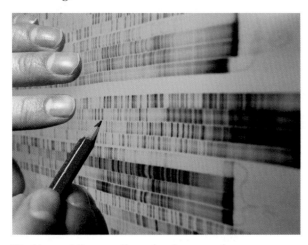

Working out the genetic code of an organism

Since 1989, the field of genetics and genetic technologies has grown exponentially. The specific technologies mentioned in the mandate of the Royal Commission still raise important issues today. At the same time, many new issues continue to arise, and several additions have been made to the 1989 mandate. These new issues range from whether or not human gene sequences may or should be patented, to how the knowledge of gene sequences may be used to create entire organisms in the laboratory. Recently, several new businesses have formed in response to the new era of genetic information. Some of these businesses are involved in:

(a) decoding the human genome

(b) bioinformatics, where human genome data are being used to create new pharmaceuticals

(c) *in silico* biology, (which means "biology in computer chips"), where computer models are used to study genes. Computer models are needed because the data bases for gene sequences of specific proteins have become so massive that only computers can decipher the data and generate results.

(d) proteomics, which uses *in silico* biology to determine the properties of the proteins that genes encode.

What issues have arisen with the development of these and other types of genetic research?

```
TTTTTTTTTTTTTTTTTCCCCCCCC
CCCCCCCCAAAAAAAAAAAAAAAA
AAGGGGGGGGGGGGGGGGGTTTTC
CCCAAAAGGGGTTTTCCCCAAAA
GGGGTTTTCCCCAAAAGGGGTTT
TCCCCAAAAGGGGTCAGTCAGTC
AGTCAGTCAGTCAGTCAGTCAGT
CAGTCAGTCAGTCAGTCAGTCAG
```

Part of the genetic code for vertebrates

Plan and Present

1. Collect newspaper articles on issues related to genetics. Post the articles on your classroom bulletin board. As a class, decide which issue you will focus on for a detailed analysis. It may be helpful to brainstorm specific sub-issues within the larger issue. The list of sub-issues will assist in gathering the necessary background information.

2. As a class, brainstorm how you could gather the following types of information to analyze the issue you have selected. Use concept maps or other graphic organizers to record your ideas.

- Factual information that explains the science behind the issue, obtained from such sources as specific Internet sites, scientific journals, science television programs, and science textbooks. List several key terms that could be used for a literature/Internet search for the information.
- Expert information that explains the perspective of several expert scientists who are working in a field related to the issue.
- Industry information that explains the perspective of private corporations that stand to profit from some techniques or information related to the issue.
- Legal information that explains the laws governing the principles related to the issue, such as the mandate of the Royal Commission.
- Political information that explains the government's position on the issue (include municipal, provincial, and federal levels of government).
- Religious information that explains the perspectives of several different religious groups on the issue.
- Other interest-group information that explains the perspectives of other interest groups, such as environmentalists and human rights activists, on the issue.

3. In small groups, complete the tasks you outlined in step 2.

4. Create a bulletin board display and post the information you gather.

5. As a class, decide on the how you could increase public awareness of the various perspectives on the issue.

6. As a class, develop an action plan to increase public awareness of the various perspectives on the issue. Divide the tasks among small groups of students. The following steps should be part of your plan.
- *Define roles* — What role will each group play in your action plan?
- *Set goals* — What are the goals of your project? What would you like to accomplish?

- *Ask permission* — The information you gather may have to be treated with sensitivity. Prior to taking action, ask your teacher to approve the method you have selected to increase public awareness of the issue.
- *Outline ethical precautions* — Establish rules and guidelines for acting responsibly when obtaining the information related to the issue. Some individuals may not wish to share their perspectives on the issue, and this wish needs to be respected.
- *Establish steps and timelines* — What will be done and when will you do it?
- *Plan a public relations strategy* — How will you inform the public about your findings? How will you get the public involved? For example, will you have a method for receiving public response to your project? One possible strategy is to create a web site where the public can access your findings and enter their responses to the project.

Evaluate the Results

1. What were some of the challenges and successes of your action plan? If you could do the exercise again, what might you do differently?

2. How important was planning to the success of your action plan?

3. How did your understanding of science and genetics-related issues help you carry out this action plan?

Web LINK

Various organizations, such as the Royal Commission on Reproductive Technologies, have been established to address the social, ethical, and legal implications of research on human genetics. To access publications and other resources related to genetic research, go to the web site shown below. Go to **Science Resources**, then to **BIOLOGY 11** to find out where to go next. What progress has been made in increasing public awareness about issues in genetic research? Who are the stakeholders and what are their interests? Based on the most current research, can we predict issues that will arise in the future? Investigate these questions as you plan and present your issue analysis. **www.school.mcgrawhill.ca/resources/**

UNDERSTANDING CONCEPTS

True-False

In your notebook, indicate whether each statement is true or false. Correct each false statement.

1. Many physical characteristics are inherited.

2. Knowledge of the mechanisms of inheritance is the result of Aristotle's work on pea plants.

3. The Punnett square is used to determine the outcome of various genetic crosses.

4. The phenotype refers to the genetic make-up of an organism.

5. If the genes for two given characteristics are found on the same chromosome, then the genes are linked.

6. If a mother has blue eyes (bb) and a father has brown eyes (Bb), then the probability their child will have blue eyes is 50%.

7. A chromosome is made up of smaller units called genes.

8. Each human somatic cell contains the haploid number of chromosomes.

9. The ABO blood group in humans is an example of multiple allele inheritance.

10. Colourblindness in males is an example of incomplete dominance.

11. An allele is one of the components that form a genotype.

12. The end product of meiosis is four diploid cells.

13. A cross that involves two traits and their associated alleles is called a monohybrid cross.

14. During meiosis, genes cannot be sorted independently if they are defective.

15. Translocation, inversion, and duplication are all types of mutations.

16. If both parents possess the genotype AaBb, they can produce nine different genotypes in the F_1 generation.

17. A tetrad is used to describe a pair of homologous chromosomes.

18. In DNA, adenine always pairs with guanine.

19. Polygenic inheritance occurs when a pair of alleles controls a single trait.

20. During spermatogenesis, four sperm cells are formed from each spermatogonium.

Multiple Choice

In your notebook, write the letter of the best answer for each of the following questions. (Only four choices are provided because of the nature of the concepts in the unit.)

21. Mendel's law of dominance states that
    (a) in an organism heterozygous for a trait, only one of the two alleles is expressed
    (b) two alleles that determine a characteristic will separate when sex cells form
    (c) an allele that is expressed is recessive
    (d) the inheritance of a particular allele is not affected by the inheritance of other alleles

For questions 22 to 24, refer to the diagram.

Male Parent

	b (blue)	b
B (brown)	Bb	Bb
b	bb	bb

Female Parent

22. What is the colour of the female parent's eyes?
    (a) brown
    (b) blue
    (c) one brown, one blue
    (d) cannot be determined

23. What would be the expected ratio of eye colour among the offspring?
    (a) 2 brown : 3 blue
    (b) 1 brown : 2 blue
    (c) 1 brown : 1 blue
    (d) 2 brown : 1 blue

24. If the parents produce four offspring, how many will probably be homozygous for brown eyes?
    (a) none   (c) 2
    (b) 1   (d) 3

25. Due to the similar behaviour of genes and chromosomes, we can conclude that
    (a) genes and chromosomes perform similar functions
    (b) chromosomes pairs separate during meiosis
    (c) genes linked on the same chromosome are sometimes separated
    (d) genes are located on chromosomes

26. The genotype describes
    (a) the physical appearance of an organism
    (b) one allele of a gene
    (c) the combination of two or more alleles
    (d) all of the above

27. The phenotypic ratio of a cross between two organisms that are heterozygous for a single trait is
   (a) 1 : 1
   (c) 1 : 2 : 1
   (b) 2 : 1
   (d) 2 : 1 : 2

The numbered structures in this diagram represent animal cells in various stages of meiosis. Use the diagram to answer questions 28 to 30.

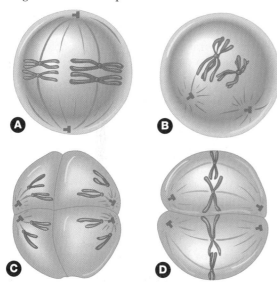

28. Which letter best represents anaphase II of meiosis?
   (a) A
   (c) C
   (b) B
   (d) D

29. What phase of meiosis is represented by letter D?
   (a) prophase I
   (c) metaphase I
   (b) metaphase II
   (d) telophase II

30. Which letter best represents crossing over?
   (a) A
   (c) C
   (b) B
   (d) D

31. Which of the following bases is not found in DNA?
   (a) adenine
   (c) thymine
   (b) uracil
   (d) cytosine

32. The sequence of DNA nucleotides that encodes the amino acid sequence of an enzyme is a
   (a) gene
   (c) phenotype
   (b) polypeptide
   (d) protein

33. Traits that exhibit continuous variation, such as height in humans, are generally controlled by
   (a) a single dominant gene
   (b) co-dominance
   (c) a single recessive gene
   (d) multiple genes

34. In DNA synthesis, the bases are attached to
   (a) phosphate groups
   (b) deoxyribose
   (c) another nitrogenous base
   (d) both (b) and (c)

35. If the sequence of bases in one strand of DNA is AATCGG, what is the sequence of the complementary strand?
   (a) TTGCAA
   (c) UUAGCC
   (b) TTAGCC
   (d) TTUGCC

36. Which of the following mutations adds one or more base pairs to a DNA molecule?
   (a) nonsense mutations
   (b) frameshift mutations
   (c) inversions
   (d) silent mutations

37. Nondisjunction results in
   (a) failure to produce a protein
   (b) a missing chromosome in a gamete
   (c) failure to produce a viable gamete
   (d) all of the above

Short Answer
In your notebook, write a sentence or a short paragraph to answer each of the following questions.

38. (a) Who was Gregor Mendel?
   (b) Identify three reasons why pea plants were an excellent choice for his study of genetic inheritance.

39. Describe the phenotypes and genotypes when two organisms that are heterozygous for a trait are crossed.

40. How would Mendel explain why certain phenotypes and genotypes are not always expressed in offspring?

41. Why is chromosome reduction necessary in sexual reproduction?

42. In a cross of purple-flowered and white-flowered plants, the F_1 generation were all purple. A cross of two F_1 plants resulted in a F_2 generation with the following numbers of phenotypes: 28 purple, 52 lavender (light purple), 19 white.
   (a) What were the F_1 generation genotypes? Explain.
   (b) Use a Punnett square to show how the results observed in the F_2 generation were obtained.
   (c) Identify and explain the type of inheritance this cross reveals.

43. **(a)** What is crossing over?

(b) Explain how crossing over promotes genetic variability among individuals.

44. Identify what contributions Watson and Crick made in the discovery of the DNA molecule.

45. A probationary nurse mixed up the identification bracelets of three newborn babies. The blood types of the parents and babies were obtained in an attempt to identify the parents of each baby.

Parent	Blood type	Baby	Blood type
Mr. Smith	AB	Baby X	O
Mr. Rene	O	Baby Y	A
Mr. Sharetsky	A	Baby Z	AB
Mrs. Smith	O		
Mrs. Rene	O		
Mrs. Sharetsky	B		

(a) Which baby belongs to which set of parents?

(b) Using your knowledge of genetics, explain how you arrived at your answer.

46. A woman, whose maternal grandfather was prematurely bald has parents who are not bald. The woman's husband is also not bald. What is the probability that her first son will show premature baldness? Explain how you arrived at your conclusion(s).

47. A female hog may give birth to as many as 16 offspring in a single litter. If black coat colour in hogs is dominant to white, show how a breeder might expect an entire litter of piglets to have black coat colour.

48. Curly hair in humans is dominant to straight hair.

(a) What are the two possible genotypes for curly hair?

(b) Show the possible genotypes and phenotypes of a cross between a man heterozygous for curly hair and a woman homozygous for straight hair.

49. Would you expect to find colourblindness and hemophilia more frequently in men or in women? Explain.

50. What type of vision can be expected in the offspring if the parents have normal colour vision but the father of each parent is colour-blind? Why?

51. Identify and describe three different ways that a genetic disease can be detected before an individual is born.

52. **(a)** A man has blood type genotype I^AI^B, whereas his wife has the genotype ii. What are the possible blood types of their children?

(b) Is it possible for this couple to have a child who is genotype I^AI^B or ii? Explain.

53. The following letters represent a normal DNA sequence.

A B C D E F G H

Indicate the type of mutation that is occurring for each of the following situations.

(a) A B C C D E F G H

(b) F G H A B C D E

(c) A B C D W X Y Z

(d) A B C D E Q G H

54. Identify the research that each of the following researchers conducted, and explain how their research contributed to our current understanding of genetics.

(a) Watson and Crick

(b) Hershey and Chase

(c) Sutton and Boveri

INQUIRY

55. Analyze this diagram by answering the questions below.

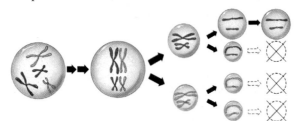

(a) Identify this process.

(b) Explain where this process takes place.

(c) Explain the specific part of the process in which differences in genetic information are created.

(d) What does "n" refer to in the ovum created in the final part of this process?

56. In humans, the allele for normal hearing (H) is dominant over the recessive allele for congenital deafness. The trait is not sex-linked.

Interpret the pedigree shown here in order to answer the following questions.

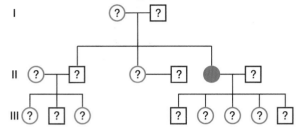

(a) Explain how it is possible for individual II-3 to be congenitally deaf if neither parent had the condition.

(b) Are boys more likely than girls to inherit the condition? Explain.

(c) What is the probability that female III-1 will be congenitally deaf? Assume that person II-1 is not a carrier for the trait.

57. Genetic information is encoded in the sequence of nucleotides in DNA. Suppose a specific nucleotide sequence on one strand of the DNA molecule is responsible for the structure of hemoglobin. Do you think the complementary sequence of nucleotides on the opposite strand also encodes useful information? Explain. Describe a method you could use to test your idea.

COMMUNICATING

58. With the development of new medical treatments for genetic diseases, more people with these diseases are surviving to reproductive age. What will happen to the number of recessive alleles in the human population as a result of this? Explain.

59. A couple has three children, two of whom have hemophilia. As their genetic counsellor, what would you tell them about the probability of their next child not having hemophilia? Explain.

60. Today, we are making advances in genetics at a tremendous rate. Do you think there should be limits on how this new knowledge is used? Explain.

61. Mendel's work with pea plants and his resulting laws have changed the course of science. Do you agree with this statement? Why or why not?

62. Why is it important that both mitosis and meiosis occur in humans?

63. Human *in vitro* fertilization is a technique in which an ovum is fertilized outside the female's body. Could this method be used to create identical twins, triplets, and so on? Argue for or against such a possibility.

MAKING CONNECTIONS

64. When Mendel performed his experiments, he worked with many individual plants that produced thousands of offspring. Do you think Mendel would have obtained the same results if he worked with only 20 or 30 plants? Explain.

65. Some species of animals, such as the northern right whale, have had their populations reduced to an extremely small number. As a result, their genetic diversity has been significantly reduced. Why might a lack of genetic diversity threaten a species? Could a lack of genetic diversity threaten a small, isolated human population as well? Explain.

66. Agriculture and medicine are just some of the industries benefiting from the advancements made in genetic technology. Identify and discuss an argument in favour of using these advancements. Identify and discuss an argument against continuing research and use of new genetic technologies.

COURSE CHALLENGE

Consider the following as you continue to build your biology research portfolio.

- Review the information you have gathered in preparation for the Biology Course Challenge. Consider any new findings to see if you want to change the focus of your project.

- Add important concepts, formulas, interesting facts, and diagrams from this unit.

- Scan magazines, newspapers, and information on the Internet to enhance your project.

Overall Expectations

In this Unit, you will discover

- how substances from the environment are absorbed, transported, and transformed within the body,

- how adaptations in internal systems allow organisms to survive in different environments,

- how your personal choices can affect your body's natural systems.

Unit Contents

UNIT PROJECT PREP

Read pages 370–372 before beginning this unit.

- You will be exploring how medical advances have changed the way we treat particular illnesses.

- As you work through the unit, think about how both illnesses and treatments can affect internal systems.

- Start planning for your project now by setting up a system to organize the information you find.

Internal Systems and Regulation

Imagine a soccer game: lots of action, plenty of activity. You move quickly, racing to make contact with the ball. Out of the corner of your eye, you see an opponent closing in and you push yourself a little harder. So much is going on inside you, but you think little of it. Nerves are sending messages, muscles are contracting and relaxing, your heart pumps, sending the oxygen it has obtained from your lungs out to all the cells in your body. Your body responds automatically as you jog, sprint, or stop to catch your breath.

Look now at the photograph of the newborn infant. The patches on its skin are hooked up to monitors that record heartbeat and rate of breathing, helping to ensure that its internal systems are functioning properly. If these systems fail to develop or function as they should, it can take a roomful of medical professionals and equipment to support life's basic processes.

What is it that goes on in the body that can seem so effortless, and yet is so difficult to accomplish artificially? Your body is constantly absorbing material from its environment, ridding itself of wastes, and transforming matter into energy. These processes are closely interconnected and carefully regulated in a way that even the best medical technology can barely reproduce.

Some of the things that affect the body's internal systems are hard to control. These include environmental changes, disease, and injuries. Other factors, such as personal lifestyles and choices, are more manageable. This unit is all about the body's systems: how they work, how they are regulated, and how the things you do can help or hurt them.

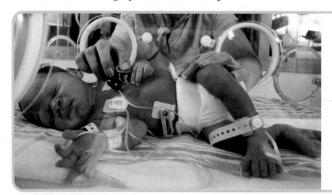

What internal systems does this newborn's life depend on?

The Breath of Life

**Reflecting
Questions**

- What features of
respiration do all
organisms have in
common?

- What adaptations allow
different organisms to
thrive in different
environments?

- What is your own
respiratory capacity,
and what can you do
to increase it?

- In what ways do changes
in the environment affect
gas exchange differently
in plants and animals?

Like most people, you probably think of your body as having an "inside" (of tissues, organs, and systems) which is clearly separated from the "outside" (the environment around you). In fact, your survival depends on your body not being so easily divided into inside and outside. There are a few places where the inside and the outside meet to take part in a constant but carefully regulated flow of materials back and forth.

One of these places is the blood-rich lining of the alveoli, which are sac-like structures that look like tiny clusters of grapes in our lungs. This is where the body exchanges gases with its surrounding environment. But what exactly is being exchanged, and how? Why is the exchange necessary? Why is it so difficult to control your breathing? What if you are a smoker — does it *really* matter?

If you have ever watched the end of a long race, you will have seen that some runners practically sprint to the finish line, while others struggle to complete the event. What role does the respiratory system play in this, and could you use this knowledge to improve your own endurance? Although issues like lung capacity often come up in connection with athletic performance, your ability to breathe obviously affects all your activities. How should you respond to an air quality alert on a day when your region is engulfed in smog? Will a bird, spider, or oak tree also be affected by air pollution?

All living organisms respire — that is, they exchange gases with their environment — although not all of them breathe. In this chapter, you will examine a number of different kinds of respiratory systems and how they are regulated. As you work through the chapter, keep in mind that respiratory systems and gas exchange systems are only one part of the complex puzzle of sustaining life. The respiratory system is closely connected to other systems in the body, including the transport and digestive systems. These other systems are described in the next two chapters. For now, however, the respiratory system will serve as a starting point for your exploration of the places where the outside meets the inside.

At the end of this marathon, one runner can barely stand while another looks relatively fresh. How might the differences in these athlete's respiratory systems affect their performance?

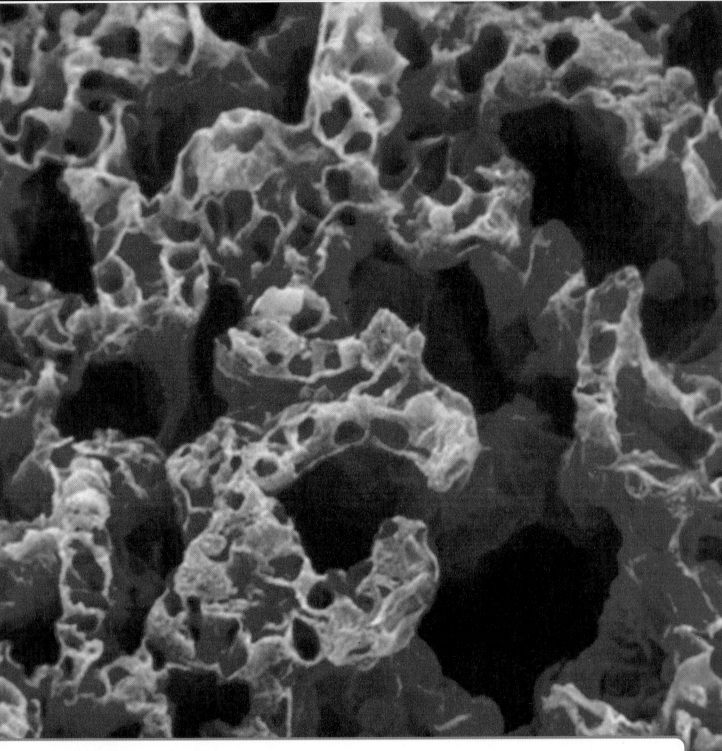

Chapter Contents

The Task of Respiration

- Describe gas exchange in simple organisms.
- Explain why some organisms do not need specialized respiratory systems.
- List the respiratory adaptations that enable organisms to live on land.
- Describe the main types of animal respiratory systems.

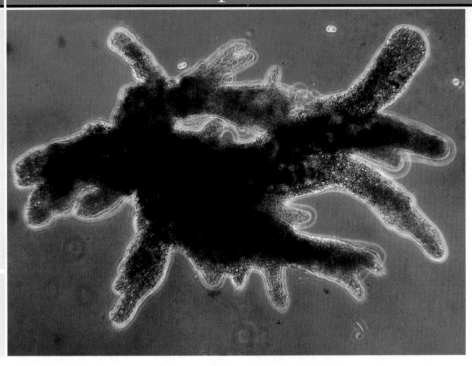

Figure 8.1 Single-celled organisms, like the amoeba shown here, do not require a specialized respiratory system.

Like most organisms on earth, the amoeba is **aerobic** — that is, it requires oxygen to survive. Whether an aerobic organism is unicellular, like the amoeba, or multicellular, each cell in the organism must have a supply of oxygen. Oxygen is necessary to carry out cellular respiration, the process that releases the energy needed to drive all cell functions. Each cell must also rid itself of the carbon dioxide that is the waste product of cellular respiration. The basic function of the respiratory system is to make sure that oxygen can enter each cell in the organism, and that carbon dioxide can leave each cell. This process is known as **gas exchange**.

◄◄ REWIND

To review the concept of cellular respiration, turn to Chapter 3, Section 3.3.

Different organisms have different kinds of respiratory systems to accomplish the task of gas exchange. Every respiratory system, however, shares two requirements. First, the surface area available for gas exchange, **or respiratory surface**, must be big enough for the exchange of oxygen and carbon dioxide to occur at a rate that will meet the organism's metabolic needs. Second, respiration must take place in a moist environment, so that the oxygen and carbon dioxide are dissolved. The respiratory systems you will examine in this chapter all demonstrate variations of these two basic features.

Gas Exchange at Its Simplest

Most single-celled aerobic organisms do not have a distinct respiratory system. Such organisms, including protists, algae, fungi, and some bacteria, rely instead on diffusion to meet their gas exchange requirements. These organisms need moist environments, and are found either in aquatic environments or in other moist places such as within the body of a host organism. Oxygen, which is dissolved in the water around the cell, diffuses through the outer membrane of each cell and thereby becomes available for cellular respiration. At the same time, carbon dioxide diffuses out. For these organisms, the cell membrane itself provides a moist surface area big enough to accommodate the organism's gas exchange requirements.

Math LINK

A number of factors affect the rate of diffusion of dissolved gases. These include the surface area available for diffusion, the concentration gradient, the size of the diffusing molecules, and the length of the diffusion path. In one set of experiments, a group of researchers found that, under a particular set of conditions, a molecule of oxygen dissolved in water diffused 1 μm in 0.0001 s, but took 100 s to diffuse 1 mm. Write an equation showing the relationship between the diffusion time and the length of the diffusion path. Now estimate the distance from your nose to your writing hand when your arm is fully extended. How long would it take oxygen to diffuse that distance, assuming the same conditions as in the experiment above?

Colonial algae, such as volvox, and simple animal organisms such as hydra (see Figure 8.2A and B) also lack specialized tissues for gas exchange. Although they are multi-celled organisms, almost all of the cells of these organisms are in direct contact with the surrounding aquatic medium. As a result, each individual cell can obtain sufficient oxygen through diffusion. In contrast to volvox or hydra, the worm-like planarian (see Figure 8.2C) has all three germ layers, or tissue types, found in higher animals. This tiny creature can still manage without a respiratory system, however, because of its thin, flat shape. A planarian's body is at most only a few cells deep, so oxygen has a short distance to travel in order to diffuse into every living cell. At the same time, the width of the body provides a large surface area for gas exchange.

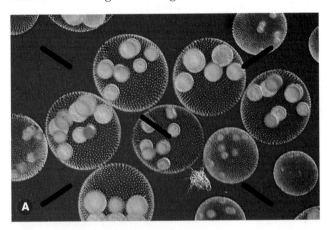

Figure 8.2 Volvox (A), hydra (B) and planarian (C). These simple organisms can also depend on diffusion alone to meet their gas exchange requirements.

Unicellular Terrestrial Organisms

Some unicellular terrestrial organisms also lack a distinct respiratory system. Bacteria and fungi living within the soil, as well as terrestrial protists, depend on the air in the tiny spaces in the soil for their source of oxygen. The organism's requirement for a moist respiratory surface is satisfied by water derived from the soil solution. As long as there is water in the soil, the air spaces will remain humid enough for the cell membrane to stay moist.

Many bacteria and fungi live on the surface of the soil, often in association with organic debris. These organisms depend on simple diffusion of gases to and from the surrounding air. As in their aquatic or soil-borne counterparts, this exchange takes place directly across the cell membrane. In general, it is the availability of moisture (either as soil moisture or as water vapour in the surrounding air) that restricts the habitat of such organisms.

Figure 8.3 This environment supports many unicellular terrestrial organisms.

The Specialized Respiratory System

The larger an organism is, the more oxygen it requires to supply its cells, and the greater the distance over which that oxygen must travel in order to reach all of the cells. This raises two problems. First, diffusion of oxygen is only effective over a distance of a few cells, so an organism with a body more than a few cells thick must use another mechanism to bring oxygen to all its cells. Second, as body parts become differentiated for uses such as locomotion or reproduction, the body surface that can be dedicated to gas exchange is reduced.

Different kinds of adaptations have made it possible for larger, more complex organisms to meet their need for oxygen. All of the higher animals have evolved a specialized respiratory system. An animal's respiratory system includes a respiratory surface, any passageways that connect this surface to the external environment, and any muscular structures that are used to help bring the respiratory medium into contact with the respiratory surface. The following pages examine several types of specialized respiratory structures found in animals.

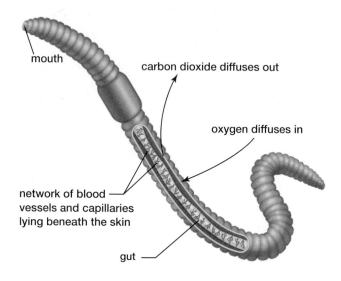

Figure 8.4 The earthworm makes use of its moist skin surface to exchange gases between its circulatory system and its environment.

❚❚ PAUSE   ● RECORD

Multicellular animals have evolved ways of storing nutrients and, to a lesser extent, water in their bodies. Your own body can survive for several days without water, and for weeks without food, but only for a few minutes without oxygen. What factors might prevent your body from storing oxygen? List your ideas and explain briefly. Hint: what does the term "oxidization" mean?

Skin Respiration

One adaptation is demonstrated by animals in the phylum Annelida, which includes the segmented worms such as earthworms and leeches. Segmented worms can survive only in water or in damp earth, because their skin must remain moist. To meet their oxygen requirements, earthworms make use of the moist surface and their simple circulatory mechanism. The skin is lined with many tiny capillary vessels, and these capillaries make contact with the skin surface all over the body of the worm. At each of these points of contact, respiratory gases diffuse into and out of the circulatory vessels (Figure 8.4). The oxygen is then carried through the circulatory vessels to other parts of the organism.

The exchange of gases across the skin of the animal is called **skin respiration**. As in volvox and planaria, the gas exchange occurs across the organism's entire body surface. The crucial difference is that the earthworm uses a circulatory system to carry oxygen to the cells that could not rely on diffusion to meet their needs.

Figure 8.5 The aquatic tube worm cannot exchange gases through its protective casing.

Gills

In contrast to the earthworm, whose whole body surface is available for respiration, most of the body of a tube worm is covered with a protective casing. Many other aquatic animals also have protective coats. These coats provide defence against predators or help maintain the animals' internal environments. In such organisms the relative area over which diffusion of respiratory

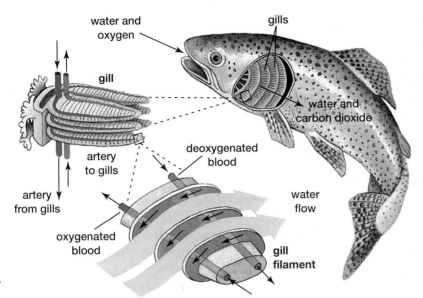

water and oxygen

gill

gills

water and carbon dioxide

artery to gills

deoxygenated blood

artery from gills

oxygenated blood

water flow

gill filament

Figure 8.6 The fish draws water through its mouth and over its gills. As water passes over the gills, oxygen diffuses into the adjacent blood vessels. At the same time, carbon dioxide diffuses out.

gases can occur is considerably reduced. Two adaptations help these organisms accomplish the task of respiration. First, structural changes have increased the surface area of the body part involved in gas exchange. Second, a mechanism has evolved that enables the animal to **ventilate** this surface — that is, to move the oxygen-containing aquatic medium over the respiratory surface. This allows the respiratory surface to be constantly exposed to a fresh supply of oxygen.

Many aquatic organisms, including molluscs, crayfish, mud puppies, tadpoles, and fish, have developed **gills**, which are feathery tissue structures that invariably consist of numerous delicate branches. When the gills are exposed to water, gases are exchanged across the thin gill membranes. The oxygen diffuses into the organism's vascular system for circulation around the body. Gills ensure that a considerable surface area is available for gas exchange in a very limited space.

Gilled animals have evolved various means of ventilation. In some animals, such as the tube worm, the gill is moved through the water. In others, such as fish and clams, water is drawn or pumped over the gill. In most gilled animals, the water flows only one way over the gills. This reduces the amount of energy the animal must expend to move the water over the respiratory surface.

Figure 8.6 shows the respiratory organ of a typical fish. Water moves in through the mouth and out behind the animal's head, passing over the gills on the way. Adjacent to the gills are a network of tiny capillaries that absorb oxygen and release carbon dioxide from the animal's circulatory system.

The ventilation mechanisms of some aquatic animals are linked with other functions. In a number of species, including many molluscs, feeding and ventilation are accomplished together. Food particles are captured as the gill moves through the water, and are filtered out by the organism at the same time that gas exchange takes place. Other animals use the currents produced by respiratory action for locomotion. A squid, for example, can move rapidly forward or backward by forcing water out of its gill siphon.

Moving out of the Water

Given how much equipment we need in order to breathe under water, it may be hard to imagine that, from an evolutionary perspective, respiration in air is actually the bigger challenge. In the water, the need for a respiratory surface that stays moist is rarely a problem. On land, however, moisture from a respiratory surface exposed to the air will evaporate, so the animal would have to release more water constantly to keep the surface moist. A terrestrial animal that made a large moist surface area available for gas exchange would therefore risk excessive water loss. Before living organisms could

Figure 8.7 People must take air with them in order to breathe under water, along with special equipment to dispense it.

begin to colonize terrestrial environments, adaptations were needed that could solve this critical problem. In much the same way that scuba divers take some of their usual respiratory medium (air) along on the dive, all terrestrial animals have evolved some way to carry a moist respiratory environment wherever they go.

In the previous paragraphs, you learned that most aquatic animals have developed some way to ventilate their respiratory surface. The same is true of most terrestrial animals. The act of ventilating a respiratory surface with air is called **breathing**. The breathing of terrestrial organisms relies on a basic law of physics: air will move from a region of higher pressure to a region of lower pressure until equilibrium is reached (Figure 8.8). Different terrestrial animals have evolved different ways to make use of this principle in their respiratory systems.

The Tracheal Respiratory System

In insects, the problem of how to maintain a moist respiratory surface without losing too much water is resolved by an internal respiratory system that consists of a series of external pores called **spiracles**. The spiracles lead to an internal network of tubes called **tracheae** (singular trachea). All of the spiracles are controlled by valves. Although the specific configuration of spiracles and tracheae varies considerably from one species to the next, the basic elements of the tracheal system are common to most insects and many other non-vertebrate terrestrial animals.

If you can, observe a living grasshopper. Note that the abdomen contracts and relaxes rhythmically. These are the breathing movements of the animal. As described in Figure 8.9, the animal's breathing causes an orderly movement of air through the tracheae, from the front of the animal to the back.

both containers same size, same pressure

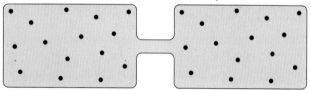

A At equilibrium, air pressure is equal in both vessels.

left container larger, lower pressure; air moves in

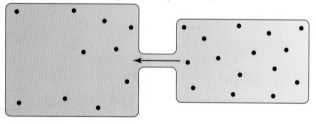

B If the volume of one vessel increases, the air pressure inside it decreases. Air flows from the vessel with the higher pressure into the vessel with the lower pressure.

same pressure in both (but lower than above)

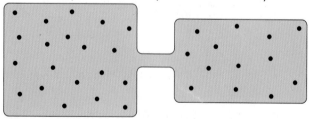

C A new equilibrium is reached with air pressure once again equal in each vessel.

Figure 8.8 Air will move from a region of higher pressure to a region of lower pressure.

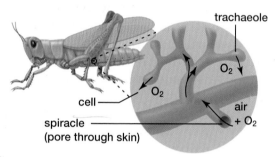

A As the abdomen expands, air pressure drops within the tracheae. At the same time, the anterior four pairs of spiracles open, while the posterior six pairs of spiracles remain closed. Air therefore flows in through the anterior spiracles.

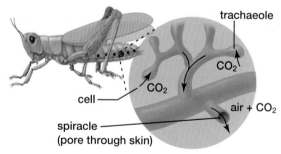

B When the abdomen contracts, the reverse situation occurs. The anterior four pairs close and the posterior six pairs open. Air pressure is now higher inside the animal than in the surrounding environment, so air flows out through the posterior spiracles.

Figure 8.9 The tracheal respiratory system of a grasshopper.

In insects, the respiratory and circulatory systems are separate from one another. The tracheal system of an insect does not require a circulatory system to transport the respiratory gases. Instead, the many branches of the tracheal tubes ensure that the respiratory surface is in close enough contact with all of the living cells to allow gas exchange to occur by diffusion across the moist tracheal walls. Because most of the tracheal system remains inside the animal, the risk of excessive water loss is reduced.

The Lung

The third general type of respiratory system, and the one that is characteristic of air-breathing vertebrates, is the internal **lung** arrangement. The lung is an internal respiratory surface connected to the air by means of internal passageways. Lung systems vary from species to species in terms of both structure and efficiency. However, all lung systems consist of three basic elements: one or two lungs that have a moist respiratory surface; some means of forcibly bringing air in contact with the lung surface; and a circulatory system to carry the gases between the lungs and the other cells of the body. Figure 8.10 outlines the various general lung types found in a number of animal species.

The frog uses a simple lung system ventilated by the movement of muscles in the nostrils, mouth, and abdomen. To breathe in, the frog first closes its mouth and opens its nostrils or *nares*, then lowers the floor of the mouth, drawing air into the mouth cavity. The nostrils are then closed, and the floor of the mouth raised. As a result the air is forced into the lungs where gas exchange takes place. In the frog, as in other amphibians, the lung system is used in conjunction with both skin respiration and the exchange of gases across membranes in the

lining of the mouth. This explains why a frog cannot live for any extended period away from either an aquatic or a very humid environment. Because it uses its skin as a respiratory surface, it has no satisfactory means of controlling water loss through the skin.

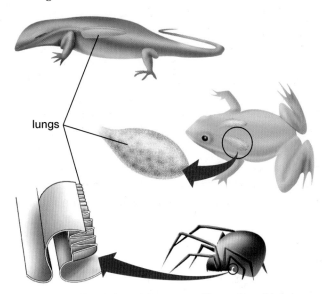

lungs

Figure 8.10 Examples of the types of lungs found in animals such as amphibians, spiders, and reptiles. Spiders' lungs are often referred to as "book lungs" because their many folds are arranged like the pages of a book.

Snakes and other reptiles that flourish on land (and even in desert environments) do not use the skin as a site for the exchange of gases. They confine this exchange to the internal lung or lungs. All these organisms possess muscle and skeletal arrangements that enable them to force air out of the lungs and draw air back over the lung surface to ventilate the respiratory tract.

SECTION REVIEW

1. **K/U** Describe how gas exchange takes place in an amoeba.

2. **K/U** Describe two ways in which the problem of getting respiratory gases to individual cells has been overcome in larger, more complex organisms.

3. **C** Imagine an argument between a tube worm and a grasshopper about the best way to respire. Working with a partner, try to create an imaginary dialogue between the two animals (assume that the two animals can speak the same language). Where are the greatest misunderstandings likely to arise? How would you suggest the two settle their argument?

4. **MC** Populations of grasshoppers and locusts occasionally skyrocket, creating plagues that can cause considerable damage to farm crops. How could knowledge of the way grasshoppers breathe be used to control their numbers?

5. **K/U** Can a frog respire under water? Why or why not?

6. **K/U** Account for the fact that you see many earthworms on the ground after a rainstorm.

7. **I** A new species of insect is discovered. This insect has 12 pairs of spiracles along its abdomen. Design an experiment to test whether the spiracles work in concert, in sequence, or some type of intermediate mechanism.

The Mammalian Respiratory System

- List the steps in the path taken by air as it moves from the outside of the animal to the internal gas exchange site in the lungs.

- Describe the role played by each part of the respiratory tract.

- Explain how the mammalian respiratory system is adapted to reduce water loss.

Figure 8.11 All mammals, including marine mammals such as seals and whales, have lungs.

What do these seals, which spend most of their lives in the ocean, have in common with a desert rat which might never see so much as a puddle in its life? Despite their very different habitats, the respiratory systems of all mammals share the same basic features.

As you have seen, respiration refers to all parts of the process that supplies oxygen to body cells and rids the body of carbon dioxide. In mammals, respiration can be subdivided into the following:

Breathing, which can be further divided into inspiration, the act of taking air into the lungs, and expiration, the act of breathing out;

External respiration, the exchange of oxygen and carbon dioxide between air and blood;

Internal respiration, the exchange of oxygen and carbon dioxide between blood and the cells of the surrounding tissue (discussed in Chapter 9); and

Cellular respiration, the complex series of chemical reactions that take place mainly in the mitochondria of cells.

The Respiratory Tract

Lungs, with their many folds and fine membranes, are delicate, fragile structures. As a result, they must be shielded not only to prevent water loss, but also to guard against damage. The lungs of mammals are located deep within the body, where they are protected by the bone and muscular structure of the thoracic cavity. This adaptation means that a suitable passageway becomes necessary to allow air to move from the external environment to the respiratory surface deep inside the animal. The organs of the lung system therefore include a number of different structures, each with an important role to play. The following paragraphs trace the passage of air through these organs, using the human respiratory system as an example.

The Upper Respiratory Tract

The air first enters the nostrils (in humans and many other animals, it can also enter via the mouth). The nostrils conduct the air into the hollow nasal passages where several things occur. Thin bones, called turbinates, hang suspended from the nasal chambers. Their presence increases the surface area of these chambers. The turbinates are covered with a thin membrane that secretes mucus, which moistens the air. The epithelial linings of the nasal chambers and the turbinate bones are well supplied with capillaries, which serve both to warm the incoming air and also to increase its relative humidity. This warming and moistening helps to protect the delicate tissues of the lungs.

The air then passes successively through the pharynx, the glottis, and the larynx (see Figure 8.12). The **pharynx** is the section of alimentary canal that connects the mouth and nasal cavity to the larynx and esophagus. The **glottis** is the opening of the trachea, the passageway that conducts air to the lungs. This opening is protected by the **epiglottis**, a flap-like structure that helps to prevent food from entering the trachea. The pharynx is the intersection between the trachea and the esophagus, the passageway for food.

The **larynx**, or "voice box," houses the vocal cords, which are held securely in place by the cartilaginous material present in the walls of the larynx (Figure 8.13). The larynx contains the two folded structures of the vocal cords. When you breathe normally, there is a large gap between the two cords. When you prepare to speak, muscles around the larynx contract, bringing the cords closer together. The passage of air through this narrower space causes the cords to vibrate, producing a sound. The pitch of the sound varies with the length of the cords: a long cord produces a low sound, while a shorter cord produces a higher sound. At puberty, the vocal cords of males grow quickly. This often produces a "breaking" quality in the voice until the vocal cords finish growing.

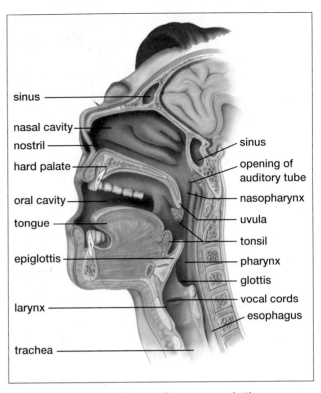

Figure 8.12 Together, the nasal passages, glottis, pharynx, larynx, and trachea are referred to as the upper respiratory tract.

> ➤ **PLAY**

To view the pathway of air through the respiratory tract, refer to your Electronic Learning Partner.

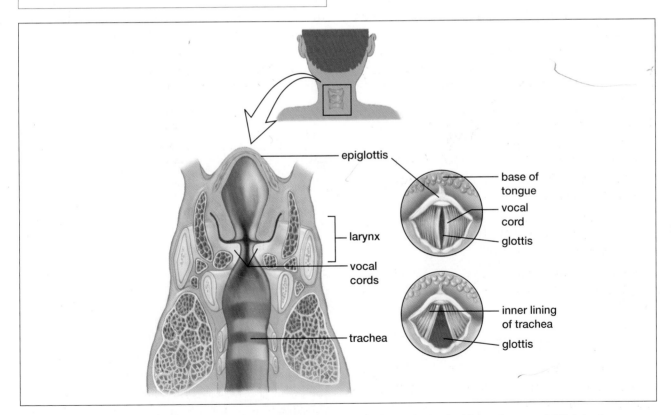

Figure 8.13 A cross section of the larynx, showing the vocal cords. Air passing between the cords causes them to vibrate, producing sound. You can change the pitch of the sound you make by expanding or tightening the glottis; the tighter the glottis, the higher the sound. Pitch is also determined by the length of the cords. The cords tend to be longer in men than in women, which is why men tend to have deeper voices.

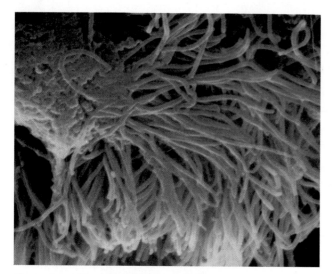

Figure 8.14 The interior of the nasal passage.

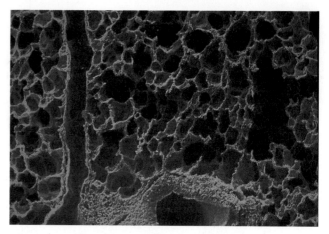

Figure 8.15 The alveolar tissue of the lung. The walls of the alveoli are only a single cell thick.

After passing through the larynx, air goes down the flexible tube of the trachea. In mammals, the trachea is commonly called the "windpipe." The trachea is supported in part by semicircular cartilage rings. These rings prevent the trachea from collapsing and are arranged so they do not interfere with the passage of food down the esophagus, which is adjacent to the trachea.

The nasal and other passages of the upper respiratory tract are lined with ciliated cells that secrete mucus. The mucus traps foreign particles such as dust and bacteria, while the continual beating of the cilia helps to propel this material back into the nose and throat where it can be expelled by coughing or sneezing. When you catch a cold, more mucus is secreted, which is why you find yourself repeatedly blowing your nose.

BIO FACT

The average healthy human adult produces about 0.9 L of mucus every day.

The Lower Respiratory Tract

At about the level of your armpit the trachea branches into two smaller passageways called **bronchi** (singular bronchus). One bronchus enters each lung (see Figure 8.16). Here, each bronchus subdivides many times to produce a network of finer and finer tubes called **bronchioles**. Like the trachea and nasal passages, the bronchi and bronchioles are lined with a ciliated mucous membrane.

Each bronchiole ends in a grape-like cluster of tiny sacs called **alveoli** (singular alveolus). It is in these sacs, which are always kept moist, that the actual exchange of gases takes place. If you could take all of the alveoli in the average human lung and spread them out on a smooth surface, they would cover approximately 70 to 90 m^2 — an area about the size of a tennis court. The wall of each sac is one cell thick and is adjacent to a network of tiny capillaries (Figure 8.15). These capillaries are the site for the exchange of oxygen and carbon dioxide in the body. While most of the exchange of gases takes place through simple diffusion, a process of facilitated diffusion accounts for some (possibly as much as 30%) of the oxygen transfer. This allows the blood to take up oxygen more quickly than would otherwise be possible. The transport of oxygen across the alveolar membrane is facilitated by a particular protein-based molecule in the alveolar cell wall.

The entire arrangement of bronchioles and alveoli is kept in a relatively permanent position by elastic connective tissue that fills the spaces between the individual structures. In addition, the alveoli are lined with a lipoprotein-based lubricating film that helps to keep them from collapsing.

Word LINK

The word "lung" comes from the Old English word *lungen*, meaning "light in weight." The lungs are the lightest organs of the body. Because of their many air sacs, they will float in water. The lungs of a livestock animal, particularly a sheep or cow, are sometimes called its "lights."

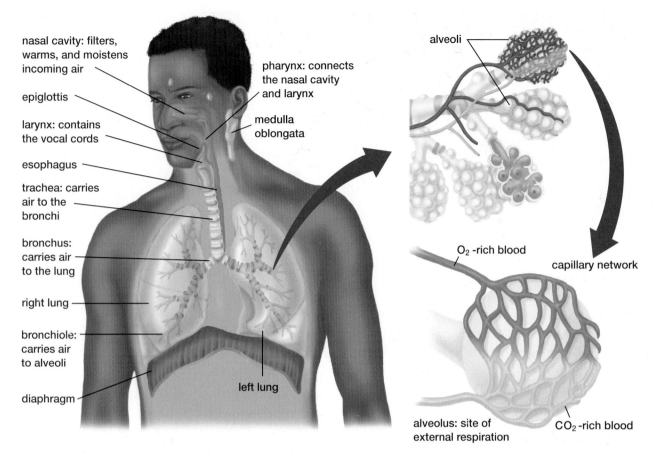

nasal cavity: filters, warms, and moistens incoming air

epiglottis

larynx: contains the vocal cords

esophagus

trachea: carries air to the bronchi

bronchus: carries air to the lung

right lung

bronchiole: carries air to alveoli

diaphragm

pharynx: connects the nasal cavity and larynx

medulla oblongata

left lung

alveoli

O_2-rich blood

capillary network

alveolus: site of external respiration

CO_2-rich blood

Figure 8.16 The path of air through the human respiratory tract. The complex structure of the lungs serves to maintain a moist respiratory surface across which gases can be exchanged between the external environment and the body.

Each lung is divided into lobes. The right lung has three lobes, while the left lung has only two (to accommodate the heart). A lobe is made up of a number of lobules, each with its own bronchiole. The lungs themselves are enveloped in layers of tissue called **pleura** (singular pleuron). This flexible membrane contains the lungs while still allowing them to expand and contract during inspiration and expiration. Each pleuron is made up of two layers separated by a thin film of lubricating fluid. The condition known as pleurisy occurs when the pleura become inflamed, typically as a secondary infection related to pneumonia or other thoracic diseases. Pleurisy can be extremely painful and requires prompt medical attention.

SECTION REVIEW

1. **K/U** Explain how the two basic requirements for gas exchange are met by the structure of the mammalian lung.

2. **K/U** In what ways does the respiratory tract alter incoming air to prepare it for gas exchange in the lung? What organs of the respiratory tract are involved in this?

3. **C** "A lung is an inside-out gill." Make one list of the ways in which this statement is true, and another list of the ways in which this statement is false. How can you summarize your findings in a single sentence?

4. **MC** Some cold-relief medications work by inhibiting the production of mucus. What side effects would you expect from these products?

5. **I** Jarvic 7 is an artificial heart. Design a device that could act as an artificial lung. Provide detailed reasoning to support your design.

UNIT PROJECT PREP

If you have decided to study a respiratory disorder in your Unit Project, make sure you can describe the location and function of the affected respiratory structures.

The Mechanics of Breathing

- Distinguish between the concepts of breathing and respiration.
- Describe the muscular processes involved in breathing.
- Explain the concepts of respiratory capacity and respiratory efficiency.

Figure 8.17 Mammalian breathing movements, including the controlled exhalation that allows singing, involve a number of muscles.

Breathing is the mechanism by which mammals ventilate their lungs. Like the insect tracheal system and the lung systems of other animals, this ventilation relies on the principle that air will flow from a region of higher pressure to a region of lower pressure.

When we breathe we use two muscular structures to control air pressure inside our lungs. These structures are the **intercostal muscles**, the muscles associated with the ventral surface of the rib cage, and the diaphragm. The **diaphragm** is a muscle layer that separates the region of the lungs (the thoracic cavity) from the region of the stomach and the liver (the abdominal cavity). The diaphragm is found in all mammals, and its prime function is to assist in the ventilation of the lungs. While the intercostal muscles and the diaphragm can each produce breathing-related movements, the two usually work simultaneously as described below.

Figure 8.18 shows how the intercostal muscles and diaphragm work together to move air in and out of the lungs. Inhalation begins when the external intercostal muscles and the diaphragm contract. The intercostal muscles expand the rib

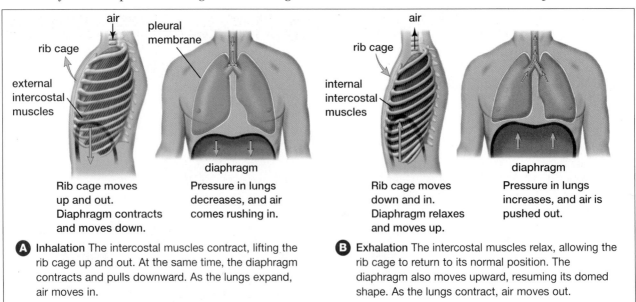

Rib cage moves up and out. Diaphragm contracts and moves down.

Pressure in lungs decreases, and air comes rushing in.

Rib cage moves down and in. Diaphragm relaxes and moves up.

Pressure in lungs increases, and air is pushed out.

A Inhalation The intercostal muscles contract, lifting the rib cage up and out. At the same time, the diaphragm contracts and pulls downward. As the lungs expand, air moves in.

B Exhalation The intercostal muscles relax, allowing the rib cage to return to its normal position. The diaphragm also moves upward, resuming its domed shape. As the lungs contract, air moves out.

Figure 8.18 The mechanics of respiration.

cage, while the diaphragm moves down in the thoracic cavity. This increases the volume of the thoracic cavity. Because the thoracic cavity is relatively airtight, an increase in its volume produces a decrease in air pressure within the cavity. This decrease in pressure draws the flexible walls of the lungs outward into the thoracic cavity, causing the lungs to expand. As a result of this expansion, the air pressure within the lungs is lower than the air pressure in the external environment. Air then enters the lungs, moving from the region of higher to lower pressure.

The reverse muscular movement expels air from the lungs. The diaphragm relaxes, returning to a dome-shaped curve. The external intercostal muscles also relax, while the internal intercostal muscles contract to help pull the rib cage back to its original position. These changes create a higher pressure in the thoracic cavity, which causes the

lungs to shrink and results in a higher pressure in the lungs. In turn, air moves out through the trachea.

> **⏸ PAUSE** **⏺ RECORD**
>
> While sitting, slowly bend forward until your head is near your knees. What effect does this have on your ability to breathe? Explain, with reference to the particular structures involved in breathing.

> **▶ PLAY**
>
> Refer to your Electronic Learning Partner for a computer animation of the mechanics of breathing.

Exchange of Gases

External respiration takes place in the lungs. As in the other respiratory systems you have examined,

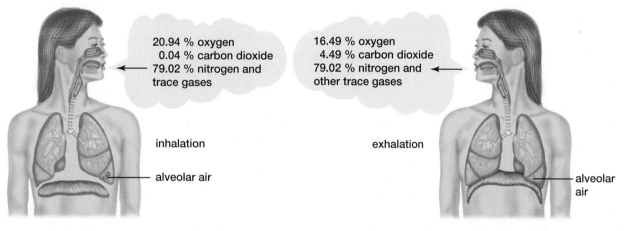

20.94 % oxygen
0.04 % carbon dioxide
79.02 % nitrogen and trace gases

inhalation

alveolar air

16.49 % oxygen
4.49 % carbon dioxide
79.02 % nitrogen and other trace gases

exhalation

alveolar air

Figure 8.19 The composition of inspired and expired air under normal conditions.

 MINI LAB

Carbon dioxide in inhaled and exhaled air

In this lab, you will observe the difference between the concentration of carbon dioxide in inhaled and in exhaled air. First, light a wooden splint and place it in a glass jar, holding it until the flame goes out. Add a small amount of limewater to the jar and shake. Record your observations. Now prepare an Erlenmeyer flask by pouring in a small amount of limewater, inserting a two-holed rubber stopper into its mouth, and inserting a glass tube through one of the holes. Insert one branch of a rubber Y-tube into the other hole. Prepare a second flask in the same way, inserting the other branch of the same Y-tube. Label one flask "inhaled" and the other "exhaled." Pinch shut the branch of the

Y-tube that leads to the "exhaled" flask, and inhale deeply through the Y-tube. You should be drawing air through the "inhaled" flask. Now pinch shut the branch of the Y-tube that leads from the "inhaled" flask, open the branch that leads to the "exhaled" flask, and exhale through the Y-tube. You should be exhaling through the "exhaled" flask. Repeat until you see a change in the limewater in one or both flasks. Record your data.

Analyze

Describe the differences between the two flasks at the end of your experiment. Explain your findings with reference to the exchange of gases during respiration. What purpose does the wooden splint serve in this experiment? Are there any variables that might not be accounted for in this experiment?

the exchange of oxygen and carbon dioxide takes place across cell membranes. The alveoli and adjacent capillaries each have walls that are only a single cell thick, so they can allow the diffusion of these gases. For inhaled oxygen to enter the bloodstream, it must first dissolve in the fluid lining of each alveolus.

Under normal conditions, the concentration of oxygen in inhaled air is greater than the concentration of oxygen in the blood of the capillaries entering the lung area. In contrast, the carbon dioxide concentration is greater in the blood than in inhaled air. Thus oxygen diffuses across the capillary wall into the bloodstream and carbon dioxide moves from the capillaries across the alveoli into the lung. The composition of inhaled and exhaled air is illustrated in Figure 8.19.

Lung Capacity

Think about the difference between your normal breathing and a deep breath, such as a heavy sigh or a yawn. Under normal conditions, your regular breathing does not use up the full capacity of your lungs. As your body's needs increase, such as when you exercise, the volume of air drawn in can also increase.

The different volumes of air drawn in or pushed out by the lungs are distinguished as follows. See also Figure 8.20.

Tidal volume is the volume of air inhaled and exhaled in a normal breathing movement.

Inspiratory reserve volume is the additional volume of air that can be taken in, beyond a regular or tidal inhalation.

Investigation   8 • A

SKILL FOCUS

Performing and recording

Analyzing and interpreting

Communicating results

Measuring Respiratory Volumes

Respiratory volumes vary from individual to individual. In this investigation, you will measure your own respiratory volume.

Pre-lab Questions

- What medical purposes could be served by measuring respiratory volumes?

- What variables might affect the measurement of respiratory volumes in a single individual? Does this investigation control for these variables?

Problem

How can you use a spirometer, which measures air as it is exhaled, to determine the volume of air you inhale on a normal or deep breath?

Prediction

Predict what percentage of your vital capacity is represented by your tidal volume.

CAUTION: Do not inhale or exhale to the point of faintness.

Materials

nose plug
materials for recording data
spirometer with disposable mouthpieces

Procedure

1. Set the spirometer gauge to zero and insert a clean mouthpiece. Put on the nose plug.

2. Inhale normally, then exhale normally into the spirometer. Record this value as your *tidal volume*.

3. Reset the spirometer. Inhale and exhale normally. At the end of the normal exhalation, put the spirometer mouthpiece into your mouth and exhale as much as you can into the spirometer. Make sure you do this all in one breath. Record this value as your *expiratory reserve volume*.

4. Reset the spirometer. Inhale as deeply as you can, and then exhale normally into the spirometer. Do not force the exhalation. Record this value as your *inspiratory capacity*.

5. To calculate your inspiratory reserve volume, subtract your tidal volume from your inspiratory capacity. Record this value as your *inspiratory reserve volume*.

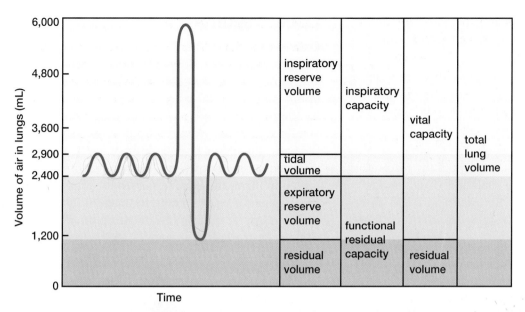

Figure 8.20 The graph shows the maximum volume of air that can be moved in and out of the lungs during a single breath: the vital capacity. The pattern shown in this graph is called a spirograph.

6. Calculate your vital capacity by adding your inspiratory reserve volume, expiratory reserve volume, and tidal volume. Record this value as your *calculated vital capacity*.

7. Reset the spirometer. Inhale as deeply as you can and then exhale deeply into the spirometer, forcing out as much air as you can. Make sure you do this all in one breath. Record this value as your *recorded vital capacity*.

Post-lab Questions

1. How does your calculated vital capacity compare to your recorded vital capacity? How would you explain any difference?

2. How does your inspiratory reserve volume compare to your expiratory reserve volume? How would you explain this difference?

3. Can you use the spirometer to measure your total lung capacity? Explain.

Conclude and Apply

4. How might an athlete use information about his or her vital capacity? How do respiratory volumes relate to athletic performance?

5. A ventilator is a piece of medical equipment that maintains respiratory movements in a person who is unable to breathe unaided. In a young, otherwise healthy patient paralyzed as a result of a car crash, should a ventilator be adjusted to maximize the volume of air inhaled and exhaled? Explain.

Exploring Further

6. Compare your respiratory volumes with those of others in your class. How much variation do you see? Do you see particular patterns in this variation? Can you suggest factors that could contribute to differences in respiratory volumes? Design an experiment to test how two of these variables affect respiratory volumes.

7. Vital capacity is one factor in determining fitness, since it shows how well individuals can ventilate their lung surface. Conduct research in your library or on the Internet to determine how vital capacity is affected in two different respiratory disorders. Prepare a brief report describing how these disorders affect the respiratory system, and what their treatments involve.

Expiratory reserve volume is the additional volume that can be forced out of the lungs, beyond a regular or tidal exhalation.

Vital capacity is the total volume of gas that can be moved in or out of the lungs. It can be calculated as tidal volume + inspiratory reserve volume + expiratory reserve volume = vital capacity.

Residual volume is the amount of gas that remains in the lungs and the passageways of the respiratory system even after a full exhalation. This volume never leaves the respiratory system; if it did, the lungs and respiratory passageways would collapse. Because the residual volume is not exchanged with air from the external environment, it has little value for gas exchange.

Table 8.1 reviews the path of air through the main structures involved in mammalian gas exchange. The rate at which oxygen can be transferred into the blood stream for transport to the rest of the body is called **respiratory efficiency**. You will learn about factors that affect your respiratory efficiency in Chapter 9. Other animals have respiratory systems with special adaptations that help to increase their respiratory efficiency. One such adaptation is the use of facilitated diffusion which, as you saw earlier, can speed the transfer of oxygen across cell membranes in mammals. Some animal respiratory systems, however, show special adaptations not found in the mammalian lung arrangement.

Table 8.1
Path of air in the body

Structure	Description	Function
Nasal cavities	Hollow spaces in nose	Filter, warm, moisten air
Pharynx	Chamber connecting oral and nasal cavities to larynx	Connection to surrounding regions
Glottis	Opening to larynx	Air passage to larynx
Larynx	Organ containing vocal cords	Sound production
Trachea	Flexible tube linking larynx and bronchi	Passage of air to bronchi
Bronchi	Tracheal divisions to lungs	Passage of air to lungs
Bronchioles	Branched tubes from bronchi to alveoli	Passage of air to each alveolus
Lungs	Soft, spongy organs in thoracic cavity	Gas exchange

Counter-current Flow

Earlier, you learned that water flows over the gills of a fish in only one direction. This saves energy, since the fish does not have to reverse the direction of the water flow. It also provides for another adaptation that increases the rate of gas exchange. While water flows from the front of the fish toward the back, the blood vessels lining the gills are arranged so the blood flows in the opposite direction (from the back to the front). This arrangement is called a **counter-current flow**, and it plays an important role in increasing the efficiency of the fish respiratory system (Figure 8.21).

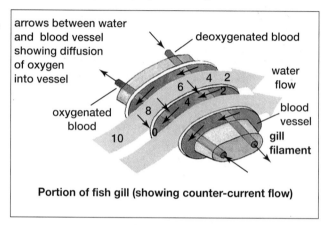

arrows between water and blood vessel showing diffusion of oxygen into vessel

deoxygenated blood

water flow

oxygenated blood

blood vessel

gill filament

Portion of fish gill (showing counter-current flow)

Figure 8.21 The illustration shows that the counter-current flow in a fish gill allows for diffusion of a great deal of oxygen across a thin wall of a blood vessel. (The numbers in the water and in the vessel represent the concentration of oxygen in the water flowing over the gill and within the vessel.) If the fish had no counter-current flow, the amount of oxygen in the water and in the blood vessel would quickly become equal, thus no further diffusion would occur.

The counter-current arrangement makes the most of the oxygen gradient between the respiratory medium and the blood. As the blood flows past the gills, the most oxygen-depleted blood meets the most oxygen-depleted respiratory medium first. However, the concentration of oxygen in the blood is still lower than that in the water, so oxygen will tend to diffuse into the blood. As the blood flows toward the head of the fish, it becomes richer in oxygen, but continues to meet water that is also increasingly oxygen-rich. The level of oxygen in the blood never reaches that in the water, so even as the blood is about to leave the gill area it continues to pick up oxygen from the respiratory medium.

In contrast to the mammalian lung, where the blood exchanges gases with inhaled air of a constant composition, the counter-current arrangement makes it possible for the blood to pass by a respiratory medium that is increasingly rich in oxygen (Figure 8.22). As a result, more oxygen can be transferred from the respiratory medium to the blood. A similar principle is used in the heat-exchange design of industrial air-conditioning systems.

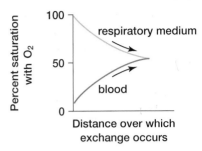

A In the mammalian lung, the oxygen gradient between the respiratory medium in the lungs and the blood in the capillaries is steadily reduced as oxygen passes across the alveoli wall. The blood may take up about 50% of the oxygen in the respiratory medium entering the lungs.

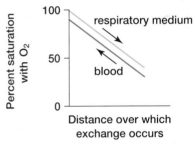

B In a countercurrent exchange system, the oxygen gradient is maintained over the whole of the gill. The blood may take up as much as 80% of the oxygen carried in the respiratory medium entering the gill.

Figure 8.22 A comparison of the efficiency of oxygen exchange in the fish gill and the mammalian lung.

The Respiratory System in Birds

The arctic tern (*Sterna paradisaea*) spends much of the year in the coastal regions of continents near the North Pole (Figure 8.23). As winter approaches, these birds can migrate nearly halfway around the world, to the waters off Antarctica. Many other species of birds also migrate hundreds or even thousands of kilometres and back again each year. Flight is an activity that requires a great deal of energy to maintain, and birds must supply their cells with enough oxygen to produce this energy. The respiratory system of birds has evolved special adaptations that allow the birds to fly for many hours without resting.

Figure 8.23 Respiratory adaptations of the arctic tern allow them to fly for many hours without resting.

Much of the efficiency of the bird's respiratory system comes from a series of air sacs that branch out from the two lungs (see Figure 8.24). These air sacs permeate most of the cavities of the bird, including some of the cavities of the bones. The exact number of air sacs varies from species to species, but the sacs can be divided into two groups. The anterior air sacs are located generally on the anterior side of the lungs (that is, between the lungs and the trachea), while the posterior air sacs are located on the posterior side of the lungs. All the air sacs have tubes connecting them to the lungs. No exchange of gases occurs in these air sacs. Instead, the regular expansion and contraction of both sets of air sacs serves to ventilate the lungs in a highly efficient manner.

In the mammalian lung, air enters the lungs and reaches the dead-end sacs of the alveoli, where gas exchange takes place. This arrangement means that much of the air that makes contact with the respiratory surface is residual air left over from the last act of inspiration. In contrast, the respiratory system of the bird permits a true circulation of the air. As a result, fresh air is continually moved across the lung surface, whether the bird is inhaling or exhaling. This means that the bird has an oxygenated respiratory medium in contact with the moist respiratory surface of the lungs at all times. The efficiency of this system is increased even further by the arrangement of the bird's circulatory system which, like the fish gill described previously, provides for a counter-current exchange across the lungs.

Probeware

If you have access to Probeware, do the activity "Cold-Blooded vs. Warm-Blooded Respiration Rates."

Biology At Work

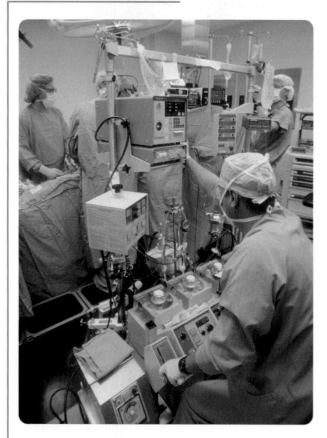

Perfusionist

Imagine a job in which you hold someone's life in your hands every day. Imagine knowing that without you, the operations that save people with heart attacks or lung cancer would not be possible. Imagine knowing that your work can keep a premature infant alive, or give an organ transplant recipient a second chance.

Holding Someone Else's Breath

Disease, exposure to harmful chemicals, and hereditary disorders can all lead to conditions that stop the lungs from working well. People who suffer from these conditions may require lung transplant surgery. But how is this surgery possible? The lungs must be kept still, perhaps for hours at a time, for the delicate operation. In any surgery where the function of the heart or lungs must be stopped, the medical team includes a perfusionist.

Cardiovascular perfusion works by directing the patient's blood out of the body and flowing it continuously through a heart/lung machine. This is called extra-corporeal circulation, which means circulation outside of the body. In fact, the perfusionist is responsible for maintaining the essential functions of respiration as well as circulation. The heart/lung machine perfuses the patient's blood with oxygen while filtering out carbon dioxide.

In the Operating Room — and Beyond

Well before each surgery, the perfusionist chooses and sets up the appropriate type of machine for the patient. This preparation is crucial — there is no room for error once the patient is attached to the machine! A perfusionist may also work in other critical care situations, such as providing cardiopulmonary support to a premature infant whose lungs have not yet developed. In cases where drugs are administered intravenously to the patient during the surgery, this may also be done by the perfusionist through the heart/lung machine.

Perfusionists must be familiar with a number of different techniques. A perfusionist might be responsible for warming or cooling the blood as it flows through the heart-lung machine, or for maintaining gas exchange functions in just one part of the body, such as an arm or leg. A perfusionist must also be prepared to deal with a patient who has a rare blood or respiratory condition.

Perfusionists regularly spend time on call to respond to emergencies. It is a position that calls for dedication and responsibility, but it is also a very rewarding career.

Career Tips

Perfusionists are highly trained medical professionals. A number of medical schools and other institutions in North America offer training in cardiopulmonary perfusion. Most of these training programs involve about two years of specialized study involving a combination of academic work, research, and practical training in a clinical setting. You can start your training by getting a degree as a Registered Nurse, or by getting a diploma in Respiratory Therapy from a community college. After you have some clinical care experience, you will be able to apply to a cardiopulmonary perfusion training program.

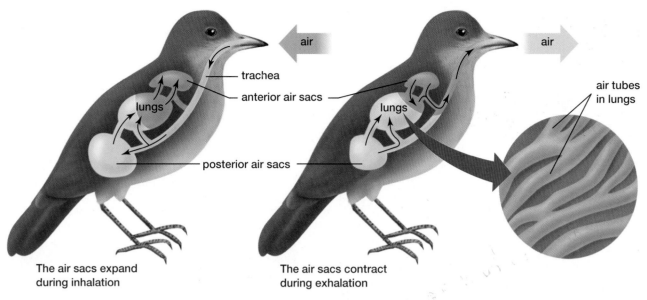

trachea
anterior air sacs
lungs
posterior air sacs

air tubes
in lungs
lungs
air

The air sacs expand
during inhalation

The air sacs contract
during exhalation

A When the bird breathes in, the air sacs expand. Most of the inhaled air passes into the posterior air sacs, and some flows from there into the lungs. At the same time, air that was in the lungs moves into the anterior air sacs.

B When the bird exhales, all the air sacs contract, forcing the air in the posterior air sacs into the capillary-lined tubes of the lungs, where the exchange of gases takes place. The air from the anterior air sacs is forced out through the trachea.

Figure 8.24 The respiratory system of a typical bird. The arrangement of air sacs around the lungs allows fresh air to flow constantly over the surface of the lungs. Note that it takes two full cycles of inspiration and expiration for a given volume of air to move through this respiratory system.

SECTION REVIEW

1. **K/U** Explain the role played by the diaphragm in inspiration and expiration. Suppose that as a result of an automobile accident, the diaphragm of a passenger is punctured. How would this affect the victim's ability to breathe?

2. **C** How would you use the apparatus shown here to explain to a group of young students how air enters and leaves the lungs? Assume that these students are not yet familiar with the concept of pressure.

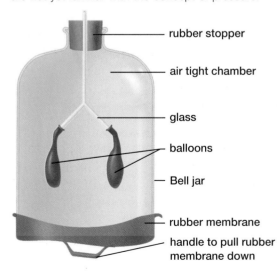

rubber stopper
air tight chamber
glass
balloons
Bell jar
rubber membrane
handle to pull rubber membrane down

3. **K/U** Distinguish between the concepts of respiratory efficiency and respiratory capacity. What is the relationship between the two?

4. **K/U** Describe three different adaptations exhibited by animal respiratory systems that help to increase the rate of gas exchange.

5. **I** The mammalian respiratory system is sometimes described as employing "negative pressure." The frog's respiratory system, on the other hand, uses "positive pressure." To what do these terms refer? Design an experiment that will test which system is more efficient at delivering oxygen from the environment to the lungs.

6. **C** Produce a Concept Organizer that relates what you have learned about the structures of the mammalian respiratory system to the mechanics of breathing. Use the Concept Organizer on page 173 as an example.

Control and Regulation

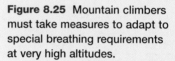
- Describe how the act of breathing is controlled.
- Explain the body's response to high altitudes.
- Describe how environmental hazards can affect respiration.

Figure 8.25 Mountain climbers must take measures to adapt to special breathing requirements at very high altitudes.

High Altitude Breathing

If you have ever travelled up into a very high mountain region, you likely found that you lacked energy and even the slightest physical exertion brought on an acute shortness of breath. You may also have experienced headaches or nausea. If you remained in the region for a period of two weeks or more, however, you probably noticed a return to a state of physical normality. The condition you experienced is known as altitude sickness, or hypoxia, and your recovery involved some temporary adaptations to meet the challenge of gas exchange at high altitudes.

At high elevations, air pressure is lower and the air is "thinner" or "rarer" than at sea level. This means that although oxygen and other gases are present in the air in the same proportions as at lower elevations, there is less air in total. Therefore, there is less oxygen available for respiration. When an individual accustomed to living at lower elevations first arrives at high altitudes, the body cannot extract enough oxygen from the air to meet its metabolic needs, and the result is altitude sickness.

The body responds to the new environment with adjustments to the respiratory and circulatory systems. The first response to hypoxia is an increased breathing rate, which helps to bring more oxygen into contact with the alveoli. For a period of about two weeks, the body also produces more and more red blood cells. Before long, the body is able to take up enough oxygen from the air to carry on normal and even athletic endeavours. After a return to a lower altitude, these extra blood cells can allow for exceptional physical endurance. This is why many serious athletes choose to train at high altitudes. This energy boost is short-lived, however. Within a few weeks, the red blood count drops back down to a level in keeping with the normal needs of the lower altitude. While these physiological adjustments are temporary, populations that have evolved at high elevations also show some genetic adaptations. People from such populations tend to have more alveoli and lung capillaries than people from populations adapted to life at lower altitudes. The changes that take place in the body as a result of short-term exposure to high altitudes involve some of the same processes that are involved in the everyday control of breathing. The next paragraphs explore these processes in more detail.

The Control of Breathing

To some extent, you can control your rate of breathing consciously. You quickly lose this control, however, with a change in your environment or in your body activity. When you hurry to catch a bus or run up a flight of stairs, for example, you breathe more quickly and deeply. You do not consciously think about this act, nor can you prevent it. Somehow the increase in body activity triggers an increased breathing rate.

Since muscles need oxygen, it seems logical that a lack of sufficient oxygen will lead to an increased breathing rate. Studies have shown, however, that a person breathes at the same rate from a tank of pure oxygen as from air with a normal concentration of oxygen. This suggests that it is not the presence or absence of oxygen that plays the main role in controlling the breathing response. So what does initiate a change in the rate of breathing?

Research has shown that an increase in the concentration of carbon dioxide in the body leads to a faster breathing rate. This faster rate can be triggered by breathing from air with a high concentration of carbon dioxide, or by a buildup of carbon dioxide from within the body itself.

Physical exertion requires an increased level of cellular respiration, which in turn means that more carbon dioxide is produced by the cells of the muscles. This carbon dioxide enters the bloodstream. After the exchange of gases has taken place in the alveoli of the lungs, any carbon dioxide still present in the blood is carried to the heart and up to the lower portion of the brain. There, it reaches a part of the brain called the **medulla oblongata**. This is the area of the brain responsible for controlling some of the body's reflexes. When the concentration of carbon dioxide in the blood exceeds a certain level, the medulla

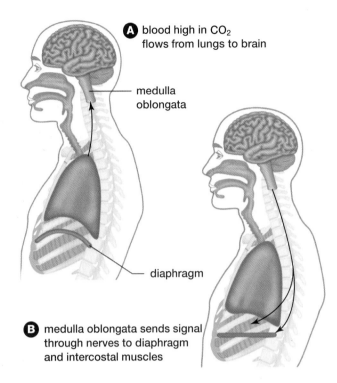

A blood high in CO_2 flows from lungs to brain

medulla oblongata

diaphragm

B medulla oblongata sends signal through nerves to diaphragm and intercostal muscles

Figure 8.26 The rate of breathing is controlled by the medulla oblongata, and is influenced primarily by the amount of carbon dioxide present in the blood.

oblongata sends out nerve impulses to initiate faster movement of the muscles of the rib cage. At the same time, other nerve impulses are sent to the muscles controlling the diaphragm, making it move more rapidly as well. Figure 8.26 illustrates this

 THINKING LAB

Coach's Corner

Background

The table shows the results of an imaginary test to find out if athletic training at a high altitude can improve performance and endurance. The test involved a single runner who normally trains at a high altitude.

You Try It

1. Make a list of the main variables that could affect the runner's time. How could you control these variables?

2. Between the first round and second round of time trials, the runner moved to a low altitude and trained there. How long should this training period be between the two rounds? Explain.

3. Explain the results shown in the table. If you were a coach, how might you use these results? Does the test tell you whether people born at a high altitude tend to be better athletes?

First round time trials (400 m run)		Second round time trials (400 m run)	
High altitude	Low altitude	High altitude	Low altitude
48.2 s	44.7 s	51.8 s	47.1 s

regulatory process. Under normal conditions, the firing of nerve impulses from the medulla oblongata happens regularly, thereby producing a rhythmic pattern of inhalation and exhalation.

While the concentration of carbon dioxide in the blood is the main factor controlling the rate of breathing, the concentration of oxygen also plays a small role. Some of the blood vessels, including the aorta and carotid, contain chemoreceptors that respond to oxygen pressure in the blood. When the oxygen content of the blood drops below a certain level, these chemoreceptors send stimuli to the medulla oblongata, causing it to increase the breathing rate.

The volume of air you breathe in also plays a role in controlling your breathing rate. If you inhale more deeply than usual, the lungs and alveoli expand and stretch. This causes stretch receptors in the walls of the alveoli to fire impulses that travel to the medulla oblongata. In turn, the medulla oblongata sends a signal to the respiratory muscles to stop the inhalation.

Respiratory Impairment

As you have seen, the human respiratory system can adjust quickly to meet the physical demands of the body or to respond to certain changes in the environment. This adaptability is limited, however. If either the internal environment of the body or the external environment changes too much, the structures and processes involved in respiration will be unable to adjust. The following paragraphs describe some common causes of respiratory failure.

Investigation 8 • B

SKILL FOCUS

Identifying variables

Hypothesizing

Performing and recording

Communicating results

Controlling the Rate of Respiration

Since the rate of respiration is not affected by the concentration of oxygen in the body, perhaps it is affected by carbon dioxide, the other gas exchanged during respiration. How could you test the effects of the concentration of carbon dioxide on the rate of respiration?

Pre-lab Questions

- What are the main differences in the composition of inhaled and exhaled air?
- What volume of air is exchanged at a normal, relaxed breathing rate?

Problem

How can the level of carbon dioxide in the body be altered?

Prediction

Predict what will happen if the level of carbon dioxide in the body is increased.

CAUTION: Students with respiratory disorders should not be subjects in this experiment. Students should not hold their breath or hyperventilate long enough to cause faintness. At the first sign of faintness or dizziness, stop the experiment and return to a normal breathing rate.

Materials

paper bag   stopwatch

Procedure

1. Find a partner and prepare a data table like the one below.

Condition	Resting	After holding breath	After hyperventilating	While breathing into paper bag
Respiratory rate				

2. Count the number of breaths that your partner takes while resting in a sitting position for a period of 3 min. Divide the number of breaths by 3, and record this value under "Resting" in your data table.

3. Have your partner hold his or her breath for about 45 s. Then count the number of breaths he or she takes in the next 3 min.

Drowning

While the term "drowning" is commonly used to refer to a death in water, the actual causes of death vary significantly. In up to 10% of cases, the victim suffers a laryngospasm, or reflex closing of the larynx. In these cases, death actually occurs from asphyxiation rather than as a result of water entering the lungs.

In cases where laryngospasm does not occur, the cause of death depends on whether the drowning takes place in fresh water or salt water. In fresh water, water entering the lungs washes away the lipoprotein lubricating film that coats the alveoli. As a result, the alveoli collapse and gas exchange ends. In salt water, the concentration gradient means that fluid is drawn out of the capillaries and into the lungs. As this fluid builds up, it prevents oxygen from reaching the walls of the alveoli.

Carbon Monoxide Poisoning

Carbon monoxide is an invisible, odourless, tasteless gas released during the combustion of organic materials. It has many common sources in our society, including car exhaust, gas ovens, and wood smoke. Carbon monoxide is toxic because it binds to the oxygen receptors in red blood cells approximately 200 times more tightly than oxygen does. Once inhaled, carbon monoxide is quickly absorbed into the bloodstream and prevents the blood from transporting oxygen to the cells of the body. The early symptoms of carbon monoxide poisoning are similar to those of hypoxia: headaches, weakness, dizziness, and nausea. If the victim is not treated promptly, permanent damage to internal organs and the nervous system is likely, followed by coma and death. Treatment usually includes administering pure oxygen; even so,

---

Divide this number by 3, and record the value under "After holding breath" in your data table.

4. Ask your partner to take 10 fast, deep breaths. Then count the number of breaths he or she takes in the next 3 min. Divide this number by 3, and record the result under "After hyperventilating" in your data table.

5. Ask your partner to breathe into a large paper bag. Count the number of breaths he or she takes in 3 min. Divide this number by 3, and record the result under "While breathing into paper bag" in your data table.

6. Switch roles with your partner and repeat the experiment.

Post-lab Questions

1. Why did you count your partner's breaths for a three minute period and then divide by three?

2. What effect do holding breath, hyperventilating, and breathing into a paper bag each have on the level of oxygen and carbon dioxide in the body? Explain your results with reference to the concentration of respiratory gases.

Conclude and Apply

3. Based on your results, what effects would you expect to see on workers in a crowded, poorly-ventilated office building? Explain your answer with reference to the process of respiration.

Exploring Further

4. Compare results with other members of your class. What similarities and differences can you identify? Provide an explanation that could account for the differences. Design an experiment to test your hypothesis.

recovery can be slow because the blood only gradually relinquishes carbon monoxide.

Victims of carbon monoxide poisoning suffocate, even though they can breathe. Even if oxygen is present at normal levels in the environment of the victim, it cannot be absorbed by the body while the blood's oxygen receptors are blocked by carbon monoxide. For this reason, carbon monoxide is toxic in very low concentrations. A concentration of as little as 20 to 30 parts per million (or 0.002%) of carbon monoxide can be harmful if exposure is maintained for more than a few hours.

BIO FACT

The inhalation of smoke and toxic gases (including carbon monoxide) is the most common cause of death in a building fire. Since the gases released in a fire are hot, they tend to rise. For this reason, if you find yourself in a building where there is a fire — even if there is not much visible smoke — you should stay close to the floor and crawl to safety.

Smoking

What exactly does cigarette smoke do to the respiratory system? First, as smoke is drawn into the trachea, it temporarily paralyzes the cilia and prevents them from sweeping foreign particles out of the passages of the respiratory system. A single drag on a cigarette will slow the action of the cilia, while more regular exposure can completely destroy them. Even light smokers have a greater tendency to cough and snore than non-smokers, partly as a result of the damage to cilia in the trachea and nasal passages.

Once the smoke reaches the lungs, the different substances in the smoke produce a number of different effects. Like any burning organic matter, cigarette smoke contains carbon monoxide. In fact, the concentration of carbon monoxide in cigarette smoke is about 50 000 ppm — over 1000 times greater than the amount known to be harmful. As a result, a steady smoker constantly suffers from a mild level of carbon monoxide poisoning. This is only part of the picture, however, since carbon monoxide is just one of more than 4000 different chemicals that make up cigarette smoke. More than 40 of these chemicals cause cancer in humans.

The particles in cigarette smoke become lodged in the fine passageways of the respiratory system, interfering with the passage of air and with oxygen exchange. One of the inhaled substances is tar, a by-product of burning tobacco. People who smoke

a pack of cigarettes a day will absorb about 250 mL of tar into their lungs a year. This tar coats the lungs with a sticky, sooty material and is a key cause of lung cancer. Tar can also cause the alveoli to become brittle, leading to the respiratory disorder known as emphysema. In this condition, the lungs lose their elasticity, making inhalation and exhalation very difficult.

COURSE CHALLENGE

The regulation of breathing involves the interaction of voluntary and involuntary muscle movements, chemical messengers, and nerves. Your understanding of the principles at work in breathing will help you, in the Biology Course Challenge, to test your ability to connect physical symptoms with their physiological effects. To help you prepare for the Challenge, try the following:

- Make a list of the ways in which the structure of the thoracic cavity contributes to the mechanics of breathing in a healthy person.

- Make another list of ways in which specific kinds of damage to the thoracic cavity will affect the mechanics of breathing.

- Prepare a short diagnostic guide that could help you trace physical symptoms back to the kinds of injuries that could cause these symptoms.

▷ PLAY

To further investigate the effects of smoking on the respiratory system, turn to your Electronic Learning Partner.

Air Pollution

All residents of Canada are exposed to varying levels of air pollution. This pollution takes different forms. Indoors, it may result from the use of chemical cleaners and particular construction materials; outdoors, the emissions from automobiles and industrial processes are a key contributor. Airborne pollutants include molecules such as carbon monoxide, nitrogen oxides, chlorine, and methane, as well as small particles of dust and other compounds. These materials can contribute to a number of respiratory problems, including asthma (a condition in which the bronchial tubes suddenly constrict, making breathing difficult). Children are especially susceptible, because they tend to have a higher respiratory rate than adults and because their lungs are still developing.

Figure 8.27 Smog can be a serious problem in urban areas.

In urban areas, the combination of pollutants, heat, and sunlight often produces smog, a characteristic brownish haze (Figure 8.27). The chemicals in smog have effects similar to those in cigarette smoke, making the lungs less elastic and more vulnerable to disease. Smog tends to be worse on hot summer days, and its concentration will be highest late in the day. For this reason, even people with no history of respiratory problems should avoid strenuous outdoor activity during the late afternoon and early evening on days when air quality is a concern. People who already suffer from asthma or other respiratory problems may have to avoid going outdoors altogether.

SECTION REVIEW

1. **K/U** Describe the process involved in the control of breathing. Why is it so difficult to control your own breathing?

2. **MC** A lifeguard pulls an unconscious swimmer from a pool and begins mouth-to-mouth resuscitation. Before long, the swimmer begins breathing again. With respect to the respiratory system, what has taken place to cause the swimmer to stop breathing, and how does artificial respiration work to initiate breathing?

3. **K/U** What signs might a coroner look for in determining the cause of death of a person in a boating accident?

4. **K/U** Two students breathe into paper bags for three minutes. At the end of this period, would you expect the level of carbon dioxide in both bags to be the same? Explain your reasoning.

5. **MC** Would you expect smog to have the same effects on an insect's respiratory system as on a mammal's? Explain.

UNIT PROJECT PREP

If you have decided to study a respiratory disorder for your Unit Project, use the information in this chapter to note the ways in which the disorder might affect the control and regulation of breathing.

Gas Exchange in Plants

- Describe the major processes and mechanisms for gas exchange in plants.
- Describe how leaves are modified to reduce water loss while enabling gas exchange.
- Compare gas exchange mechanisms in plants and animals.

Figure 8.28 Plants are complex organisms — but they have no lungs. How can such organisms survive without a respiratory system?

At the beginning of this chapter, you saw that single-celled organisms such as protists do not require any specialized respiratory structures. The small size and moist habitat of these organisms mean that a direct exchange of gases across the cell membrane is sufficient to meet the organisms' metabolic needs. You also saw that as animal organisms became larger and more complex, different kinds of respiratory systems evolved to increase the respiratory surface area and facilitate the exchange of gases.

Like animals, plants must respire to supply their cells with oxygen and remove waste carbon dioxide. Many terrestrial plants are large and complex organisms. Although plants have specialized structures for many functions, including nutritive and reproductive functions, they have neither a distinct respiratory surface area nor a circulatory system that carries gases from one part of a plant to the other. This means that each plant organ must rely on a direct exchange of gases with its environment. Like terrestrial animals, terrestrial plants also face the challenge of maintaining a moist respiratory surface for gas exchange while preventing excessive water loss.

>> **FAST FORWARD**

To review plant anatomy turn to Chapter 15, Section 15.2.

Gas Exchange in Roots

Like the soil-borne organisms you saw in section 8.1, the roots and rhizoids of plants depend on gas exchange with the air in the soil. The surface of the root is covered with many outgrowths called **root hairs** (Figure 8.29). These outgrowths add considerable surface area to the root, and provide a moist surface for gas exchange. As long as the soil is sufficiently aerated and contains water, oxygen will diffuse from the air into the air spaces of the soil and then into the moisture film surrounding the soil particles and root hairs. The dissolved oxygen then enters the root hair cell and by diffusion passes to the other cells of the root. At the same time, carbon dioxide diffuses from the cells of the root through the root hairs and out into the soil. The rate of respiration in roots is relatively low, so this mechanism is sufficient to meet the roots' gas exchange needs.

Figure 8.29 Root hairs on the surface of the root of a germinating radish.

Root cells can also obtain oxygen from the intercellular spaces often found in plant tissues. Some plants, including certain plants found in swampy areas, have large air canals linking the root and stem. These canals allow oxygen to diffuse internally to the roots directly from other regions of the plant.

Gas Exchange in Leaves

In most plants, leaves are the primary organs responsible for photosynthesis, the process that produces plant nutrients (in a few species, such as cacti, the stem is the main site of photosynthesis). During photosynthesis, plants absorb carbon dioxide and give off oxygen. But plants also respire constantly, absorbing oxygen and giving off carbon dioxide. During the day, both photosynthesis and respiration occur simultaneously in the leaf.

Both photosynthesis and respiration require the leaf to exchange gases with its environment. At the same time, the leaf must guard against losing too much water. Most of the surface of the leaf is covered with a waterproof coating, or cuticle. In order to allow for the gases to pass into and out of the leaf, the cuticle is perforated with small structures called **stomata** (singular stoma). Each stoma consists of a pore bordered by a pair of guard cells. The guard cells allow the pore to be opened to permit the exchange of gases, or closed to prevent the loss of water. You will learn more about how the stomata function in Unit 5.

As shown in Figure 8.30, the stomata open into intracellular air spaces within the leaf. The arrangement of different tissues within the leaf ensures that all cells are close to, or directly in contact with, these air spaces. The surfaces of the leaf cells are moist to permit the gaseous exchange to occur by diffusion across the cell membranes. As the plant photosynthesizes, oxygen is released into the intracellular air space and can be reused by the cells for respiration. Similarly, carbon dioxide released by the respiring leaf cells enters the intracellular air space and can be taken up by cells for photosynthesis. Additional oxygen reaches the cells from the external environment through the stomata, while excess carbon dioxide leaves the plant through the same openings.

Gas Exchange in Stems

The stem of a plant — whether it is the flexible stem of a tulip or grass, or the thick woody bark of a giant sequoia — contains small pores. The flexible green stems of grasses and other non-woody plants perform photosynthesis and, like leaves, contain stomata through which gases can enter the leaf. On woody stems you can often see the small white markings of **lenticels**. These are arrangements of cells that provide openings from the environment into the tissue of the stem.

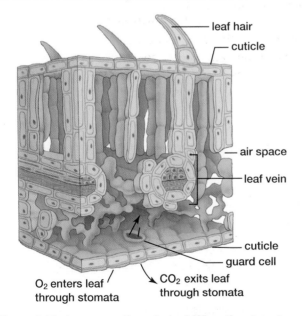

leaf hair
cuticle
air space
leaf vein
cuticle
guard cell
O_2 enters leaf through stomata
CO_2 exits leaf through stomata

Figure 8.30 A cross section of a leaf. When the stomata are open, gases can enter and leave the air spaces within the leaf.

Figure 8.31 The bark of the giant sequoia tree can protect the plant from forest fires. Even this thick bark has pores through which the stem exchanges gases with the environment.

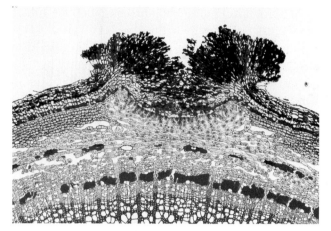

Figure 8.32 A lenticel. On the woody stems of tree trunks, lenticels usually appear as small white spots.

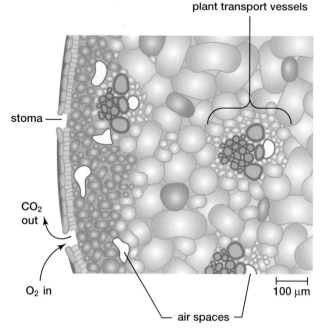

Figure 8.33 Portion of a cross section of the stem of a young corn plant. Gases are exchanged through the stomata. The air channels in the stem help respiratory gases reach all the cells of the stem.

Lenticels often occur at the same place where a stoma was once situated when the stem was younger and capable of carrying on photosynthesis.

Oxygen diffuses through the stomata or lenticels into the intercellular air space of the plant, and from these air spaces can reach every cell in the stem. The arrangement of cells in the stem is shown in Figure 8.33. Inside the plant, oxygen dissolves in the water of the moist cell membrane and then diffuses across the cell membrane into the cell. Carbon dioxide follows the opposite path, diffusing across the cell membrane into the intracellular air space and then out through the pores.

Looking at the stem of a large tree, it may be hard to imagine that diffusion alone can allow gas exchange to take place at a sufficient rate to meet the needs of all the cells of the stem. In woody stems, however, only a relatively thin layer at the outer surface of the stem is made up of living cells. The central portion of the stem is composed of dead cells that do not require oxygen.

In this chapter you learned how different organisms obtain oxygen from their environments. As you saw, most animals need a mechanism to deliver that oxygen to all the cells of the organism. In most organisms, substances such as nutrients, waste materials, and hormones must also be moved from one tissue or organ to another. Both plants and animals have intricate transport networks that help maintain their vital processes. In the next chapter, you will explore how some of these transport systems operate.

SECTION REVIEW

1. **K/U** How are plants adapted to reduce water loss while still allowing for gas exchange?

2. **K/U** What are some of the features of roots that assist plants with the exchange of gases?

3. **MC** With respect to water loss and gas exchange, what are some of the features you would expect to find in plants that live on the forest floor?

4. **MC** Would you expect a shade-tolerant plant to have more or fewer stomata per leaf than a plant that grows best in full sunlight? Why?

5. **MC** You are planning a vegetable garden. What are some of the things you should do, both as you prepare the garden bed and as you care for the plants, to make sure the plants can respire properly?

6. **MC** Beaver dams often flood large areas of wooded land. Knowing what you do about respiration in plant stems and roots, what effect would you expect this flooding to have on trees? Explain.

Chapter Expectations

Briefly explain each of the following points.

- Living organisms need oxygen in order to produce energy. (8.1)
- An animal's respiratory surface may be many times larger than its body surface area. (8.1)
- Respiration in a terrestrial environment requires special adaptations. (8.1)
- Breathing involves controlled changes in air pressure. (8.3)
- The human respiratory system can adapt to some environmental changes. (8.4)
- Smoking is bad for the respiratory system. (8.4)
- Plants do not have a respiratory system. (8.5)

Language of Biology

Write a sentence using each of the following words or terms. Use any six terms in a concept map to show your understanding of how they are related.

- aerobic
- respiratory surface
- ventilate
- breathing
- trachea
- pharynx
- epiglottis
- bronchioles
- pleura
- diaphragm
- tidal volume
- inspiratory reserve volume
- residual volume
- counter-current flow
- stomata
- gas exchange
- skin respiration
- gills
- spiracles
- lung
- glottis
- larynx
- bronchi
- alveoli
- intercostal muscles
- lung capacity
- vital capacity
- expiratory reserve volume
- respiratory efficiency
- medulla oblongata
- root hairs
- lenticel

UNDERSTANDING CONCEPTS

1. Decide whether each of the following statements is true or false. If false, write a correct version of the statement.
   (a) In animals, a specialized respiratory system is always linked to a circulatory system.
   (b) Respiration can be divided into two processes: inspiration and expiration.
   (c) Carbon dioxide is the most important factor in regulating the rate of breathing.
   (d) The body's response to hypoxia is an increase in the number of capillaries and alveoli in the lungs.
   (e) The counter-current exchange system works by maintaining the oxygen concentration gradient between the respiratory medium and the blood.

2. Explain how these two processes are involved in gas exchange:
   (a) dissolving
   (b) diffusion

3. What are the two basic requirements of a gas exchange system? How are these requirements met in a typical fish?

4. What are three important adaptations in the mammalian respiratory system? What advantages do these adaptations provide?

5. Arrange these structures into the order in which they are encountered by air entering the mammalian lung: bronchiole, turbinate, pharynx, alveoli, larynx.

6. Explain the difference between lung capacity and respiratory efficiency.

7. Write a brief comparison of the structure and function of a) a lenticel, b) a spiracle, and c) a stoma. In your response, include answers to the following questions:
   (a) Which of these structures open and close?
   (b) Does opening and closing serve the same purpose for the different structures?

8. A tadpole starts life under water and respires through gills. As it grows into a frog, it loses its gills and develops lungs instead.
   (a) What are some factors that make gills unsuited to life out of water?
   (b) If the adult frog tried to use its lungs to breathe under water, what would happen?

9. What role do root hairs play in plant respiration? Do roots help absorb oxygen for use by other parts of the plant?

10. Give two reasons why children tend to be more susceptible than adults to respiratory disorders resulting from air pollution.

11. Practitioners of some forms of exercise claim that special breathing techniques can help relieve stress and improve physical well-being. One school of yoga recommends first inhaling normally and exhaling deeply, then inhaling deeply and exhaling normally. What would be the effect on the body after a few minutes of this breathing pattern?

12. Design an experiment to test the effect of temperature on breathing rate.

13. This illustration shows the spirograph results obtained by three students.
    (a) Which of these students is most likely to be a smoker?
    (b) Which of these students is most likely to be an excellent long-distance runner?

(c) Which of these students might have just finished breathing into a paper bag for three minutes?
(d) From this information, can you determine which student has the greater respiratory efficiency?

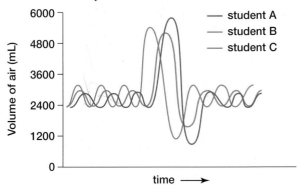

14. During an experiment to test for the presence of carbon dioxide in inhaled and exhaled air, limewater became cloudy in the flask labelled "inhaled." Is this the result you would expect? Explain.

15. What reasoning could you use to argue that the respiratory system of a rose bush is similar to that of an amoeba? What adaptations to this system allow the rose to live on land, while the amoeba can only survive in an aquatic environment?

16. "Diffusion is not an effective mechanism for gas exchange in multicellular organisms." Explain why this statement is neither entirely true nor entirely false, using examples of different kinds of respiratory systems.

17. Some species of fish do not pump water past their gills. Instead, they swim with their mouths open so water flows in through the mouth and out past the gills. Draw a diagram to illustrate what would happen if such a fish

were to try swimming backwards. Include an explanation for your conclusions.

18. Draw a flowchart that illustrates why you breathe faster during strenuous exercise.
    (a) Write a caption for this chart that includes all of the following terms: inspiratory reserve volume, waste product, oxygen concentration, intercostal muscles, hypoxia.
    (b) In the early spring, one variety of clematis vine may grow very quickly — perhaps as much as several centimetres in a day. Will the plant respond to this vigorous activity by respiring more quickly? Draw another flowchart comparing the plant's response to increased metabolic demands to your body's response to increased metabolic demands.

19. "Just because the air doesn't stink, doesn't mean the air doesn't stink," states a Canadian Lung Association bulletin. Explain what you think the CLA means by this statement, using examples.

20. You are having lunch at a restaurant when someone at the next table begins choking. A bystander rushes over, stands behind the choking victim, and wraps her arms around him. Then, holding her hands together just below the victim's rib cage, she squeezes with a rapid, upward movement.

(a) What is this technique (known as the "Heimlich manoeuver") intended to accomplish? Explain how it works, with references to the structures and processes involved in respiration.

(b) Another bystander suggests giving the choking person a glass of water. Would this be a good idea?

(c) The rescuer is successful in dislodging the obstruction that caused the choking. By this time, however, the victim has stopped breathing. A medical team with resuscitation equipment arrives on the scene. If you could measure the composition of the gas in their ventilator, what would you expect to find? How does this compare to the composition of the air we normally breathe?

21. An algae bloom in a lake is a condition in which a species of algae present in the lake suddenly starts reproducing at a very high rate, thereby producing an exceptionally high concentration of algae in the water. What effects might such a bloom have on the fish and aquatic plants in the lake? Draw a consequences map to illustrate the immediate impact of an algae bloom on the lake ecosystem. On the same map, identify some of the factors that will help restore the algae population to its normal level.

22. Compare the air canals found in some plant stems to the tracheal tubes of a grasshopper and to the trachea of a bird.

    (a) Do these air passages all have the same basic structure and function? Explain.

    (b) A pesticide is sprayed over the habitat shared by the three organisms. This chemical works by disrupting muscle movements so that the grasshopper cannot control the opening and closing of its spiracles. What effect might such a pesticide have on the bird and plant? Explain with reference to respiratory structures.

23. Some plants grow well in swampy areas. Others die if they stand in wet soil for too long. How would you explain this difference? What structural differences would you expect to see between the roots of these two plants?

24. You are walking through town when you come to a construction site where waste material is being burned. You want to minimize the amount of smoke you inhale as you pass the site, but the distance is too far for you to simply hold your breath. Will the total amount of smoke you inhale be greater if you take occasional deep breaths, or more frequent shallow breaths? Or will it make any difference? Explain your answer.

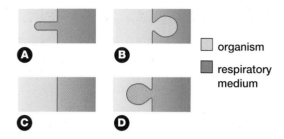

25. The illustrations above are very simplified drawings of different types of animal respiratory systems. Name the respiratory structure represented in each drawing, and explain how it is suited to a particular environment.

26. A tracheotomy is a procedure performed when a person is unable to breathe through the nose or mouth. It involves creating an opening that connects the trachea directly with the outside air.

    (a) What functions are lost with this alteration to the respiratory system?

    (b) What are some of the features that must be incorporated into the artificial tracheal cover?

27. As part of an employee health promotion initiative, a factory manager brings a number of potted plants into the factory garage. "The plants will increase the level of oxygen in the garage, and help to reduce the risk of carbon monoxide poisoning from the exhaust," the manager explains to the staff.

    (a) Assume that there is enough natural light in the garage for the plants, and that the factory does not operate night shifts. Will the manager's plan work? Why or why not?

    (b) Will the plants suffer from exposure to the carbon monoxide present in the garage? Explain.

28. When time-out is called during a fast-paced sporting event and the athletes stop to catch their breath, you often see them bending over and placing their hands on their knees. Is this a good position for recovery? Explain.

29. Many heavy smokers develop a characteristic "smokers' cough." What do you think causes this cough? What substances would you expect to be coughed up?

Transport and Circulation

Your hand contains well over a kilometre of blood vessels. Some of these you can see through the skin on the back of your hand, and many more can be revealed with the use of different medical technologies. Even such spectacular images as the X-ray shown here, however, do not show all the blood vessels of the hand. The circulatory system extends through every part of your hand, right down to the microscopic level, so that no cell of your hand is more than a cell's breadth away from a blood vessel.

Each cell of your hand — like the self-sufficient cell of an amoeba — can only exchange materials with the fluid surrounding it. Your hand is made up of individual cells, each of which pick up oxygen, nutrients, and other materials and release carbon dioxide and other waste products. The movement of blood around the hand accomplishes both of these tasks.

This example indicates the importance of internal transport. Your circulatory system, however, does much more than maintain a healthy environment for your cells. You breathe oxygen into your lungs, and it reaches the cells of your fingers; you swallow a tablet, and it eases the swelling in a sprained wrist. The transport system provides an essential link that helps to create a single organism from a group of cells.

Most people think of the internal transport system as being made up of blood, blood vessels, and a heart, but living organisms have evolved many kinds of transport systems that may or may not incorporate these components. Your own body has two circulatory systems and only one heart, while an insect may have several hearts but only a single blood vessel. A Douglas fir tree has no specialized heart or pump, and yet it can transport water from its roots to its crown — a distance that may exceed a hundred metres. In this chapter, you will learn how these different types of transport mechanisms work, and how they are adapted to suit particular requirements.

A tree has no blood vessels, but it still has a powerful internal transport system.

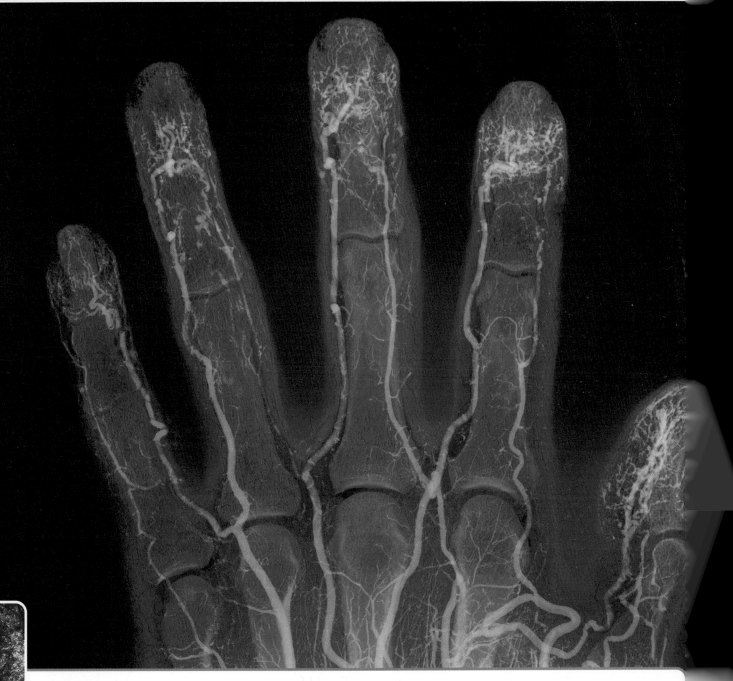

Chapter Contents

The Task of Transportation

EXPECTATIONS

- Explain the functions of a transport system in multicellular organisms.

- Identify the main types of transport system found in animals.

- Distinguish between an open and closed transport system.

- Explain how adaptations such as double circulation alter the efficiency of a transport system.

Figure 9.1 A jellyfish does not require a specialized internal transport system.

Organisms like those shown in Figure 9.1 can rely on their external environments to supply what they need for all their life activities. In most animals, however, the transport system plays a key role in keeping the body in a state of general physical well-being. Its functions include delivering nutrients and oxygen to each and every cell of the body, removing the waste products of cellular processes, and serving as the pathway from one part of the body to another for disease-fighting agents, hormones, and other chemical messengers. In warm-blooded animals, the transport system also assists in the important function of controlling body temperature. The transport system is therefore an essential link among the cells and organs within the body, and between individual cells and the external environment.

In Chapter 8 you learned that while all aerobic organisms must exchange gases with their environment, different organisms have evolved different kinds of respiratory systems to meet this challenge. The same is true of transport systems. Almost all multicellular organisms have a **vascular system**, a system of fluid tissue that plays a role in transporting nutrients and other materials to the cells of the organism. Most animals have a **circulatory system**, which is a vascular system in which the progress of fluid is controlled by muscle movements so that it follows a specific pattern. A cardiovascular system, found in the higher animals,

is a circulatory system in which the vascular fluid is pumped around the body by the action of a specialized organ, the heart. The following paragraphs describe the transport mechanisms found in different kinds of organisms.

Internal Transport at Its Simplest

A self-sufficient unicellular organism such as *Amoeba* has no need for an organized transport system. Respiratory gases and nutrients enter the cell through diffusion or active transport across the cell membrane. Once inside the cell, these substances are distributed to the cell's organelles by the streaming or flowing of cytoplasm. Waste materials diffuse or are carried back across the cell membrane to be released into the environment. As you can see in Figure 9.2, such an organism exchanges the materials it needs directly with the external environment.

Some multicellular animals, such as those in the family Cnidaria (which includes hydra and jellyfish), also lack an organized transport system. In these animals, fluid taken in through the mouth enters a body cavity that extends through most of the organism, including the tentacles. Materials are exchanged directly between the fluid in the body cavity and the individual cells of the organism, none of which are more than a few cells away from the body cavity.

≪ REWIND

For more information about diffusion, turn to Chapter 1, Section 1.3.

Although planaria have a higher metabolic rate than cnidaria (and therefore need a faster exchange of materials), planaria can still rely on diffusion to meet their metabolic needs. Nutrients dissolve directly into individual cells from a digestive cavity. This cavity branches and rebranches within the organism to provide a surface for the exchange of materials with individual cells (see Figure 9.3). A separate cavity absorbs waste materials that are then expelled from the animal.

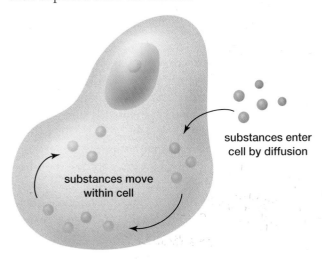

Figure 9.2 The movement, or streaming, of cytoplasmic fluid helps to distribute materials to the organelles within a cell.

None of these organisms have blood, which is a vascular tissue adapted to carry particular substances.

They also lack a specialized mechanism for pumping fluid from one body part to another. Instead, fluid containing dissolved respiratory gases, nutrients, and other substances is ingested directly from the external environment. This fluid flows freely within the organism's body cavities, sometimes assisted by the contraction of cells and muscle fibres as the animal moves.

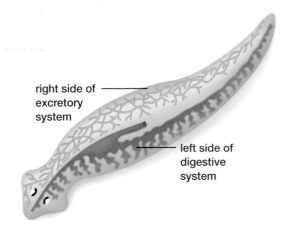

right side of excretory system

left side of digestive system

Figure 9.3 In the multicellular planarian, the movements of the animal help to stream fluid through a central cavity, from which material can diffuse into and out of its cells.

The Specialized Transport System

Most multicellular organisms cannot rely on diffusion or active transport to bring materials from the external environment to cells of the internal tissues quickly enough to meet the cells' metabolic requirements. For such organisms to survive, some means of speeding the exchange of materials between the inside of the organism and the outside world is required. Before organisms could evolve to

MINI LAB

How Effective Is Diffusion as a Transport Mechanism?

In this lab, you will compare the rate of diffusion of a solution into tissues of different sizes. Carefully cut a potato into sections of different shapes and sizes. Select four sections for this experiment. Your thinnest section should be no less than 1 mm wide, and your thickest section no more than 3 cm wide. The sections should be of varying dimensions and volumes. Immerse the potato sections into a solution of potassium permanganate, and leave them for 30 min. At the end of this period, use forceps to remove all the sections. Cut each one in half and measure how far the purple solution penetrated the potato flesh. Record your results in a table.

Analyze

Calculate the rate of diffusion in each section by dividing the diffusion distance by the time the potato was immersed in the solution. Was the diffusion rate constant for each section? Provide an explanation for any variation. Assuming that the same diffusion rate you measured here could be applied to your body. Use this information to calculate approximately how long it would take for an oxygen molecule absorbed in your lung to reach the fingers of your writing hand (if you had no specialized transport system).

sizes more than a few cells thick, adaptations providing for an organized transport system were necessary. The evolution of a transport system also made it possible for larger animals to dedicate specially-adapted organs and structures to specific tasks, and then distribute the products of these tasks to other organs and structures. This, in turn, allowed for the emergence of multicellular organisms capable of undertaking complex activities.

The Open Transport System

If you dissect a grasshopper, you will find only one blood vessel. This vessel, the aorta, carries blood into the animal's body cavity. The body cavity is subdivided into a number of sinuses (or chambers) that bring the blood and other body fluids into contact with the internal cells of the animal. The exchange of materials takes place within the sinuses. Co-ordinated movements of body muscles help to move the blood around inside the insect and then back to a sinus surrounding the long, tubular heart. From there, the blood is again pumped through the aorta to the sinuses of the body cavity (see Figure 9.4). In this circulatory system, the blood bathes the cells directly. A transport system in which the blood does not always stay contained within blood vessels is called an **open transport system**.

In an open transport system, fluid can slosh back and forth; therefore it circulates relatively slowly. The result is a system that cannot provide for the rapid delivery of materials around the body. This is one reason why the open transport system is best suited to insects and other arthropods that have relatively small body cavities. Another reason is that (as you saw in Chapter 8) insects have a

tracheal respiratory system that delivers oxygen directly from the environment to the animals' cells. The respiratory and circulatory systems are separate in these animals, so even a very active insect can meet its oxygen requirements despite its relatively slow circulation.

BIO FACT

Because there is no reason for the blood of grasshoppers and other insects to carry oxygen, it lacks an oxygen-carrying respiratory pigment and thus appears clear and watery.

The Closed Transport System

Animals that rely on the circulatory system to carry respiratory gases need a faster flow of blood than can be provided by an open transport system. These organisms, including the annelids (segmented worms such as earthworms) and vertebrates, have a **closed transport system**. In this type of system, the blood does not bathe the cells directly, but rather is pumped around the body within a network of vessels. This network includes larger vessels that collect blood for pumping, smaller vessels that distribute the blood throughout the body, and tiny capillaries that provide a surface for the exchange of materials with individual cells. In a closed transport system, blood circulates in only one direction, passing through the animal's gas exchange system in its cycle through the body.

Although all closed transport systems share these features, they differ in ways that result in varying levels of efficiency. The efficiency of a circulatory system is measured by the rate at which

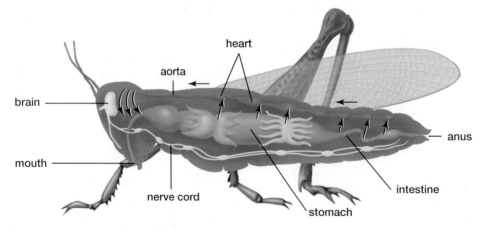

Figure 9.4 The transport system of a grasshopper. The long, tubular heart extends most of the length of the abdomen. Some insects have additional hearts located at the base of their wings or antennae to help pump blood into these body parts.

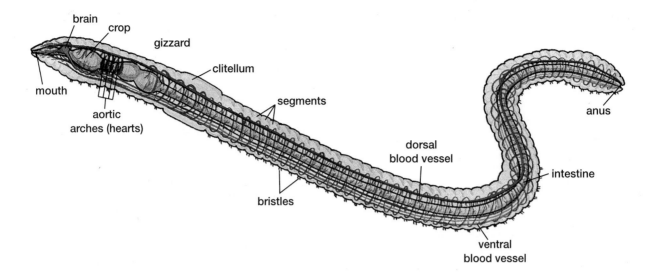

brain
crop
gizzard
clitellum
mouth
segments
aortic
arches (hearts)
bristles
dorsal
blood vessel
anus
intestine
ventral
blood vessel

Figure 9.5 The earthworm has a relatively simple closed circulatory system. The five aortic arches located near the head link the dorsal and ventral blood vessels.

it can transport substances around the body. Factors that affect this efficiency include the composition of the blood, the path of circulation, and the speed of blood flow (usually measured in terms of blood pressure). The circulatory systems of different animals show adaptations related to their unique metabolic requirements.

Circulation in Annelids

The simplest closed circulatory system is found in annelids. This system consists of two main blood vessels connected by a series of five pairs of heart-like pumps called aortic arches. Blood enters the aortic arches from the dorsal vessel, which (like the arches) contracts to pump the blood forward. From the aortic arches the blood is pumped into the ventral vessel located under the intestinal tract. The blood then flows through a branching series of smaller and smaller vessels to the internal organs and tissues, where the exchange of materials occurs across the thin walls of the capillaries. Some vessels also lead to the animal's body walls, where the exchange of gases takes place between the capillaries and the external environment. The capillaries lead into larger vessels, which in turn direct the blood into the dorsal vessel and aortic arches to complete the cycle.

Dissolved in the blood of the earthworm is a respiratory pigment, a molecule that binds to oxygen. The presence of this pigment allows the blood to pick up and transport more oxygen than would otherwise be possible. The respiratory pigment found in earthworms is the same pigment that is found in the blood of vertebrates.

Figure 9.6 Unlike the earthworm, the bird breathes through lungs. It needs a different kind of circulatory system to deliver oxygen around its body.

As you saw in Chapter 8, the earthworm uses its entire skin surface to exchange gases. This means that the blood is being oxygenated as it circulates around the animal. For animals with specialized respiratory structures such as gills or lungs, however, a more complex circulatory system is required. This is necessary to ensure that the blood is first passed through the respiratory surface where the exchange of gases takes place, and then is delivered to the rest of the body.

In contrast to the circulatory system of the earthworm, which lacks a true heart, all vertebrates have a closed circulatory system in which the regular contractions of a muscular heart force blood past the respiratory surface, through a network of vessels, and into the **capillaries** where the exchange of materials takes place. Blood travels from the heart to the capillaries through a distinct set of vessels called **arteries**, and returns from the capillaries to the heart through another set of vessels called **veins**. The path of circulation and the structure of the heart both play a role in determining the efficiency of the circulatory system in the different animals discussed in the following pages. See Figure 9.7 for a comparison of these systems.

Circulation in Fish

The heart of a fish has two main chambers and two lesser cavities organized in a row. Blood flows through this series of chambers and is pumped out through a ventral artery to the network of capillaries in the gills, where the exchange of respiratory gases takes place. From the gills the blood travels to a dorsal artery that branches through the body to deliver oxygenated blood. This kind of circulation, in which the blood travels through the heart only once during each complete circuit around the body, is called single circulation.

The circulatory system of the fish offers the advantage that all the blood travelling from the heart to the body has been oxygenated in the gills. In this circulation pathway, however, much of the blood pressure generated by the heart is lost as the blood passes through the capillaries in the gills. This happens because the finer tubes of the capillaries offer more resistance to the blood, slowing it down. The relatively slow passage of blood through the rest of the body limits the rate of oxygen delivery and therefore limits the metabolic rate of the animal. Since fish are cold-blooded, they do not need to generate as much energy as warm-blooded animals such as birds and mammals.

Circulation in Amphibians

Animals in the class Amphibia (which includes frogs, toads, and salamanders) have a heart with a third chamber. The blood is pumped from the heart to the lungs, and then flows back to the heart where it is pumped again before flowing into the arteries that carry blood to the rest of the body. The structure of the heart means that there is some mixing of oxygenated and deoxygenated blood — that is, some of the blood that returns to the heart from the body then flows back to the body without first passing to the lungs.

The extra chamber of the heart allows blood to be pumped through the heart twice during every complete cycle of the circulatory system, creating a double circulation. Since only some of the blood is pumped twice in each circuit, the amphibian circulatory system is called an *incomplete* double circulatory system. The incomplete separation of oxygenated and deoxygenated blood in the heart reduces the efficiency of the respiratory system. Remember, however, that amphibians can respire through their skin as well as through their lungs, so the blood does not have to pass by the lungs to pick up oxygen.

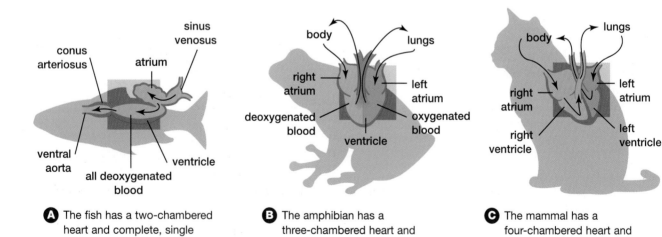

A The fish has a two-chambered heart and complete, single circulation.

B The amphibian has a three-chambered heart and incomplete, double circulation.

C The mammal has a four-chambered heart and complete, double circulation.

Figure 9.7 The circulatory systems of a fish, an amphibian, and a mammal. Variations in the structure of the heart and in the path of circulation affect the efficiency of the circulatory system in these different animals.

Figure 9.8 Adaptations in the circulatory system of mammals provides them with a much higher metabolic rate than is found in fish.

Circulation in Birds and Mammals

Active, warm-blooded vertebrates have very high energy requirements. Their bodies demand lots of oxygen, and need it delivered quickly. The high level of cellular activity also generates wastes that must be removed quickly from the fluid surrounding individual cells in order to keep those cells healthy. The circulatory systems of birds and mammals show two important adaptations that allow this more efficient circulation. The first is a mechanism to keep oxygenated and deoxygenated blood completely separate, so the blood that flows from the heart to the body contains as much oxygen as possible. The second is a mechanism to maximize blood pressure in order to force blood through the capillaries quickly.

All birds and mammals have a heart consisting of four chambers: two **atria** (singular atrium) and two **ventricles**. Blood entering the right atrium from the body is pumped into the right ventricle. From there it moves through an artery to the lungs, where the exchange of respiratory gases occurs. The blood loses pressure as it flows through the capillary networks of the lungs — but rather than flowing out to the body, this oxygenated blood is carried back to the heart. It flows into the left atrium, enters the left ventricle, and from there is pumped into the **aorta** and other arteries that deliver blood to the body. This system is called a closed, complete, double circulatory system. In the sections that follow, you will examine the mammalian transport systems in more detail, using the human system as an example.

SECTION REVIEW

1. **K/U** Describe the differences in the transport mechanisms found in an amoeba and in a planarian.

2. **K/U** Explain why an open transport system is well suited to the metabolic needs of an insect.

3. **C** Using landmarks that your classmates will be familiar with, map out a walking or cycling route that could illustrate a path of single circulation, and another route that could illustrate a path of double circulation. Trade maps with a partner and try to explain how your partner's two routes compare to the circulatory systems of different animals.

4. **I** The heart rate of mammals is inversely proportional to their size. Accumulate, graph, and analyze data that will either support or discredit this hypothesis.

5. **K/U** Reptiles have two aorta — one travels down the right side of the body, and the other down the left. In contrast, birds and mammals each have only one aorta; in mammals it is on the left side of the body, and in birds it is on the right. What does this suggest about the evolution of the circulatory system? What selective advantage is offered by the loss of one aorta?

6. **MC** Amphibian species are sometimes referred to as "indicator species" because changes in their health can provide information about damage to an ecosystem. With reference to the transport of respiratory gases, explain why a frog would be more sensitive than a muskrat to chemical changes in the water of the pond they share.

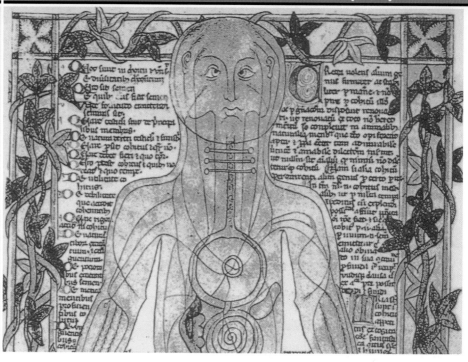

Figure 9.9 This illustration of the circulatory system dates from the thirteenth century.

Throughout history, different theories have been proposed to explain the purpose and structure of the heart and blood vessels. The ancient Greeks believed that the heart was the seat of intelligence. In the second century, the Greek physician, Galen, proposed that blood ebbed and flowed within the body like the tides of the ocean, causing the heart to enlarge suddenly and rhythmically. He also believed that the arterial and venous systems were largely separate, and that blood flowed out of both vessels to be absorbed by the flesh. This theory held sway for over a thousand years. It was not until the seventeenth century that an Englishman named William Harvey established that mammals have a cyclic circulatory system.

Web LINK

Put yourself in the shoes of William Harvey, a physician and surgeon in the 1600s (before the invention of the microscope). What kinds of experiments could you conduct to demonstrate that the blood is pumped by the heart and moves in a cycle around the body? Make a note of your ideas, then go to the web site shown below to find out how Harvey solved this puzzle. Go to **Science Resources**, then to **BIOLOGY 11** to find out where to go next. How do your ideas compare to Harvey's methods? In his discussion, Harvey compares the cycle of blood to the water cycle on Earth. Why does he make this comparison, and in what way is it inaccurate?
www.school.mcgrawhill.ca/resources/

Although Harvey established that blood travels in only one direction through the circulatory system (flowing away from the heart in arteries, and back toward the heart in veins), he was never able to find the place where the blood stops flowing away from the heart and begins its return journey. This discovery was made in 1657 (not long after Harvey's death) by Marcello Malpighi, an Italian physiologist. Malpighi used the recently invented microscope to identify the capillaries, which completed the picture of the overall pathway of blood through the body.

Figure 9.10 shows the main pathway and the largest vessels of the human circulatory system. As you saw in the previous section, the mammalian circulatory system is a closed, complete, double system. The blood vessels are organized into the three primary cycles. The route taken by the blood within the heart is called **cardiac circulation**. The pathway of the blood from the heart to the lungs and back is called **pulmonary circulation**. The route from the heart to the rest of the body is called **systemic circulation**. The systemic circulatory cycle includes all the blood vessels other than those associated with the lungs. Almost all of these blood vessels are named.

The average adult man has about five to six litres of blood, while the average adult woman has about four to five litres. Of the volume of blood in your body right now, 80 to 90% is currently in your systemic circulation, while most of the remainder is in your pulmonary circulation.

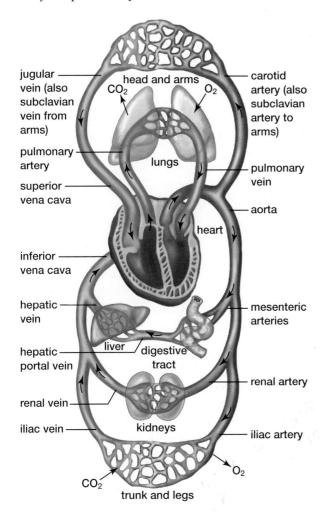

jugular vein (also subclavian vein from arms)

CO₂

head and arms

O₂

carotid artery (also subclavian artery to arms)

pulmonary artery

lungs

pulmonary vein

superior vena cava

aorta

heart

inferior vena cava

hepatic vein

mesenteric arteries

liver

hepatic portal vein

digestive tract

renal artery

renal vein

kidneys

iliac vein

iliac artery

CO₂

O₂

trunk and legs

Figure 9.10 The human circulatory system. Only the main vessels are shown here.

A circulatory system has three main elements: the transport vessels, which conduct fluid from one area to another; the transport medium, which is the specialized fluid tissue that carries substances around the body; and the pumping mechanism. The rest of this section describes the vessels (the arteries, veins, and capillaries) and transport medium (blood) of the mammalian cardiovascular system. The mammalian pumping mechanism, the heart, is examined in Section 9.3.

The Transport Vessels

As you have seen, the mammalian circulatory system includes three main types of blood vessels — the artery, the vein, and the capillary. The classification of blood vessels also includes the arteriole, which is a small artery, and the venule,

which is a small vein. Remember that all arteries carry blood away from the heart, while all veins carry blood toward the heart. This means that most arteries carry oxygenated blood, and most veins carry deoxygenated blood. The one exception is in the pulmonary circulatory cycle, where the pulmonary artery carries deoxygenated blood from the heart to the lungs, while the pulmonary vein returns oxygenated blood from the lungs back to the heart to be pumped into systemic circulation.

Table 9.1
Examples of blood vessels and their associated organs

Vessel	Artery or vein	Associated organs
aorta	artery	principal arteries of the body, distributing to all organs
carotid	artery	head region
jugular	vein	head region
hepatic	both	liver
renal	both	kidney
vena cava	vein	principal veins of the body, collecting from all organs
celiac	artery	serves coelom (major body cavity) and contained organs (e.g., stomach)

Word LINK

Each of the many blood vessels in the body takes its name from a Latin, Greek, or English term for its associated organ or organs. Portal, for instance, derives from the Latin *porta*, meaning gate. It is the name given to vessels that enter particular organs. For example, the hepatic portal vein carries the end products of digestion into the liver, while the renal portal vein carries waste products into the kidneys for processing.

Blood travels from an artery to an arteriole and then into a capillary network where gases, foods, wastes, and hormones are exchanged across the capillary wall between the blood and the interstitial fluid bathing each cell of the body. The capillaries then empty into venules and progressively larger veins that carry blood back to the heart.

A key factor that has influenced the evolution of the circulatory system is the need to keep the blood flowing as quickly as possible through this cycle. As vessels get smaller and smaller, friction increases and blood pressure drops (see Figure 9.11 on the following page). This means that blood moves very slowly through the capillaries. The heart alone is incapable of exerting enough pressure to drive the blood around the entire circulatory system. So how can blood be forced all the way through the capillary beds, into the veins, and back to the heart? Adaptations in each of the different kinds of blood vessels help keep the blood moving.

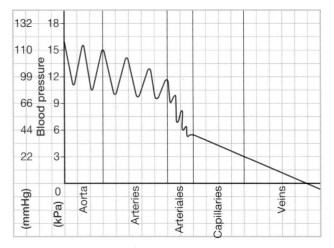

Figure 9.11 Blood pressure in different parts of the body. Note that the pressure approaches zero in the capillaries. When the blood must travel a long distance against the pull of gravity, as it must in large animals such as the giraffe, the veins may show a negative blood pressure.

Arteries

A cross section of an artery or arteriole reveals three different structural layers (see Figure 9.12). The outer layer is a covering of connective tissue mixed with a few elastic fibres. The middle layer — the thickest of the three layers — is made up of alternating, circular bands of elastic fibres and smooth muscle. The inner layer is only a single cell thick, and consists of smooth epithelial cells that serve to reduce friction as blood courses through them.

A distinguishing feature of the artery is its elastic walls. This elasticity allows the artery to first expand as a wave of blood passes through it, and then snap back again. This movement keeps blood flowing in the right direction, and provides an additional pumping motion to help force the blood through the blood vessels. When you measure your pulse, what you actually feel is the rhythmic expansion and contraction of an artery as blood courses through it.

BIO FACT

If the arteries, veins, and capillaries in your body were arranged end to end, they would stretch a distance of approximately 160 000 km.

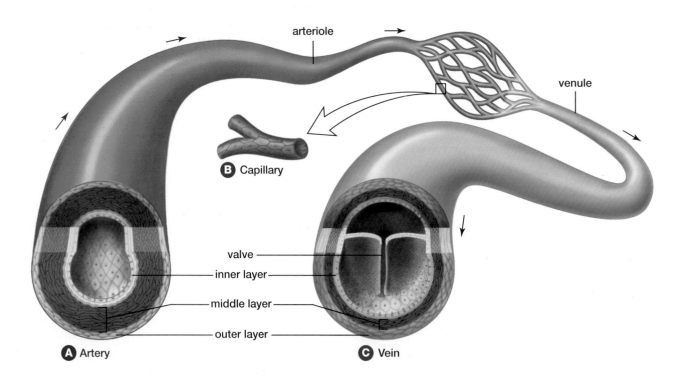

Figure 9.12 Sections through an artery, capillary, and vein. At any given moment, about 30% of the blood in your systemic circulation will be found in the arteries, 5% in the capillaries, and 65% in the veins.

Veins

Compared to an artery, a vein has a thinner wall and a larger inner circumference (see Figure 9.12). As a result, the vein lacks the elasticity of the artery, but has a greater capacity. At any given time in a living mammal, the venous system contains approximately twice as much blood as the arterial system.

Once blood reaches the veins after passing through the fine network of capillaries, it is travelling very slowly. Since veins lack the ability to contract, some other mechanism must be used to keep the blood moving toward the heart. For the regions above the heart, the pull of gravity can help draw blood back down through the veins. Below the heart, however, the blood must be pushed against the force of gravity. This movement comes largely from the contractions of the muscles, which exert pressure on the vessels lying between them. Although these muscle movements are not always rhythmic, they do assist the flow of blood. This is especially true when the body is moving, which is when a faster blood flow is most needed. Veins cannot contract behind the blood to keep it moving forward, but they are equipped with one-way valves that help to keep the blood moving toward the heart. These valves prevent the blood from flowing backward.

BIO FACT

Do you ever have trouble staying alert during a long exam? Some studies have found that people who jiggle their feet and legs perform better on long tests than those who sit still. This may be because the movement assists the flow of blood and speeds the delivery of oxygen around the body.

Capillaries

The smallest of the blood vessels, capillaries reach every corner of the body. The capillary wall is a single layer of endothelial cells. The size of capillaries varies, but their average diameter is about 8 μm — just large enough for the largest blood cells to pass through in single file.

The capillary wall regulates the movement of fluids and other materials into and out of the blood stream. Remember that in a closed circulatory system the blood itself is always contained in capillaries, and never flows out to bathe the body's cells directly.

Math LINK

The flow of blood through a blood vessel is affected by the pressure gradient along the vessel, the radius of the vessel, the length of the vessel, and the viscosity of the blood itself. The relationship among these factors can be expressed according to the following equation:

$$F = \Delta P \frac{\pi r^4}{8} \ell \mu$$

where F = flow, ΔP = pressure gradient, ℓ = length and μ = viscosity. Assuming a constant pressure and viscosity, calculate the change in blood flow that would result if the radius of a blood vessel were doubled. On a graph, plot the relationship between vessel radius and blood flow through the same vessel at a constant pressure and viscosity. Now calculate the change in blood pressure that would result if blood flow remained constant but the original vessel became partially blocked so that its radius was 80% of its original value. On the same graph, plot the relationship of blood pressure to vessel radius at a constant blood flow and viscosity. For all of these calculations, assume that the length of the vessel remains constant.

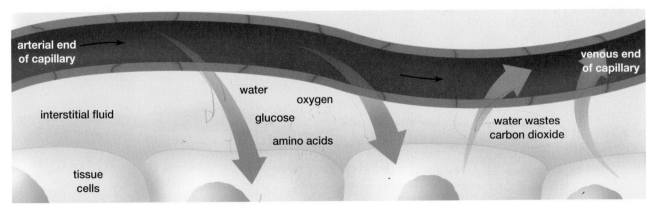

Figure 9.13 The exchange of material between the circulatory system and the fluid surrounding the individual cells of the body takes place across the wall of the capillaries. The direction of diffusion of each material is a product of its concentration gradient. Nutrients diffuse out of the blood, while carbon dioxide and other waste materials diffuse in.

> PLAY

To view and explore the paths that the circulatory system takes, refer to your Electronic Learning Partner. To explore the circulatory system of the fetal pig, turn to Appendix 10.

Blood: The Transport Medium

Blood is a collection of cells that have been specialized to perform a set of particular tasks within an organism. For this reason, blood is considered a tissue even though (unlike most of our body tissues) it appears liquid. In fact, blood consists of two distinct elements. The fluid portion is called **plasma**, and the solid or "formed" portion is made up of different kinds of cells. About 55% of blood is plasma, which is made up of water plus dissolved gases, proteins, sugars, vitamins, minerals, and waste products. The remaining 45% of the blood is composed of cells (see Figure 9.14).

Table 9.2 compares the features of the main components of the formed portion of human blood. Note the marked differences in the form and function of these cells, which all belong to the same tissue.

Red Blood Cells

Red blood cells (also called **erythrocytes**) make up 44% of the total volume of your blood. The average adult male has about 5.5 million red blood cells per millilitre of blood, while the average adult female has about 4.5 million red blood cells per millilitre of blood.

The red blood cell is specialized for oxygen transport (see Figure 9.15). Only about two percent of the dissolved oxygen that enters the blood stream is transported by the fluid portion of the blood (the plasma). Since the remainder is transported by red blood cells, these cells vastly increase the oxygen carrying capacity of the blood. A mature red blood cell has no nucleus. Instead, each disk-shaped red blood cell is packed with about 280 million molecules of the respiratory pigment hemoglobin, an iron-containing molecule

Table 9.2
Cellular components of blood

Point of comparison	Red blood cells	White blood cells		Platelets
		Leucocytes	Lymphocytes	
Origin	red bone marrow	red bone marrow	spleen, lymph glands	red bone marrow, lungs
Cells present per mm³ of blood (approx.)	5 500 000 (male) 4 500 000 (female)	6000	2000	250 000
Relative size	small (8 μm diameter)	largest (up to 25 μm)	large (10 μm)	smallest (2 μm)
Function	to carry oxygen and carbon dioxide to and from cells	to engulf foreign particles	to play a role in the formation of antibodies	to play a role in the clotting of blood
Life span	120 days	a few hours to a few days	unknown	7–8 days

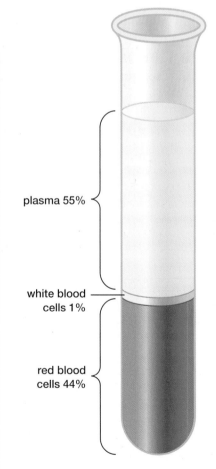

plasma 55%

white blood cells 1%

red blood cells 44%

Figure 9.14 A medical device can be used to separate the three main components of the blood. When the blood is separated it settles into layers as shown here.

that binds with oxygen. Hemoglobin allows the oxygen to be transported in the blood.

As you saw in Chapter 8, the respiratory system relies on the blood being able to pick up oxygen from the lungs and deliver it to the cells of the body. For this to work, there must be some way to ensure the red blood cells will bind with oxygen as it is absorbed into the body, but will release this bond in the presence of the cells that require oxygen. The special properties of hemoglobin allow this molecule to alternately pick up and release oxygen as the body requires.

Red blood cell

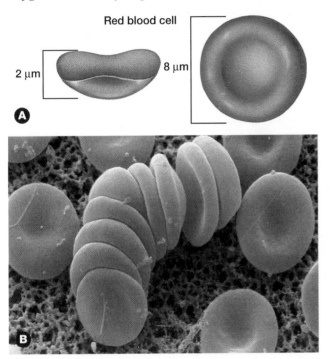

Magnification: 6900x

Figure 9.15 A red blood cell is a biconcave disk as shown in both A and B. It takes its colour from the respiratory pigment hemoglobin. Oxygenated blood is bright red; as oxygen is released, the colour becomes a darker blue-red.

A hemoglobin molecule contains four iron atoms, each of which forms part of a separate binding site or heme group. When the concentration of oxygen is high (as it is in the capillaries that line the alveoli of the lungs), the heme group may form a loose bond with a molecule of oxygen. Theoretically, four molecules of oxygen can become attached to one molecule of hemoglobin. In practice, not all of the possible heme positions in any one molecule of hemoglobin will be occupied by oxygen.

Table 9.3
Blood colour is determined by different respiratory pigments

Pigment	Colour	Metal element	Animal
hemoglobin	red	iron	mammals birds reptiles amphibians fishes
hemocyanin	blue	copper	molluscs
chlorocruorin	green	iron	some annelids
hemoerythrin	red	iron	some annelids

Oxygen Pick-up and Release Factors

In mammals, two factors play a major role in determining when oxygen is picked up and when it is released by the respiratory pigment. These factors are the concentration of oxygen and the acidity of the surrounding fluid.

The concentration of oxygen is usually measured in terms of its partial pressure. In any mixture of gases, the total pressure of the mixture is made up of the individual pressures exerted by each of the component gases. At sea level, the total atmospheric pressure is about 101 kPa. Since oxygen makes up about 21% of the atmosphere, the partial pressure of oxygen = 0.21 × 101 kPa = 21.21 kPa. Figure 9.16 illustrates the different partial pressures of respiratory gases measured in different parts of the body.

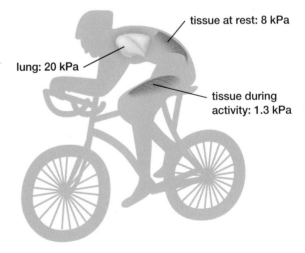

tissue at rest: 8 kPa

lung: 20 kPa

tissue during activity: 1.3 kPa

Figure 9.16 The partial pressure of oxygen is highest in the lungs, and lowest in the tissues where oxygen is consumed by the cells to meet metabolic needs. The partial pressure of carbon dioxide, in contrast, is highest in the tissues and lowest in the lungs.

When the partial pressure of oxygen is low, the bond that links oxygen to the heme group weakens. The hemoglobin molecule will then tend to release the oxygen molecules it carries. Similarly, an increase in acidity will loosen the bond and lead to the release of oxygen. This acidity, in turn, is influenced by the presence of dissolved carbon dioxide. An increase in the concentration of carbon dioxide results in an increase in acidity in the blood, which in turn weakens the bond between oxygen and hemoglobin.

In the capillaries of the alveoli of the lungs (where the partial pressure of oxygen is relatively high), the blood picks up oxygen. In the fluid surrounding the cells in other body tissues, the partial pressure of oxygen will be relatively low as the tissue cells take up oxygen to fuel their metabolic processes. At the same time, the partial pressure of carbon dioxide will be relatively high as the cells release carbon dioxide (a waste product of respiration). Under these conditions, hemoglobin releases the oxygen it carries. The result of this process is that the oxygen carried by the blood is released at the same rate as the cells' rate of respiration.

A dissociation curve is a graphic representation of how much oxygen is saturated in the hemoglobin at different partial pressures of oxygen in the blood (see Figure 9.17). The characteristic shape of the dissociation curve is the result of co-operation between the four heme groups on a hemoglobin molecule. When no binding sites are occupied by oxygen, it is relatively difficult for the first oxygen molecule to bind. After the first heme group is occupied, however, subsequent oxygen binding becomes easier. As a result, hemoglobin picks up oxygen slowly at first and then more quickly.

Another factor that influences the rate at which oxygen dissociates from hemoglobin is temperature. In cooler temperatures, hemoglobin releases oxygen more slowly. This is not a significant issue in warm-blooded animals, whose body temperature remains fairly constant, but it is an important factor in determining the activity level of cold-blooded animals such as amphibians and reptiles (see Figure 9.18).

The loose bond that hemoglobin forms with oxygen is the key to hemoglobin's ability to pick up and deliver oxygen in response to the different requirements in different parts of the body. In contrast, carbon monoxide forms a very tight bond with hemoglobin. The heme groups that are

bonded to carbon monoxide are no longer available for oxygen, which prevents oxygen from reaching the body's cells. Hemoglobin is very slow to release carbon monoxide, so this toxic chemical can continue to harm the body even after the victim's exposure has ended.

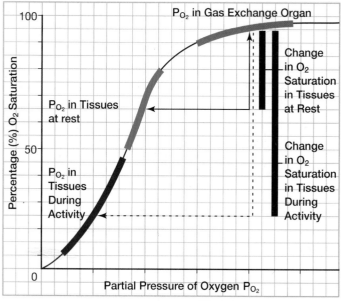

Figure 9.17 The different partial pressures of oxygen in different parts of the body can be plotted against the relative saturation of hemoglobin with oxygen. Since the resulting curves depict the dissociation, or breaking apart, of the oxyhemoglobin, the graph is referred to as a dissociation curve. During activity, a large increase in the amount of oxygen released to the tissues can be produced by a relatively small decrease in the partial pressure of oxygen in those tissues.

Figure 9.18 Cold-blooded animals like this one must use external heat sources to warm their blood before the blood can deliver oxygen to their cells effectively. Such animals tend to be very sluggish at night and in cooler temperatures.

Red blood cells also contribute to the transport of carbon dioxide in the blood. Carbon dioxide is released by the cells of the body as a waste product of cellular respiration. It diffuses into the bloodstream from the interstitial fluid. About nine percent of the carbon dioxide released by cells is carried in the plasma. About 40 to 45% of the carbon dioxide that enters the blood stream binds to hemoglobin, forming a compound called carbaminohemoglobin. The remainder of the carbon dioxide combines with water in the blood plasma to form carbonic acid (H_2CO_3). This conversion is facilitated by an enzyme in the blood. As carbon dioxide converts to carbonic acid, the partial pressure of carbon dioxide in the blood remains low, so carbon dioxide continues to diffuse into the blood from the cells of the body.

Carbonic acid tends to dissociate into bicarbonate ions ($H_2CO_3^-$) and hydrogen ions (H^+). An accumulation of hydrogen ions would increase the acidity of the blood, and could be harmful. Hemoglobin plays a role in picking up the loose hydrogen ions to help maintain the optimal pH in the blood.

A red blood cell rarely lives more than three or four months. When it dies, the remains are carried into the liver where much of the iron from the hemoglobin molecules is salvaged and recycled. A healthy body replaces its red blood cells at the rate of approximately one to two million every second. Any condition that reduces the level of oxygen in the blood will cause a reaction that stimulates the bone marrow to produce more red blood cells. Such conditions might include certain illnesses or the loss of blood from a bad injury. The body will also adjust its red blood cell count to respond to environmental changes. For example, people used to living at high altitudes may have almost double the number of red blood cells as those who are used to lower altitudes.

White Blood Cells

White blood cells, which are also called **leucocytes**, make up about one percent of your total blood volume. The number of white blood cells present in your blood may increase to more than double normal levels, however, when your body is fighting an infection. White blood cells play a number of different roles that help protect the body from disease-causing agents, or pathogens. In contrast to red blood cells, all white blood cells have nuclei and appear colourless.

There are several different types of white blood cells. Two of the most important disease-fighting cell types are **macrophages** and **lymphocytes**. Macrophages are phagocytic cells that can pass through the walls of the capillaries to engulf and digest pathogens. These cells behave much like amoebae and use pseudopodial action to move. Macrophages are part of the body's **innate immune response**, which is the body's generalized response to infection.

 THINKING LAB

Comparing Dissociation Rates

The dissociation rate of oxygen from hemoglobin varies from one animal to the next. These different dissociation curves will affect the rate at which oxygen is delivered to the tissues of the animal. In this lab, you will compare the dissociation curves of five different animals.

You Try It

1. The table shows oxygen saturation levels measured in five different animal species. Prepare a dissociation graph and plot each animal's dissociation curve on the same graph.

2. Examine the different dissociation curves. What factors would need to be controlled for a comparison among these curves to be possible?

3. Which animal is most efficient at releasing oxygen in response to tissue demand? What adaptive advantages or disadvantages do you think having each of the dissociation curves gives the organism?

Hemoglobin oxygen saturation in different representative organisms

Oxygen partial pressure (kPa)	Percent saturation of hemoglobin with oxygen				
	Worm	Fish	Reptile	Bird	Mammal
0	0	0	0	0	0
1	85	19	2	3	9
2	95	42	10	9	24
3	-	61	22	16	42
4	-	71	37	22	59
5	-	80	44	30	74
6	-	83	60	41	85
7	-	85	70	52	89
8	-	86	78	60	92
9		87	84	72	95
10		-	-	81	-

In contrast, lymphocytes are non-phagocytic cells that play a role in the body's **acquired immune response**. This is the response that enables the body to recognize and fend off specific pathogens. There are two main types of lymphocytes: T cells, which mature in the thymus gland, and B cells, which arise from the bone marrow. There are several kinds of T cells and B cells, each contributing a specific part of the response that allows the body to become immune to certain toxins. Figure 9.19 illustrates some of the roles played by both macrophages and lymphocytes in the body's reaction to pathogens.

As shown in Figure 9.20, an **antibody** is a Y-shaped protein molecule that is made up of a heavy polypeptide chain bound to a light polypeptide chain. Each chain includes one region that remains constant and another region (at the tip of each branch of the Y) that is variable.

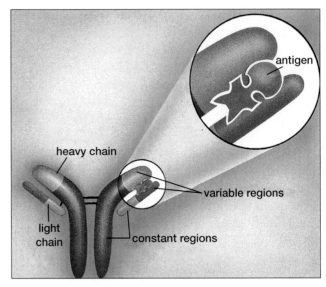

Figure 9.20 The structure of an antibody. Variations in the amino acid sequence produce the distinctive shape of the variable regions on different antibodies.

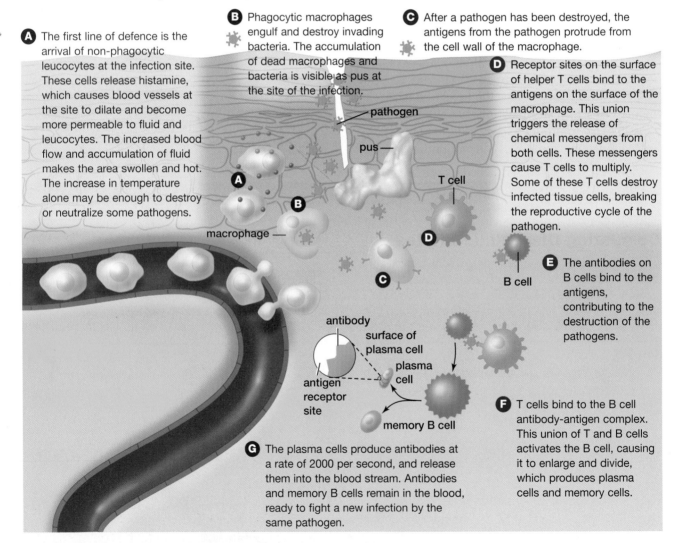

A The first line of defence is the arrival of non-phagocytic leucocytes at the infection site. These cells release histamine, which causes blood vessels at the site to dilate and become more permeable to fluid and leucocytes. The increased blood flow and accumulation of fluid makes the area swollen and hot. The increase in temperature alone may be enough to destroy or neutralize some pathogens.

B Phagocytic macrophages engulf and destroy invading bacteria. The accumulation of dead macrophages and bacteria is visible as pus at the site of the infection.

C After a pathogen has been destroyed, the antigens from the pathogen protrude from the cell wall of the macrophage.

D Receptor sites on the surface of helper T cells bind to the antigens on the surface of the macrophage. This union triggers the release of chemical messengers from both cells. These messengers cause T cells to multiply. Some of these T cells destroy infected tissue cells, breaking the reproductive cycle of the pathogen.

E The antibodies on B cells bind to the antigens, contributing to the destruction of the pathogens.

F T cells bind to the B cell antibody-antigen complex. This union of T and B cells activates the B cell, causing it to enlarge and divide, which produces plasma cells and memory cells.

G The plasma cells produce antibodies at a rate of 2000 per second, and release them into the blood stream. Antibodies and memory B cells remain in the blood, ready to fight a new infection by the same pathogen.

Figure 9.19 A simplified illustration of the body's immune response, triggered by the entry of pathogens at the site of an infection. Pathogens may include bacteria, viruses, fungi, protists, etc.

The variable regions recognize **antigens**, or toxins, carried by invading pathogens. Most antibodies are so specific that they can bind with only one antigen. Different types of B cells, however, carry different kinds of antibodies, and this variation increases the possibility that the body will have an antibody that can recognize and bind to an invading pathogen. Once a B cell is activated, it enlarges and divides to produce memory B cells and plasma cells. The plasma cells produce enormous quantities of the same antibody carried by the B cell, and release these antibodies into the bloodstream to fight the invading pathogens. After the infection has been fought off, memory B cells remain in the blood, ready to trigger another immune response when necessary (see Figure 9.21).

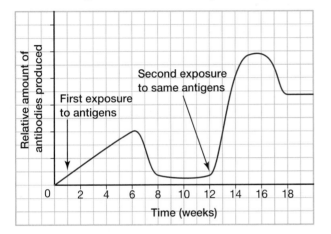

Figure 9.21 On the first exposure to an antigen, the immune response takes time to produce the antibodies necessary to fight the infection. If the same antigen is introduced again, the response is much faster and generates much higher levels of antibodies.

In addition to their role in fighting disease, lymphocytes can (under particular conditions) undergo changes to become a variety of cell types. If lymphocytes enter the bone marrow, they can be converted into red blood cells. If they enter other tissues of the body, they can play a role in the construction of different kinds of connective tissue fibres.

Platelets

Platelets make up the third major component of the formed portion of the blood. Platelets are not cells — they are fragments of cells that were created when larger cells in the bone marrow broke apart. These fragments contain no nucleus and break down quickly in the blood (each platelet lasts only about a week to 10 days). Nevertheless, platelets play an important role in clotting blood and

therefore help to protect the body from excessive blood loss after an injury.

While the process of clotting is not fully understood, it is clear that a number of steps are involved. Your blood does not clot until a blood vessel is broken, which indicates that the first step is triggered by the injury. Substances released by the broken blood vessels attract platelets to the site of the damaged vessels. As the platelets collect, they rupture and release certain chemicals. These substances combine with other clotting agents in the plasma of the blood to produce the enzyme thromboplastin. As long as there are calcium ions in the blood, the thromboplastin will react with prothrombin (a serum protein produced by the liver) to produce thrombin. Thrombin is an enzyme that reacts with fibrinogen (another plasma protein) to produce **fibrin**. Fibrin is an insoluble material that forms a mesh of strands around the area of the injury. This matted material serves to trap escaping blood cells and form the clot.

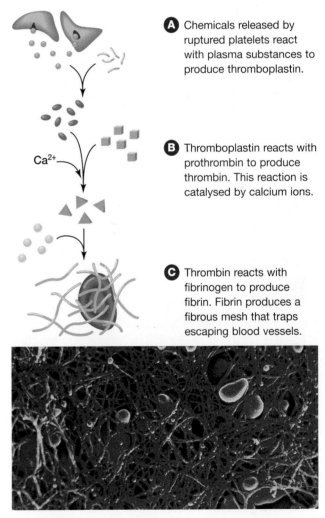

A Chemicals released by ruptured platelets react with plasma substances to produce thromboplastin.

B Thromboplastin reacts with prothrombin to produce thrombin. This reaction is catalysed by calcium ions.

C Thrombin reacts with fibrinogen to produce fibrin. Fibrin produces a fibrous mesh that traps escaping blood vessels.

Figure 9.22 Clotting helps to prevent the loss of blood when an injury breaks blood vessels.

Blood Plasma

Plasma, the fluid portion of the blood, is the medium in which the blood cells are suspended. But this fluid does more than simply carry all the blood cells. Plasma itself contains substances that play an important role in maintaining the body's well-being (see Table 9.4). The dissolved protein components of plasma include fibrinogen, serum albumin, and serum globulin. Serum albumin plays an important role in maintaining the blood volume and blood pressure. Serum globulin is the name given to a number of protein components, some of which act as antibodies to defend the body against disease.

Plasma also plays a role in the transport of carbon dioxide in the blood. Carbon dioxide dissolves in the water portion of the plasma to form carbonic acid. This carbonic acid is carried in the plasma from tissues to the lungs for gas exchange.

Table 9.4
The composition of plasma

Constituent	Percentage
Water	92%

Blood proteins
  Fibrinogen
  Serum albumin
  Serum globulin
	7%

Other organic substances
  Nonprotein nitrogen (urea)
  Organic nutrients
	0.14%

Inorganic ions:
  calcium, chlorine,
  magnesium, potassium,
  sodium, bicarbonates,
  carbonates, phosphates
	0.93%

Biology *Magazine* — TECHNOLOGY • SOCIETY • ENVIRONMENT

Fake Blood: A Real Alternative?

Donated natural blood has a limited shelf life.

Each year, approximately 600 000 Canadians undergo surgery or medical treatments that require donated blood — but donations to blood banks have dropped almost 25% in the last ten years. As a result, hospitals in major Canadian cities face a critical shortage of fresh blood every day. These shortages are not the only problem associated with the use of donated blood. Blood typing and careful screening are required to make sure the donated blood is compatible with the recipient's blood type, and that it is not contaminated by bacteria or viruses. Supplies of donated blood must be refrigerated, and they have a shelf life of only 42 days. Even where a safe supply of compatible donor blood is available, the time it takes for donated blood to circulate around the patient's body means that there is a delay in oxygen delivery to the patient. These problems have led researchers to look for artificial blood substitutes.

A Challenge for Scientists

Red blood cells are extremely efficient vehicles for transporting oxygen. Each red blood cell contains about 280 million molecules of hemoglobin, the protein responsible for absorbing oxygen when the red blood cell passes through the lungs. In the human body, about five litres of red blood cells travel through approximately 160 000 km of blood vessels, releasing oxygen to the body along the way. Creating a blood substitute that can match this efficiency is not just a matter of duplicating the molecular structure of hemoglobin, however. Every hemoglobin molecule is enclosed by a protective membrane. Once this covering is removed, the hemoglobin molecule disintegrates into particles called dimers. These particles can cause severe damage to the lungs and kidneys. Therefore, the search for an artificial blood substitute starts off with a challenge — how can we mimic the oxygen-carrying capacity of hemoglobin without the risk of producing toxic dimers?

When the fibrinogen and other clotting agents are removed from the blood, the straw-coloured liquid that remains is called serum. This liquid contains cellular nutrients, hormones, electrolytes, enzymes, hormones, antibodies, and waste materials. Serum from an animal or a person immune to a particular disease can be injected into a patient to provide temporary immunity from that disease.

Other Functions of the Blood

Blood is sometimes called a connective tissue, because it plays a role in linking all the body's cells and organs. As the blood circulates around the body, it provides an ideal pathway for the distribution of materials. Within a very short time, a substance that enters the bloodstream in one part of the body will come into contact with almost every other body part. In mammals, the blood serves as a channel for many of the body's systems. This means that blood is closely connected to other body systems that are responsible for digestion and for the action of hormones.

Capillaries in the walls of the small intestine absorb many of the nutrients that are end products of digestion. The blood also absorbs nutrients synthesized by cells in parts of the body other than the digestive tract. These materials, which include glucose and amino acids, are carried to the liver where they are converted into storage products or prepared for transport to other parts of the body. The blood also serves a critical body function by removing the waste products of cellular processes. Substances such as uric acid, end products of protein metabolism, and excess amounts of various mineral ions are carried by the blood to the kidneys for processing and excretion.

Several pharmaceutical research companies are working on developing blood substitutes. Some of these substitutes rely on natural blood products. For example, one company collects blood from slaughtered livestock, while another obtains human blood from blood banks. In these cases, scientists extract and purify the hemoglobin molecules, which then become building blocks for the synthetic product. Other researchers are exploring ways to create artificial blood without using hemoglobin at all. One possibility is to use a perfluorocarbon (PFC) emulsion that can act like a liquid sponge to absorb and deliver oxygen.

Artificial blood molecules developed through these techniques are up to 30 or even 40 times smaller than red blood cells. Because they are so small, these particles can travel around blockages in vessels and into very small capillaries. This lets them deliver oxygen around the body more quickly than red blood cells can — something that could be especially important in an emergency, where every second counts.

Blood substitutes can address many of the problems involved in dealing with real blood. The artificial products being developed are compatible with all blood types and are free of contamination by bacteria or viruses. Some of these products can be stored without refrigeration for up to two years. In addition, once blood substitutes are in the human body, they offer immediate oxygen delivery. They can keep working for about 36 h — long enough for the body to begin reproducing its own blood. These characteristics could make blood substitutes helpful in planned medical procedures such as scheduled surgery and chemotherapy, as well as in emergency situations such as accident scenes.

Although blood substitutes can offer some medical advantages, real blood does much more than just deliver oxygen. The artificial products being developed today still lack two key ingredients of real blood: white blood cells to fight infection, and platelets to help blood clot. The search is on for a substitute that performs all of the blood's vital functions, and the stakes are high. A successful blood substitute could help save thousands of lives every year.

Follow-up

1. In the 1990s, concerns about the safety of donated blood led to a nationwide inquiry known as the Krever inquiry. What were the main recommendations of the inquiry, and what changes were made in the blood bank system as a result? Following the Krever inquiry, has the search for alternatives to donated blood become more important, or less important? Explain briefly.

2. Other than in surgeries, emergency transfusions, and medical treatments such as chemotherapy, what uses might a blood substitute have? Conduct research to determine what risks may be associated with the use of a blood substitute. Given the potential benefits and risks, prepare a brief report arguing whether or not the use of artificial blood should eventually replace natural blood in all cases.

➤➤ FAST FORWARD

For more information about digestion, turn to Chapter 10.

The blood also serves as a medium for conveying chemical messengers, or hormones, from their origins in various glands to the organs on which the hormones act. Hormones play a central role in regulating and co-ordinating the internal systems of the body. Without the bloodstream to serve as a pathway for these substances, the body would be unable to respond effectively to fluctuations in its external or internal environment, and the finely-balanced mechanisms that keep the many different components of the organism functioning together would quickly break down.

Human Blood Groups

William Harvey's seventeenth-century discovery that the blood circulates through the body made it possible for physicians to consider blood transfusions as a treatment for patients. The first transfusions were conducted within 50 years of Harvey's work. A number of transfusions were successful, but there were also a number of dramatic failures in which the patient died almost immediately after receiving the transfused blood. In England, concerns about the risks meant that blood transfusions were made illegal in 1678.

In the early 1900s, scientists identified the four major human **blood groups**: A, B, AB, and O. Each blood group is characterized by the presence or absence of particular protein markers on the walls

of the red blood cells. The four blood groups result from different combinations of two protein markers, A and B (see Table 9.5).

Table 9.5
The human blood groups

Blood type	Protein markers	Serum antibodies
A	A	anti-B
B	B	anti-A
O	neither	anti-A and anti-B
AB	both A and B	neither

The blood serum carries antibodies against the protein markers that are not present on the red blood cells. This means that a person with type A blood will carry anti-B antibodies, a person of type O blood will carry both anti-A and anti-B antibodies, and a person with type AB blood will carry neither antibody.

Figure 9.23 illustrates how these antibodies are responsible for the clumping, or agglutination, of blood cells when incompatible blood groups are mixed together. For a blood transfusion to be successful, physicians must ensure that the donor and recipient blood are compatible. If a patient with type O blood receives a transfusion of type B blood, the patient's anti-B antibodies will react with the type B red blood cells, causing them to agglutinate. Agglutinated red blood cells can clog blood vessels, blocking circulation and causing severe damage to the body.

 THINKING LAB

Operating Room Puzzle

Imagine you are part of a medical team preparing to conduct a blood transfusion. You see on the patient's chart that she has type B blood, and the label on the donor blood container also says B. As an extra precaution before beginning the transfusion, you mix samples of the patient and donor blood together on a glass slide. You find that agglutination occurs.

You Try It

You need to discover whether it is the information on the patient's chart or the information on the blood container that is incorrect. You have access to samples of blood types A, AB, and O, but there is no more type B blood in the blood bank.

1. Prepare a table illustrating the results you would expect to see if you combined type B blood with each of the other blood types.

2. Explain how you would set up an experiment to determine which label was incorrect. Is there a control in this experiment?

3. If it turns out that the label on the stored blood container is incorrect and you have no type B blood for the transfusion, what other blood type could be used instead?

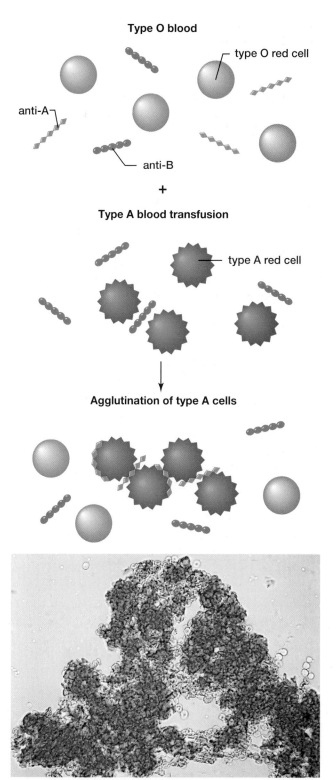

Type O blood

type O red cell

anti-A

anti-B

+

Type A blood transfusion

type A red cell

↓

Agglutination of type A cells

Figure 9.23 The agglutination or clumping of red blood cells that occurs when type A blood is injected into a type O patient. The recipient's anti-A antibodies recognize and bind to the A markers on the donor blood, causing them to clump together. The agglutination of blood cells can be fatal.

A second factor that affects the compatibility of human blood is the rhesus factor, another protein marker. People who carry the Rh protein are called Rh-positive, while people without the protein are called Rh-negative. Unlike the A and B antibodies, the anti-Rh antibody is not always present in the blood. It is manufactured by the body only after an exposure to the Rh protein marker. Therefore, the first transfusion of Rh-positive donor blood into an Rh-negative recipient is usually safe, since the anti-Rh antibodies develop over a two to four month period after the transfusion. A second transfusion of Rh-positive blood will cause agglutination of the blood entering the donor's bloodstream.

A similar problem may occur when a Rh-positive father and a Rh-negative mother conceive a child who is Rh positive, as red blood cells from the fetus may leak across the placenta into the mother's circulatory system. As a result, the mother's immune system may be stimulated to produce anti-Rh antibodies that can in turn cross the placenta. These will destroy the child's red blood cells and put all subsequent pregnancies at risk. The solution has been to give the mother an injection containing anti-Rh antibodies midway through her first pregnancy or no later than 72 h after giving birth to a Rh-positive baby. The anti-Rh antibodies destroy any of the child's red blood cells that have crossed the placenta before the mother's immune system begins producing antibodies.

This section has examined the transport vessels and the transport medium of the mammalian circulatory system. The next section takes a closer look at the third major element of this circulatory system: the heart, the pump that powers the circulatory system.

Word LINK

Is it clotting or is it clumping? These two words apply to two different processes. Blood *clots* when platelets are ruptured, but blood cells *clump* when blood of an incompatible type is injected into a patient.

1. **K/U** List three functions performed by the blood and identify the cells involved in each.

2. **K/U** Complete the following table in your notebook.

Vessel	Artery or vein	Associated organs
aorta		principal arteries of the body, distributing to all organs
carotid	artery	
jugular		head region
hepatic	both	
renal		kidney
vena cava	vein	
celiac		serves coelom (major body cavity) and contained organs (e.g., stomach)

3. **K/U** Explain the difference between the body's innate and acquired immune responses. Which cells are involved in both processes? Which cells are involved only in one or the other?

4. **K/U** The blood of a mother and her fetus sometimes mix during birth, and the Rh factor in maternal blood can cross the placenta to enter the fetus. Knowing this, explain how an Rh⁻ mother carrying an Rh⁺ baby could encounter no complications during her first pregnancy, but face blood compatibility problems during a second pregnancy with an Rh⁺ baby.

5. **K/U** Unlike most viruses, the human immunodeficiency virus (HIV) first binds to the receptor sites on a T cell and then becomes engulfed by that T cell. Explain why this characteristic helps to make HIV a difficult antigen for the body to fight.

6. **C** A volunteer firefighting team wants to increase the water pressure delivered by its fire truck. They have only enough money in their budget to do either (a) replace their 75 mm diameter hose with a 100 mm diameter hose, or (b) buy a new pump that will increase the pressure by 25%. Which of these options will provide the greatest gain in pressure? How does this relate to the organization of the circulatory system in mammals?

7. **I** Develop a simple test, based on using just a few drops of a person's blood, that could determine whether or not that person was anemic. Provide detailed reasoning to support your design.

8. **MC** Iron deficiency, or anemia, often results in fatigue and pallor. Explain how these symptoms could result from inadequate iron in the diet. What reasons can you suggest for why women are statistically more likely to be anemic than men?

9. **MC** A pharmaceutical company develops an artificial red blood cell that is very effective at transporting oxygen but is unable to transport carbon dioxide. Explain what would take place in the blood vessels if this substance were used in a blood transfusion. How would this affect the test patient? Assume the transfusion has no effect on the level of plasma in the blood.

10. **I** In a typical individual, 100 mL of venous blood holds 14 mL of oxygen, and the ventricles each have a volume of 70 mL. Given these data and additional information that you may have to research, how much oxygen does the blood absorb from the lungs in one minute?

11. **C** Describe the events that occur in each step of the blood-clotting process illustrated below.

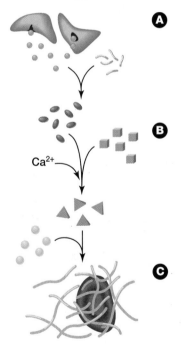

Ca^{2+}

The Mammalian Heart

EXPECTATIONS

- Describe the pathway of circulation through the mammalian heart.

- Identify the major compartments of the heart and its associated blood vessels.

- Design a feedback diagram to illustrate how the heartbeat is regulated.

- Explain how personal choices can affect the functioning of the heart.

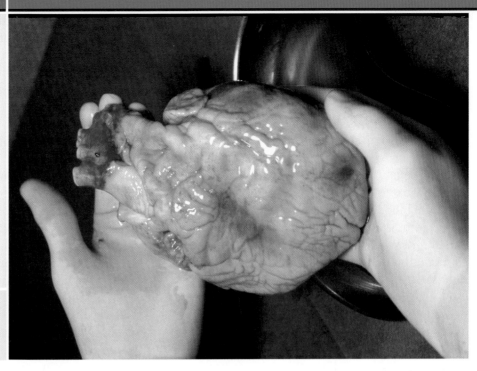

Figure 9.24 This heart is about to be transplanted into a patient needing a new heart.

Imagine you are an engineer, and a client asks you to design a pump that will push fluid through a closed system. It may seem like a simple task, until you see the client's specifications. This pump must work constantly, day after day, pumping about 70 times per minute, or approximately 90 000 times per day. With each beat, it must be able to pump fluid through about 160 000 km of vessels. It must maintain a steady flow, but be able to adjust quickly — and without any conscious controls — to demands for an increase or decrease in the pressure of fluid within the system. It must be able to pump in two directions at once, without mixing the fluid travelling in the two directions. It must have a life expectancy of about 80 years without any major repairs or part replacements (assuming it is well cared for). To top it off, it must be compact — about the size of your fist. As an

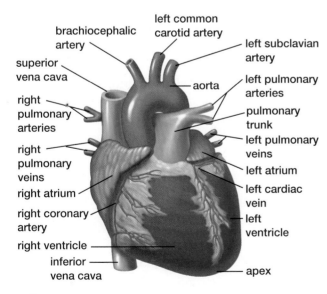

A An external view of the human heart. The left ventricle is more muscular than the right, giving the heart a lopsided shape.

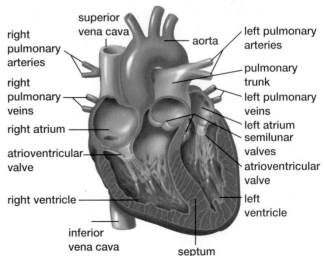

B An internal view of the human heart. Note the thick septum or wall separating the right and left ventricles.

Figure 9.25

engineer you would find this project daunting, and yet these are only some of the features of the human heart.

As you saw in Section 9.1, the heart of a mammal is divided into four chambers: a right and left atrium, and a right and left ventricle. Blood enters the heart through the atria, and leaves the heart through the ventricles. The two atria contract simultaneously, and the two ventricles contract simultaneously shortly afterward. This double pump action forces the blood through the cardiac cycle.

As the blood returns from the body, it is collected in a vein called the **superior vena cava**, which flows into the right atrium. When the atria contract, the right atrium pumps the blood into the right ventricle. When the ventricles contract, the right ventricle then pumps blood from the heart out to the lungs through the pulmonary artery. The oxygenated blood returns to the heart through the pulmonary veins, which are blood vessels that enter the left atrium. When the atria contract again, the left atrium pumps the blood into the left ventricle. When the ventricles contract, the left ventricle pumps the blood out through the **aorta** to the systemic circulatory system.

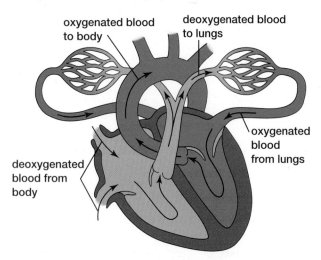

oxygenated blood to body

deoxygenated blood to lungs

oxygenated blood from lungs

deoxygenated blood from body

Figure 9.26 The flow of blood through the heart. Note that the atria contract at the same time, and the ventricles contract at the same time. Thus, only two contractions are required to force blood through all four chambers.

The contraction of each chamber of the heart produces a certain amount of pressure. The atria, which only have to push blood into the adjacent ventricles, have relatively thin walls and do not generate much force. The ventricles, on the other hand, have thicker, muscular walls that can push blood out through blood vessels and capillary beds in the pulmonary and systemic circulatory systems.

The left ventricle has the thickest walls, since it must force blood the greatest distance.

A series of valves prevents blood from flowing the wrong way through the cardiac cycle. On both sides of the heart, the atrium and ventricle are separated from one another by a set of three valves called atrioventricular valves. These are also known as **tricuspid valves** because each valve has three parts or cusps.

Between the left ventricle and the aorta, and between the right ventricle and the pulmonary artery, other valves work to prevent blood from being sucked back into the heart when the ventricle relaxes after forcing blood out of the heart. When you listen to a heartbeat through a stethoscope, the classic "lub-dup" sound you hear is caused by the opening and closing of these valves. The softer "lub" is the sound of the atrioventricular valves closing, while the louder, sharper "dup" is the sound of the valves between the ventricles and the arteries snapping shut following the contraction of the ventricles.

> PLAY

To view an animation of the function of the heart and the pathway of cardiac circulation, refer to your Electronic Learning Partner.

Control of the Heartbeat

You can probably hold your breath for more than a minute, and yet you cannot hold your pulse even for a single beat. Your heart continues beating regularly if you are knocked unconscious, and may even continue beating for a while after you die. In fact, a heart kept in a saline solution of the correct composition may beat for a long time. The impulse that triggers the heartbeat actually originates from within the heart itself. A bundle of specialized muscle tissue, located in the wall of the right atrium, stimulates the muscle fibres to contract and relax rhythmically. This tissue is called the **sinoatrial node**, or the S-A node. More commonly, the S-A node is known as the pacemaker.

BIO FACT

The first artificial pacemaker was invented by Canadian John Hopps in 1950. Hopps was conducting experiments with body temperature when he discovered that artificial stimulation could restart regular contractions in a heart that had stopped beating after being chilled. Hopps used this information to design a large external pacemaker.

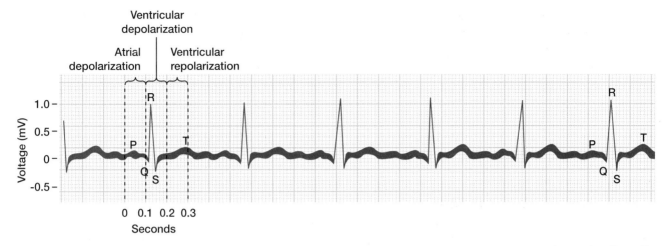

Figure 9.27 An electrocardiogram records the electrical activity measured by an electrocardiograph. The small voltage increase from P to Q shows the electrical depolarization that accompanies the contraction of the atria. The large spike from Q to S shows the depolarization that accompanies the contraction of the ventricles. As the ventricles recover from the contraction, the small spike at T shows the electrical repolarization that precedes the next firing of the S-A node. The repolarization of the atria cannot be measured, because it takes place at the same time as the depolarization of the ventricles.

Recording the Heart Rate

The S-A node generates an electrical impulse that spreads over the two atria and makes them contract simultaneously. As the atria contract, the impulse reaches another node called the **atrioventricular**, or A-V, **node**. This node, located near the atria on the partition between the two ventricles, transmits the electrical impulse over the walls of the ventricles to start their contraction. The change in voltage produced by these electrical signals can be measured using a device called an electro-cardiogram (ECG). The tracing produced by an electrocardiogram is called an electrocardiograph.

Figure 9.27 shows a typical ECG tracing. To take the tracing, a doctor or technician will place electrodes on the skin over the heart. The electrodes transmit signals to an instrument that measures the electrical changes in the heart muscle.

In a normal ECG reading, the small voltage increase marked as P shows the electrical depolarization that accompanies the contraction of the atria. The large spike from Q to S shows the depolarization that accompanies the contraction of the ventricles. As the ventricles recover from the contraction, the small spike at T shows the electrical repolarization that precedes the next firing of the S-A node. The repolarization of the atria cannot be measured because it takes place at the same time as the depolarization of the ventricles.

Some conditions, such as a drug overdose, can cause the ventricles to start contracting randomly. This condition is known as *ventricular fibrillation*. Fibrillation can sometimes be stopped by applying a sudden strong electrical current to the heart. After the fibrillation has stopped, the S-A node may be able to initiate a regular heartbeat again.

Chemical Regulators

When you are relaxed, your S-A node fires regularly, probably around 70 times a minute. This firing rate adjusts, however, to meet your body's needs. When you run to catch a bus, the increased activity in your muscles produces a faster rate of cellular respiration. This leads to an increase in the amount of carbon dioxide in your blood. Receptors in your blood vessels transmit this information to the medulla oblongata (the part of your brain that plays a role in controlling the rate of respiration). As shown in Figure 9.28, the medulla oblongata sends impulses along the nervous system causing the release of a chemical called noradrenaline. When it reaches the S-A node, noradrenaline makes the node fire more rapidly.

Once you have boarded the bus and found a seat, your heart gradually slows down again until it resumes its resting rate. This response is also controlled by the medulla oblongata. A fast heart rate leads to an increase in blood pressure, since blood is being pumped more quickly through the vessels. Receptors in the blood vessels sense the increase in blood pressure and carry this information to the medulla oblongata. In turn, the medulla oblongata causes the nervous system to release a substance called acetylcholine (see Figure 9.29). This chemical slows the firing of the S-A node.

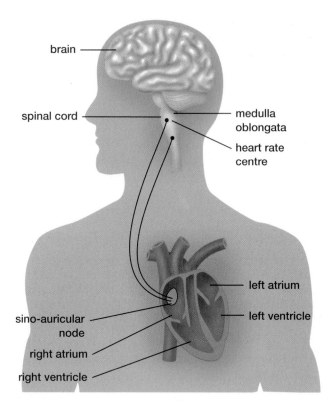

brain

spinal cord

medulla oblongata

heart rate centre

left atrium

left ventricle

sino-auricular node

right atrium

right ventricle

Figure 9.28 While the firing of the S-A node happens spontaneously, the rate of firing can be temporarily increased or decreased by chemical messengers. The release of these chemicals is controlled by the medulla oblongata in the brain.

Physical activity is not the only trigger for an increased heart rate. Your nervous system releases adrenaline when you are nervous, angry, or excited, or after a sudden shock or sharp pain. All of these conditions produce what is called a "fight or flight" response — a physiological change that prepares the body for anticipated activity including attack, defence, or escape. As the heart rate increases, so does blood flow to the muscles, resulting in more oxygen being delivered to the muscle cells.

Cardiac Output and Fitness

The amount of blood pumped by the heart is often referred to as the **cardiac output**. This is a measure of the volume of blood pumped from each ventricle per unit of time. Therefore, it is also a measure of the level of oxygen delivery to the body, and an indicator of the total level of work the muscles can perform.

Two factors affect the cardiac output. These are the heart rate and the **stroke volume**. Stroke volume is the amount of blood forced out of the heart with each heartbeat. Cardiac output can be calculated as

cardiac output = stroke volume × heart rate

The average person has a stroke volume of about 70 mL and a resting heart rate of about 70 beats per minute, for a cardiac output of about 4900 mL/min. Remember that the average person has about 5 L of blood in the body. This means that for the average person, the total volume of blood in the body circulates through the heart about once every five minutes.

Table 9.6 shows the relationship between stroke volume, heart rate, and cardiac output. In this table

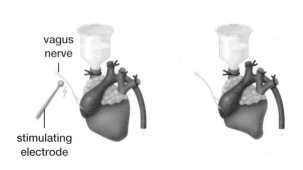

vagus nerve

stimulating electrode

A Loewi removed the hearts from two anesthetized frogs and passed a saline solution through each heart to keep them beating. He then electrically stimulated the vagus nerve of one of the hearts. This caused the heartbeat to slow down and eventually stop.

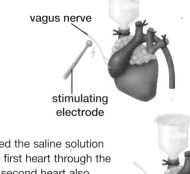

vagus nerve

stimulating electrode

B When Loewi passed the saline solution collected from the first heart through the second heart, the second heart also slopped. Loewi concluded that since there was no physical connection between the hearts, the nerve must have secreted a chemical inhibitor that was carried to the second heart in the saline solution. This substance was later shown to be acetylcholine.

Figure 9.29 An experiment conducted by a German scientist in 1921 demonstrated that chemicals are involved in the control of the heart rate. Loewi and a colleague later received a Nobel prize for their work.

individual C is exceptionally fit, having a very high stroke volume. C can maintain the same level of oxygen delivery at a much lower heart rate than the less fit individual B. This means that C's heart is working more efficiently than B's. A low resting heart rate is considered an indicator of physical fitness because it means that stroke volume is high.

Table 9.6
Relationship between stroke volume, heart rate, and cardiac output

Individual	Cardiac output mL/min	Stroke volume mL/beat	Heart rate beats/min
A	4900	70	70
B	4900	50	98
C	4900	140	35
D	9800	70	140

BIO FACT

Elite endurance-trained athletes such as Olympic cross-country skiers have demonstrated resting heart rates as low as 30 beats per minute. The maximum cardiac output in such individuals may reach 40 L per minute – 8 times that of an average person!

Heart Rate and Fitness

Your maximum heart rate is the highest heart rate you can attain during an all-out physical effort. This value will diminish as you get older. Maximum heart rate does not appear to be related to fitness. The more important indicator is the length of time it takes for your heart rate to return to its resting level following physical activity. The recovery time will diminish as you become more fit.

≫ FAST FORWARD

You should not exercise at your maximum heart rate. Instead, aim for a target level of about 80% of this rate. For tips on determining your maximum heart rate and on exercising to promote cardiovascular fitness, turn to Chapter 10, Section 10.5.

Stroke Volume and Fitness

Two sets of factors affect stroke volume. The first set affects how easily the heart fills with blood, while the second set affects how readily the heart empties again. The first set of factors include the volume of blood returning to the heart from the veins and the *distensibility*, or stretchiness, of the ventricles. The second set includes the strength of the ventricular contraction and the pressure exerted by the artery walls.

Regular cardiovascular exercise will increase the resting stroke volume of your heart. Cardiovascular exercise enlarges the ventricular chambers, increases the distensibility of the ventricles and strengthens the ventricle walls. As a result, the heart develops more power to push blood out with each contraction. Strength training such as weightlifting, on the other hand, may simply increase the thickness of the ventricle walls. This may actually limit stroke volume by reducing the elasticity of the ventricles. A good exercise program will include regular cardiovascular activity.

 MINI LAB

Measuring Recovery Rates

In this lab you will see how long it takes your heart to return to its resting rate following a short period of exercise. If you have a physical condition that makes it unadvisable for you to exercise vigorously, try the modification described below.

Find your pulse either at the wrist or under your jawbone. Record your pulse rate for 15 s and multiply this number by four to determine your resting heart rate. You may wish to do this twice to ensure an accurate measurement. Record the number. Now have a partner time you while you do jumping jacks or another vigorous activity for one full minute. Immediately after you finish, measure your pulse rate again and record this number. Measure your pulse rate at one-minute intervals until your heart returns to its resting rate. Plot the results on a graph.

Modification: After recording your resting heart rate, sit very quietly and breathe deeply. Try to relax your body and mind as much as you can. After a few minutes, record your pulse rate again to see if you have managed to bring your heart rate down to below your usual resting rate. Then measure your heart rate at one-minute intervals until your heart returns to its resting rate. Plot the results on a graph.

Analyze

Describe the shape of the graph you have produced. Compare your results with other members of the class. Provide an explanation for the differences you see. What do you think these results tell you about your level of fitness? Explain.

Stroke volume also increases while you exercise. The more fit you are, the greater will be the increase in stroke volume. Table 9.7 shows the relationship between resting and maximum stroke volumes for individuals of different fitness levels.

Heart Defects

A newborn baby will sometimes have a distinct bluish tinge. This is a sign that not enough oxygen is reaching the body. Such "blue babies" may have one or more congenital heart defects. Some of the more common defects include problems in the walls dividing the chambers of the heart, in the valves, or in the structure of the blood vessels near the heart.

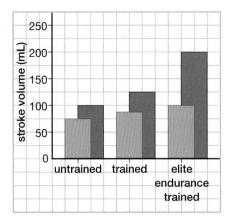

Table 9.7 The difference between resting (green bars) and maximum stroke volume (purple bars) increases with physical fitness.

Investigation 9 • A

SKILL FOCUS

Performing and recording

Analyzing and interpreting

Communicating results

The Heart Rate of Daphnia

Although Daphnia is commonly called a water flea, it is actually a crustacean rather than an insect. You will be able to see the heart of this animal through its transparent skin, and will be able to gauge the effects of various substances on its heart rate.

Pre-lab Questions

- How will substances in the environment reach the heart of a crustacean to cause a change in its heart rate?

- What effect will a change in the heart rate of a crustacean have on its circulatory system?

Problem

How can you compare the effects of different substances on the heart rate of a single animal?

Prediction

Predict how you would expect a change in temperature to affect the activity level of a crustacean.

CAUTION: Be careful when using chloroform

Materials

several live daphnia
microscope slide (with a
  small well or concavity)
medicine dropper
cover slip
ASA (such as Aspirin™)

adrenaline solution
magnesium sulphate
  (Epsom salts)
chloroform (very small
  amount)
ice water

Procedure

1. Place a single healthy Daphnia on the microscope slide and examine it under low-power magnification with a microscope. See if you can count the number of heartbeats in a one minute interval. If so, record this figure.

2. Gently lift the cover slip slightly and inject a drop or two of ice water. It may be necessary first to blot up the existing water in the well. Record any change you see in the heart rate. If you have not been able to count the heart rate, simply note whether the ice water caused an increase or decrease in the heart rate, or whether there was no noticeable effect.

3. Repeat the procedure several times, adding any or all of the following substances: adrenaline solution, ASA, magnesium sulphate, chloroform.

4. Prepare a table compiling your observations.

A septal defect is a hole in the **septum**, the wall that separates the right and left ventricles. This defect allows oxygenated and deoxygenated blood to mix in the heart. Such mixing may also happen when a small fetal blood vessel connecting the aorta and the pulmonary artery does not close properly at birth. Both of these conditions can usually be treated with surgery.

Another relatively common congenital defect is a heart murmur, a condition that occurs when one or more of the heart valves does not open or close properly. A failure of the valve to open readily restricts the flow of blood from the heart, while a failure of the valve to close properly results in blood being drawn back into the heart after a contraction. A heart murmur takes its name from the characteristic whooshing or rasping sound caused by the blood escaping from the valve. This sound can be heard with a stethoscope. A heart murmur is not necessarily a problem. Physicians grade heart murmurs according to their severity and according to the location of the valve defect. The location can be determined by identifying when the murmur is heard in relation to the different elements of the heartbeat.

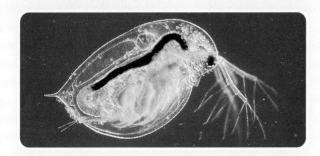

Post-lab Questions

1. Which substances caused a change in the daphnia's heart rate? Explain how you think these substances worked.

2. ASA is said to "thin" the blood because it prevents platelets from sticking together. Explain how this characteristic might have contributed to the result you saw.

3. Another classmate points out that your experiment lacks a control. Could this affect the validity of the conclusions you may draw from your findings? Explain. What control could be set up for this experiment?

4. Compare your findings with those of others in your class. Are all the findings consistent? If not, explain what factors may have produced any variations.

Conclude and Apply

5. What effect did the ice water have on the heart rate? What advantage could this response give to the animal? Assuming that the mammalian heart responds to a drop in temperature in the same way, how could knowledge of this response be used to increase the success rates of heart surgery?

Exploring Further

6. Daphnia, a very small crustacean, has a heart rate much faster than your own. If you were able to measure the heart rate of your daphnia, calculate the ratio of your own resting heart rate to the daphnia's. Why would such a small animal have such a fast heart rate? Would you expect the heart rate of large animals to be, on average, slower than that of small animals? Explain.

7. This investigation provides information about factors that affect the heart rate of a small crustacean. How much can this information contribute to scientists' knowledge of the factors that affect the hearts of other animals, including a fish or a mammal? Conduct research to determine the structure and function of the heart of a daphnia, and compare this to what you know about the structure and function of the human heart. In what ways are the two similar? How do they differ? Using this information, write a brief report explaining whether or not the data gathered from this investigation could help to predict what might happen in another organism.

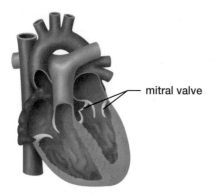

The most common heart valve defect is mitral valve prolapse, a condition in which the flaps of the mitral valve (Figure 9.30) close unevenly, allowing blood to flow backwards from the left ventricle into the left atrium. This condition is thought to affect between five to 15% of the population of North America. It is not usually a serious condition, although it does require regular monitoring.

mitral valve

Figure 9.30 The mitral valve is located between the left atrium and left ventricle.

Biology At Work

Pathology: Investigating Medical Questions

Dr. Jagdish Butany

Dr. Jagdish Butany seldom has a dull moment. His workday includes a variety of responsibilities: practicing regular pathology, serving as Chief of Autopsy Services at the University Health Network/Toronto General Hospital, conducting research, and teaching at the University of Toronto's medical school. With so many obligations, he must juggle priorities so no one suffers. Doing the work he likes, doing it well, and doing it on time are among Dr. Butany's biggest challenges.

Responsibilities

Pathology is a branch of medicine that studies disease by examining tissues and body fluids obtained during surgery or autopsy. Ontario law states that any tissue a surgeon removes must be sent for pathological examination. Dr. Butany first examines the tissue visually and records a description of his findings. He then has microscope slides made of sections of the tissue, and examines the slides in order to make a diagnosis. On rare occasions, the diagnosis may be that the tissue is normal. More commonly, Dr. Butany will diagnose a lesion, which is an abnormal change in the tissue. His report will mention the lesion, describe it, and (when possible) explain its significance and how it relates to the patient's symptoms.

Dr. Butany's specialty is cardiovascular pathology. He performs autopsies on patients who have died after undergoing open-heart surgery, a heart transplant, or a bypass graft operation. He must report on the procedure that was done and draw a conclusion about why the patient died. He tries to make sure that nothing went wrong in the surgical procedures or in the patient's treatment at any other time.

Research

Dr. Butany considers research to be a very enjoyable part of his work. He publishes reports and presents his findings at meetings all over the world. He is particularly interested in artificial cardiovascular devices, such as the artificial heart valve. Manufacturers consult him about new heart valves and other cardiac devices that are being developed for human use. Usually, Dr. Butany works with manufacturers in the testing stage, when the device is implanted into animals. It is essential to know how well the device is working and how it can be improved. Dr. Butany must use his skills as a pathologist to come up with definitive answers to these important questions.

Rewards

A career in pathology, according to Dr. Butany, is a huge challenge. Clinical colleagues ask for his advice when diagnosing a disease and when planning a course of treatment. He is rewarded by his confidence in his work and by the opportunity to make a significant contribution to the well-being of the patient. His work as a pathologist gives him an extraordinary sense of fulfilment.

Career Tips

Becoming a pathologist requires a strong background in biology and biochemistry, as well as good detective skills. If you are drawn to solving medical mysteries, you can contact the pathology department of your local hospital to learn more about the education and other qualifications you will need to pursue work in this field.

1. **K/U** Arrange the following into the order by which blood flowing through the cardiac cycle encounters them: pulmonary artery, pulmonary vein, aorta, superior vena cava, right atrium, left atrium, right ventricle, left ventricle.

2. **K/U** Explain how noradrenaline and acetylcholine are involved in the regulation of the heart rate.

3. **I** Can an ECG reading provide information about a person's cardiac output? Explain and give examples.

4. **C** Copy the following illustration in your notebook. Use arrows to show the flow of oxygenated and deoxygenated blood. Indicate the source and destination for each of these blood supplies.

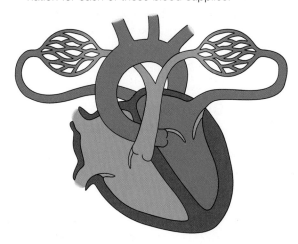

5. **C** Prepare a drawing and a set of up to four flash cards that you could use to explain to a Grade 1 class why regular exercise is good for the heart.

6. **I** Plot a graph of your heart rate versus time over a 24 h period. Account for any variations in the shape of the curve.

7. **K/U** Study the normal ECG trace shown below.

    (a) What effect does the increase in voltage at R have on the ventricles of the heart?

    (b) Describe what the trace might look like during ventricular fibrillation.

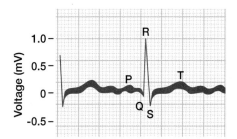

8. **MC** In one form of congenital heart defect, the major blood vessels are transposed. That is, the aorta is connected to the right ventricle, and the pulmonary artery is connected to the left ventricle. At the same time, a hole exists in the septum separating the right and left sides of the heart.

    (a) Draw a diagram to explain how this defect will affect the flow of blood through the heart, and explain the implications for the efficiency of oxygen delivery in the body.

    (b) How would you expect the ECG reading for an individual with this heart defect to differ from the ECG reading of a normal individual? Explain.

UNIT PROJECT PREP

If you have decided to study a heart disorder in your Unit 3 Project, draw a labeled diagram showing which heart structures are affected by the disorder. Include a note explaining what effect the disorder will have on the flow of blood through the heart.

EXPECTATIONS

- Explain the relationship between the lymphatic and cardiovascular systems.

- Describe the role of the circulatory system in temperature regulation.

- Describe how personal choices can affect the function of the circulatory system.

- Explain how blood pressure relates to fitness.

Figure 9.31 Some mammals and birds are well suited to life in very cold climates.

The coldest regions of the world are the terrestrial regions of the north and south poles. The only animals that inhabit these lands are mammals and birds. These animals have a number of physiological adaptations that enable them to maintain an optimal body temperature despite the cold environment. This is one example of homeostasis, or a steady internal state, working at a macroscopic level. In Chapter 1, you saw that an individual cell must maintain a steady internal state in order to continue its life functions. A multicellular organism must also maintain near-constant conditions throughout its internal environment for all of its individual cells to continue working together as one unit.

As you have already seen, the circulatory system helps maintain healthy conditions in the interstitial fluid surrounding each cell by transporting nutrients, respiratory gases, and wastes. Hormones and other chemical messengers are also carried around the body in the blood, enabling different organs and processes to communicate with one another. The circulatory system also has a direct role to play in maintaining the body's steady state. This section examines the contributions of the internal transport mechanisms to some homeostatic mechanisms, including water balance and temperature regulation. You will also learn about some of the factors that affect the well-being of the circulatory system.

Osmotic Balance: Lymphatic Circulation

Your circulatory system is not your body's only vascular transport system. Closely associated with the blood vessels of the circulatory system is the **lymphatic circulatory system**, a network of glands and vessels that extends throughout your body. These glands and vessels contain a fluid called **lymph**, which is either colourless or pale yellow and is much like the plasma of blood in composition. The lymphatic vascular system is found only in mammals and a few other animals (such as the frog). This accessory circulatory system helps maintain the balance of fluids within the body.

As the blood circulates through the body, some of the plasma escapes from capillaries to become the **interstitial fluid** that constantly bathes all the cells of the body. Rather than re-entering the capillaries, much of this interstitial fluid is absorbed into the vessels of the lymphatic circulatory system. It eventually rejoins the main circulatory system through ducts that empty into the large veins near the heart. This steady flow of water and other substances between the blood, the interstitial fluid, and the lymphatic system helps maintain constant conditions in all three areas.

<< REWIND

For more information on homeostasis and osmosis, turn to Chapter 1, Section 1.3.

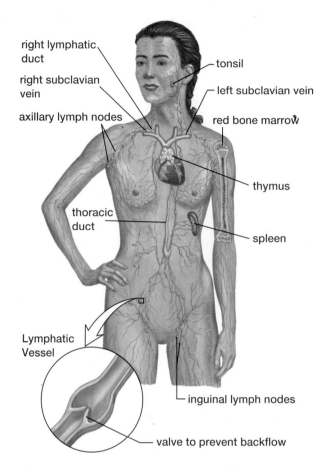

right lymphatic duct

right subclavian vein

axillary lymph nodes

thoracic duct

tonsil

left subclavian vein

red bone marrow

thymus

spleen

Lymphatic Vessel

inguinal lymph nodes

valve to prevent backflow

Figure 9.32 The human lymphatic system is spread throughout the body. Its largest vessels are in the region of the abdomen and thorax.

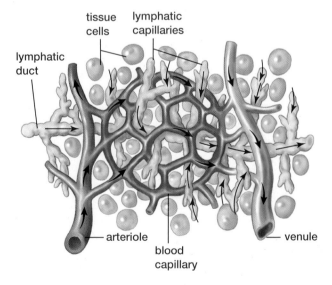

tissue cells

lymphatic capillaries

lymphatic duct

arteriole

blood capillary

venule

Figure 9.33 Lymph vessels are closely associated with the blood vessels. Fluid that escapes from the capillaries forms part of the interstitial fluid. Some of this fluid is collected in lymph vessels and eventually returned to the blood.

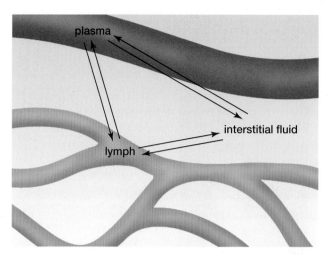

plasma

interstitial fluid

lymph

Figure 9.34 The lymphatic system plays an important role in maintaining the right water balance in the interstitial fluid of the body. The arrows indicate a steady-state relationship between the lymphatic system, the circulatory system, and the interstitial fluid.

The lymphatic system also works with the white blood cells in guarding the body against infection. Remember that one group of important cells in the body's defence against infection is lymphocytes. As the name suggests, these cells originate in the lymphatic system. Lymphocytes are produced in lymph nodes, the glands found in a number of places around the lymphatic system. The lymph nodes also contain macrophages, which serve to trap and destroy bacteria circulating within the body. An infection may cause an increase in the number of macrophages and lymphocytes in the lymph notes. When you get sick, you can sometimes feel the swelling in the lymph glands behind your jawbone or in your armpits.

The lymphatic system has no pump, so some other means must be used to move the lymph around in the body. Recent evidence suggests that the system is not a series of open-ended vessels, but rather a close-knit network of closed tubes. This means that the fluid must be forced from one end of each tube to the other in order to circulate around the body. In fact, like the flow of blood in the veins, the flow of lymph depends almost entirely on the movement of muscles outside the circulatory system. The contraction and relaxation of muscles in the area of the intestines, along with the muscular movements associated with breathing, help to move lymph through the vessels.

Facts on Fish That Fight

Dr. Louise Milligan

Whether or not you are an angler, you have probably heard your share of fish stories. Have you ever wondered what gives a particular fish the ability to put up a fight? What happens to that fish afterwards? These and other questions are being explored by Dr. Louise Milligan, an Associate Professor in the Department of Zoology at The University of Western Ontario in London. Dr. Milligan specializes in fish physiology and biochemistry. She also teaches two courses at Western.

Using commercially raised rainbow trout, Dr. Milligan and her team are studying how hormones in the blood contribute to the feedback mechanisms that affect the body's response to exercise. The trout in Dr. Milligan's lab have been implanted with catheters that allow blood samples to be taken without harm to the fish.

The team places trout in a fast swim tunnel, or simply chases the fish around in a tank, in order to exercise them to exhaustion. They take blood samples immediately after the exercise, and again following a recovery period. The changes in hormone levels in the blood indicate some of the feedback mechanisms that operate through the circulatory system.

How do fish respond to exercise?

When fish fight, they are "burst swimming" or sprinting. In order to meet the oxygen demand produced by this intense activity, the muscles of the fish convert glycogen (a type of starch) into lactate, a process that releases energy. Lactate accumulates in the muscle tissue. You will have experienced the effects of a lactate buildup yourself, if you have ever felt a "burn" while exercising.

If the sprint activity is prolonged, the muscles eventually use up their store of glycogen and become exhausted. Recovery from exhaustive exercise involves clearing away the accumulated lactate and restoring muscle glycogen. In fish, recovery from such exercise can take from eight to 12 h.

Exploring the feedback mechanisms at work

Dr. Milligan and her team found that fish blood showed elevated levels of a hormone called cortisol for up to six hours after exercise. When they injected the fish with a substance that inhibits cortisol, they found that recovery was much quicker (taking as little as two to four hours). Therefore, presence of high levels of cortisol appears to inhibit recovery from exhaustive exercise.

More recently, Brian Hooke — a graduate student working with Dr. Milligan — demonstrated that recovery can also be speeded up if the fish are allowed a "cool-down" period after exercise. Hooke showed that if an exhausted fish is placed in a current and allowed to swim slowly, cortisol levels in the blood do not increase and the fish recovers within two hours.

Another graduate student on the team, Jason Frolow, has produced research that helps to explain how cortisol and glycogen together affect recovery in trout muscle. Frolow prepared a slice of trout muscle which he kept alive *in vitro*. Using this muscle, he demonstrated that when glycogen levels in the muscle are above a certain level, cortisol stimulates the metabolism of glycogen into lactate. When the level of muscle glycogen is below this threshold, the muscle tissue produces glycogen instead of breaking it down.

What are the applications of this research?

Cortisol is just one of the many substances transported in the blood. The research being conducted by Dr. Milligan and her team will help scientists learn more about how exercise and recovery feedback mechanisms work in fish, and what role the circulatory system plays in these mechanisms. This research may contribute to a better understanding of how substances in the blood can contribute to muscle recovery in human systems.

Temperature Regulation

Birds and mammals are homeotherms. This means they keep their body temperature relatively constant (*homeo* = same; *therm* = temperature). In contrast, the body temperature of a cold-blooded animal, or poikilotherm, fluctuates depending on the temperature of the animal's environment. Many animals are not complete homeotherms or complete poikilotherms, but rather fall somewhere in the range between these two extremes.

Your normal body temperature is about 37.5°C. Your body generates heat as a by-product of metabolic processes, and uses several different mechanisms to control the rate at which this heat

Figure 9.35 The sea gull maintains a constant body temperature. It can remain active in a wide range of temperature conditions, from below freezing to over 40°C. The coho salmon, whose body temperature is the same as that of the water it is in, is found almost exclusively in water temperatures between 4 and 14°C — a temperature range of only 10°C.

is lost through the skin. Some of these mechanisms are behavioural; for example, on a hot day you will stretch out in the shade, while on a cold day you might curl up by a fire. Other mechanisms are physiological. The circulatory system plays an important role in the physiological regulation of heat.

Blood coming to the skin from the interior of the body is usually warmer than the skin. As more blood passes by the skin, more heat is lost from the body. Just as the rate of diffusion is affected by the concentration gradient, the rate of heat loss is affected by the heat gradient — the difference in temperature between the skin and the external environment. The greater the heat gradient, the faster the heat loss through the body surface.

When your body needs to conserve heat, blood vessels close to the skin constrict to limit the blood flow. When you get very cold, your extremities (including your fingers, toes, nose, and ears) may go numb and develop a bluish tinge as the circulation to these areas is reduced. On the other hand, when your body needs to release excess heat, vessels near the skin dilate to increase the flow of blood just under the skin's surface. You feel hot to the touch, and your skin becomes flushed.

Under normal conditions, a countercurrent heat exchange system helps maintain a steady body temperature. This system works because the deep arteries and veins entering and leaving the body's extremities lie adjacent to one another, so the warmer blood that flows from the body core to the extremities exchanges heat with the cooler blood returning from the extremities to the body core. Blood returning from the extremities can flow

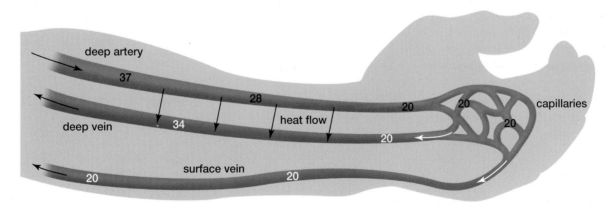

Figure 9.36 The countercurrent heat exchange mechanism between blood vessels in the human arm. The deep vein and artery are adjacent to one another, so heat is exchanged from one to the other. As a result, arterial blood is cooled as it nears the hand, and venous blood is warmed as it leaves the hand and returns to the body core. When

heat conservation is important, more blood will return to the heart through the deep vein. In warmer temperatures, when heat conservation is not a concern, more blood will return through the surface vein. You may have noticed that the veins on your inner arm are more visible when you feel hot.

either through a surface vein or through a deep vein. Figure 9.36 illustrates how the countercurrent exchange mechanism works to regulate temperature in your arm.

The constriction of blood vessels is called **vasoconstriction**, while the dilation of blood vessels is called **vasodilation**. Some substances can interfere with the body's internal temperature regulation mechanisms by promoting either vasodilation or vasoconstriction. Alcohol, for example, promotes vasodilation, causing blood to rush to the surface of the skin.

BIO FACT

Cold hands, warm heart! In cool temperatures, people whose skin temperature approaches the environmental temperature have a small heat gradient at the body surface. As a result, they conserve heat better than people whose body surface stays warm.

Blood Pressure

As discussed in the previous section, heart rate and blood pressure will increase temporarily in response to an increased demand for oxygen in the body's tissues. In a healthy body, this increase is short-lived. When blood pressure goes up, stretch receptors in the arterial walls are stimulated by the expansion of the arteries. At the same time, chemical receptors in the blood respond to changes in the level of oxygen and carbon dioxide. Both types of receptors trigger a response in the medulla oblongata, causing a release of acetylcholine that slows the heart rate and returns blood pressure to optimal levels.

The highest pressure in the cardiac cycle is generated by the contraction of the left ventricle as it forces blood out of the heart. This pressure is called the **systolic pressure**. Pressure in the cardiac system reaches its lowest point immediately before another contraction of the ventricles. This pressure

DESIGN YOUR OWN
Investigation 9 • B

The Effect of Stress on Blood Pressure

How can the effects of stress on blood pressure be isolated and studied? In this investigation, you will design an experiment to determine how blood pressure changes following a stressful experience.

SKILL FOCUS

Hypothesizing

Identifying variables

Performing and recording

Communicating results

Conducting research

Problem

How can you distinguish stress from other factors that might affect blood pressure?

Hypothesis

Make and record a hypothesis about the effect of stress on blood pressure.

CAUTION: Do not over-inflate the blood pressure cuff. Students with circulatory or blood pressure problems should not be subjects in this experiment.

Materials

blood pressure cuff   watch with a second hand

Experimental Plan

1. Working in a group, prepare a list of ways you might test your hypothesis using the materials available in the classroom.

2. Decide on one approach for your experiment that could be conducted in the classroom.

3. Your design should test one variable at a time. Plan to collect quantitative data.

4. Outline a procedure for your experiment, listing each step. Assemble the materials you will require.

5. Design a table for collecting your data.

Checking the Plan

1. What will be your independent variable? What will be your dependent variable(s)? What will be your control variable(s)?

2. How will you cause a temporary stress for the subject? What stress will you apply, and how long will you apply it? How many trials will you run?

3. Has your teacher approved your plan?

is called the **diastolic pressure**. In medical practice blood pressure is typically measured at an artery in the arm and recorded in millimetres of mercury, or mm Hg (1 mm Hg = 0.133 kPa). The systolic pressure is presented over the diastolic pressure. In an average, healthy young person, blood pressure is about 120 mm Hg over 80 mm Hg, or $\frac{120}{80}$. As the heart rate increases, the ventricles must push a greater volume of blood per unit of time, so pressure within the arterial system also increases.

Blood Pressure Risks

A chronically elevated blood pressure, or hypertension, is associated with a number of health problems, including a greatly increased risk of heart disease. Since blood pressure is the measure of the force of blood against the arterial walls, conditions that either increase the volume (or rate) of blood or reduce the elasticity of the arteries can produce hypertension. A diet high in salt will cause the blood to retain more water, thus increasing the volume of blood that must be pumped by the heart. A diet high in cholesterol can cause arteries to become clogged, reducing their elasticity and narrowing the vessels. Both diets can lead to high blood pressure.

Artificial stimulants such as caffeine, nicotine, and alcohol imitate the effects of noradrenaline and cause a temporary increase in your heart rate. Regular use of such stimulants can lead to hypertension. Other factors that affect blood pressure include heredity, age (blood pressure tends to increase as you get older), lack of exercise, smoking, and obesity.

Data and Observations

Conduct your experiment and record your results. Enter the data into the table. Prepare a graph or chart that can help you communicate your findings to other groups in the class.

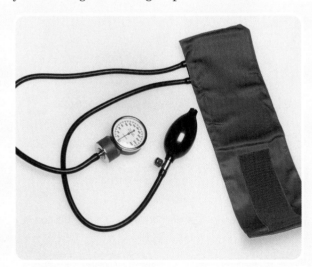

Analyze

1. What was the subject's resting blood pressure?

2. How did the blood pressure change as a result of stress?

3. How long did this change in blood pressure last?

Conclude and Apply

4. How did your results compare with those of other groups in the class? How can you explain any differences?

5. What is the adaptive advantage of a temporary increase in blood pressure?

Exploring Further

6. High blood pressure is a common problem in North America. Many different kinds of treatment are available for individuals suffering from the effects of high blood pressure. Some examples include the techniques found in western medicine, naturopathy, acupuncture, massage therapy, and herbal remedies. Conduct research on three different approaches to the treatment of high blood pressure, and prepare a brief report comparing the main features of these treatments. If you had high blood pressure, which treatment would you consider first?

High blood pressure may occur in combination with arteriosclerosis, a condition in which cholesterol or other fatty material becomes deposited under the inner lining of arteries. The fatty material (or plaque) builds up over a period of years, primarily due to poor diet. The plaque blocks the flow of blood in the artery. The obstruction, in turn, can cause damage to platelets, which will then trigger the formation of a blood clot. If a clot occurs in an artery, it may block the blood supply and cause body tissues to die. Sometimes a blood clot will break free and be pushed through the blood vessels by the circulating blood. Eventually, such a clot — known as an embolism — may make its way to a vessel in the heart or brain, causing serious damage.

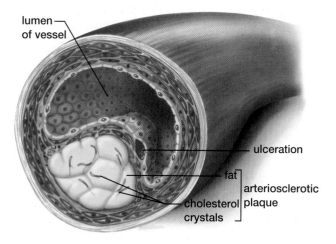

Figure 9.37 An accumulation of cholesterol or other fatty substances can restrict blood flow through the artery. The ulceration is a site at which the buildup has caused a tear in the artery wall, which could result in the formation of a blood clot.

If a clot reaches the brain, it may block a vessel and cause a portion of the brain to be starved of oxygen. This condition is called a stroke. If a blood clot reaches the heart, it can interfere with the movement of blood through the heart and result in a heart attack. During a heart attack, the heart beats irregularly and may stop functioning altogether.

The treatment of patients with a high risk of blood clots can include preventive medicine, including more exercise and a better diet, as well as medications. Aspirin™ is often prescribed because it helps prevent platelets from sticking to one another, and therefore reduces the formation of blood clots. Another common medication is derived from digitalin, a substance produced by foxgloves. Although digitalin is toxic in large doses, in small doses it helps strengthen heart contractions and slow the heart rate. It reduces blood pressure in the body while maintaining cardiac output.

Occasionally, circulatory problems require surgical treatment. In an angioplasty procedure, a cardiologist inserts a fine plastic tube into a clogged artery. When the tube reaches the site where the artery is constricted by plaque, a tiny balloon is pushed out from the tip of the tube. Inflating the balloon forces the vessel to open.

Another relatively common surgical procedure is a coronary bypass. This involves removing a segment of healthy blood vessel from another part of the body and using it to create a new pathway around a blockage in a blood vessel near the heart. The new segment is attached at one end to the aorta, and at the other end to a point in the blood vessel beyond the blockage. The term "double" or "triple" refers to the number of vessels containing blockages that must be bypassed (see Figure 9.39).

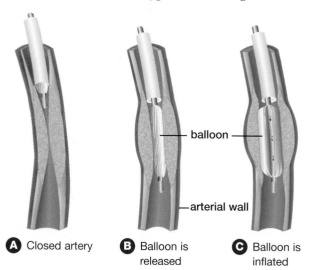

A Closed artery **B** Balloon is released **C** Balloon is inflated

Figure 9.38 An angioplasty procedure. The inflation of a balloon pushes open the walls of the artery.

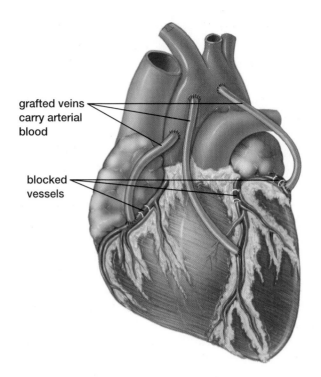

grafted veins carry arterial blood

blocked vessels

Figure 9.39 Coronary bypass operation. A triple bypass means that three new pathways are constructed to avoid blockages in three separate blood vessels.

The diastolic blood pressure is the pressure to which blood vessels are exposed the majority of the time. The systolic blood pressure, on the other hand, is exerted on blood vessels only in short bursts following the ventricular contractions. This observation led researchers to believe that a high diastolic blood pressure was the most important

indicator of health risks associated with hypertension. Recent studies, however, suggest that both systolic and diastolic pressure are linked to cardiovascular health, and that systolic pressure may in fact be the stronger indicator of risk. In young people, a systolic pressure of about 140 mmHg or more is associated with a higher risk of cardiovascular disease.

Web LINK

Some marine mammals such as seals and whales can dive for long periods of time. Go to the web site shown below to learn more about the adaptations that allow for extended dives. Go to **Science Resources**, then to **BIOLOGY 11** to find out where to go next. Draw a diagram comparing your own circulatory system to that of a whale. What additional challenges will a whale face as it returns to the surface after a deep dive? Is this something human divers have to be concerned about as well? **www.school.mcgrawhill.ca/resources**

COURSE CHALLENGE

A diagnosis of "heart failure" tells you that the victim's heart has stopped working, but not why. Make a consequences map that shows how different kinds of circulatory problems might affect different elements of the body's internal well-being such as water balance, blood pressure and temperature regulation. Use this map to think about what physical signs could help you to narrow down the possible causes of death by heart failure.

SECTION REVIEW

1. **K/U** Describe two ways in which the lymphatic system contributes to the body's well-being.

2. **K/U** A penguin's body is well protected from the cold by thick down and blubber, but its feet have no insulation. Explain how it is possible that a penguin does not lose heat through its feet.

3. **MC** An athletic wear company is marketing a new form of winter glove. The glove is very thin, but it includes heat capsules in the palm that will remain warm in cold weather. Would you expect this new glove to be effective?

4. **MC** One form of lie detector measures changes in skin temperature. If skin temperature suddenly increases as the subject responds to a question, the machine indicates that the subject is lying. What is the theory behind this technology? How could you foil the machine if you were the subject?

5. **K/U** A person's blood pressure is measured before and after exercise. What effect would you expect the activity to have on the systolic blood pressure? on the diastolic blood pressure? Explain.

6. **I** The metabolic rate of an active mouse is 100 times that of a human in the same environment. How would you explain this difference? What experiment could you conduct to test your hypothesis?

UNIT PROJECT PREP

If you have decided to study a cardiovascular disorder in your Unit 3 Project, make a list of the ways in which this disorder will directly affect the body's internal well-being. Make a second list showing the indirect effects that might arise from the direct effects on your first list.

Transport in Plants

- Distinguish between the two sets of transport tissues.

- Illustrate the different ways water and minerals can move through a typical plant.

- Describe how the mass flow theory can account for the movement of organic materials within a plant.

Figure 9.40 Campers stripped the bark and outer layer of tissue from this birch. This action damaged the tree's transport vessels and will likely kill the tree.

In the seventeenth century, the Italian scientist Marcello Malpighi removed the bark and outer layer of tissue in a complete ring around the trunk of a tree. Shortly after this treatment, a swelling appeared in the bark of the tree immediately above the stripped ring. Sweet-tasting fluid oozed out from this swelling. Although the tree initially appeared to be unaffected, it died a few weeks later.

From this experiment, Malpighi concluded that water is not transported in the outer tissue layer of the plant. If it had been, the leaves of the tree would have wilted almost immediately when their source of water was cut off. He also concluded that the sweet fluid that normally flows down the tree carries nutrients from the leaves to the roots. When the transport of this fluid was cut off, the roots continued to survive for a while on the food stored below the cut, but eventually died. This experiment provided evidence that plants divide the task of transport, with water following one pathway and nutrients following another.

The movement of materials from one part of a plant to another is called **translocation**. Translocation in plants involves two specialized tissues: **xylem** and **phloem**. The specific structure and arrangement of xylem and phloem differs in different kinds of plants, and also varies in different parts of the same plant. The general principles at work, however, remain the same.

Xylem tissue is formed when certain plant cells thicken, providing structural support to the plant.

Some xylem cells die and their contents disintegrate to leave a strong, hollow cylinder. These cells are stacked one on top of another to form a hollow tube that extends up the plant. Xylem conducting cells carry water and minerals from the roots of the plant to the stem and leaves.

The other transport tissue in plants is called phloem. In contrast to xylem, phloem tissue is made up of cells that contain living cytoplasm. The cell walls are porous, allowing the exchange of materials with neighbouring cells. Phloem transports organic materials including nutrients and hormones throughout the plant.

> **⤻ FAST FORWARD**
>
> Some plants do not have any specialized transport tissue. In other plants, the xylem and phloem tissues serve additional functions beyond transport. For more information on plant anatomy, turn to Chapter 15, Section 15.2.

Over 400 years have passed since Malpighi conducted his experiments. In that time, scientists have learned a great deal about the two main transport mechanisms in plants. Even so, many aspects of plant transport remain a mystery. The following pages outline what is known — and what remains unknown — about how plant transport systems work.

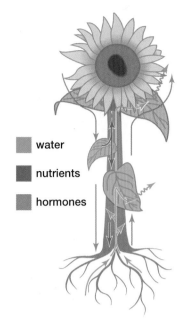

water

nutrients

hormones

Figure 9.41 Different substances move in different directions within a plant. A typical flowering plant has two distinct sets of transport vessels.

Transport in Xylem

Roots take in water through the root hairs and epidermal cells by osmosis. Water flows through the cell walls, into the intercellular spaces within the root, and enters the xylem. The water is then transported in the xylem tissue up through the root into the stem. Within the stem, water and minerals move by diffusion (and, to a lesser extent, active transport) into the other tissues of the plant.

As the xylem tissue carrying water and minerals enters the leaf, the conducting vessels branch and rebranch into the numerous veins visible in the leaf. From the end of each vein, water and minerals can diffuse into the cells of the leaf. About 99% of the water that reaches the leaf is lost through transpiration. This might, at first glance, seem like a waste. But as you will see below, the loss of this water may be an important part of the movement of water through the plant.

Earlier, you saw that blood can be moved through the veins against the force of gravity. This is possible in animals only because the movements of the muscles help push blood through the veins, while one-way valves keep the blood from flowing back down. A plant has neither muscles nor valves, so how does it move water up from its roots to its leaves? The following paragraphs explain the three main theories that have been developed to account for the translocation of water in plants. It is important to note that these mechanisms are not mutually exclusive. Any or all of these may be at work in a single plant at any one time.

Root Pressure

The **root pressure** mechanism relies on the fact that plant roots can build up pressure that forces water upward (see Figure 9.42). This theory suggests that water builds up in the xylem of the roots for one of two reasons. The first explanation is that cells may actively pump or secrete water into the xylem tissue. Or, cells may actively transport ions and, in turn, create a concentration gradient that causes water to move into the xylem by osmosis. In either case, the accumulation of water in the xylem builds pressure that forces the water upward.

Under conditions of high humidity, water cannot vaporize from the leaves and the sap forced up by the roots is pushed out from the tips of the leaves.

What Path Is Taken by Water and Nutrients as They Travel up a Plant?

In this lab, you will identify the path of the transport vessels involved in the translocation of water in a flowering plant. Using a long-stemmed white carnation flower, make two lengthwise slices about 5 cm long in the base of the stem. You should end up with three sections of stem, each still attached to the uncut portion of the stem. Fill two small test tubes with diluted food colouring, using a different colour for each tube. Fill a third small test tube with plain water. Place each of the sectioned ends of the carnation stem into one of the three test tubes. Support the carnation upright with the aid of clamps and a retort stand. Make a prediction about how you think the flower will look the next day. Allow the arrangement to stand overnight and then make an illustration to record your observations.

Analyze

Describe what you observed on the second day. With respect to the transport vessels of the plant, what do you think has taken place? What do the results tell you about the arrangement of transport vessels in the plant? Did the results support your prediction? Explain any changes you had to make in your hypothesis to account for your observations.

This process, called guttation, occurs almost exclusively in relatively short plants, where the leaves are not far from the source of the pressure.

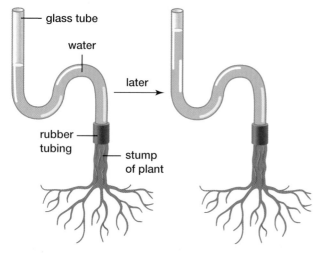

Figure 9.42 A demonstration of root pressure. The root pressure is measured by the final height reached by the water in the pipe. Aside from tomato plants, which have been known to build up a root pressure of up to 900 kPa, most plants have root pressures of less than 200 kPa.

Figure 9.43 Guttation sometimes occurs in conditions of high humidity.

The root pressure theory can account for the movement of water in some plants. For the roots of a tall tree to raise a column of water 100 m, however, the difference in pressure between the roots and crown would have to exceed 1000 kPa — approximately ten times the atmospheric pressure. Such root pressures have never been demonstrated in a tree. Indeed, many tall trees show no measurable root pressure at all.

Therefore, root pressure cannot account for the translocation of water in many plants. It also cannot account for the variations in flow that are measured in some plants. For example, some plants show a diurnal pattern where the volume of

flow rises and falls over the course of a day, despite showing no measurable change in root pressure.

Capillary Action

A second translocation mechanism, **capillary action**, relies on the adhesive properties of water. If you touch the end of a glass capillary to the surface of water, water rises into the tube. This happens because the polarity of the capillary walls attracts water molecules, which cling to the sides of the capillary. The narrower the capillary tube, the higher the water will climb (Figure 9.44). Capillary action could account for the movement of water up a very narrow vessel to a height of about 60 to 90 cm, but still cannot explain how water rises to the height of a tree.

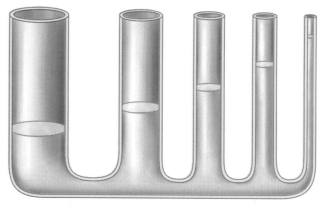

Figure 9.44 A demonstration of capillary action. The finer the capillary, the higher the water will climb.

Cohesion-tension

While the root pressure mechanism indicates that water is forced up the plant from below, and the capillary action mechanism indicates that water climbs the vessels on its own, a third mechanism may act to pull water up the plant from above. This process, known as **transpiration pull** or **cohesion-tension**, is the most widely accepted explanation of how water moves up a tall plant.

As each molecule of water vapour evaporates from a stomata on the surface of the leaf into the surrounding air, another molecule is right behind it. This second molecule moves up to replace the first. The water is not dependent on atmospheric pressure to support it. Instead, it depends on the cohesive forces within the water itself and the adhesive forces between the water and the walls of the vessels. These cohesive forces result from the attractive forces of water molecules for each other.

A As water evaporates from the leaf cell, the water pressure in the cell falls. Water moves by osmosis from the xylem in a leaf vein into the leaf cell. The removal of water from the leaf xylem lowers the water pressure in the leaf xylem, which causes water to flow from the stem xylem into the leaf. This, in turn, causes water to flow from the root xylem into the stem.

B As water continues to transpire from the leaf, pressure continues to drop in the leaf until a tension is created. The continuous flow of water from the stem to the leaf, and from the root to the stem, draws water steadily from the soil into the root xylem and up the plant.

Figure 9.45 A demonstration of the cohesion-tension theory. The action might be compared to someone at the top of the tree pulling on a long, continuous thread that originally entered the root and passed up through the stem. The thread will continue to pass through provided it does not break.

The daily water intake of a kilogram of plant tissue may be more than 15 times that of a kilogram of human tissue.

Even though the cohesion-tension theory involves transpiration, water will still move up the xylem even when there is no transpiration taking place from the leaves. More important is that the water remain under tension — a pull that will draw the water up the plant. In a plant, water follows a pressure gradient from the soil (where it is likely to be at a positive pressure) up into the stem (where pressure quickly decreases and usually becomes negative). This creates a tension that remains even if transpiration stops when the stomata close to prevent the loss of water.

In large trees, the tension may become high enough that the column of water is "stretched" and the circumference of the tree trunk actually shrinks measurably. Even under these conditions, the column of water will not break. The force of the cohesion between water molecules can withstand tensions of up to 20 000 kPa — more than ten times the pressure needed to raise the water to the top of a tall tree.

Although the cohesion theory is widely accepted as an explanation for the movement of water in tall plants, some questions remain unanswered. For example, scientists still do not know how water begins to move up a maple tree in the spring, before the tree's leaves are out.

Mineral Transport

Like water, minerals are transported within plants in the xylem tissue. The absorption of water and minerals, however, take place through different processes. As you saw above, water moves into the roots of the plant by osmosis. In contrast, the concentration of minerals in the soil is often not high enough for diffusion to be effective as a way for the plant to take up an adequate supply of the minerals it requires. Furthermore, the rate at which a plant takes up minerals does not match the rate of water uptake. Researchers have also found that the concentration of minerals in certain tissues of the root may exceed the concentration in the surrounding soil. The movement of minerals against the concentration gradient provides evidence that a mechanism other than diffusion is at work in the transport of minerals into plant roots.

Minerals exist in the soil in the form of ions dissolved in the water contained in the soil. These mineral ions are taken up by the roots through active transport (when conditions allow, this active transport may be supplemented by diffusion). The ions pass through a layer of living cells, where they may be incorporated into various compounds. The ions and mineral compounds are then released into the xylem tissue, where they move with the water up the plant. The ions or compounds will be taken up by cells of the plant tissue along the way.

While the absorption of minerals and water take place through separate processes, they are not entirely independent of one another. For minerals to be taken up by the plant they must be dissolved in water. At the same time, the uptake of minerals can increase the osmotic gradient between the soil and the root tissue, leading to an increase in the uptake of water as well.

Transport in Phloem

Plant scientists are still debating how transport occurs in phloem. Any theory must be able to account for a number of observations. First, phloem cells must be living for transport to occur. Second, material can move through the phloem in more than one direction at the same time (experiments with radioactive carbon and phosphorous show these substances move in opposite directions in the phloem of geranium stems). Third, phloem may transport large amounts of material quite rapidly within the plant — a pumpkin, for example, can gain 5500 g in less than a month. Fourth, oxygen deficiency and low temperatures both inhibit but do not stop phloem transport. Finally, the characteristics of movement of a particular substance may vary from one plant to another. For example, carbohydrates tend to enter cotton bolls

during the daytime, but they tend to enter date fruits at night.

The Mass-flow Theory

The most broadly accepted theory of phloem transport is the **mass-flow theory**. This theory relies on a combination of osmosis and pressure dynamics to explain the movement of materials. The principles at work in this theory are illustrated in Figure 9.46. In this illustration, two membranes that are permeable to water but not to sucrose are connected by a tube and immersed in water to form a closed system.

If sucrose is added to membrane X, then water will tend to flow into this membrane. The pressure in the membrane will increase, forcing some of the contents of the membrane into the tube connecting the two membranes. In this way, the sucrose solution will flow from membrane X to membrane Y. As pressure builds up in membrane Y, some water will be forced out. Eventually the solution in the two membranes will be at an equal concentration, and the flow will stop. If there were a way to continuously add more sucrose to membrane X and withdraw it from membrane Y, the flow would become continuous.

> **BIO** **FACT**
>
> The speed of phloem transport varies from 20 to 100 cm per hour, while the speed of transport in xylem is estimated to reach up to 50 m per hour.

This is, in fact, what happens in a plant. Sucrose is manufactured in the leaves as the plant converts the Sun's energy into nutrients. The sucrose travels in solution to other parts of the plant, including storage areas (where the sucrose is transformed into starch) and plant tissues (where the sucrose is consumed as food).

Figure 9.46 A model of mass-flow. The red dots represent sucrose. Red arrows represent the movement of sucrose solution; blue arrows represent the movement of water.

> PLAY

For more information about transport in xylem and phloem, turn to your Electronic Study Partner.

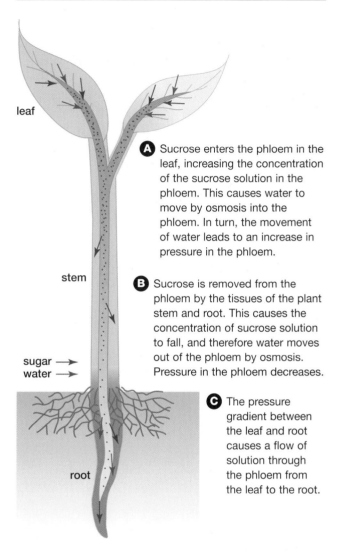

A Sucrose enters the phloem in the leaf, increasing the concentration of the sucrose solution in the phloem. This causes water to move by osmosis into the phloem. In turn, the movement of water leads to an increase in pressure in the phloem.

B Sucrose is removed from the phloem by the tissues of the plant stem and root. This causes the concentration of sucrose solution to fall, and therefore water moves out of the phloem by osmosis. Pressure in the phloem decreases.

C The pressure gradient between the leaf and root causes a flow of solution through the phloem from the leaf to the root.

Figure 9.47 A simplified illustration of how the mass-flow hypothesis applies to the transport of sugar in a typical plant. Dots represent the concentration of sucrose, while the diagonal lines represent pressure.

The mass-flow theory is a widely accepted explanation of how materials can move within a plant. Even so, this theory does not answer all the questions about plant transport. One problem for supporters of this theory is that the pressures involved in mass flow should lead to a higher internal pressure within the phloem cells than is actually observed. Another problem is that it is not clear that mass flow can account for the speed or distances over which transport in phloem is effective.

The mass-flow theory also cannot account for several observations relating to the characteristics of phloem transport. These include the simultaneous bi-directional movement of substances within phloem vessels and the retarding effects that oxygen deficiency and low temperatures have on the rate of translocation. These observations suggest that the living tissue of the phloem cells itself plays a role in controlling the movement of organic materials. Some researchers have proposed that a form of cytoplasmic streaming within the plasma of the phloem cells is responsible for the movement of materials through the phloem vessels.

While the precise mechanisms of phloem transport remain a mystery, it is clear that the xylem and phloem together provide a plant the means of moving almost any substance to every cell of the organism. While the movement of materials typically takes place in opposite directions between the xylem and phloem vessels, substances can pass from one set of vessels to the other. This provides the plant with a complete transport system that serves a number of the same functions as the animal circulatory system.

You have seen how the circulatory system transports materials around the body and delivers them to the individual cells of the tissues. These substances include the nutrients that provide the energy needed by each cell to undertake its life functions. The next chapter will examine the structures and processes involved in transforming the food you consume into the nutrient molecules your body needs. You will see how your body begins the process of changing matter into energy, and the effects your own choices can have on this process.

Web LINK

Go to the web site shown below to learn more about transport mechanisms in plants. Go to **Science Resources**, then to **BIOLOGY 11** to find out where to go next. Explore new ideas that have been added to the mass-flow theory of transport of materials in plants. Add to the ideas presented in this section in order to produce an oral presentation or written report on current developments in this area.
www.school.mcgrawhill.ca/resources/

1. **K/U** Describe the path taken by water from the soil through a plant. Identify the structures and molecular processes that play a role in this movement.

2. **K/U** Explain how the consumption of sucrose in the roots of a plant contributes to the movement of sucrose from the leaves.

3. **C** Prepare a table to show how each of the following factors will influence the rate of transpiration from a plant: high humidity, bright sunshine, light wind, freezing temperatures.

4. **MC** When you buy a bouquet of cut flowers, the florist tells you to cut the stems again before putting the flowers in a vase. Why might this help the flowers last longer?

5. **C** What property of water is demonstrated in the illustration. How does this property help to move water through plant tissues?

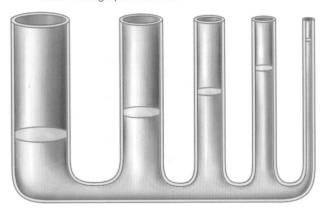

6. **K/U** One experiment found that sap in a tree moves slowly at night. In the morning, the sap began to move more quickly in the twigs. Later in the day, sap began to move more quickly in the lower trunk of the tree. How can you explain these results?

7. **MC** When a plant begins to wilt from lack of water, will the leaves near the top or the bottom of the plant be affected first? Explain.

8. **C** Describe the three stages of the mass-flow hypothesis, illustrated below.

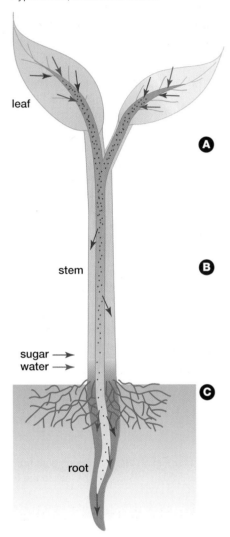

9. **I** Construct a graph that demonstrates the concentration of sugar in the phloem cells of a plant stem over a 24 hour period. Sugar concentration should be on the y axis and time on the x axis. Include a brief explanation for the shape of your graph. What effect, if any, would a sudden daytime rainstorm have on the shape of your graph? Explain.

Chapter Expectations

Briefly explain each of the following points.

- Some animals do not require a specialized transport system. (9.1)
- Blood is often described as a connective tissue. (9.2)
- In a mammal, blood pressure in some blood vessels may be less than zero. (9.2)
- Your body has more than one circulatory system. (9.2)
- The human cardiovascular system has both general and specialized transport functions.
- The left side of the heart is more muscular than the right side. (9.3)
- Blood flows only one way through the entire mammalian circulatory system. (9.4)
- Plants have transport systems but no circulatory system. (9.5)
- The loss of water through the leaves of a plant contributes to the transport of water within the plant. (9.5)
- Both osmosis and pressure dynamics are believed to be at work in the transport of organic materials within a plant. (9.5)

Language of Biology

Write a sentence including each of the following words or terms. Use any six terms in a concept map to show your understanding of how they are related.

- vascular system
- circulatory system
- open transport system
- closed transport system
- capillary
- artery
- vein
- atria
- ventricle
- cardiac circulation
- pulmonary circulation
- systemic circulation
- plasma
- erythrocyte
- leucocyte
- macrophage
- lymphocyte
- innate immune response
- acquired immune response
- antibody
- antigen
- platelet
- fibrin
- blood group
- superior vena cava
- aorta
- tricuspid valve
- sinoatrial node
- atrioventricular node
- noradrenaline
- cardiac output
- stroke volume
- septum
- lymphatic circulatory system
- lymph
- vasoconstriction
- interstitial fluid
- systolic pressure
- vasodilation
- translocation
- diastolic pressure
- phloem
- xylem
- capillary action
- root pressure
- cohesion-tension
- transpiration pull
- mass-flow theory

UNDERSTANDING CONCEPTS

1. Grasshoppers have green blood because insects have a different respiratory pigment in their blood than mammals do. True or false?

2. White blood cells are responsible for the swelling that occurs at the site of an infection. True or false?

3. The cohesion-tension theory is the most widely accepted explanation for the movement of sugars around a plant. True or false?

4. Explain why red blood cells are well-suited for oxygen transport.

5. List four functions of the mammalian circulatory system.

6. Distinguish between systolic and diastolic blood pressure.

7. Name three factors that affect blood pressure, and explain how each factor produces its effect.

8. List three factors that assist the flow of blood through the veins.

9. What is the difference between a heart attack and a stroke?

10. Arrange the following organs and vessels into the order in which they are encountered by blood travelling through the mammalian circulatory system: superior vena cava; lung capillaries; pulmonary vein; pulmonary artery; tricuspid valve; semilunar valve; left atrium; right atrium; left ventricle; right ventricle; venule; aorta; arteriole.

11. In the nineteenth century, deadly outbreaks of a viral disease called smallpox were not uncommon. During these outbreaks, people who had already had cowpox (which is a similar but less serious illness) rarely contracted smallpox. Explain this observation, with reference to the body's immune response.

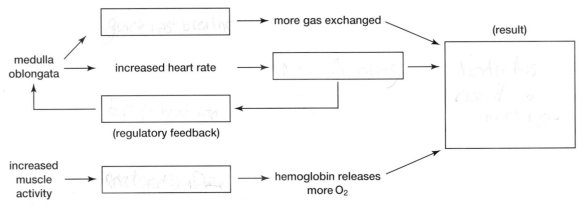

more gas exchanged

(result)

medulla oblongata → increased heart rate →

(regulatory feedback)

increased muscle activity →

hemoglobin releases more O_2

12. Complete the concept map shown above, using appropriate labels.

13. Describe three different mechanisms by which water moves from the roots of a plant to its leaves.

INQUIRY

14. Examine the following graphs.
    (a) Match each graph with its correct label from the choices below.
        (i) distribution of blood volume in the mammalian cardiovascular system
        (ii) variation in systolic blood pressure in the mammalian cardiovascular system
        (iii) variation in blood flow velocity in the mammalian cardiovascular system
    (b) How does the structure of the different blood vessels contribute to the shape of each graph?
    (c) How would an increase in the heart rate affect the shape of each graph?

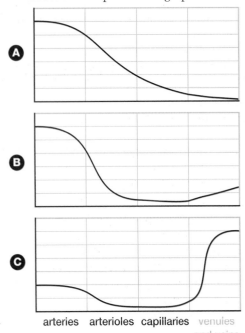

arteries arterioles capillaries venuies and veins

15. Describe how you would use a stethoscope to determine each of the following. Include details of what you would expect to find in each case.
    (a) damage to the mitral valve
    (b) damage to the tricuspid valve
    (c) damage to the aortic valve
    (d) damage to the pulmonary valve
    (e) damage to the A-V node

16. You are in charge of the Institute of Circulatory Studies. In one experiment, you have a test subject sitting in a hot tub, smoking a cigarette, and drinking a glass of wine. What do you predict will be happening to this subject's circulatory system?

17. The following diagrams illustrate an experiment conducted in the eighteenth century to explore the movement of water within a plant. The accompanying graph records the results.
    (a) What is the independent variable?
    (b) What is the dependent variable?
    (c) Is there a control in this experiment? If so, what is it? If not, how could you design a control?
    (d) What does the experiment indicate with respect to the movement of water? How does this relate to the different mechanisms for the translocation of water within a plant?
    (e) This experiment used cut tree branches. Would the results be different if a whole plant, with roots intact, had been used instead? Explain.

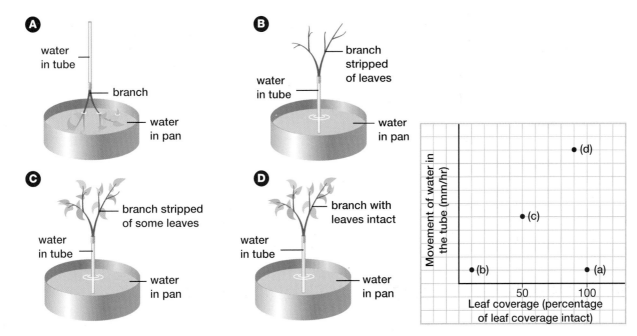

18. Design an experiment to test the effect of two separate factors on blood clotting. Provide detailed reasoning to support your design.

COMMUNICATING

19. A baby is born with a septal defect (a hole in the septum separating the right and left ventricles). Draw a diagram comparing the heart of this baby to the heart of a frog.
    (a) In what way are the two hearts similar? In what way do they differ?
    (b) What are the implications of this defect for the baby? Do these implications apply to the frog as well? Why or why not?

20. A classmate observes that the circulatory system of a grasshopper is inefficient. How would you respond? What evidence would you provide to support your argument?

21. "All living organisms need a transport system." Provide evidence that supports this statement and evidence that refutes it. How could you rewrite the statement to make it accurate in all circumstances?

MAKING CONNECTIONS

22. A sudden shock may make one person flush, while another person turns pale. Explain how each of these responses has an adaptive advantage.

23. A snowboarder is buried in snow by an avalanche. By the time the rescue team tracks down the locator signal and pulls the snowboarder out, he is hypothermic and barely conscious. One of his friends suggests giving him a shot of brandy. Is this a good idea? Explain.

24. Astronauts are subjected to large changes in gravitational force. During blast-off they are subjected to gravitational forces many times normal, and once in space they experience zero gravity. How would you expect these extremes to affect their circulatory systems?

25. A florist is showing a new employee how to care for the potted plants on display. "These ones grow best when their foliage is misted with water every day," says the florist. The new employee thinks "I can save time, and get the same result, by watering the plants more." Is the employee right? Explain.

Nutrients, Digestion, and Nutrition

Reflecting Questions

- How do organisms get the nutrients they need to survive?
- What nutrients are needed for life?
- In what ways do substances digested affect our health?

Orcas, or killer whales, are one of the ocean's most successful predators. Found in all oceans of the world, these swift, strong, and agile creatures have a diet that varies depending on the food source available to them. While fish and squid comprise a large part of their diet, some orcas will eat seals, sea lions, or birds. Occasionally they will even hunt in groups to attack other whales.

Orcas are predators and eat only other animals. They do not eat the kelp through which you see the orca swimming. Sea urchins, snails, and other types of marine animals do, however, graze on the long fronds of kelp, along with other ocean vegetation. These animals are adapted to survive on the nutrition supplied by plants, while the orcas and other predators survive solely on meat. The nutritional requirements of these animals are very different. The kelp also has nutritional requirements. It gains its nutrients from the ocean as well as through the process of photosynthesis.

On land, as in the ocean, many organisms survive solely by eating animals. Chameleons, with their extraordinary ability to change colour to match their surroundings, capture invertebrate prey such as the dragonfly pictured here with lightning speed. However, they will not eat the plant and fruit that other lizards, such as the green gecko, depend upon.

Unlike orcas and chameleons, humans have a more varied diet that usually includes foods from both plant and animal sources. What does this tell us about our digestive systems and those of other animals? How are the structure and function of digestive systems related to the nutritional requirements of an organism? How does your body digest and use different foods? What would happen if certain nutrients were missing from your diet? In this chapter you will learn more about digestion and nutrition, and how good nutrition and sound lifestyle choices can complement your health.

Chapter Contents

Obtaining and Processing Food

- Describe how nutrients and digestion provide materials for energy and growth.
- List the six nutrients required by heterotrophs.
- Describe how plants use nutrients.
- Describe three feeding types.
- Describe the tube concept as it applies to nutrition.

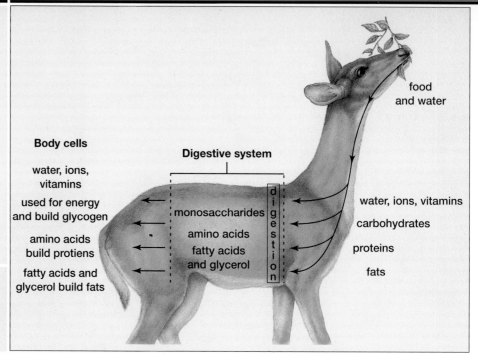

Figure 10.1 All heterotrophs, like this deer, are dependent on autotrophs for most of their nutrients.

All organisms, regardless of their size or complexity, must have some way of obtaining **essential nutrients**, the basic raw materials they need to make their own structures, perform their life functions, and obtain energy for survival. Organisms that depend on organic molecules manufactured by other living things are called **heterotrophs** (see Figure 10.1). This category includes organisms that lack chlorophyll: animals, fungi, and some kinds of bacteria, protists, and plants. Organisms that can nourish themselves using inorganic material are called **autotrophs** (see Figure 10.2). Autotrophs have the unique ability to build organic molecules from simple inorganic starting materials such as water and carbon dioxide. This category includes all photosynthetic organisms (chlorophyll-containing plants, protists, and bacteria) as well as chemosynthetic bacteria (such as those found in mineral hot springs and undersea volcanic vents). As their name suggests, autotrophs are self-sufficient. The heterotrophs are not. Directly or indirectly, the survival of heterotrophs depends on the organic molecules synthesized by the autotrophs. These organic molecules are commonly known as food. In summary, autotrophs produce food while heterotrophs consume it.

Regardless of an organism's food source, the nutrients that it takes in or derives from its food must be in a form that can readily pass through the organism's cell membranes. Many organisms produce digestive enzymes that reduce their food to a form from which nutrients can be absorbed.

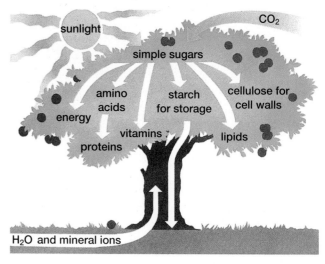

Figure 10.2 Green plants are typical autotrophs — they produce simple sugars by photosynthesis. These molecules can then be combined and rearranged to form a variety of other nutrient molecules.

>> FAST FORWARD

To find out more about heterotrophs and autotrophs, turn to Chapter 12, Section 14.2.

How Green Plants Use Nutrients

Green plants, as well as other autotrophs, need only mineral elements – not preformed, organic molecules – to survive. There is, then, no need for the function of digestion, which is associated with a digestive system. Terrestrial plants obtain these mineral elements from the soil. The fertility of a soil is, in fact, a reflection of the abundance of the elements that are available to plants. Although green plants do not need preformed organic molecules, they are able to make use of the elements that make up simple carbohydrates, amino acids, etc., if they are available (as in a culture solution).

In some cases the line between autotroph and heterotroph is blurred (Figure 10.3). The pitcher plant, the Venus flytrap, and the sundew are insect "eating" plants. They all possess chlorophyll-containing leaves, so they are able to perform photosynthesis. Although they can survive without insects, they do not thrive. This is because they grow in bogs where the water is very acidic and low in nitrogen compounds. Insects, however, are high in protein and hence rich in nitrogen-containing amino acids. These plants have adapted to capture insects and use them as a secondary source of nitrogen.

Figure 10.3 The pitcher-shaped leaves of the pitcher plant can be likened to the digestive cavity of an animal. Water fills the leaves' cavities, and enzymes secreted by the cells lining the cavities digest the captured insects.

>> FAST FORWARD

Turn to Unit 5 for a thorough analysis of how plants use nutrients.

Feeding Devices and Behaviours

For organisms that cannot produce their own food, the intake of food involves complex mechanisms and complex behaviour. It brings senses such as smell, taste, and vision into play, as well as various devices that enable the organism to search for, seize, and somehow convey food into its digestive system.

Filter Feeding

Since organisms come in all shapes and sizes and consume all sorts of things as food, you might reasonably expect to find considerable diversity in feeding devices. As a rule, there is a rough relationship between the size of an organism and the size of its food. As with most rules, though, there are exceptions — some of them startling.

Consider the blue whale, a mammal over 20 m in length and 90 t or more in mass (Figure 10.4). It is the largest animal in the world and quite possibly the largest that has ever existed. Yet it lives mainly on krill, which are tiny shrimp-like crustaceans that swim in countless numbers in parts of the ocean. Engulfing barrels of food-laden water at a time, the blue whale strains out the water by pushing up its tongue between horny plates of baleen that hang like vertical blinds from the roof of its mouth. The krill are captured on the inner fringes of the baleen and swallowed. This mighty whale, in other words, lives by filtering its food from its surroundings.

On a far smaller scale, clams, oysters, mussels, scallops, and similar shellfish feed in much the same way. They filter water through the plates of

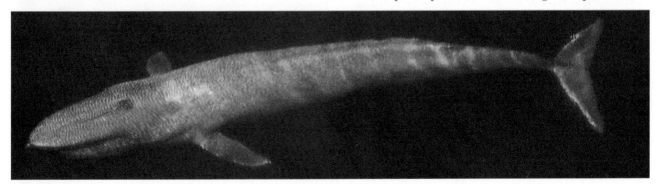

Figure 10.4 The blue whale, the world's largest living animal, is a filter feeder. Other whales that use baleen to filter food from their surroundings include the northern right, bowhead, humpback, fin, sei, minke, and grey whales.

their gills to collect microscopic organisms (see Figure 10.5). Water birds such as many ducks and flamingos also live by filter feeding. Their beaks are specialized to strain food from water.

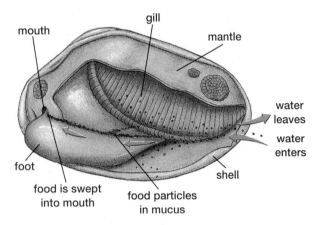

Figure 10.5 Clams and other molluscs draw in water containing food using an incurrent siphon. The food is then filtered out of the water by the gills and swept toward the mouth on a layer of mucus. The water is then expelled from the animal by an excurrent siphon.

Fluid Feeding

Some animals (such as insects) have mouth parts adapted for piercing and sucking the juices of plants and animals. These are the fluid feeders. Well-known examples include mosquitoes and leeches, which feed on blood. To keep the blood flowing in the wounds, they use anti-coagulants, which are chemicals manufactured in their bodies that keep the blood from clotting while they are feeding.

Another means of fluid feeding is demonstrated by the tapeworm (Figure 10.6). The tapeworm attaches itself firmly to the intestinal lining of its host using the tiny hooks and suckers on its mouth.

Here, it simply absorbs nutrient-rich fluids from the host's digestive tract.

A human tapeworm can grow as long as 6–7 m while attached to the walls of a person's intestines. Do some research to find out about the life cycle of these organisms and how they manage to infest humans.

The spider represents yet another example of fluid feeding. After killing its prey, the spider injects digestive enzymes into the prey's body. These enzymes break down or hydrolyze the contents of the prey by acting on its proteins. The spider then sucks its newly liquefied meal into its digestive tract.

Other Devices and Behaviours

Many animals, including a large number of insects (see Figure 10.7) and most vertebrates, ingest relatively large amounts of food at a time. As a result, they do not feed continuously. These animals display great variety in feeding devices and behaviour. This is true even for those animals that are related and are within the same group. In the group we call mammals, for instance, we find the grasping trunk of the elephant, the mobile lips and tongue of the cow, and the hands of the human as food gathering and feeding devices. What if organisms were separated into new groups based on their different feeding devices and behaviours? What kind of relationships would such a system show? How would these new groupings change our understanding of animals as we know them today?

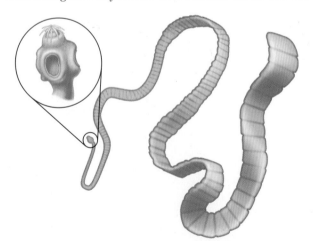

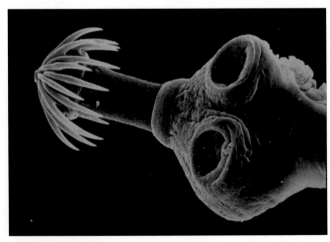

Figure 10.6 Tapeworms are examples of fluid feeders. Because they lack digestive systems, they depend on the hosts in which they live to digest food before they absorb some of the nutrients for themselves.

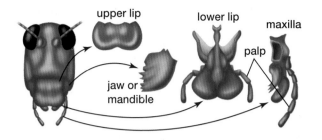

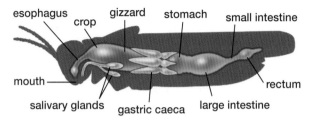

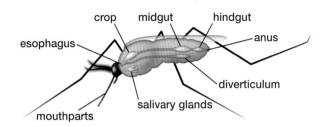

Figure 10.7 The feeding devices and digestive systems of the grasshopper and female mosquito differ dramatically, even though both are classified as insects. The biting-and-chewing mouth parts (like the kind belonging to the grasshopper) assist in the mechanical breakdown of food, and the piercing-sucking system of the female mosquito serves it well.

THINKING LAB

Feeder Types

Background

Animals have evolved to take on countless different shapes, eat a myriad of different foods, and live in practically every kind of earthly habitat. The number of known insect species alone is over 1 000 000, with more being discovered every day. Yet in spite of this phenomenal diversity, it seems that all animals obtain their food through one of only three means: filter feeding, fluid feeding, or (as we humans do) chunk feeding. By carefully observing the mouth or other feeding device of an organism, it is usually possible to tell which type of feeder it is.

Hawk

Vampire bat

Sponge

Monarch butterfly

Deer fly

Little brown bat

Honey bee

Canada goose

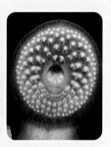
Lamprey eel

You Try It

1. Make a data table with the columns shown below in your notebook.

2. Look carefully at the feeding devices of the animals shown in the illustration. Decide on the feeder type you think each one is, and put a checkmark in the appropriate column alongside its name.

Animal	Feeder type		
	Filter	Fluid	Chunk
Hawk			
etc.			

3. Add more animals to the list, if you like.

4. Now do some research to find out how each animal actually feeds. How many feeder types did you get right?

5. Which animals in the list would you place together as belonging to the same group? Did such animals always fall into the same feeder type? Explain.

6. Explain why you think there are or are not other feeder types besides those listed in the chart.

Digestion: Essential Food Processing

Getting food brings a source of nutrients to the organism, but the problem of getting the nutrients out of the food and into the individual cells of the organism in a useable form remains. In single-celled organisms, the food is often taken into the cell by the process of pinocytosis. The food is not in a form that can be used immediately, however. It must still be acted upon by enzymes before it is of any value to the cell.

<< REWIND

For more information about pinocytosis, see Chapter 1.

In larger organisms such as fish, frogs, birds, and mammals, the cells are numerous and packed in tissues far from the internal surface of the digestive tract. To further complicate matters, most of the digestive tract is not permeable to substances in food. These organisms have solved the problem of distributing nutrients to their cells by developing digestive and circulatory systems. The **digestive system** breaks down food masses into useful substances that can be absorbed into the circulatory system. The circulatory system then transports these substances to the individual cells where they are again absorbed.

On the surface, it may seem a waste of time and energy for an organism to break down its food into simple substances, only to use those substances to make compounds in its cells similar to the ones originally in its food. Remember, though, that the substances have to move across a cell's boundary membrane to get inside. To do this, the molecules

of the substances must be both small enough to pass through the membrane and be in solution. Additionally, if larger molecules such as proteins could pass into a cell across its membrane, it would be equally possible for the proteins in the cell's cytoplasm to leak out. Thus, the essential role of the digestive system is to break food down into small, soluble units that can pass through cell membranes.

To more fully understand digestion, we need to explore some of the processes and anatomical structures involved. Essentially, these are

1. the digestive tract through which food travels;
2. the mechanical means by which food moves through this tract;
3. the chemical digestion of food;
4. the roles of the liver, pancreas, and gall bladder (these organs, plus the digestive tract, make up the digestive system); and
5. the roles played by nutrients, diet, and health.

To begin, consider the following different digestive tract arrangements.

The Tube Arrangement

A very useful arrangement for transporting food in larger multicellular animals is the tube. The tube enables digestion to be carried out in a small isolated portion of an organism's internal environment. In the open tube variation, the animal has an intake (mouth) at one end, and an outlet (anus) at the other (Figure 10.8). Food proceeds along the tube, which functions somewhat like a production line in a factory. In a number of other organisms, such as the hydra and sea anemone, a single opening serves as the place where food enters and wastes leave. Think of this

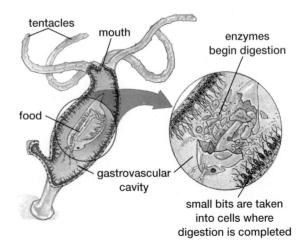

Figure 10.8 The open tube of the earthworm and the closed tube of the hydra illustrate variations on the tube digestive tract arrangement.

variation as a closed tube. Digestive enzymes may enter the tube in one area (as they do in many invertebrates) or at more than one point along its length (as in the vertebrates).

Intracellular Digestion

Protists generally do not have tubes, although some (such as *Paramecium* with its food-collecting groove) have the beginning of one. Other protists (such as *Amoeba*) engulf food particles by phagocytosis (Figure 10.9). In both cases, the prey or food particles are enclosed in a vacuole into which digestive enzymes are secreted. As the vacuole follows a path through the cytoplasm, it shrinks as water and the products of digestion leave the vacuole. Finally, the vacuole reaches the cell boundary (often at a particular point), where any indigestible residue is expelled. The vacuole itself then disintegrates.

This form of digestive arrangement, in which particles are first taken into a cell before being subjected to the action of enzymes, is termed **intracellular digestion**. This name is used even though digestion actually occurs inside the food vacuoles (and thus, for all intents and purposes, outside of the cell). Intracellular digestion occurs to some extent in other forms of life, including clams and sea anemones, in conjunction with extracellular digestion. **Extracellular digestion**, or digestion outside the cells (as in the tube arrangement) is far more common among animals. It is the method used along the mammalian tract, as you will see in the next section.

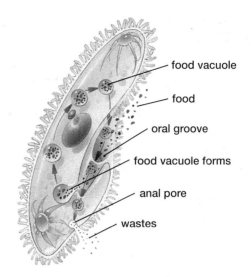

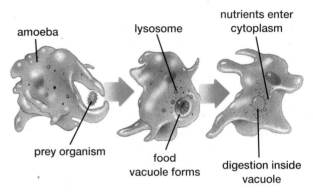

Figure 10.9 *Paramecium* and *Amoeba* illustrate intracellular digestion, in which food is digested inside vacuoles formed with the cell.

SECTION REVIEW

1. **K/U** Define the word "nutrient."

2. **K/U** Indicate whether you agree or disagree with the following statement: "Cola drinks do not qualify as food." Explain you answer.

3. **K/U** A snail uses a rasping organ to "file" off bits of food from surfaces. Which feeder type is it?

4. **K/U** Name three feeder types and give two examples of each. Explain how each obtains its food.

5. **K/U** What is the purpose of the digestive system?

6. **K/U** Does the "plant food" bought at a hardware store or garden centre really contain food? If not, what does it contain?

7. **C** Would you expect digestion in filter feeders to be mainly intracellular or extracellular? Explain in a way that someone new to the subject could understand.

8. **K/U** How does the intracellular digestion in *Amoeba* and *Paramecium* resemble extracellular digestion?

9. **K/U** Cats have pointed, cutting teeth; cows have flat, grinding teeth. Why do you think humans have teeth that are generally in between these two extremes?

10. **K/U** How does some of the food taken in by a chunk feeder eventually start to resemble the food taken in by a fluid feeder?

11. **K/U** Several kinds of whales are carnivores (meat eaters). What you would expect to find in their mouths instead of baleen?

The Human Digestive Tract

- List, in order, the structures through which food passes in the human digestive tract.

- Distinguish clearly between the structure of the stomach and the small intestine.

- Describe how the digestive system helps maintain our internal environment.

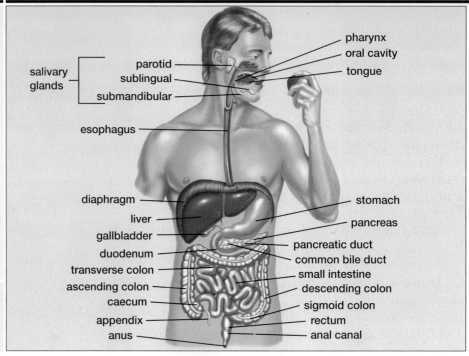

Figure 10.10 A view of the human digestive tract and its associated organs.

Within mammals, there is considerable variation in digestive system details. There is even more variation among invertebrate digestive systems. The human digestive tract will serve, however, to point out the essential features characteristic of an open tube arrangement (see Figure 10.9). On average, it takes about 24–33 h for each meal you eat to complete its passage through your digestive tract.

Parts of the Human Digestive Tract

The Mouth

In mammals, the mouth is equipped with a number of teeth arranged along the upper and lower jaws. The teeth vary in number and structure, depending on species. The structure, number, and arrangement of teeth in the human mouth is shown in Figure 10.11, as are details of the structure of the mouth itself. Not evident from the diagram is that the upper surface of the tongue is covered with tiny pimple-like structures called **papillae**. The papillae house most of the taste buds that allow us to tell whether our food is sweet, sour, bitter, salty, or some combination thereof. The **uvula** hanging from the middle of the back edge of the soft palate prevents food from entering the pharynx when we swallow.

Upon entering the mouth, food quickly comes in contact with **saliva**, which is secreted by three pairs of **salivary glands** that assist in the chemical process of digestion (Figure 10.10). Saliva also

moistens or lubricates food so it will pass into the next part of the digestive system more readily.

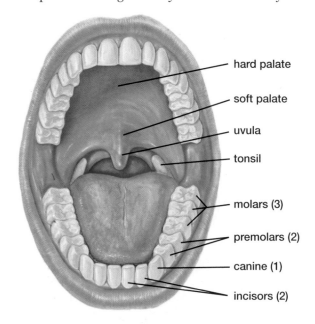

Figure 10.11 This illustration of the human mouth shows the number, type, and arrangement of the teeth, plus other details.

The two parotid glands, which are located slightly below and in front of the two ears, are the largest of the salivary glands. The smallest of the salivary glands, called the sublingual glands, are in the floor of the mouth just inside of the incisor teeth. Slightly below and behind the sublinguals are the third and final pair of salivary glands, known as the submaxillary glands. In all cases, the glands open up into the mouth cavity by means of **ducts** — tubular canals for carrying glandular secretions from one part of the body to another.

The Esophagus or Gullet

After leaving the mouth, the food passes into a tube called the **esophagus**, passing the covered opening of the trachea or windpipe on the way. If you place your fingers over your "Adam's apple" and swallow, you will notice that both it and your trachea move up. This movement closes the trachea against the covering called the epiglottis. This action seals off the glottis in order to prevent food from entering the trachea (Figure 10.12).

The esophagus is lined with circular and longitudinal muscles along its length, which is about 24 cm. These muscles work together to push the food along. Mucin, a lubricant, is secreted by a number of small, tubular glands located in the back of the throat and in the walls of the esophagus. The circular muscle ring at the lower end of the esophagus (before the entrance to the stomach) is thickened considerably to give its owner (whether a person or another mammal) some involuntary control over the flow of food into or out of the stomach. The movement of food out of the stomach, up the esophagus, and out of the mouth is called **regurgitation**. Most of us have experienced regurgitation when we are sick.

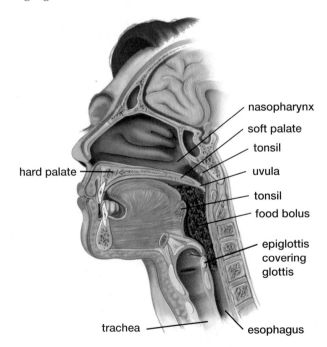

Figure 10.12 During the act of swallowing, the trachea moves up against the epiglottis to seal off the glottis and prevent food from entering the trachea.

The Stomach

After passing through the esophagus, the food enters the next organ of the digestive tract, the stomach (Figure 10.13). The **stomach** is a muscular, J-shaped, sac-like organ whose interior lining is packed with millions of gastric glands. These glands secrete the gastric juice so important in digestion. The stomach differs structurally from the esophagus by having a third layer of muscle fibres called the oblique layer. Muscles lining the stomach work to break food physically into smaller pieces and mix it with the gastric juices, rendering it into a thick liquid called **chyme**.

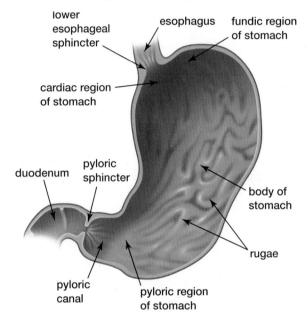

Figure 10.13 A cross sectional view of the stomach. Note the multitude of folds called rugae on the inner walls, and the esophageal and pyloric sphincters.

The circular muscle layer at the junction of the stomach and the next part of the digestive tract is also thickened, much like the ring at the junction of the esophagus and stomach. Here, however, the muscle layer forms a valve called the **pyloric sphincter**, which contracts and relaxes to control the flow of food leaving the stomach.

The Small Intestine

After exiting the stomach, the food enters the **small intestine**, which is subdivided into three regions. The **duodenum**, which is generally U-shaped, is the shortest and widest of these regions. Like the esophagus, it lacks a layer of oblique muscle. The pancreatic and bile ducts open into the duodenum, making it an important site for the further chemical breakdown of the partially digested materials received from the stomach.

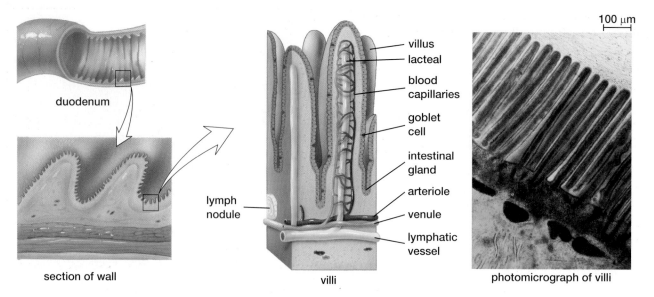

100 μm

villus
lacteal
blood capillaries
goblet cell
intestinal gland
arteriole
venule
lymphatic vessel

lymph nodule

duodenum

section of wall

villi

photomicrograph of villi

Figure 10.14 The permanent circular folds in the mucous membrane of the duodenum bear tiny projections called villi, which in turn bear microvilli. The presence of all three vastly increases the absorptive surface of the intestine.

Like the rest of the small intestine, the duodenum has permanent, circular folds in its mucous membrane. These folds greatly increase the surface area of the intestine. This larger surface, in turn, increases the amount of digested food that can be absorbed (Figure 10.14).

Along these folds, and in particular along the folds in the duodenum, are minute, visible, finger-like projections called **villi** (singular villus). The villi, in turn, have a fine brush-like border of microvilli. Both serve to further increase the absorptive surface of the intestinal tract. Minute, tube-shaped, intestinal glands are in the spaces between the villi. Their role is to secrete intestinal juices.

There are also lacteal or lymph vessels in the villi. The role of these **lacteal** vessels is to accept and carry the larger fat particles that are absorbed from the intestine. These vessels flow into vessels of the lymphatic circulatory system, as described in Chapter 9.

Following the duodenum are the jejunum and the ileum. These last two regions differ only slightly in structure from the duodenum. The **jejunum** (which is about 2.5 m long) contains more folds and intestinal glands than the duodenum. Its function is to break down remaining proteins and carbohydrates so the end products can be absorbed. The **ileum**, which is about 3 m long, contains fewer and smaller villi. Its function is also to absorb nutrients, as well as to push remaining undigested material into the large intestine.

The Large Intestine

The **large intestine** consists of the caecum, colon, rectum, and anal canal (see Figure 10.10). At about 1.5 m long, it is much shorter than the small intestine. Its diameter, however, from which it takes its name, is much greater. A valve separates it from the small intestine. The sac-like **caecum** is the blind end of the large intestine. The **appendix**, an organ that plays no role in digestion but which may play some role in fighting infection, hangs suspended from the caecum.

Undigested food entering the large intestine passes up, along, and down the **colon**, the main portion of the large intestine. In the colon, water and dissolved minerals are absorbed from the undigested food, while intestinal bacteria help to break it down further to provide more nutrients. These bacteria also produce vitamins B-12 and K and some amino acids. The damp mass of indigestible material that remains at the end of this process is called **feces**. It passes into the **rectum** and **anal canal**, which comprise the last 20 cm of the large intestine. From here, the feces passes out of the body through the **anus**, which has rings of circular muscle called the anal sphincters. These sphincters allow the body to control the timing of elimination to some extent.

The Movement of Food

So far, we have considered what happens to food in the digestive tract, but not how the food actually moves through it. This movement is accomplished by a series of wavelike muscular contractions and relaxations known as **peristalsis**. Peristalsis involves the circular and longitudinal muscles that surround the various parts of the digestive tract. To move food, the circular muscles over a food mass relax while the longitudinal muscles immediately in front of it contract. The circular muscles immediately behind the food mass then contract while the longitudinal muscles over the food mass relax. As succeeding muscular regions relax and contract, the food is pushed along (Figure 10.15). If you ever have the chance to observe a snake after it has swallowed a mouse, you will see peristalsis in action.

Another action related to peristalsis is used by the body to mix partially digested food in the intestines. During this action, known as rhythmical segmentation, the food is held in approximately the same part of the intestine while rhythmical contractions of the circular muscles squeeze it back and forth (Figure 10.16).

> PLAY

Your Electronic Learning Partner has video and animation clips that will enhance your understanding of the human digestive system.

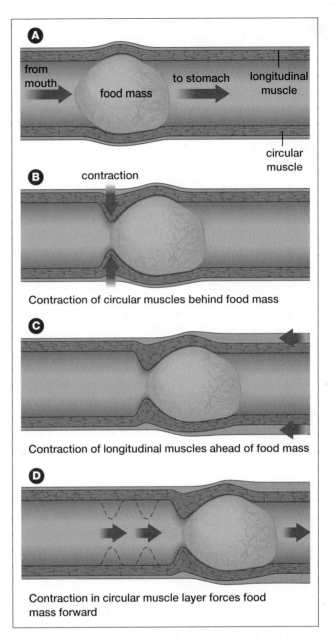

Figure 10.15 Waves of peristalsis like the one shown here move food along the digestive tract.

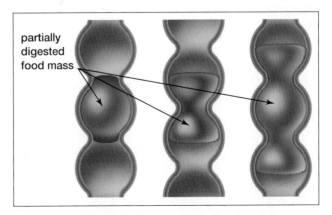

Figure 10.16 Rhythmical segmentation is a form of peristalsis that allows partially digested food to be thoroughly mixed in the intestines.

Modelling Peristalsis

You can gain a good idea of how peristalsis works in the esophagus by conducting a simple experiment using a few readily available materials. You will need a tennis ball (or rubber ball of similar size), liquid soap or detergent, a knee-high nylon stocking, scissors, and a hand lens. To begin, stretch the stocking gently in all directions with your hands. Observe what happens to the width and length of the stocking as you do this. Now cut off the toe end of the stocking with the scissors. Next, soak the stocking and ball in water for a few seconds before applying a squeeze or two of soap or detergent to each. Use your hands to spread the soap or detergent throughout the stocking and around the ball.

Hold the stocking up by its reinforced end in one hand and push the ball inside the stocking opening until it is well below the top of the reinforced end. With your free hand, squeeze the stocking material at the top of the ball in the web between your thumb and forefinger. What happens to the ball and the stocking? Repeat this squeezing action

over and over, bringing the other fingers of same hand in play as well, if you like, until the ball exits the stocking at the toe end.

Rinse the stocking, tennis ball, and your hands free of the soap or detergent when you are through. Place the stocking and tennis ball where they can dry.

Analyze

1. Use one hand to stretch the stocking from the inside while you observe it with the hand lens. How do the textile fibres you see correspond to the muscle fibres that surround the esophagus and other parts of the digestive tract? Explain how your squeezing action modelled the action of these muscle fibres.

2. What did the water and soap or detergent do? What two secretions serve the same purpose in the esophagus?

3. Could someone swallow a mouthful of juice while upside down? Why or why not?

SECTION REVIEW

1. **K/U** List, in order, the organs of the digestive tract through which food passes.

2. **K/U** Name two secretions that help to lubricate food.

3. **K/U** Describe two features of the stomach that make it an important organ of digestion.

4. **K/U** Explain how chyme is made.

5. **K/U** What purposes do the villi and microvilli serve? Where are they located?

6. **K/U** Where is the appendix located and what role does it play in digestion? Does it have another role?

7. **C** Using diagrams, illustrate how peristalsis and rhythmical segmentation work.

8. **C** Draw a diagram that shows where the three sphincters in the human digestive tract are located. Label it with the functions that each performs.

9. **K/U** What would be the effect on the digestive system if mechanical digestion did not take place?

10. **MC** What do people mean when they talk about "food that went down the wrong way"? Could this prove dangerous? Explain your answer.

11. **I** Explain how you could design an experiment to model rhythmical segmentation, including the equipment and materials you would use.

12. **MC** Doctors, after examining a person with colon cancer, decide to surgically remove the cancerous region of the person's large intestine. Suggest what dietary adjustments that person might have to make afterward in order to live a healthy life.

13. **MC** A detective is assigned to investigate a suspicious death. What kinds of information could an autopsy of the person's digestive tract reveal?

The Chemical Digestion of Food

- List the three types of enzymes associated with chemical digestion.

- Design an activity to show that enzymes are not used up when involved in a reaction.

- Describe how hormones and the nervous system regulate the release of enzymes.

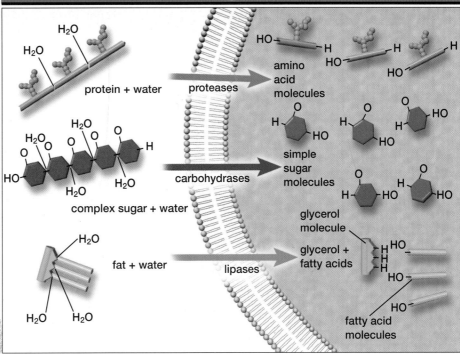

Figure 10.17 Hydrolysis of proteins, carbohydrates, and lipids is greatly speeded up by enzymes. The smaller molecules produced as a result can pass through cell membranes.

As food moves through the digestive tract to be physically broken down into smaller and smaller pieces, it is also being acted upon by digestive chemicals. These chemicals work to break complex molecules into smaller ones that can pass through cell membranes.

Chemical Digestion and Enzymes

The term **digestion** is usually applied to the chemical breakdown of food by the process of hydrolysis. During hydrolysis, a water molecule is added at the point where a link in a more complex molecule is being broken (Figure 10.17). Hydrolysis can occur spontaneously at a very slow rate, but it is immediately speeded up by enzymes. These enzymes are biological catalysts which, being proteins, are manufactured in the ribosomes of cells.

Word LINK

"Hydrolysis" comes to us from two Greek words: *hydro*, meaning "water," and *lysis*, meaning "to loosen." In other words, hydrolysis means to break apart with water.

◀◀ REWIND

For more information about enzymes and their action, return to Chapter 2, Section 2.2.

As shown in Figure 10.17, three kinds of enzymes are associated with digestion: carbohydrases, lipases, and proteinases. Each is named after the class of compounds (carbohydrates, lipids, and proteins, respectively) that it helps to break down. These enzymes are formed by secretory cells and then secreted into the digestive tract. The secretory cells can exist singly, in simple sacs, or in the lining of the walls of glands. A gland is a structure made up of a complex system of tubules (see Figure 10.14). The digestive glands are usually connected to the digestive tract by ducts.

Hydrolytic enzymes act very specifically. They catalyze hydrolysis for only particular linkages. For example, the fat-splitting lipase can act on a wide variety of lipid compounds, but in each case the same linkage is hydrolyzed. These digestive enzymes often require special conditions in order to act. Some perform best in acid media, for instance, while others work best in neutral or alkaline media. Other chemicals, such as sodium carbonate and bicarbonate, are often secreted with the hydrolytic enzymes. These chemicals assist in establishing and maintaining the pH level at which the enzymes work best (see Appendix 9 to review pH).

Enzymes are adversely affected by high temperatures. Many also require the presence of metallic ions (such as those of cobalt and magnesium), vitamins, or coenzymes in order to function properly.

The contents of the stomach are very acidic, with a pH of around 2. A short distance farther on in the duodenum, however, the contents that have left the stomach are slightly basic, with a pH of around 8. What could account for these dramatic differences in pH, and why do you think the body maintains the contents of these organs at these pH levels?

Digestive Enzymes

Most of the digestive enzymes that we know today have been named by starting with the substrate they attack and adding an "-ase" ending. A **substrate** is a molecule on which an enzyme acts. Thus, the enzyme maltase acts on the sugar maltose, its substrate. Other enzymes discovered

DESIGN YOUR OWN
Investigation

10 • A

SKILL FOCUS

Initiating and planning

Hypothesizing

Identifying variables

Performing and recording

Analyzing and interpreting

Factors That Affect the Rate at Which Enzymes Act

Catalase is a non-digestive enzyme produced by the liver. It breaks down the toxin hydrogen peroxide in the body according to the equation $H_2O_2 \xrightarrow{\text{Catalase}} H_2O + O_2$. The presence of the flammable gas oxygen can be used to detect this reaction. The volume produced can be used to calculate the rate of the enzyme's activity. In this investigation, you will design experiments to test for factors that may affect the rate of this reaction. Factors to consider include pH, temperature, the quantity of the substrate hydrogen peroxide, and the quantity of the enzyme. Test for each factor separately.

Problem

How do different factors affect the rate of enzyme activity?

Hypothesis

Make hypotheses about three factors you would like to test.

CAUTION: Hydrogen peroxide is a bleaching agent and an irritant. Take care not to get it, the vinegar, or the sodium bicarbonate solutions in your eyes or on your skin or clothes. Wash spills away immediately with lots of water and inform your teacher. Exercise caution when testing for flammable gas. Make sure there are no cracks in the glassware you use.

Materials

30 mL square bottle	stock solution of puréed
one-holed rubber stopper	liver (contains catalase)
to fit above	medicine dropper
100 mL graduated cylinder	vinegar (acid)
10 mL graduated cylinder	sodium hydrogen
plaster tray or pneumatic	carbonate solution (base)
trough	graph paper

forceps	dilute hydrogen peroxide
600 mL beaker	solution (substrate) (3%)
watch or clock	matches
absorbent paper disks	wooden splints

Experimental Plan

1. Using the materials and considering the set-up shown in the illustration, prepare a list of possible ways in which you can test your hypotheses.

2. Decide on an approach that you can carry out in your classroom.

3. Make sure your approach will test for only one possible factor (independent variable) at a time. Prepare to collect and record quantitative data for at least three variables on the graph paper, and to summarize this data in a data table (like the one shown here) that can be interpreted by others.

Independent variable	Elapsed time	Volume of gas evolved	Gas flammable?

many decades ago, such as pepsin, are known by their original, trivial names. Known human digestive enzymes, and their places of origin and activity, substrates, and products are listed in Table 10.1 on the following page. More digestive enzymes will likely be discovered as our knowledge of body chemistry increases.

COURSE CHALLENGE

If you have not yet done a dissection (or a virtual dissection) of the digestive system of a vertebrate, this is a good time to do so. A fetal pig dissection guide is presented in Appendix 10. Keep in mind how you might use knowledge and skills gained from this dissection to assist you in your Biology Course Challenge on forensic science.

4. Outline a procedure for your experiment listing each step. Include all necessary safety procedures. Provide a list of materials and the quantities you will require. Obtain your teacher's approval before starting any reaction. One step you must do is soak as many of the paper disks in the puréed liver extract as you think you will need. Make sure you soak them all for the same length of time. To begin the reaction, the bottle containing the hydrogen peroxide and disks is turned over. Wash your hands thoroughly at the end of the investigation.

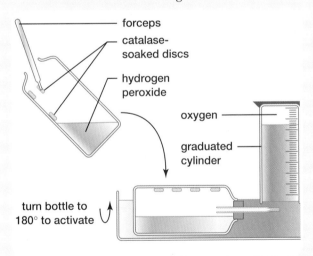

forceps
catalase-soaked discs
hydrogen peroxide
oxygen
graduated cylinder
turn bottle to 180° to activate

Checking the Plan

1. What will be the dependent variable for each of the independent variables you want to test? What will the controlled variables be?

2. What will be your control?

3. What will you measure, and how will you record this information on the graph paper?

4. How will you safely test whether any resulting gas is flammable?

Data and Observations

Conduct your investigation and make your measurements. Graph your results first, and then enter your summary data in the table.

Analyze

1. Changes in which factors (independent variables) influenced the rate at which gas was produced? Which changes, if any, meant that little or no gas was produced?

2. Changes in which factor produced the greatest amount of gas in the shortest amount of time?

3. Why was it necessary to test only one variable at a time?

Conclude and Apply

4. Based on your results, which factors affect the rate at which enzymes such as catalase act?

5. Explain how variations in these factors could affect digestive enzymes, and how they could affect the general well-being of a person.

Exploring Further

6. Ask a pharmacist at a local drugstore to show you some of the products intended for use by customers with digestive problems. How many of these products contain digestive enzymes, mild acids, or mild bases? Explain why these ingredients might be used in these products, in light of what you have learned about factors that affect the rate at which enzymes work.

7. Why do you suppose the human body is kept at a near constant temperature of 37°C? Could it have anything to do with enzymes? Do some research to find out more.

Table 10.1
Enzymes of the human digestive system

Enzyme	Place where enzyme acts	Substrate	Products	Origin of enzyme
salivary amylase (also called ptyalin)	mouth	starch, glycogen	maltose (a double sugar)	salivary glands
pepsin	stomach	protein	peptides	a product of pepsinogen and hydrochloric acid, both secreted by stomach glands
lipase	small intestine	fats	glycerol and fatty acids	secreted by stomach glands but not very active in the stomach (too acid)
pancreatic amylase (also called amylopsin)	small intestine	starch	maltose	pancreas
pancreatic lipase (also called steapsin)	small intestine	fat	glycerol and fatty acids	pancreas
trypsin	small intestine	peptides	simpler peptides	product of trypsinogen from the pancreas, and of enterokinase from the walls of the duodenum
chymotrypsin	small intestine	peptides	simpler peptides	product of trypsin and chymotrypsinogen (from the pancreas)
carboxypeptidase	small intestine	peptides	simpler peptides	pancreas
ribonuclease	small intestine	ribonucleic acid	nucleotides	pancreas
deoxyribonuclease	small intestine	deoxyribo-nucleic acid	nucleotides	pancreas
aminopeptidase	small intestine	peptides	simpler peptides	glands in the walls of the small intestine
tripeptidase	small intestine	tripeptides	dipeptide and an amino acid	glands in the walls of the small intestine
maltase	small intestine	maltose	two glucose molecules	glands in the walls of the small intestine
sucrase	small intestine	sucrose	one molecule of glucose and one of fructose	intestinal glands
lactase	small intestine	lactose	one molecule of glucose and one of galactose	intestinal glands

A Summary of Chemical Digestion

In humans and other mammals, chemical digestion begins in the mouth, where the enzyme, **amylase**, breaks down starch to smaller disaccharide sugar molecules. In the stomach, gastric juice contains hydrochloric acid and the enzyme, pepsin. Pepsin begins the breakdown of protein in the stomach while the amylase swallowed from the mouth continues breaking down starch until the pH in the stomach becomes too low for it to act (see Appendix 9 for a review of pH). Pepsin functions well within a pH range of 1 to 2. Amylase requires a high pH to function.

The thick liquid chyme then passes into the small intestine, a muscular tube about 6 m in length. The first 25 cm, called the duodenum, secretes enzymes from its lining, and the pancreas and liver both empty their enzymes into the duodenum to complete the process of digestion.

Pancreatic juice is alkaline and thus neutralizes the acidity of partially digested food coming from the stomach, stopping any further action of pepsin. (Again, refer to the table above to see the wide variety of enzymes secreted and used to digest food.)

As noted previously, no enzymes are produced in the large intestine; water is simply absorbed from indigestible material through its walls. Anaerobic bacteria living there, however, do digest more of this material, and some of it is absorbed for use by the body, as well. These bacteria also synthesize some B vitamins and Vitamin K which is then used by the body. The total digestion of a large meal takes about 24–33 h.

The Regulation of Digestive Secretions

The secretion of digestive enzymes is regulated by both nerves and hormones. A **hormone** is a

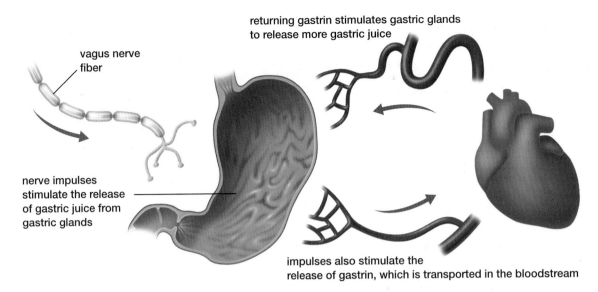

returning gastrin stimulates gastric glands
to release more gastric juice

vagus nerve
fiber

nerve impulses
stimulate the release
of gastric juice from
gastric glands

impulses also stimulate the
release of gastrin, which is transported in the bloodstream

Figure 10.18 The secretion of gastric juices is controlled by nerve impulses and the hormone gastrin.

chemical regulator that is secreted in one part of the body and transported by the bloodstream to another part, where it causes a response. For instance, the digestive glands lining the walls of the stomach are stimulated by nerves and by a hormone called **gastrin** (Figure 10.18). In response, individual glands secrete mucin (which both lubricates food and protects the walls of the stomach), pepsin, hydrochloric acid, and lipases.

The glands that produce gastrin are located in the lower part of the stomach. Because these glands are ductless, however, the hormone must be transported by the bloodstream until it arrives at the upper part of the stomach before it is able to stimulate the digestive glands to secrete their products (Figure 10.19).

In a similar way, the presence of the chyme in the duodenum stimulates ductless glands in the walls of the duodenum to secrete the hormone **secretin** into the bloodstream. Arriving at the pancreas, secretin stimulates duct cells there to release an alkaline fluid containing sodium

carbonate and sodium bicarbonate. This fluid raises the pH of the chyme from 2 to approximately 8.

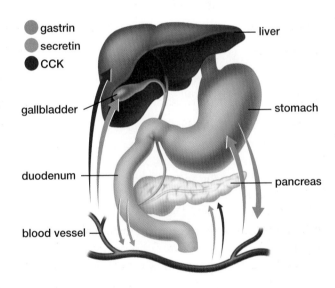

○ gastrin
○ secretin
● CCK

liver

gallbladder

stomach

duodenum

pancreas

blood vessel

Figure 10.19 Gastrin, secretin, and CCK are hormones produced by ductless glands. All must be transported by the bloodstream from their place of origin to the place where they can stimulate the release of digestive juices.

Trypsin, one of the enzymes produced by the pancreas, requires a pH of approximately 8 to function efficiently. At this pH, pepsin is no longer functional. Secretin, along with the hormone cholecystokinin (CCK, which is also produced in the walls of the duodenum), also causes the pancreas to secrete its enzymes and the gall bladder to secrete bile.

Digestion of a Protein

Digestion involves the breakdown of a substance to the point where its nutrient products can be absorbed into the bloodstream and carried to the individual cells where they can be used. Proteins are complex molecules, and several enzymes and other chemicals are involved in their digestion. Two protein-digesting enzymes are pepsin, secreted in the stomach, and trypsin, secreted in the pancreas. Trypsin is a component of pancreatin, along with pancreatic amylase and lipase. In this investigation, you will explore some of the conditions under which these digestive enzymes work. As with fats and carbohydrates, the chemical digestion of protein takes place by means of hydrolysis.

Pre-lab Questions

- What happens during hydrolysis?
- What kind of molecules are formed when proteins undergo hydrolysis?

Problem

How can you demonstrate that pepsin and trypsin (in pancreatin) will digest protein?

Prediction

Predict the kind of environments that pepsin and trypsin require in order to digest egg white, which is essentially protein.

CAUTION: Hydrochloric acid is a strong acid and sodium hydroxide is a strong base. Both are very corrosive and must not be mixed together. Other chemicals used may be toxic. Be extra careful not to get them in your eyes, on your skin, or on your clothes. Flush spills away immediately with lots of water and inform your teacher. Exercise care with boiling water and hot objects.

Materials

4 beakers (250 mL)
Bunsen burner
ring clamp
wire gauze
retort stand
12 test tubes
egg white
pepsin solution (1%)
pancreatin solution (1%)
acid-base indicator
  (bromthymol blue,
  litmus, or congo red)

dilute hydrochloric acid (1%)
distilled water
sodium hydrogen carbonate
  solution (1%)
copper (II) sulfate
  solution (1%)
dilute sodium hydroxide
  solution (1%)

Procedure

1. Coagulate a small quantity of egg white by placing it in a beaker of boiling water. Divide the coagulated product into 9 small cubes. Place the egg white cubes into separate test tubes, and number the tubes 1 through 9.

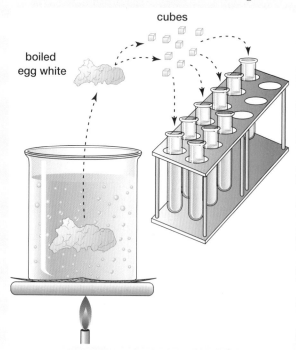

cubes

boiled egg white

2. Test the egg white samples in the test tubes by adding the following substances:

Test tube 1 — 5 mL of distilled water

Test tube 2 — 5 mL of distilled water and 1 mL of 1% sodium hydrogen carbonate solution

Test tube 3 — 5 mL of distilled water and 1 mL of hydrochloric acid

Test tube 4 — 5 mL of 1% pepsin solution

Test tube 5 — 5 mL of 1% pepsin solution and 1 mL of 1% sodium hydrogen carbonate solution

Test tube 6 — 5 mL of 1% pepsin solution and 1 mL of dilute hydrochloric acid

Test tube 7 — 5 mL of 1% pancreatin solution

Test tube 8 — 5 mL of 1% pancreatin solution and 1 mL of 1% sodium hydrogen carbonate solution

Test tube 9 — 5 mL of 1% pancreatin solution and 1 mL of dilute hydrochloric acid (1%)

3. Set the test tubes aside for 24 h in a place where the temperature can be kept as close to 37°C as possible. Observe their contents after the elapsed time, and then add a few drops of an acid-base indicator. Record the approximate pH in a data table like the one shown here.

Test tube	Observed results and pH	Biuret colour change?
1		
2		
3		
etc.		

4. Although the end products of protein digestion cannot be obtained through a single enzyme reaction, you can confirm that intermediate products have been produced by testing for them with a Biuret solution. Make this solution just before using it by adding two or three drops of a 1% copper (II) sulfate solution to 3 mL of a 1% sodium hydroxide solution. Carefully pour approximately 3 mL of liquid from each of the test tubes and replace it with approximately 3 mL of the Biuret solution. Test tubes whose contents change colour contain partially digested protein. Make sure to record your observations in the table. Wash your hands thoroughly at the end of the investigation.

Post-lab Questions

1. What was the purpose of adding sodium hydrogen carbonate solution to test tubes 2, 5, and 8?

2. According to the Biuret solution test, which test tubes showed evidence of protein digestion?

3. In which test tube was the digestion of protein most evident? What does this suggest about the action of protein digestion enzymes in our stomachs?

4. In what pH range does the digestion of protein occur most favourably? By inference, what must be the approximate pH of the chyme in our stomachs?

5. Explain why is it necessary to have more than one enzyme in order to fully digest a protein.

Conclude and Apply

6. What were the controls in this investigation? Why were they necessary?

Exploring Further

7. You can demonstrate the presence of protein-digesting enzymes in plant material by adding 10 mL of fresh or frozen pineapple juice to a test tube containing a small piece of egg white and allowing it to stand for 24 h. Set up a second test tube using distilled water in place of the fresh or frozen juice, and a third test tube using boiled pineapple juice. What effect did boiling the pineapple juice have on its effectiveness as a protein digester? What was the purpose of the second test tube?

8. Cuts of meat that would otherwise be tough are often treated with meat tenderizers before they are cooked and served. Do some research to find out more about meat tenderizers and how they work.

9. You arrive home after a few days away during a heat wave to find you had left fresh fish fillets uncovered on the kitchen counter. What you see and smell is hardly appealing or palatable, but decay organisms seem to be having a feast. How are these organisms able to do what they do? Why would the story have been different if you had remembered to put the fish in the refrigerator?

You are walking down the street at dinnertime. You begin to smell the pleasant aroma of cooking food. Suddenly, your mouth starts to water. Explain what you think might be causing this reaction.

How Do We Know What We Know?

The process of digestion in human beings is now well known and well understood. This was not always the case. Of the early research that was done, we only know about that which was published. In 1833, an innovative physician took advantage of a patient's situation to provide some important early information about how digestion occurs. William Beaumont (1785–1853) had, as a patient, a man who had been shot in the stomach. When his gunshot wound healed, it did so improperly. The lining of his stomach fused to the outer wall of his body, leaving a small opening (or fistula) to his stomach. Beaumont used this man for a series of studies of digestive processes. He introduced specific foods directly into the stomach through the opening, always with a string attached. Beaumont was able to ascertain from this the relative rates of digestion for different kinds of foods. He also noted that the stomach produces gastric juice, and identified the acid in it as hydrochloric acid. He noted the movements of the stomach and was probably the first person to report the effects of the emotions on the secretion of gastric juice. Beaumont's experiments stimulated many others to begin to investigate digestion and nutrition. Most of these used other animals as subjects, and over the next two hundred years, led to our present understanding of how digestion occurs.

The Roles of Related Organs

Three other organs associated with the digestive tract are the liver, pancreas, and gall bladder. These organs play vital roles in the digestive process. The liver also carries out many other functions essential to the body's general good health, some of which have an impact on the digestive process.

The Liver

In its digestive role, the **liver** is responsible for producing bile salts from cholesterol. These bile salts are released into the small intestine as needed, where they break up fat globules into tiny fat droplets. This allows a stable emulsion of the droplets to form in the contents of the intestines.

The action is similar to the action of detergent on greasy pots and pans — the detergent breaks up the grease into fine droplets that form an emulsion with water, allowing the emulsion to be washed away.

The tiny fat droplets in the small intestine are much more readily acted on by the water-soluble enzyme lipase, which the bile salts also activate. Evidence suggests that the fatty acid and glycerine molecules that result are engulfed through pinocytosis by the epithelial cells of the villi. Once inside the villi, the fatty acid and glycerine molecules enter the very porous lacteal vessels, where they frequently reunite to make fat molecules. These molecules are then transported by the lacteal vessels through the lymphatic circulatory system and into the main bloodstream near the left shoulder. A high percentage of fats may even be emulsified and absorbed directly, without the need for lipase action.

BIO FACT

The liver is the largest organ in the body and has been identified as having over 500 different functions.

The liver also functions as a demolitions expert, recycler, storehouse, and detoxification centre in addition to performing many other tasks. As a demolitions expert, it breaks down old red blood corpuscles, after which the hemoglobin component of the old cells is further broken down. Then, in its function as a recycler, parts of the decomposed hemoglobin molecules are used to make bile salts. As a storehouse the liver collects from the bloodstream chemicals that are in excess of the amount needed by the body at any given time. All monosaccharides except glucose, for instance, are removed and converted into glycogen by the liver. This glycogen is stored, then reconverted as needed to keep the glucose level in the bloodstream constant. The fat-soluble vitamins A, D, E, and K are also stored in the liver.

Because the body cannot store amino acids, any excess must be de-aminized or broken down into smaller molecules. Some of these molecules are converted to fats, while others are eliminated from the body (see Figure 10.20).

As a detoxification centre, the liver works to detoxify various poisons ingested with food and drink in addition to those produced in the intestines. The liver is, in short, a marvellous and highly evolved organ that performs a wide range

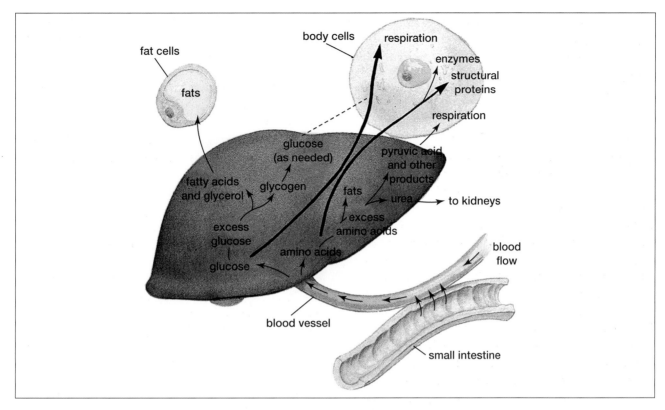

Figure 10.20 The liver plays many roles in the digestive process. Shown here are some of the paths taken by the products of carbohydrate and protein digestion that enter the liver.

of important, specialized functions for the body as a whole.

The Pancreas

Like the liver, the pancreas is an important member of "Team Digestion." As shown in Table 10.1, the **pancreas** is the source of several enzymes that act on carbohydrates, fats, and peptides, all of which are sub-units of proteins. As mentioned earlier, the pancreas also produces and releases a basic solution that changes the pH of chyme (from a strongly acid mixture to a weakly basic one) after it enters the duodenum.

The Gall Bladder

Like every successful team, the contributions of each and every member matter. The **gall bladder**, although not involved in enzyme production, serves as the storage warehouse for bile produced in the liver. Bile contains a number of chemicals that include cholesterol and the bile salts so important to the digestion of fats. The release of bile from the gall bladder is triggered by a hormone that stimulates the contraction of the smooth muscle cells of the gall bladder and makes the sphincter muscle at the neck of the gall bladder

relax. This relaxing of the sphincter muscle allows the bile to enter the duodenum via the bile duct. As this is happening the hormones CCK and secretin, produced in the duodenum, inhibit the contraction of the stomach muscles, thus putting the stomach into a temporary resting condition.

As lipids are absorbed by the intestine, so are the components of bile. They are picked up in blood vessels, carried back to the liver, and recycled to make more bile.

Back to the Plants

This section has concentrated on digestion in human beings. Other heterotrophs similarly must have digestive systems to break down their food. Even green plants (which, as autotrophs, are capable of producing their own starch, proteins, and fats) need some way to digest or convert these substances into a soluble form for transport to the rest of their cells. For example, food stored as insoluble starch in the cotyledons (embryonic leaves) of a very young seed-bearing plant must first be converted to soluble sugar before it can be transported to an actively growing part of the plant (see Figure 10.21). Thus, although the solution for how to obtain food varies, the problem of deriving and transporting nutrients to the cells remains the same for all living organisms. In fact, every living organism must either bring its cells to the source of its life-supporting nutrients or carry those nutrients to its cells.

>> FAST FORWARD

For more about plant nutrition and growth, turn to Chapter 16, Section 16.1.

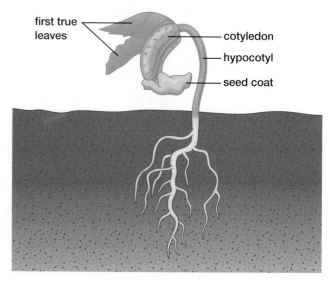

Figure 10.21 Food stored as starch in the cotyledons of this bean seed is being converted to sugar for the use by the growing leaves and roots.

SECTION REVIEW

1. **(K/U)** Name the three kinds of enzymes associated with digestion.

2. **(K/U)** What kinds of conditions affect the action of enzymes?

3. **(K/U)** How are hormones transported and what do they do?

4. **(K/U)** Describe the role played by the nervous system in the secretion of gastric juices.

5. **(K/U)** Why are most digestive enzymes not found in the stomach?

6. **(C)** Create a line graph showing the comparative length of the esophagus, small intestine, and large intestine. Under each segment, offer explanations for why it is longer or shorter than its neighbours.

7. **(MC)** A condition called heartburn afflicts many people occasionally. What causes this malady, and what can people do about it?

8. **(I)** A student has placed the enzyme lipase in a test tube along with a solution of hydrochloric acid and a protein. Explain why digestion will or will not take place.

9. **(I)** Describe an activity that could be used to test whether or not an enzyme is used up in a reaction.

10. **(C)** Create a concept map that shows the relationship among the three accessory organs of the digestive system.

11. **(K/U)** Describe at least four different functions of the liver.

12. **(K/U)** What does the gall bladder do?

13. **(MC)** Cirrhosis of the liver is a serious disease. What environments and lifestyle choices can put someone at risk for this condition? How would it affect the person's health?

14. **(C)** Some foods we eat contain toxins, or poisons. Explain why we do not normally suffer from the effects of these toxins.

15. **(C)** Create a diagram showing the accessory organs and their ducts in relation to the stomach and small intestine.

16. **(MC)** As a result of a major car accident, the pancreas of an injured driver has been badly damaged. What role does the pancreas play in the digestive system? What will happen to the driver if he loses his pancreas? Could a person live without one? Explain, giving reasons.

17. **(MC)** An older friend of the family has just had her gall bladder removed. Describe the kind of diet you think she would be wise to follow.

Nutrition, Fitness, Lifestyle, and Health

- Describe the importance of proper nutrition.
- Demonstrate how fitness level is related to the efficiency of metabolism.
- Describe how drugs can disrupt or help maintain homeostasis.
- Present informed opinions about nutrition and lifestyle.

Figure 10.22 Do you tend to eat well-balanced meals, or is grabbing a "fast-food" meal more typical for you?

You are rushing from class to your after-school job. You meant to pack a sandwich, some juice, and an apple, but you ran out of time. Fortunately, you can always pick something up at the fast-food outlet. Besides, they have great fries. You are getting concerned, though — you seem to be going for the fast-food solution more often than not these days, and your clothes are feeling snug. This situation is typical of our fast-paced lives — always occupied or on the run, with little or no consideration given to the food we eat or how it is prepared. Yet our food and the lifestyle we lead combine to influence the nutrition we get, which has significant consequences for our health. A little time spent learning about how diet, lifestyle, and health are all related may have you vowing to change your eating habits and to start leading a more active, healthier life.

Good nutrition is important for at least two reasons. First, it provides the energy we need to carry out the many metabolic activities of our bodies such as nerve transmission, contraction of muscles, and repair and replacement of cells. Second, it provides us with essential raw materials that we need as building blocks but that we are unable to manufacture for ourselves.

The digestive process that makes nutrients available to us is controlled and matched to the needs of the body by nerve signals and hormones. In other words, we do not have to think about the food we eat once we have swallowed it. Muscles, activated by nerves, make sure our food is broken down physically and moved through the digestive tract. Some hormones (as you have already learned) stimulate the release of digestive secretions. The hormones **insulin** and **glucagon**, both produced by the pancreas, work with the liver to regulate the level of glucose, a simple sugar, in our blood. Insulin, which is released when blood glucose rises after a meal, causes body cells to become permeable to glucose. In active cells like those in muscles, the glucose is metabolized or chemically broken down. Excess glucose is converted and stored by liver cells as glycogen. Glycogen is a molecule that is easily converted back to glucose by glucagon when blood glucose drops too low. If too much food is eaten, however, the amount in excess of what is needed to maintain the glycogen reserve is converted to fat and stored in fat cells. The cartoon on the following page shows the result — an increase in fat deposition, and thus a gain in weight.

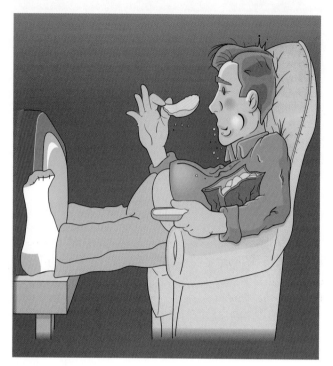

Figure 10.23 Fat is deposited when more energy is consumed in the form of food than is expended in the form of activity.

Math LINK

Most people can use their Body Mass Index (BMI) as a guide to indicate whether they are underweight or overweight for their height, and therefore whether they are at an increased risk for certain diseases. To calculate your BMI, divide your mass in kilograms by your height in metres squared. A score from 20–25 is considered good for most people. How did you do?

Essential Nutrients

A healthy diet must include six essential nutrients: carbohydrates, fats, proteins, minerals, vitamins, and water. Your body and mind function at their best when all these nutrients are present in your diet in the correct proportions. A diet that satisfies these conditions is called a **balanced diet**.

During enzymatic digestion, carbohydrates are broken down into simple sugars such as glucose, fructose, and galactose; fats are broken down into fatty acids and glycerine; and proteins are broken down into amino acids. With the exception of fatty acids and glycerine, these nutrients along with vitamins, minerals (as salts), and water pass readily into the capillaries, arterioles, and venules of the villi. The fatty acids and glycerine pass into the lacteals at the core of each villus.

Carbohydrates

Carbohydrates are made up of atoms of carbon, hydrogen, and oxygen. These molecules are sources of energy that can be accessed very quickly by an organism. When we speak of "burning off energy," it is usually carbohydrates that are supplying us with that energy. Carbohydrates can be relatively simple molecules such as glucose (the same six-carbon sugar found in our blood), or more complex molecules such as starch. Two other examples of simple sugars are fructose, found in fruit, and galactose, found in milk. Chocolate bars give you an energy "rush" because of the simple sugars they contain.

Recall from Chapter 1 that, when two simple sugars combine chemically, the result is a disaccharide or double sugar (Figure 10.24). For example, if two molecules of glucose are chemically combined and a molecule of water is removed, a molecule of the disaccharide maltose results. If a molecule of glucose is combined with a molecule of fructose, the disaccharide that results is sucrose, which we know as table sugar. Disaccharides are easily broken into simple sugars through hydrolysis.

Recall that starch (which is made by plants) and glycogen (which is made by animals) are examples

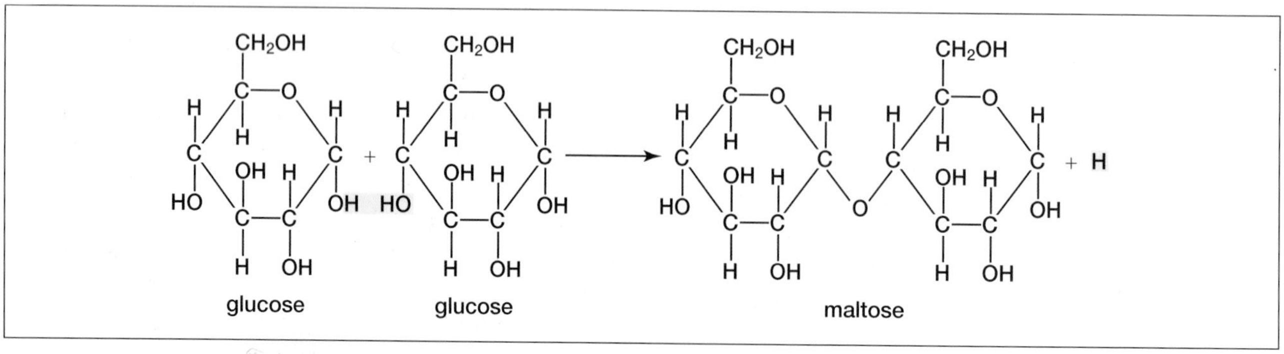

Figure 10.24 Two glucose molecules combine to form a molecule of maltose and a molecule of water.

of complex carbohydrates called polysaccharides. These molecules are energy storehouses for living things. In humans, for example, glucose is converted to glycogen in the liver. When our bodies are very active, some of this glycogen is converted back down to glucose by hydrolysis. This glucose is carried by the bloodstream to cells that need energy. The starch we get by eating such plant products as cereals, bread, vegetables, beans, and pasta is broken down in a similar way.

Another polysaccharide made by plants is cellulose. Cellulose gives plant cells their structural support. Although cows and other ruminants can digest cellulose with the help of bacteria, humans cannot. Nevertheless, cellulose (or fibre) forms an important part of healthy diets, because it helps to hold water and provide bulk in the large intestine. Thus, it helps us eliminate our wastes.

Fats (Lipids)

Some people are surprised to learn that fats (lipids) are an essential nutrient. We need fats in our diet both as a source of energy and to provide building materials for cell membranes and hormones. Layers of fat are also needed to insulate the body against cold and protect vital organs from injury. Fats also store certain vitamins and help conduct nerve impulses.

Major sources of fat in the diet include nuts, grains, seeds, meat, eggs, cheese, milk, butter, cooking oils, and margarine. When fats are consumed, they are broken down into fatty acids and glycerol in the small intestine. From here they are absorbed through the microvilli. Some of the fatty acids are then transported to the liver, where they may be converted to glycogen. Others are passed to fat cells in the body, where they are reconverted to fat.

Eating fat does not cause weight gain unless you eat too much. However, as with anything else, some fats may be better for you than others. Fats can be categorized as either saturated or unsaturated fats. Saturated fats are solid at room temperature. They are called saturated because all the available bonding sites on the carbon atoms in their fatty acids are occupied by hydrogen. These are the so-called animal or "bad" fats that (along with cholesterol) can cause plaque to form in the arteries. Some plant oils, such as coconut oil, are also highly saturated. Food producers sometimes force hydrogen into fats in a process called hydrogenation, thus making them even more saturated.

◄◄ REWIND

For more information about fatty acids, return to Chapter 1, Section 1.1.

Unsaturated fats, known as "good" fats, are usually liquids or soft solids at room temperature. They fall into at least two groups. Polyunsaturated fats, found in plants such as sunflower, corn, and soybeans, help lower blood cholesterol levels. Some fish oils also contain a form of polyunsaturated fat that has been found to lower certain types of fats in the bloodstream. Monounsaturated fats, found in animals and in plants such as olives, peanuts, and avocados, also tend to lower blood cholesterol. If you have margarine in your refrigerator, take a moment to read the label to see whether the product is unsaturated or hydrogenated. If the margarine is hard, it has probably been hydrogenated.

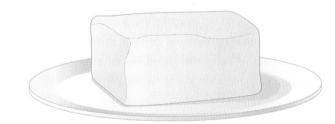

Figure 10.25 Hydrogenated margarine contains saturated fat, just like butter.

Cholesterol

Cholesterol is a soft, waxy lipid found in body cells and among the lipids (fats) in arteries and veins. Everyone needs cholesterol. It is used to form cell membranes, insulate nerves, and produce vitamin D, bile acids, and some hormones. Dietary sources such as meat, shellfish, whole-milk products, and egg yolks are especially rich in cholesterol. It is also produced by cells in the liver. Too much cholesterol in the diet, however, can lead to life-threatening problems.

Why is there so much concern about the presence of cholesterol in our bodies and our diet if it performs so many useful and necessary metabolic functions? The liver already produces as much cholesterol as the body needs — it is the amount and type of extra cholesterol that we consume that causes problems. Cholesterol and other fats cannot dissolve in the bloodstream, so they are transported to where they are needed in the form of lipoproteins. There are several types of lipoproteins, but the most important ones are low-density lipoprotein (LDL) and high-density lipoprotein (HDL). There is general agreement in the medical community that LDL is the "bad" cholesterol while HDL is the "good" cholesterol.

If too much LDL cholesterol is circulating in the blood, it combines with other substances to form plaque. Plaque becomes incorporated into arterial walls, causing obstructions that can lead to blood clots.

<< REWIND

For more information about plaque, return to Chapter 9, Section 9.4. To see a photograph of an artery clogged with plaque, return to Chapter 7, Section 7.4.

Therefore, it is important that we limit our intake of foods that are rich in both cholesterol and saturated fats. In this combination, the cholesterol is predominantly of the LDL type. Food from plants, including fruit, vegetables, grains, and nuts, does not contain cholesterol. Exercise may play a role in increasing the level of HDL cholesterol in our blood. High levels of HDL cholesterol, compared to LDL cholesterol, are linked to reduced risk for heart disease.

Proteins

Enzymes, molecules that enable the hundreds of metabolic reactions to take place in the body, are all proteins. Antibodies to disease and many hormones are also proteins. Proteins help build and repair muscles and cell membranes. Proteins are made up of chains of peptides that, in turn, consist of strings of amino acids. The human body is unable to make eight of the 20 amino acids it needs. These eight acids are called the essential amino acids. If a protein contains all eight of the essential amino acids, it is called a **complete protein**. Sources of complete protein include meat, legumes, eggs, cheese, milk, and whole grain products.

Proteins from dietary sources are broken down into their component amino acids during digestion. After being absorbed into the bloodstream in the small intestine, they are carried to the liver. From here, most are transported to the cells, where they are used to create new proteins. The liver may also break down amino acids to provide energy when all your fat and glycogen reserves have been exhausted. Obviously, this process is a last resort.

Minerals

Minerals are inorganic compounds that the body needs in small amounts. Minerals enable certain chemical reactions and help build bones and cartilage (see Table 10.2). They do not contain carbon, like carbohydrates, fats, and proteins, and are readily absorbed into the bloodstream. Minerals are essential components of hemoglobin, hormones, enzymes, and vitamins.

Table 10.2
Essential minerals

Mineral	Sources	Functions
Calcium	leafy green vegetables, dairy products	bone formation, nerve transmission, muscle contraction, blood clotting
Phosphorus	dairy products, meat, eggs, vegetables	bone formation, soft tissue growth, manufacture of nucleic acids and ATP
Potassium	fruits, vegetables	nerve conduction, muscle contraction
Sodium	table salt, vegetables	nerve conduction, osmotic balance
Magnesium	leafy green vegetables, grains, meats, potatoes	enzyme functions, protein synthesis
Chloride	table salt	water balance
Zinc	meats, whole grains	enzyme synthesis, immune system functions, growth
Iron	meats, whole grains, raisins, leafy green vegetables	hemoglobin synthesis
Selenium	seafood, eggs, meat	tissue elasticity
Copper	whole grains, leafy vegetables, nuts, meats	hemoglobin synthesis
Iodine	seafood, table salt	thyroid hormone synthesis, thyroid gland function

Vitamins

Like minerals, **vitamins** are required in the body in relatively small amounts. Nevertheless, vitamins are vitally important. For example, they serve as **coenzymes** — chemicals needed to make enzymes function. They are also involved in tissue

Table 10.3
Vitamins

Vitamin	Sources	Functions
A (Carotene)	eggs, butter, whole milk, yellow-orange vegetables, fruits	antioxidant needed for healthy eyes and skin, growth and repair of tissues and bones
B$_1$ (Thiamin)	whole grains, legumes, nuts, meats	carbohydrate metabolism, growth, muscle tone, maintenance of healthy nervous system
B$_2$ (Riboflavin)	whole grains, nuts, dairy products, eggs, leafy green vegetables, poultry	carbohydrate, fat, and protein metabolism, cell respiration, red blood cell and antibody formation
B$_6$ (Pyridoxine)	whole grains, nuts, cereals, legumes, poultry, leafy green vegetables	carbohydrate, fat, and protein metabolism, antibody formation, sodium regulation
B$_{12}$ (Cyanocobalamin)	meats, fish, poultry, eggs, dairy products	carbohydrate, fat, and protein metabolism, maintenance of healthy nervous system, red blood cell formation
Niacin (Nicotinic acid)	poultry, whole grains, legumes, leafy green vegetables	carbohydrate, fat, and protein metabolism, maintenance of healthy skin and digestive system
Folic acid (Folacin)	dark leafy green vegetables, nuts, whole grains, legumes	protein metabolism, red blood cell formation, DNA formation, normal growth and development
Biotin	eggs, yeast, most foods	carbohydrate, fat, and protein metabolism, maintenance of healthy skin
Pantothenic acid	dark leafy green vegetables, nuts, legumes, poultry, milk, fruits	oxidation of carbohydrates and fats, hormone formation, enhances body's ability to withstand stress
C (Ascorbic acid)	tomatoes, cabbage, potatoes, leafy green vegetables, citrus fruits	antioxidant, helps heal injuries, strengthens blood vessels, enhances resistance to disease
D	milk, eggs, fish liver oil; also made in skin exposed to sunlight	bone formation, maintenance of nervous system and heart action
E	leafy green vegetables, fruits, whole grains, nuts	antioxidant, protects red blood cells and helps prevent blood clots, needed in cellular respiration
K	leafy green vegetables, cabbage	needed for normal blood clotting

development, tissue growth, and helping the body fight and resist disease. The body can produce vitamin D when exposed to sunlight, while vitamin K and some B vitamins are produced by beneficial bacteria in the intestines. Only vitamins A and D, two of the four fat-soluble vitamins, can be stored in the body. (The other fat-soluble vitamins are E and K.) The remaining vitamins must be consumed on a regular basis. Some water-soluble vitamins are removed when we cook foods in water and then discard the water.

Choosing Healthy Foods

You can get all the nutrients you need every day by using the rainbow in *Canada's Food Guide to Healthy Eating* shown on the following page. Each rainbow colour represents a different food group. Yellow represents grain products, green represents vegetables and fruits, blue represents milk products and substitutes, and red represents meat and alternatives. Each group provides a different set of nutrients that complements the nutrients provided by the other groups (see Figure 10.27). By choosing foods from each of the four groups every day, your body will get the complete nutrition it needs.

To make sure you receive the correct proportion of each nutrient, *Canada's Food Guide to Healthy Eating* recommends that you stay within the following ranges of daily servings:

Grain products	5–12 servings
Vegetables and fruit	5–10 servings
Milk products or substitutes	2–4 servings
Meat and alternatives	2–3 servings

The food group colour bars on the rainbow give you a general idea of how many servings of each group you should be receiving relative to the others. Be sure to choose leaner, lower fat choices from each group more often. That way, you will also limit your fat intake to healthy levels.

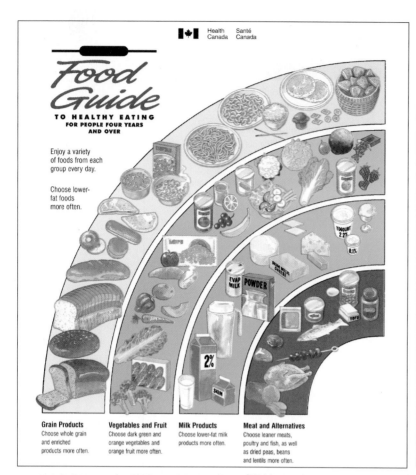

Figure 10.26 The rainbow in *Canada's Food Guide to Healthy Eating* will help you choose foods that will supply you with the right amount of all the nutrients your body requires.

Food Guide TO HEALTHY EATING FOR PEOPLE FOUR YEARS AND OVER

Health Canada / Santé Canada

Enjoy a variety of foods from each group every day.

Choose lower-fat foods more often.

Grain Products
Choose whole grain and enriched products more often.

Vegetables and Fruit
Choose dark green and orange vegetables and orange fruit more often.

Milk Products
Choose lower-fat milk products more often.

Meat and Alternatives
Choose leaner meats, poultry and fish, as well as dried peas, beans and lentils more often.

‖ PAUSE ● RECORD

Vitamin deficiencies have been recognized for several centuries. As early as 1794, work was published about scurvy. Hundreds of sailors died of this disease caused by the lack of vitamin C, before the discovery was made that citrus fruits in the diet could prevent it. Scurvy also affected early European colonists to Canada. Fortunately, aboriginal people shared knowledge that they had with the early colonists. They had learned that drinking a "tea" of the bark of black spruce or tamarack during the long winters would prevent them from becoming ill from the disease we now know as scurvy. Only in the early part of the 1900s were vitamins actually isolated, and their molecular structures determined. What other vitamin deficiencies can be avoided by simply eating the "right" foods? Use Table 10.3 on the previous page as a guide when considering this question. Also, go to your Electronic Learning Partner for more guidance.

Grain Products	+	Vegetables & Fruits	+	Milk Products	+	Meat & Alternatives	=	The Food Guide
protein				protein		protein		protein
				fat		fat		fat
carbohydrate		carbohydrate						carbohydrate
fibre		fibre						fibre
thiamin		thiamin				thiamin		thiamin
riboflavin				riboflavin		riboflavin		riboflavin
niacin						niacin		niacin
folacin		folacin				folacin		folacin
				vitamin B$_{12}$		vitamin B$_{12}$		vitamin B$_{12}$
		vitamin C						vitamin C
		vitamin A		vitamin A				vitamin A
				vitamin D				vitamin D
				calcium				calcium
iron		iron				iron		iron
zinc				zinc		zinc		zinc
magnesium		magnesium		magnesium		magnesium		magnesium

Figure 10.27 Each food group in *Canada's Food Guide to Healthy Eating* provides a set of complementary nutrients.

The Role of Fitness and Lifestyle Choices

Fitness can be easily divided into two categories: cardiovascular fitness and muscular fitness. Consider the differing activities of weight lifters and soccer players. Weight lifters have very well-developed muscles, enabling them to "press" or lift heavy weights. But if asked to run 100 m, they might be out of breath by the end of the run. Soccer players, on the other hand, are constantly running throughout each match — this requires cardiovascular fitness.

Cardiovascular fitness can be achieved and maintained if you eat a healthy diet, exercise regularly, and avoid harmful substances such as alcohol, nicotine, and other drugs. Of the two types of fitness, cardiovascular fitness delivers the greatest benefits.

Figure 10.28 Cross-country skiing is an excellent way to build cardiovascular fitness.

Exercise

The benefits we derive from exercise depend on four variables: the intensity, frequency, duration, and type of exercise.

Heart rate is the simplest, most commonly used indicator of the benefit gained from exercise.

 THINKING LAB

Interpreting Canada's Nutrition Labels

Background

Canada has recently implemented new nutrition labelling regulations. These regulations make it mandatory for most manufacturers of packaged foods to display a Nutrition Facts label. A Nutrition Facts label for a breakfast cereal is shown here. These new labels present facts on food energy units and 13 important nutrients in a standard format. These labels are designed to make it easier for consumers to assess and compare the nutritional value of the foods they buy, and therefore to manage their diets more effectively. The Daily Value percentage (on the right side of the label) indicates what percentage of the average person's total daily requirement for that nutrient that one serving of the product supplies.

You Try It

1. The table to the right lists the major nutrients and states (as a percentage) how much of an average person's daily value (DV) intake should be composed of each nutrient. In other words, it shows what percent of your total food energy units should come from each source. In the case of fats, for instance, no more than 30% of total food energy units should come from this source.

Nutrition Facts

Serving Size 1 cup (40 g)

Amount Per Serving	
Calories 147*	
	% Daily Value
Fat 0.8 g	1%
Saturated Fat 0.1 g + Trans Fat 0.5 g	3%
Cholesterol 0 mg	0%
Sodium 252 mg	11%
Carbohydrate 33 g	11%
Fibre 5 g	20%
Sugars 6 g	
Protein 4 g	
Vitamin A 0% • Vitamin C 0%	
Calcium 1% • Iron 39%	

* 615 kJ

Percentage of Daily Value	
Fats	30%
Saturated Fats	10%
Cholesterol	1.5%
Carbohydrates	60%
Protein	10%

2. Compare the values given for the breakfast cereal with those listed in the Percentage of DV table. By itself, is the cereal a good source of any nutrients or minerals? If so, which ones?

3. What nutrients and minerals would you want to be sure to get from other sources in order to balance your daily diet?

Proper cardiovascular exercise should raise your heartbeat to a level that produces a "training effect." This effect begins when your pulse rate (in beats per minute) rises above 170 minus your age. There is a higher pulse rate that represents the upper, safe limit which your body should not exceed. This limit is the difference between 200 and your age. You should exercise within these pulse rate limits. As your fitness improves, you will be able to exercise more vigorously and still stay within these limits. Your capacity for physical activity will increase, and you will enjoy such activity more. These are two of the benefits of fitness!

Math LINK

Determine your own pulse rate limits. Subtract your age in years from 170 to find the lower limit, and subtract your age from 200 to find your upper limit. In what range do you have to keep your pulse rate in order to achieve a training effect?

Table 10.4 lists a number of common activities and the levels of fitness to which they can lead. Before engaging in regular physical exercise after a period of inactivity, it is advisable to see your doctor and explain your plans. Your doctor can help you decide what kinds of activities to begin with, how long you should engage in them, and how often you should exercise. Remember to set realistic targets for yourself. Realistic targets help to ensure your success, and to prevent you getting frustrated and giving up. Once you have achieved

one target, you can consider going on to another. Eventually, you will know the limits of your body better than anyone!

Can you think of at least two additional activities that could be added to each of the three columns in the table? Give reasons why you would place them there. What about the issue of gender — should it be included in the table? Why or why not?

Table 10.4
Activities to improve your cardiovascular fitness

Activity and Level		
High-level fitness	**Moderate-level fitness**	**Low-level fitness**
ice hockey	cycling	bowling
jogging	basketball	golf
cross-country skiing	squash	baseball
hiking in hilly terrain	swimming	curling
Activities in this column should be carried out for at least 20 min, three times each week.	Activities in this column should be done for 30 min, three times a week. If done briskly, the benefits will be comparable to those derived from activities in column A.	Most of the activities in this column are not sustained long enough to provide training effect benefits. They do improve co-ordination, muscle tone, and flexibility.

 MINI LAB

Deconstructing a Pizza

How nutritious is pizza? Pizza is a combination food, or one that contains foods from more than one food group. Examples of other combination foods include sandwiches, chop suey, soups, and stews. To conduct this lab, you will need a slice of your favourite pizza, a butter knife, some paper plates, and some serviettes. Don't eat any of this pizza slice, as you are handling it in a lab where it may get contaminated. Let it cool to room temperature. Then use the butter knife and your gloved fingers to separate each kind of food onto separate plates. Green peppers and anchovies, for example, would go on separate plates. List how many different kinds of food were on your pizza slice — don't forget to count the sauce. Then determine where each food is represented in *Canada's Food Guide to Healthy Eating* rainbow and list its food group in your note-

book. If you cannot locate a particular food on the guide, classify it as "other." Using Tables 10.2 and 10.3, see if you can also determine what kinds of vitamins and minerals each food supplies.

Analyze

1. How many food groups were represented on your pizza slice? How many minerals and vitamins do you think were represented?

2. Estimate the percentage of each food group comprising the full slice of pizza.

3. Is pizza a good source of nutrients? Could pizza form part of a balanced diet? Explain.

4. How would you change the toppings on your next slice of pizza?

Fitness will do much more than improve your "game" and how much you enjoy of it. Losing excess weight and maintaining a healthy, fit body can reduce the levels of lipids (fats) in your blood and reduce your blood pressure, thus preventing conditions that can lead to a stroke or heart attack later in life. The general metabolic well-being of the body — all of the intricate chemical events that take place inside us, including digestion — improves with exercise and a balanced diet. Simply put, the body does not have to work as hard when you eat the right foods and stay active. When you are fit, you feel more confident and energetic. The result goes a long way toward improving your self-image and your ability to handle stress.

If you are still convinced that your busy schedule will not allow you to work in some exercise, try doing the following.

- Get off the bus one stop early and walk the rest of the way home.
- Forget the elevator; take the stairs.
- If there are too many stairs, get off the elevator three floors before your destination, and walk up the rest of the way.
- Get out your bike, put a couple of panniers on the back, and use it to run errands in your area. Ride your bike to school in good weather.
- Get a few of your friends together for a three-on-three basketball game after school.
- Take dancing classes.
- Shovel your neighbour's driveway and mow your neighbour's lawn when you do your own.

Diets and Dietary Supplements

Our diets are closely linked to our lifestyles and life choices. Although diets differ (as you can see by the many books on the subject in any bookstore), it is still necessary to maintain a balance of grain products, vegetables and fruit, milk products or substitutes, and meat or meat alternatives in order to obtain proper nutrition. This is true in spite of claims made for any particular diet.

Figure 10.29 In spite of claims made by the authors of various diets, it is still necessary to maintain a balanced diet for good health and proper nutrition.

The ever-present threat of a heart attack in both men and women after the age of 40 is unique to the highly industrialized countries of the world. In no small measure, this is related to the high-fat foods we eat. Numerous scientific studies have shown that the consumption of too much fat, especially saturated fats, certain unsaturated fatty acids, and dietary cholesterol, contributes significantly to heart attacks and certain cancers. In parts of the world where heart attacks are not nearly as common, people eat very low-fat diets and little if any meat. Although meats are rich in protein and B vitamins, many also contain large quantities of fat. If you eat meat, choose lean cuts and limit the amount you consume.

Vegetarian Diets

If excess fat is the dietary villain in our nutrition drama, then every attempt should be made to reduce or replace it in our daily meals. **Vegetarians** attempt to avoid meat and fish altogether on moral or other grounds, although most consume dairy products and eggs. **Vegans** are vegetarians who use substitutes for even these products, preferring to rely strictly on foods derived from plants. Such restrictive diets must be carefully planned and followed, however, or their practitioners may be put at risk.

Consider, for example, that milk is an important source of calcium, along with protein and vitamin D. If you are not drinking milk or eating other dairy products, it becomes important to eat other foods that are rich in calcium, such as kale, broccoli, and Brussels sprouts. If you follow a vegetarian diet, keep track of the foods you eat, to ensure that you are consuming representatives of the four major food groups or their substitutes. Some people express concerns about whether they can get balanced nutrition on a vegetarian diet, and in particular whether they can get adequate amounts of protein. A diet rich in beans, whole grains, and vegetables will satisfy this requirement. However, vegetarians may have a higher risk of iron and vitamin B_{12} deficiencies than non-vegetarians, because the richest sources of these nutrients are in fish, red meats, liver, and egg yolk. Dried beans, brewer's yeast, spinach, and dried fruits can supply iron, but the only substantial source of vitamin B_{12} is animal protein or dietary supplements.

Biology *Magazine*   TECHNOLOGY • SOCIETY • ENVIRONMENT

Nutrition for the Unborn

Folic acid is a tasteless vitamin with the power to prevent serious birth defects, such as defective spines. Extensive studies show this vitamin is effective in preventing birth defects that develop in the third and fourth weeks of pregnancy, often before many women even know they have conceived. Yet few Canadian women realize they should be getting a daily dose of folic acid. They are not aware that by including folic acid (which is available as an inexpensive dietary supplement pill) in their diet, they can prevent serious problems for their unborn children. It is estimated that 75% of Canadian women do not take folic acid before they get pregnant or during the crucial early weeks of their pregnancies. Consequently, Canadian doctors and public health officials are debating how they can raise awareness about folic acid.

"This is old news, yet young women in particular are not paying attention," says Dr. Judith Hall, a researcher at the University of British Columbia. She notes that humans evolved with a much different diet (one based on more fruits and vegetables than many people consume), but that we still need folic acid to make healthy babies. Women with plenty of folic acid in their diets will likely produce healthy babies.

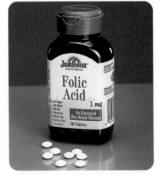

Folic acid is readily available as a dietary supplement.

Sources and Benefits

Folic acid is a B vitamin, found naturally in small quantities in foods such as strawberries, spinach, romaine lettuce, frozen peas, orange juice, cauliflower, cantaloupe, Brussels sprouts, broccoli, beans, and cooked beets and asparagus. Since the human body is not very good at storing it, and since half of all pregnancies are unplanned, Health Canada recommends that all women of childbearing age take a daily supplement of 400 μg of folic acid every day, either separately or as part of a multivitamin.

Natural dietary sources of folic acid include fresh fruits and vegetables.

Folic acid protects the developing embryo against what are known as neural tube defects. The neural tube gives rise to the brain and spinal cord. If the neural tube does not close properly, the baby will be born with a condition such as spina bifida or anencephaly. In Canada, about 500 babies a year are born with these problems. In spina bifida, the bones around the spinal cord are formed with

Supplements and Aids

A balanced diet will normally contain all the nutrients, in their correct proportions, that a healthy person requires. Vitamin and mineral supplements will probably not provide any benefit to these people, and may even do harm if taken indiscreetly. But for others who are ill, planning to have children, recovering from injury, suffering from digestive problems, following a special diet, or who cannot or choose not to eat an optimal diet, supplements may prove of significant value.

Some people worry about being overweight. If you are concerned about your weight and want to make changes, the best, first thing you can do is see your doctor. There are a number of weight-loss aids and programs on the market, some requiring a prescription. In consultation with your doctor, you can decide on a program that is both safe and right for you. The best program is one that will help you lose weight gradually while encouraging you to adopt better eating habits, a healthier lifestyle, and a positive self-image.

Under no circumstances should you begin to restrict your food intake severely. In addition to causing nutrient deficiencies, such behaviour can lead to a dangerous condition called anorexia nervosa. Many anorexics keep trying to lose weight even after they have lost all their body fat. This can cost them their lives.

---

a cleft, which can lead to serious physical problems or mental disabilities. In anencephaly, the brain and skull do not develop properly. This condition usually leads to death shortly after birth.

Folic acid cannot protect against all neural tube defects, but studies show it can prevent up to 70 percent of them. There is also new evidence that it helps prevent congenital heart defects, cleft palates, and urinary tract anomalies. About five per cent of all babies are born with serious birth defects. Some researchers estimate that half of these could be prevented if women of childbearing age either took supplements or ate a diet that contained an adequate amount of folic acid.

How Does It Work?

Nobody knows for sure, but researchers believe that human bodies need folic acid to make DNA. They think folic acid is also involved in turning genes on and off, something that happens frequently as an embryo develops. In the early 1980s, researchers in China and Scotland began working with mothers who had already had one baby with a neural tube defect. These women had a higher risk of having a second child with a similar problem. The study showed that after following a diet with increased levels of folic acid, 70 percent of the women delivered healthy babies. Ten years of follow-up studies done around the world, including studies in Canada, Hungary, and China, have added to the compelling evidence.

What Is Being Done?

In 1998, the U.S. government required that flour pasta, cereals, rice, and other grain products sold in the United States be fortified with 100 µg of folic acid. A recent study showed that, as a result, American women of childbearing age had more than doubled the amount of folic acid in their diet. The Canadian government allows companies here to similarly fortify grain products but does not require them to do so. Instead, it recommends that women take a daily supplement if they are old enough to have babies.

Researchers and doctors are urging the Canadian government to do more, especially since new evidence indicates folic acid is good for almost everybody and may play a role in fighting heart disease and cancer. The problem, however, is that foods enriched with folic acid may cause problems for elderly people who have a vitamin B_{12} deficiency. A Canadian study is presently examining whether foods fortified with folic acid yield the same benefits as vitamin supplements, and whether foods so enriched will cause problems for the elderly. The study is being done in an area of the country where people have the greatest percentage of neural tube defects.

Follow-up

1. What could be causing the high percentage of neural tube defects in some areas? List some ideas, being sure to consider environmental, economic, geographic, and other factors that might contribute to this phenomenon.

2. Suppose food fortified with folic acid was found to cause problems for the elderly, but to benefit the general population. In small groups, discuss the controls these foods should be subject to, including how they should be marketed, advertised, and displayed.

Drugs and Other Toxins

Nicotine, Caffeine, and Alcohol

The drugs we call nicotine, caffeine, and alcohol are used much more commonly than marijuana, heroin, and other drugs used to change feelings and emotions. Like other drugs, these everyday drugs present their users with unique problems, all of which result from the users' choice to make them part of their lifestyle.

Nicotine is a highly poisonous substance found in tobacco that increases pulse rate and blood pressure. It also increases stomach acidity, which is accompanied by a lack of appetite. Smoking reduces the effectiveness of the cilia in our nostrils, which filter particulate matter from the air that we breathe. It also interferes with the body's ability to absorb vitamin C, making smokers more susceptible to colds and other ailments. As the tars and residues in smoke accumulate in the lungs, the efficiency of the respiratory surface of the alveoli is reduced. Hence, smokers are not able to sustain vigorous exercise activities without "running out of breath." Over time, smokers can look forward to such serious risks as narrowing or hardening of the arteries, respiratory infections, emphysema, stomach ulcers, chronic cough, and cancer of the mouth, throat, and lungs.

Many tobacco users claim that smoking suppresses their appetite and helps them stay slim. If they stopped smoking, they argue, they would gain weight. You might want to do some research to find out how much weight smokers really gain after they quit.

Figure 10.30 Smoking interferes with the body's ability to absorb vitamin C and puts people at risk for a host of serious diseases.

What does caffeine do in your body? You likely know that it will keep you awake at night if you drink a cup of coffee after an evening meal. You may not know that **caffeine** also acts as a diuretic. Diuretics are chemicals that increase the amount of water excreted by the kidneys. Both caffeine and alcohol act on the hypothalamus (at the base of the brain) to inhibit the production of ADH, the antidiuretic hormone. The result is the formation of more dilute urine and the desire to urinate more frequently. Caffeine also increases your blood pressure by making your blood vessels constrict. Check this out the next time you drink a cup of coffee or tea, or a glass of cola. Take your pulse before you drink and five minutes after.

The negative short-term consequences of consuming too much alcohol are well known. Less well-known is that excess alcohol destroys B vitamins and results in the formation of poisonous acetaldehyde in the body. The acetaldehyde is eventually metabolized into essentially harmless products, but first it usually causes a hangover for the alcohol drinker who drinks excessively. Long-term excessive use of alcohol can cause serious physical, social, and psychological problems.

There are many other drugs that also affect, either directly or indirectly, our metabolism, digestion, and nutrition. Antacids, for instance, purchased across the drugstore counter, are taken by people who have eaten a meal high in acid content.

> **Probeware**
>
> If you have access to probeware, do the activity, Caffeine and the Human Heart.

Psychoactive Drugs

Psychoactive drugs are chemicals that affect the central nervous system and interfere with the normal functioning of the brain. This includes stimulants (for example, amphetamines and cocaine), depressants (such as alcohol, barbiturates, and tranquilizers), hallucinogens (such as LSD), and narcotics (for example, morphine, codeine, and heroin), which are derived from plants in the poppy family. The following are but a few examples of the many psychoactive drugs used in society.

LSD is a major hallucinogen. It is made from lysergic acid (the 'L' in the name), a chemical present in ergot, which is a fungus found on rye and other grain crops. Often called, "acid," it has a slightly bitter taste. The drug is usually taken orally.

The effects of LSD vary significantly from one person to the next, and the resulting mood swings can be very large and unpredictable. LSD "trips" can last for several hours and often prove quite frightening for the user.

Heroin is made from morphine, which is extracted from the seedpods of the Asian poppy. The drug is highly addictive. Once injected into a blood vessel, the user experiences a "rush," followed by alternating periods of alertness and sleepiness. Many complications are associated with the continued use of heroin, including liver disease, infections of the heart, and collapsed veins. Because heroin users often do not take care of their health or well-being in other ways, they are prone to pneumonia and other lung-related problems.

Ecstasy (MDMA) differs from the drugs above in that it has both stimulant and hallucinogenic qualities. In addition, ecstasy is a *neurotoxin*, or nerve poison. In high doses it can increase the body temperature markedly and lead to failure of the cardiovascular system. Research also indicates that this drug affects neurons that use the chemical serotonin to communicate with other neurons. Serotonins, in turn, are involved in a major way in sleep, sensitivity to pain, mood regulation, and other body activities. The use of ecstasy has in recent years been associated, rightly or wrongly, with large, after-hours dance parties.

Anabolic Steroids

Another category of drugs, which is often in the news during sports coverage, is **anabolic steroids**. Anabolic steroids are synthetic derivatives of the male hormone testosterone. These drugs can be used under medical supervision to build muscle tissue in chronically ill patients. They have also been used by unscrupulous athletes to temporarily improve their performance during competitions, a practice that is banned by Olympic rules and most competing countries. This practice can also lead to disastrous after-effects, including an increased risk of liver damage, heart problems, high blood pressure, and serious mood swings. Anabolic steroids are one example of the increasing number of synthetic "designer drugs" appearing in the underground market.

Web LINK

Do some research to find out how much public money is spent on smokers' health costs each year or on people who drink alcohol excessively, versus the money raised in taxes on tobacco, or alcohol. Are governments really making money on these taxes? Explain. A good place to begin you research is the following web site.

www.school.mcgrawhill.ca/resources/

Figure 10.31 Athletes like Silken Laumann, the Olympic medal-winning rower, have made it to the top of their form without using anabolic steroids.

All these drugs are involved, in one way or another, with the metabolism of the body. Some affect digestion, others affect the cardiovascular system, and still others affect the nervous system. They are all drugs of choice — they are used as a result of decisions we make individually and as a society. Unfortunately, if you decide to take these drugs, your decision will affect not only you but also the people around you to whom who you are closest.

It is undeniable that the majority of drugs produced by pharmaceutical companies have improved the lives of people suffering from a variety of diseases. However, individuals and society pay a terrible price for the use of non-medicinal drugs like those described. This price goes far beyond economics.

1. **K/U** What are the six essential nutrients a healthy diet must include?

2. **K/U** Why is it important to limit our intake of saturated fats and dietary cholesterol?

3. **K/U** Name at least three benefits that we derive from exercise.

4. **K/U** List three common non-medicinal drugs and their effects on the body.

5. **K/U** Name some of the risks associated with the use of psychoactive drugs.

6. **MC** Many professional athletes are known to use drugs of one kind or another. In small groups, discuss whether the use of certain drugs or all drugs should be prohibited in professional sports. How would you enforce your ruling?

7. **C** Draw a large food group rainbow like the one in *Canada's Food Guide to Healthy Eating*, but leave the bars blank. Fill in the bars with the names of the foods in your refrigerator and cupboards, making sure you put each one where it belongs.

8. **MC** One of your friends talks constantly about losing weight, while another has decided she is going to become a vegan. What advice would you give each of them, and why?

9. **MC** A teenage acquaintance comes back from a jog and tells you her pulse rate is way up to 145. Explain why she is or is not receiving training effect.

10. **MC** It has been said that the following foods should be included in everyone's diet: oranges, cantaloupe, broccoli, multi-grain bread, sweet potatoes, beans, salmon or sardines, spinach, skim or 1% milk. Make a case for their inclusion.

 UNIT PROJECT PREP

The disease or disorder you select for your Unit 3 Project could be a disease of the digestive system. Consider diet deficiencies or consider addictive substances and their effects as possible project subjects.

- Are organ transplants an option for the disease you chose?
- What new technologies can help in its treatment?
- Is there current research on the disease being done in Canada?

Chapter Expectations

- Describe and explain the major processes, mechanisms, and systems of digestive systems. (10.1, 10.2, 10.3)
- Conduct laboratory investigations to be able to illustrate and explain digestive systems. (10.3)
- Evaluate the impact of personal lifestyle decisions on the health of humans. (10.4)
- Describe the importance of nutrients and digestion. (10.1, 10.2, 10.3, 10.4)
- Select and integrate information about the digestive systems from various print and electronic sources. (10.1, 10.2, 10.3, 10.4)
- Analyze and explain how societal needs have led to scientific and technological developments related to the digestive system. (10.3, 10.4)
- Present informed opinions about how scientific knowledge of the digestive system influences personal choices concerning nutrition and lifestyle. (10.4)

Language of Biology

Write a sentence using each of the following words or terms. Use any six terms in a concept map to show your understanding of how thay are related.

- essential nutrient
- autotrophs
- intracellular digestion
- papillae
- saliva
- ducts
- regurgitation
- chyme
- small intestine
- villi
- jejunum
- large intestine
- appendix
- feces
- anal canal
- peristalsis
- substrate
- hormone
- secretin
- pancreas
- insulin
- balanced diet
- complete protein
- vitamin
- vegetarian
- nicotine
- psychoactive drugs

- heterotrophs
- digestive system
- extracellular digestion
- uvula
- salivary glands
- esophagus
- stomach
- pyloric sphincter
- duodenum
- lacteal
- ileum
- caecum
- colon
- rectum
- anus
- digestion
- amylase
- gastrin
- liver
- gall bladder
- glucagon
- cholesterol
- mineral
- coenzyme
- vegan
- caffeine
- anabolic steroids

UNDERSTANDING CONCEPTS

1. In what way does the intracellular digestion in single-celled organisms resemble extracellular digestion?

2. Describe the tube concept as it relates to the digestion of food.

3. List, in order, the organs of the digestive tract through which food passes in a human.

4. Explain the function of the esophagus.

5. What role(s) do the salivary glands play in the process of digestion?

6. Explain the significance of the change in pH from the stomach to the small intestine.

7. Describe the structure of the walls of the stomach and how this structure aids the digestive process.

8. Create a word equation for the digestion of an example of each of the following: carbohydrate, fat, protein.

9. Why is the liver such a major component of the digestive system?

10. What role do hormones play in the secretion of chemicals involved with digestion?

11. What is the consequence of having a gall bladder removed with respect to a person's health and diet?

12. Why is it important to chew your food when you eat?

13. Why must the stomach be so acidic?

14. Given the acidic condition of the stomach, explain how the stomach wall is maintained.

15. How would you expect the relative lengths of the small intestines of a wolf and a cow to compare? Explain.

16. Why must the pancreas secrete a an alkaline (basic) substance, into the small intestine?

17. In terms of what takes place in the liver, explain why it is important for vegetarians to eat lots of grains and vegetables that contain a variety of proteins.

18. Give two reasons why good nutrition is important.

19. What two hormones work to regulate the level of glucose in the blood, and where are they produced?

20. Explain the difference between saturated and unsaturated fats, and give dietary examples of each.

21. What effects does nicotine have on the body? What long-term risks are associated with tobacco use?

22. Account for the fact that people around the world eat vastly different foods and yet they can all be healthy.

23. What would happen if a person was no longer able to produce gastrin? Describe what effect this would have on the digestion of food.

INQUIRY

24. Design a simple lab activity to determine what effect, if any, altering the concentration of an enzyme would have on the rate of enzyme action.

25. Design a "better" digestive system than the one you have

26. The experiment below was set up to investigate the digestion of egg white by pepsin. Answer the following questions about the experiment.
    (a) What was the researcher's hypothesis?
    (b) Explain the reason for having each test tube.
    (c) At approximately what temperature do you think the incubator was set?
    (d) What conclusions can you make about your observations?

27. Design a similar experiment for the digestion of a food by amylase in the saliva.

28. René Réaumur (1683–1757) wrote a great treatise on insects. He also invented a method of coating iron with tin which is still used today. This diverse scientist did an interesting experiment on digestion in 1752. He put perforated metallic tubes containing food into the beaks of certain birds. Because he was a good naturalist, he knew which birds regurgitate the indigestible remains of their food, thus he used these birds for his experiment. When he removed the tubes from the birds' digestive tracts, they were empty. This gave evidence that something in addition to grinding or crushing was occurring in the stomach.
    (a) What do you think Réaumur's hypothesis was?
    (b) Some people would say this experiment is cruel to the animal. Do you think such experiments should have been done? Should they be done today? Support your answer with an explanation.
    (c) Describe a follow-up experiment you think Réaumur might have considered.

Incubator

1	2	3	4
water	pepsin water	HCl water	pepsin HCl water
egg white	egg white	egg white	egg white

| no digestion | little or no digestion | no digestion | digestion |

29. You have been asked to speak to a group of mothers-to-be about the benefits of a healthy diet and of folic acid in particular. Using full sentences, outline the key points your speech will emphasize.

30. Do some research to find out more about the way in which Venus flytraps and sundews catch and digest their food. Write a short report that compares their feeder type and digestive process with that of mammals. Be sure to include drawings that show how the plants capture their prey.

31. Alcoholism is considered to be a disease by some health professionals, marked by, among other things, the inability of the alcoholic to control his or her drinking. Excessive consumption of alcoholic beverages can also lead to other diseases such as cirrhosis of the liver. In cirrhosis, liver cells die and are replaced by scar tissue, which can prove fatal. If cirrhosis has progressed too far, the only treatment may be a costly human liver transplant. Such livers are in very short supply, and may in turn be damaged if their recipients continue drinking alcohol. In small groups, debate the ethics of offering organ transplants to people who place their health at risk because of lifestyle choices. Note that some professionals have suggested that genetic factors may predispose certain people to alcoholism.

32. The rate of colon cancer is relatively high among Canadians and relatively low among citizens of China. How can you account for this difference?

33. For health reasons, particularly to fight cancer, certain organs of the digestive system may be removed or altered. Which organs are vital to digestion and, thus, could not be removed?

Making Medical History

Background

Imagine that, year after year, your community is rocked by epidemics of a frightening disease. Health authorities move in and close down public places, such as shopping malls, movie theatres and swimming pools. Homes are quarantined and people avoid contact with one another. Nobody knows what causes the disease or how it spreads — all they know is that it tends to attack otherwise healthy babies and children. Year after year, your community is thrown into a panic. This may seem far-fetched now, but your grandparents may remember the fear that accompanied regular outbreaks of polio throughout North America. These outbreaks occured from the 1930s until the mid-1950s, when an effective polio vaccine first became available.

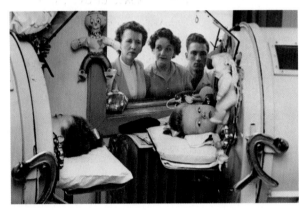

The iron lung, which came into common use in the 1930s, was designed to help ventilate the lungs of patients unable to breathe on their own.

Polio causes an inflammation of the spinal cord and affects the nerves that control muscle movement. Some of its victims suffered complete paralysis of the chest muscles and diaphragm. This meant that they were unable to breathe on their own. Beginning in the 1930s, many of these patients were encased in devices called "iron lungs." The iron lung was an air-tight chamber from which only the patient's head emerged. A bellows pump rhythmically increased and decreased the air pressure within the chamber. As the pressure decreased, the patient's chest would expand and air would be drawn into the lungs through the mouth. As the pressure rose, the chest would contract and air would be forced out. A number of patients lived

for years inside their iron lungs, making this one of the first long-term life support systems.

Over time, advances in medical technology meant that smaller, more portable ventilators became available. One modern ventilator fits into a small mask that can be worn over the patient's nose. Advances like this have allowed victims of respiratory paralysis and other respiratory disorders to lead more independent lives. At the same time, social values have changed, making it easier for people with disabilities to be active participants in their communities.

The history of the iron lung — like the history of all medical treatments — has biological, technological, and social dimensions. The past 50 years has seen tremendous changes in the treatment of diseases and disorders affecting the internal systems of respiration, circulation and digestion. In this project you will trace the history of one such treatment.

Challenge

Working individually or in a small group, research, design and present a report on the history of a single disease or disorder that affects one or more of the internal systems you have studied in this unit. Describe how the diagnosis and treatment of the disease or disorder has changed over the past 50 to 100 years. As part of your research, interview people from your grandparents' generation to find out what they knew about the disease or disorder and its treatment. Try to include first-hand accounts in your report. Your presentation may be in any one of the following forms:

■ an oral, video, or computer presentation;

■ a drama you write and perform, either live or on video;

■ a "walk through medical history" tour on a web site.

Materials

You will need materials for collecting your data and for recording interviews. Aids that accompany an oral presentation should be visible to the entire class, so consider using an overhead projector or use various art and construction supplies to build models that can be passed around. A drama — whether live or on video — will require suitable props. If you prepare your presentation on a web site, make sure that it can be viewed on computers or audio-visual equipment available at your school.

Design Criteria

A. Working individually or in a small group, prepare a report discussing medical advances over the last century in relation to a particular disease or disorder. The disease or disorder should be one that affects one or more of the respiratory, circulatory and digestive systems.

B. Your report should combine information you have learned in one or more chapters of this unit with your own research.

C. You may wish to include in your report a working model to demonstrate the past and present treatment of the disease or disorder you are studying.

D. Your report should explain how changes in the treatment of the disease or disorder over time have been linked to changes in our understanding of the structures and processes involved in the affected internal system.

Action Plan

1. Choose a disease or disorder to study.

2. Develop a plan to find, collect, and organize the information you will need.

3. Identify the materials you will need to prepare your report and presentation. If you are going to build a model, identify the materials you will need for this as well.

4. Interview a number of people from your grandparents' generation about their personal memories of particular illnesses and their treatments. If you can, interview people with different perspectives. Find out what they knew about the disease or disorder you are studying, and also how they felt about it — for example, were particular treatments considered especially powerful or frightening? Think about how

attitudes towards medicine and health have changed (if at all) in your own family over the generations. You may wish to record these interviews to form part of your presentation.

5. As you collect information, think about how you might discuss some of the following questions:

   - how has our understanding of the symptoms, causes and treatments of the disease or disorder changed over the last 50 to 100 years?

   - how have social and cultural values affected the diagnosis and treatment of the disease or disorder?

   - how have advances in knowledge and technology contributed to the treatment or prevention of the disease or disorder?

   - what do you think will be the next major advance in the treatment or prevention of the disease or disorder?

6. Design a rubric for assessing your project. With your teacher, decide on the assessment categories you will use.

7. Obtain your teacher's approval, then carry out your plan and make modifications as necessary.

8. Present your report to the class. Review each presentation and make a note of any common themes or differences of opinion.

Evaluate

1. Using the rubric you have prepared, evaluate your own work and presentation. How effective do you think they were?

2. Evaluate the presentations by other members of your class. Do these other presentations raise issues that are similar to the ones raised in your presentation? Are there differences of opinion about any of these issues? If so, try to explain where these differences come from.

3. After seeing these presentations, what changes would you make to your own project? Explain your reasons.

4. How did working on this project help you think about what you have learned in this unit?

UNDERSTANDING CONCEPTS

True-False

In your notebook, indicate whether each statement is true or false. Correct each false statement.

1. All organisms require a respiratory system.

2. In order for gas exchange to take place in the alveoli of the lungs, the gases must be dissolved.

3. The volume of the lungs is the most important factor in determining their efficiency.

4. Hemoglobin has a greater affinity for carbon monoxide than for oxygen.

5. In plants, gas exchange takes place only through the stomata present on leaves.

6. The stomata of plants are open during the day and closed at night.

7. The more active an organism is, the more it needs a circulatory system.

8. A closed circulatory system is more efficient than an open one.

9. A four-chambered heart ensures the separation of oxygenated and deoxygenated blood.

10. A person with Type O blood can receive blood from a Type AB donor.

11. High blood pressure indicates that you are very physically active.

12. In plants, most mature xylem cells are dead while phloem cells contain living cytoplasm.

13. Both nerves and hormones regulate the secretion of enzymes.

14. The most important site for the absorption of nutrients is the large intestine.

15. It is important to eat representative foods from the four food groups every week.

16. Cholesterol is an unsaturated fat.

Multiple Choice

In your notebook, write the letter of the best answer for each of the following questions.

17. The process that uses oxygen to break down glucose to produce energy takes place
    (a) only in the lungs
    (b) in the lungs and in cells
    (c) when the diaphragm contracts
    (d) in alveoli
    (e) within cells

18. A process that is *not* associated with cellular respiration is
    (a) the breakdown of glycogen

(b) gas exchange in the lungs
(c) ATP formation
(d) gas exchange in cells
(e) metabolic processes

19. One thing that does not occur during inspiration is
    (a) the intercostal muscles of the rib cage contract
    (b) the rib cage rises
    (c) the rib cage extends out from the body
    (d) the diaphragm relaxes
    (e) air moves into the lungs

20. Hyperventilation
    (a) increases the amount of carbon dioxide in the lungs
    (b) increases the vital capacity of the lungs
    (c) increases the concentration of oxygen in the bloodstream
    (d) reduces the time a swimmer can remain under water
    (e) reduces the body temperature slightly

21. Gas exchange in plants takes place
    (a) across the membranes of cells in the main roots of the plants
    (b) across the membranes of the root hairs
    (c) in individual cells
    (d) in stomata
    (e) in phloem cells

22. Cardiopulmonary circulation does not involve
    (a) the pulmonary veins
    (b) the right ventricle
    (c) the left atrium
    (d) the carotid artery
    (e) the pulmonary arteries

23. The true statement among the following is
    (a) Type O blood can only be given to Type AB individuals.
    (b) Type O blood does not contain any antibodies.
    (c) Type AB blood contains A and B antigens on the surface of the cells.
    (d) Type AB blood is called the universal donor.
    (e) Type A blood cannot receive Type O blood.

24. The series of involuntary muscular contractions by which food moves through the digestive tract is called
    (a) mechanical digestion
    (b) osmosis

(c) chemical digestion

(d) peristalsis

(e) stimuli

25. The release of food from the stomach to the small intestine is controlled by the

(a) villus

(b) larynx

(c) epiglottis

(d) uvula

(e) pyloric sphincter

26. The duodenum is

(a) the middle section of the colon

(b) the bottom part of the stomach

(c) the first section of the small intestine

(d) 10 fingers wide

(e) located in the appendix

27. The body's preferred energy source is

(a) carbohydrates

(b) fats

(c) vitamins

(d) proteins

(e) minerals

28. Vitamins

(a) provide energy to the body

(b) regulate processes in the body

(c) remove wastes

(d) supply building materials

(e) digest proteins

29. Anaerobic bacteria in the large intestine

(a) help with the absorption of water

(b) synthesize vitamin K and some B vitamins

(c) change glucose to glycogen

(d) eliminate indigestible matter

(e) recover minerals from the feces

30. The surface area of the small intestine is greatly increased by

(a) villi

(b) chemical digestion

(c) peristalsis

(d) rhythmical segmentation

(e) lacteals

31. A balanced diet contains

(a) water and vitamins

(b) proteins

(c) fats and carbohydrates

(d) minerals

(e) all of the above in the correct proportions

32. Unsaturated fats

(a) will make you sick

(b) are the "bad" fats

(c) are cholesterol

(d) are the "good" fats

(e) contain extra vitamins

33. A fit person usually

(a) suffers from greater stress

(b) feels confident and energetic

(c) needs extra saturated fat in the diet

(d) has a higher risk of heart attack and stroke

(e) has high blood pressure

34. Smoking

(a) makes people more susceptible to colds and other illnesses

(b) increases a person's lung capacity

(c) improves a person's ability to absorb vitamin C

(d) lowers blood pressure

(e) prevents emphysema

Short Answers

In your notebook, write a sentence or a short paragraph to answer each of the following questions.

35. Distinguish between external and internal respiration.

36. Describe how the volume of the chest cavity increases during inhalation.

37. Explain how the respiratory system prevents most of the foreign matter in the air from reaching our lungs.

38. Describe the effects that smoking has on the lungs of a smoker.

39. Describe stomata and lenticels, indicating how they are similar and how they differ.

40. Distinguish between blood serum and blood plasma.

41. A human blood sample at a blood clinic has A antigens in the red blood cells and anti-B antibodies in the plasma. Identify the blood type and who can receive it.

42. Explain how a pacemaker sets the heart rate of its user.

43. Distinguish between systolic and diastolic pressure.

44. Over time, arteriosclerosis reduces blood flow through the arteries to the brain. Explain how this might affect a patient with this condition.

45. When a person has pneumonia, their alveoli become inflamed and the air spaces within them become clogged. Describe some of the effects these symptoms will have on a pneumonia patient.

46. Identify the means by which the liver ensures that the body has a constant supply of energy.

47. Describe what is meant by someone having a fast metabolic rate.

48. Describe what happens to a hamburger as it goes through the digestive system.

49. Explain how hormones secreted by the small intestine affect digestion in both the stomach and the small intestine.

50. Identify the uses of proteins in the body.

51. Explain the role of insulin.

52. Explain the role of glucagon. What controls the release of this hormone?

53. A person suffering from diarrhea may become dehydrated. Predict how might this might cause a problem in the body.

54. Describe the major components of a healthy vegetarian diet.

INQUIRY

55. Olympic swimmers can increase the amount of blood pumped by their hearts (heart output) from a resting rate of 5 L/min to over 30 L/min during competition. As shown in the graph, their heart rates, measured in beats/min, and stroke volumes, measured in mL/beat, also increase. Based on the graph, which would you conclude has the greater effect on heart output, stroke volume or heart rate? Justify your answer.

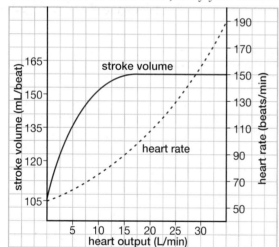

56. You are a scientist on a team in the search of extraterrestrial life. Part of your team has found an organism that cannot be classified as any known species. These teammates believe that this creature is starving, and they ask you to determine what to feed it. Using your knowledge of digestion and nutrition, detail the steps you would take to ensure this creature, possibly from another world, does not starve.

57. In a scientist's experiment, a frog is anesthetized, its heart is exposed, and the nerve connections to the various areas of its heart are selectively blocked. Frogs have a three-chambered heart, with right and left atria and a single ventricle. They also have a sinus venosus, which receives oxygen-depleted blood from all parts of the body except the lungs. The sinus venosus (the pacemaker in this case) is

where contractions begin. In the experiment, probes from the sinus venosus, right atrium, and ventricle are each attached to a fine pen on a kymograph, an instrument that graphs pressure changes. The upward pulses in the following graphs represent contractions.

(a) Interpret the data under the "Normal" heading of each graph.

(b) What can you conclude from this experiment about the rate of beat for the three different parts of the heart?

(c) To understand how the heart beats when the impulse from the sinus venosus is blocked, a thread is tied around the heart between the sinus venosus and the atrium. In the graphs, this is called an S-A block. How does the S-A block affect the rate of the beat of the sinus venosus?

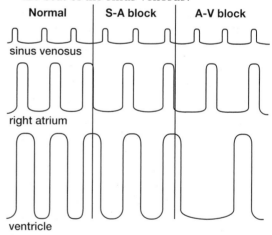

(d) Based on the graphs, how does blocking the sinus venosus affect the rate at which the atrium and ventricle beat?

(e) The action between the atrium and the ventricle is also blocked. How does this action, which is called an A-V block, affect the beat of the sinus venosus, the atrium, and the ventricle?

(f) Record your conclusions.

58. You are working for the Humane Society. A family comes in to adopt a cat. They are strict vegans and want to raise their pet on a vegan diet. Write them an e-mail detailing your advice and providing your supporting reasons.

59. Summarize clearly the relationship between cardiovascular fitness and diet.

60. Controversy stills surrounds the topic of smoking and its effects on both smokers and non-smokers. You are given the responsibility of preparing a case to a parliamentary committee that outlines the impact of smoking on the health, lifestyle, and economics of Canadians. As you prepare your speech and accompanying report, consider how you will address questions and arguments that may be raised by those who support smoking.

61. Being overweight is a concern for many North Americans. A weight-loss consultant claims the problem can easily be solved by surgically removing sections of obese people's digestive systems. You wish to demonstrate to your friends that such a solution could prove dangerous. Prepare a chart that lists the components of the human digestive system in one column and the consequences of removing (a) part of and (b) the entire component in a second column.

62. Cystic fibrosis I is a serious condition of the respiratory system that can lead to death. You are given the responsibility of preparing literature for a new campaign to raise public awareness of this disease. What information would you include in your material?

63. Explain how your knowledge of cells and cell metabolism could be applied to your study of digestion and nutrition.

64. Evaluate how training for a sport requiring strength would differ from training for a sport requiring cardiovascular fitness.

65. The laboratory where you work wants to invent a blood vessel substitute. After evaluating both synthetic and natural materials, which would you recommend to be most suitable? Why?

66. Decide why an individual with an inflammation of the gall bladder might also develop an inflammation of the pancreas.

67. The Canadian government is funding a special five-year study to help determine the causes of heart disease and heart attacks in Canadians. The citizens of Caledon East, a small Ontario town, have agreed to participate. You are in charge of designing the Caledon East study. What will your plan be? What data will you need to collect? How will you obtain the data? What will your hypotheses be? Give reasons for your choices and proposed course of action.

COURSE CHALLENGE

No organ system functions independently of any other. They are all intimately connected and related. Your understanding of these connections will serve you well when you carry out the Biology Course Challenge. This challenge will test your ability to apply what you have learned and to demonstrate your understanding of the relationships between systems. To help prepare for the challenge you will want to

- Describe the links that you have made between breathing and respiration, the circulatory system, and digestion and nutrition.

- Examine how your study of internal systems and regulation has helped you gain a clearer understanding of the interrelationships between these systems.

- Prepare a concept map showing the links and relationships between these systems. To do this, first make separate concept maps of each of the three systems and then join them together in a larger concept map.

4

Overall Expectations

In this Unit, you will

- understand the diversity of living organisms and viruses by applying concepts of taxonomy and phylogeny,

- sample and classify organisms,

- examine how similarity and diversity within the kingdoms of life affect biodiversity, and examine connections between biodiversity and survival of species, and

- learn how scientists use the characteristics of organisms in biotechnology.

Unit Contents

UNIT ISSUE PREP

Read pages 512–513 before beginning this unit.

- Begin collecting information about endangered species in Canada.

- Choose the organism you will be investigating.

- Start planning by setting up files for information on your endangered species.

Diversity of Living Things

In the early 1980s, a biologist studying life forms in the tropical forest canopy in Panama astonished the world with his estimate that there may be 30 million species of insects alone — many times more than previously thought. At the same time, he suggested that many of these insects were rare, specialized organisms found only in association with certain other animals or plants. As tropical forests and other ecosystems are being altered by human activities, millions of species are at risk of extinction before we even know they exist.

This unit introduces you to the remarkable variety of living things on Earth. Is there any value in all this diversity? The more scientists study the relationships among organisms, the more we understand the significance of biodiversity and the risks of high rates of extinction. All of our food and many of our medicines come from living things which depend for their survival on a network of other organisms. Research in biotechnology shows that many species have unexpected genetic properties that could be beneficially applied in the fields of agriculture, medicine, and pollution control.

During your lifetime, humanity will have the challenge of slowing a rate of extinction that is already approaching rates found during the most catastrophic eras in life's history. Part of the challenge is to understand the pattern of life's diversity and the place of *Homo sapiens* in the web linking every species with every other.

These tiny leafcutter ants belong to just one of the millions of insect species that are critical to the health and survival of ecosystems all over the planet. How would their extinction affect the rainforest where they live?

Patterns of Life

Reflecting Questions

- How can you know internal features of an organism by looking at its external characteristics?

- What evidence do scientists need to accurately classify an organism?

- How could you determine which of these organisms are most similar to each other: a sea squirt, a bee, a human?

Suppose you are lost in a strange forest and want to build a wooden shelter. You have an axe, a saw, and other tools, but there are many different types of trees to choose from. Which tree might you pick to make your shelter, and why? Carpenters are aware that different woods have different properties, such as colour, hardness, and strength. They divide trees broadly into softwoods and hardwoods. Softwoods are from coniferous trees, such as pine, spruce, and fir. Hardwoods come from deciduous species, such as oak, maple, and ash. If you know how to identify and classify trees, you can choose a species with the characteristics of wood best suited to your project.

Not only trees, but all plants, animals, and other organisms can be organized into groups sharing certain characteristics. These categories may have a practical advantage, such as grouping together plants with medicinal properties, or animals that are poisonous. For biologists, classification is a valuable way of learning how organisms are related to one another. For example, based on the numbers of characteristics they share, a pine and a spruce are more closely related to one another than either is to an oak.

In this chapter, you will discover the principles that biologists use to organize and classify all species — including those that are extinct. Although the details of classification change as scientists gather new information, the principles used to classify organisms are generally standard. By the end of the chapter, you will be able to identify, name, and classify organisms from all the major groups of organisms. With this information, you can make sense of the amazing diversity of life on our planet, and begin to interpret patterns in the structure and distribution of living things around the world.

This barn owl is included in a classification scheme that contains other birds. The same classification principles allow you to organize and identify species present in this mixed wood forest.

Chapter Contents

EXPECTATIONS

- Describe characteristics of representative organisms.
- Compare the structure and function of prokaryotic and eukaryotic cells.
- Classify organisms living in your neighbourhood.

Figure 11.1 Is this an animal or a plant? How would you decide?

Everyone classifies. You classify your books by grouping them in a particular order on a shelf. You classify your clothes by putting them in particular drawers or hanging them up in the closet. The groups we make and the names we give the groups reflect patterns in the world around us. Some groups are clearly defined. For example, "people under 18 years of age" and "people 18 years of age or older." Other groups are more fuzzy. For example, "people who speak French" and "people who don't speak French." In which group would you place people who know a few French phrases but are not fluent? One of the most interesting challenges for biologists is finding a way to classify Earth's millions of species.

If you were given the task of separating all organisms into categories, how could you begin? What characteristics would you use to classify living things? Among the most obvious are the characteristics that separate animals and plants. Over two thousand years ago, the Greek philosopher Aristotle divided all living things into these two large groups, **Plantae** and **Animalia**. He called each group a **kingdom**, a term still used today.

Classifying organisms is not always straightforward. You could start with the fact that most animals are motile (have a method of locomotion) and ingest the food they have obtained. Most plants, on the other hand, are non-motile and obtain their food through photosynthesis. However, some organisms, such as the ones shown in

Figure 11.1, appear to have characteristics of both plants and animals. For example, sponges and corals, like those in Figure 11.2, spend most of their lives fixed in one place like plants. Unlike plants, however, sponges and corals do not make their own food through photosynthesis.

Figure 11.2 Some organisms, such as these sponges and the coral reef that they live on, can be difficult to classify using obvious characteristics such as the ability to move.

Micro-organisms

Classifying organisms became more difficult after the microscope was invented in the seventeenth century. The new magnifying tool revealed a previously unknown world of living things. Some microscopic organisms have methods of locomotion and capture their food, as animals do. Some carry out photosynthesis, as plants do. However, some micro-organisms have characteristics of both animals and plants. For example, euglena are common single-celled organisms that swim by means of a flagellum but also carry out photosynthesis.

In 1866, the German biologist Ernst Haeckel proposed classifying micro-organisms that are neither animals nor plants in a third kingdom, which he named **Protista**. As biologists learned more about the structure and way of life of different organisms, they added more kingdoms to the classification system. Fungi, such as mushrooms and moulds, were originally included in the plant kingdom. However, fungi do not carry out photosynthesis. They obtain food by absorbing materials into their bodies. They are classified in a fourth kingdom, named **Fungi**.

Bacteria consist of very small cells that differ in appearance from the cells of animals, plants, protists, and fungi. Bacteria lack a nucleus and other organelles, and are able to grow and obtain energy in a wide range of environments. They are classified in a fifth kingdom, named **Bacteria**. Some textbooks refer to this kingdom as Eubacteria, Prokaryotae, or Monera.

During the 1990s, there was growing interest in certain types of bacteria found living in extreme environments, such as salt lakes or hot, acidic springs. Detailed studies showed that these organisms have unique structures and mechanisms that allow them to live in conditions where no other organisms — including other bacteria — can survive. The new data led scientists to rename these micro-organisms and to reclassify them in a sixth kingdom, named **Archaea**. Some sources may refer to these organisms as Archaebacteria. These six kingdoms are shown in Figure 11.3 on the next page.

MINI LAB

Organizing Life

How many different organisms live in your neighbourhood? In this activity, you will make an inventory of and classify local species. Make a list of all the different organisms you observe during a 15-minute walk around your school or home. Be as specific as possible (for example, robin, not bird; earthworm, not worm). You should have at least 20 species in your list. Organize your list into groups based on the similarities and differences you observe among the various types of organisms. Begin by choosing a characteristic that lets you divide your list of organisms into two groups: one group that has the characteristic and one group that does not (for example, wings and no wings). List the organisms in each group on a separate sheet of paper. Record the group characteristic in your notebook. Next, decide if you can subdivide one or both of your groups using another characteristic. If so, list the organisms in your new subgroups on separate sheets of paper. Continue subdividing your lists until you cannot see another way to do so. Record the classification characteristics you use in your notebook.

Analyze

1. What characteristics did you use to define your groups of organisms? How many different subgroups did you make? Suggest a way in which you could improve the classification of your groups.

2. Exchange your collection of groups with a partner. Can you discover the characteristics used by your partner to create each group? Record the characteristics you think your partner used. How accurately did your partner identify the characteristics of each group you created? Explain.

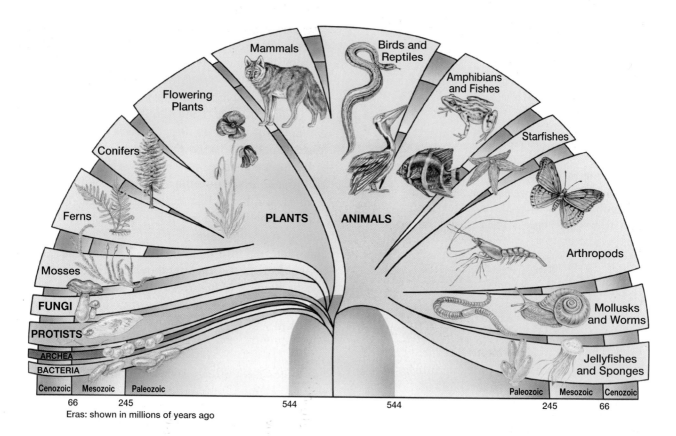

Figure 11.3 This fan diagram represents the six kingdoms of life extending out over the geologic time scale. The origin of life is shown at the base during the Precambrian Era, and present-day species are represented along the outer edge of the fan. Each kingdom is represented by a different colour.

> PLAY

The incredible diversity of living things can be difficult to appreciate with only a few examples. Go to your Electronic Learning Partner for videos showing the biodiversity present in different ecosystems.

Classifying to Kingdom

Kingdoms describe very large groups of organisms. Usually, you need more than one single characteristic in order to identify which kingdom an organism belongs to. The best way to classify organisms is to study as many of their different characteristics as possible.

Your teacher will provide you with samples of two organisms you have probably never seen before. Your task is to classify each by kingdom. Observe the samples both with the naked eye and under a microscope. Record as many characteristics of each specimen as possible. Review your list and determine the kingdom to which each organism belongs.

Analyze

1. What characteristics of each organism helped you make your decision? Explain why these characteristics were helpful.

2. Your teacher will provide you with other examples of organisms in different kingdoms. List characteristics that you could use to classify these organisms just by looking at them. Would you need more information? Explain your answer.

3. What characteristics on your list are present in more than one kingdom? Are there any characteristics that were not helpful in your classification scheme? List the characteristics that you did not find helpful. Discuss why you feel they are not helpful.

Prokaryotes and Eukaryotes

The study of cells is an important first step in understanding the diversity of life. Biologists recognize two basic types of cells based on differences in their size, structure, and other characteristics, shown in Figure 11.4. Recall from Chapter 2 that cells lacking a true nucleus and most other types of organelles are called prokaryotic cells (*pro* means before, *karyon* means nucleus). Bacteria and archaea, the smallest and simplest type of cells, are referred to as prokaryotes. The cells of other organisms are larger and have a more complex internal structure. They contain nuclei and other types of membrane-bound organelles. Such cells are called eukaryotic cells (*eu* means true), and organisms with these cells are called eukaryotes. Table 11.1 summarizes some of the differences between these cells.

Table 11.1
Two types of cells

Prokaryotes	Eukaryotes
bacteria, archaea	protists, plants, fungi, animals
small (1–10 μm)	large (100–1000 μm)
DNA circular, not bounded by membrane	DNA in nucleus bounded by membrane
genome made up of a single chromosome	genome made up of several chromosomes
cell division not by mitosis and meiosis	cell division by mitosis and meiosis
asexual reproduction common	sexual reproduction common
multicellular forms rare	most forms are multicellular
mitochondria and other membrane-bound organelles absent	mitochondria and other organelles present
many are anaerobic (do not require oxygen)	most are aerobic (require oxygen)

Fossil evidence shows that the first forms of life were prokaryotic organisms similar in appearance to bacteria. Remains of these single-celled organisms have been found in rocks dated at 3.5 billion years old. The first eukaryotes did not appear until about 2 billion years later (1.5 billion years ago). The first multicellular forms of life appeared only 700 million years ago. In other words, unicellular organisms have a much longer history than do multicellular organisms such as plants, animals, and fungi.

Math LINK

Draw a graph or pie chart illustrating the proportions of the following relationships:
- First prokaryotes appear 3.5 billion years ago.
- First eukaryotes appear 1.5 billion years ago.
- First multicellular organisms appear 700 million years ago.

For what percentage of time that life has existed on Earth did it consist only of prokaryotes?

For what percentage of time that life has existed on Earth did it consist only of unicellular organisms?

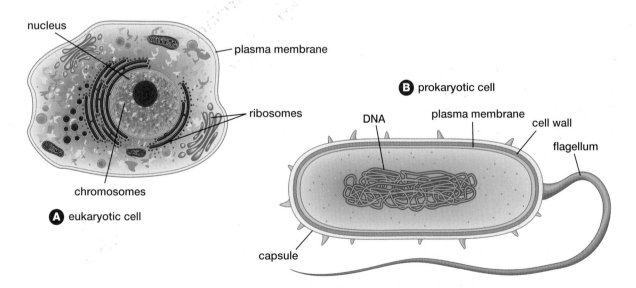

Figure 11.4 Plants, animal, fungi, and protists are referred to as eukaryotes. They contain eukaryotic cells like the one shown in (A). Bacteria and archaea are referred to as prokaryotes. They are prokaryotic cells like the one shown in (B).

The Three Domains

Although today's prokaryotes look little different from the earliest forms of life, recent research has shown that living prokaryotes are far more diverse than anyone had previously suspected. Details of the molecular biology of bacteria and archaea, especially studies of their RNA structure, show that they are as different from each other as either is from eukaryotes. This led to these three groups being organized into a new level of classification above kingdoms, known as **domains**. The three domains — Bacteria, Archaea, and Eukarya — are shown in Figure 11.5.

Within the Domain Eukarya, the greatest biological diversity occurs within the Kingdom Protista. For example, there is a much greater genetic difference between some species of protists than there is between, for example, corn and humans. Protists have lived on Earth for a much longer time than plants and animals, which has given this group more opportunity to change and diversify. Many scientists believe the Kingdom Protista should be divided into several different kingdoms, but no one new system of classification for it has been generally accepted.

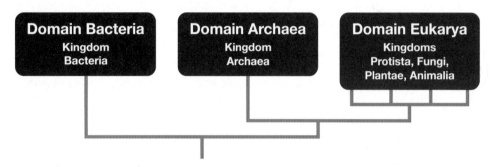

Figure 11.5 Kingdoms are grouped into three domains based on the types of cells the organisms in each kingdom have. Note that Eukarya are linked more closely to Archaea than to Bacteria.

SECTION REVIEW

1. **K/U** List examples of classification systems you use every day.

2. **K/U** Would a group identified as "flying animals" be useful to a biologist? Explain why or why not.

3. **K/U** Why should all scientists use the same scheme to classify living things?

4. **C** Create a concept organizer to show the different domains and kingdoms. Include the appropriate characteristics that define each grouping in list form.

5. **I** You have discovered an unknown organism while on a field trip. You think it is a new species of protist. How could you test to identify this species as a protist? What data would you need to have to classify it in the Kingdom Protista?

6. **K/U** Plants and fungi have been classified in the same kingdom in the past. Most scientists today classify fungi in their own kingdom. Explain how these two different classification schemes are supported by data.

7. **I** You discover an unusual organism growing on the bark of a dying tree. Later, in the laboratory, you look at some of its cells under a microscope. It is a multicellular organism with eukaryotic cells, but no chloroplasts. To what kingdom does it belong?

8. **C** Using the information contained in Table 11.1 and Figure 11.4, create a handout contrasting prokaryotic and eukaryotic cells. If you were to teach this material to students in an earlier grade, what information would be the most important to teach them the basic differences between the two cell types?

9. **MC** When a new development is being proposed, the developer usually has to submit an Environmental Impact Assessment. This is a scientific study that outlines the effect of the development on the local environment. Explain how a knowledge of classification would be necessary to prepare your Environmental Impact Assessment. Why would you need to know about the different kingdoms?

EXPECTATIONS

- Describe characteristics of a representative virus.
- Learn the life cycles of representative viruses.
- Explain the relevance of current studies of viruses to the field of biotechnology.

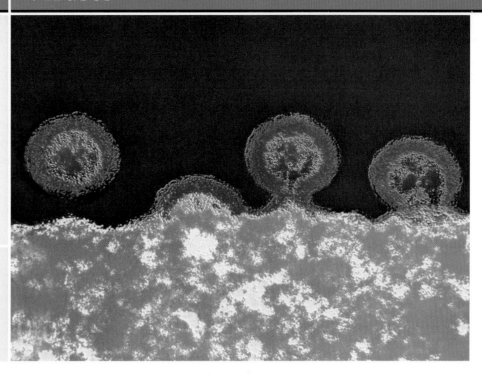

Figure 11.6 HIV viruses budding from the surface of a host T-lymphocyte white blood cell. The viruses are acquiring their protein coat from the host cell's plasma membrane.

Many diseases of plants and animals (including humans) are caused by bacteria or viruses that invade the body. You might think, because of this, that bacteria and viruses are roughly similar kinds of micro-organisms. Yet bacteria are classified as living organisms, while viruses are not.

What are viruses? You have probably learned that scientists consider cells to be the basic units of life. **Viruses** have no cellular structure, so by this definition, viruses are not organisms and they are not classified in any kingdom of living things. Viruses have no cytoplasm, organelles, or cell membranes. They do not carry out respiration or many other common life processes. Viruses consist of little more than strands of DNA or RNA surrounded by a protective protein coat called a **capsid** (Figure 11.6). In effect, viruses are mobile genes that parasitize cells. The capsid protects the virus from attack by the host cell enzymes, and it helps the virus attach itself to specific receptors on the host cell.

Classifying Viruses

Since viruses were first identified in 1935, scientists have described more than 160 major groups. Members of different groups differ in their size and shape as shown in Figure 11.7. The shape is determined by the type and arrangement of proteins in the capsid. Polyhedral viruses such as the polio virus resemble small crystals and may

have as many as 20 sides. The HIV virus that causes AIDS, has a spherical shape. The tobacco mosaic virus has a cylindrical shape. The T4 virus infects bacteria. It has a polyhedral head attached to a protein tail and several tail fibres. Some groups of viruses are able to replicate only in a particular species, while others may be found, for example, in both animals and plants, or in both plants and fungi. Viruses are also grouped by the types of diseases they cause. Viruses that infect humans are currently classified into 21 groups. These groups differ in their genomes (set of genes) and their method of replication.

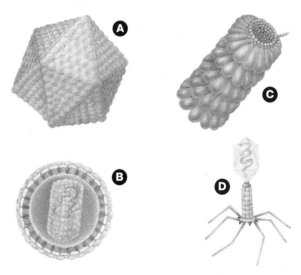

Figure 11.7 Virus particles have a variety of shapes. The viruses shown here, include (A) the polio virus, (B) the HIV virus, (C) the tobacco mosaic virus, and (D) the T4 virus.

Viral Reproduction

One characteristic viruses do share with living things is the ability to multiply. However, a virus cannot do this on its own. It depends entirely on the metabolism of a eukaryotic or prokaryotic cell to replicate its DNA or RNA and to make protein coats for each newly formed virus particle.

Before a virus can enter any cell, it must attach to a specific receptor site on the plasma membrane of the host cell. The proteins on the surface of the virus act as keys that fit exactly into a matching shape on the host cell membrane. For example, a protein in the tail fibres of the T4 virus shown in Figure 11.7 on the previous page, recognizes and attaches the T4 to the specific host cell. In other viruses, the attachment protein is in the capsid or in the envelope. This attachment sequence, where the virus recognizes and attaches to the host cell, is like two jigsaw pieces fitting together. Because each virus has a specifically shaped attachment protein, the virus can only attach to a few specific types of cells. The T4 virus mentioned above, for example, can only infect certain bacterial cells. It cannot attach to a plant or animal cell. Some viruses are even specialized to the type of cells within an organism. The polio virus, for example, infects human nerve and intestinal cells. This specificity is very important for controlling the spread of viral diseases. Therefore, each virus can only enter particular cells with specific receptor sites. Outside of their host cell, viruses are completely inert.

Viruses can enter cells in two different ways. In the first, once attached to the host cell, the virus can inject its nucleic acid into the cell. Figure 11.8 shows the steps to this cycle of viral replication, called the **lytic cycle**. A typical lytic cycle takes about 30 min, and may produce up to 200 new viruses. If a virus is contained in an envelope, it may enter in a second way. After the virus attaches, the membrane of the host cell surrounds the virus. This creates a vacuole inside in the host cell's cytoplasm that contains the virus. When the virus breaks out of the vacuole, it releases its nucleic acid into the cell.

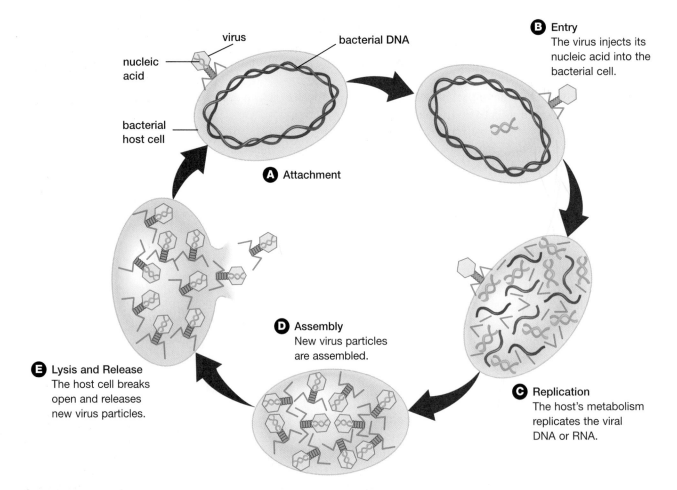

Figure 11.8 The lytic cycle occurs when a virus inserts its nucleic acid into a cell, and then uses the cell's metabolism to replicate its DNA or RNA and make new viruses.

Viruses and Disease

In the lytic cycle of a virus, shown in Figure 11.8, newly formed viruses burst from the host cell, usually killing it. In multicellular hosts, these new viruses then infect neighbouring cells, thereby causing damage to their host. The amount of damage and its effects on the host vary.

Human immunodeficiency virus (HIV) is an example of a type of RNA virus called a **retrovirus**. Retroviruses contain an enzyme called reverse transcriptase. This enzyme causes the host cell to copy the viral RNA into DNA (Figure 11.9). In this form, the viral genome can enter the chromosomes of the host cell and be copied when the cell divides. You will learn more about RNA viruses in the viral genome section on page 389.

In other cases, viruses can invade a cell but not kill it. These viruses undergo a different type of replication cycle in which their DNA becomes integrated with the host cell chromosomes. Once inserted into the host chromosomes, the viral DNA is called a **provirus**. When the host cell divides through the process of mitosis, it replicates the provirus along with its own DNA. Every descendant of the host cell will carry a copy of the provirus in its chromosomes. This process can continue for years, with no harm to the host. As part of the host chromosomes, the virus cannot be easily detected by medical tests. At any time, however, the provirus can separate from the host chromosomes and complete the more damaging lytic cycle shown in Figure 11.8.

The replication strategies of viruses help explain certain patterns of disease. For example, the herpes simplex virus causes cold sores in people. These sores may appear and disappear on the skin of an infected person throughout her or his lifetime. The sores appear when the viral cycle destroys cells, and they disappear when the virus is in its provirus stage. The exact trigger that causes the switch from one phase to another is not known.

Other viruses follow variations of the replication strategies already described. For example, HIV forms a provirus in the host cell chromosomes, but it also produces small numbers of new viruses while the cell continues to function normally. This explains why people may test positive for HIV but remain healthy for many years. Only when the infection spreads to more and more cells do the symptoms of AIDS (Acquired Immune Deficiency Syndrome) eventually appear. The symptoms result from infections by other micro-organisms because the HIV virus has destroyed the body's T-lymphocytes, which help the immune system fight off other diseases.

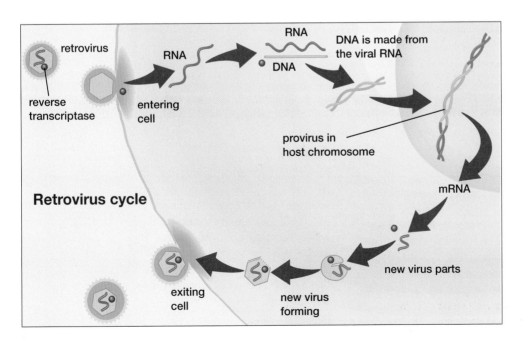

Figure 11.9 Reproductive cycle of a retrovirus. Retroviruses contain an enzyme that causes the host cell to copy viral RNA into DNA. This DNA becomes a provirus that continues to produce new viruses without destroying the cell.

▶ PLAY

Your Electronic Learning Partner has animations to demonstrate the lytic cycle and the retrovirus reproductive cycle.

Viruses and Biotechnology

Because viruses enter host cells and direct the activity of the host cell's DNA, they can be useful tools for genetic engineers. For example, if researchers want to clone a gene, they first splice the gene into the genome of a virus. The virus then enters a host cell and directs the cell to make multiple copies of the virus. Each new virus in each new cell contains the added gene that the researchers wanted copied. This process is illustrated in Figure 11.10.

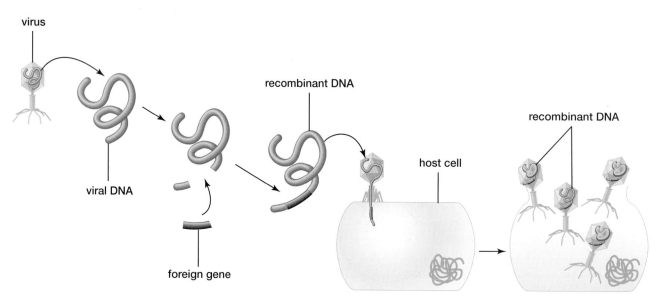

Figure 11.10 Genetic engineers use viruses to introduce new genes into a cell and to clone copies of genes.

MINI LAB

Viral Replication

Viruses are very successful at invading the cells of organisms because they can only reproduce using the metabolism of a host cell. In this lab you will diagram the steps involved in viral replication in cells. Your teacher will give you 5 photocopies of a drawing showing a bacterial cell. Put one of the following labels on each sheet: Attachment; Penetration; Biosynthesis; Maturation; Release. Using these headings as a guide, on each figure draw the different stages in the process of viral replication. At the bottom of each diagram, summarize each step in words.

Analyze

How do replication and protein synthesis occur in a cell? In what way is viral replication different from cell reproduction? Examine your completed diagrams of viral replication. What two processes are directed by viral genes that are activated inside the host cell? Describe the stage that occurs before viruses are released from the cell. To summarize and enhance what you have learned in this lab, write an essay that explains the different ways viruses invade host cells and replicate. Use your library or the Internet to gather your information.

The Viral Genome

The genome of a virus consists of either DNA or RNA. The entire genome may occur as a single nucleic acid molecule or several nucleic acid segments. The DNA or RNA may be single-stranded or double-stranded, and either linear or circular.

Because viruses are so small, the size of the genome is limited. For example, the genome includes coded instructions for making only a few different proteins that are needed to make the capsid. In contrast, the human genome codes for over 30 000 different proteins. Most DNA viruses have their genome on a single, linear, double-stranded DNA molecule. Some groups of these viruses require the presence of helper viruses to reproduce themselves. They are said to be replication defective.

RNA viruses comprise 70% of all viruses. The process of RNA replication frequently involves errors, and as a result these viruses usually have much higher mutation rates than do DNA viruses. Mutations provide new variants of the virus, some of which may be better adapted to invade new hosts.

Origin of Viruses

Where do viruses fit into the history of life? Because they cannot replicate without host cells, they must have evolved after the first cells came into existence. They probably originated as fragments of nucleic acid that escaped from their original cell. They survived by becoming parasites of the same or similar types of cell. Viruses and their hosts evolved together, and each type of virus is probably more closely related to its host cells than to other viruses in different groups.

BIO FACT

Viruses are much smaller than prokaryotic cells and cannot be seen with a light microscope. They vary in size from about one half to one one-hundredth the size of the smallest bacterium. While bacteria were first observed in the 1670s, viruses were not identified until 1935, after electron microscopes had been invented.

SECTION REVIEW

1. **K/U** Describe the structure of a virus. Why are viruses considered to be non-living?

2. **K/U** Why must a virus enter a host cell in order to reproduce itself?

3. **K/U** What are the different ways a virus can reproduce using a host cell?

4. **C** Draw the lytic and retrovirus reproductive cycles to show the similarities and differences between these two processes.

5. **K/U** A doctor tells a patient that an antibiotic will not help cure a cold sore. Explain the doctor's reasoning.

6. **K/U** How is viral replication similar to the making of a product in a factory? How does it differ from the making of a product in a factory?

7. **MC** Explain how viruses might be used to copy the gene for producing human insulin.

8. **K/U** Consider the data table above right, on incubation time of different viral diseases. Use the data to predict which diseases are caused by viruses that undergo the lytic cycle, versus diseases that include a provirus stage. What is a possible public health consequence of the incubation time for diseases caused by proviruses?

Disease	Incubation time
Measles	9-11 days
Shingles	years
Warts	months
Cold	2-4 days
HIV	2-5 years

9. **I** The following table records the estimated numbers of viruses found in samples taken from a bacterial culture at hourly intervals.

Plot the data on a graph and interpret them to explain what was happening in the bacterial culture.

Hour	Number of viruses
1	15
2	17
3	49
4	128
5	385
6	386
7	386
8	387

10. **MC** If you were a scientist developing a drug that would block viral replication, which steps would you choose to block? Explain your answer in detail.

The Classification of Living Things

EXPECTATIONS

- Define the fundamental principles of taxonomy.
- Demonstrate the usefulness of the system of scientific nomenclature.
- Construct a key for the identification of different organisms.

Figure 11.11 Features such as petals are used to classify flowering plants into different groups or taxa.

When detectives ask an eyewitness to describe a getaway vehicle, the more specific the description the witness gives, the more likely it is that the detectives will be able to identify the car. The model, colour, and year of the car all narrow down the search. But there may still be hundreds or thousands of vehicles that fit this description. Of course, the license plate number is the best evidence of all. Together with the other details, it accurately describes one particular car.

In the same way, biologists need specific details to identify organisms. For example, if you ask a zoologist to help you identify a species of bird, it is not very useful to describe the bird as small and brown. Many dozens of species of small brown birds live in Canada. One purpose of a classification system, therefore, is to allow the accurate identification of a particular organism.

The practice of classifying organisms is known as **taxonomy** (*taxis* means arrangement and *nomos* means law). The system of taxonomy used by scientists today was founded nearly 300 years ago by a Swedish botanist named Carolus Linnaeus (1707–1778). Linnaeus used simple physical characteristics to identify different species and organize them into groups. For example, he based his classification of flowering plants, like the one shown in Figure 11.11, on the number and arrangement of features such as petals and stamens. Using this system, people could accurately identify an organism by comparing its appearance against a checklist of characteristics.

During the 1700s, explorers from Europe were discovering more and more of the world's rich diversity of plants and animals — including many species Europeans had never seen before. Thanks to the work of Linnaeus, they were able to classify these unknown organisms into groups of similar species. Linnaeus's system was so easy to use that it quickly became popular.

Naming Organisms

Biologists still use Linnaeus's method of naming each species using two words, such as *Felis domesticus* (the house cat). Many of these names are based on Latin or Greek words because when Linnaeus developed his system of classification in the 1700s, these classical languages were the common languages of science. When scientists find and describe new species, they are required to give the species a Latin scientific name. These names often reflect characteristics of the organisms, or in other cases, the names are given to honour a fellow scientist or historical figure. Latin continues to be used for these new names.

Figure 11.12 A bee, shark, horse, dog, and oyster are all members of the animal kingdom.

Hierarchy of Groups

As members of the animal kingdom, the bee, shark, horse, dog, and oyster shown in Figure 11.12 have certain things in common. On the other hand, these animals are obviously not very much alike. There are different degrees of similarity among animals. For example, a horse is more like a dog than like a shark (horses and dogs are mammals; sharks are fish). However a horse is more like a shark than like an oyster (horses and sharks are vertebrates; oysters are invertebrates). To distinguish such different degrees of similarity, each kingdom is subdivided several times into a series of progressively smaller groups. Each group is called a **taxon** (plural taxa).

Kingdoms are the largest and most general taxa — they include many thousands of species. Species are the smallest taxa — they include only a single type of organism. Between kingdoms and species, organisms are classified into a minimum of five other taxa, which form a hierarchy of groups. Table 11.2 lists the names of these taxa and gives an example of each. In some systems, additional taxa are used to help subdivide large groups. For example, subphylum is an added taxon between phylum and class.

Table 11.2
An example of hierarchical classification

Taxon	Example	Organisms included in this taxon
Kingdom	Animalia	bee, shark, horse, oyster, frog, dog, cougar, lynx, bobcat
Phylum	Chordata	shark, horse, frog, dog, cougar, lynx, bobcat
Class	Mammalia	horse, dog, cougar, lynx, bobcat
Order	Carnivora	dog, cougar, lynx, bobcat
Family	Felidae	cougar, lynx, bobcat
Genus	*Lynx*	lynx, bobcat
Species	*Lynx canadensis*	lynx
Species	*Lynx rufus*	bobcat

You can see from Table 11.2 that a species is classified in a particular taxon at every level of the hierarchy. For example, a bobcat is a member of the Kingdom Animalia, the phylum Chordata, the class Mammalia, and so on. As you move down the table, each taxon contains fewer species. As well, the smaller the taxon, the more similar the organisms within it. The taxon species includes members that resemble each other so closely that they can interbreed and produce fertile offspring.

❚❚ PAUSE **● RECORD**

Over 75% of named living species belong to the phylum Arthropoda, which includes such diverse organisms as lobsters, crabs, shrimp, barnacles, sow bugs, scorpions, spiders, mites, millipedes, and insects. The insects are by far the most abundant arthropods. What physical characteristic(s) do you think all arthropods have in common? List your ideas and explain them briefly.

◀◀ REWIND

To learn about the genetic basis for differences among species, turn to Chapter 6, Section 6.1.

Creating a Dichotomous Key

If you find an insect you have never seen before, how could you discover its identity? Many field guides help you match up the characteristics of your specimen with those of similar organisms using a dichotomous key. This identification key uses a series of paired comparisons to sort organisms into smaller and smaller groups. In this investigation, you will learn how to make your own keys to identification.

Pre-lab Questions

- What characteristics do all insects have in common?
- Name two characteristics that scientists use to tell different insects apart.

Problem

How do you make a dichotomous key?

Prediction

Predict which characteristics of insects will be most useful in creating an identification key.

Materials

illustration of 18 beetles	sample dichotomous keys
paper	pencil

Procedure

1. Copy the diagram of a dichotomous tree shown here onto a separate piece of paper.

2. Study the illustration of 18 beetles shown on the next page.

3. Select one characteristic and sort the beetles into two groups based on whether they have the characteristic or not.

4. List each beetle's number under either Group 1 or Group 2 on your diagram.

5. Record the characteristic that identifies each group.

6. Select another characteristic of each subgroup, and repeat steps 4 and 5 for the next level down on your diagram.

7. Continue to subdivide the groups until you have 18 groups with one beetle in each.

8. Using the characteristics shown on your diagram, construct a dichotomous key that someone could use to identify any beetle from the original large group. To do this, create a series of numbered steps with the first step showing the first characteristic you used. At each step, offer two choices for classifying the beetle based on a single characteristic. For example, you may have used the characteristic "antennae longer than front legs" as your first dividing characteristic. Your first numbered step in your key would be (1a) antennae longer than front legs or (1b) antennae not longer than front legs. Use the sample keys provided by your teacher to help you.

9. Exchange your key with a partner. Use your partner's key to classify a beetle, and record all the characteristics of the species you chose.

Post-lab Questions

1. Did your partner produce a dichotomous key identical to yours? Explain why or why not.

2. Which beetle characteristics were not useful for creating your key? Explain why not.

Conclude and Apply

3. Why does a key offer two choices at each step and not more than two?

4. In your own words, define a dichotomous key.

Exploring Further

5. Your teacher will provide you with several different "mystery" beetles. Use your dichotomous key and see if you can identify what species the beetles are. You may be unable to completely identify your beetle using your key. If this is the case, how far could you go with your key? Visit the library or the Internet and get a field guide to beetles. Use this to identify the mystery beetles. What characteristics would you have needed in your key in order to fully identify them?

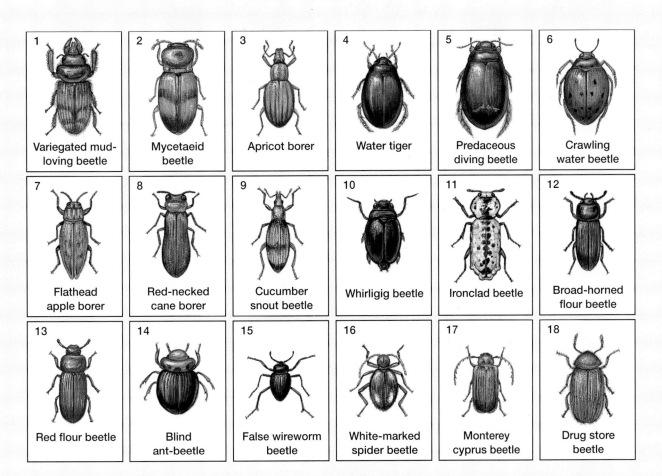

1 Variegated mud-loving beetle	2 Mycetaeid beetle	3 Apricot borer	4 Water tiger	5 Predaceous diving beetle	6 Crawling water beetle
7 Flathead apple borer	8 Red-necked cane borer	9 Cucumber snout beetle	10 Whirligig beetle	11 Ironclad beetle	12 Broad-horned flour beetle
13 Red flour beetle	14 Blind ant-beetle	15 False wireworm beetle	16 White-marked spider beetle	17 Monterey cyprus beetle	18 Drug store beetle

The system of using a two-word name for each species is called **binomial nomenclature**. The first word is the name of the genus (plural genera) in which the organism is classified. The first letter of this name is capitalized. Because a genus may contain more than one species, there may be several species with the same first name. For example, the genus *Canis* includes *Canis lupus*

(wolf), *Canis latrans* (coyote), and *Canis familiaris* (domestic dog). The fact that these three animals have the same first name tells you that they are all in the same genus of dog-like animals and are very similar to one another. The second word in the name identifies the particular species. Thus, each species name has a unique two-word combination.

 THINKING LAB

Classifying Dinner

Background

For dinner one evening, you are served a seafood stew containing lobster, squid, mussels, and two types of oysters. In the same way that the marine organisms are mixed up together in your bowl, the various names of the taxa that identify these five species are mixed up in the chart to the right. In this lab, you will redraw the chart and place each organism in its proper taxon at each level of the hierarchy.

Common name	Market squid, American lobster, blue mussel, Virginia oyster, European oyster
Phylum	Arthropoda, Mollusca, Mollusca, Mollusca, Mollusca
Class	Malacostraca, Bivalvia, Bivalvia, Bivalvia, Cephalopoda
Order	Decapoda, Decapoda, Mytiloida, Pterioida, Pterioida
Family	Ostreidae, Ostreidae, Nephropidae, Mytilidae, Loliginidae
Genus	*Homarus, Mytilus, Ostrea, Loligo, Crassostrea*
Species	*americanus, virginica, edulis, edulis, opalescens*

You Try It

1. Draw a chart with six columns and seven rows. At the top of the first column, write "Taxon." At the top of each of the other columns, write the common name of one organism from the chart. Label the rows: Phylum, Class, Order, Family, Genus, and Species, matching the order on the chart. Use reference books or the Internet to gather enough information to classify each organism correctly at each taxon level.

2. According to your classification scheme, which is the only taxon level in which all five organisms have a different name? Which order name is found in both the Arthropoda and Mollusca phyla (plural of phylum)? What does this name mean? Which two genera (plural of genus) have species with names containing the same word? What does this word mean?

3. Which two organisms are most closely related to each other? Give a reason for your answer. Which organism is least closely related to the other four? Give a reason for your answer.

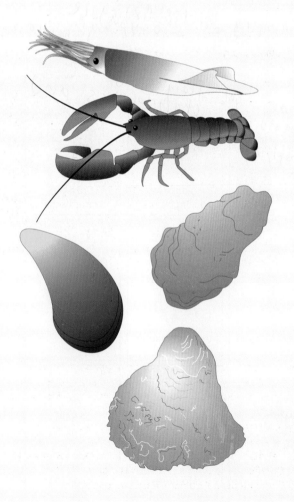

Common Names

You may wonder what is wrong with referring to organisms by their everyday names, such as "cat." Common names are not precise. The animal you think of when you hear the word "cat" may not be the same animal being described. There are different species of cats, such as wild cats and ring-tailed cats. Animals such as lions and tigers are also called cats. In addition, people in different regions may use different common names to refer to the same species. For example, puma, cougar, and mountain lion are three different common names for the same animal. Over 300 different species of trees around the world are called "mahogany." Each has its own scientific name.

Common names can give you misleading ideas about the basic characteristics of an organism and the group in which it should be classified. For example, should shellfish, starfish, jellyfish, crayfish, and catfish all be in the single group, fish? All these organisms are animals that live in water, but there are more significant differences between a shellfish and a starfish than between a catfish and you. In fact, biologists place each of these five members of the animal kingdom in a separate phylum (Figure 11.13).

A shellfish: phylum Mollusca

B starfish: phylum Echinodermata

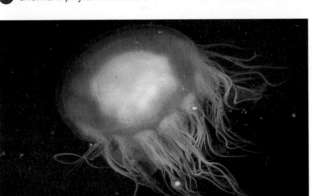

C jellyfish: phylum Cnidaria

D crayfish: phylum Arthropoda

E catfish: phylum Chordata

Figure 11.13 The common names of all these animals include the word "fish," but each animal is classified in a different phylum. You are classified in the same phylum as a catfish.
(A) Shellfish (Pacific pink scallop): *Chlamys hericia*
(B) Starfish (vermilion star): *Mediaster aequalis*
(C) Jellyfish (upsidedown jellyfish): *Cassiopea xamachana*
(D) Crayfish (blue crayfish): *Cambarus bartoni*
(E) Catfish (channel catfish): *Ictalurus punctatus*

The same common name may be used for different species. For example, the bird called a robin in Canada is a different species from the bird called a robin in Great Britain (Figure 11.14).

Figure 11.14 Bird A is called a robin in Canada. Bird B, a different species, is called a robin in Great Britain.

SECTION REVIEW

1. **K/U** List two reasons why the system of binomial nomenclature is useful.

2. **K/U** Cats, goldfish, and humans are in the same phylum. What characteristics do they have in common? What characteristics place cats and humans in a different order from goldfish?

3. **I** Based on your own knowledge, place the following species into three different phyla: ant, crow, spider, turtle, salmon, snail, octopus.

4. **I** The Greek philosopher Aristotle classified animals based on where they lived. Classify objects in your classroom in the same way, based on where they are found.

5. **I** Referring to the table shown here, which two animals are most closely related? Explain your answer.

6. **I** The information in this table shown here shows that a skunk is more closely related to a coyote than it is to a bat. Explain how you know this.

7. **I** What kind of an animal is *Myotis myotis*? How do you know? Use the table shown here to help you.

8. **C** Using the information contained in the table shown here, create a display showing the relationships of the organisms. You may draw them, create a flow chart or a concept map, or you may even create a key.

9. **MC** There is a growing concern worldwide about the numbers of species that are going extinct. Conservation organizations work to protect endangered species, however, there may be disagreement about what exactly a "species" is. How can naming an organism influence our attitudes about that organism? For example, is a fish more likely to be protected if it is a known endangered species, or if it is newly discovered and different from all known species of fish? How can a name influence our feelings about a particular organism? Discuss this topic and write a short essay about your ideas.

Organism	House cat	Dog	Coyote	Skunk	Brown bat	Praying mantis
Kingdom	Animalia	Animalia	Animalia	Animalia	Animalia	Animalia
Phylum	Chordata	Chordata	Chordata	Chordata	Chordata	Arthropoda
Class	Mammalia	Mammalia	Mammalia	Mammalia	Mammalia	Insecta
Order	Carnivora	Carnivora	Carnivora	Carnivora	Chiroptera	Mantodea
Family	Felidae	Canidae	Canidae	Mustelidae	Vespertilionidae	Mantidae
Genus	*Felix*	*Canis*	*Canis*	*Mephitis*	*Myotis*	*Stagmomantis*
Species	*domesticus*	*familiaris*	*latrans*	*mephitis*	*lucifugus*	*carolina*

 UNIT ISSUE PREP

You have just learned about how scientists name and classify organisms. You will be picking an endangered species to study for your Unit 4 Issue Analysis. Does the species that you are considering have a common name? What are the organisms' names in binomial nomenclature? Make sure you are considering organisms based on their proper Latin names, not the common names that might be confusing.

Origins of Diversity

- Explain the importance of sexual reproduction to variability within a population.
- Define the fundamental principles of phylogeny.
- Apply the concept of phylogeny to the kingdoms of life.

Figure 11.15 Each of these Galapagos finches is adapted to collecting and eating a different type of food. This variation is the result of initial variation within ancestral species of finches.

You know that species differ from one another. You have probably also noticed that the individual members of a single species differ. Although you are similar to all other humans, you are not exactly like any other person (unless you have an identical twin.) The diversity between species begins with this diversity *within* a species. For example, certain characteristics found in two populations of a single species may change and become dissimilar in response to differences in the environment where each population lives. Eventually, the characteristics of the two populations may diverge so much that they form new species (see Figure 11.15). The process by which new species evolve is called natural selection. This process was first described in 1859 by British naturalist Charles Darwin in his book, *On the Origin of Species by Means of Natural Selection.*

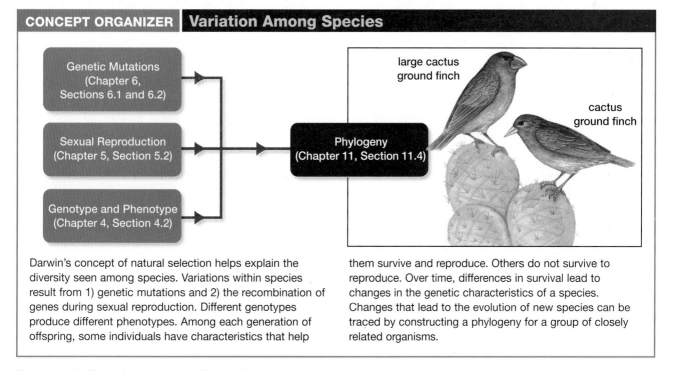

CONCEPT ORGANIZER | **Variation Among Species**

Darwin's concept of natural selection helps explain the diversity seen among species. Variations within species result from 1) genetic mutations and 2) the recombination of genes during sexual reproduction. Different genotypes produce different phenotypes. Among each generation of offspring, some individuals have characteristics that help them survive and reproduce. Others do not survive to reproduce. Over time, differences in survival lead to changes in the genetic characteristics of a species. Changes that lead to the evolution of new species can be traced by constructing a phylogeny for a group of closely related organisms.

Figure 11.16 Natural selection and the development of phylogeny.

Genetic Variation

Changes in the characteristics of a species are produced by a combination of random genetic mutations and selection for a particular characteristic that increases the organism's chances of survival and breeding in a particular environment (Figure 11.16 on the previous page). Random genetic mutations generate variety in all organisms but especially in organisms that usually reproduce asexually (such as prokaryotes). Asexual reproduction produces offspring genetically identical to the parent, so it normally results in no variation in characteristics. Mutation is the only mechanism that generates variety. Most organisms, however, reproduce sexually. The great advantage of sexual reproduction is that it provides genetic variation in every generation.

Investigation 11 • B

SKILL FOCUS

Performing and recording

Modelling concepts

Analyzing and interpreting

Communicating results

Variation and Selection in the Paper Bird (*Avis papyrus*)

The paper bird (*Avis papyrus*) depends on flight for its survival. Specifically, only those birds that can fly a long distance in a straight line can survive long enough to breed successfully and raise a new generation. In this investigation, you will work in groups to model natural selection by breeding several generations of paper birds from one ancestral bird and to observe how the characteristics of the species change over time. In this model, the source of variation is genetic mutations that affect the birds' wings. Since mutations are random, you will flip a coin and roll a die to determine the nature of the variation in traits in your group's young paper bird.

Pre-lab Questions

- How do characteristics of a species change?
- Explain how variation within a population will eventually affect variation among populations.

Problem

How can you model changes in characteristics to show the process of natural selection?

Prediction

Predict how variation in the paper birds' wings could cause the characteristics of the species to change over time.

Materials

paper	tape (clear or masking)
rigid drinking straws	six-sided die
scissors	penny
tape measure	masking tape

Procedure

1. Using this illustration and your teacher's instructions as a guide, construct an ancestral paper bird.

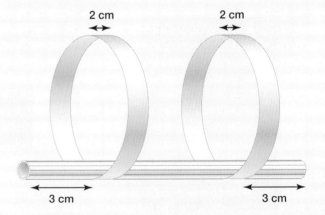

2. Create a flight-test area that is open and free of obstacles.

3. Using masking tape, mark a starting line from which to release the paper birds. Mark off regular intervals (for example, one metre) along a straight line perpendicular to the starting line.

For most organisms, the process that ensures variation in genetically-determined characteristics from generation to generation is meiosis. Meiotic cell division produces gametes containing half the number of chromosomes found in other body cells. At fertilization, two gametes fuse to produce a new combination of genes.

The continual re-assortment of traits in each generation allows the evolution of many new characteristics. Over time, this leads to the evolution of new species. The potential for variation made possible by sexual reproduction is enormous. For example, a male and female of an imaginary species having only 100 traits could produce more than 10^{30} different genetic combinations among their offspring. Of course, they could not have that many offspring, but if they could, each of those offspring could be unique.

4. Test the bird's flying skill by releasing it at the starting line with a gentle, overhand pitch. Try to release your paper bird in as uniform a way as possible each time you test its flying skill.

5. Create a chart to record your mutations and observations. The headings should include generation number, changes to bird, distance of flight, and successful or unsuccessful mutation.

6. Make a chick by modifying the parent bird. To determine how to mutate the chick's wings, first toss a coin then throw a die. Use the results to adjust the parent bird into a chick.

Coin flip
heads = anterior (front) mutation
tails = posterior (back) mutation

Die throw
1 = position of wings moves 1 cm distally (toward the end of the straw)
2 = position of wings moves 1 cm proximally (toward the middle of the straw)
3 = circumference of the wings increases 2 cm
4 = circumference of the wings decreases 2 cm
5 = width of the wings increases 1 cm
6 = width of the wings decreases 1 cm

NOTE: After several generations, some mutations may prove lethal. For example, the wing may fall off the bird. In this situation, begin again with a new chick made from the previous generation.

7. Repeat steps 4 and 5 for each generation of your paper bird.

8. Repeat the process for a total of 15 generations.

Post-lab Questions

1. Did your selection process result in a paper bird able to fly farther than its original ancestor?

2. Describe how the characteristics of your last paper bird differed from those of the original ancestral bird.

3. Did the same group of students always produce the most successful bird in each test?

4. What were your criteria to determine if a mutation was successful or unsuccessful?

Conclude and Apply

5. Describe two aspects of this investigation that model the evolution of biological organisms.

6. Describe two ways in which the processes in this investigation differ from the situation found in nature.

Exploring Further

7. What might happen to the descendants of your last bird if it was transported to a small, remote island where continual strong winds pose a danger that flying birds may be blown out to sea and die? How will the selection criteria for the species' survival change? Design a variation on the investigation to answer these questions.

8. Add a column to your observation chart and indicate whether you think each mutation would still be successful or unsuccessful in the new environment described in question 7.

<< REWIND

To review the process of meiosis, turn to the genetics unit, Chapter 5, Section 5.2.

Determining Relatedness

The science of taxonomy is about more than classifying and naming organisms. It is part of a much wider field that overlaps many aspects of biology, particularly the study of evolution. One goal of taxonomy is to determine the evolutionary history of groups of organisms. This can be done by comparing different species living today with each other and with species that existed in the past.

To study evolutionary relationships, scientists can use several different types of evidence. Physical characteristics of anatomy, including those that show up in fossil remains, are very valuable in helping determine how closely related different organisms are. Scientists also use data from development, biochemistry, DNA, and even differences in behaviour and ecology of organisms to develop hypotheses of evolutionary relationships.

Evidence from Anatomy

Figure 11.17 shows the fossil remains of a feathered animal named *Archaeopteryx*. It lived about 150 million years ago but is now extinct. All feathered animals living today (birds) are classified in the class Aves, in the phylum Chordata, which suggests that *Archaeopteryx* might have been an ancestor of today's birds. However, *Archaeopteryx* also shares several characteristics with modern reptiles, which are classified in the class Reptilia, in the phylum Chordata.

Figure 11.17 This fossil shows the remains of *Archaeopteryx*, now extinct.

Evidence like this shows that even major taxa are not so clearly different from one another as they might at first appear. As scientists uncover more fossil evidence, the exact relationships between birds and reptiles continue to be studied. Most scientists now think of birds as modern descendants of dinosaurs.

You do not have to dig up fossils to find anatomical evidence of evolution. Compare the bones found in a human arm, a horse's leg, a bat's wing, and a whale's flipper (Figure 11.18). Although these four species look very different on the outside, they all have similar bone structures inside. The size and proportions of the bones have been modified for different uses (walking, flying, and swimming), but the overall arrangement and similarities of the bone structures indicate that they have the same evolutionary origin. Biological features that have a common evolutionary origin are said to be **homologous**.

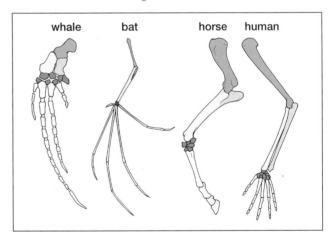

Figure 11.18 The same bones are present in different groups of vertebrates. This is evidence of a common ancestor for these groups.

|| PAUSE   ● RECORD

Until recently, the great apes (chimpanzees, gorillas, and orangutans) and gibbons were included in the family Pongidae, while humans were the only members of the family Hominidae. Scientific evidence contradicted the idea that humans are so different from great apes that they should be included in their own separate family. What effect does this have? Why is it important for scientists to continue to classify and reclassify organisms? What might happen if different types of evidence support different relationships among organisms? Write a short essay that outlines your thoughts about these questions.

Evidence from Development

It is not always possible to determine relatedness between organisms on the basis of similarity in appearance. For example, do you think the two organisms shown in Figure 11.19 are closely related? In fact, they are two stages (larva and adult) of the same organism.

Comparisons of early stages of embryonic development can reveal relationships among species that are not obvious from comparisons of adult organisms alone. For example, sea squirts (tunicates) are potato-shaped organisms that anchor themselves to rocks in the sea and filter their food from the water (Figure 11.20). Their larvae, however, have structures that look similar to those found in tadpoles. Larval tunicates have long dorsal nerve cords and flexible, rodlike supporting structures called notochords. Because of these and other characteristics, biologists classify tunicates in the phylum Chordata, together with such animals as fish, reptiles, and mammals (including humans).

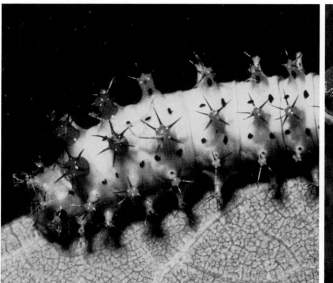

Figure 11.19 Are these two organisms closely related? Although their structures appear quite different, the one on the left is the larval form of the adult cecropia moth (*Hyalophora cecropis*), on the right.

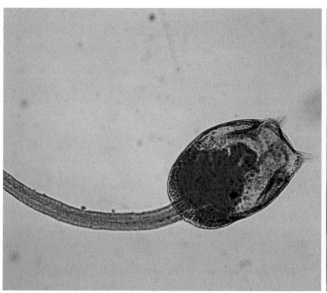

Figure 11.20 Adult tunicates (right) remain attached to rocks and filter food from the water. Their larvae (left) are about 1 cm long and swim freely. The larval structure is evidence that these animals are related to vertebrates.

Evidence from Biochemistry

Technology has given scientists new tools for comparing species at a fundamental level — the molecules from which they are made. The particular proteins that form the body of an organism are determined by the organism's genes. (Many genes are simply encoded instructions to make proteins.) Therefore, comparison of protein molecules among organisms can indicate genetic similarities and differences. On the basis of this evidence, some species have been reclassified. For example, do you think the guinea pig and the mouse shown in Figure 11.21 are closely related?

Comparison of insulin molecules from these two animals suggests that they are not as closely related as they may appear. Insulin is a hormone. Like all proteins, this hormone is made up of chains of amino acids. When the sequence of amino acids in this hormone is compared between guinea pigs and mice, 18 out of insulin's 51 amino acids, or 35% of the structure of this molecule, differs. Similarly, studies of blood proteins in the horseshoe crab (Figure 11.22) have revealed that this animal is more closely related to spiders than to crabs.

Figure 11.21 Guinea pigs (left) were once considered to be rodents, like mice (right). As a result of molecular studies, they were reclassified into a taxon of their own.

Figure 11.22 Horseshoe crabs (left) are related more closely to modern spiders and to an ancient extinct form called trilobites (right) than they are to crabs.

Evidence from DNA

Suppose that a human skull were dug up in your neighbourhood and that forensic scientists estimate its owner died two hundred years ago. The scientists could also determine if the skull belonged to an ancestor of a particular local family. To do this, they would extract samples of DNA from the remains. Then, they would compare the DNA with DNA samples from families who have lived in the area for several generations.

DNA analysis is a powerful and precise method for measuring the closeness of relationships among different organisms. As you may have learned in earlier grades, genes consist of sequences of nucleotide bases in a segment of DNA. In one DNA comparison method, DNA from each of two organisms is separated into single strands, then single strands from the two samples are mixed. Where their nucleotide bases are complementary,

strands from the two organisms will bond together. The greater the amount of bonding, the more genes the two organisms have in common, and the closer their relationship. Using DNA analysis, scientists have found that human DNA matches closely with that from other primates. For example, 93% of our genes match those of macaque monkeys and 98% match those of chimpanzees (Figure 11.23).

DNA analysis can also help us to determine how long ago two species began to diverge from a common ancestor. This is done using DNA found in a cell's mitochondria rather than from the cell nucleus, because mitochondria pass directly from a mother to her offspring in each generation. Scientists hypothesize that mitochondrial DNA mutates at predictable rates, which means that it provides a molecular clock for measuring rates of evolution.

Macaque ←———— 93% ————→ Human ←———— 98% ————→ Chimpanzee

Figure 11.23 Humans share 93% of genes with macaque monkeys and 98% with chimpanzees. Humans, chimpanzees, gorillas, and orangutans are now classified in the same family, Hominidae.

◀◀ REWIND

Turn to Chapter 6, Sections 6.1 and 6.2, for a review of DNA and the process of DNA analysis.

COURSE CHALLENGE

Now that you have learned about different lines of evidence that allow scientists to organize and compare organisms, think about the usefulness of this type of evidence for your Biology 11 Course Challenge. These data are commonly used in forensic science to recreate many scenarios, including crime scenes. How could you use evidence from anatomy in your course challenge? Evidence from biochemistry? Evidence from DNA? Would you be able to use developmental evidence to help recreate your crime scene? Consider the strengths and weaknesses of these different types of evidence. Keep an ongoing file of how this information could be useful to you in developing your Biology 11 Course Challenge.

Phylogeny

When taxonomists classify species into various taxa, they are presenting a hypothesis about the evolutionary history, or **phylogeny**, of the organisms. For example, Figure 11.24 illustrates the phylogeny of four species of hooved mammals in a phylogenetic tree. Like a family tree, the roots or base of the phylogenetic tree represents the oldest ancestral species. The upper ends of the branches represent the present-day descendant species. Forks in each branch represent the points in the past at which an ancestral species split into two new species.

The common ancestor at the base of the tree had general characteristics that are shared by all the species that evolved from it. These features, called primitive characteristics, define the Order in which these species are grouped. For example, all members of the Order Artiodactyla have an even number of hooved toes on each hindfoot and have specialized teeth and digestive systems adapted to eat plants. There are about 150 members of this order worldwide, including goats, deer, cattle, camels, giraffes, antelopes, and pigs.

By definition, new species that evolved from the common ancestor had new features. These additional features are called derived characteristics. Different lines of descent have different derived characteristics. The combination of primitive and derived characteristics help define each family level of classification on this tree. For example, members of the family Bovidae (wild cows and antelopes) are artiodactyls that have horns. Members of the family Cervidae (deer) are artiodactyls that have antlers. There are about 110 species of Bovidae and 40 species of Cervidae.

With continuing evolution, further new derived characteristics are added. On the time scale of the tree, members of different genera have split apart from one another more recently than members of different families. Smaller differences help distinguish one genus from another. For example, the family Cervidae includes 16 genera. The genus *Cervus* includes deer with highly branched antlers, while animals in the genus *Rangifer* are deer with broad, palmate antlers (having the shape of a hand).

Cladistics

You have learned that a phylogenetic tree represents a hypothesis about the evolutionary relationships among groups of organisms. A classification scheme that is based on phylogeny is called **cladistics**. This system is based on the idea that each group of related species has one common ancestor, and organisms retain some ancestral characteristics and gain some unique derived characteristics as they evolve and diverge from the common ancestor.

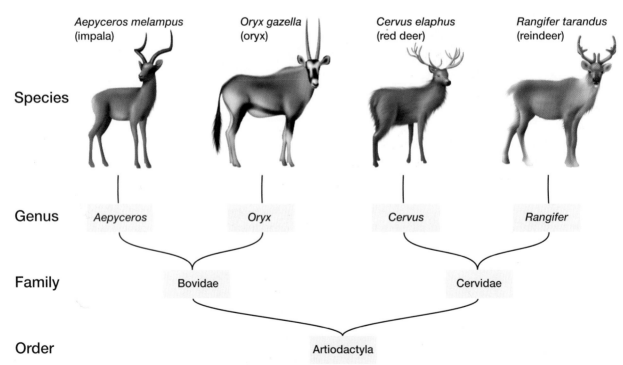

Figure 11.24 A phylogenetic tree showing relationships among various species of plant-eating hooved mammals.

The use of different types of characteristics can shed light on otherwise uncertain relationships because some organisms are easier to classify than others. For example, would you consider the giant panda in Figure 11.25 to be more closely related to bears or to raccoons? Giant pandas have characteristics of both groups, and scientists debated the puzzle of where to classify them for more than 100 years. Eventually, biochemical and genetic comparisons placed this species closer to the bears (Figure 11.26).

A **cladogram**, like the one in Figure 11.27 on the next page, is a branching diagram that resembles a phylogenetic tree but that can be used to test alternative hypotheses. For example, suppose you have three species that share primitive characteristics from a common ancestor. Since the three species share a common ancestor, you know they are related. However, you are not sure which species diverged from the main branch first. Which two of the three species split apart more recently and are therefore more closely related?

Figure 11.25 How are these different yet similar species related to one another?

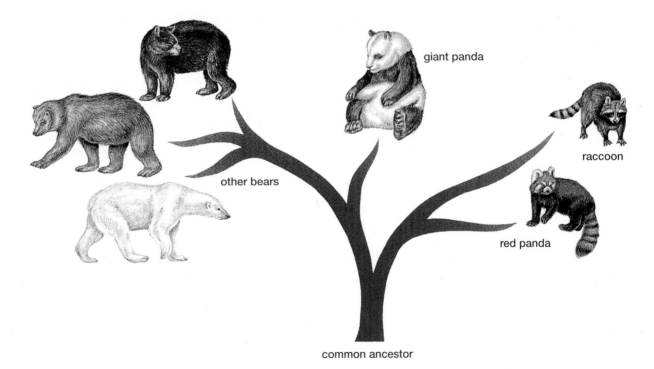

Figure 11.26 This phylogenetic tree shows the relationships among giant pandas, bears, and raccoons.

Figure 11.28 shows three possible hypotheses. By matching the shared derived characteristics of the species, you can conclude that one cladogram is more likely than the other two.

The Value of Phylogeny

Understanding evolutionary relationships among species and groups of organisms can have important consequences. For example, when looking for sources of drugs, hormones, and other important medical products, scientists can narrow their search to species closely related to organisms already known to produce valuable proteins or chemicals.

As you have learned, the kind of proteins produced by a cell depends on the genes in that cell. Closely related species have similar genes. As well, understanding phylogeny can help us trace the transmission of disease and develop and test possible treatments. Diseases can spread more rapidly between species that share certain genetic characteristics. For example, Creutzfeldt-Jakob disease may be transmitted from cows to people.

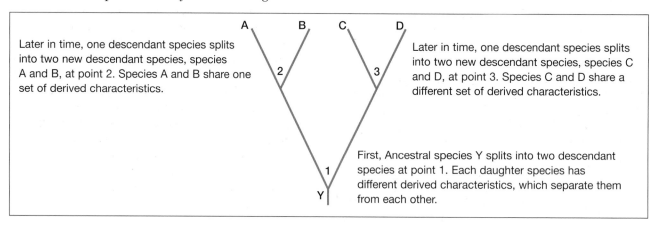

Later in time, one descendant species splits into two new descendant species, species A and B, at point 2. Species A and B share one set of derived characteristics.

Later in time, one descendant species splits into two new descendant species, species C and D, at point 3. Species C and D share a different set of derived characteristics.

First, Ancestral species Y splits into two descendant species at point 1. Each daughter species has different derived characteristics, which separate them from each other.

Figure 11.27 Species A, B, C, and D share a common ancestor, Y. They all share certain primitive characteristics retained from this ancestor.

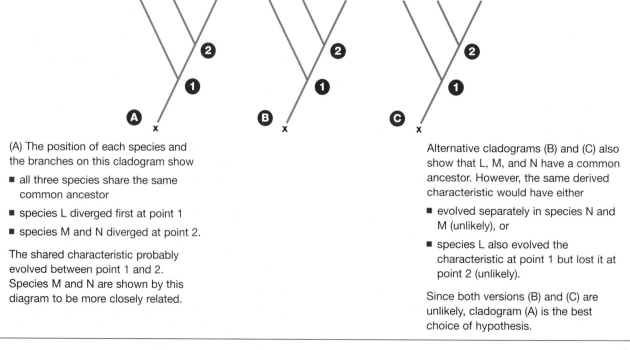

(A) The position of each species and the branches on this cladogram show

- all three species share the same common ancestor
- species L diverged first at point 1
- species M and N diverged at point 2.

The shared characteristic probably evolved between point 1 and 2. Species M and N are shown by this diagram to be more closely related.

Alternative cladograms (B) and (C) also show that L, M, and N have a common ancestor. However, the same derived characteristic would have either

- evolved separately in species N and M (unlikely), or
- species L also evolved the characteristic at point 1 but lost it at point 2 (unlikely).

Since both versions (B) and (C) are unlikely, cladogram (A) is the best choice of hypothesis.

Figure 11.28 Species L, M, and N share primitive characteristics inherited from their common ancestor, X. In addition, species M and N share derived characteristics (symbolized by the box). Which of these three cladograms best shows the relationships of species L, M, and N?

Foods for Tomorrow

Do you ever wonder where the fruits and vegetables in your grocery store originally came from? Common foods such as rice, potatoes, sugar, citrus fruits, bananas, tomatoes, coffee, and chocolate originated in the tropics. They have been cultivated and traded for hundreds or even thousands of years. Scientists trace the history of different foods by studying the wild ancestors of modern cultivated plants. For example, bananas, coconuts, and sugarcane came from southeast Asia. Rice, soybeans, and tea originated in China. Coffee and kola nuts (used in soft drinks) are native to Africa, and potatoes and peanuts to South America.

Many common foods are cultivated varieties of tropical plants.

Although there are several thousand wild species of plants known to be edible, only about 150 crops are significant in world trade. Many familiar foods became part of our diet as a result of historical chance, when tropical countries were first exploited for their resources as colonies of Europe. For example, tomatoes were originally cultivated in Mexico and were unknown in Europe until Spanish explorers carried the new food back home with them in the early 1500s. Today they are the third most widely consumed vegetable in North America.

New and Improved

For centuries, the foods we eat have been genetically modified. Ever since agriculture was developed in prehistoric times, farmers have attempted to improve their crops by selectively growing plants with desirable qualities such as larger size or improved flavour. For example, the wild ancestor of tomatoes produced small, ridged fruits about the size of a raspberry. Today, there are over 50 genetic varieties of tomatoes, all developed by selective breeding.

What might the grocery stores of tomorrow look like? Genetic modifications will continue to alter the qualities of our foods, but the changes will come more from biotechnology than selective breeding. Millions of hectares of fields in Canada today already produce crops that have been altered by genetic engineering. Some people fear these new techniques of food production pose dangers to human health. For example, soybeans containing genes added from Brazil nuts may trigger harmful reactions in people allergic to Brazil nuts. There may also be dangers to the environment. For example, genes for herbicide resistance may spread from engineered crops to weeds. But are the risks from the new techniques any greater than from older methods of food production?

Old and Undiscovered

Another way in which your grocery shelves might look different in the future is by carrying more different fruits and vegetables from the tropics. Many edible tropical plants are currently used only by local populations and are not widely cultivated or marketed for export. Instead of buying the usual bananas and apples, you may pick up some naranjillas or guanabanas. Many underutilized foods are more nutritious and tasty than some staples that we now commonly use. The development of a wider variety of foods depends on maintaining a diversity of ecosystems in different parts of the world.

Follow-up

1. What exotic or unusual foods from the tropics can you find in your local store that were not widely available a few years ago? List the advantages and disadvantages of eating locally produced foods rather than imported foods.

2. Can you identify genetically engineered foods? What are the arguments for and against clearly labelling such foods?

3. Using the Internet or your library, find out about organizations that help preserve rare and unusual food plants. These include fruits and vegetables that were once common in Canada but have since been replaced by new varieties.

In agriculture, ways to increase crop yields and disease resistance have already been developed by cross-breeding closely related species. Biological control through the use of natural predators, parasites, and diseases also depends on a knowledge of different taxa and their particular characteristics.

By understanding the history and diversity of life on Earth, we may eventually understand why some groups of organisms (such as insects) have become diverse and widespread while others are less numerous, as shown in Table 11.3. What characteristics have allowed humans to become so successful, while similar species such as chimpanzees now face the threat of extinction? Might our own species (*Homo sapiens*) also become extinct? These fundamental questions help us understand how living things respond to the long-term challenges of Earth's changing environment. In the next two chapters of this unit, you will study members of the different kingdoms in more detail.

Table 11.3
Overview of the six kingdoms

Kingdom	Major subdivisions	Number of described species
Archaea		200
Bacteria		4560
Protista	Protozoa	30 800
	Algae	26 900
Fungi		46 983
Plantae		248 428
Animalia	Insects	751 000
	Other Invertebrates	238 761
	Vertebrates	43 853
TOTAL		1 391 485

SECTION REVIEW

1. **K/U** Arrange the following in a hierarchy:

   (a) Ontario, Regional Municipality of Durham, Canada, Oshawa

   (b) organ system, organ, organism, organelle, tissue, cell

2. **K/U** Which organisms are more closely related: those in the same genus or those in the same family?

3. **C** Make a chart showing what different types of evidence might lead scientists to conclude that two species have a common ancestor.

4. **K/U** Which types of evidence would be most useful to trace evolutionary relationships of dinosaurs? of insects? of fish? Explain your answers.

5. **C** Choose any three organisms and create alternative cladograms showing the possible relationships among them. Decide which cladogram supports the most likely evolutionary relationship. Redraw this cladogram, showing where the shared characteristics are found that support the relationships.

6. **I** Describe the relationships in the phylogeny shown above right. Which two species are most closely related? Explain your answer.

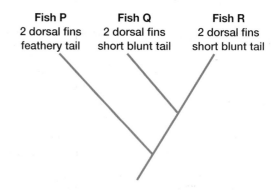

Fish P — 2 dorsal fins, feathery tail
Fish Q — 2 dorsal fins, short blunt tail
Fish R — 2 dorsal fins, short blunt tail

7. **MC** Fish R above, has been found to contain a hormone that improves human health. Unfortunately, Fish R is very rare. Fish P and Fish Q are both common. What might you do if you wanted to obtain more of the hormone? Explain your answer. How might this impact local fishers who make a living catching Fish P and Fish Q?

UNIT ISSUE PREP

You may have already chosen the organism you will be examining for the Unit 4 Issue Analysis, or you will be choosing it soon. How might knowledge of your organism's evolutionary history help you explore why it is endangered today? Could knowledge of your species' characterisitics, and characteristics of its close relatives (which may be abundant or may be extinct) give you any information on its present endangered status?

Chapter Expectations

Briefly explain each of the following points:

- All organisms may be classified into one of six large groups called kingdoms. (11.1)
- All organisms are composed of either prokaryotic or eukaryotic cells. (11.1)
- Viruses are non-cellular and are not classified as living things. (11.2)
- The science of taxonomy classifies organisms into a series of taxa, which form a hierarchy of groups from kingdoms (largest) to species (smallest). (11.3)
- A dichotomous key is used to identify unknown species. It is based on a series of comparisons between two alternative sets of characteristics. (11.3)
- Each species is identified by a unique two-word name. (11.3)
- Variations in the characteristics of a species in each generation result from genetic mutations and the random assortment of genes produced by the process of sexual reproduction. (11.3)
- The reconstruction of a species' evolutionary history is called phylogeny. (11.4)
- A hypothesis of evolutionary relationships can be illustrated using a cladogram. (11.4)

Language of Biology

Write a sentence using each of the following words or terms. Use any six terms in a concept map to show your understanding of how they are related.

- Plantae
- Animalia
- kingdom
- Protista
- Fungi
- Bacteria
- Archaea
- domain
- virus
- capsid
- lytic cycle
- retrovirus
- provirus
- taxonomy
- taxon
- binomial nomenclature
- homologous
- phylogeny
- cladistics
- cladogram

UNDERSTANDING CONCEPTS

1. In your notebook, state whether each of the following statements is true or false. If the statement is false, explain why.
   (a) Some species of bacteria are eukaryotes.
   (b) Species in the same family are more closely related to one another than species in the same class.
   (c) In most species, genetic mutation is the most important source of variation from one generation to the next.

2. List three differences between prokaryotic cells and eukaryotic cells.

3. Why is a tree classified in a different kingdom than a slug?

4. Explain briefly why two species classified in the same family must also be in the same order.

5. Which two of the following have the most similar characteristics: a horse, a cow, a wolf? Explain your answer.

6. List four types of evidence that may be used to help classify a species in the most appropriate taxa.

7. Give an example of homologous structures.

8. Explain how the classification of an organism is related to its phylogeny.

9. Tigers and zebras are both mammals with striped fur coats. Why is this characteristic not useful in determining the closeness of their evolutionary relationship?

10. Describe three types of independent evidence that can be used to establish the closeness of relationships among species, and give an example of each.

11. Scientific names often describe a characteristic of the organism. What can you conclude about the rabbits *Sylvilagus aquaticus* and *Sylvilagus floridanus* based on their names?

12. Aristotle divided the animal kingdom into three main groups: species living in the air, on land, and in water. Explain how this system is different from the one developed by Carolus Linnaeus. Why is it less useful than Linnaeus's system?

13. All vertebrates share some characteristics, including passing through similar embryonic stages. What conclusion does this support?

14. Based on your own knowledge, classify the following organisms into various groups and subgroups. Name the characteristics shared by the members of each group. Organisms: butterfly, chimpanzee, dog, dogfish, dolphin, eagle, earthworm, fern, frog, human, maple tree, moss, mosquito, shark, toad, toadstool.

15. Put these Latin names in order from most general to most specific:

    order —— Perciformes   (a)
    class —— Actinopterygii   (b)
    kingdom —— Animalia   (c)
    phylum —— Chordata   (d)
    species —— *tridigitatus*   (e)
    family —— Dactyloscopidae   (f)
    genus —— *Dactyloscopus*   (g)

    The organism you have classified is a fish called a sand stargazer. What is its scientific name?

16. Make a list of all of the furniture in your classroom or a room at home. Classify it into groups based on function. Make as many groups as possible. Did any of your final groups contain more than two items, or were you able to distinguish between all objects?

17. Explain why a classification based on phylogeny is more natural than a classification scheme based on other characteristics such as shape, size, function, or colour? List five organisms and classify them based on phylogeny and then reclassify them using some other trait (such as size). Are the two classifications different? Explain how they differ.

18.

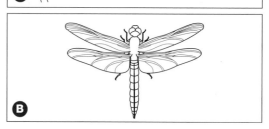

Key

1A Front and hind wings similar in size and shape, and folded parallel to the body when at rest… damselflies

1B Hind wings wider than front wings near base, and extend on either side of the body when at rest… dragonflies

Use the dichotomous key above to answer the following questions.

(a) Identify the organisms shown in the diagrams. Explain how you came to your decision.

(b) From the key and the diagrams above, explain why you could conclude that dragonflies and damselflies evolved from a common ancestor.

19. Draw a fictional organism that can be recognized as a member of one of the six kingdoms. Label its features. Swap your description with another student. Based on the information given, can you classify your partner's organism into its correct kingdom?

20. Imagine that four new species of bird have been discovered. All four birds have similar decorative plumage on their heads. Three of the four birds have tails that are longer than their bodies. Two of those birds have beaks that are sharp and hooked, while the third has a long slender beak. Using this information, draw a cladogram showing the probable evolutionary relationships of these birds. Indicate on the

cladogram where the shared characteristics probably arose.

21. Study the cladogram shown here. Which animal is most closely related to the squirrel? Which two animals are the most dissimilar? Which animals have limbs?

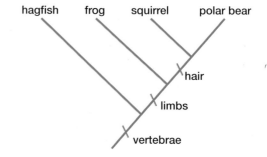

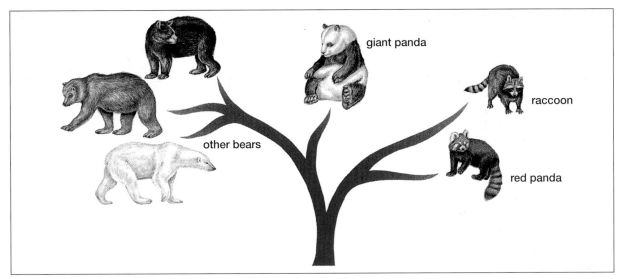

giant panda

raccoon

other bears

red panda

22. Based on the phylogenetic tree diagram above, state whether each of the following statements is true or false. If the statement is false, explain why.

(a) The giant panda's closest living relative is the red panda.

(b) Pandas, bears, and raccoons all have a common ancestor.

(c) The most recent common ancestor of giant pandas and bears is different from the most recent common ancestor of red pandas and raccoons.

23. Study the organisms shown on the right. Make a key that would allow you to identify them. Once your key is complete, draw a cladogram showing an hypothesis of their evolutionary relationships. Indicate which characteristics you have used to build your cladogram.

MAKING CONNECTIONS

24. How do genetic mutations and sexual reproduction help produce diversity among living things? What other process leads to the evolution of new species? How are humans affecting these processes? Explain your answer.

25. Describe how the extinction of a particular species might affect

(a) an ecosystem.

(b) your own life.

Think of an example where the extinction of one species would have a greater impact on your life than the extinction of a different species. What conservation implications does this have?

26. Draw a flowchart that traces the effects of a species of fly going extinct. Include five to ten steps in your chart. For example: The fly goes extinct → the birds that eat the flies lose a major source of food → those birds start eating another species of fly …

27. Medical scientists claim that the smallpox virus has been eradicated in the human population. However, one sample of this virus still exists at the Center for Disease Control in Atlanta, Georgia. Write a short essay outlining your feelings about this. Why might this be a positive or a negative situation?

CHAPTER 12

Mostly Micro-organisms

Reflecting Questions

- How might a micro-biologist persuade you that "bacteria run the world?"

- What is the link between the most common algal species in the ocean and toothpaste?

- How is a mushroom like an animal?

Invisible, or barely visible to the naked eye, micro-organisms include the oldest and most abundant forms of life on Earth. Some micro-organisms have vital roles in the environment, such as decomposing wastes and producing oxygen, but others can be deadly to humans.

Malaria is a devastating and often fatal disease carried by the mosquito shown in the photo on the next page. Each year between 400 million and 600 million cases of malaria are diagnosed, and 1.5 million to 2.7 million people die of the disease. Malaria has long been eradicated from North America. Recently, however, a case of malaria was diagnosed in New York State, in a woman who had not travelled to an area where malaria exists. Other deadly diseases once thought to be under control are making a comeback.

How can this happen? The reason is that many diseases are caused by species of micro-organisms, which, like all living things, can change their characteristics and distribution over time. The changes in these species are produced by changes in the environment, usually caused by human activity. For instance, increasing international travel has helped carry once restricted diseases, such as the plague and malaria, around the world. The growing use of antibiotics has led to the appearance of new strains of drug-resistant bacteria such as those causing tuberculosis. And changes in climate and habitats may help some newly introduced organisms spread in Canada.

Only a few species of micro-organisms are harmful to people. In this chapter you will study the characteristics and classification of four kingdoms: Archaea, Bacteria, Protista, and Fungi. Most species in these kingdoms are unicellular, but protists and fungi also include many larger and more familiar members, such as seaweeds and mushrooms. These organisms have helped shape human history and culture, yet most people know very little about them. New species are discovered every year, and the field of microbial taxonomy is still changing, and waiting for new discoveries by the biologists of tomorrow.

Micro-organisms spread to new geographical areas, passively carried by world travellers.

Chapter Contents

Kingdom Archaea

Figure 12.1 Archaea thrive in environments that would destroy most other organisms, such as the hot, acidic pools in Yellowstone National Park shown here.

Does life exist on other planets? We are most familiar with the other planets in our own solar system, such as Mars, Saturn, or Venus. Most organisms on Earth could not survive the conditions on these other planets: some are boiling hot, others freezing cold; they lack atmospheres containing oxygen and water vapour; some have extremely acidic surfaces, others surfaces under high pressure. However, the world of micro-organisms includes species that thrive in these kinds of extreme environments.

Earth's most extreme-loving micro-organisms are prokaryotes classified in the Kingdom Archaea. Species of archaea have been found living in hot springs (see Figure 12.1) and near sea-floor vents at temperatures near 100°C. They have been found in alkaline or acidic waters, and in extremely saline environments such as the Dead Sea. Some live inside volcanoes, some in piles of hot coal, and some in rocks deep below Earth's surface (see Figure 12.2). All members of archaea live without oxygen. They obtain their energy from inorganic molecules or from light.

Archaea do not look very different from bacteria and were initially even classified as a type of bacteria, the archaeabacteria. However, when scientists began analyzing the cells of these

remarkable organisms in more detail, they made an unexpected discovery. Biochemically and genetically, archaea are as different from bacteria as they are from plants and animals.

BIO FACT

Molecular analysis has revolutionized the study of taxonomy. This method presumes that the longer the period of time since two organisms had a common ancestor, the greater the number of differences in the structure of their macromolecules (such as proteins and RNA).

Classifying Archaea

How can archaea survive in such extreme environments? Their appearance does not offer an obvious answer. Only detailed studies of their molecules and metabolism provide the key. Archaea have many genes that differ significantly from those of bacteria. As well, there are chemical differences between the RNA of archaea and bacteria, and the cell membranes of archaea have a different structure and chemical composition than those of bacteria. For example, the cell membranes of some archaea contain unusual lipids (fats). Unlike most lipids, these remain stable at very high temperatures, allowing the archaea to function in environments hot enough to kill most cells. Archaea that function at low temperatures have high contents of other fatty substances that remain fluid and functional at cold temperatures.

≪ REWIND

To remind yourself of the metabolic processes common to most organisms, turn to Chapter 3, Sections 3.3 and 3.4.

Methanogens, or methane-producing archaea, live in oxygen-free environments, such as below the surface of swamps, marshes, as shown on the left, and sewage-disposal plants. They use carbon dioxide, nitrogen gas, or hydrogen sulfide as a source of energy and give off methane gas as a waste product.

Halophiles, or salt-loving archaea, live in extremely saline environments such as the salt pools shown on the right. Salt concentrations may reach up to 15% (seawater is 3.5% salt). They are so well adapted to these conditions that they cannot grow in weaker salt solutions.

Thermoacidophiles, heat- and acid-loving archaea, live in extremely hot and acidic environments. For example, some species live in hot sulfur springs and use sulfur as their source of energy. Others prefer spots on volcanoes, like the one shown on the left, or near deep sea vents, and grow best at temperatures above 80°C.

Figure 12.2 Based on their metabolism, scientists identify three main groups of archaea.

Web LINK

Exciting new discoveries about the Kingdom Archaea are made every year. To find the latest news and reports from this research, go to **Science Resources**, then to **BIOLOGY 11** and follow the links. Where have archaea been found? What extreme environmental conditions exist in these locations? What characteristics of the archaea allow them to survive there? **www.school.mcgrawhill.ca/resources/**

Archaea and Biotechnology

Archaea's ability to survive and flourish in conditions of heat, cold, and acidity is unique and poorly understood. Scientists do know that enzymes present only in archaea allow these organisms to successfully carry out chemical and metabolic processes. Biotechnology and industry depend on the use of enzymes for many different processes, including DNA analysis and diagnosing diseases. While standard enzymes break down and stop working when they are exposed to extreme conditions, this is not the case for archaean enzymes. This makes them very valuable, both for reducing production costs and because new biotechnology techniques can be developed that are not affected by harsh conditions.

For example, polymerase chain reaction, or PCR, is now a widespread technology thanks to an archaean species that can grow at temperatures greater than 70°C. During PCR replication, an enzyme called DNA polymerase repeatedly copies a small piece of DNA. This produces a large supply of DNA. In order to have the copying procedure work, the enzyme is cycled between very high and very low temperatures. PCR used to be a slow and expensive process because standard enzymes would be destroyed during the heated portion of the cycle, and would have to be replaced by hand each time. However the DNA polymerase from archaea can withstand these high temperatures, and the PCR process is now fully automated. This revolutionary technology has become commonplace.

> **◄◄ REWIND**
>
> To review the process of polymerase chain reaction technology, turn to Chapter 6, Section 6.2.

Canadians in Biology ✦

Oasis Under the Sea

You are probably aware of the abundant life under the sea. Marine plants and algae harness the energy of the sun and synthesize food to support the rest of the ocean food webs. But at depths as low as 1500-3000 m you will find no green plants or algae, fishes, whales, or dolphins. The Sun's energy does not penetrate to these depths. As well, the temperatures and pressures are too extreme for those creatures to survive. However, there *are* ecosystems at these extreme depths, whose biomass rival any of the largest and most productive terrestrial ecosystems.

Dr. Verena Tunnicliffe, a professor at the School of Earth and Ocean Science at the University of Victoria in British Columbia is a researcher of these ecosystems. She earned her B.Sc. at McMaster University in Ontario and her M.Phil. and Ph.D. at Yale University. In addition to research, she teaches marine biology and paleobiology at University of Victoria.

Dr. Verena Tunnicliffe

What are Vent Ecosystems?

These deep marine ecosystems obtain their energy from hydrothermal vents that dot the ocean floor. Hydrothermal vents are formed when tectonic plates spread, allowing hot magma to rise and cold sea water to seep into the Earth's crust. The water heats up which causes substances like iron, zinc, copper, manganese and hydrogen sulfide (H_2S) to dissolve from the surrounding crust. The water is heated up to 380°C, and it rises forth in spectacular clouds called "smokers" or it percolates slowly but surely from the crust.

At these depths exist a special species of bacteria that are able to react H_2S with CO_2 to sustain their lives, much the same way plants harness the Sun's energy and CO_2 to produce sugar. These bacteria are the first trophic level of vent ecosystems in the same way that plants are the first trophic level of terrestrial ecosystems.

One organism that these bacteria support is the tubeworm. This creature has no mouth, gut, or digestive system. It appears, as its name implies, as a tube that is open to the water surrounding the vent. Instead of eating the bacteria, a symbiotic relationship has developed where the bacteria actually live inside of the tube of the worm. The tubeworm is able to capture H_2S from the surrounding water and delivers the H_2S to the bacteria. The bacteria use the H_2S and their organic carbon by-products (analogous to sugar made by plants) to feed the tubeworm.

ROPOS

The Juan de Fuca Ridge (JdFR) is a geological formation on the ocean floor off the coast of British Columbia. It has many hydrothermal vents along its line which support vent ecosystems. Dr. Tunnicliffe and her team study the vent ecosystems along this ridge. At 1.5–3.0 km deep,

Archaea and the Origin of Life

Earth's early atmosphere lacked oxygen. Evidence shows that it consisted of water vapour and probably methane and ammonia. How could life begin in such an atmosphere? This was the question posed by Alexander Oparin in the 1930s, which led to his hypothesis that life began early in Earth's existence in the ocean. He proposed that the Sun's energy and electrical energy from lightning initiated chemical reactions among the atmosphere's gases, resulting in the formation of organic compounds.

In 1953, Stanley Miller and Harold Urey set up the now famous experiment, shown in Figure 12.3 on the next page, to test Oparin's hypothesis. Miller and Urey simulated what was thought to be Earth's early atmosphere — water vapour, methane, hydrogen, and ammonia. They used a high voltage electrical source, simulating lightning, to send sparks through the gaseous mixture. The result? Chemical reactions within the chamber produced several different amino acids, sugars, and other simple organic compounds in a week's time.

The results of this experiment stimulated many scientists to consider other conditions on the early Earth's surface. They continued to experiment, combining substances that formed more and more complex compounds. Sidney Fox, for example, heated solutions of amino acids, and his experiments led to the formation of other amino acids and polypeptides, the precursors of proteins. Scientists have not, however, been able to produce any entities capable of attaining all the characteristics of living cells during experiments that approximate conditions on early Earth.

the temperature (ranging from 2°C-380°C) and pressure is too great for diving expeditions by humans. Dr. Tunnicliffe and her team rely on ROPOS (remotely operated robotic submersibles) that can function at depths of 5 km to conduct their field studies.

The ROPOS (as shown in the photo) are equipped with still and video cameras. They also have two arms that allow the team to take samples of the life forms and rocks in the vent ecosystems. The ROPOS can also be custom outfitted to sample water for chemical analysis or measure temperatures with extreme accuracy and precision.

What Scientific Questions Are Dr. Tunnicliffe and Her Team Addressing?

Since the vents are spread out along a ridge, the ocean temperature drops significantly between them. This results in virtually lifeless regions between the vents. Therefore, vent ecosystems that are quite unique from each other have emerged along the JdFR. Research questions include how, exactly, these vent ecosystems along the JdFR differ in terms of the number and types of species that inhabit them. Further questions include how vent ecosystems compare to existing, general models of ecosystems. In other words, are the patterns found in known ecosystems similar or different from vent ecosystems, and why is this so? Also being studied is the distribution and diversity of a specific organism called a copepod along the JdFR.

Additional research focusses on how vent ecosystems form. In 1998, a volcanic eruption atop the JdFR occurred, spilling lava along its South Rift. Obviously, any organisms living along the lava flow were destroyed during this eruption. However, this occurrence has provided model conditions for asking questions about the formation of new vent ecosystems. As organisms move into the South Rift, a new vent ecosystem is forming. Research comparing this new vent ecosystem with the existing mature vent ecosystems along the JdFR is ongoing. Another advantage of studying vent ecosystems is that they recover much faster than terrestrial ecosystems that have experienced volcanic eruptions and lava flow. The team also continues to identify previously unknown species within the vent ecosystems.

The conditions seen in and around the hydrothermal vents are believed by scientists to be similar to the conditions when life on Earth began 3.5 to 4 billion years ago. As Dr. Tunnicliffe and her team conduct their research, they continue to expand humanity's knowledge of what could be the descendants of Earth's first life forms.

Present-day archaea can thrive in conditions similar to those presumed to have existed in Earth's early atmosphere. Were they, or a similar group of organisms, the first living things on Earth? Did all other life originate from them? The answers to these questions are still to be learned.

❚❚ PAUSE ● RECORD

In Chapter 11 you learned about the three domains of life. The Domain Archaea is more closely related to the Domain Eukarya than it is to the Domain Bacteria. However, until recently and based on appearances, archaea were considered to be a type of bacteria. Does changing the classification of archaea have any real effect? List your ideas, and explain briefly.

◀◀ REWIND

Some of the organic compounds that led to life on this planet may also have come from outer space. As the introduction to Unit 1 discussed, these "molecules of life" have also been shown to travel between stars on comets.

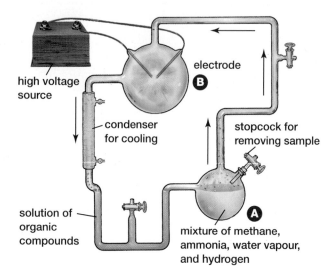

Figure 12.3 This experimental equipment shows how the experiment of Miller and Urey worked. The solution in A, containing ammonia, methane, and hydrogen was circulated as steam, and subjected to electric sparks simulating lightning in B. It is now recognized that the starting conditions Miller and Urey used were probably not as close to the conditions on early Earth as was thought. However, their experiment stands as an indication of how the "molecules of life" might have evolved.

SECTION REVIEW

1. **K/U** Explain why archaea are anaerobic.

2. **K/U** What makes members of the Kingdom Archaea so unusual?

3. **K/U** Originally, members of archaea were thought to be closely related to bacteria and were called the eubacteria. Give two reasons that this classification is no longer used. What does this indicate about taxonomy and classification?

4. **❶** A biologist is analyzing the metabolic information shown in the table below. Unfortunately, the identity of the organisms has been accidentally deleted from the computer. Could she be studying any members of the Kingdom Archaea? Explain your answer.

	Organism A	Organism B	Organism C	Organism D
Main energy source	hydrogen and carbon dioxide	oxygen	hydrogen sulfide	carbon dioxide
Main waste product	methane	carbon dioxide	methane	oxygen

5. **❶** Using the information in the table above, identify any possible archaea. Explain what other information you would need to make a positive identification.

6. **K/U** If you discovered small micro-organisms growing beside a hydrothermal vent on the ocean floor, what could you infer about their metabolism? Where would you look to find closely related species? Explain your answers.

7. **C** Write a criticism of the following points:

    (a) Archaea have been identified as unusual for over 100 years.

    (b) Archaea and bacteria look very similar, so they should be classified in the same kingdom.

    (c) Organisms that can live in extreme environments teach us very little applicable biology.

8. **MC** Humans influence the environment in many different ways, particularly as a result of waste disposal. By creating extreme conditions (for example, toxic waste disposal sites and landfills) are we encouraging the evolution of new species of archaea? Create two lists. The first list should include any possible positive consequences of creating extreme conditions, and the second list should outline the negative consequences.

EXPECTATIONS

- Describe characteristics of members of the Kingdom Bacteria.
- Explain the process of reproduction in bacteria.
- Classify representative bacteria.
- Explain the relevance of current studies of bacteria to the field of biotechnology.

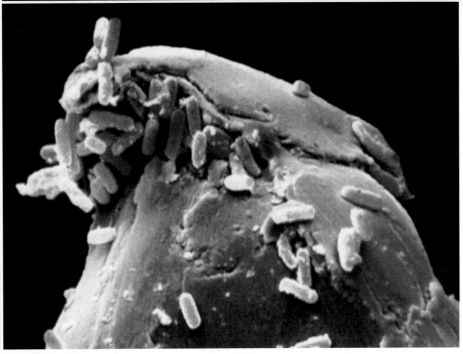

Figure 12.4 Bacteria are present everywhere. Here bacteria are shown on the tip of a needle.

Magnification 5600x

Wherever you go on Earth, no matter how isolated it may seem, you will be surrounded by tiny, invisible organisms in the air, in the soil, in the water, and on your skin. They even live in our bodies. These organisms are members of the Kingdom Bacteria, and their numbers exceed those of all other forms of life.

When most people think of bacteria, they think of pathogenic (disease-causing) organisms such as the *Streptococcus* bacteria that can cause Necrotizing Fasciitis, or flesh-eating disease. But disease-causing species represent only a tiny fraction of the bacteria species. Bacteria also play critical roles in all ecosystems and are of great importance to humans. For example, different stages in the nitrogen cycle, which is critical to soil fertility, require bacteria. We also use bacteria to make many edible products, including vinegar, butter, cheese, and yogurt.

As you have already learned, bacteria are prokaryotes. The great majority live as single cells, although some produce colonies or link up in chains to form filaments.

≪ REWIND

Turn to Chapter 1, Section 1.1, to review the characteristics of a bacterial cell.

Classifying Bacteria

What characteristics make one group of bacteria different from another? Bacteria have been classified by their shape, the structure of their cell walls, and their sources of food and energy. More recently, bacterial phylogenies have been constructed based on analysis of RNA sequences.

The concept of species used to classify animals and plants is difficult to apply to bacteria. A species is defined as a group of organisms that can only breed with one another. Bacteria reproduce mainly by asexual methods, but are also potentially able to swap genes with any other bacteria. Because of this, they are not genetically separated from one another in the way animals and plants are. As well, genetic change by mutation occurs rapidly in bacteria so genetic differences can arise in populations of bacteria within a few generations.

COURSE CHALLENGE

Can identifying different types of bacteria give you useful information for your course challenge? Details about which bacteria are present in a decomposing body may provide evidence for the time of death. Investigate this to consider whether or not data on bacteria can help you as you prepare your forensic scenario, the Course Challenge at the end of the book.

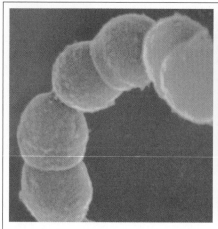

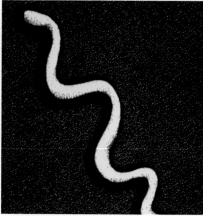

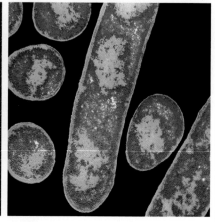

Streptococcus mutans, a coccus, causes tooth decay. Its metabolism converts sugars to an acid that eats away at tooth enamel.

Treponema pallidum, a spirillum, causes syphilis, a potentially fatal sexually transmitted disease.

Clostridium botulinum is a bacillus that can cause food poisoning. The products of its metabolism are highly toxic if eaten by humans.

Figure 12.5 The round coccus, spiral-shaped spirillum, and rod-shaped bacillus are common bacterial shapes.

Shape

When an entire organism consists of only a single cell, the shape of the cell is especially important. The simplest way to classify bacteria is by separating them into groups based on their shape as shown in Figure 12.5. Bacterial cells have three main shapes:

- **cocci**, or round (singular coccus)
- **bacilli**, or rod-shaped (singular bacillus)
- **spirilli**, or spiral-shaped (singular spirillum).

Each shape gives bacteria different advantages. For example, cocci resist drying better than bacilli.

Can you say why? Bacilli have a relatively greater surface area for absorbing nutrients from their surroundings than cocci do. Spiral bacteria can move through fluids with less resistance than either cocci or bacilli can.

Bacteria often grow in characteristic patterns, or groupings. These are shown in Figure 12.6. The prefix **diplo-** describes cells arranged in pairs. The prefix **staphylo-** describes cells arranged in clusters resembling grapes. The prefix **strepto-** refers to bacteria arranged in a chain.

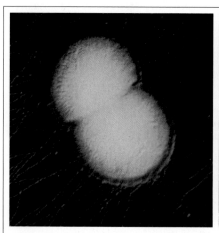

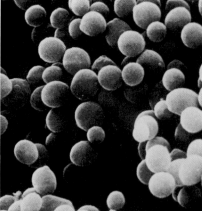

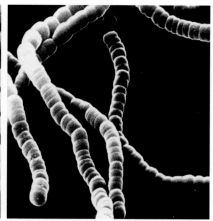

The diplococci shown here can cause the sexually transmitted disease gonorrhea.

The staphylococci shown here can cause many different infections including boils and food poisoning.

The streptococci shown here cause the throat infection known as strep throat.

Figure 12.6 Bacteria often link together in characteristic patterns.

Cell Wall Structure

Bacteria differ significantly in the structure and thickness of their cell walls. In 1884, the Danish physician Hans Gram used a stain on bacteria that allowed these differences to be seen. The stain, now called Gram stain, highlights basic differences in the arrangements of amino acid and sugar molecules in bacterial cell walls. **Gram-positive bacteria** have a thick protein layer on their cell wall and stain purple. **Gram-negative bacteria** have a thin protein layer on their cell walls and stain pink. Figure 12.7 shows these differences. The Gram-negative group of bacteria is larger and more diverse than the Gram-positive group.

Carbon and Energy Sources

In order to grow and maintain itself, every organism needs a source of energy, a source of nutrients (such as carbon and nitrogen), and a suitable range of physical conditions (such as temperature and pH). In this respect, bacteria are like all other living things. Bacteria, however, can use widely different sources of energy and materials that other organisms cannot. That is one reason why bacteria are found in almost every kind of environment.

Based on their sources of nutrients and energy, bacteria can be grouped into four major types, shown in Figure 12.8. Bacteria can be divided based on whether they use light as an energy source or whether they use chemicals as an energy source. They can be divided further into autotrophs or heterotrophs.

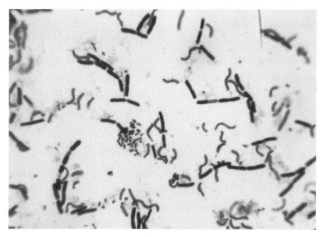

Figure 12.7 Based on your knowledge, which bacteria in this photograph are Gram-positive and which are Gram-negative?

Word LINK

The following are some terms used to identify and classify bacteria based on differences in their metabolism:
- aerobic — require gaseous oxygen for their growth and metabolism
- obligate anaerobes — die when exposed to oxygen
- facultative anaerobes — can grow either in the presence or absence of oxygen
- phototrophs — use light as an energy source
- chemotrophs — use chemical compounds as an energy source
- saprotrophs — feed on dead organisms or organic wastes
- thermophiles — grow at temperatures above 50°C
- psychrophiles — grow best at temperatures below 15°C and die when exposed to normal room temperature

Look up the meaning of the suffixes "-troph" and "-phile." Use these meanings to find out what is meant by at least two terms in the list above that include these suffixes.

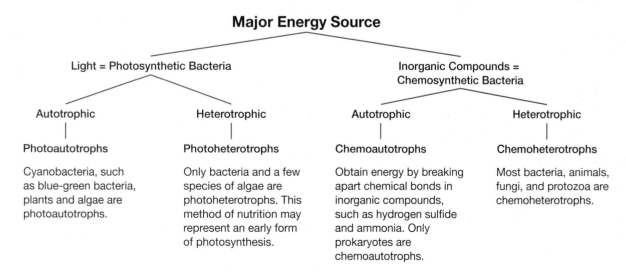

Major Energy Source

Light = Photosynthetic Bacteria

Autotrophic

Photoautotrophs

Cyanobacteria, such as blue-green bacteria, plants and algae are photoautotrophs.

Heterotrophic

Photoheterotrophs

Only bacteria and a few species of algae are photoheterotrophs. This method of nutrition may represent an early form of photosynthesis.

Inorganic Compounds = Chemosynthetic Bacteria

Autotrophic

Chemoautotrophs

Obtain energy by breaking apart chemical bonds in inorganic compounds, such as hydrogen sulfide and ammonia. Only prokaryotes are chemoautotrophs.

Heterotrophic

Chemoheterotrophs

Most bacteria, animals, fungi, and protozoa are chemoheterotrophs.

Figure 12.8 Major nutritional groups of bacteria

The Bacteria Around You

You can find bacteria everywhere, even on your desk and on your skin. Although they are much too small to be seen individually without the help of a powerful microscope, you can see evidence of their presence by growing colonies of them in the lab. In the first part of this investigation, you will collect bacterial samples from your school environment and provide them with food and warmth so that they multiply rapidly. After a few days, you will examine them and describe your results.

Note: Some schools do not permit labs using bacteria. If this is the case for your school, go to your Electronic Learning Partner for a simulation instead.

Pre-lab Questions

- Describe the conditions necessary for bacterial growth.
- Describe two factors that might inhibit bacterial growth.

Problem

How can you observe the bacteria that live in different areas in your school?

Prediction

Predict the levels of bacterial growth in different areas of your classroom.

CAUTION: Be careful when working with live bacterial cultures. Always wear gloves. Also, wash your hands with soap immediately after handling any bacterial culture. Carefully clean and disinfect your work area after you finish. Follow your teacher's instructions about disposal of your swabs, cultures, and petri dishes.

Materials

grease pencil or marker
sterile tweezers
incubator
disinfectant cleaner
paper towels
sterile agar plate
sterile swabs
4 sterile jars or bags
biohazard disposal bags
clear tape
dissecting microscope or magnifying glass

Procedure

Note: Carefully follow the steps of this investigation to maintain sterile conditions and to avoid contaminating your cultures with unwanted bacteria.

1. Wipe your desk top thoroughly with disinfectant cleaner. Dry the desk top with paper towels. Then wash your hands with soap and dry them with paper towels.

2. Turn the petri dish upside down and using a grease pencil, label the bottom of the dish as shown below. (The letters are written backwards so that they will appear correctly when the dish is placed on its bottom.) Add your initials and the date at the edge to identify your dish.

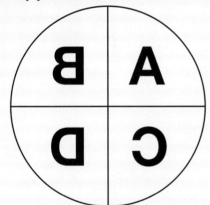

3. Collect bacteria from four different locations around your classroom.

   (a) Use one sterile swab for each sample held with tweezers. Gently wipe the surface to be sampled (for example, the floor near the door, on your desk, near the sink, and near the garbage can).

   (b) Place the swab back into its original wrapping or into a sterile container.

(c) Label the container with the name and conditions of the sample's location (for example, clean, dusty, seldom used, etc.).

4. To transfer your samples to your sterile agar plate, follow these directions:

(a) Slide the lid off the petri dish.

(b) Streak the agar by taking a swab of each sample and running it gently over a different quadrant of the agar (see below). Be careful not to damage the agar jelly.

(c) Replace the lid as soon as you have finished.

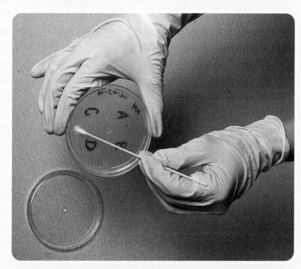

You may trace a wiggly line, circle, or other pattern with your swab. What effect will this have?

5. Discard the swabs in special biohazard disposal bags provided by your teacher.

6. Tape the petri dish closed, turn it upside down, and return it to your teacher. The dishes will be placed in an incubator at 30°C.

7. After a few days, examine your bacterial cultures with the dissecting microscope or a magnifying glass. Do *not* open the petri dishes.

(a) Record the appearance of each culture by sketching your petri dish. Show the distribution and type of bacterial growth.

(b) Note the colour and the texture of the culture's surface (for example, smooth and glistening, dry and powdery, or rough). You may wish to put your observations in a chart listing colour, manner of growth, texture of surface, etc.

Post-lab Questions

1. Which areas around your classroom appeared to have large populations of bacteria? Which areas had fewer bacteria? Suggest reasons for these findings.

2. Based on your knowledge of micro-organisms, where did the bacteria on the sampled surfaces come from? Now list at least three factors that might restrict the growth of bacteria.

Conclude and Apply

3. Did this experiment have a control? If not, suggest what control you could set up and why.

4. Based on your observations of bacterial distribution and growth, what general statements can you make about bacterial growth and conditions that support their growth?

Exploring Further

5. Did any of your bacterial cultures grow in a particular shape? If so, research the shapes of bacterial growth and determine if this provides you with any more information on your cultures.

6. Examine prepared and stained slides of various bacteria provided to you by your teacher. Draw and label diagrams describing your observations of them.

This researcher is checking growth patterns of a culture.

How Bacteria Reproduce

If you leave an uncovered dish of warm food on a kitchen counter one morning, you may return in the late afternoon to a population of bacteria that has increased over one millionfold. The potential for bacteria to multiply very rapidly in favourable conditions (such as in leftover food) can lead to food poisoning. Other examples that involve the rapid reproduction of bacteria include throat infections, compost heaps, sewage treatment plants, and various fermentation processes.

Asexual reproduction

Bacterial cells cannot reproduce by mitosis or meiosis (as animal and plant cells do) because they lack nuclei. Their genetic material is contained in a single chromosome within the cell. Figure 12.9 shows the process of **binary fission**, or cell division, in the bacterium *E. coli*. As a bacterial cell grows, it makes a copy of its original, single chromosome. When the cell reaches a certain size,

Math **LINK**

The rate at which materials can move in and out of a cell determines the metabolic rates, and therefore the growth rates, of microbial cells. The smaller the cell, the larger the surface area of its membrane relative to its volume, and therefore the faster the potential growth rate. Copy and complete this table to illustrate the difference.

	Cell A	Cell B
Radius (r)	1 μm	2 μm
Surface area (SA) $4\pi r^2$	12.6 μm^2	?
Volume (V) = $4/3\pi r^3$	?	33.5 μm^3
Ratio of SA to V	?	?

it elongates, separating the two chromosomes. The cell then builds a partition between them, and eventually the original cell splits into two smaller, genetically identical cells.

In favourable conditions, a bacterium can grow and divide in as little as 20 min. Each new cell can then grow and produce two more cells 20 min later. A sequence like this of repeated doubling is called exponential growth. It allows bacteria to produce huge populations in a fairly short time. For example, a single bacterium and its descendents multiplying every 20 min would produce a population of over 30 000 in only five hours. As with all other organisms, however, bacterial numbers are limited by predators, unfavourable environmental conditions, and the availability of resources.

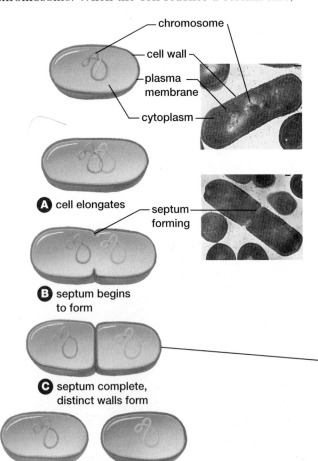

A cell elongates

B septum begins to form

C septum complete, distinct walls form

D cells separate

Figure 12.9 The bacterium *E. coli* dividing by binary fission.

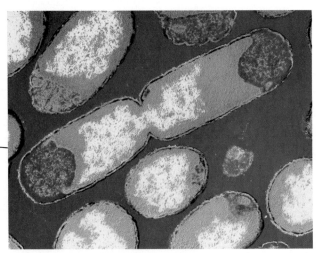

Sexual reproduction

In less favourable conditions, some bacteria are able to reproduce sexually by a process called **conjugation**. This process produces cells with new genetic combinations, and thereby provides a chance that some may be better adapted to changing conditions. During conjugation, bacterial cells become linked to one another through bridging structures called **pili** (singular pilus). One bacterium transfers all or part of its chromosome to the other across this structure, as shown in Figure 12.10. With its new gene content, the receiving cell then undergoes binary fission to produce more cells with the same genetic make-up.

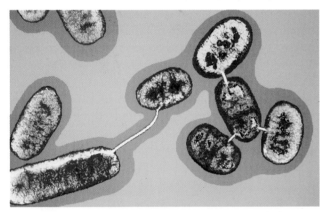

Figure 12.10 Genetic material being transferred through a long, tube-like pilus.

Gene transfer

In most bacteria, the chromosome is not the only part of the cell containing genes. **Plasmids** are small loops of DNA that are separate from the main chromosome. Plasmids contain from one to a few genes, and these genes are different from those found in the chromosome. Plasmids can split from the bacterial chromosome and rejoin it, and they are an important method of producing genetic recombination in bacteria.

Plasmids may be transferred from one bacterial cell to another during the process of conjugation. Scientists can use this mechanism as a tool for genetic engineering to introduce new genes into cells. For example, suppose scientists want to clone a human gene for producing insulin. First they separate the gene from its chromosome, and then they splice it into a plasmid. The next step is to insert the plasmid, with its recombined DNA, into a bacterial cell. Each time the bacteria divide, the new gene is copied along with the bacteria's own genes. Figure 12.11 summarizes this technique of cloning genes using plasmids.

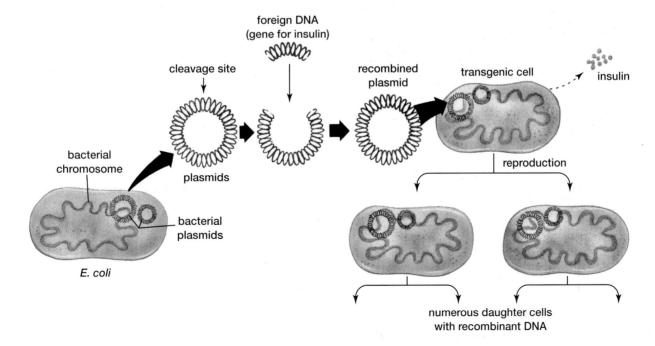

Figure 12.11 Plasmids are used to introduce foreign genes into bacterial cells. When the cells divide, the foreign gene is cloned.

Spore formation

The life cycle of some bacteria includes a dormant phase, in which they are able to survive an unfavourable environment. The bacteria develop a tough outer covering that surrounds their DNA and a small amount of cytoplasm. This forms small seedlike structures called **endospores** such as the one shown in Figure 12.12. While in the endospore stage, bacteria do not grow or reproduce. Endospores can resist extreme heat or cold, drying out, and damaging chemicals. When favourable conditions return, the endospore loses its coat and begins to grow and divide like a normal cell. Some endospores have survived thousands of years in the resting state. While endospores can resist most extreme environmental conditions, they can be killed. One reliable method is to subject the endospores to an autoclave, a container that contains pressurized steam.

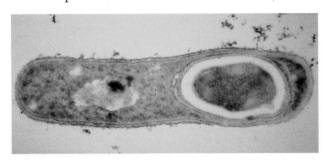

Figure 12.12 The bacterium shown here, *Bacillus subtilis*, contains an endospore.

Bacteria and Human Health

Why does food spoil and become sour or toxic? Why do some diseases spread from person to person? These events are the result of bacteria carrying out their normal life functions. Knowing which types of bacteria are involved, and the characteristics of the bacterial group, allows people to develop ways of avoiding certain health risks.

For example, botulism is a type of food poisoning caused by a species of anaerobic bacteria, *Clostridium botulinum*, commonly found in the soil. It forms endospores that are very resistant to heat and that germinate in anaerobic conditions. The metabolism of these bacteria produces toxic products that can cause nausea or even death in humans. The bacteria are not dangerous, however, unless they are trapped with food for a period of time under anaerobic conditions. This sometimes occurs when people seal food into bottles or jars at home without proper care (Figure 12.13). To ensure that bacterial endospores are killed, the food must be heated under high pressure at temperatures above the boiling point of water.

> **❙❙PAUSE**   **●RECORD**
>
> You have learned that bacteria are all around you, in every environment on Earth. Make a list of all of the positive ways that bacteria affect humans. Now make a similar list of all of the negative ways that bacteria affect humans. Compare your two lists. Which list is longer? Write down your ideas about the overall impact of bacteria on human life.

MINI **LAB**

Modelling Gene Splicing

Bacteria are useful for genetic engineering because a) it is relatively simple to add new genes into plasmids and b) bacteria reproduce rapidly, making multiple copies of their genes. Genetically altered bacteria are then used in many different ways in the fields of medicine, agriculture, industry, and pollution control. In this lab, you will make a model that represents the process of gene splicing. Study the technique of making recombined DNA illustrated in Figure 12.11. Create a flowchart explaining the steps in your own words. Using paper, string, wire, or other suitable materials, construct a model that can be used to explain this process to others. You may mount your model, with labels, as a display, or prepare a short demonstration.

Analyze

1. How is a strip of DNA cut into fragments containing the desired genes? What part of your model represents DNA fragments? Why does a strip of foreign DNA join onto a plasmid?

2. Genes are transferred from one species to another in order to produce characteristics of value in agriculture, medicine, or industry. Carry out your own research to find out more about this topic. Focus on one application, such as medicine or agriculture, that interests you. Produce a brief report of your findings. Your report should include the following information:

   - How are bacteria used in the application?
   - What other species are involved?
   - What characteristic is altered, and why?
   - What are the advantages and disadvantages of this technology?

Figure 12.13 Commercially canned foods are heated to 121°C for at least 20 min to destroy all *C. botulinum* endospores. Care must be taken with home canning to ensure high temperature is used for a long enough time to kill the toxic germinating endospores.

Bacteria and Medicines

The ability to identify and classify bacteria is especially useful in medicine because infection occurs when bacteria build up in large numbers in affected parts of the body. To grow and divide into these large numbers, bacteria must have suitable environmental conditions as well as a supply of nutrients and energy. To stop infections, it is necessary to keep bacteria from spreading.

Antibacterial agents, or **antibiotics**, work to stop bacteria from growing by interfering with the specific processes that are essential for bacterial growth and reproduction. Antibiotics stop infections in a number of different ways. In general, they prevent the bacteria from building or repairing cell walls and membranes, or from making more RNA or DNA. Some antibiotics kill the bacteria, while others inhibit the bacteria's growth, which allows the normal defences of the host body to destroy the micro-organisms.

How might it help a doctor to know whether the bacteria found in a patient are classified as either Gram-positive or Gram-negative? Recall that these two groups of bacteria differ in the structure of their cell walls as shown in Figure 12.14. The bacterial cell wall is like a wall around a castle, protecting the bacterium from dangers present in the external environment. Damage to the cell wall can destroy its rigidity and may result in the death of the bacteria. Doctors use the knowledge of which type of cell is present to choose which antibiotics or other antibacterial agents to prescribe for a particular bacterial infection.

Web LINK

People have faced the challenge of preserving foods for centuries. Drying, smoking, pickling, and salting are traditional methods. How does each method discourage bacteria from growing in the food? How do more modern methods help protect food from bacteria? To research this topic, use the web site shown below. Go to **Science Resources**, then to **BIOLOGY 11** and follow the links shown there.
www.school.mcgrawhill.ca/resources/

peptidoglycan

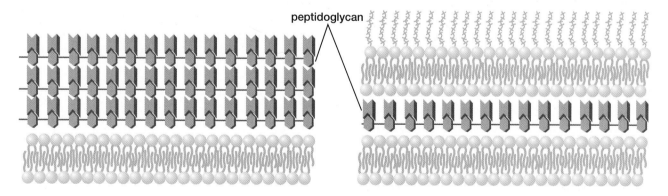

Figure 12.14 Structure of the cell wall in Gram-positive (left) and Gram-negative (right) organisms. The cell wall contains a layer of material called peptidoglycan, which makes up as much as 90% of the thicker walls of Gram-positive bacteria. However, the peptidoglycan layer is porous and allows most antibacterial agents to enter the cell. The thinner walls of Gram-negative bacteria are surrounded by outer membranes made of materials that block the entry of antibacterial agents.

Bacterial Resistance

Over time, bacteria exposed to antibiotics evolve new strains that are resistant to the effects of the antibiotic. For example, the bacterium may be modified so that it reduces the amount of the drug entering the cell. Or, the changes may make the drug inactive in some way, perhaps by altering the molecular structure of the drug or changing the target site of the drug within the cell. Changes like these may occur as a result of a single genetic mutation. For example, bacterial resistance to early drugs called sulfonamides resulted from a single amino acid change in one enzyme. This one change

DESIGN YOUR OWN
Investigation   12 • B

SKILL FOCUS

Initiating and planning

Hypothesizing

Performing and recording

Analyzing and interpreting

Observing Variations in Bacterial Response to Antibiotics

Drug researchers test the effectiveness of antibiotics by observing the size of the area where antibiotics inhibit bacteria from growing. Any substance that inhibits the growth of bacteria is called an inhibitor. The area in which bacteria do not grow is called the zone of inhibition. The photograph on this page shows colonies of penicillin-producing mould surrounded by zones of inhibition. These zones are where the antibiotic has killed the bacteria. In this activity, you will use different inhibitors to carry out similar tests of your own.

Note: Some schools do not permit labs using bacteria. If this is the case for your school, do *not* conduct this lab.

Problem

Which antibiotic is most effective in killing a particular culture of bacteria?

Hypothesis

Make a hypothesis about the effect of each different inhibitor you test on bacteria.

CAUTION: Always wear gloves when handling bacterial cultures. Also, wash your hands thoroughly with soap after handling the cultures. Clean your work area and dispose of your cultures and petri dishes as directed by your teacher. Always wear eye protection in the lab. Be aware, and do not spill the cultures. Once your experiment has begun, tape the lid securely to the bottom of the petri dish and do not open it.

Materials

cultures of bacteria	petri dishes containing
antibiotic disks	sterile nutrient agar
marking pen	sterile disks of blank filter
forceps	paper
cotton swabs	incubator
metric ruler	tape

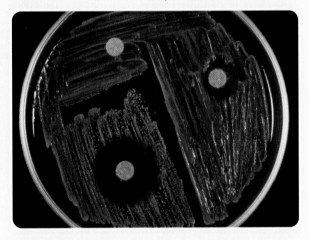

Experimental Plan

1. Using the materials provided, outline several possible procedures to test your hypothesis. Use all the safety procedures outlined in Investigation 12·A as your guide to ensuring sterile conditions.

2. Decide on one experiment that you can carry out in the classroom. Ensure that you will be testing only one variable at a time, and include a control. Make sure you obtain your teacher's approval.

428 ● MHR • *Diversity of Living Things*

reduced the ability of the sulfonamides to bind onto molecules in bacterial cells.

In the late 1950s, researchers found that disease-causing bacteria had become resistant not only to sulfonamides, but also to other drugs such as tetracyclines. This resistance was not due to a genetic mutation, but rather to the presence of extra genes that were transmitted between bacterial cells via plasmids. In recent years, the ability of plasmids to rapidly transfer genes for drug resistance among different bacteria has greatly reduced the effectiveness of many antibiotics.

3. List the details of the materials and quantities you will need. What data will you collect? How will you quantify these data? How often will you record data?

4. Create a table to record your data.

Checking the Plan

1. What is your independent variable? Your dependent variable? Your control?

2. How will you determine if the different antibiotics are effective? Will you add the bacteria or the inhibitor first?

3. How will you prevent contamination from other bacteria in the room?

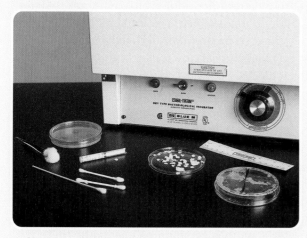

Data and Observations

When your outline has been approved by your teacher, carry out the experiment. Collect and enter your data into a table. Draw your petri dish showing how you set up your test substances and your control. Shade in the bacterial growth on your petri dish after two days.

Analyze

1. How did you measure the effectiveness of each antibiotic? Why did you choose this measurement?

2. Which inhibitor was most effective at inhibiting bacterial growth? How do you know?

3. Rank the inhibitors you used according to their effectiveness. Give the highest ranking to the most effective inhibitor. Explain how you made your decisions.

Conclude and Apply

4. Why is it important for a physician to know the exact identity of the bacteria involved in an infection? How might this knowledge help the physician choose the best treatment for a patient?

5. Suggest why some types of inhibitors worked better on the particular type of bacteria that you cultured. Would the same inhibitor be equally effective on inhibiting other types of bacterial growth?

Exploring Further

6. Why might the excessive or improper use of antibiotics eventually lead to an increase in the number of infections? How can this risk be reduced?

Bacteria and the Environment

Ecosystems depend on a wide diversity of bacteria. In earlier grades, you have studied the various processes by which materials and energy move into, through, and out of ecosystems. Bacteria are an important part of all these processes. In some cases, members of a particular species of bacteria are the only organisms able to carry out certain ecological roles. Without a variety of bacteria, the chemical cycles and food chains that maintain all life would soon come to a halt.

Processes such as the carbon, nitrogen, and sulfur cycles depend on the fact that chemicals excreted into the environment by one type of organism can be used as nutrients by another type. These links join together different types of bacteria into microscopic food webs. In many cases, bacteria that use one anothers' products live in clusters that grow and interact in groups called consortia. For example, one type of bacterium uses hydrogen sulfide and produces sulfate. This type is usually found stuck onto the surface of another type of bacterium that uses sulfate and produces hydrogen sulfide. The two live in a consortium, providing food for each other continuously.

- **Cyanobacteria** (often referred to as "blue-green algae"), such as the photoautotrophs shown in Figure 12.15, are major producers of oxygen through the process of photosynthesis. They were probably among the first organisms on Earth to carry out this vital process. Two billion years ago, Earth's atmosphere had little or no oxygen. By combining water and carbon dioxide to produce carbohydrates, and by releasing oxygen as a waste product, bacteria altered the composition of the atmosphere and literally changed the world.

- Other species of cyanobacteria are the only organisms able to fix atmospheric nitrogen. This process produces nitrates, which are essential for the growth of plants on land and in water (see Figure 12.16).

- Most bacteria are chemoheterotrophs. As decomposers, they break down organic materials and release carbon, hydrogen, and other elements into the environment for use by other organisms.

- The stinking odour of rotten eggs that rises from the muck at the edge of a swamp is hydrogen sulfide. Chemoheterotrophs, such as anaerobic sulfate-reducing bacteria, convert waste materials into hydrogen sulfite and sulfur. Sulfur, an essential ingredient of all proteins, is required by all organisms, and chemoheterotrophs produce the element in a form that other organisms can use.

- Cyanobacteria are important producers in aquatic ecosystems. Given sunlight and water, they reproduce rapidly to form huge colonies that are visible to the unaided eye. You can find them in the green scum on pools and lakes, and in the slimy coats on seaside rocks. In the oceans, they form the base of many food chains.

- Plant-eating animals would be unable to digest much of their food without the help of symbiotic bacteria living in their intestines. Huge populations of these anaerobic bacteria convert specialized parts of the intestine into fermentation chambers. They produce enzymes that digest the cellulose and other large molecules found in plant matter. Other symbiotic bacteria synthesize vitamins needed by their animal partners.

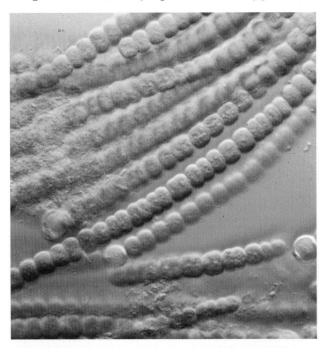

Figure 12.15 Cyanobacteria may contain blue, red, or yellow pigments. Depending on the combination, they may appear any colour from blue-green to black, yellow, or red. *Anabaena*, shown here, contains only chlorophyll *a*, which is found in its cell wall.

BIO FACT

Bacteria can digest almost anything. Even though many synthetic chemicals have been introduced to the environment only during the last 100 years, it is possible to find micro-organisms that degrade them. These micro-organisms can break down molecules that are toxic to most other species, including detergents, creosote, TNT, and PCBs.

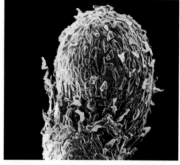

Figure 12.16 *Rhizobium* bacteria (shown on the right) live in the root nodules of plants (shown on the left) and convert atmospheric nitrogen into nitrates that the plant can use for growth.

SECTION REVIEW

1. **K/U** Which of the following is not a bacterial shape: round, pyramidal, spiral, rod?

2. **K/U** Which of the following are true of prokaryotes:

    (a) they include both archaea and bacteria

    (b) they lack a nucleus

    (c) they are only found in extremely hot environments

    (d) they are all parasitic

    Explain your answers.

3. **K/U** Describe what is meant by these terms, and give an example of each:

    (a) obligate anaerobe

    (b) halophile

    (c) chemoheterotroph

4. **I** Cans of tinned food sometimes begin to bulge and lose their shape. Infer what is happening inside the can. Would you eat the food contained in this can? Explain your answer.

5. **I** Hypothesize why you would not suffer from food poisoning if you ate fresh fruit contaminated with the endospores of *Clostridium botulinum*. Hypothesize why you might suffer food poisoning if you ate home-preserved fruit that spoiled.

6. **I** There are bacteria that undergo binary fission every 20 min. If one bacterium were present at 2 p.m., what time would it be when the population of bacteria reached 1 million?

7. **C** Describe two processes that kill harmful bacteria. Write a paragraph explaining how one of the processes works.

8. **K/U** How do antibiotics combat bacteria?

9. **K/U** The images above are illustrations of a bacterial cell dividing into two cells. In your notebook, redraw the figures in the proper sequence and explain what is happening at each step.

10. **C** What is one way that an antibiotic-resistant strain of bacteria can arise? Draw a diagram contrasting a bacterium that is affected by an antibiotic and an antibiotic-resistant bacterium of the same species. Use labels to explain how the antibiotic resistance works.

11. **MC** This section has discussed some of the ways that bacteria are used in biotechnology. What are some of the precautions that would have to be considered before starting to develop a new biotechnological process that uses bacteria? Explain your answer.

12. **MC** Predict how bacteria could help reduce or prevent acid rain.

13. **MC** Bacteria are responsible for many deadly and disabling diseases of humans. They are also invaluable in many ways, keeping our world free from wastes of all different kinds. If you were a scientist starting a new research program, would you focus your research on eradicating a particular disease, or on finding new positive ways to use bacteria in biotechnology? Write a short essay outlining what you would do and why.

Kingdom Protista

- Describe characteristics of members of the Kingdom Protista.

- Learn the life cycle of representative protists.

- Collect various organisms in an ecosystem, and classify them using taxonomic principles.

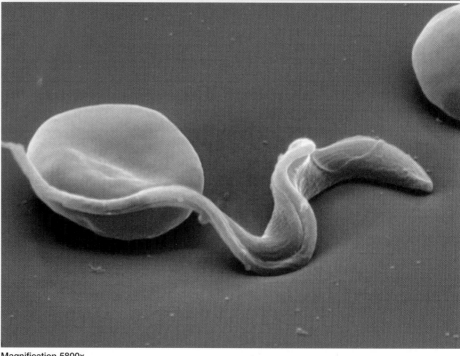

Figure 12.17 Protists live in aqueous environments, including human blood.

Magnification 5800x

The photograph in Figure 12.17 shows *Trypanosoma brucei* in human blood. It is one of many species of protists that cause disease in humans, in this case, African Sleeping Sickness. Most protists, however, do not cause disease and are free-living. For example, if you look at a sample of pond water under a microscope, you will probably see many tiny organisms of various shapes, colours, and sizes. Some of these organisms are autotrophs and some are heterotrophs. Like bacteria and archaea, most are single-celled. On the other hand, they are also eukaryotes like plants, animals, and fungi.

These microscopic organisms are classified in the Kingdom Protista. The members of this kingdom, such as the ones in Figure 12.18, are classified together mainly because they do not fit into the other kingdoms, rather than because they are similar or closely related to one another. They are less diverse than bacteria and archaea, but, as you can see from Figure 12.19, they are more diverse than the other eukaryote kingdoms.

Classifying Protists

Protists are classified into three major groups based on their type of nutrition. **Protozoa**, or animal-like protists, are heterotrophs that ingest or absorb their food. **Algae**, or plant-like protists, are autotrophs that carry out photosynthesis. **Slime moulds** and **water moulds** are fungus-like protists that are also heterotrophs.

Figure 12.18 The three groups of protists are (A) Algae, (B) Protozoa, and (C) Slime and Water moulds.

Characteristics of Protists

- 60,000+ species described
- eukaryotes
- most are unicellular, a few are multicellular
- range in size from 10 μm to 60 m
- some have cell walls, some do not
- some are motile, some are not

- some have pigments, some do not
- have various feeding methods
- most are aerobic
- lack specialized features of fungi, plants, and animals
- do not develop complex sex organs
- do not form embryos

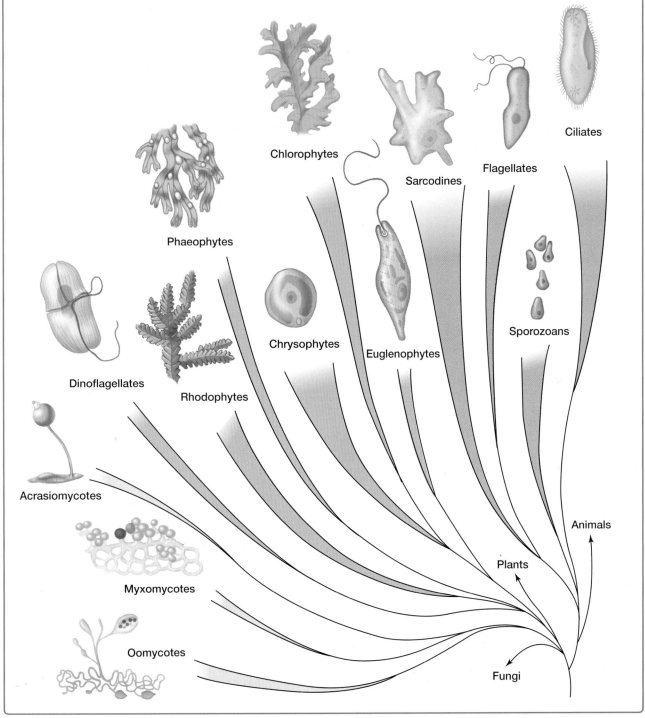

Chlorophytes

Sarcodines

Flagellates

Ciliates

Phaeophytes

Dinoflagellates

Rhodophytes

Chrysophytes

Euglenophytes

Sporozoans

Acrasiomycotes

Myxomycotes

Oomycotes

Plants

Animals

Fungi

Figure 12.19 An overview of the Kingdom Protista.

Investigation 12 • C

Sampling Pond Organisms

The microscopic organisms found floating in bodies of water are collectively known as plankton. Phytoplankton are plankton that carry out photosynthesis. They may be members of the Kingdom Bacteria, Protista, or Plantae. Zooplankton move and consume other organisms. They may be members of the Kingdom Protista or Animalia. In this investigation, you will use techniques of sampling and classification to measure the diversity of organisms in pond plankton.

Pre-lab Questions

- What factors determine the number of species found in an ecosystem?

- How might a particular environmental factor affect biodiversity?

- List some factors that might make some species over-represented and other species under-represented in one sample. (For example, the depth at which species live, or their response to light.)

Problem

How can you collect and classify pond plankton to accurately reflect the diversity of the organisms in the pond?

Prediction

Predict which types of organisms will be present in a pond ecosystem.

Materials

samples of pond water
prepared slides of various
  pond organisms
small vials for
  collecting samples
microscope

cover slips
methyl cellulose solution
collecting nets
microscope slides
dropper

Procedure

1. Obtain samples of pond water from your teacher or by collecting them yourself during a class field trip.

2. Prepare a table in your notebook to record the name of each organism, the kingdom and subgroup in which it is classified, its relative abundance, and a labelled sketch of the organism.

3. To become familiar with the appearance and identity of some common pond micro-organisms, study the illustrated field guide to protists on the next page. Examine several prepared slides under the microscope.

4. Place a drop of the sample on a slide and prepare a wet mount. See *Appendix 4, Preparing a Wet Mount*, if you need to review this procedure.

5. Observe the slide under low power of your microscope. If the zooplankton move too quickly, add a drop of methyl cellulose to slow them down.

6. Select one species from your slide sample and study it under medium and then high power. Using the illustration shown on the next page, decide which group it belongs to. Record the identity and relative abundance of the organism in your table. If you cannot identify it, make a sketch. Note if your organism is very common in your sample, or if it is relatively rare.

7. Return to low power and repeat the procedure with another species. Observe as many different species as you have time for. If you observe all of the species on your slide sample, prepare another wet mount using a different sample of pond water taken from a different location.

Post-lab Questions

1. How did you distinguish between protists and the members of other kingdoms?

2. Name three factors that might increase the diversity of plankton species living in a pond. Name three factors that might decrease the diversity of plankton species in the pond.

Conclude and Apply

1. Did your sampling have any biases that might have affected your results? Explain your answer.

2. Did you record more species of phyto-plankton or zooplankton? Suggest why.

3. Compare your results of pond organism diversity with the results of other students in your class. Note any differences. Using this information, explain why knowledge of sampling methods and taxonomy might be important for studying diversity in different environments.

Exploring Further

4. You have been chosen to assess and manage the quality of a watershed that supplies drinking water. Based on your experiences during this investigation, develop a plan to show how you would proceed with this task. List at least two questions you would need to answer before you could make your plan.

5. Sampling organisms in different environments is a common scientific procedure. Write a scenario about sampling organisms in an environment other than a pond. Explain why the sampling needs to be done, and how the results of the study could be used.

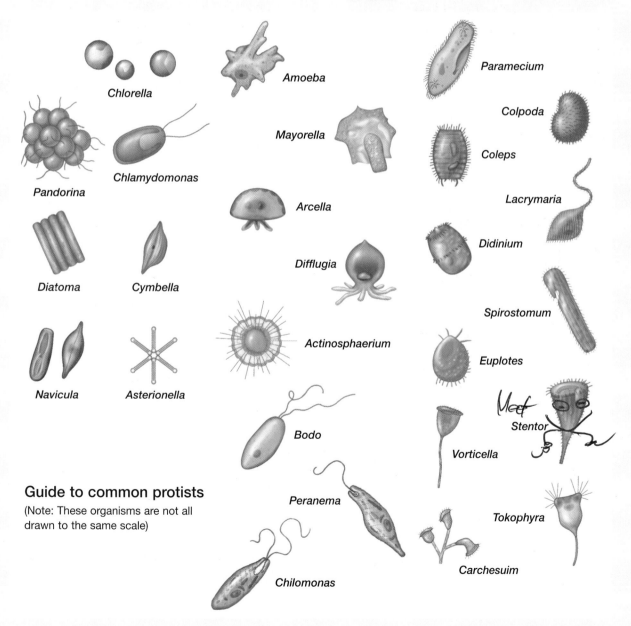

Chlorella

Amoeba

Paramecium

Colpoda

Pandorina

Chlamydomonas

Mayorella

Coleps

Lacrymaria

Diatoma

Cymbella

Arcella

Didinium

Difflugia

Spirostomum

Navicula

Asterionella

Actinosphaerium

Euplotes

Bodo

Stentor

Vorticella

Guide to common protists
(Note: These organisms are not all drawn to the same scale)

Peranema

Tokophyra

Carchesuim

Chilomonas

Protozoa (Animal-like Protists)

Protozoa means "first animals." Like animals, protozoa obtain their food by feeding on other organisms or dead matter. Some are scavengers that absorb or ingest materials from their surroundings. Others are predators that actively hunt down or ambush small organisms such as bacteria and other protozoa. Parasitic species of protozoa live inside larger organisms, including humans.

There is little about a protozoan that makes it immediately recognizable. Protozoa vary in shape from a jelly-like blob to a spherical sunburst to a flattened leaf (Figure 12.20). They vary in size from tiny blood parasites only 2 μm long to shell-covered marine forms 5 cm or more in diameter. Most live as single cells, although a few form colonies.

Many protozoa, especially parasitic species, have complex life cycles with multiple stages. Sometimes the different life cycle stages are so dissimilar that the organisms have been mistaken for completely different species. Most protozoa can move, and species are traditionally classified in four phyla based on their methods of locomotion.

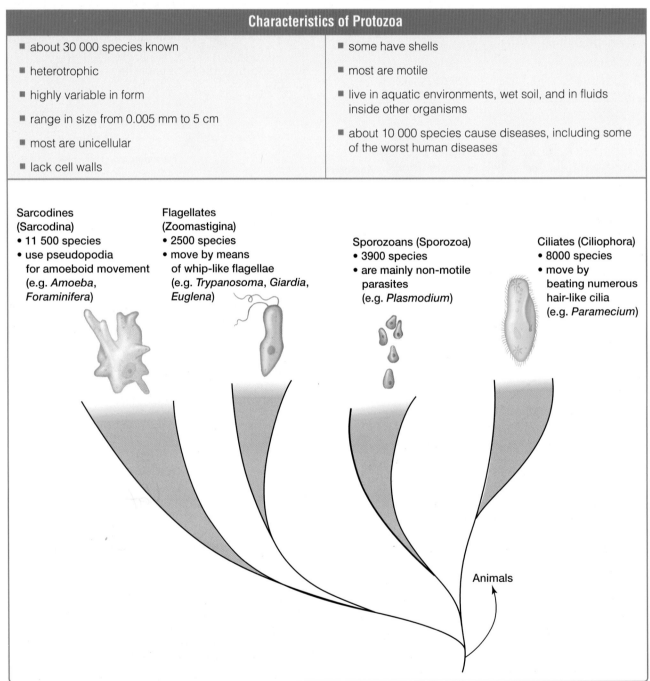

Characteristics of Protozoa

- about 30 000 species known
- heterotrophic
- highly variable in form
- range in size from 0.005 mm to 5 cm
- most are unicellular
- lack cell walls

- some have shells
- most are motile
- live in aquatic environments, wet soil, and in fluids inside other organisms
- about 10 000 species cause diseases, including some of the worst human diseases

Sarcodines (Sarcodina)
- 11 500 species
- use pseudopodia for amoeboid movement (e.g. *Amoeba*, *Foraminifera*)

Flagellates (Zoomastigina)
- 2500 species
- move by means of whip-like flagellae (e.g. *Trypanosoma*, *Giardia*, *Euglena*)

Sporozoans (Sporozoa)
- 3900 species
- are mainly non-motile parasites (e.g. *Plasmodium*)

Ciliates (Ciliophora)
- 8000 species
- move by beating numerous hair-like cilia (e.g. *Paramecium*)

Animals

Figure 12.20 An overview of the Phylum Protozoa

Flagellates (Zoomastigina)

Protists in the phylum Zoomastigina are called flagellates because they have one or more flagellae that whip from side to side to move them about. They have a hard, protective covering over their outer membrane. Some species are free-living, some are parasites, and some live in symbiotic relationships.

Among the symbiotic flagellates are many species that live in the digestive tracts of animals and help the host animals digest plant material. For example, termites feed on wood, but they are unable to digest the tough cellulose that makes up a large part of their diet. Flagellates, like the ones shown in Figure 12.21, live in termite guts and produce enzymes that convert cellulose to carbohydrates, which the termites can use. In return, the flagellates receive a steady supply of food and a warm and protected environment.

There are many species of parasitic flagellates. *Trypanosoma*, shown in Figure 12.17 at the beginning of this section, is the parasite that causes a disease called trypanosomiasis, or African Sleeping Sickness. The complex life cycle of *Trypanosoma* passes through three different stages. They spend part of their life cycle in the salivary glands of tsetse flies. They are then transmitted to humans by the bite of these insects. In the second stage, the trypanosomes reproduce and spread in the blood and spinal fluid of the person who has been bitten. In the third stage of their life cycle, the trypanosomes begin to affect the body tissues of the patient, who gradually becomes dizzy, falls into a coma, and dies.

African Sleeping Sickness also affects domestic animals, including cattle that humans depend on for food. This is a major issue in parts of Africa where raising livestock is critical to human survival.

Wild mammals have built up resistance to the parasite, but domesticated livestock have no such protection. Presently, forested areas are being cleared to provide grazing land for livestock, and this land is located in areas where tsetse flies are common. The overlap in territory has caused the infection rate of livestock to increase dramatically.

In Zimbabwe, a national campaign to eradicate the tsetse fly is underway. The tsetse fly is attracted to the dark colours blue and black. Traps of these colours are covered with poison and set out. It is hoped that the flies will land on the traps and be killed. A poster created by the government of Zimbabwe to inform the public is shown in Figure 12.22.

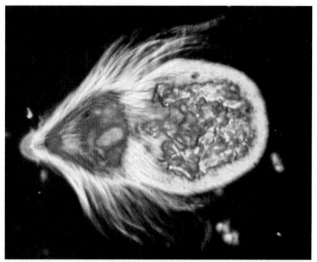

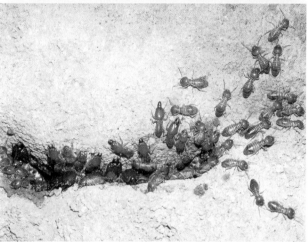

Figure 12.21 This flagellated protozoan (top) lives in the gut of termites (bottom).

Figure 12.22 A warning sign created by the Zimbabwean government to increase public awareness of infection by *Trypanomosa brucei*.

Medical Laboratory Technologist

Have you ever wondered what happens to the blood or tissue samples your doctor takes when trying to solve a medical problem? It is sent to a lab where a Medical Laboratory Technologist (M.L.T.) analyzes the material and searches for biological clues to determine what is making you sick.

Giardiasis

An example of this process occurs when people are infected with *Giardia intestinalis*, a parasite some Canadians encounter when they drink untreated water from lakes and rivers. *Giardia* is a teardrop shaped flagellate, 7 to 15 μm in size. These protozoans have a simple life cycle where cysts are taken in orally (usually in contaminated drinking water). The cysts develop flagella at their next growth stage, and swim in the small intestine. They then use a suction cup to attach to the intestine of their host where they develop into cysts, and pass out in the faeces. The symptoms of the disease include diarrhea, vomiting, dehydration, abdominal pain, and/or a low-grade fever. In order to positively identify *Giardia* in a patient, the doctor must turn to a Medical Laboratory Technologist.

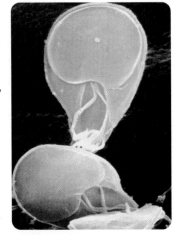

Giardia intestinalis in the human digestive tract. This protozoan causes painful symptoms in humans.

The Medical Analysis

Identifying the presence of cysts is still the most common way to diagnose a *Giardia* infection. The Medical Laboratory Technologist uses a centrifuge to separate out the heavier organic material from the rest of the stool sample. This organic material is suspended in saline solution, and placed under a microscope. The Medical Laboratory Technologist inspects the sample for any signs of parasites, worms, eggs, or amoebas. If *Giardia* cysts are present, they would be found in this organic matter. Any organisms are identified and reported back to the doctor who can then treat the patient.

Identifying parasites is just one example of a Medical Laboratory Technologist's responsibilities. Medical Laboratory Technologists must also be competent in examining and analyzing samples of various types in other fields, including the following: biochemistry (chemical analysis), hematology (blood cells), histology (preparation and analysis of tissue), immunochematology (blood transfusions), bacteriology (infections and micro-organisms), mycology (fungi), virology (viruses), cytology (cancer screening), molecular genetics (molecular basis for disease), and cytogenetics (chromosone abnormalities).

Educational Requirements

Medical Laboratory Technologists complete a three-year Medical Laboratory Technologist's course at a provincial college of medical laboratory technology. The first two years are academic, but the third year is an apprenticeship, working in a lab under the supervision of a qualified M.L.T. When completed, the Medical Laboratory Technologist must write a national certification exam and maintain proficiency by completing 60 hours of professional upgrading each year.

Sarcodines (Sarcodina)

Protists of the phylum Sarcodina, also called amoebae (singular amoeba), move and engulf their prey by producing limb-like extensions of their cytoplasm called **pseudopodia**.

Foraminifera, like the one shown in Figure 12.23, are marine amoebae that have shells made of calcium carbonate. Foraminifera are incredibly abundant, and much of the thick layers of sediment on the ocean floor is made of their shells that have piled up over millions of years. Compressed sediments eventually form sedimentary rock, which may later be raised to the surface by geological upheaval.

For example, the white cliffs of Dover on the south coast of England are made of sedimentary limestone rock composed largely of foraminiferan shells.

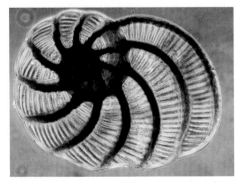

Figure 12.23 Foraminifera extend sticky pseudopodia through tiny holes in their shells to capture food.

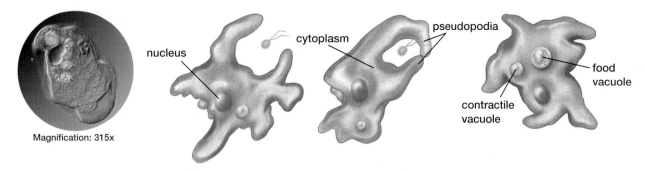

nucleus   cytoplasm   pseudopodia   food vacuole   contractile vacuole

Magnification: 315x

Figure 12.24 Amoebae feed on small organisms including single-celled bacteria. Freshwater amoebae contain contractile vacuoles that collect and expel the excess water that diffuses into their cytoplasm.

In earlier grades, you may have studied the common freshwater amoeba, *Amoeba proteus*, like the one shown capturing prey in Figure 12.24. These species constantly alter their shape as they move, and lack any hard external covering.

As well as free-living species, there are also symbiotic and parasitic amoebae. For example, *Entamoeba hystolitica* feeds on the lining of the gut in humans and causes a serious illness called amoebic dysentery. Many other species of intestinal amoebae also live inside us without causing significant problems. Intestinal amoebae can be spread by drinking contaminated water, or eating produce that has been contaminated.

Ciliates (Ciliophora)

Paramecium, shown in Figure 12.25, is a common ciliate protozoan found in ponds. It is covered by

hundreds of **cilia** that beat in a co-ordinated rhythm to move the micro-organism about. The cilia also help to sweep food particles into the paramecium's gullet, which leads to a food vacuole.

Many species of ciliates are large and complex, growing to over 100 µm in length. As with the other groups of protozoa, some members of this phylum are free-living (like *Paramecium*), some are symbionts, and some are parasites. Only one species of ciliate is known to parasitize humans — *Balantidium coli* lives in the large intestine and causes diarrhea.

« REWIND

You have learned about intracellular digestion in single-celled organisms in Chapter 10, Section 10.1. Turn back to this section if you need to review this process.

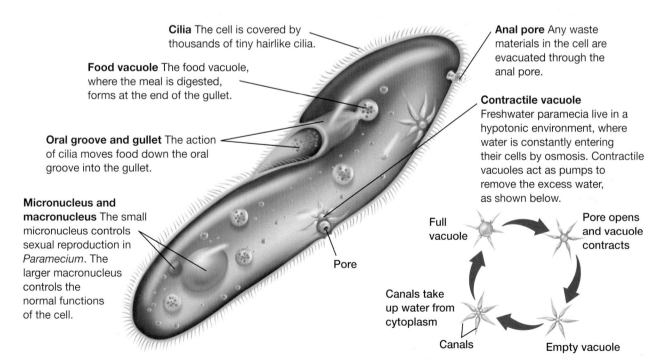

Cilia The cell is covered by thousands of tiny hairlike cilia.

Food vacuole The food vacuole, where the meal is digested, forms at the end of the gullet.

Oral groove and gullet The action of cilia moves food down the oral groove into the gullet.

Micronucleus and macronucleus The small micronucleus controls sexual reproduction in *Paramecium*. The larger macronucleus controls the normal functions of the cell.

Anal pore Any waste materials in the cell are evacuated through the anal pore.

Contractile vacuole Freshwater paramecia live in a hypotonic environment, where water is constantly entering their cells by osmosis. Contractile vacuoles act as pumps to remove the excess water, as shown below.

Pore

Full vacuole

Pore opens and vacuole contracts

Canals take up water from cytoplasm

Canals

Empty vacuole

Figure 12.25 *Paramecium* is a complex unicellular organism.

Sporozoans (Sporozoa)

Sporozoans are parasites. The name of this group comes from the fact that they form spores at some point in their life cycle. Like many other parasites, they have a complex life history, adapted to transferring their offspring from one host to another. They contain a number of complex organelles at one end of their bodies that may help them invade their host's cells or tissues. Many species are so small that they are parasites within the cells of their host.

The most widespread human parasite, and one of the most devastating, is the sporozoan *Plasmodium vivax*, which causes one type of malaria in humans. These parasites pass into the bloodstream when a person is bitten by an infected mosquito, like the one in the opening photograph

for this chapter. The **sporozoites** (spore cells) of the parasite invade and reproduce in the liver, creating a second sporelike stage. These cells make their way into the red blood cells where they multiply by reproducing asexually. Eventually, the red blood cells rupture and release the spores, which re-infect new red blood cells. This is the stage where the fever and chills associated with malaria occur. Some spores become male or female **gametocytes**, which form gametes that combine to reproduce sexually. When an infected person is bitten by a mosquito, the gametocytes enter into the mosquito's gut, combine, and form more sporozoites. The mosquito bites another human, and so the cycle continues. This complete cycle is shown in Figure 12.26.

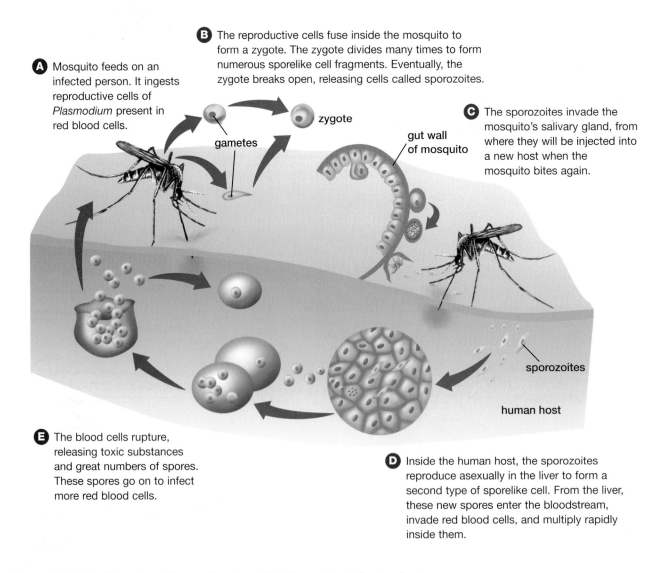

A Mosquito feeds on an infected person. It ingests reproductive cells of *Plasmodium* present in red blood cells.

B The reproductive cells fuse inside the mosquito to form a zygote. The zygote divides many times to form numerous sporelike cell fragments. Eventually, the zygote breaks open, releasing cells called sporozoites.

gametes

zygote

gut wall of mosquito

C The sporozoites invade the mosquito's salivary gland, from where they will be injected into a new host when the mosquito bites again.

sporozoites

human host

E The blood cells rupture, releasing toxic substances and great numbers of spores. These spores go on to infect more red blood cells.

D Inside the human host, the sporozoites reproduce asexually in the liver to form a second type of sporelike cell. From the liver, these new spores enter the bloodstream, invade red blood cells, and multiply rapidly inside them.

Figure 12.26 The life cycle of *Plasmodium vivax*. The life cycle includes two hosts, mosquitoes and humans.

Algae (Plant-like Protists)

Algae are simple, aquatic, chlorophyll-containing organisms. They range in size from single cells that live in puddles and wet soils to giant seaweeds 60 m in length. Because these organisms carry out photosynthesis, they were once classified as plants. However, they lack the leaves, stems, roots, and water-conducting tissues of true plants. As well, the organisms in this group may or may not be closely related to one another. The term "algae" is not a proper taxonomic group but is used for convenience to mean all aquatic eukaryotes that carry out photosynthesis.

Algae of one kind or another have been on Earth for more than 2 billion years, and scientists are still discovering new species. Algae are classified into six phyla, based partly on the type of chloroplasts and pigments they contain. The chloroplasts in different types of algae have different types of chlorophylls and other pigments. This suggests that chloroplast-containing cells evolved independently at least three times. Of the six algal phyla, three are mainly multicellular and three are mainly unicellular. These characteristics are shown in Figure 12.27. Other differences among the groups include the chemistry of their cell walls, the number and position of flagellae (if any), and the form that food reserves take in their cells.

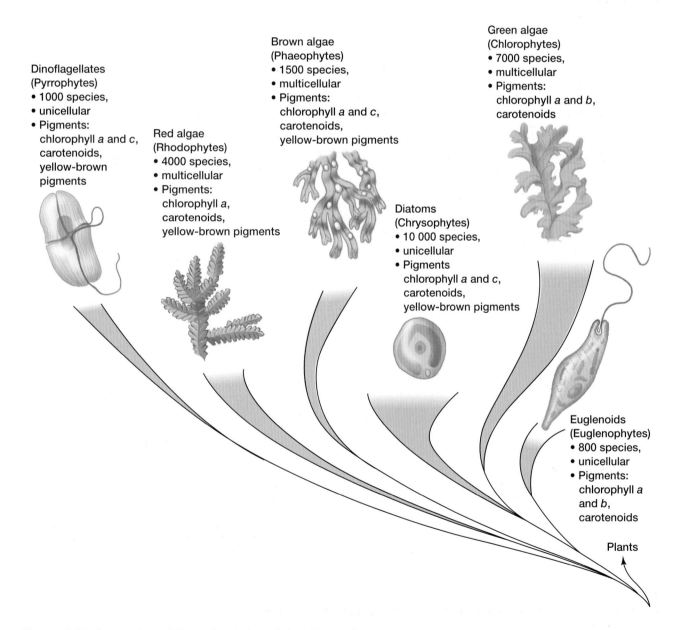

Dinoflagellates (Pyrrophytes)
• 1000 species,
• unicellular
• Pigments: chlorophyll *a* and *c*, carotenoids, yellow-brown pigments

Red algae (Rhodophytes)
• 4000 species,
• multicellular
• Pigments: chlorophyll *a*, carotenoids, yellow-brown pigments

Brown algae (Phaeophytes)
• 1500 species,
• multicellular
• Pigments: chlorophyll *a* and *c*, carotenoids, yellow-brown pigments

Green algae (Chlorophytes)
• 7000 species,
• multicellular
• Pigments: chlorophyll *a* and *b*, carotenoids

Diatoms (Chrysophytes)
• 10 000 species,
• unicellular
• Pigments chlorophyll *a* and *c*, carotenoids, yellow-brown pigments

Euglenoids (Euglenophytes)
• 800 species,
• unicellular
• Pigments: chlorophyll *a* and *b*, carotenoids

Plants

Figure 12.27 An overview of Algae, the phylum of plant-like protists

Green Algae (Chlorophytes)

Green algae, shown in Figure 12.28, are the most plant-like of the algae. They have the same types of chlorophyll and the same colour as most land plants. Also like plants, their cell walls contain cellulose, and they store food reserves in the form of starch.

Green algae are most commonly found in freshwater and in damp places on land. Some species of green algae even live in the fur of tree sloths. These large, slow-moving mammals live in tropical rainforests of South and Central America. One common marine algae is *Ulva*, or sea lettuce, as shown in Figure 12.28. It is often found attached to rocks and exposed at low tide. *Ulva* may grow to one metre in length. During reproduction, it produces spores with flagellae that can swim through the water.

Flagellae are also found on many unicellular green algae, such as *Chlamydomonas*, shown in Figure 12.28. The large chloroplast of this species contains a red-pigmented eye-spot — a light-sensitive organ that helps the *Chlamydomonas* swim toward well-lit areas to carry out photosynthesis. During asexual reproduction, the cell divides to form flagellated spores that resemble the parent. *Chlamydomonas* can also reproduce sexually, forming gametes of two different types that fuse to form a zygote. This type of reproduction occurs when conditions are unfavourable. The zygote is protected by a heavy wall to form a zygospore, which survives until the environment is suitable for it to germinate.

A *Volvox* colony, like the one shown in Figure 12.28, is composed of hundreds or even thousands of flagellated cells arranged in a single layer, forming a hollow ball-shaped structure. Small balls of daughter colonies form inside the large sphere, and the large colony eventually breaks open and releases the daughter colonies.

Investigation 12 • D

SKILL FOCUS

Performing and recording

Analyzing and interpreting

Communicating results

Observing Algae

Although some multicellular algae look like plants, they are classified in the Kingdom Protista. In this investigation, you will distinguish among diverse forms of algae and examine the characteristics they all have in common.

Pre-lab Questions

- What characteristics do algae have in common?
- What characteristics help identify different algal groups?

Problem

Observe and identify characteristics of algae, and use them to classify samples of algae.

CAUTION: Iodine stains. If any iodine spills, wash at once with water and inform your teacher.

Materials

compound light microscope microscope slides
cover slips droppers
paper towel iodine solution
living or prepared specimens of: *Closterium, Oedogonium, Scenedesmus, Synedra, Ulothrix, Ulva, Volvox*

Procedure

1. Prepare a table to record your data. Include space to record the cellular organization, any evidence of reproduction, and method of locomotion.

2. Prepare wet mounts of each type of alga. Refer to *Appendix 4, Preparing a Wet Mount*. Examine each species under low and medium power.

3. Add a drop of iodine to the edge of the cover slip. Draw the iodine across the slide using a piece of paper towel, as shown in the figure on the next page.

4. Examine the stained alga under high power and make a labelled drawing. Identify the cell wall, chloroplasts, holdfast cell (which some filamentous species use to attach themselves to rocks), and any other identifying characteristics.

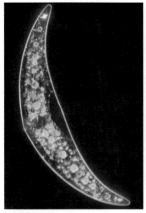

Magnification: 350x

A *Chlamydomonas* is an example of a one-celled green alga.

B *Ulva*, or sea lettuce, is a multicellular alga. It grows in thin sheets that are only two cells thick.

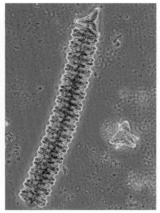

Magnification: 100x

C *Spirogyra* is a freshwater alga that grows in chains. Its chloroplasts are spiral-shaped.

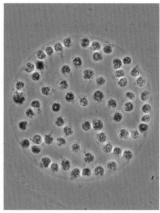

Magnification: 125x

D *Volvox* is a freshwater alga that moves using its flagella. It occurs in ball-shaped colonies, which roll through the water.

Figure 12.28 Examples of Chlorophytes or green algae. Some are unicellular, some are colonial, some form filaments, and others are multicellular.

5. Make clear, labelled sketches of each of your samples.

6. Record the form of cellular organization in each species.

7. Describe any evidence of reproduction seen in your samples.

8. Describe any methods of locomotion you observe.

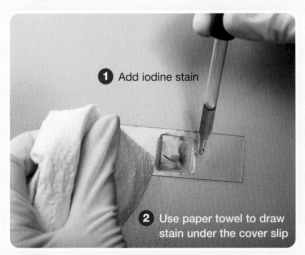

1 Add iodine stain

2 Use paper towel to draw stain under the cover slip

Post-lab Questions

1. Among the samples you examined, which species are unicellular?

2. Describe differences in the shape of the chloroplasts in two or more species. Use illustrations to support your answer.

3. Which species are filamentous? If there is more than one, how do the filamentous species differ?

4. Which species are colonial? How were you able to determine this?

Conclude and Apply

5. Based on your observations, describe a procedure you could use to identify an unknown sample of algae.

6. Obtain a sample of pond water. Prepare a wet mount of this water and locate algae. Many different species will be present, so look carefully. Identify as many species as possible, and draw each specimen you see.

Exploring Further

7. Do some research to determine what other characteristics are used to classify algae. List two characteristics that are used to distinguish members of each phylum into order, genus, and species.

Brown Algae (Phaeophytes)

Brown algae, as shown in Figure 12.29, are nearly all multicellular marine organisms, which we commonly call seaweeds. They have cell walls made of cellulose and alginic acid — a substance similar to pectin, which is used to thicken jams and jellies.

If you have ever observed seaweeds along a beach, you may have noticed some other adaptations brown algae have made to their tidal environment. Their large, flat fronds are tough enough to withstand pounding by the waves. Their bases have root-like holdfasts that anchor the algae to the rocky seabed and prevent them being washed out to sea. In cold, deep waters off the shore, giant brown seaweeds called kelp (*Laminaria*) form huge underwater forests that provide shelter, habitat, and food for a wide variety of marine animals. *Laminaria* is the only multicellular protist that has well-differentiated tissues. Transport tissues resembling those found in land plants are used to carry nutrients through the large fronds.

Figure 12.29 An example of a Phaeophyte, or brown algae. A mucilage-like material in their cell walls helps retain water and keeps seaweeds from drying out when exposed to air at low tide.

BIO FACT

In November 1493, Christopher Columbus sighted landfall after a long voyage westward across the Atlantic. One of the observations that may have led him to the unknown coast was a drifting brown seaweed called Sargasso weed, an algal species common in warm waters. One form of Sargasso weed floats freely on the ocean's surface far from land. A second form grows in shallow coastal waters, secured to underwater rocks by a holdfast. However, parts of this weed may be ripped from their anchor and float out to sea during storms. From notes made by Columbus, it seems he could distinguish between these two forms of Sargasso weed. When he sighted loose strands of the coastal form out at sea, he deduced that land was not far away.

Red Algae (Rhodophytes)

While brown algae are typically found in cold oceans, red algae are multicellular seaweeds found mainly in warmer seawater. They are more delicate and smaller than brown seaweeds. Many are branched, with feathery or ribbonlike fronds (Figure 12.30). The pigments that give red algae their colour are efficient absorbers of green, violet, and blue light. Since these wavelengths penetrate deepest below the water surface, red algae are able to grow at greater depths than other algae.

Species called coralline algae deposit calcium carbonate in their cell walls, making them hard and crusty. They look like pinkish-grey patches of paint splashed over rock surfaces. These algae, together with coral animals, help to build up coral reefs.

Both brown algae and red algae are important economically. Mucilaginous material in the walls of some species of red algae is the source of agar. This gel material is used not only in the lab for culturing bacteria but also to make edible capsules for vitamins and drugs, as a base for cosmetics, and to make jellies and desserts set rapidly.

Figure 12.30 An example of a Rhodophyte, or red algae. The largest do not exceed a metre in length.

Diatoms (Chrysophytes)

Diatoms are the most abundant unicellular algae in the oceans. They are also one of the biggest components of plankton — the free-floating collection of micro-organisms, eggs, and larvae found in the surface waters of oceans and lakes. Diatoms are thus a major food resource at the base of marine and freshwater food webs. As photosynthetic organisms, they are also a major source of atmospheric oxygen.

Diatoms have rigid cell walls with an outer layer of silica, a common ingredient in sand and glass. As you can see from Figure 12.31, they look like small jewel boxes, with one half fitting over the other like a lid. During asexual reproduction, they split in two. Each then grows a new half to fit inside the old one. The rigid cell wall cannot grow once it has been formed, so each generation of diatoms is smaller than the one before. The reduction in size over generations continues until the diatoms reproduce sexually, producing a zygote that grows to the original size before secreting a new cell wall. This process is shown in Figure 12.32.

The remains of diatom shells accumulate on the ocean floor and are mined as diatomaceous earth.

This material is used in filters, soundproofing materials, insulation, and as a gentle abrasive in metal polishes and toothpastes.

Figure 12.31 A single millilitre of seawater may hold many thousands of diatoms like these.

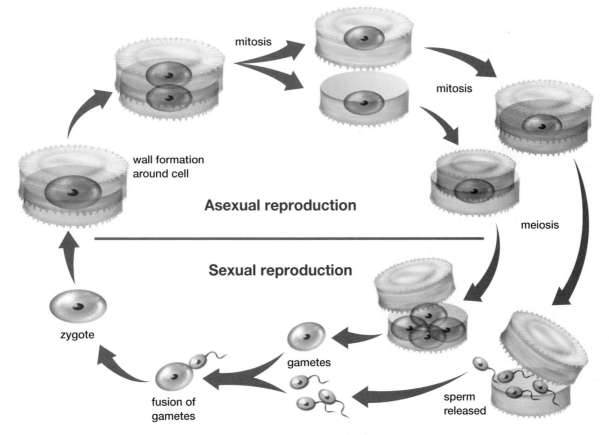

Figure 12.32 Diatoms reproduce asexually and sexually.

Dinoflagellates (Pyrrophytes)

Dinoflagellates, like the one shown in Figure 12.33, are unicellular, photosynthetic, and mostly marine. They have protective coats made of stiff cellulose plates. They are identified as a group by the presence of two flagellae. One lies in a long groove on the covering plate with only its far end free. The second is flat and ribbonlike and lies in a groove that encircles the dinoflagellate. The beating of this second flagellum moves the organism in a spinning path, while the first flagellum acts as a rudder.

Dinoflagellates, like diatoms, are extremely numerous and form an important food source for small marine animals. Reproduction is mainly by cell division, although they are also capable of sexual reproduction. Under certain conditions, species of dinoflagellates increase rapidly in numbers to form a "red tide" like the one shown in 12.34. These dense populations produce toxins that can kill fish and poison people who eat shellfish that have fed on the algae.

Some species of dinoflagellates are symbiotic, living within the bodies of invertebrates such as sea anemones, molluscs, and corals. Called zooxanthellae, these species lack the characteristic cellulose plates of this phylum. In return for the shelter of their partner, they provide carbohydrates which they produce through photosynthesis. This symbiotic relationship is the main reason for the high productivity of coral reefs in nutrient-poor waters.

Figure 12.34 Species containing a red pigment sometimes increase in numbers and produce a "red tide" like this one.

Euglenoids (Euglenophytes)

Euglenoids, such as the *Euglena* shown in Figure 12.35, are small unicellular freshwater organisms with two flagellae — one usually much longer than the other. Although classified among the plant-like protists, over one half of euglenoid genera do not have chloroplasts and are heterotrophs. As well, species with chloroplasts that are raised without light will lose their chloroplasts and ingest or absorb food. So, these algae can be autotrophic or heterotrophic.

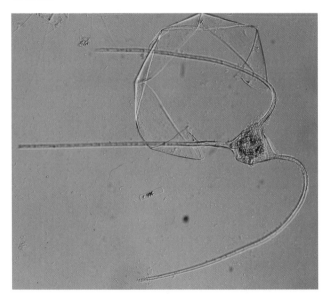

Figure 12.33 Dinoflagellates have a protective coat of cellulose cell plates.

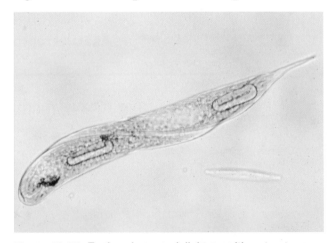

Figure 12.35 *Euglena* has a red, light-sensitive structure called an eye-spot. This structure helps *Euglena* orient itself toward areas of bright light, so photosynthesis can occur.

Slime moulds and Water moulds (Fungus-like Protists)

Slime moulds and water moulds are difficult to classify. They have the characteristics of fungi, protozoa, and plants. Like fungi, they produce spores. Like protozoa, they glide from place to place and ingest food. Like plants, they have cellulose cell walls. Neither one thing nor another, they are included among the diverse kingdom of protists. There are two groups of slime moulds and one group of water moulds as shown in Figure 12.36.

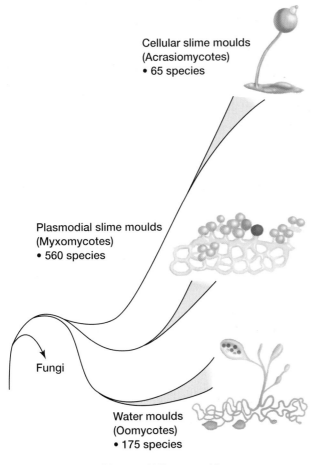

Cellular slime moulds (Acrasiomycotes)
• 65 species

Plasmodial slime moulds (Myxomycotes)
• 560 species

Fungi

Water moulds (Oomycotes)
• 175 species

Figure 12.36 The Slime and Water moulds

⏸ PAUSE ⏺ RECORD

You have learned that protists are classified together in the same kingdom because they do not fit into any other kingdoms. This means that the relationships among these organisms are poorly understood. List some other characteristics that you could use to organize protists. For example, could you classify protists based on their method of feeding, or their method of movement? Would a new classification make any difference to a biologist studying slime moulds? Explain your ideas.

Water moulds (Oomycotes)

The phylum Oomycota includes water moulds, white rusts, and downy mildews. They are filamentous organisms that resemble fungi. Most live as **saprotrophs** on dead organic matter. Some species, however, are parasites on fish, insects, and plants. They extend fungus-like threads into their host's tissues, where they release digestive enzymes and absorb the resulting nutrients. You may have seen them as furry growths on the gills of fish. This process is shown in Figure 12.37. One species, *Phytophthera infestans*, infects potato and tomato crops, causing them to rot. It was responsible for the Irish potato famines during the 1840s in which over 30% of the Irish population either died or emigrated. Oomycotes differ from other fungus-like protists by the nature of their spores and their sexual life cycle.

Figure 12.37 Water mould consumes a dead insect.

Plasmodial slime moulds (Myxomycotes)

Plasmodial slime moulds are visible to the naked eye as tiny slug-like organisms that creep over damp, decaying plant material in forests and fields. This streaming blob, called a **plasmodium**, contains many nuclei. Like amoebae, these slime moulds feed by engulfing small particles of food into their cytoplasm. Under the microscope, you can see that some of the cytoplasm is concentrated to form a sort of skeleton made of tubules, through which the liquid cytoplasm flows.

During sexual reproduction, the plasmodium develops spore-bearing structures called **sporangia** (singular sporangium). Inside these structures, the nuclei divide by meiosis to produce haploid spores. These spores allow the organism to survive dry periods that would otherwise kill the plasmodium. When damp conditions return, the spores germinate. Some spores produce amoeboid cells, and some produce cells with flagellae. The two different types of cells fuse to make a zygote that feeds and grows into another multinucleated plasmodium.

Cellular slime moulds (Acrasiomycotes)

The second type of slime mould, cellular slime mould, exists as individual amoeboid cells with one nucleus each (Figure 12.38). Like protozoa, each cell feeds by ingesting tiny bacteria or yeast cells. When food becomes scarce, the cells release a chemical that causes them to gather together to form a **pseudoplasmodium**. This is a jelly-like mass which then produces sporangia that release spores like the plasmodial slime moulds. The spores fuse and the life cycle continues. This cycle is shown in Figure 12.39 on the next page. Despite their names and similarities, there is no strong evidence that the two types of slime moulds are closely related.

Figure 12.38 These are different stages in the life cycle of a cellular slime mould. Can you identify which stages these are by looking at Figure 12.39 on the next page?

THINKING LAB

Plasmodial Life Cycle

Background

Plasmodial slime moulds have a life cycle that moves through many different stages. The most visible stage is the plasmodial stage, where the organism is a mass of slime. This stage is followed by a stage that is too small to be seen by the naked eye, and therefore less noticeable.

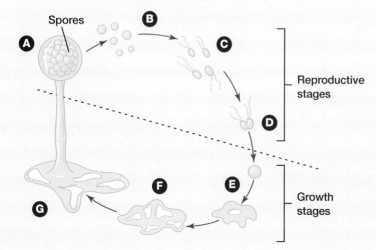

You Try It

Examine the illustration of the plasmodial slime mould's life cycle. The structures below the dashed line are diploid in chromosome number. Using your knowledge of meiosis and mitosis, and the diagram, answer the following questions. Turn to Chapter 5, Sections 5.1 and 5.2, if you need to review these processes.

1. Between F and G, which cell process is occurring, meiosis or mitosis? Between A and B? Explain your answers.

2. Indicate the letter shown beside each of the following stages: fertilization; motile spores; an embryo. For each answer, explain your reasoning.

3. At what point in the illustrated life cycle does the slime mould feed? Explain your answer.

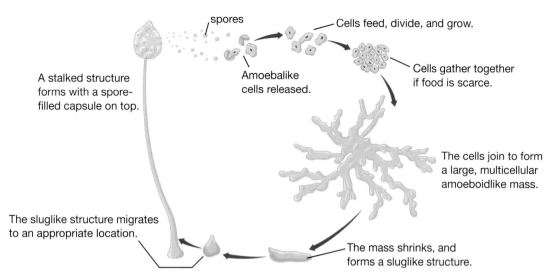

spores

A stalked structure forms with a spore-filled capsule on top.

Cells feed, divide, and grow.

Amoebalike cells released.

Cells gather together if food is scarce.

The cells join to form a large, multicellular amoeboidlike mass.

The sluglike structure migrates to an appropriate location.

The mass shrinks, and forms a sluglike structure.

Figure 12.39 The complex life cycle of a cellular slime mould.

SECTION REVIEW

1. **K/U** List three main divisions in the Kingdom Protista. What are their modes of nutrition?

2. **K/U** List four main divisions of protozoa, with an example of each. What are their methods of locomotion?

3. **K/U** Freshwater paramecia live in a hypotonic environment. How might the contractile vacuoles of a paramecium respond if the organism were placed in a dilute salt solution?

4. **K/U** What are algae? How are they classified?

5. **K/U** What evidence suggests that plants evolved from a species of green alga?

6. **K/U** Name three phyla of seaweeds and give an example of each.

7. **C** Draw a diagram that distinguishes between cellular and plasmodial slime moulds. Use labels to explain the differences and/or similarities.

8. **K/U** Study the following drawings and correctly identify the phylum to which each organism belongs. Explain how you decided where each organism belongs.

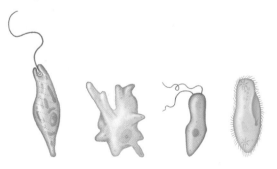

9. **I** The following data were collected by two students observing *Paramecium* and *Euglena* react to light. Is there any pattern to their data? What can they infer about the differences in *Paramecium* and *Euglena* reacting to light?

Organism	Time in min	% of individuals in the light
Euglena	3	55
Euglena	6	70
Euglena	9	90
Paramecium	3	45
Paramecium	6	30
Paramecium	9	15

10. **C** Make a concept map that relates the following terms. You must come up with the linking words for your map: protists, algae, dinoflagellates, protozoans, amoebae, ciliates, slime moulds, *Paramecium*, *Trypanosoma*, *Foraminifera*.

UNIT ISSUE PREP

You may have chosen the species you will be studying for the Unit 4 Issue Analysis. Many larger species of plants and animals have close relationships, either positive or negative, with members of the Kingdom Protista. During your research keep notes about any interactions the species you have selected has with species of protists. Try to include this information in your Unit 4 Issue Analysis.

- Describe characteristics of members of the Kingdom Fungi.
- Learn the life cycle of representative fungi.
- Classify representative fungi.

Figure 12.40 Some species of mushrooms are poisonous. The *Amanita muscaria* shown here can be fatal if eaten.

The mushrooms that spring up after a rain may look like a type of plant, but they also have much in common with animals. Mushrooms and toadstools, along with moulds, mildews, and yeasts, are all members of the Kingdom Fungi. Like animals, fungi are heterotrophs. They feed by releasing digesting enzymes into their surroundings, then absorbing the digested nutrients into their cells.

A few types of fungi are unicellular. For example, yeasts consist of individual oval or cylindrical cells. The majority of fungi, however, are multicellular. Their bodies are made up of **hyphae** (singular hypha) a network of fine filaments. In a mushroom, the hyphae are densely packed together in a tight mass and difficult to see as separate structures. But the mushroom is only a specialized reproductive part of the whole fungus. The main bulk of the organism is under the soil in the form of a loose, branching network of hyphae called a **mycelium**.

Many types of fungi have hyphae that are divided into cells by cross walls called **septa**. Each individual cell has one or more nuclei. The septa are porous, allowing cytoplasm to flow through the hyphae from cell to cell. In other species of fungi that lack septa, each hypha appears to be one large, multinucleate cell (Figure 12.41). Within these hyphae, the nuclei can be seen moving in streams through the undivided cytoplasm. The boundary of a fungal cell is a cell wall. However, unlike plant cell walls, these are made of chitin — a hard material found in the external skeleton of invertebrate animals like insects.

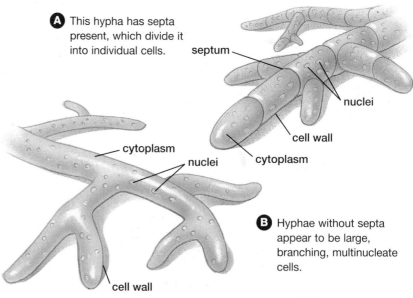

A This hypha has septa present, which divide it into individual cells.

septum

nuclei

cell wall

cytoplasm

nuclei

cytoplasm

cell wall

B Hyphae without septa appear to be large, branching, multinucleate cells.

Figure 12.41 Differences in the structure of hyphae.

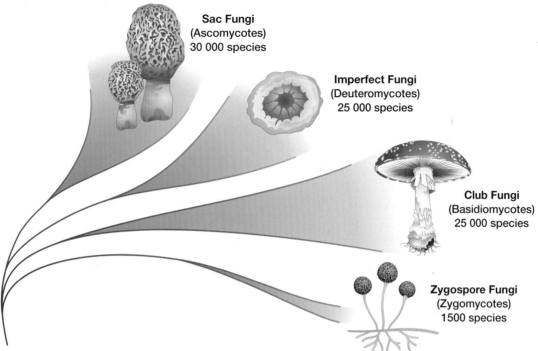

Sac Fungi
(Ascomycotes)
30 000 species

Imperfect Fungi
(Deuteromycotes)
25 000 species

Club Fungi
(Basidiomycotes)
25 000 species

Zygospore Fungi
(Zygomycotes)
1500 species

Figure 12.42 An overview of the Kingdom Fungi

How Fungi Feed

Most fungi are saprophytes that break down dead matter and play a vital role in the recycling of nutrients. As hyphae grow across a source of food, such as a piece of dead wood, an orange peel, or a piece of bread, they release digestive enzymes (Figure 12.43). The enzymes break down large organic molecules in the substrate into smaller molecules. This is essentially the same method of digestion that occurs in your stomach. Because the digestion of food occurs outside the body of the fungus, it is called **extracellular digestion**. The smaller molecules diffuse into the fungus, where they are used to fuel growth and repair. The more extensive the mycelium, the greater the surface area available for absorbing nutrients.

Some fungi are parasites of plants and animals and can cause diseases such as athlete's foot and ringworm. Parasitic fungi are specialized to feed on living cells. They produce hyphae called **haustoria** (from the Latin word meaning "to drink"), which can penetrate host cells without immediately killing them. Some parasitic fungi feed on plants, such as the species that causes Dutch elm disease. Other parasitic fungi such as *Cordyceps myrmecophila* (the last name means ant-lover) parasitize animals. When a spore of this fungus lands on an ant, it germinates and grows into the ant's body as shown in Figure 12.44. Hyphae slowly spread through the ant like a cancer, digesting the insect's tissues to feed the fungus. Another fungus feeds on nematodes — tiny worms that live in the soil. It actually uses its hyphae to snare its food, making a small loop that holds onto any nematode unfortunate enough to enter it.

Figure 12.43 This turkey-tail fungus (*Trametes versicolor*) is decomposing this dead tree. The mycelium of this fungus actually extends deep within the tissue of the tree branch.

Figure 12.44 This ant is being digested from within by the hyphae of a parasitic fungus.

Symbiotic Fungi

Many fungi live in symbiotic relationships with plants or animals, benefiting both species. For example, most trees have fungi living in close contact with their roots. This relationship is called a **mycorrhiza** (from the Greek words *mykes* meaning fungus and *rhiza* meaning root). Fine, threadlike hyphae grow from the fungus around the plant roots, often entering the root cells. The hyphae absorb minerals from the soil and release them into the roots. In effect, the fungal mycelium increases the absorptive surface of the plant roots, helping them take up more nutrients. Another benefit to the plant may be that the fungus helps to maintain air and water flow in the soil around the roots. The fungus benefits from this relationship by absorbing organic nutrients (such as sugars and amino acids) from the plant. Experiments have shown that trees lacking mycorrhiza do not grow as well as those in the same environment that have the symbiotic fungi. (See Figure 12.45 below.)

How Fungi Reproduce

Many fungi have both asexual and sexual methods of reproduction. The simplest asexual method is **fragmentation**, in which pieces of hyphae are broken off and grow into new mycelia. This can happen, for example, when the soil is disturbed by a gardener or a burrowing animal, which breaks up a mycelium under the soil surface. The resulting fragments of hypha can each continue to grow and produce new mycelia.

Figure 12.45 A fungus and a tree root form a mycorrhiza. The fungal hyphae, visible here as white strands, encase the root and provide it with nutrients.

Most fungi live on land, and as an adaptation to terrestrial life they produce spores, which are windblown reproductive cells that help the fungi disperse to new locations. Spore-bearing structures help keep the spores from drying out. To further increase their chances of survival and dispersal, spores are produced in vast numbers. A single puffball, like the one shown in Figure 12.46, can produce as many as one trillion dustlike spores. The lightweight structures can be transported on the bodies of insects or birds, or be blown on the wind for distances of hundreds of kilometres.

Like plant seeds, spores can grow directly into a new organism in a suitable environment. Spores may be asexual (produced by mitosis) or sexual (produced by meiosis). The life cycle and pattern of sexual reproduction is one of the key features used to classify fungi into various groups. Details of the various methods of reproduction are described under each group in the following pages.

Figure 12.46 Almost any type of movement will help to disperse fungal spores. A strong wind or a falling raindrop will cause puffballs, like the one shown here, to release a cloud of spores. The spores will be carried away by the wind.

Classifying Fungi

The original ancestors of fungi are not known. In fact, different groups of fungi living today may have evolved separately from more than one origin. At one time, fungi were included in the plant kingdom. Like plants, they grow in the ground and have cell walls. Today, fungi form a separate kingdom, with four subgroups. An overview of these groups is shown in Figure 12.42 on the previous page.

Zygospore Fungi (Zygomycotes)

You have encountered a type of Zygomycote if you have ever seen fuzzy black patches on a slice of stale bread. Small black dots in the fuzz are the reproductive structures that identify this group. Zygospore fungi include bread moulds and other saprotrophs, as well as a few parasites of protists and small invertebrate animals.

As with bacteria, this group of fungi keep sexual reproduction in reserve for unfavourable times. During sexual reproduction, they produce zygospores, giving the group its name. **Zygospores** are diploid structures that develop after two haploid hyphae of opposite types (called mating strains + and −) combine and fuse their nuclei together (Figure 12.47). The mycelium of a bread mould, such as *Rhizopus stolonifera*, is made up of two forms of hyphae. Horizontal hyphae called

stolons spread out over the bread surface. Downward-growing hyphae called **rhizoids** penetrate the bread and anchor the mycelium. Rhizoids also secrete enzymes that digest the surrounding food and then absorb the digested nutrients. A thick wall develops around the zygospore after the nuclei fuse, protecting the contents from drying and other hazards. The zygospore remains dormant until conditions for growth are favourable again. Then, it absorbs water and the nuclei undergo meiosis. To reproduce asexually, bread mould develops a third form of hyphae that project up above the mycelium. These stalk-like hyphae, called **sporangiophores**, carry sporangia (spore-bearing capsules) like the one in Figure 12.47a, at their ends. Asexual spores develop inside the sporangia, and are released when the capsules split open.

Figure 12.47a This scanning electron micrograph of a *Rhizopus* sporangium shows the clustering of thousands of haploid spores.

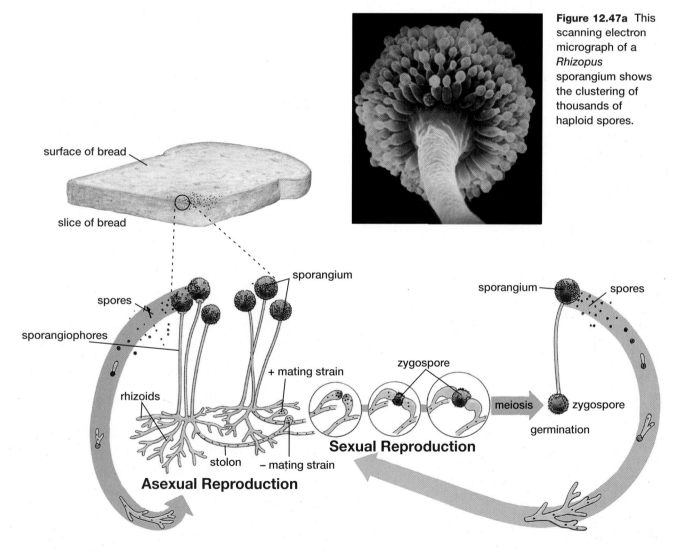

Figure 12.47 The life cycle of the black bread mould, *Rhizopus stolonifera*. Asexual reproduction is the norm, but sexual reproduction also occurs in certain circumstances.

Club Fungi (Basidiomycotes)

The Basidiomycotes include the mushrooms that grow on lawns, the bracket fungi on dead tree trunks, and the puffballs and stinkhorns found on woodland floors. These are all short-lived reproductive structures called fruiting bodies or **basidiocarps**. They bear spores called **basidiospores** on club-shaped hyphae called **basidia**, which give this group its name. Some club fungi are parasites of plants and these species of club fungi do not form basidiocarps. Commonly called smuts and rusts, you can see the serious damage they cause to cereal crops such as corn, wheat, and rye in Figure 12.48.

Although it is easy to imagine that the mushrooms we see growing on the ground are the complete organism, the largest part of the club fungus is a vast, sprawling network of hyphae that spread underground. You can see evidence of this hidden mycelium in the "fairy rings" or circles of mushrooms that sometimes appear on lawns and forest floors. The centre of the circle is the point at which the mycelium began growing, expanding outward like the spokes of a wheel to produce basidiocarps at their ends as shown in Figure 12.49. The complete reproductive cycle of a club fungus involves a complex sequence of events that you can follow in Figure 12.50 on the next page.

Web LINK

The mushrooms that you see growing on lawns are probably the most familiar type of fungus to most people. Fungi of all types, however, have an enormous impact on the world that we live in. Smuts and rusts are parasitic fungi that have an enormous impact on many agricultural crops. What types of crops are affected by rusts and smuts? Choose one particular parasitic club fungus, and do research to discover what its impact is. How are agricultural experts dealing with the threat presented by your parasitic club fungus? To answer these questions, and any others you may have thought of, go to the web site shown below. Prepare a presentation on how a parasitic club fungus has influenced what is available at your local grocery store. Go to **Science Resources**, then to **BIOLOGY 11** and follow the links to find out where to go next. **www.school.mcgrawhill.ca/resources/**

PAUSE **RECORD**

Fungi are heterotrophs that carry out extracellular digestion. List the different types of feeding relationships that fungi have, and describe an example of each relationship.

Figure 12.48 Smuts (A) and bracket fungi (B) are both Basidiomycotes, or Club Fungi.

Figure 12.49 A "fairy ring." The basidiocarps are produced in a circle around the origin of the mycelium.

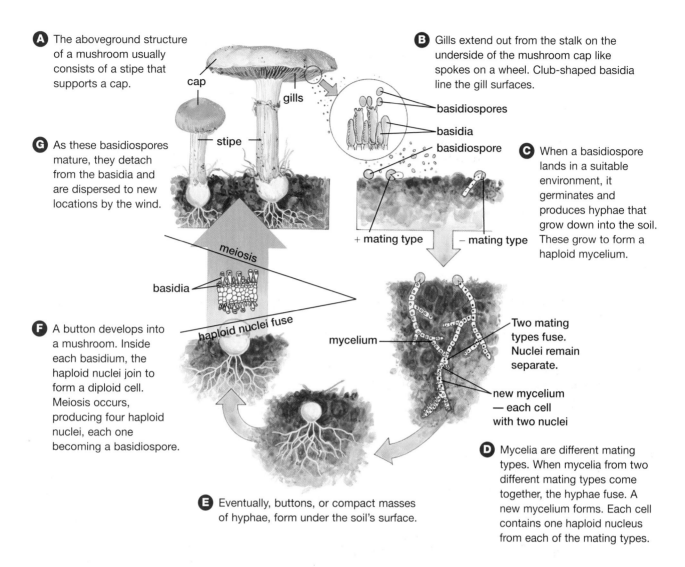

A The aboveground structure of a mushroom usually consists of a stipe that supports a cap.

cap

gills

stipe

B Gills extend out from the stalk on the underside of the mushroom cap like spokes on a wheel. Club-shaped basidia line the gill surfaces.

basidiospores

basidia

basidiospore

G As these basidiospores mature, they detach from the basidia and are dispersed to new locations by the wind.

C When a basidiospore lands in a suitable environment, it germinates and produces hyphae that grow down into the soil. These grow to form a haploid mycelium.

+ mating type   − mating type

meiosis

basidia

haploid nuclei fuse

mycelium

Two mating types fuse. Nuclei remain separate.

new mycelium — each cell with two nuclei

F A button develops into a mushroom. Inside each basidium, the haploid nuclei join to form a diploid cell. Meiosis occurs, producing four haploid nuclei, each one becoming a basidiospore.

D Mycelia are different mating types. When mycelia from two different mating types come together, the hyphae fuse. A new mycelium forms. Each cell contains one haploid nucleus from each of the mating types.

E Eventually, buttons, or compact masses of hyphae, form under the soil's surface.

Figure 12.50 The life cycle of a mushroom. The portion of a mushroom that is visible above the ground is the sexual structure of the fungus. Most types of mushrooms usually reproduce sexually.

MINI LAB

What Are Lichens?

The colourful, crusty growths often seen on exposed rocks are lichens. They do not form a taxonomic group but are a symbiotic association of two organisms from two different kingdoms! One organism is an alga or cyanobacterium and the other organism is a fungus. Obtain a small sample of lichen from your teacher and study it under a magnifying lens. Tear apart a small section of the sample with pins and prepare a wet mount. Observe the lichen under a microscope.

Analyze

1. Describe the appearance of the two organisms that make up the lichen. Can you easily tell them apart? Make a labelled sketch of your sample.

2. Do some research in the library or on the Internet to determine how each partner feeds. How does each organism benefit in this symbiotic association?

Sac Fungi (Ascomycotes)

From the powdery mildews on leaves to the morels and truffles used in gourmet meals, the Ascomycotes is the largest group of fungi. They are identified by small fingerlike sacs called **asci** (singular ascus), which they develop during sexual reproduction. Most sac fungi are saprotrophs that break down the hard-to-digest materials in wood and bone. Other species are parasites of plants, producing leaf curl, chestnut blight, and Dutch elm disease. The usual method of reproduction among ascomycotes is asexual. Species with mycelia do not produce specialized sporangia as zygospore fungi do, but develop spores directly at the tips of modified hyphae exposed to the air. Released spores are dispersed by wind, water, or animals. Sexual reproduction in this group involves the fusion of two different mating types to form spore-bearing asci.

This group also includes single-celled yeasts. Yeast cells usually reproduce asexually by budding as shown in Figure 12.51. The cell nucleus divides by mitosis, and a small part of the cell containing one of the nuclei pinches off from the parent to form a new individual.

Investigation 12•E

SKILL FOCUS

Performing and recording

Analyzing and interpreting

Communicating results

Identifying Common Fungi

The different groups of fungi you have learned about can be distinguished by their reproductive structures. In this investigation, you will study various fungi, note their characteristics, and classify them into their appropriate groups.

Pre-lab Questions

- What characteristics do fungi have in common?
- What characteristics help identify different fungal groups?
- List the reproductive structures of different fungi. Note which groups have sexual and/or asexual reproduction.

Problem

Observe and identify characteristics of fungi, and use them to classify samples of fungi.

CAUTION: Wash your hands after handling fungi.

Materials

cultures of fungi
clear adhesive tape
compound light microscope
microscope slides

Procedure

1. Prepare a table to record your data. Include a title and columns to record the appearance, the colour, and the type of reproductive structure. As well, ensure you have space for a drawing of each sample.

2. Examine a fungus sample and record its colour and appearance.

3. Gently touch the sticky side of a piece of clear adhesive tape to the reproductive structures of the fungus.

4. Carefully place the tape, sticky side up, on a microscope slide.

5. Observe the reproductive structures under low power and draw them in your table. Label the drawing using the illustration on the next page as a guide.

6. Identify the group to which the sample belongs and record it in your table.

7. Repeat the procedure for each sample of fungi provided by your teacher.

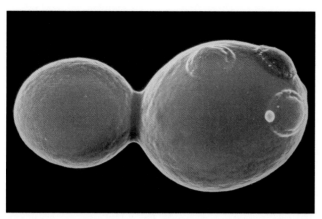

Figure 12.51 Yeast cells form a tiny bud scar every time a bud pinches off from its parent cell. Can you find the bud scars on the parent cell in this photograph?

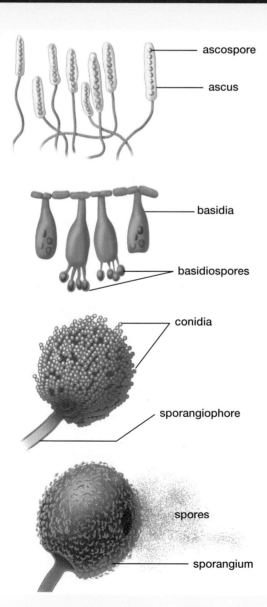

Post-lab Questions

1. Describe the spores you observed in this activity. Include information on their shape, size, and numbers.

2. Describe any differences, other than those based on reproductive structures, that you were able to distinguish among your samples.

Conclude and Apply

3. Why are fungi identified by their reproductive structures rather than by spores alone?

4. Write a short description of the reproductive strategies of the different fungi. Based on your observations, comment on how the physical structures of the fungi relate to these different strategies.

Exploring Further

5. Bring samples of fungi from home and follow the procedures given above to classify them. You may find fungi on mouldy cheese, bread, or fruit, or in damp areas.

6. Grow spores from a sample of fungi on a nutrient medium in a petri dish. Observe and record different stages of its growth.

Imperfect Fungi (Deuteromycotes)

Deuteromycotes are fungi that reproduce only asexually. They appear not to have a sexual phase of reproduction as other fungi do. Because of this, they were named "imperfect fungi." Like basidiomycotes and ascomycotes, they develop mycelia from spores called **conidia**.

This group is diverse, and many of its members are of importance to humans. For example, the antibiotic penicillin was first obtained from a species of the mould *Penicillium.* This greenish-coloured deuteromycote fungus is often seen growing on mouldy fruit. Another drug, cyclosporin, is obtained from a fungus that lives in soil. Cyclosporin is used after transplant operations to suppress the patient's immune system, helping avoid rejection of the transplanted organ. Other deuteromycotes are used to make soy sauce and some kinds of blue-veined cheeses, such as Roquefort. The blue streaks in these cheeses are patches of fungal spores.

You have now read about members of the Kingdom Archaea, Kingdom Bacteria, Kingdom Protista, and Kingdom Fungi. The members of each of these groups have special characteristics that make them belong to one of the kingdoms. As you study the next chapter, you will learn about organisms classified in the Kingdom Plantae and Kingdom Animalia, and about the characteristics that make them unique.

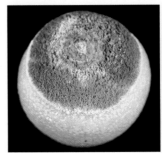

Figure 12.52 Deuteromycotes are useful in many ways. *Penicillium* mould growing on an orange is the same mould that produces the powerful antibiotic penicillin. Many cheeses have a strong flavour due to the presence of deuteromycotes. The blue veins in this cheese are patches of conidia.

SECTION REVIEW

1. **K/U** What are the characteristics of the Kingdom Fungi?

2. **K/U** How are fungi classified?

3. **K/U** Contrast sexual and asexual reproduction in sac fungi.

4. **K/U** Describe examples of fungi that are economically important.

5. **C** Draw diagrams to explain what hyphae and mycelium are. Label your diagrams.

6. **K/U** Your neighbour tells you that mushrooms used to grow in only one small area in the corner of the lawn, but now they grow all over the lawn. How would you explain this observation?

7. **K/U** Your friend tells you that lichens are classified in the Kingdom Fungi. Explain why you would agree or disagree with this statement.

8. **C** You are teaching a junior school classroom about the life cycle of fungi. Create a script for a play that would outline the life cycle of a basidiomycote. List the actors that you would need, and write out what lines and actions they would have.

9. **I** You are preparing to study bread mould. Outline a scientific procedure which would allow you to investigate the conditions needed for bread mould to grow. What would your hypothesis be? What would your control be? What variables would you look at?

10. In an investigation, you inferred that yeast is living because it produces carbon dioxide, a waste gas. In an experiment, you measured the height of gas bubbles produced in three test tubes, and recorded your results in the table below. Create a graph in your notebooks and plot the data shown in the table below. What can you infer from the results of your graph.

Test tube contents	Time			
	0 min	10 min	20 min	30 min
A. yeast without sugar	0 cm	0 cm	1 cm	1 cm
B. yeast + 1 pinch of sugar	0 cm	0 cm	1 cm	2 cm
C. yeast + 2 pinches of sugar	0 cm	1 cm	2 cm	3 cm

UNIT ISSUE PREP

Members of the Kingdom Fungi are not commonly seen as threatened or endangered species. When you were researching your species for the Unit 4 Issue Analysis did you discover any fungi on your lists? Make a list of fungi that you feel may be threatened. Could these species have an impact on the species you have chosen to examine for your Unit 4 Issue Analysis?

Chapter Expectations

Briefly explain each of the following points.

- Archaea are prokaryotes that live in extreme environments. (12.1)
- Bacteria may be classified by their shape. (12.2)
- Bacteria are either Gram-positive or Gram-negative. (12.2)
- Bacteria may be autotrophs or heterotrophs; phototrophs or chemotrophs. (12.2)
- Bacteria reproduce asexually by binary fission and sexually by conjugation. (12.2)
- Bacteria are an essential part of ecosystem processes such as chemical cycles and food chains. (12.2)
- Protists may be classified as animal-like, plant-like, or fungus-like. (12.3)
- Protozoa are classified in four phyla based on their methods of locomotion. (12.3)
- Algae are classified into six phyla based on their type of pigment and whether they are unicellular or multicellular. (12.3)
- Fungus-like protists consist of slime moulds and water moulds. (12.3)
- Fungi are heterotrophs. (12.4)
- Fungi may reproduce sexually or asexually. (12.4)
- Fungi are classified in four major groups. (12.4)

Language of Biology

Write a sentence using each of the following words or terms. Use any six terms in a concept map to show your understanding of how they are related.

- methanogens
- halophiles
- thermoacidophiles
- cocci
- bacilli
- spirilli
- diplo-
- staphylo-
- strepto-
- gram-positive bacteria
- gram-negative bacteria
- binary fission
- conjugation
- pili
- plasmids
- endospores
- antibiotics
- cyanobacteria
- protozoa
- algae
- slime moulds
- water moulds
- pseudopodia
- cilia
- sporozoites
- gametocytes
- saprotrophs
- plasmodium
- sporangia
- pseudoplasmodium
- hyphae
- mycelium
- septa
- extracellular digestion
- haustoria
- mycorrhiza
- fragmentation
- zygospores
- stolons
- rhizoids
- sporangiophores
- basidiocarps
- basidiospores
- basidia
- asci
- conidia

UNDERSTANDING CONCEPTS

1. Describe a characteristic that allows archaea to survive in extreme environments.

2. In your notebook, state whether each of the following statements is true or false. If the statement is false, explain why.
   (a) Most bacteria cause diseases.
   (b) There are three main shapes of bacterial cells.
   (c) Gram-negative bacteria have thick cell walls.
   (d) Bacterial cells can reproduce by mitosis but not meiosis.

3. Explain why the Kingdom Protista might be considered an artificial taxon.

4. What characteristics do algae have in common with plants?

5. Sketch a diagram showing the life cycle of the malaria-producing sporozoan *Plasmodium vivax*.

6. (a) What is an advantage of sexual reproduction over asexual reproduction?
   (b) Why is sexual reproduction the preferred reproductive method of many protists when environmental conditions are unfavourable?

7. Why are red algae found at greater depths in the ocean than brown or green algae?

8. In what way do slime moulds resemble (a) fungi, (b) plants, (c) protists?

9. Describe the difference between plasmodial slime moulds and cellular slime moulds.

10. How do fungi obtain their food? Describe the process in detail for one type of fungus.

11. A mushroom is only a small part of a fungus. Explain what the bulk of a club fungus consists of. What is the function of a mushroom in the life cycle of the fungus?

12. What argument could you use to support the idea that archaea were the first kinds of organisms on Earth?

13. Many unicellular green algae have flagellae and are able to swim. What is the advantage of movement to these plant-like protists?

14. Name three ways in which a protozoan resembles a human and three ways in which it differs from a human.

15. What characteristics of bacteria make them useful tools for genetic engineers?

16. What shape is *Pneumococcus*, the organism that causes bacterial pneumonia?

17. In coastal areas of Canada where shellfish are harvested for human consumption, local authorities monitor the populations of dinoflagellates in the water during the harvesting season. Why do they do this?

18. What evidence might you find in a limestone cliff that tells you the rock material it is made of originated in the ocean?

19. Fish may be preserved from spoiling by adding salt. Fruits may be preserved by adding sugar. Explain how salt and sugar protect foods from invasion by bacteria.

20. When might you deliberately eat (a) bacteria, (b) fungi, and c) algae?

INQUIRY

21. Design an experiment that could help you decide if a particular type of bacteria could grow in anaerobic conditions. Be sure to include a control and to list the different variables you would use.

22. You have designed an experiment to show that mould spores landing on a favourable surface will germinate and produce hyphae. You have placed two slices of bread on a plate for several hours, and then sealed them into plastic bags and put the bags into the dark. Complete the procedure for this experiment. How long would you wait before checking the bread? What would you look for? Would you check both slices at the same time? What data would you collect? Create a data table showing results from your two pieces of bread if (a) conditions were not adequate to support the growth of mould, and (b) conditions were adequate to support the growth of mould.

23. In an experiment, a species of freshwater protozoa was observed to study its behaviour in different circumstances. Water, vinegar, and sugar water were added to the protozoan's environment while the temperature stayed the same. Answer the following questions concerning the experiment.
    (a) What was the control situation?
    (b) What were the variables in the different trials?
    (c) Write a hypothesis that might go with this experiment.

24. During an ecology field trip, a group of students collected data about unicellular algae at a site in the middle of a pond. They measured the number of cells in the water a various depths. They produced the following graph based on their data.

Locations of Diatoms

Use the graph to answer the following questions.
(a) At what time were the highest concentrations of diatoms at the surface?
(b) At what time were the highest concentrations of diatoms about half a metre below the surface?
(c) Why might the diatoms show the pattern found by the students?

25. Construct a table comparing the characteristics of archaea and bacteria. Use the information from your table to describe one way in which these organisms are similar and one way in which they are different.

26. A museum has a collection of four algae specimens which they need to classify to display in an exhibit. Two of the algae have chlorophyll *a* and *b* and two have chlorophyll *a* and *c*. Two of the algae are unicellular and two are multicellular. Both the unicellular algae have flagellae. Based on this information, name the four different groups to which the algae belong, listing the identifying characteristics beside each.

27. There are approximately 85 000 species of fungi presently named in the world and 30 000 of these are sac fungi. Using these data, calculate the percentage of fungi that are sac fungi. If there are 25 000 species of imperfect fungi, 25 000 species of club fungi, 1500 species of zygospore fungi, and 20 000 species of lichens, create a pie chart showing the relative sizes of these groups. For the purposes of this question, include lichens as a type of fungi.

28. There are many products on the market such as soaps, hand lotions, and bathroom cleansers, that claim to be anti-bacterial. Do you believe it is a good idea to rely on these products to keep our homes and bodies free of harmful bacteria? Explain your answer, supporting it with information about bacterial resistance. Based on your answer, create a poster to give information about these products to consumers at grocery stores.

29. What precautionary steps can be taken to prevent food poisoning? Create a checklist that consumers could use to ensure the food they are eating is safe from dangerous bacterial infection.

30. The American chestnut tree was once a common deciduous tree in North America. Unfortunately, it has become increasingly rare as a result of a disease called chestnut blight caused by the fungus *Cryphonectria parasitica*. The spores of the fungus germinate on the bark of the chestnut tree, and the hyphae spread underneath the bark. The spores of *C. parasitica* are carried by the wind, or passively on birds and insects, to other trees, which then become infected. The Japanese chestnut tree is somehow chemically resistant to chestnut blight. You are a scientist reviewing ideas to reduce infection of American chestnut trees. One solution is to apply fungicide on the bark of chestnut trees. Based on your knowledge, why is this not likely to solve the problem? Suggest a solution that involves biotechnology and the Japanese chestnut tree.

31. A tiny bacterium called *Mycobacterium tuberculosis* causes the often fatal disease tuberculosis (TB) in humans. TB, which attacks the lungs, was thought to be almost eradicated from North America, but in recent times this disease is making a comeback. The bacterium is easily passed between people. As social problems such as homelessness increase, people are crowding in shelters in larger and larger numbers. As well, many strains of the bacteria are becoming resistant to antibiotics. Some people feel that new technology is the answer to this disease. Science and technology should produce new medicines, and discovering these drugs should be a priority to the medical community. Others feel that prevention is the solution. Society must eliminate conditions that support passing the bacteria, and ensure that infected people finish prescribed medications. Write an essay about your ideas concerning this problem. What do you feel the priorities should be? Outline a strategy to deal with the rise in cases of TB in Canada.

32. In the 1800's, malaria was a relatively common disease in parts of North America. One approach to fighting the incidence of malaria was to fill in swampy and marshy areas. Explain why this would make a difference in the prevalence of the disease. If this is a successful method to fight malaria, why is this approach not being taken in areas of the world where malaria still exists?

Plants and Animals

Reflecting Questions

- Why are flowering plants more common than any other type of plant?
- Where do most species of animals on Earth live?
- Which animals have no organs?

A caterpillar chews through a leaf on a plant. Like all animals, it must ingest its food. By contrast, the leaf it is eating makes its own food through the process of photosynthesis. These different methods of obtaining food are a key difference between members of the plant and animal kingdoms. A fleeting shadow overhead makes the caterpillar suddenly drop from the plant. This behaviour is its defence against insect-eating birds that may be looking for a meal. Response and movement is another characteristic that distinguishes animals from plants. How is this characteristic related to their different methods of obtaining food?

All plants and animals are multicellular, but they range greatly in size from microscopic organisms to giants such as redwood trees and whales. The earliest animals evolved in the sea, and most animal phyla today are mainly aquatic. Sponges, jellyfish, crabs, mussels, clams, and worms are examples of common marine animals. The only major groups of animals found mainly on land are insects, spiders, some molluscs such as snails, and some vertebrates such as mammals, birds, and reptiles. Plants, on the other hand, evolved on land. Today, grasses, shrubs, and trees dominate the landscape, and land animals (including humans) depend on them for food and shelter, and countless other products.

In this chapter, you will trace the relationships between and among groups of plants and animals. You will learn what adaptations allowed plants to evolve from small, green, moss-like organisms into the vast array of different species that surround us. You will discover what important changes have occurred in the bodies of animals since their origins in the sea millions of years ago. By the end of the chapter, you will have discovered why flowering plants are by far the most numerous of all plants, and why insects and vertebrates are among the most successful of all animals.

Spanish " moss" is not a moss at all. It is an epiphyte, a plant that lives on another plant, and yet it is independent, producing its own food.

Chapter Contents

From Water to Land

- Describe anatomical and physiological characteristics of plants.

- Learn the life cycle of select plants.

- Classify representative organisms.

- Use techniques of classification to illustrate the principles of taxonomy.

Figure 13.1 Mosses can live on land, but need very wet conditions to survive and reproduce.

What are plants, and how do they differ from other living things? All species of plants are multicellular eukaryotes that obtain their food by photosynthesis. You learned that algae and some bacteria also carry out photosynthesis. Unlike these two groups, which are sometimes called "the grass of the waters," plants such as the mosses in Figure 13.1 live on land. For photosynthetic organisms, one advantage of living on land instead of in water is the greater availability of light. Another advantage is the more rapid diffusion of carbon dioxide and oxygen into and out of the organism. One disadvantage of living on land is the risk of dehydration. Many characteristics of plants are adaptations to living in a dry environment.

Adaptations to Life on Land

Fossil evidence shows that the first land plants appeared about 400 million years ago. Their ancestors were most likely filamentous green algae (see Figure 13.2). Like green algae, plants have chlorophylls *a* and *b* in their cells. Plants and green algae also both have cellulose cell walls. A third similarity is that plants and green algae store food energy in the form of starch, whereas bacteria, fungi, and animals store food as glycogen.

Imagine taking a thin filament of algae floating in a pond and moving it to land. What changes would have to happen in order for it to survive on land? One major need is protection from drying out. Other major needs include a system to transport

water and dissolved substances from the outside environment to cells within the body of the plant, and a system to support the body of the plant, lifting it up into the light and air.

The adaptations of plants to life on land did not all occur at once. The earliest land plants were small and delicate. They grew in moist places and transferred water and dissolved substances from cell to cell by osmosis and diffusion. These processes are slow and inefficient, and they limited the maximum size of these plants as well as the types of environments in which they could live. Despite this, land plants flourished, and there are still many plants that continue to survive using these adaptations. Of the plants living today, mosses and their relatives most closely resemble the first land plants.

Vascular and Non-vascular Plants

You may have learned that most plants consist of three main parts: roots, stems, and leaves (as shown in Figure 13.3 on the next page). These specialized organs are all adaptations to life on land. Roots penetrate the soil to anchor the plant and reach sources of water. Leaves provide a greater surface area to carry out photosynthesis. Stems supply rigid tissues that raise and support the leaves.

In order for roots, stems, and leaves to grow, they need a regular supply of water, energy, and

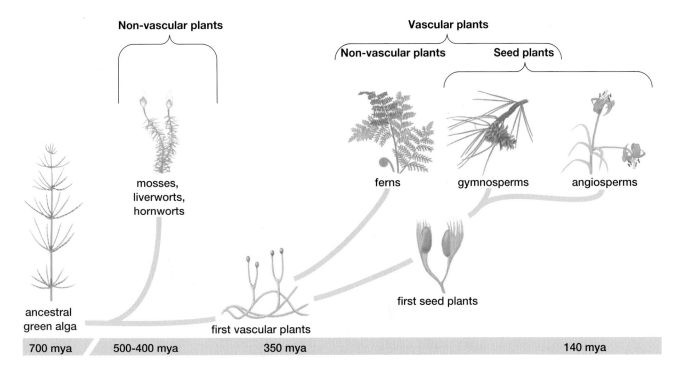

Non-vascular plants

Vascular plants

Non-vascular plants   **Seed plants**

mosses,
liverworts,
hornworts

ferns   gymnosperms   angiosperms

first seed plants

ancestral
green alga

first vascular plants

| 700 mya | 500-400 mya | 350 mya | 140 mya |

Figure 13.2 Phylogeny of relationships among land plants showing green algae as the ancestor (mya = millions of years ago)

nutrients. How does a cell in a tree branch get water? How do roots receive sugars made in the leaves? In most plants, these tasks are carried out by vascular tissue, which is made of cells able to conduct solutions throughout the plant, and which links the tips of the roots to the highest leaves. A plant's vascular system has a similar function to the circulatory system that carries blood around in your body. It transports water, dissolved minerals, and sugars to all parts of the plant, providing cells with materials they need to carry out their life functions. The evolution of vascular tissue has allowed plants to increase in size, with some growing to be giants compared to their ancestors.

This characteristic is so significant that it divides the plant kingdom into two major groups: vascular and non-vascular plants. Mosses, liverworts, and hornworts are non-vascular plants; they have no or poorly developed roots, leaves, and stems. All other plants contain vascular tissue.

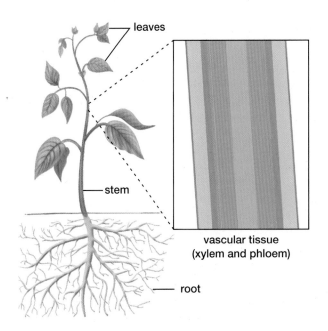

leaves

stem

vascular tissue
(xylem and phloem)

root

Figure 13.3 Most plants have roots, stems, leaves, and vascular tissue.

> **>> FAST FORWARD**

For more information on characteristics of plants and their specialized tissues, turn to Chapter 14, Section 14.1–14.3.

Reproductive Strategies

A further challenge faced by land plants is how to carry out sexual reproduction. For fertilization to occur, gametes must move from one organism to another. Algae do this by releasing unprotected gametes into the surrounding water. But gametes are single-celled structures and cannot survive exposure to air for very long. To shield their gametes from drying out, the first land plants had a layer of thick-walled cells around their reproductive parts. However, they could only release their gametes when a film of water covered the plant. For millions of years, this mechanism limited the conditions under which plants could reproduce. Today, mosses, ferns, and their relatives still depend on external water in the form of dew or rain in order to reproduce.

How do other plants carry out sexual reproduction? You can see the answer in the air each spring. Male gametes in these plants consist of pollen grains such as those in Figure 13.4 on the next page. These tiny, waterproof structures are carried to female plants not by water but on the wind, by insects, or by other animals. After fertilization, the zygote develops inside another protective, waterproof coat forming the seed. A **seed** is a structure made up of an embryo, stored food, and a tough waterproof coat. Seeds can remain dormant for long periods of time, which allows plants to survive exposure to drought, freezing, and, in some cases, even fire. As a result of these characteristics, seed-bearing plants are more widespread and diverse than seedless plants.

≪ REWIND

To review information on haploid and diploid cells, turn to Chapter 5, Section 5.2.

Investigation 13 • A

SKILL FOCUS

Performing and recording

Analyzing and interpreting

Communicating results

How Do Mosses Differ from Algae?

Mosses and green algae are both multicellular eukaryotes that carry out photosynthesis. Yet mosses are classified in the plant kingdom, while green algae are not. In this investigation, you will compare the characteristics of these two types of organisms.

Pre-lab Questions

- Describe the environments of a typical moss and a typical alga.
- List two characteristics of each of the kingdoms to which mosses and algae belong.

Problem

What differences can you observe between mosses and algae that would explain their classification in different kingdoms?

Prediction

Predict which characteristics of mosses and algae will be useful to classify them to kingdoms.

Materials

magnifying lens	microscope
slides	cover slips
dropper	samples of mosses and green algae

Figure 13.4 The small flowers of the alder plant shed their pollen to be dispersed by wind.

Alternation of Generations

The life cycle of plants consists of two generations which alternate between a haploid and a diploid stage. Figure 13.5 on the next page shows this cycle. The diploid generation of a plant is called the **sporophyte**. Through the process of meiosis, sporophytes produce haploid spores, which can develop without fertilization. The haploid spore grows into a plant body called the **gametophyte**. Gametophytes produce male and female gametes, which fuse at fertilization and develop into another sporophyte. The cycle then repeats itself.

Although all plant life cycles include a sporophyte and gametophyte generation, one stage or the other is characteristically dominant in different plant groups. In non-vascular plants the dominant stage (the familiar green plant) is the gametophyte. In vascular groups the sporophyte is the more dominant generation. In flowering plants, the gametophyte is reduced to a small group of cells entirely dependent on the sporophyte.

Procedure

1. Make a table to record features of both types of organisms. Include such variables as overall size, and structures for obtaining water and nutrients, for support, for reproduction, and for photosynthesis.

2. Study your samples with a magnifying lens. Use your textbook or other references supplied by your teacher to identify structures. Make labelled sketches of each structure and record your notes and observations in your table.

3. Prepare wet mounts of the samples, making sure that each contains the organism's photosynthetic structures. Observe them under low and high power. Record observable similarities and differences.

4. Prepare wet mounts of the structures the organisms use for absorbing water and nutrients. Observe them under low and high power. Record similarities and differences.

5. Prepare wet mounts of the structures the organisms use for reproduction. Observe them under low and high power. Record similarities and differences.

    Ensure you wash your hands thoroughly at the end of the procedure.

Post-lab Questions

1. Using your notes and sketches, describe two pieces of evidence that indicate mosses are better adapted to life on land than algae are.

Conclude and Apply

2. Based on your observations of their structure, give a reason why mosses do not grow to the size of trees.

Exploring Further

3. Obtain samples of other terrestrial and aquatic plants. Using the same procedure as above, record your observations. What are the similarities to your other samples? What are the differences? Offer explanations for your findings.

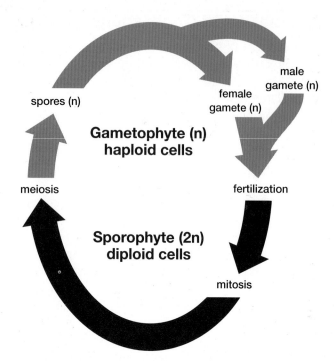

spores (n)

male gamete (n)

female gamete (n)

Gametophyte (n) haploid cells

meiosis

fertilization

Sporophyte (2n) diploid cells

mitosis

Figure 13.5 The life cycle of a plant consists of the alternation of generations of diploid sporophytes with haploid gametophytes.

BIO FACT

The first eukaryote organisms were probably haploid, and some eukaryotes today are haploid all their lives. Plants and animals, however, are diploid at some stage in their lives. Diploid cells seem to have developed early in the history of life by the fusion of two haploid cells that later divided by meiosis. This fusion process was the origin of sexual reproduction. Its value is in producing genetically variable offspring — the raw material for the evolution of new characteristics. The alternation of different diploid and haploid forms found in plants is called the alternation of generations, but the word "generation" here means simply "phase in a life cycle." It does not refer to the more common meaning relating to offspring and time.

‖ PAUSE ● RECORD

Think of the different challenges faced by organisms living in water versus organisms living on land. Make a list outlining as many differences as possible. Think of some examples of organisms that live on land, organisms that live in water, and organisms that use both land and water habitats. How have they solved the different challenges you listed?

SECTION REVIEW

1. **K/U** Name two pieces of evidence to support the idea that filamentous green algae were the ancestors of land plants.

2. **K/U** List three changes that had to occur in order for plants to move from a life in water to a life on land.

3. **K/U** Why is a temperate rainforest the ideal habitat for mosses? Is this also true for a tropical rainforest? Explain your answer.

4. **K/U** Explain why the alternation of generations is an adaptation for plants living on land.

5. **K/U** How does the size of a plant indicate how it transports water and nutrients? Explain your reasoning.

6. **C** Write a short essay explaining why the evolution of seeds was so important.

7. **C** Draw a generalized life cycle of a plant, showing the alternation of generations. Label your diagram to fully explain the life cycle.

8. **C** Create an illustrated time line to show the evolution of plants from water to land. Be sure to indicate what the first land plants looked like. How does the appearance of plants today differ from those early land plants?

9. **I** Suppose, on a field trip with your class, you collected several samples of plants growing near the edge of a pond. Can you identify the samples as mosses? Explain how you would do this.

10. **C** Based on your knowledge of the alternation of generations, which of the following life cycles, A, B, or C describes the condition found in **(a)** non-vascular plants; **(b)** non-flowering vascular plants; and **(c)** flowering plants?

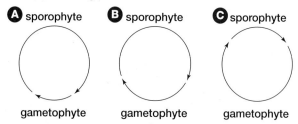

A sporophyte

B sporophyte

C sporophyte

gametophyte

gametophyte

gametophyte

Support your answer with a short written explanation.

11. **MC** Consider the different relationships that terrestrial organisms have with land plants. Detail three interactions between land organisms and land plants. Now, write a short story describing the effect it would have on humans if land plants were to die off. What effects would this have on other land organisms? What effects would it have on aquatic plants and animals?

Kingdom Plantae

- Describe anatomical and physiological characteristics of plants.
- Learn the life cycle of select plants.
- Classify representative plants.
- Demonstrate an understanding of the diversity of living organisms.

Figure 13.6 Members of the plant kingdom are able to thrive in unexpected locations, such as this epiphyte, which lives on the surface of another plant.

Imagine you are walking beside a stream in a forest. Beds of soft green moss cover rocks beside the water and clumps of ferns spring from the decaying trunk of a fallen tree. Seeing a patch of sunlight ahead, you leave the shade of the tall pines and enter a clearing filled with the pinkish-purple spikes of fireweed. This short journey has taken you past examples of all four major groups within the plant kingdom. In fact, a short walk through most places on Earth will take you past members of the same four groups: mosses and their relatives, ferns and their relatives, cone-bearing plants, and flowering plants.

Classification of Plants

There is a huge variety of plants in the world, but they can all be arranged into a few major groups on the basis of several fundamental characteristics, such as the presence or absence of vascular tissue and seeds. Figure 13.7 shows members of these four groups. Each large group contains several Divisions, which are each roughly equivalent to a Phylum.

Figure 13.7 The Kingdom Plantae is divided into four major groups. Plants range in size from tiny mosses to giant pine trees.

Non-vascular Plants (Mosses and Their Relatives)

There are three divisions of **non-vascular plants**: mosses (Bryophytes), hornworts (Anthocerophytes), and liverworts (Hepatophytes). These plants do not have vascular tissue, and they are dependent on the processes of diffusion and osmosis to transport nutrients. They usually grow in mats of low, tangled vegetation that can hold water like a sponge, allowing them to survive periods of cold and dry. Non-vascular plants have no roots.

Instead, they have small root-like structures called **rhizoids**, which develop from their lower surfaces.

Non-vascular plants are the only groups of plants in which the life cycle is dominated by the gametophyte phase. The identifiable green plants that are common in moist shady areas are gametophytes. Male gametophytes produce sperm, and female gametophytes produce eggs. For fertilization to occur, there must be enough moisture on the plant surface for the sperm to swim to an egg. After fertilization, the zygote remains on the female plant and develops into a sporophyte.

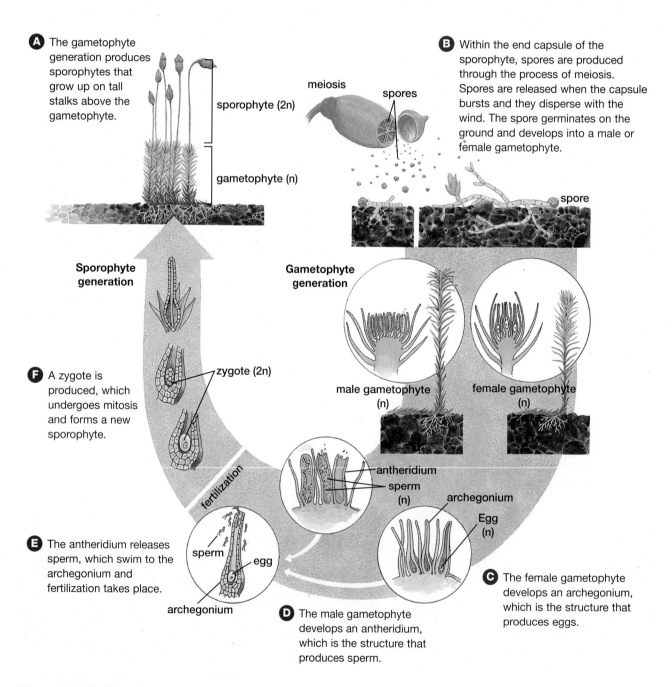

A The gametophyte generation produces sporophytes that grow up on tall stalks above the gametophyte.

sporophyte (2n)

gametophyte (n)

B Within the end capsule of the sporophyte, spores are produced through the process of meiosis. Spores are released when the capsule bursts and they disperse with the wind. The spore germinates on the ground and develops into a male or female gametophyte.

meiosis

spores

spore

Sporophyte generation

Gametophyte generation

male gametophyte (n)

female gametophyte (n)

F A zygote is produced, which undergoes mitosis and forms a new sporophyte.

zygote (2n)

fertilization

antheridium

sperm (n)

archegonium

Egg (n)

E The antheridium releases sperm, which swim to the archegonium and fertilization takes place.

sperm

egg

archegonium

D The male gametophyte develops an antheridium, which is the structure that produces sperm.

C The female gametophyte develops an archegonium, which is the structure that produces eggs.

Figure 13.8 The life cycle of a moss

Mosses (Bryophytes)

Bryophytes, commonly known as mosses, lack vascular tissue and do not have well-developed roots, so they absorb most of their water directly through their surface. When the air is dry, mosses become dry; when wet conditions return, mosses quickly absorb water. Although they seem to have disadvantages compared with other plants, mosses are very successful and widespread. They thrive in such diverse habitats as bogs, tundra, on bare exposed rocks, and in deep shade where other plants may be unable to grow. In fact, mosses are the most diverse group of plants after flowering plants, and there are twice as many species of mosses as of mammals.

A typical moss sporophyte consists of a spore-bearing capsule growing on the end of a stalk called the **seta**. Sporophytes do not contain chlorophyll and receive all their nourishment from the gametophyte. Spores are produced by meiosis in the capsule of the sporophyte as shown in Figure 13.8 on the previous page. As the sporophyte dries out, the capsule releases spores. If these spores germinate once they land on the ground, they will become either a male gametophyte, called an **antheridium** (plural antheridia) or a female gametophyte, called an **archegonium** (plural archegonia). Sperm are released from the antheridium and swim to the archegonium, where they fertilize the egg. A zygote develops, and grows to become a new sporophyte. You can often see a scattering of sporophytes standing up above a bed of green moss gametophytes as shown in Figure 13.9.

Figure 13.9 The spore-bearing capsules of a moss stand up on brown stalks above the leafy gametophyte.

Liverworts (Hepatophytes)

Hepatophytes, known commonly as liverworts, grow flat and close to the ground and are rarely more than 30 cells thick. There are two types of liverworts, with different appearances shown in Figure 13.10. About 80% of species have "leafy" gametophytes that resemble mosses. Leafy liverworts are most abundant in tropical forests and in humid climates. In appearance, their gametophyte generation resembles mosses. The remaining species are thallose liverworts, called this because the gametophytes are made up of flattened, lobed bodies called **thalli** (singular thallus). The common name, liverwort, comes from the appearance of these gametophytes, which resemble the lobes of animals' livers.

Figure 13.10 Liverworts may be (A) thallose or (B) leafy. The leafy liverwort resembles moss.

Liverworts produce sporophytes that grow on the body of the gametophyte. Spores are formed inside an egg-shaped capsule held at the top of a translucent or white stalk. When it matures, the capsule splits open into four equal quarters, releasing the spores into the air. Liverwort sporophytes are not often seen because they shrivel up and disappear shortly after releasing their spores. Liverworts can also reproduce asexually by means of tiny pieces of tissue that become detached from the thallus.

Hornworts (Anthocerophytes)

Anthocerophytes are commonly known as hornworts. Their gametophytes are broad, flat, usually less than 2 cm in diameter, and have a blue-green colour. Figure 13.11 shows the mature

Investigation 13 • B

Alternation of Generations in Mosses

In mosses, both the spore-bearing sporophyte and the gamete-bearing gametophyte are visible to the naked eye. In this investigation, you will study the structure of both generations.

Pre-lab Questions

- Is the gametophyte haploid or diploid?
- In which generation does meiosis occur?

Problem

What are the characteristics of the alternating generations in mosses?

Prediction

Predict the importance of identifying the reproductive structures of both generations of mosses.

CAUTION: The scalpel blade is sharp. Always cut away from your body.

Materials

microscope
single-edged razor
  blade or scalpel
dropper
moss plants with male and female
  gametophytes and sporophytes
paper towels

microscope slides
forceps

water

Procedure

1. Obtain moss gametophytes with both male and female reproductive structures. You may use Figure 13.8 on page 470 for reference.

2. Using forceps, remove all leaves from the upper part of one stem, being careful not to damage the reproductive structure at the tip of the stem. Repeat with a stem of the opposite sex.

sporophyte, which look like miniature green cattle horns thus giving the group its common name. The sporophyte continues to grow throughout its life. As in other bryophytes, it remains attached to its parent. Eventually the sporophyte splits into two halves lengthwise, releasing the maturing spores.

Although hornworts and liverworts are similar in appearance, they can be distinguished from each other. The best way to differentiate them is to look at their cells under a low-power microscope. Hornworts usually have one large chloroplast per cell, while liverworts typically have many small chloroplasts per cell.

Figure 13.11 Hornwort sporophytes and gametophytes.

3. With a sharp blade, cut off the top 1 cm of each stem you have prepared.

4. Place each stem tip at opposite ends of a clean slide. Add several drops of water, and place a second glass slide over the first.

5. Gently press down with the eraser end of a pencil to slightly squash the reproductive structures.

6. Place the sandwiched slides on a microscope stage, using the stage clips to keep them from slipping apart. Observe the reproductive structures under low-power magnification only.

7. Draw both types of reproductive structures. Using Figure 13.8 as a guide, label the male and female gametophytes, antheridium, and archegonium.

8. Obtain a sample of moss with sporophytes.

9. Using forceps, carefully remove a small capsule from the tip of a stalk, and mount it in several drops of water on a microscope slide.

10. Add a second slide on top of the first and carefully squash the capsule as in the procedure above.

11. Observe the squashed capsule under low-power magnification only. Draw and label the sporophyte, capsule, and spores.

Wash your hands thoroughly at the end of this procedure.

Post-lab Questions

1. Which structure is responsible for a) sexual reproduction? b) asexual reproduction?

2. What type of reproductive cell is formed by the a) archegonium? b) antheridium? c) sporophyte?

3. Which cells are a) haploid? b) diploid?

Conclude and Apply

4. Diagram the life cycle of a moss, using your own observations. Use different colours to indicate the haploid and diploid stages. Mark where fertilization and meiosis occur.

5. Are eggs or sperm cells produced in greater numbers? Suggest an explanation for your answer.

Exploring Further

6. The most important bryophytes to humans are probably peat mosses. Prepare a brief report describing these plants and some of the ways in which they are useful to people.

Seedless Vascular Plants (Ferns and Their Relatives)

Non-vascular plants represent the pioneers of plant life on land, but about 300 million years ago they were literally overshadowed by the first vascular plants. If you could travel back to this time in Earth's history, you would find vast swampy forests. You would notice insects and some amphibians, but no birds, mammals, or even dinosaurs. The plants you would see growing in forests around you would contain vascular tissues, roots, stems, and leaves. These first forests are the source of some of our non-renewable fossil fuels.

> ⯈ PLAY

To view videos on the alternation of generations and on fern development, turn to your Electronic Learning Partner.

These early **seedless vascular plants** were different from the non-vascular plants in several ways. Not only had they developed the vascular tissue that allowed them to grow tall, but they had the sporophyte generation as the dominant stage in their life cycle. Their gametophytes were reduced to tiny, short-lived structures that still depended on moisture to carry out sexual reproduction. Nearly all the trees that covered the land in that era are now extinct. There are a few remaining groups of those early vascular plants that live on today, however. They include the whisk ferns, club mosses, horsetails, and ferns like the one shown in Figure 13.12.

Figure 13.12 Giant relatives of ferns like these helped form Earth's forests millions of years before dinosaurs evolved.

Whisk Ferns (Psilotophytes)

Looking like small green whisk brooms, psilotophytes or whisk ferns are among the simplest of living vascular plants (Figure 13.13). They do not have leaves or roots, but grow to about 30 cm in height from short **rhizomes**, which are horizontal underground stems. Photosynthesis takes place in the outer cells of the branching stems.

Figure 13.13 The small yellowish clusters on this whisk fern are sporophytes.

The tips of the stems of a whisk fern produce yellow sporangia. After the spores are released, they disperse and germinate into tiny, colourless gametophytes beneath the soil surface. Only a few millimetres long, the subterranean gametophytes obtain their nutrition by absorbing dissolved substances from the surrounding soil. At sexual maturity, they develop both egg and sperm cells. Fertilization produces the next generation of sporophytes, which begin to grow on their parent gametophyte. Eventually, the sporophyte grows into a mature whisk fern.

BIO FACT

Young fern sporophytes first appear as tightly coiled fiddleheads that later unroll to form a mature frond. Today, fiddleheads are eaten as a seasonal delicacy. At one time, the fine silky hairs that cover the fiddleheads of some larger tropical tree ferns were stripped off and used to stuff pillows and mattresses. During the late 1800s, over 1900 metric tons of this fern hair were shipped from Hawaii to North America.

Club Mosses (Lycopodophytes)

The lycopodophytes, or club mosses, that we see today are mostly small evergreen plants that grow in dense mats on moist temperate and tropical forest floors. Extinct club mosses, however, were prominent members of Earth's forests for 40 million years. They formed trees more than 35 m tall and up to 2 m in diameter. Despite their name and appearance, club mosses are not related to true mosses.

The sporophytes of all club mosses have true stems and roots. Tiny leaves grow from their stems in spirals, whorls, or pairs. Each narrow leaf has a single, unbranched vein of vascular tissue along its centre, whereas most plant leaves have multiple, branching veins. At the end of a stem, specialized spore-bearing leaves form compact clusters called **strobili** (singular strobilus), which protect the reproductive cells. Strobili resemble pine cones, and because of this club mosses are sometimes called ground pines (Figure 13.14).

A lycopodophyte spore germinates to form a tiny, independent gametophyte called a **prothallus**. Some species of lycopodophytes produce two different types of spores: large megaspores and small microspores. The megaspore germinates to form a female prothallus and the microspore produces a male prothallus. The prothallus lives on the soil and produces either sperm or eggs. In wet conditions, sperm swim to an egg and fertilize it. The resulting zygote grows into the larger, dominant sporophyte.

Web LINK

The vast swampy forests found on early Earth about 300 million years ago are the source of most of our non-renewable fossil fuels. Find out more about the extinct species of vascular plants that made up these forests. To conduct your research, go to **Science Resources**, then go to **BIOLOGY 11** and follow the links to find out where to go next. What was the geographical distribution of these forests? Did the species of plant vary from place to place? Think about where fossil fuel reserves are located in Canada. Is this correlated to these forests? **www.school.mcgrawhill.ca/resources/**

Figure 13.14 This club moss, *Lycopodium*, is sometimes called a ground pine because it is evergreen and looks similar to a tiny pine tree.

Horsetails (Sphenophytes)

Sphenophytes, or horsetails, are another group of seedless vascular plant that once included tree-sized members but now contain plants that only grow to about a metre in height. These plants are often found in damp areas or along roadsides. Their hollow stems have a ribbed appearance, with whorls of tiny, scale-like leaves growing from each joint or node along the stem (Figure 13.15 on the next page). These plants are also known as scouring rushes, because they have a rough texture that can be used for scrubbing pots or polishing wood. The roughness is due to granules of silica stored within the plant cells.

The life cycle of horsetails is similar to that of club mosses. In spring, the tips of the stems produce spore-bearing strobili. The spores germinate to form male and female gametophytes. Each female gametophyte has several eggs and may develop more than one sporophyte after fertilization.

Figure 13.15 Horsetails have small leaves, and their photosynthesis occurs mainly in the stems.

Horsetails have traditionally been used by North American Aboriginal people and Asians for various medicinal purposes. Some Aboriginal groups burned the stems and used the ashes to treat burns or sore mouths; some ate the strobili to cure diarrhea; and others boiled horsetail stems in water to make a shampoo for controlling head lice.

Ferns (Pteridophytes)

Pteridophytes, commonly known as ferns, dominated the forests during the Carboniferous Period (315 million to 280 million years ago). Although their numbers have declined since their peak, pteridophytes remain the most familiar and successful of seedless vascular plants. Ferns evolved several adaptations to life on land that are also found in seed-bearing plants. In addition to roots and vascular tissue, ferns have a waxy, thickened outer epidermis that reduces water loss by evaporation. Small openings in the epidermis, called **stomata**, allow gases to enter and leave for the processes of photosynthesis and cellular respiration.

Ferns have an enormous range of form and structure, with the greatest diversity being found in the tropics. It is possible to find tiny ferns less than 1 cm in diameter as well as giant tree ferns up to 25 m tall. The **fronds**, or fern leaves, grow up from a thick, underground rhizome and are commonly

divided into small leaflets called **pinnae**. The conspicuous fern plant is the sporophyte, and you can often see small spore-producing structures called **sori** (singular sorus) clustered on the underside of the pinnae (Figure 13.16).

>> FAST FORWARD

Turn to Chapter 14, Section 14.3 to learn more about the processes and structures involved in gas exchange in plants.

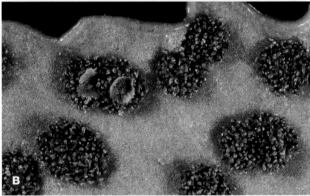

Figure 13.16 The small round structures often seen on the underside of a fern frond (A) are called sori. They consist of clusters of sporangia (B).

Ferns produce millions or even billions of spores during their lifetime, but very few ever land in a spot suitable for growth. A germinating spore does not produce a new fern plant with fronds; rather, it grows into a small, heart-shaped prothallus. The gametophyte generation is unnoticed by most people, because the prothallus is usually just over 1 cm across and lies flat on the ground. It is an independent structure with its own rhizoid system to provide it with nutrients and water. The prothallus contains female organs, called archegonia, and male organs called antheridia. You can observe the structure of a fern prothallus for yourself in the next mini lab.

Gymnosperms (Conifers and Their Relatives)

There are two groups of plants that disperse by means of a seed, gymnosperms and angiosperms. Seeds allow plants to reproduce sexually without needing water, and also provide protection against harsh environmental conditions. As seeds, plants can survive without water for many years. They can be carried by different means to disperse across continents and begin growing in new areas. The first small seed-bearing plants appeared about 280 million years ago, among forests of ferns, club mosses, and horsetails. At that time, the global climate had begun to grow cooler and drier. Most of the large spore-producing plants could not survive long periods of drought and freezing, and they became extinct. **Gymnosperms** have seeds that are exposed on the surface of cone scales. The word gymnosperm actually means "naked seed." This group includes the cone-bearing trees (conifers) such as pines, firs, yew, spruce, cedars, redwood, and many other large trees (Figure 13.17). As well as the conifers, gymnosperms include three other small groups: cycadophytes, gnetophytes, and ginkgophytes shown in Figure 13.19 on page 479.

Reproduction in Gymnosperms

Recall that club mosses and horsetails bear spores in strobili — structures made of compact clusters of specialized leaves. Cones are simply large, woody strobili. Female cones develop ovules in archegonia that grow on the upper surface of each cone scale. Male cones produce microspores that develop into pollen grains. Each pollen grain is a four-celled male gametophyte enclosed in a hard, water-resistant coat. Many hundreds of thousands of dust-like pollen grains are produced in each male cone and dispersed to female cones by wind. When a pollen grain lands next to an archegonium, it produces a **pollen tube**, which grows into the tissue of the female gametophyte. Sperm pass along this tube to the egg. After fertilization, the zygote develops into an embryo in the female cone. The embryo, together with a small supply of stored food, is covered by a tough, waterproof coat to form a seed. Female cones remain on the tree until the seeds have matured, which may take from several months to two years. The evolution of pollen, pollen tubes, and seeds allowed plants to reproduce sexually without the need of moisture. This ability helped them survive cold, dry conditions.

Figure 13.17 This conifer is one example of a gymnosperm.

 MINI LAB

Investigating the Fern Prothallus

Most people have seen fern plants, but few have observed the gametophyte generation, which produces the gametes. In this lab, you will study the structure of a fern prothallus. Obtain a mature fern prothallus from your teacher and prepare a wet mount. Observe all standard safety procedures, especially when using electricity and glass. Examine the prothallus under the low power of a microscope. Make a labelled sketch indicating its general shape and features. Use Figure 13.18 on the next page as a reference if you need to. Identify the female organs, located near the notch of the heart-shaped plant, and the male organs, located near the pointed end of the prothallus.

Using the eraser end of a pencil, press gently on the cover slip over the area bearing the male organs. Study your specimen under medium power to see if any sperm were released. If so, observe their structure and behaviour.

Analyze

1. What is the name of the structure that produces eggs? that produces sperm?

2. Is the prothallus haploid or diploid?

3. What type of cell division produces the gametes?

4. Sketch and label a diagram showing the stages in the fern life cycle between the gametophyte generation and the sporophyte generation.

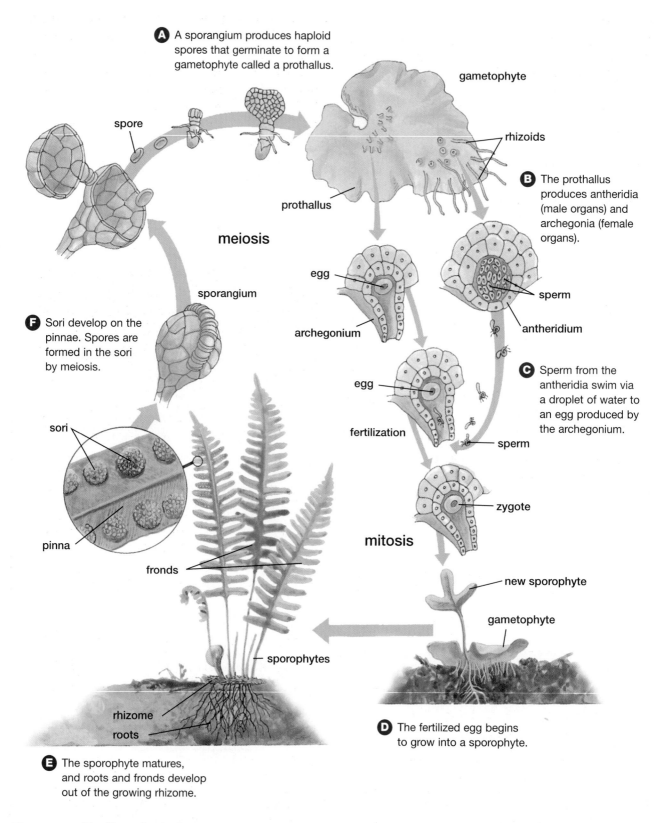

A A sporangium produces haploid spores that germinate to form a gametophyte called a prothallus.

spore

gametophyte

rhizoids

prothallus

meiosis

B The prothallus produces antheridia (male organs) and archegonia (female organs).

egg

sperm

antheridium

archegonium

sporangium

F Sori develop on the pinnae. Spores are formed in the sori by meiosis.

egg

fertilization

C Sperm from the antheridia swim via a droplet of water to an egg produced by the archegonium.

sperm

sori

zygote

pinna

mitosis

fronds

new sporophyte

gametophyte

sporophytes

rhizome

roots

D The fertilized egg begins to grow into a sporophyte.

E The sporophyte matures, and roots and fronds develop out of the growing rhizome.

Figure 13.18 The life cycle of a fern.

Conifers

Conifers are the largest group of gymnosperms, and they form vast forests in cold regions of the world. As well as being able to reproduce without water, they have other adaptations to cold, dry habitats. Their protective covering of bark helps protect the stem and reduce water loss.

The pyramidal shape of many conifers, such as the one shown previously in Figure 13.17, together with their flexible branches, helps snow and ice slide off the tree. This reduces the risk of a heavy buildup of snow that could break branches.

The needle-like leaves of conifers have a thick, waxy cuticle and sunken stomata, which reduce the rate of evaporation (Figure 13.20 on the next page). Pine needles are usually semicircular or round in cross section, resembling a cylindrical leaf. The shape reduces surface area, which in turn reduces water loss by evaporation. Most conifers are evergreen, so they continually lose and replace their needle-like leaves all year long rather than losing all of their leaves at once like a deciduous tree.

A Conifers bear seeds in cones like the ones on this Eastern Hemlock.

B *Welwitschia* (Gnetophyta) is an odd-looking plant found only in deserts in southern Africa, where the average rainfall is less than 2.5 cm per year. Its short stem produces two broad leaves that continue growing throughout the life of the plant. *Welwitschia* may live 100 years, and the older ends of its leaves become tattered and weathered.

C Cycads (Cycadophyta) were common trees during the Mesozoic era when dinosaurs shared the forests with the first birds and mammals. About 100 species exist today, mainly in the tropics. They are short, palmlike trees with scaly trunks, but they are not closely related to palms. Male and female cones grow on separate trees. The cones of some cycads may grow to a metre in length.

D *Ginkgo biloba* (Ginkgophyta) is the only living species of a group of plants common during the Jurassic period 200 million years ago. It has distinctive lobed leaves. Ginkgos were cultivated in Asian temple gardens for thousands of years, which may have helped protect them from extinction.

Figure 13.19 Gymnosperms bear their seeds in cones. This group includes conifers, gnetophytes, cycads, and ginkgos.

By keeping leaves through winter, they are able to start photosynthesis early in the spring, as soon as the weather grows warmer. This is a great advantage at high latitudes where the growing season is short. Conifers are also better able to grow in nutrient-poor soils, because they do not need to grow a complete new set of leaves all at once.

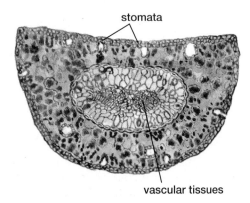

Figure 13.20 A cross section of a pine needle

Angiosperms (Flowering Plants)

Each spring, brightly coloured packages of plant seeds, like those shown in Figure 13.21, are displayed in gardening stores. On the outsides of the packages are pictures of flowers or vegetables. Inside each package is a number of small, dry, hard seeds. These tiny waterproof capsules contain plant embryos, ready to grow as soon as you add water.

Figure 13.21 The dry hard seeds of angiosperms are often sold in packages in order to be planted in a garden.

DESIGN YOUR OWN
Investigation

13 • C

SKILL FOCUS

Initiating and planning

Performing and recording

Analyzing and interpreting

Communicating results

Identifying Conifers

How can you tell one coniferous tree from another? In this investigation, you will study the characteristics of several different species of coniferous plants and develop a key to identify them.

Problem

Identify different species of conifers found in your area.

Hypothesis

Make a hypothesis about what specific characteristics will best distinguish among several coniferous species.

Materials

twigs, needles, and cones collected from several different conifers in your area
a field guide to trees

Experimental Plan

1. Make a list of characteristics in which species of conifers might differ in order to test your hypothesis. From the characteristics in your list, decide which ones would be most useful in a key.

These plants grow and develop seeds that are enclosed within a fruit. Plants that protect their seeds within the body of a fruit are called **angiosperms** or flowering plants.

The first flowering plants appeared on Earth about 150 million years ago. More than three quarters of all species of living plants are seed-bearing, flowering plants. Angiosperms include trees, shrubs, herbs, grasses, vines, and water plants, which may have inconspicious flowers, and they grow almost everywhere on land from the tropics to the tundra.

Angiosperms are divided into two large classes, based on the number of seed leaves, or **cotyledons**, on the embryo within the seed. Angiosperms with one seed leaf are called **monocots**, and those with two seed leaves are **dicots**. Figure 13.22 on the next page shows examples of these different flowering plants.

> ⯈ PLAY

To see a video of different types of seed dispersal, use your Electronic Learning Partner.

> ⯈⯈ FAST FORWARD

Turn to Chapter 14, Section 14.1, for more information on monocots and dicots.

Reproduction in Angiosperms

What are flowers, and what advantages do they provide to plants? One clue is that colourful and scented flowers are not only attractive to people but also to some other animals. The flower contains the structures used for sexual reproduction in the plant, and when animals visit flowers to get pollen or nectar, they help flowering plants carry out the process of reproduction.

Recall that the pollen grains of gymnosperms are dispersed in vast numbers by wind. This method of transport is quite imprecise, and most pollen grains do not land on an appropriate female cone. Some angiosperms also scatter their pollen on the wind, but the majority of flowering plants have more specific methods of transferring pollen from the male to the female of the same species. This is known as **pollination**, and flowers play an active role in this process.

2. Decide in which order the characteristics should appear in the key.

3. Collect samples of different local conifers.

Checking the Plan

1. Traits are described in a key as sets of two alternative choices. For example, if you decide that the arrangement of needles is a useful characteristic for identification, one choice in your key might be:
   - needles grouped in bundles, or
   - needles growing singly

2. When writing your key, remember that it must be clear enough to be used by any person not familiar with conifer identification.

Data and Observations

Create your key. Examine your conifer samples and list the characteristics you observe. Identify the samples of conifers that you have brought into class using your key.

Analyze

1. Was your hypothesis supported? Explain your answer.

2. Exchange your key with students from a different group. Using the new key, identify your conifer specimens. Does the key work? Are you able to correctly identify your specimens?

Conclude and Apply

3. Is there only one correct way to design a key to identify conifers? Explain your answer.

Exploring Further

4. Mount and label your specimens. Display them in your classroom along with other students' specimens. Try to provide examples of all the conifers in your area. Be sure to highlight the identifiable characteristics of each sample.

Figure 13.22 Monocots include (A) lilies and (B) grasses while dicots include (C) daisies and (D) deciduous trees.

Many different organisms depend on flowers for food, because most flowers produce nectar — a concentrated liquid mixture of proteins and sugars. When an insect, a bird, or even a bat lands on a flower to collect nectar, it becomes brushed with pollen from the anthers (Figure 13.23). Then, as the organism flies on to the next flower, the pollen grains are brushed onto the stigma, where they can fertilize the ovum.

Figure 13.23 As a bee lands on the lower petal of this flower, the anther deposits pollen on the bee's back.

BIO FACT

Civilization as we know it would not have been possible without members of the grass family. Nine species in this family, including wheat, barley, rice, oats, and corn, provide over 75% of the food eaten by people worldwide today. The development of agriculture and the cultivation of cereal crops thousands of years ago allowed people to produce surplus food, settle in large populations, and create cities for the first time.

❚❚ PAUSE ● RECORD

You have learned about the different ways that plants reproduce. What are the similarities in how all plants reproduce? What are the main differences among the four groups of plants? Create a short checklist or diagram to organize these similarities and differences.

Adaptations for Pollination

Most methods of pollination in flowering plants involve close relationships between flowers and certain species of insects, birds, and bats. Flowering plants and the animals that pollinate them evolved together. For example, flowers pollinated by bats are open at night (Figure 13.24). Flowers pollinated by butterflies usually store their nectar at the base of a long corolla, where it can only be reached by moths or butterflies with their longer specialized mouth parts.

Specialization is an advantage to both the plant and the pollinator. The distinct colour, shape, and scent of a flower helps the pollinator easily recognize it as a reliable source of food (Figure 13.25). Differences between the flowers of different species increase the chance that a pollinator will search for nectar from only one species at a time. Transporting rose pollen to a daisy, or vice versa, would not help either plant become pollinated and complete its life cycle (which is shown in Figure 13.27 on the next page).

After a pollinator deposits pollen on a stigma, each pollen grain grows a pollen tube to reach the ovule. Only the first tube to reach the ovule will penetrate and fertilize it. This process leads to **pollen-tube competition**. The fastest growing pollen tube usually carries the best genes and results in more vigorous offspring.

Because a single plant often produces many flowers, there is a risk that the plant may self-pollinate (that is, that pollen may be transferred from one flower to another flower on the same plant). Although self-pollination results in the development of seeds, it does not involve the exchange and recombination of genetic material that helps create diversity within a population. Self-pollination produces offspring with the same genome as the parent.

Flowering plants have evolved several strategies to favour cross-pollination over self-pollination. Some plants have separate male and female flowers that mature at different times. This ensures that male flowers have already dispersed their pollen before female flowers on the same plant are ready to be fertilized. Other species have chemical barriers that prevent fertilization by pollen from the same plant. In flowers with both male and female parts, the stigma usually extends much farther than the anthers, keeping the two parts well separated so they do not self-pollinate accidentally.

Figure 13.24 Flowers pollinated by bats must be large enough to support the weight of the bat.

Figure 13.25 The markings on this flower are only visible to the human eye when illuminated with ultraviolet light. These same markings are easily seen by pollinating insects.

◀◀ REWIND

Turn to Chapter 4, Section 4.2, to review cross- and self-fertilization.

Seed Development and Dispersal

Flowering plants are diploid sporophytes. Unlike the earlier plant groups you have studied, however, angiosperms do not produce spores. The pollen grains and ovum cells are all that remain of the gametophyte generation in flowering plants. Fertilization produces a diploid sporophyte embryo, which is enclosed in a hard case to form a seed.

Angiosperm seeds are further protected by the fleshy walls of the ovary. As the ovary matures, it swells to form a fruit or seed pod like the one shown in Figure 13.26. Fruits also help in seed dispersal. When the fruit is eaten by an animal, seeds are carried away from the parent plant in the animal's digestive tract. The seeds resist digestion and pass out with the animal's feces to germinate in a new spot.

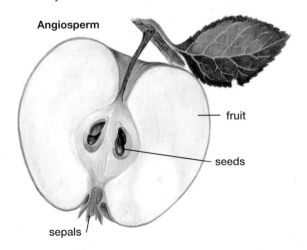

Angiosperm

fruit

seeds

sepals

Figure 13.26 A fruit such as an apple consists of the fleshy walls of the ovary enclosing the seeds. You can see the remains of the flower sepals at the bottom of the apple, opposite the stalk that attaches the fruit to a stem.

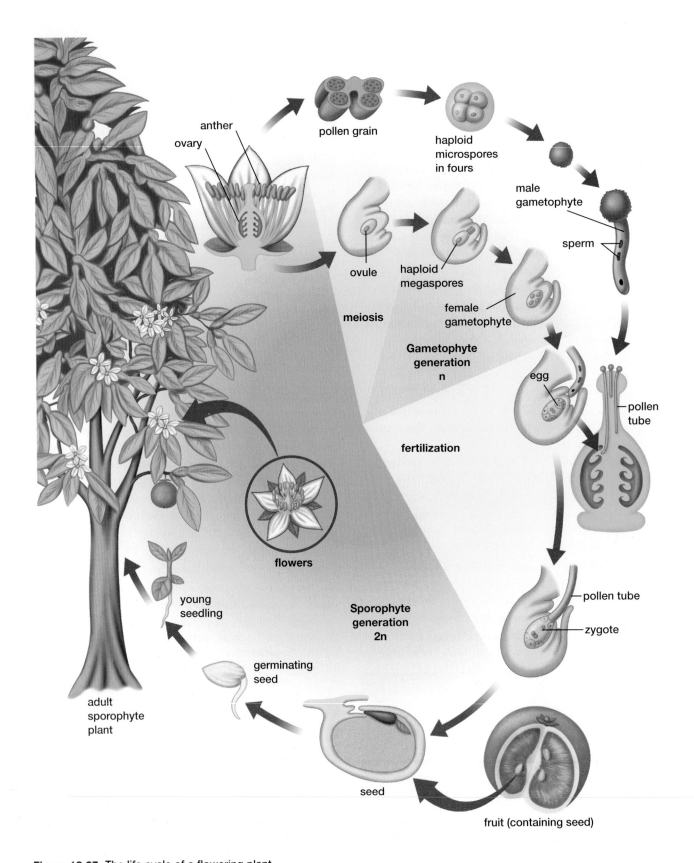

Figure 13.27 The life cycle of a flowering plant

Adjusting the Balance

Animal and plant species change over time, sometimes evolving into different forms and sometimes going extinct. As the human population grows, it disturbs more and more land mass, driving many plants and animals into extinction. For example, the vast forests in the Mediterranean region disappeared by Roman times. Some scientists believe humans may have caused the extinction of large mammals like the North American mammut (a kind of mastodon) more than 10 000 years ago. The list of species that have been negatively affected by humans keeps growing.

The loss of plant and animal species affects all other animal and plant species with which the lost species interact. It is only recently that biologists have begun to study such interactions and to understand the far-reaching impact of mismanaging our ecosystems. As our understanding of the importance of interactions grows, so does the need to protect the plant and animal species threatened by human expansion.

Maintaining a keystone species in a community — a plant or animal that is crucial to the overall health of the ecosystem — may have a direct economic benefit for humans. But conservation efforts sometimes have indirect economic benefits that seem surprising. The work being done by conservationists to protect monarch butterflies and the forests they live in is an excellent example of this.

The Monarchs and the Oyamel Forests

The Oyamel fir forests in central Mexico are the winter home of monarch butterflies, whose yearly migration from Canada and the eastern United States has captured the imaginations of people worldwide. Unfortunately, the indigenous farmers (*ejidatarios*) who live in the area depend on logging these forests for their livelihood. For the past 20 years, the Oyamel forests have been slowly shrinking, thus threatening the monarchs' winter habitat.

Monarch butterflies migrate by the thousands to these forests in Mexico.

In 1986, the Mexican government created monarch sanctuaries by banning logging in parts of the Oyamel forests. However, logging continued in and around the sanctuaries, and more and more of the monarchs' winter home was converted into oat and corn crops. To make matters worse, as the trees were cut, the remaining trees became subject to strong winds, drying the normally moist habitat and making the standing trees more prone to disease. Some conservationists rallied to the cause of the monarch butterflies, calling for stronger policing of the Oyamel sanctuaries. However, they ignored the economic needs of the farmers. The competing needs of the butterflies and the people created a dilemma — how to find a solution that would take into account the needs of both the monarchs and the people who live in the area.

Forests for People and Forests for Monarchs

Robert L. Small of Oakland, California and Jose Luis Alvarez of El Rosario, Mexico started a project in 1997 that may satisfy the needs of both the monarchs and the farmers. With the help of donations from conservationists in the United States, Small has been able to send fir seedlings to Alvarez, who distributes them to willing farmers. The goal is to use the donated trees to create a new forest that can be planted, harvested, and replanted by the farmers, while at the same time allowing the monarchs their current habitat. Five farmers planted 7000 donated trees in 1997, 20 farmers planted 40 000 trees in 1998, and the project continues to grow. The reforestation project promises so much success that the Mexican government is considering similar projects of its own.

Follow-up

1. The Oyamel reforestation project shows how even the conservation of species that do not affect the human economy can have a positive impact on whole communities, including human populations. Briefly write down your thoughts on conservation that is not driven directly by economic need.

2. A new potential threat to monarch butterflies has surfaced. Genetically modified corn crops, whose pollen kills certain corn pests, may be affecting the monarch caterpillars in the United States. Studies of the corn/butterfly connection have brought attention to the controversy surrounding genetically modified plants (and animals) and how they affect whole communities. Write a paragraph outlining possible steps that could be taken to avoid further damage to the monarch butterfly populations. Which do you think is more important: developing a better food source for hungry people, or conserving the monarch butterfly? Explain your answer.

Asexual Reproduction and Multiple Chromosomes

Nearly half (47%) of all angiosperms are **polyploid** — that is, they have more than two (2n) sets of chromosomes. They may have 3n, 4n, or more. This situation is caused by irregularities during meiosis. It results in sterile offspring that can still reproduce asexually, and has been an important mechanism in the evolution of plants. For example, polyploidy can produce larger cells, thicker and fleshier leaves, and larger flowers and fruits. The original South American ancestor of the potato is tetraploid (4n), and many common food plants such as strawberries and apples are polyploid. A species of wheat commonly grown for bread (*T. aestivum*) is hexaploid (6n = 42 chromosomes).

Odd-number polyploids are sterile because they cannot segregate chromosomes evenly into gametes during meiosis (odd numbers are not divisible by two). Sterility caused by triploidy produces such results as seedless bananas and less bitter cucumbers.

Word LINK

To most people, it is fairly clear that carrots are a type of vegetable, and apples are a type of fruit. Some people argue that tomatoes can be classified as either a fruit or a vegetable. What are the differences? To botanists, a fruit is a mature plant ovary that contains seeds. Thus, tomatoes, string beans, cucumbers, and squashes are all fruits. Make up your own definition of a vegetable. Do all vegetables fit your definition?

SECTION REVIEW

1. **K/U** Which three characteristics do plants share with green algae?

2. **K/U** Name two characteristics that adapt plants to life on land.

3. **K/U** Name the four broad groups into which the plant kingdom is divided.

4. **K/U** What are the products of meiosis in the four different groups of plants?

5. **K/U** What are bryophytes? How do they differ from the other groups of plants?

6. **K/U** Which two plant groups produce seeds?

7. **C** Sketch the life cycle of a fern, clearly showing the sporophyte and gametophyte generations. Indicate which is haploid and which diploid.

8. **I** How does the graph below show that these conifers grow according to their own growth pattern?

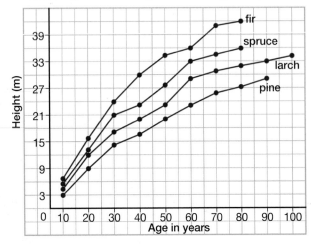

9. **I** Suppose you find yourself in a wilderness area in a part of the world you have never been before. How might a knowledge of plant classification help you determine the typical climate of the area? Describe the steps you would take to do this.

10. **I** Copy and complete the following table about the growth patterns of certain conifers. Use the graph shown on the left below for your information. Give your table a title.

	Maximum height	Age at maximum height	Height at 45 years
fir			
spruce			
larch			
pine			

11. **MC** Why do some angiosperms have showy flowers while others have inconspicuous flowers? What does flower type indicate about the plant? If you wanted to farm a plant with showy flowers, name one challenge you would face and explain how you would deal with it.

UNIT ISSUE PREP

If you have decided to investigate the status of a plant species in your Unit 4 Issue Analysis, make sure you have noted the characteristics of the phylum to which your species belongs. These characteristics may have an impact on how your species can be protected.

Kingdom Animalia

- Describe anatomical and physiological characteristics of animals.

- Learn the life cycle of select animals.

- Classify representative organisms from the Kingdom Animalia.

- Demonstrate an understanding of the diversity of living organisms.

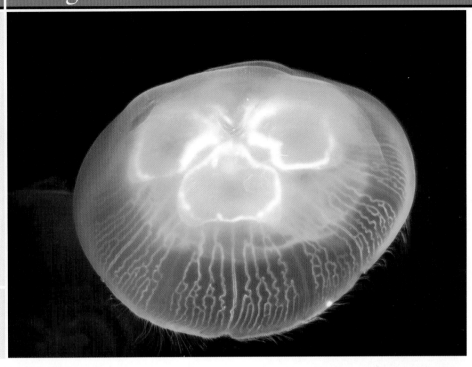

Figure 13.28 What does this jellyfish have in common with you?

What is an animal? Humans and jellyfish, like the one in Figure 13.28, are both members of the Kingdom Animalia, but at first they appear to have little or nothing in common. However, if you recall what you have learned so far, you should be able to list some characteristics they share not only with one another but also with plants.

Like plants, animals are multicellular, eukaryotes, and reproduce sexually. But while plants make their own food by photosynthesis, animals must ingest and then digest sources of food from outside their own bodies. Figure 13.29 shows different methods animals use to obtain food.

Figure 13.29 Different animals have different methods of feeding.

Plants make their food using light, air, and water. They can obtain all three without moving from one place. In contrast, most animals must move to obtain their food. Figure 13.30 shows different animals that locomote in different ways. Feeding and methods of locomotion are therefore two key characteristics of animals.

Figure 13.30 Different animals have different methods of locomotion.

THINKING LAB

Animal Similarities and Differences

Background

Animals are organized into phyla on the basis of similarities and differences in their structure and way of life. Superficial resemblance is not always a reliable guide to classification. For example, whales and mice are in the same phylum because they share many basic features such as a bony skeleton and a nerve cord located on the dorsal side or back. Snakes and worms, although superficially alike, are classified in different phyla and have few features in common.

You Try It

1. Whether you already know a lot or only a little about the animal kingdom, try grouping the following animals into phyla. If you do not know what any animal on the list looks like, use a reference to find out. The 20 animals on the list are representatives of eight common phyla that you will study in this chapter. Note that some animals in the list may be the only representative of their phylum, while other phyla may include two, three, or more of the animals listed.

2. Chart your answers in a notebook, and suggest what characteristic(s) is typical of each phylum. Modify your chart when necessary as you learn more about each group. Add the name of the phylum when you know it.

Animals from Eight Phyla

butterfly, cat, centipede, chimpanzee, coral, crab, earthworm, frog, grasshopper, jellyfish, leech, octopus, oyster, salmon, seagull, snail, snake, spider, sponge, tapeworm, starfish

Classifying Animals

By now you may realize that the word "animal" has a different meaning for biologists than it does for most people. Most animals do not have fur, feathers, or scales. Most animals (95%) do not have bones. Most animal phyla do not live on land.

Almost all of the animals we commonly think of — mammals, birds, fish, and reptiles — belong to a single subgroup in one of 33 phyla comprising the animal kingdom. Over half of animal phyla consist of various worms that are generally unknown to non-scientists. The largest number of animal species that have been identified (about 800 000) are in the Phylum Arthropoda, and most of them are insects, some of which are shown in Figure 13.31. Animals are classified on the basis of differences in their structure, tissues, and organ systems.

For example, the phylum Chordata (to which humans belong) includes all the animals with an internal bony skeleton. Such animals are often called vertebrates because they have a backbone made of a series of bones called vertebrae. Backbones and bony skeletons stiffen an animal's body and provide solid surfaces for the attachment of large muscles. Bones also protect the spinal cord, brain, and other internal organs. As a result, vertebrates include the largest of all animals, such as dinosaurs, whales, and elephants. All animals without backbones are called invertebrates. The largest invertebrates are species of giant squid that can grow to 5 m or more in length, but most invertebrates are relatively small animals such as insects, snails, and worms.

To continue your study of the animal kingdom, you will survey representatives of eight major phyla. As you compare these groups of animals, ask yourself how and why they differ from one another. You will be able to interpret these differences as evidence of different stages in the evolution of the animal kingdom.

Figure 13.31 Shown here are the following (A) sucking louse (Order Anoplura), (B) monarch butterfly (Order Lepidoptera), (C) grasshopper (Order Orthoptera), (D) ichneumonid wasp (Order Hymenoptera), (E) flesh fly (Order Diptera), (F) dog flea (Order Siphonoptera), (G) cicada (Order Homoptera), (H) dragonfly (Order Odonata), and (I) Madagascar hissing cockroach (Order Orthoptera).

The First Animals

If you could travel back in time to 700 million years ago, you would find the ancestors of today's animals living in warm, shallow seas. There were no fish, and no animals living on land. In appearance and behaviour, the animals of that period were similar to some of the simpler groups of animals living today — the sponges, jellyfish, and worms shown in Figure 13.32.

Figure 13.32 Sponges, jellyfish, and marine worms resemble the earliest forms of animals.

Sponges (Porifera)

Porifera, commonly known as sponges, do not appear to have changed much in hundreds of millions of years. Fossil remains show that they were widespread early in the history of life, and they remain well adapted to their ocean home today. Adult sponges spend their lives permanently attached to a solid surface and filter their food from the passing stream of water. The cells that make up a sponge have little more organization than a colony of protists. In fact, individual cells are so independent that if you squeeze a sponge through a filter to separate it into clumps of cells, the cells will be able to reassemble themselves again into a whole sponge. This experiment suggests that the first animals evolved from protist colonies, and were made of cells very similar to one another. Animals that evolved later have a division of labour among their cells, which are organized in specialized groups to form tissues and organs.

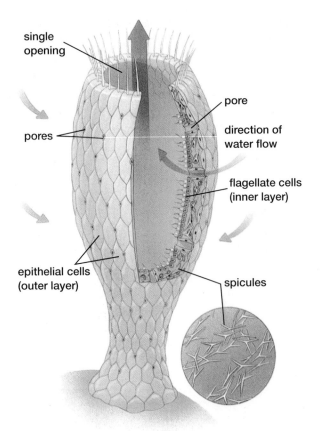

Figure 13.33 The structure of a sponge

The body of a sponge has a single opening through which food enters and waste matter leaves. A sponge has no tissues and no organs. Its body consists of only two layers of cells. Figure 13.33 shows the structure of a sponge. The outer layer is made of flattened epithelial cells that form a protective wall. Water is taken in through pores in this wall. Facing to the inside of the body cavity is a layer of flagellated cells. The beating of the flagellae drives water through the sponge, bringing the sponge food and oxygen and expelling wastes. Between the two cell layers is a gelatinous material containing **spicules**, which are needle-like fibres that help strengthen the body of the sponge.

Jellyfish, Corals, and Anemones (Cnidaria)

Cnidaria is a diverse group of animals that share a similar basic structure and life history. Like sponges, the bodies of these animals have only two cell layers and a single opening. However, cnidarians also have a simple nervous system and muscle tissue. This allows them to swim and capture prey, which they accomplish by using the stinging tentacles around their mouth opening.

While sponges can only digest food particles after absorbing them into their cells, cnidarians begin to digest their food before absorbing it. To do this, they secrete digestive enzymes into their body cavity to carry out extracellular digestion. You may recall from the last chapter that this process is also used by fungi. Extracellular digestion allows cnidarians to digest organisms larger than themselves, giving them a wider range of possible food sources. Cnidarians do not, however, have any specialized excretory or respiratory organs.

Jellyfish and sea anemones are classified in the same phylum although they do not look much alike. The explanation is that cnidarians have two different body forms (see Figure 13.34). One form, called the **polyp**, is cylindrical. Polyps are usually attached to a rock with their mouths directed upward, like a sea anemone or fresh-water hydra. The other form, called the **medusa**, is umbrella-shaped. Medusae float with their mouths pointing downward, like a jellyfish. Some species of cnidarians occur only as polyps, some only as medusae, and some alternate between these two forms during their life cycle (Figure 13.35).

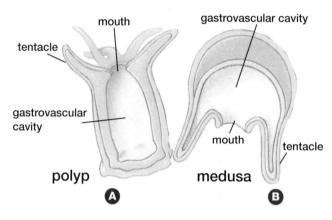

Figure 13.34 Like sponges, cnidarians have two cell layers and a single opening. There are two basic forms of cnidarians. (A) Polyps (such as hydra and anemones) and (B) Medusae (such as jellyfish). How can you turn one form into another?

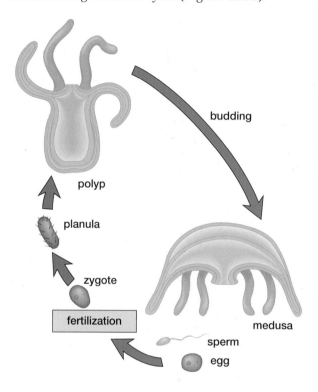

Figure 13.35 Life cycle of a cnidarian. In some cnidarians, the polyp generation is dominant; in others, the medusa generation is dominant. In some cnidarians, one generation is absent.

 THINKING LAB

Diversity of Cnidarians

There are over 9000 species of cnidarians, classified in three classes. Hydrozoa includes hydras and the Portuguese man-of-war. Scyphozoa includes jellyfish. Anthozoa includes sea anemones and corals. Working in groups of three, pick one class of cnidarians to research. As a group, you will make a presentation describing the characteristics of the class you chose. Include details of their life cycle and sexual and asexual methods of reproduction. Describe their general anatomy and feeding methods. Where do they live? Are they solitary or colonial? Include any interesting or unusual facts you discover about these animals.

Analyze

The soft bodies of cnidarians do not preserve well as fossils. The oldest known cnidarians date from the Precambrian era, about 630 million years ago. From your research of this group, suggest why scientists believe they evolved from protists.

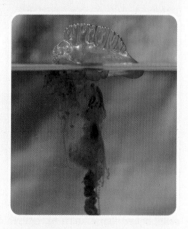

The Portuguese man-of-war shown here is not a single animal but a colony of polyps with different specialized functions.

Worms

Worms are long, wiggly invertebrate animals like the one shown in Figure 13.36. This description is not very useful for taxonomists, but it describes a form of body found in a wide variety of different animals. Of the approximately 30 animal phyla, about half have a wormlike body shape. Most are aquatic, some live in the soil, and many are parasitic. They range in size from 1 mm or less to several metres in length. They include acorn worms, arrow worms, bristle worms, hair worms, hook worms, pin worms, round worms, and tongue worms.

This chapter describes two worm phyla: Phylum Platyhelminthes (flatworms) and Phylum Annelida (segmented worms). By comparing the body organization in these two groups, you can discover further changes in the evolution of animal anatomy from simplicity to complexity.

Flatworms (Platyhelminthes)

The least complex worms are Platyhelminthes, also known as flatworms. This group includes parasitic tapeworms and flukes, as well as free-living planarians. Like sponges and cnidarians, their digestive system is a closed pouch with a single opening through which food enters and waste matter is expelled. Flatworms lack a circulatory system, but have a simple excretory system made up of specialized cells and a simple nervous system with a brain-like concentration of nerve cells at the head end (Figure 13.37). The evolution of a body with a distinct head end is a significant change from the body organization of earlier animals.

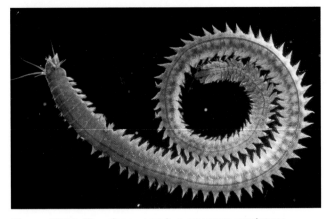

Figure 13.36 The clam worm is a common predatory species of marine worms.

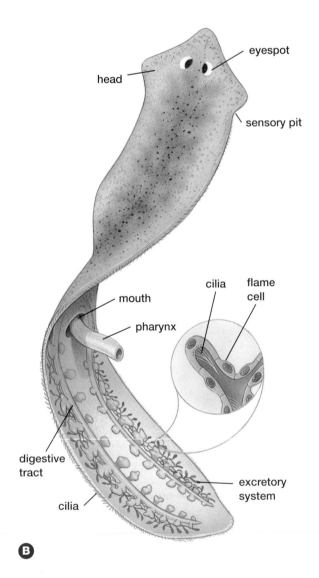

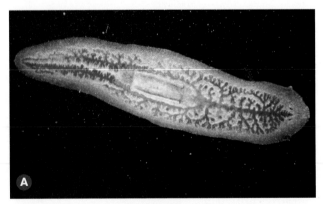

Figure 13.37 The photograph of planaria (A) shows the excretory and nervous system. Greater detail of the excretory system is shown in (B). Planaria have specialized cells, called flame cells, to remove excess water from their bodies. The water moves from the flame cells into tubules connected to pores on the body surface.

Segmented Worms (Annelida)

Members of the phylum Annelida are commonly known as segmented worms. As well as earthworms, they include marine bristle worms, featherworms, and leeches. Their long, tube-like bodies are divided into a series of ringed segments. If you looked inside an earthworm, you would see that many of these segments contain similar sets of organs for excretion, circulation, and nerve control (Figure 13.38). Can you think of an advantage to this type of body organization?

Web LINK

There are many worm phyla that are not explored in this chapter. Do some research to find out about other phyla of worms which include acorn worms, bristle worms, pin worms, or round worms. You may wish to compare several worm phyla to look at their characteristics, or you may wish to explore one phyla in detail. Go to **Science Resources**, then to **BIOLOGY 11**, then follow the links. What worm phyla can you find that have not already been mentioned? Where do they live? What do they eat?

www.school.mcgrawhill.ca/resources/

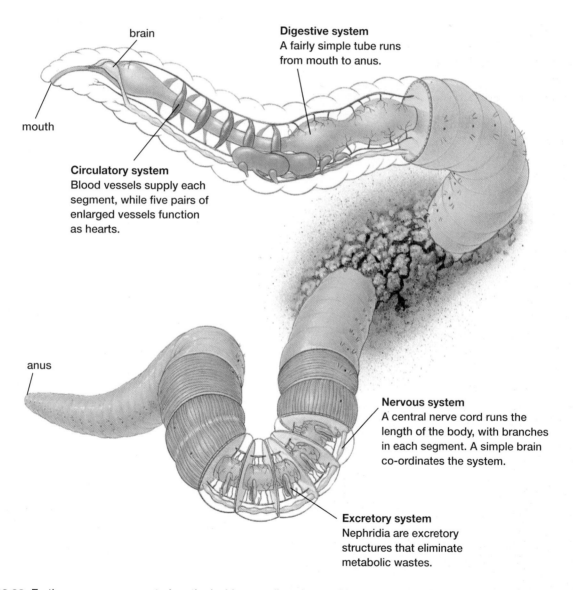

brain

mouth

Digestive system
A fairly simple tube runs from mouth to anus.

Circulatory system
Blood vessels supply each segment, while five pairs of enlarged vessels function as hearts.

anus

Nervous system
A central nerve cord runs the length of the body, with branches in each segment. A simple brain co-ordinates the system.

Excretory system
Nephridia are excretory structures that eliminate metabolic wastes.

Figure 13.38 Earthworms are segmented on the inside as well as the outside.

Development of a Mesoderm

If you were to study a flatworm in cross section, you would see that it has three layers of cells. Between the **ectoderm** (outer layer) and the **endoderm** (inner layer) is the **mesoderm**. All animals other than sponges and cnidarians have these three layers.

Blastula formation is the earliest developmental stage of an embryo. Continuous cell divisions in a sea urchin embryo as shown in Figure 13.39, result in a blastula. The total number of cells present in blastula stages of different classes of animals varies. As the embryo continues to grow, some of the cells of the blastula fold inward, forming the gastrula. The mesoderm develops in an animal embryo following a stage called the gastrula.

The development of three layers in the embryo helps sort cells into an arrangement that produces the specialized tissues and organs of the adult animal. For example, in humans, the ectoderm produces the skin, nerve tissue, and some sense organs. The endoderm produces the lungs, liver, pancreas, bladder, and lining of the gut. The mesoderm produces the muscles, blood, kidneys, and reproductive organs.

> ➤ PLAY
>
> To see a simulation of embryonic development, go to your Electronic Learning Partner.

Investigation   13 • D

SKILL FOCUS

Predicting

Performing and recording

Analyzing and interpreting

Conducting research

Observing Planarian Behaviour

You may have seen planarians if you have ever looked under rocks in a shallow stream. They are tiny, flat, soft-bodied organisms that glide over the surface of submerged rocks in search of a meal of tiny snails, worms, protozoa, or dead matter. Movement and ingestion are two key characteristics of all animals. In this investigation, you will observe the form and behaviour of planarians.

Pre-lab Questions

- How do planarians move?
- What stimuli do planarians respond to?
- How and why do they respond to these stimuli?

Problem

How is the shape of planarians related to their methods of locomotion and feeding?

Prediction

Predict what stimuli planarians might use to locate their food.

Materials

dropper	aquarium water
hand magnifying glass	watch glass
chopped cooked egg white	
live planaria (3–4)	petri dish
dissecting probe	

Procedure

1. Using a dropper, carefully transfer at least two planarians to a watch glass. Add enough aquarium water to just cover the bottom. Always wipe up any spills.

2. Observe the body plan and method of locomotion of a planarian. If necessary, use a magnifying glass. Identify the head, eye-spots, cilia, pharynx, and mouth (see Figure 13.37 on page 492). Make a labelled sketch of one of your specimens.

3. Place a small speck of egg in the watch glass. Observe the response of the planarians. In your notebook, describe your observations, noting how quickly the planarians respond, their position in relation to the food, and their feeding behaviour.

4. Transfer at least two planarians to a clean petri dish. Add enough aquarium water to just cover the planarians. Allow a minute or two for them to recover from handling.

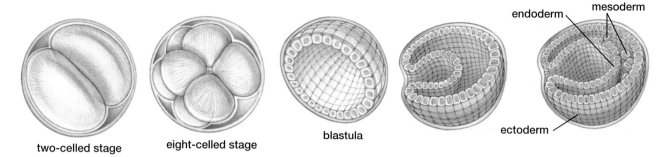

two-celled stage   eight-celled stage   blastula

endoderm   mesoderm

ectoderm

Figure 13.39 Most animals develop three layers of cells at an early stage in the growth of the embryo.

5. Tap gently on one side of the petri dish with a dissecting probe. Observe and record how the planarians respond.

6. Wait for at least one minute for the planarians to relax, then gently touch the head of a planarian with one side of the probe. Observe its reaction. Gently touch the tail. Record your observations.

   Wash your hands thoroughly at the end of this procedure.

Post-lab Questions

1. Describe how planarians move.

2. Describe as positive (toward the stimulus) or negative (away from the stimulus) the responses of planaria to: a) food, b) tapping the petri dish, c) touching the head, d) touching the tail.

Conclude and Apply

3. Suggest an explanation for each response recorded in question 2.

4. How is the flat shape of a planarian an advantage for a) its method of locomotion? b) its method of feeding?

5. Consider the entire digestive system of a planarian. What is an advantage of having its mouth located in the centre of its body rather than at the head end?

6. What part of a planarian's body reacts first to changes in its environment? Suggest an explanation for your answer.

Exploring Further

7. Hypothesize a function for the eye-spots located on the head of a planarian. What advantage might this provide? Design and conduct an experiment to test your hypothesis after getting your teacher's approval.

Body Symmetry

If the fish shown in Figure 13.40 were to begin moving, in which direction would it start? You can safely predict it would move from left to right, not from right to left. You could make a similar prediction from a photograph of a horse, or a planarian. Although these animals have very different shapes, sizes, and methods of locomotion, they all have an obvious front or head end, a back or tail end, a dorsal surface, and a ventral surface. This observation may seem trivial, but it is not true of all animals. Could you locate a head end on a sponge or jellyfish?

Figure 13.40 Which way will this fish move? How do you know?

The body plan of most animals is related to the necessity for them to move in order to locate food. Their sense organs are concentrated at the end that leads, so as to help orient them to their environment. It is also important for most organisms to distinguish between up (going against gravity) and down (going with gravity). These needs determine the basic body plans of all animals.

Sponges are the simplest of animals. They do not move as adults, and their shape is generally irregular or **asymmetrical**. Most animals, however, have a **symmetrical** body plan — one that is regular and balanced. There are two types of symmetry among animals, which are shown in Figure 13.41. For species that attach themselves to one spot, or that move very little, the most important orientation is up and down. For example, *Hydra* has a base that anchors it and a top

end that obtains food. All horizontal directions around its centre are equally significant. Such animals have **radial symmetry**, with their bodies organized equally around a central vertical axis like a wheel around its axle. You could divide these animals through their centre in many different vertical planes to obtain two halves of the same shape. The great majority of animals, including you, have **bilateral symmetry**. This means they can be cut into two equal, mirror-image halves through only one vertical plane.

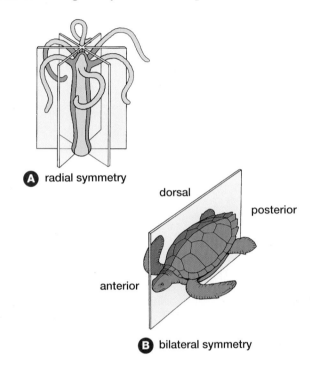

Figure 13.41 A hydra shows radial symmetry, (A) while a turtle shows bilateral symmetry (B).

BIO FACT

Most animals with bilateral symmetry are more complex and evolved later than animals with radial symmetry, but there are a few exceptions. For example, starfish and sea urchins (classified in the phylum Echinodermata) are radially symmetrical, but scientists believe that echinoderms evolved their present shape from ancestors that were bilaterally symmetrical and more mobile. Evidence for this is seen during their immature larval stage, when echinoderms are tadpole-like in appearance.

Development of a Coelom

The bodies of platyhelminthes are flat, solid, and compact, with a digestive tract and other organs sandwiched tightly into the mesoderm layer. Annelids have a similar general shape to flatworms, but with an important advance. Inside their mesoderm layer, the digestive tract and other organs are suspended in a fluid-filled body cavity called the **coelom** (Figure 13.42). Animals with a coelom (which includes all the remaining groups you will study) are called **coelomates**. Animals without a coelom, such as cnidaria and flatworms, are called **acoelomates**.

Why is a coelom important? Imagine a length of thin rubber tubing. Now imagine the same tubing closed at both ends and filled with water. The empty tube is like a flatworm, while the water-filled tube is like an earthworm. With fluid inside it, the tube is more solid and rigid. For animals, this gives their muscles a structure to brace against, allowing them to move and respond more quickly.

In addition, a fluid-filled body cavity allows for the development of more complex organ systems. For example, the digestive tract can grow longer than the body, because it can bend and fold back on itself within the coelom. In more advanced animals, such as vertebrates, the coelom is subdivided into separate cavities around the heart and lungs, as well as around the digestive tract.

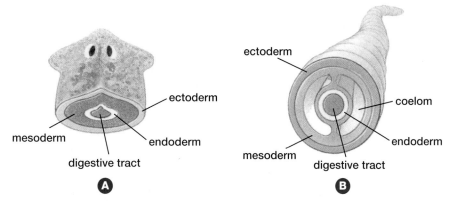

Figure 13.42 Acoelomate animals (A) have flattened bodies. Coelomate animals (B) have a body cavity or coelom in which complex internal organs can develop.

 THINKING LAB

How Does the Mesoderm Affect Tissue Development?

Background

What causes cells in one part of an embryo to develop into one type of tissue while cells in another part of the embryo develop into a different kind of tissue? Perhaps the position of the cells plays a part. For example, only the ectoderm cells on the dorsal side of an embryo develop into nervous tissue. Biologists hypothesized that the ectoderm may be influenced by the mesoderm cells lying directly beneath them. To test this idea, they removed a piece of mesoderm from beneath the dorsal surface of an embryo. They then transplanted this piece of mesoderm to a spot beneath the ventral surface of a second embryo (from which a similar piece of mesoderm had been removed). The ectoderm was sealed back over the top of the mesoderm transplant.

You Try It

1. The three diagrams shown here illustrate steps in the experiment described above, but they are not in order. Copy the diagrams into your notebook in the correct sequence of events.

2. Suggest what might happen as the embryo develops if the mesoderm influences the ectoderm as the hypothesis predicts.

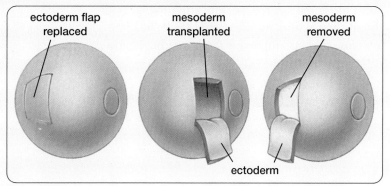

The coelom develops in the embryo in two different ways in animal phyla. In Annelida, Mollusca, and Arthropoda, it originates from a split in the mesoderm layer. In Echinodermata and Chordata, it forms from pouches in the embryonic gut (Figure 13.43). These differences in the embryonic origin of the coelom are evidence of the early evolutionary split of multicellular animals into two groups.

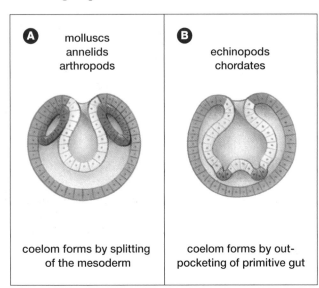

A molluscs annelids arthropods

coelom forms by splitting of the mesoderm

B echinopods chordates

coelom forms by out-pocketing of primitive gut

Figure 13.43 The two different origins of the coelom

║ PAUSE   ● RECORD

You have been learning about the amazing diversity found within the Kingdom Animalia. Make a list of the characteristics of members of this kingdom. For each of the characteristics that you have listed, describe the variety of ways that animals show the characteristic. For example, animals are motile. Describe the different ways that the animals you have learned about move. As you complete this chapter, continue to add to your list.

Molluscs (Mollusca)

Members of the Mollusca, or molluscs, are soft-bodied animals such as slugs, snails, clams, oysters, and squid. (The Greek word *mollis* means soft.) Most species are marine, and most protect themselves with a hard external shell. In some species, such as slugs, the shell is reduced and internal (Figure 13.44).

► PLAY

To see videos on locomotion and characteristics of different molluscs, go to your Electronic Learning Partner.

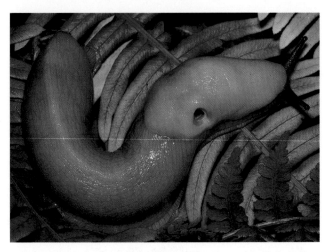

Figure 13.44 A slug is a mollusc without an external shell. Molluscs are all soft-bodied animals.

All molluscs have bilateral symmetry, a coelom, and two body openings. The phylum is diverse, but molluscs share a similar pattern of development. The larval stages of molluscs are similar in appearance, however, the adult shapes are very different.

The first molluscs appeared in the seas about 600 million years ago. They were simple, worm-like animals with segments similar to those of annelid worms. Because of this, and the pattern of early cell division in their embryos, biologists think that molluscs and segmented worms are closely related. Within 100 million years, molluscs had diversified into at least six classes, three of which are shown in Figure 13.45 on the following page. By about 100 million years ago, they were found around the world on land and in fresh-water habitats as well as in the sea. Some species are herbivores, many are predators, and some are parasites. The molluscs are the second-largest animal phylum after the Arthropods, which you will study next.

BIO FACT

There are so many different molluscs that a handful of shell grit from the deep ocean floor near the equator may contain the remains of about 500 species, of which about one fifth are unknown (that is, not yet named by scientists). Since exploration of the deepest ocean trenches began, scientists have discovered over 1100 species of molluscs living more than 1600 m below the surface of the ocean. At least one species lives at depths of 4500 m, and there may be hundreds more still unrecorded.

Bivalvia (about 10 000 species). Includes oysters, scallops, clams, and mussels. Range in size from 0.5 mm to about 1.4 m. Have two shells, called valves, connected by a flexible ligament and an adductor muscle for closing the valves tightly. There is no head region. Most are filter feeders, using their gills to collect food. Found in all marine and fresh-water habitats with a pH greater than about 5 (more acidic water would dissolve their calcium shells).

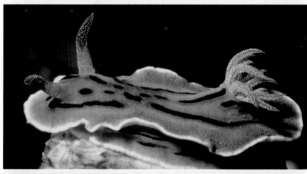

Gastropoda (at least 60 000 species). Includes snails and slugs. Range in size from 0.5 mm to 75 cm. Most, except slugs, have a spiral shell with single opening. Head has tentacles. A well-developed foot is used for locomotion. Widespread in marine, fresh-water and terrestrial habitats.

Cephalopoda (about 650 species). Includes octopus, squid, cuttlefish, and nautilus. Range in size from 10 mm to 20 m. Bilaterally symmetrical, often highly streamlined. Move by jet propulsion produced by a funnel from the mantle. Only a few species produce a shell. All are marine predators or scavengers.

Figure 13.45 The three largest classes of molluscs are (A) bivalves, (B) gastropods, and (C) cephalopods.

One feature common to all molluscs is a fleshy **mantle**, which wraps around the body like a cloak and secretes the shell on the organism's outer surface (Figure 13.46). Between the mantle and the body organs is the mantle cavity. This space contains the gills used for gas exchange in aquatic species. Terrestrial molluscs have a lunglike space in the mantle. Behind the mouth is a large, muscular foot used for locomotion.

A mollusc's body includes all the organ systems found in any animal: digestive, circulatory, respiratory, excretory, reproductive, and nervous. Some species have well-developed eyes and other sense organs. The octopus has a relatively large brain and is capable of learning complex tasks, as well as showing flexible behaviour and even play.

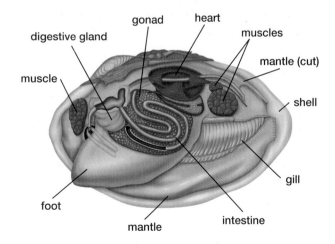

Figure 13.46 The internal anatomy of a mollusc

Joint-Legged Animals (Arthropoda)

If you turn over a rock in your garden, or a rotting log in the forest, you will almost certainly surprise some animals that have jointed legs and no spine. Some of the most fantastic and dramatic organisms in the world are members of this phylum, the Arthropoda. Scientists have described over 500 000 species of arthropods and believe there may be 10 million or more species alive today. Members of this phylum are so diverse that some species can be found living at the bottom of the deepest oceans while other species can be found floating through air high above Earth's surface.

Several classes of arthropods are shown in Figure 13.49 on page 502.

BIO FACT

About 120 000 species of flies have been formally described by scientists. This means that about one in every 10 animals known in the world is a fly. True flies are classified in the insect order Diptera (meaning two-winged). They include many familiar insects such as mosquitoes, black flies, midges, fruit flies, blow flies, and house flies.

Investigation   13 • E

SKILL FOCUS

Performing and recording

Analyzing and interpreting

Communicating results

Classifying Arthropods

The three largest classes of arthropods are insects, arachnids, and crustaceans. As arthropods, all of these animals share certain characteristics. The members of each class, however, are classified based on their differences.

Pre-lab Questions

- What are the characteristics of arthropods?
- What are the characteristics of insects?
- What are the characteristics of arachnids?
- What are the characteristics of crustaceans?

Problem

What characteristics are most useful for identifying members of different arthropod classes?

Prediction

Different classes of a phylum can be correctly identified using observable characteristics.

Materials

preserved spider
preserved grasshopper
dissecting probe

preserved crayfish
hand lens
dissecting tray

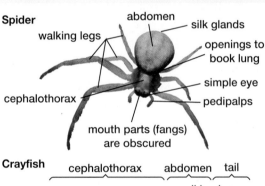

Spider

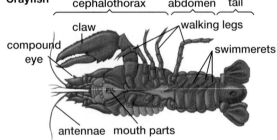

Crayfish

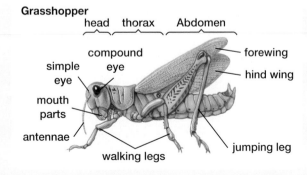

Grasshopper

Figure 13.47 The red velvet mite is a giant among mites, easily visible to the human eye.

Procedure

1. Place all three arthropods in the dissecting tray. Prepare a table to record your observations and comparisons.

2. Carefully examine the exterior of each animal in turn and record your answers to the following questions for each:

   (a) Is any part of its body segmented? If so, which part?

   (b) Does it have an external skeleton (that is, hard like the material of your fingernails, not soft like the material of your skin)?

   (c) How many legs does it have?

   (d) Are its legs jointed?

   (e) Does it have any other limb-like appendages? If so, describe each different appendage and suggest a function for each based on its appearance.

   (f) Does it have wings? If so, how many?

   (g) The body regions of an arthropod are the head, thorax, and abdomen. In some arthropods, the head and thorax are fused into one cephalothorax. Does the animal have three body regions or two?

   (h) How many simple eyes and compound eyes does it have? (Use a reference if you are not sure of the difference).

   (i) Does it have antennae? If so, how many?

   (j) Wash your hands thoroughly at the end of observing your organisms.

3. When you have recorded all your data in a table, prepare a taxonomic key that can be used to identify members of the three arthropod classes.

Post-lab Questions

1. Which characteristics are the same in all three animals you studied, and therefore identify the phylum arthropoda?

2. Which characteristics identify arachnids?

3. Which characteristics identify insects?

4. Which characteristics identify crustaceans?

5. In which taxon (class or phylum) do members of a group have the most characteristics in common?

Conclude and Apply

6. What characteristics would you expect to find in a centipede (a member of the arthropod class Chilopoda)?

7. Suggest what characteristic might distinguish a centipede from other arthropods.

In basic structure, arthropods resemble annelids, indicating that the two phyla had a common origin about 500 million years ago. You can see the resemblance most clearly in larval stages, such as the caterpillar larvae of butterflies and moths, or the maggot larvae of flies (Figure 13.48). As arthropods evolved, they developed several distinct differences from annelids.

- They have fewer body segments, with a tendency for segments in the head and thorax regions to fuse and become specialized.
- They have a hard, external cuticle, which acts as an exoskeleton for muscle attachment.
- They have legs that are divided into moveable segments connected by joints.
- They have separate muscles organized into groups related to specific movements of body parts. (Annelids have simple sheets of muscle throughout the body.)
- They have strongly developed jaws.
- They have better-developed nervous systems and sense organs.

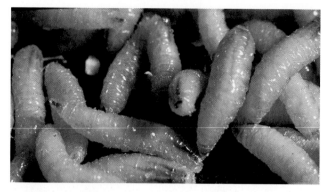

Figure 13.48 The larval stage of some insects shows the relationship of this group to the segmented worms.

Starfish (Echinodermata)

This diverse group of 6 000 species has some characteristics of very simple animals, some characteristics of very complex animals, and some characteristics unique to this phylum. All echinoderms are marine, and include starfish, sea urchins, sea cucumbers, feather stars, sea lillies, and sand dollars, some of which are shown in Figure 13.50. Like cnidarians, echinoderms are radially symmetrical as adults. Their larvae,

Figure 13.49 The Phylum Arthropoda is a very diverse group. Shown here are four large taxa of Arthropods, (A) spider (Subclass Arachnida), (B) lobster (Subphylum Crustacea), (C) centipede (Subclass Chilopoda), and (D) millipede (Subclass Diplopoda).

however, are bilaterally symmetrical and later undergo metamorphosis to change their body form. Like chordates, the coelom of echinoderms develops in the embryo from an outpocketing of the gut.

You may have seen starfish at the seaside or in an aquarium. If you looked at the underside of one of these animals, you would have seen the unusual system they use both to move and obtain their food. Locomotion depends on a water vascular system — a series of tubes or canals throughout the body in which water is moved under pressure. This system is shown in Figure 13.51. Water enters the system through a sieve plate called a madreporite. From canals along each arm of the starfish, water enters round, muscular structures called ampullae, each of which leads to a flexible tube foot. Ampullae act like the bulb on the end of an eyedropper. When the ampulla contracts, it pushes water into the tube foot, making the tube foot extend until it touches a solid object. When the ampulla relaxes, water is withdrawn from the tube foot, creating suction that holds the tube foot onto the surface.

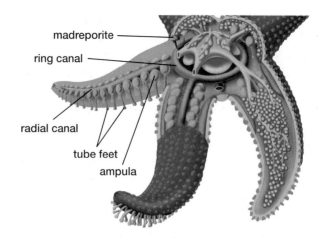

Figure 13.51 The water vascular system of the starfish provides water pressure that works the starfish's tube feet.

Starfish creep over the sea floor by alternately expanding and contracting their many dozens of tube feet. They also use these tube feet to capture molluscs, urchins, and similar slow-moving prey. To begin a meal, a starfish attaches its tube feet to the shell of the prey and holds it against its mouth. It then pushes its stomach out from its mouth until it contacts the soft parts of the prey.

Figure 13.50 These organisms are all members of the phylum Echinodermata, which means "spiny-skinned." Shown here are (A) starfish or sea star (Class Asteroidea), (B) sea cucumber (Class Holothuroidea), (C) sea urchin (Suborder Echinacea), and (D) sand dollar (Order Clypeasterioda).

The starfish secretes enzymes that begin digesting the prey and later takes the partly digested food into its body to continue the process. When attacking bivalve molluscs such as mussels, starfish use their tube feet to pull the shell open so they can get at the soft body inside. Other echinoderms have different diets. Most sea urchins graze on algae, while brittle stars, sea lillies, and sea cucumbers feed on dead and decaying matter drifting through the water.

Echinoderms lack respiratory, excretory, and circulatory systems. Gases are exchanged and wastes are eliminated by diffusion across the thin membranes of the tube feet. They have no head or brain, but have a central nerve ring with branches. Starfish have light-sensitive eyespots at the tip of each arm, and other echinoderms have cells that detect light and touch.

Starfish can reproduce asexually and sexually. If a starfish is split in half or loses one or more arms,

it can regenerate itself into a whole organism again. During sexual reproduction, female starfish can release as many as 60 million eggs. These eggs are fertilized by sperm released by male starfish and develop into free-swimming larvae which eventually settle on the sea floor and metamorphose into adults.

Chordates (Chordata)

Most members of the phylum Chordata are vertebrates, with bony skeletons and backbones, and most are bigger than the animals you have read about so far. As a result, they are better known and more familiar, including the animals shown in Figure 13.52. Although these animals appear to be the most dominant on land and in water, there are only about 45 000 species of vertebrates, compared with millions of species of invertebrates.

Figure 13.52 Five of the classes of vertebrates. Shown here are (A) fish (Class Osteichthyes), (B) salamander (Class Amphibia), (C) snake (Class Reptilia), (D) bird (Class Aves), and (E) cheetah (Class Mammalia).

Invertebrate Chordates

Odd though it seems, the phylum chordata also includes two groups of invertebrate animals shown in Figure 13.53. Tunicates, or sea squirts, are in the subphylum Urochordata. They are squat, thick-walled organisms that live on the ocean floor. Tunicates get their name from a protective layer called a tunic that covers their bodies. Lancelets, classified in the subphylum Cephalochordata, are small marine animals that look like the two-edged surgical knife called a lancet. Only a few centimetres long, lancelets usually lie buried in muddy sediments beneath the shallow water near the coast, with only their mouths and gill slits exposed.

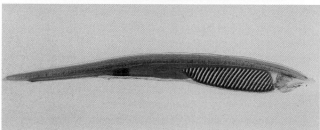

Figure 13.53 Tunicates (top) and lancelets (bottom) are invertebrate members of the chordate phylum. Both groups lack a head and brain.

The reason tunicates and lancelets are considered chordates is that they share three key features with all other chordate animals, described in Figure 13.54. At some stage in their life history, all chordates have:

- A dorsal nerve cord, from which nerves branch to all parts of the body.

- A **notochord**, or rod of cartilage, which runs along the dorsal length of the body. In most vertebrates, the notochord occurs only in the embryo. A backbone of cartilage or bone replaces the notochord.

- Gill slits in the pharynx, or throat. In terrestrial vertebrates, the gill slits appear only in the embryo. For example, in humans, one of the gill slits in the embryo develops into the ear canal in the adult.

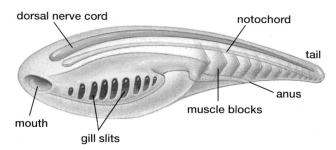

Figure 13.54 The lancelet shows all three chordate characteristics — a hollow dorsal nerve cord, a notochord, and gill slits — throughout its life. Tunicates have a dorsal nerve cord and notochord only in their tadpole-like larval stage, but retain gill slits as adults. Which chordate characteristics did you have as an embryo, and which do you have now?

Vertebrate Chordates

The vertebrate chordates are subdivided into two groups: Agnathans, or jawless fishes, and Gnathostomata, or jawed animals (see Table 13.1). Jawless fishes are the oldest group of vertebrates, and were widespread in the oceans from 500 to 300 million years ago. Today, they consist of a small group of about 60 species of lampreys and hagfish. These smooth, tube-shaped fishes grow up to one metre long and are scavengers or parasites. Hagfish drill a hole in dead or dying fish and suck out their contents. Parasitic lampreys attach themselves to other fish by a their suckerlike mouths and feed on their victim's blood as shown in Figure 13.55 on the next page.

Table 13.1
Chordate classification

Phylum Chordata
Subphylum Urochordata (tunicates)
Subphylum Cephalochordata (lancelets)
Subphylum Agnatha (jawless fishes such as hagfish and lampreys)
Subphylum Gnathostomata (jawed chordates)
Class Chondrichthyes (cartilaginous fish such as sharks and rays)
Class Osteichthyes (bony fish)
Class Amphibia (amphibians)
Class Reptilia (reptiles)
Class Aves (birds)
Class Mammalia (mammals)

Jawless fishes most likely evolved from an ancestor similar to a tunicate larva or a lancelet. Jawless fishes are mobile and ferocious predators (Figure 13.55), and they came to dominate the oceans, lakes, and rivers. The jawless fishes, in turn, were ancestors to fishes with jaws. Today, fishes are the most diverse group of vertebrates. They are divided into two classes: the cartilaginous fishes such as sharks and rays, and the bony fishes.

About 370 million years ago, the first land-living vertebrates appeared. The ancestors of these first land dwellers were lobe-finned fishes, which had muscular fins supported by limb-like bones. This group of fishes became extinct millions of years ago — with one remarkable exception (Figure 13.56). A species of fish called the coelacanth was first identified in 1938 as the only living member of the ancient group of vertebrates that took the first steps from sea to land.

Figure 13.56 The coelacanth is the only surviving species of lobe-finned fishes. Its relatives evolved into the first vertebrates with limbs for moving on land.

In 1938, the curator of a small museum near Cape Town, South Africa found "the most beautiful fish" in the catch of a fishing trawler. She drew the fish, described it as best she could, and sent the description off to a professor at Rhodes University. He replied with an urgent message to preserve the fish. Unfortunately, it had already been mounted to display and important identifying features had been thrown away. It took another 14 years of searching to find another specimen. That specimen confirmed that it was actually a coelacanth, a prehistoric fish presumed to have gone extinct. A second, different population has been discovered in Indonesia, and it appears that the "extinct" fish is uncommon but does exist.

Figure 13.55 The lamprey is a jawless fish. It feeds by rasping the flesh of other fish and feeding on their blood and body fluids.

Observing Bones

All vertebrates have a bony skeleton. Among species with four limbs, the basic shapes of bones in the skeleton are remarkably similar, whether in a bird, reptile, mammal, or amphibian. The shape and size of a bone depends on its function. As a class, gather labelled diagrams of different skeletons. Be sure to include a model or diagram of a human skeleton in your selection. You may find these diagrams in biology textbooks, anatomy textbooks, or on the Internet. You may also assemble a collection of bones, such as chicken or beef bones. Can you identify the bones in your class collection by matching each bone to a similar bone in the human skeleton?

Analyze

Which parts of a vertebrate's body are most likely to have long, straight bones? Which parts of a skeleton consist of large, broad bone surfaces to which other bones and muscles are attached? How does the spine provide evidence of a segmented organization of the body?

Evolution of Jaws

The evolution of jaws enabled animals to grasp, hold, crush, and break up their food. Without jaws, animals such as jawless fish and worms are restricted to sucking liquids and ingesting small particles. These animals are scavengers, mud-eaters, or parasites. With jaws, animals have a much wider range of possible food. They can be active predators, capturing and killing prey and tearing off large chunks of meat. They can bite through and chew the tough leaves and stems of plants. Ingesting food is one of the key characteristics of all animals, and the evolution of jaws was a huge advantage. You may recall that jaws are also one of the characteristics that distinguishes arthropods from worms. Jaws helped make arthropods and vertebrates the most diverse and successful groups of animals on the planet.

Amphibians, reptiles, birds, and mammals are the four classes of vertebrates that evolved on land. Despite their apparent differences, they all have many anatomical features in common.

Biology At Work

Marine Biologist

Right whales are marine mammals that live in the Atlantic Ocean off the coast of Florida in winter, the coast of Cape Cod in winter and spring, and in the Bay of Fundy in summer. They feed on plankton, have no predators, and live about as long as humans do. Presently, there are only about 300 right whales left alive in the North Atlantic Ocean. During the days of whaling, these whales were considered to be the "right" whales to hunt because their bodies contained so much fat that retrieving the floating carcasses was easy. Now we no longer hunt them, but right whales' lives are still in grave danger because they collide with ships or become entangled in fishing gear.

Protecting the Right Whale

Dr. Moira Brown works as a marine biologist, focussed on saving the right whale from extinction. In 1985, she founded the East Coast Ecosystems Research Organization in Freeport, Nova Scotia. Since the whales spend winter and spring off Cape Cod, she also began to work at the Center for Coastal Studies in Cape Cod, and she has become a spokeswoman for right whales both in Canada and in the United States.

Dr. Moira Brown

Forty percent of Dr. Brown's time is spent working directly with the whales. Dr. Brown and her colleagues chart sightings of individual whales and follow their migration patterns. They track the whales by identifying individual callosities — the tough, cornified skin patches on the top and sides of the whale's head. These callosities may look white because they are covered with white lice, and each right whale has a unique pattern. She also traces the ancestry of individual whales by collecting DNA samples with a crossbow.

Dr. Brown also works to disentangle trapped whales from fishing nets. Although a whale may break free from a net, if it does not, it can drown. The netting gets wrapped around the whale's body, cutting deeper and deeper, until the animal dies. In fact, sixty percent of the right whales in the North Atlantic have scars from fishing nets.

The rest of Dr. Brown's work is with people. She sets up educational programs to publicize the plight of the right whale, applies for grant money to support further research, and lobbies for shipping lanes to be changed so vessels do not travel through the whales' habitat.

Becoming a Whale Researcher

If you want to explore this field, you can get practical experience working or volunteering with scientists, tour operators, or educators who work with whales. A B.Sc. degree may help you get involved in research projects with whales on a part-time or seasonal basis. In order to find permanent or long-term positions, a Ph.D. is required.

Go to the Internet or your school's resource centre to find out how many different species of whales there are. Learn how many species are endangered or threatened, and find out what kind of research is being done to protect these whales. Write several paragraphs outlining your ideas on what you would do if you were given funding to protect marine organisms.

Relationships of Chordates

Because bones are more readily preserved as fossils than softer tissues, scientists have a much more detailed record of evolution among vertebrates than among invertebrates. Figure 13.57 outlines the evolutionary relationships between groups of vertebrates.

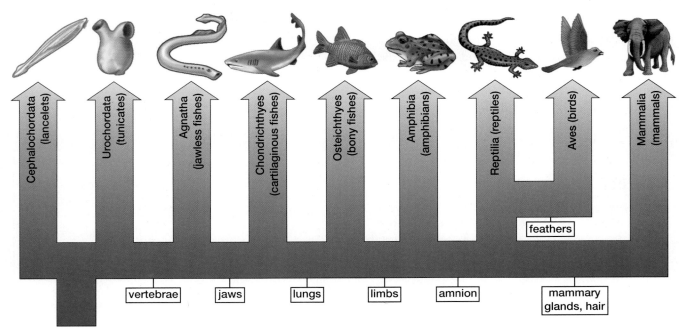

Ancestral chordates

Figure 13.57 This tree shows the relationships among chordates and the characteristics that evolved along the branches. Each characteristic shown in a box along a branch is shared by the groups to the right of that point.

SECTION REVIEW

1. **K/U** How does a sponge obtain its food?

2. **K/U** In what way is the feeding method of a cnidarian different from that of a sponge? What advantage does this give?

3. **K/U** How is the body of a flatworm (a) similar to and (b) different from the body of a sponge and a cnidarian?

4. **K/U** What is a coelom? What are the advantages of a coelomate body over an acoelomate body?

5. **C** Sketch a diagram illustrating the difference between radial symmetry and bilateral symmetry in animal bodies.

6. **I** What characteristic does a garden snail have in common with an octopus?

7. **I** How might a knowledge of insect taxonomy help scientists control insect pests?

8. **I** Construct a key that would allow you to differentiate between the four phyla you studied in this section.

9. **I** Design an imaginary arthropod that could be adapted to one of the following conditions: water, soil, dry sand, or snow. Be sure to sketch your arthropod, and indicate how it feeds itself, defends itself, and how it is adapted to use its environment.

10. **MC** Research the importance of earthworms in agriculture. Prepare a presentation to show your findings. How important do you think earthworms are to the food that we eat?

11. **MC** Explain why the origin of earthworms is not as well understood as the origin of molluscs. How could this influence the study of evolutionary biology?

UNIT ISSUE PREP

Many organisms on the endangered species list in Canada are members of the Kingdom Animalia. If you have chosen to research an animal for the Unit 4 Issue Analysis, make sure you understand how the organism's characteristics make it unique. This may be important for you to understand how and why the organism is threatened or endangered.

Chapter Expectations

Briefly explain each of the following points.

- The evolution of plants involved a number of adaptations to life on land. (13.1)
- Plant life cycles include a sporophyte and gametophyte generation. (13.1)
- The Kingdom Plantae is divided into four major groups. (13.2)
- Most non-vascular plants are small and live in damp habitats. (13.2)
- Some vascular plants are seed bearing, others are seedless. (13.2)
- There are two groups of seed-bearing plants. (13.2)
- Animals are multicellular heterotrophs. (13.3)
- The simplest animals have two cell layers and a single body opening. (13.3)
- The evolution of three cell layers and a coelom allowed animals to become more complex and mobile. (13.3)
- Vertebrates are members of the phylum Chordata and have bony skeletons and backbones. (13.3)

Language of Biology

Write a sentence using each of the following words or terms. Use any six terms in a concept map to show your understanding of how they are related.

- seed
- sporophyte
- gametophyte
- non-vascular plants
- rhizoids
- seta
- antheridium
- archegonium
- thalli
- seedless vascular plants
- rhizomes
- strobili
- prothallus
- stomata
- fronds
- pinnae
- sori
- gymnosperms
- pollen tube
- angiosperms
- cotyledons
- monocots
- dicots
- pollination
- pollen-tube competition
- polyploid
- spicules
- polyp
- medusa
- ectoderm
- endoderm
- mesoderm
- asymmetrical
- symmetrical
- radial symmetry
- bilateral symmetry
- coelom
- coelomates
- acoelomates
- mantle
- notochord

UNDERSTANDING CONCEPTS

1. Name two similarities between green algae and plants.

2. State whether each of the following is true or false. If false, explain why. Plants are adapted to life on land by:
   (a) a system to transport water
   (b) the ability to carry out photosynthesis.
   (c) a system of rigid support for the body of the plant.

3. Give two examples of non-vascular plants.

4. How do water and dissolved substances move through non-vascular plants?

5. Why do mosses and ferns need moist conditions to reproduce?

6. Why must plant seeds be stored in a cool, dry place?

7. In which generation of a plant life cycle does the process of meiosis occur? Why?

8. State whether each of the following concepts is true or false. If false, explain why.

   (a) Most plants are multicellular eukaryotes that obtain their food by photosynthesis.
   (b) In vascular plants, specialized tissues transport water, dissolved minerals, and sugars to all parts of the plant.
   (c) The diploid generation of a plant is called the gametophyte.

9. Explain the advantages of seeds to plant dispersal and survival.

10. Describe two significant differences between vascular and non-vascular plants.

11. What is the dominant generation among fern plants?

12. Describe the main differences between gymnosperms and angiosperms.

13. What advantages do flowers provide to plants?

14. How are flatworms (Platyhelminthes) similar to cnidarians? How are they different?

15. What advantages do coelomate animals have over acoelomate animals?

16. Name the three largest classes of molluscs and give an example of each. What do all three groups have in common?

17. Describe two ways in which arthropods differ from annelids and explain how each difference is significant.

18. Describe the differences between the symmetry found in a larval echinoderm and an adult echinoderm. Why is the symmetry in an adult echinoderm considered to be unusual?

19. Why are tunicates classified as Chordates?

20. Why do most animals have a method of locomotion while plants do not?

21. Are damp conditions more important for the sporophyte or the gametophyte of a fern? Explain why.

22. A friend tells you that dolphins and bats have nothing in common. What facts could you use to explain that they are both members of the same phylum?

23. How is the presence of a nervous system an adaptation for the lifestyle of a free-living planarian?

24. What advantages do multicellular organisms (such as sponges) have over unicellular organisms for obtaining food?

INQUIRY

25. Your brother shows you a few green leaves he found in a pond. How could you determine if they are from an algae or a plant?

26. During a holiday in the tropics, you see a palm-like tree. How could you determine whether it was a true palm (angiosperm) or a cycad (gymnosperm)?

27. On a pie chart, plot the relative numbers of species in each of the four major groups of plants: non-vascular plants, seedless vascular plants, gynmosperms, and angiosperms. Suggest an explanation for the pattern you observe.

28. Suppose you find a packet of unlabelled plant seeds. How could you determine if they were monocots or dicots?

29. What can you infer about the lifestyle of an organism that has no mouth or digestive system, but does have a sucker present?

30. Earthworms spend their time burrowing underground, eating soil, and digesting the organic material contained in the soil. They spend much of their time in the soil and avoid surfacing more than absolutely necessary. You are interested in the responses of earthworms to various stimuli, and decide to run an experiment to explore their behaviour. Write an hypothesis for each of the following questions:

    (a) How do earthworms respond to light?
    (b) How do earthworms respond to excess moisture?
    (c) How do earthworms respond to temperature?

31. The graph shown below illustrates the number of species of coral found at different temperatures in the ocean. Examine the graph and answer the following questions.

    (a) What biotic and abiotic factors are being examined in this study?
    (b) What is the correlation between the number of species present and the temperature of the ocean? Use the numerical data in the graph to explain your answer.
    (c) The deeper the water in an ocean, the colder the temperature. Given this fact, draw a graph showing the relationship between number of species and depth of ocean. You do not have to add real depth values, but include the same numbers of species as shown in the graph above.

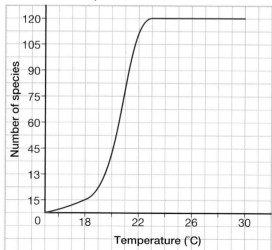

Number of Species Versus Temperature in the Ocean

32. Using one of your hypotheses from question 30, outline an experimental procedure that you could use to test your hypothesis. Be sure to include a control, a list of materials, and a detailed procedure. Based on your present knowledge, what would you expect to find if you ran the experiment as you outlined it above? Explain your answer in a presentation to the class.

33. Make a sketch comparing the polyp and medusa body forms found in Cnidarians.

34. Which part of a moss is roughly equivalent to the fronds of a fern plant? Explain your answer.

35. Design and sketch an imaginary animal using your knowledge of the animal kingdom. Indicate the animal's symmetry, and whether it is coelomate or acoelomate, vertebrate or invertebrate. Describe its method of locomotion and source of food.

36. Make a chart comparing the characteristics of animals in five different phyla. Give a specific example of an animal in each phylum, including its genus, order, and class.

37. Copy the diagram below showing alternation of generations and add the labels indicated by each letter.

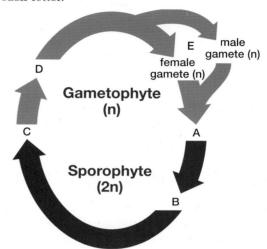

38. Make a simple sketch showing the life cycle of a moss. Use the following labels: gametophyte, sporophyte, haploid, diploid, meiosis, sperm, egg, fertilization, zygote, spores.

39. Use a diagram or a chart to compare the spore-bearing structures of ferns with the seed-bearing structures of gymnosperms.

40. Coral reefs have many different roles, including providing homes to many different marine organisms and protecting nearby shorelines from erosion. Unfortunately, coral reefs are being damaged and destroyed at a high rate. Create a consequences map (similar to a concept map but showing related consequences that arise from a single event) outlining the possible sequence of events that might occur when a section of coral reef is permanently damaged by a storm. Be sure to include the effects on ocean life, nearby shorelines, and humans who collect food from the reef.

41. Make a list of all of the possible roles that insects play in ecosystems around the world. Based on your list, what would happen to different plants and animals if all the insects in the world were to die suddenly? Explain your answers.

42. The numbers of freshwater fishes species in North America is declining. There are many different reasons for this, but three of the main threats to their survival are (a) run-off from agricultural land; (b) the presence of dams and other water diverting structures; and (c) competition for resources from introduced (non-native) species of fishes. Explain how and why these three different events have a negative impact on the survival of freshwater fishes. Choose one of the threats and think about how you could develop a solution. What impacts would your proposed the solution have on humans? and on fishes? Explain your answer.

After you complete this Issue Analysis,

- Assess your report and presentation based on how clearly your information was conveyed;
- Assess your strategy for protecting your species based on the response from your classmates;
- Assess your research skills during the development of your strategy. Did you improve?

Conserving Biodiversity

Background

The northern riffleshell (*Epioblasma torulosa rangiana*) is a small freshwater mussel that lives in swift-flowing streams. Thirty years and more ago, when your parents were children, these mussels were commonly found in rivers connected to Lake Erie and Lake St. Clair. Today, they survive only in low numbers in a 40 km stretch of the Sydenham River in Ontario, and within a few years this subspecies may disappear completely from Canada.

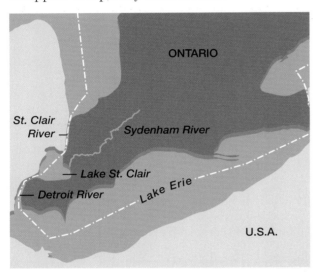

Does it matter if a small, rare, and obscure type of mussel becomes extinct? To answer this question, you need to consider the reasons why a species has declined in numbers. For example, the northern riffleshell lives mainly in highly oxygenated riffle areas of rivers or streams. Its distribution in North America has been reduced by more than 95% due to a decline in the quality of stream habitats. Table 1 lists some human activities and their effects on stream quality.

All species are connected to their environment by ecological processes such as succession and nutrient cycles, so the disappearance of any species is a sign of broader environmental changes. These changes, in turn, affect other species, perhaps including humans. For example, other endangered riffle species found in southern Ontario rivers include two species of molluscs, nine species of fish, and two species of turtles.

Table 1
Factors affecting stream quality

Activity	Effect on streams
logging and construction	increases the silt and water volume in watersheds carried into streams; alters water temperature; damages stream bed habitat
run-off of toxic chemicals from farmland and tree plantations	kills aquatic organisms
addition of sewage and industrial wastes	kills some organisms; adds nutrients; reduces oxygen content of water
introduction of alien species	reduces populations of some indigenous species
acid precipitation	alters water pH; reduces populations of some aquatic species

Over 300 species of Canadian plants and animals are already extinct or threatened with extinction. You will analyze the issue of declining biodiversity by presenting a case study of one or more species threatened with extinction. Your analysis will answer the question: Does it matter if a species becomes extinct? You will also plan and carry out an activity designed to help prevent the loss of the species you have studied.

Plan and Present

1. In small groups or individually, choose an endangered species or a group of species to study. Your analysis should answer the following questions.

   - What is the scientific name and taxonomic classification of the species?
   - What is the estimated population size of the species?
   - Where does it live (a) in Canada and (b) elsewhere in the world?
   - What type of habitat does it occupy?
   - What are its feeding and breeding habits?

- What are the main causes of its decline in numbers?
- What is the value of this species and why?
- What can be done to reverse the decline in numbers and remove the threat of extinction?

2. As part of your research, consider the following ideas.

- Some species may be more important than others because of their role in the environment. For example, some species influence the survival of a large number of other species. They may be a significant source of food for several predators, or alter the vegetation and therefore alter food and shelter for other organisms.

- The loss of some species can have a direct economic impact on people. For example, production of fruits in orchards may depend on only one or two species of pollinating insects. Without these insects, there would be no fruit harvest.

- Some species have unique genetic characteristics that may have important applications in medicine, agriculture, or pollution control. For example, the bark of the Pacific yew contains drugs that help in the treatment of ovarian and breast cancer.

- The loss of a species in one place can have consequences far away. For example, a large percentage of the world's coral reefs are in danger of destruction. The reefs are home to a huge variety of species, including the newly hatched fry of many large fish that live in the open ocean as adults. Without the coral reefs, these open sea fish may decline or disappear.

- Isolated species with small populations, such as those living on islands, are more vulnerable to extinction than species with widespread populations.

- The current rate of extinction is many times higher than normal. Today's losses are caused mainly by human activities such as habitat destruction, pollution, and the introduction of foreign species from one part of the world to another.

- Apart from their direct or indirect value to people, species should be protected from extinction for aesthetic or ethical reasons.

3. Use concept maps, tables, flow charts, or other graphic organizers to record and illustrate your findings.

4. Use the information you have gathered to prepare a report answering the questions listed above. Your presentation may be in any suitable form you choose. Use data to back up your arguments.

5. Plan a strategy you could use to help protect the endangered species you have studied. This might include habitat restoration, public education, and lobbying of politicians or industries for changes in legislation or business practices. Local community strategies may include writing letters to newspapers or producing flyers. Organizations that can help with ideas or resources include:
Canadian Environmental Law Association (CELA)
Canadian Parks and Wilderness Society (CPAWS)
Nature Conservancy Canada
World Wildlife Fund Canada (WWF)

6. Carry out your plan as a class or in small groups.

7. As a class, design two rubrics: one to assess your presentations on your species and the other to assess your protection strategy.

Evaluate the Results

1. How would you decide whether species at risk of extinction in Canada are any more or less important to protect than species in other parts of the world (such as those in tropical forests)?

2. Based on the presentations, do you think some species are more important to save from extinction than others? Explain your rationale.

3. Use your rubrics to evaluate your presentation and the success of your action strategy.

4. How did your understanding of science help you analyze this issue?

UNDERSTANDING CONCEPTS

True-False

In your notebook, indicate whether each statement is true or false. Correct each false statement.

1. All organisms are currently classified in one of five kingdoms.

2. Bacteria and protists are eukaryotes.

3. Viruses are not classified as living organisms.

4. The system of using a two-word name for each species is called trinomial nomenclature.

5. Archaea is a phylum of prokaryotes that live in extreme environments.

6. Round bacterial cells are called bacilli.

7. Gram-positive bacteria have thick cell walls and stain purple with Gram stain.

8. Chemoautotrophs obtain energy by breaking apart chemical bonds in inorganic compounds.

9. Bacterial cells can divide by mitosis but not meiosis.

10. Bacteria reproduce sexually by a process called conjugation.

11. Protozoa are heterotrophic protists.

12. Red algae are microscopic protists responsible for producing red tides.

13. Acrasiomycota and Myxomycota are two groups of slime moulds.

14. Fungi are multicellular autotrophs.

15. Penicillin is a deuteromycote fungus.

16. The diploid generation of a plant is called the gametophyte.

17. Mosses, liverworts, and ferns are all examples of non-vascular plants.

18. The gametophyte of a fern is called a prothallus.

19. Platyhelminthes have three layers of cells and no coelom.

20. Annelids have three layers of cells and no coelom.

21. Squid and cuttlefish are examples of crustaceans.

22. Sea squirts are examples of chordates.

Multiple Choice

In your notebook, write the letter of the best answer for each of the following questions.

23. Bacteria
    (a) can only reproduce asexually
    (b) occur in three shapes — round, cube-shaped, and spiral
    (c) may be autotrophs or heterotrophs
    (d) are eukaryotes
    (e) are commonly known as "extremophiles"

24. Plasmids
    (a) are small blobs of plasma
    (b) are an important method of producing genetic recombination
    (c) help amoebae to move and capture food
    (d) contain genes that are different from those found in the chromosome
    (e) can split from the bacterial chromosome and rejoin it

25. Diatoms
    (a) have rigid cell walls with an outer layer of silica
    (b) have two flagellae
    (c) are mainly fresh-water organisms
    (d) are prokaryotes
    (e) increase in size at each generation

26. A fungus is an example of a
    (a) photoautotroph
    (b) chemoautotroph
    (c) photoheterotroph
    (d) chemoheterotroph
    (e) none of the above

27. Mushrooms
    (a) are the basidiocarps of club fungi
    (b) produce spores
    (c) are made of compacted hyphae
    (d) none of the above
    (e) all of the above

28. Bryophytes
    (a) are the only group of plants in which the gametophyte is larger than the sporophyte
    (b) are vascular plants
    (c) produce specialized spore-bearing structures called strobili
    (d) are adapted to very dry conditions
    (e) are the most diverse group of plants

29. Conifers
    (a) have small, inconspicuous flowers
    (b) produce spores
    (c) are examples of bryophytes
    (d) are examples of gymnosperms
    (e) have co-evolved with specialized pollinators such as insects

30. Jellyfish are in the phylum
   (a) Porifera
   (b) Cnidaria
   (c) Platyhelminthes
   (d) Gnetophyta
   (e) Cephalochordata

31. Molluscs
   (a) are acoelomates
   (b) have a coelom that originates from a split in the mesoderm layer
   (c) have a coelom that forms from pouches in the embryonic gut
   (d) are all characterized by a large external shell
   (e) include segmented worms

32. Arthropods have
   (a) eight legs
   (b) a hard exoskeleton
   (c) no coelom
   (d) a single body opening
   (e) ten legs

Short Answers

In your notebook, write a sentence or a short paragraph to answer each of the following questions.

33. What is a halophile, and where would you look for one?

34. Describe two differences between Gram-positive and Gram-negative bacteria.

35. What is the main difference between a eukaryote and a prokaryote?

36. Define the term "chemoautotroph."

37. What is a retrovirus?

38. The taxonomic table shown here has four errors. Identify each error and write the correction.

Taxon	Example	Organisms included in this taxon
Kingdom	Animalia	shark, horse, oyster, frog, cougar, lynx, bobcat
Phylum	Chordata	horse, oyster, frog, cougar, lynx, bobcat
Class	Mammalia	horse, frog, cougar, lynx, bobcat
Order	Carnivora	frog, cougar, lynx, bobcat
Family	Felidae	cougar, lynx, bobcat
Genus	*Lynx*	lynx, cougar
Species	*Lynx canadensis*	lynx

39. Give three reasons why scientists do not generally use common names to identify a particular species.

40. Give an example of homologous characteristics. What is the significance of these characteristics?

41. "Diversity between species begins with diversity within a species." Briefly explain what is meant by this sentence, using an example.

42. Why has there been an increase in the number of bacterial strains that have resistance to antibiotics?

43. Describe an example of symbiotic bacteria.

44. This diagram illustrates three protists. In which group is each organism classified (algae, protozoa, or fungus-like protists)? Explain your answer.

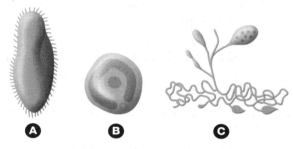

Ⓐ   Ⓑ   Ⓒ

45. Foraminifera have shells made of calcium carbonate. Why are they classified as amoebae?

46. Name two groups of unicellular algae and two of multicellular algae.

47. Describe what is meant by the term "mycorrhiza."

48. The menu of a gourmet restaurant lists a type of underground fungus. What is the common name and classification of this edible fungus?

49. Describe two adaptations of plants that help them survive in dry conditions.

50. The complete life cycle of a plant includes two generations that alternate in a regular sequence. Name each generation and describe its characteristics.

51. Name an example of a group of plants that has (a) no vascular tissue or seeds; (b) vascular tissue but no seeds; (c) both vascular tissue and seeds.

52. Name two phyla of animals that have a single body opening through which food enters and waste matter leaves.

53. Name two phyla of animals that are mainly or completely marine and two that are mainly terrestrial.

54. This figure illustrates the body plans of two organisms. Copy the diagram into your notebook, identify which is a polyp and which is a medusa, and label the parts. Give an example of each type of animal. In which phylum are they classified?

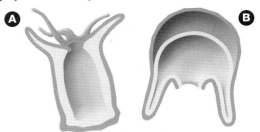

55. How does reproduction differ in pines and ground pines?

56. How would you distinguish between diatoms and dinoflagellates?

57. Suggest one or more reasons why very few fossils of bryophytes have been found.

58. In the life cycle of a moss, where does the chromosome number change from 2n to n, and vice versa?

59. Although viruses can reproduce, they are not considered to be living organisms. Why is that?

60. Suggest why sponges are able to regenerate new bodies from a few cells while humans are not, with reference to differences in degrees of body organization.

61. Name three types of evidence indicating that humans should be classified in the same (a) phylum as other chordates, (b) class as other mammals, and (c) family as chimpanzees and gorillas.

62. The classification of the Kingdom Protista is artificial. Explain what is meant by this statement, using examples.

INQUIRY

63. All organisms use the same coding of DNA bases to produce amino acids (which combine to form proteins). Degrees of similarity in the sequence of their DNA bases indicate how recently organisms descended from a common ancestor and, therefore, how closely they are related. The table on the right shows the degrees of difference in the DNA base sequence for six pairs of species. Interpret these data and describe in your own words what they suggest about human evolution.

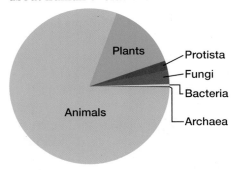

64. The circle graph shown above represents Earth's six kingdoms. Each degree of the circle graph is equal to 10 000 species. Archaea represent $\frac{1}{20}$ of a degree, and Bacteria represent 1 degree. List the approximate number of species for each of the six kingdoms. What approximate percent of the total life forms on Earth are in each kingdom? Why are these numbers approximate?

Pairs of animals	Percent difference in DNA base code sequences
human/chimpanzee	2.5
human/gibbon	5.1
human/African green monkey	9.0
human/capuchin monkey	15.8
human/lemur	42.0
mouse/rat	30.0

65. Design an experiment to test the effectiveness of four commercial antibacterial soaps. Make sure that your procedural steps are complete. Write out your hypothesis and your predictions. What variables will you test? What variables will you control?

66. Bacteria from an infected person were tested for their sensitivity to three antibiotics A, B, and C. Based on the results of the tests, the patient's physician decides to prescribe antibiotic A. Given this information, describe the test results that would lead to this conclusion for the doctor. Draw the results of the test procedure and describe what happened during the test.

67. Why do you suppose many people who own aquariums add snails to them? Design an experiment to test your ideas. What is your hypothesis? What predictions do you have? Write out the procedural steps you would follow to run your experiment. What data would you expect to collect if your hypothesis is supported? What data would you expect to collect if your hypothesis is not supported?

68. Outline the steps you would take to calculate the approximate number of spores in a puffball fungus with a circumference of 10 cm.

COMMUNICATING

69. Growing and distributing some plants is promoted by governments. At the same time, growing other plants or producing certain biologically engineered crops is restricted or made illegal by governments. Discuss the arguments for and against such policies.

70. We try to reflect evolutionary relationships through a system of classifying living things. Using an example, explain why you can say that the members of one group are more closely related to one another than they are to the members of another group.

71. Use reference books and web sites to find the scientific names of ten species of animals and ten species of plants. What is the basis and meaning for each genus and species name?

72. Make a table to compare the characteristics of archaea and bacteria.

73. Many species of organisms are in danger of extinction. Some plants are being preserved as seeds in botanical collections, and some rare animals are being bred in captivity in zoos. Carry out research on one of these conservation approaches and compare its advantages and disadvantages versus preserving species in the wild.

74. Make a table to compare the characteristics of flatworms and segmented worms.

75. To what phyla might the fungus in the photograph belong? What other information would you need before you could confidently classify this species in its correct phylum?

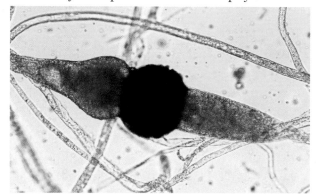

MAKING CONNECTIONS

76. How might people be affected if all conifers became extinct?

77. Which algae do you think are at the base of more marine food chains, unicellular forms or multicellular forms? Explain your answer. How might human activities on land end up affecting these organisms at the base of the marine food chain?

78. Suppose there were no system of scientific classification for flowering plants. What might be the consequences if plants only had common names?

79. Choose one of the six kingdoms you have studied in this unit and describe what direct significance the members of this kingdom have in your life.

80. Should people be as concerned about mosses becoming extinct as they are about whales becoming extinct? Explain.

81. Compare the role of free water in the reproduction of mosses and flowering plants.

82. Antibiotics are obtained from certain species of micro-organisms. Explain why antibiotic-producing organisms might evolve in nature.

COURSE CHALLENGE

As you continue to prepare for your Biology Course Challenge, consider these ideas about biodiversity and the characteristics of organisms.

- How could different kinds of organisms affect forensic data?
- Which characteristics of organisms would impact on a forensic scenario?
- How could you use your knowledge of organisms and their life cycles as a clock in a forensic study?

UNIT PROJECT PREP

Read pages 612–613 before starting this unit.

- Begin making a list of as many plant-based industries as possible.

- Consider the societal implications of these industries. Compile an ongoing list of concerns.

- Collect different sources that you can use once you choose your industry.

Plants: Anatomy, Growth, and Functions

On May 18, 1980, Mount St. Helens in the state of Washington erupted, devastating the nearby ecosystems. The area surrounding the volcano was completely devoid of life. This photograph of the area, taken several years later, shows plants making a comeback as life returns to the region. The bare surface around the volcano provides a reminder of how the surface of early Earth must have appeared before the existence of plants.

Our biosphere has not always been the same as we know it today. Life-giving oxygen did not begin to accumulate in the atmosphere until 2500 million years ago. For another 2000 million years, only the oceans held organisms capable of using energy and reproducing their own kind. Exposed rock was abundant, but it was barren. Planet Earth was a world without plants.

About 500 million years ago, the ancestors of plants began to evolve in the oceans. In another 50 million years, plants began to colonize the previously barren rock. Today, living blankets of green cover vast portions of Earth's land, which supports over six billion humans. We owe our survival to the presence of plants. Through their own life functions and their interactions with other species, plants sustain the biosphere.

In this Unit you will focus on the anatomy and physiology of plants. You will also learn how people have altered plants and their environment to make use of plants and plant products.

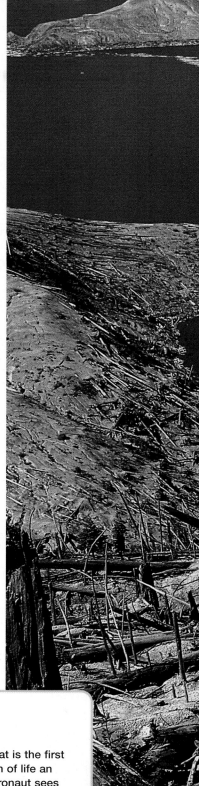

What is the first sign of life an astronaut sees on returning to Earth?

CHAPTER 14

Plant Characteristics and Functions

Reflecting Questions

- What are the parts of a plant and how do they function?
- How do water and food move around in a plant?
- How does a plant grow?

Few animals live past 100 years, but advanced age is not at all unusual in the plant kingdom. Unlike animals such as humans, plants continue to grow throughout their entire life cycle. This ability is only one of the identifying characteristics of plants.

Plants can be thought of as self-reliant chemical factories. For example, the appearance of new leaves in the spring is evidence that a living tree can collect materials from its external environment and use those materials to manufacture the new substances that it uses for growth. Perhaps the most important substance used by trees and other plants is the food they produce called glucose. The tree's cells release energy from glucose by cellular respiration, and use the energy to build new substances. The tree uses these new substances for life functions, such as repair and growth.

In this chapter, you will learn how plants use materials from the environment for their growth and survival. Some plants, such as mosses and liverworts, do not have a sophisticated system of transporting water and nutrients within their bodies. Other plants, which make up the greatest number of species and the greatest biomass on Earth, have systems that transport water and nutrients between the parts of the plant. The majority of plants have developed specific structures such as leaves, stems, and roots to collect materials from the environment, manufacture food for the plant's growth, and transport materials throughout the plant. Materials are transported through specialized cells that are found in each of the leaves, stems, and roots.

The rings on the tree stump in the large photograph on the next page show that the tree was 600 years old when it was cut down. It is not necessary to cut down a tree in order to measure its age, however — a core sample can be taken instead.

Chapter
Contents

EXPECTATIONS

- Distinguish between non-vascular and vascular plants and between gymnosperms and angiosperms, based on structural differences.

- Understand differences between monocots and dicots.

Figure 14.1 Scientists believe that terrestrial plants have descended from a type of green algae.

Scientists think it is probable that vascular and non-vascular plants have common ancestors with one group of the plant-like protists, the green algae (see Figure 14.1). Members of the plant kingdom have characteristics that they share with algae. For example, both plants and algae use starch as their primary food resource, they have cellulose in their cell walls, and they use chlorophylls *a* and *b* during photosynthesis. Protists, which can be unicellular or multicellular organisms, have no roots, stems, or leaves. Algae do not need to develop sophisticated systems to transport nutrients and water because they live in a medium of water and dissolved nutrients. The algae absorb nutrients and water directly from the external environment, and the material diffuses from one cell to another. There are no specialized cells to move materials within the organism.

In contrast, members of the plant kingdom live in terrestrial environments, from wetlands to deserts and from tundra to tropical rain forests. They have adapted many ways to survive these environments, such as protecting their reproductive cells and having more sophisticated ways of transporting material both to and from their environment and within the plant.

In Chapter 13, you studied the different groups of plants in the plant kingdom and the general characteristics of each group. Now, you will examine how plants are classified by their structures.

◀◀ REWIND

Turn to Chapter 13, Section 13.2, to review the differences between non-vascular and vascular plants, gymnosperms and angiosperms, and monocots and dicots.

Non-vascular Plants

Non-vascular plants, such as the mosses, liverworts, and hornworts (shown in Figure 14.2), require a moist environment for two reasons. First, they cannot reproduce unless a film of moisture is available to carry gametes between plants. Second, they lack **vascular tissue**. That is, they have no system of tubes to carry water and dissolved substances through the plant.

Although some non-vascular plants appear to have root-like, stem-like, and leaf-like parts or structures, these are not true roots, stems, and leaves because they do not contain vascular tissue. The root-like structures anchor the plant but do not absorb water for other parts. The stem-like structures hold the leaf-like parts up to the light, but they cannot transport food or water. The leaf-like structures carry out photosynthesis and make food, but the dissolved food must diffuse to the other parts of the plant.

Non-vascular plants are restricted in size. Even in a very moist environment, they cannot grow very tall because they have no specialized vascular tissue to support them or to transport water upward. Non-vascular plants play only a minor role in providing food or other materials for people. Sphagnum moss, for example, is used as a base for flower arrangements, used as a source of organic material for potting and gardening soils, and, in countries such as Ireland, "mined" and cut into blocks as fuel. The princess pine, despite its name, is a non-vascular plant that is used in winter flower arrangements. All trees and many of our food plants are vascular, as are the food plants used to nourish domestic animals such as poultry and cattle.

BIO FACT

Peat makes up almost 10% of Ireland's primary energy consumption. Raw peat is formed into pellets, sod, and briquettes. These fuel products yield from 7 to 22 MJ/kg of raw peat found in Ireland. In comparison, coal has a value of about 25 MJ/kg and wood has a value of about 12 MJ/kg.

Vascular Plants

Some plants developed a specific system of vascular tissue to transport materials within the plant. Many early forms of vascular plants are now extinct. Only a few of these groups of plants still exist today — they are the whisk ferns, club mosses, horsetails, and ferns.

Figure 14.2 Mosses, liverworts, and hornworts are non-vascular plants.

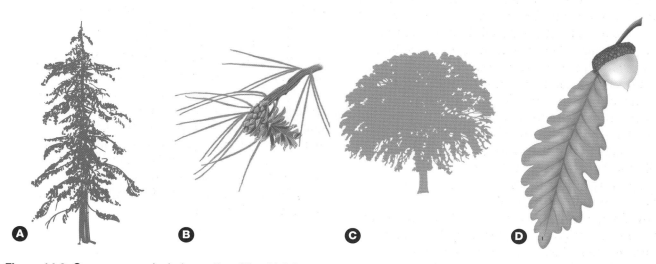

Figure 14.3 Gymnosperms include conifers (A), which have specialized leaves and cones (B). Angiosperms, such as oak trees (C) have leaves and acorns (D).

Figure 14.4 Gymnosperms and angiosperms produce seeds.

Gymnosperm or Angiosperm?

All trees living today are either gymnosperms or angiosperms (Figure 14.3 on the previous page and Figure 14.4). The "sperm" ending indicates that both groups grow from seed. A seed is a complex multicellular structure that contains an embryo and a food supply (Figure 14.5). The embryo includes an immature root, an immature shoot, and one or two "seed leaves" or cotyledons. Inside the seed, the food supply consists of nutritive tissue made up of starch, oils, and other molecules needed for development of the embryo. As you learned in Chapter 13, gymnosperms have seeds without a seed coat and are attached to the scales of cones.

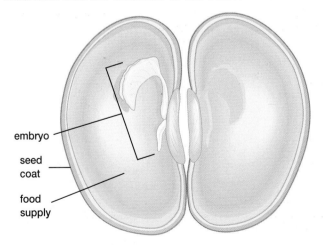

Figure 14.5 A seed contains an embryo and a food supply.

Many gymnosperms, such as conifers, are adapted to thrive in environments with long cold winters and low amounts of nutrients in the soil. Gymnosperms dominate in large parts of Canada, northern Europe, and northern Asia.

About 67% of Canada's forest area is made up of softwoods, a forestry term for gymnosperms.

The gymnosperms contribute a large portion of Canada's forestry exports, in total valued at almost $45 billion.

Coniferous trees are used for pulp and paper, lumber, wood pulp, furniture, other construction materials, fuel for heating, and many other products.

Figure 14.6 Gymnosperms are important to Canada's economy.

The boreal forest, which is characterized by conifers, is the largest biome in Canada. In addition, gymnosperms are vital to Canada's economy. Gymnosperms provides fibre for making paper and wood for building materials. Figure 14.6 illustrates the importance of gymnosperms to Canada's economy.

The total number of angiosperm species is far greater than the total number of gymnosperm species. Angiosperms as a group are more diverse in structure than gymnosperms. As well, angiosperms are so widely distributed around the world that their total biomass exceeds that of gymnosperms. Thus, angiosperms dominate many parts of the biosphere and they are important as a source of food for many organisms, including humans.

Angiosperms are also known as flowering plants. Flowers are the angiosperm's reproductive organs, which mature into a seed-containing fruit. The extra protection of the surrounding fruit gives angiosperm seeds a strong adaptive advantage over gymnosperm seeds, which lack an enclosing fruit. Once gymnosperm seeds fall or are blown out of their cones, they have only a thin cover to protect them. As well, the fruits of angiosperms are adapted to facilitate seed dispersal. Some fruits are tasty (like apples), and the seeds are dispersed when the fruit is eaten. Some are sticky (like burrs) and are dispersed in the feathers or fur of animals. Others are shaped for flight, such as maple keys, and are dispersed by the wind.

The group of plants we call angiosperms includes trees, grasses, vegetables, wildflowers, and herbs. All angiosperms produce fruits, many of which are edible. In addition, the roots, leaves, and stems of many angiosperms provide food for humans and other animals.

The number of angiosperm species is so large that biologists needed a way to group them for study purposes. They found that all angiosperm seeds have either one or two (never more) embryonic seed leaves, or cotyledons, inside the seed, and agreed to use this difference as a basis for classification. The two major angiosperm classes are the monocots, which have one cotyledon, and the dicots, which have two cotyledons. Figure 14.7 shows the major differences between monocots and dicots, including some of the structural differences in the leaves, stems, and roots.

Monocots

About 10% of all monocots have **woody** (tough and rigid) stems. Examples of woody monocots include palms and bamboos. Such species are grown for ornamental purposes in Canada, but only where the climate is mild. Most woody monocots grow in warmer climates and are sources of food such as dates, coconuts, bananas, palm oil, and sugar. Sugar cane, a woody monocot, is a type of grass. Few monocots are suitable to use as building materials. However, the hollow stems of bamboo provide a light, strong structural material often used in Asia for scaffolding and furniture. In contrast, the stems of palm trees are heavy and crumbly, with little strength for their weight. Bamboo shoots are used as food by humans and by giant pandas (see Figure 14.8).

Figure 14.8 Bamboo shoots and roots are the only food giant pandas can eat in the wild.

	Seed leaves	Veins in leaves	Vascular bundles in stems	Flower parts
Monocots	one cotyledon 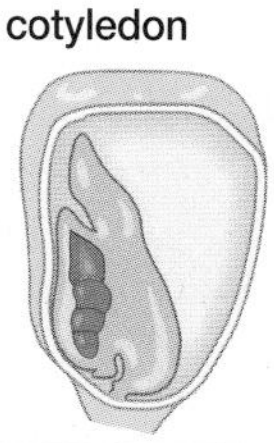	usually parallel 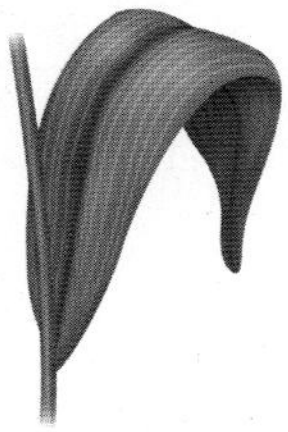	scattered 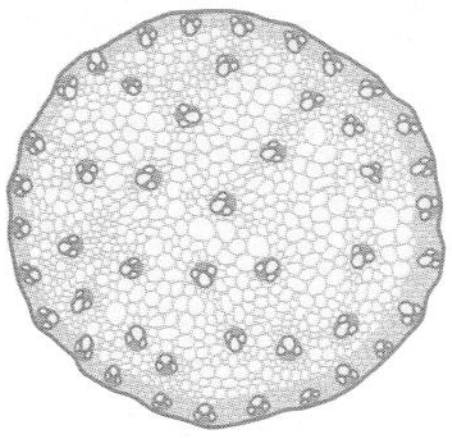	multiples of threes 
Dicots	two cotyledons 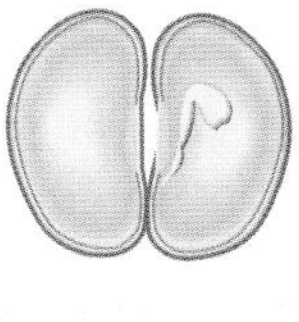	usually netlike 	arranged in ring 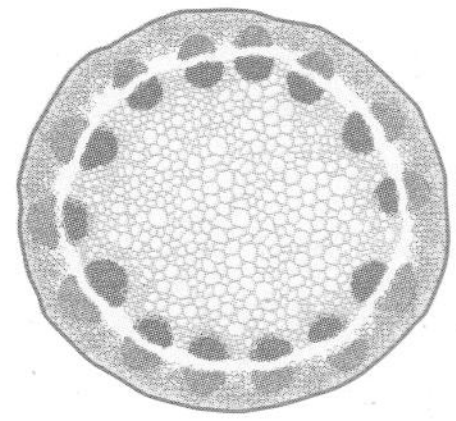	multiples of fours and fives 

Figure 14.7 Distinguishing characteristics of monocots and dicots

Two monocots, bananas and their near relatives, plantains, are a major source of carbohydrates for many of the world's people. During the 1980s, agronomists feared that a fungal infection would wipe out these important food plants. They were able to develop a new disease-resistant banana variety. This proved to be much more difficult than developing a new wheat variety, for instance, because cultivated bananas and plantains do not contain seeds. Why do you think this is so?

Web LINK

Researchers established a banana breeding program by going back to early wild varieties, which do contain seeds. However, developing plump, sweet, cultivated bananas from wild ones presents a considerable challenge. How do researchers overcome the challenge? Go to the web site shown below to find the answer. Go to **Science Resources**, then to **BIOLOGY 11** to find out where to go next.
www.school.mcgrawhill.ca/resources/

Investigation 14 • A

SKILL FOCUS

Performing and recording

Analyzing and interpreting

Communicating results

Comparing Monocots and Dicots

In this investigation, you will compare the parts of monocot and dicot plants. Apart from differences in their number of cotyledons, monocots and dicots differ in the appearance of their flowers and leaves. In monocots, the flower parts (such as petals) occur in groups of four or five (or multiples of four or five), while dicots have parts that occur in groups of three (or multiples of three). As shown below, the vascular tissue in the leaves of monocots is found in parallel veins; vascular tissue in dicot leaves is found in branching veins.

Monocot leaves (A) have parallel veins. Dicot leaves (B) have branching veins.

Pre-lab Question

■ What characteristics distinguish a monocot and a dicot? Refer to Figure 14.7 on page 525 to review these characteristics.

■ Are there any differences in growth patterns between monocots and dicots?

Problem

Use live plant specimens and photographs of plants to determine whether a plant is a monocot or a dicot.

Prediction

Predict which external characteristics of angiosperms can be used to determine if the plant is a monocot or a dicot.

CAUTION: Wash your thoroughly after the investigation. Use care when cutting the seeds. Scalpel blades are very sharp, so follow your teacher's instructions.

Materials

pre-soaked seeds of beans, corn, peas, etc.
stem, leaves, and flowers of various plants (such as onion, herbs, house plants, and others)
magnifying glass
sketching materials
scalpel

Procedure

1. Dissect one sample of each type of seed to find out whether its embryo has one or two cotyledons. Alternatively, if you let the seeds germinate, the number of cotyledons

Most monocots are non-woody or **herbaceous** — that is, their stems are soft and fleshy. Ornamental examples include orchids, lilies, tulips, and other spring bulbs. In terms of food for land animals, the most important monocots are the grasses. Cows and rabbits eat grasses, and so do you. However, there is a difference in what plant parts are eaten. Rabbits and cows obtain energy from the leaves of grass. They are able to do this because both have bacteria in their digestive systems that produce enzymes able to cut the "crossties" in cellulose molecules, and thereby release glucose units. (This relationship between bacteria and animals such as rabbits and cows is one that benefits both species; it is called mutualism.)

Humans do not have bacteria that can digest grass blades (leaves), even if the leaves are boiled or chopped. Our bodies cannot produce the enzymes needed to break down the cellulose of grass leaves into simple glucose units. We do, however, eat the seeds of grasses as you will learn next.

will be obvious once the young plants emerge from the ground.

2. Obtain samples of stems, flowers, and leaves of various plants. Use their characteristics to classify the plants as monocots or dicots.

3. Sketch an example of each structure you examined. Identify as many differences among the samples as you can.

4. Each of the plants shown below is the floral emblem of a Canadian province or territory. Look at the photos and determine whether the floral emblems are monocots or dicots. Use Figure 14.7 (on page 525) to help you in your classification.

Post-lab Questions

1. What differences did you observe in the external appearance of monocot and dicot plants?

2. Which class dominates the official list of floral emblems? Identify the province or territory for each floral emblem.

Conclude and Apply

3. Create a chart or table listing the differences you noted between monocots and dicots. Name the most significant differences.

4. Develop a hypothesis to test whether or not there are any functional differences between monocots and dicots.

trillium

wild rose

prairie crocus (pasque flower)

violet

dogwood tree

prairie lily

blue flag

pitcher plant

lady slipper

purple saxifrage

fireweed

mountain avens

mayflower

Figure 14.9 Important monocot species in many countries include rice (A), wheat (B), and corn (C).

Humans can digest most of the matter in the seeds of grass plants such as wheat, corn, and rice (see Figure 14.9). Each of these seeds has large stores of carbohydrates, along with smaller amounts of protein and oils. Wild grasses produce seeds much smaller than those of today's prairie wheat. Varieties have been developed that produce more usable human food per plant. As well, hybridization techniques have produced new varieties of wheat, oats, and barley that are both more climate-tolerant and disease-resistant than earlier varieties.

> **>> FAST FORWARD**
>
> Turn to Chapter 15, Section 15.2, to learn about the technologies for increasing production or quality of crops.

Dicots

Most of Canada's native tree species are dicots. Some of these deciduous trees are important economic resources in Canada (see Figure 14.10). Most native wildflower species are also dicots (see Figure 14.11) and a typical salad contains a diversity of dicots such as lettuce, tomatoes, radishes, and sunflower sprouts. Only the onions are monocots. The staple foods of many cultures, past and present, are dicots — yams, potatoes, rutabaga, and cabbage are all rich in starch. Bean seeds are rich in protein, while bean pods are rich in vitamins.

About 15% of Canada's forest area is made up of hardwoods, a forestry term for angiosperm trees.

The wholesale value of Canada's maple products is about $150 million.

Deciduous trees contributed a portion of Canada's forestry exports, in total valued at almost $45 billion.

Deciduous trees are used to make furniture, hockey sticks, fuel for heating, carvings, and many other products.

Figure 14.10 Deciduous trees are important to Canada's economy.

Figure 14.11 Most native wildflowers are dicots.

Figure 14.12 Which produce are dicots?

Canadians in Biology

Naturalist and Artist

Many know him best for his animal art, but Robert Bateman thinks of himself as a naturalist. He spends just as much time studying and painting rocks and plants as he does on the animals that are featured in most of his paintings.

Robert Bateman's painting of a Northern saw-whet owl

When Robert Bateman was in high school, he and two friends used to go on secret bird-watching expeditions. Why secret? "We were afraid the other fellows would laugh at us," he says. In order to locate the birds, the three friends had to learn how to identify the birds' habitats: the trees and other plants where the birds lived. Inevitably, they also learned about the other animals that

shared the birds' habitats. Bateman chose to study geology at university, "because I knew there would be lots of field trips — I would get outdoors." He went on to become a teacher of art in his home province of Ontario, painting whenever he could find time. By the time he reached his 40s, he was able to earn his living solely through artistic endeavours.

Robert Bateman believes that the biological knowledge gained by observing the organisms that share our world could be used by high school graduates throughout their lives. When speaking in public, he urges people to go outdoors and "meet the neighbours." Plants would make a good starting point because they are much easier to observe and identify than birds or other animals. Even if you are a city dweller, you may have access to natural areas set aside by your city's parks department. In addition, some public gardens have signs identifying the different kinds of plants.

Knowing the names of the plants around you can be a great source of personal satisfaction. For example, do you know the names of the native and ornamental plants that grow near your home? What about the summer weeds? Nuisance or not, they are also part of the biosphere.

To become familiar with plants in your community you might organize your own field trip, perhaps with a friend, or relative. You can borrow a field guide to native plants from a public library. You might want to take a bird guide along as well. Bird-watching is now one of the fastest growing activities in North America. When you return the guides, borrow one of Robert Bateman's books from the library. Each one consists mainly of pictures, and each picture includes meticulous renderings of plants and animals from around the world.

What factors can contribute to diversity among organisms? Vascular plants may be either angiosperms or gymnosperms, and are grouped according to the number of embryonic leaves the seeds have. Factors that can contribute to their diversity are summarized in the Figure 14.13. How does studying various structures of plants and other organisms help us to learn about their functions?

CONCEPT ORGANIZER   Predicting the Outcome

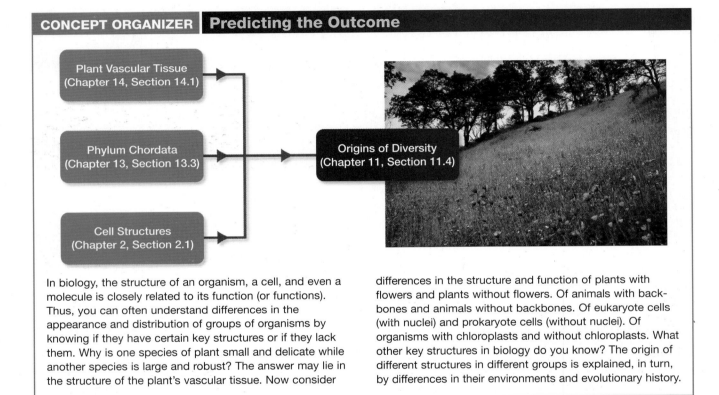

In biology, the structure of an organism, a cell, and even a molecule is closely related to its function (or functions). Thus, you can often understand differences in the appearance and distribution of groups of organisms by knowing if they have certain key structures or if they lack them. Why is one species of plant small and delicate while another species is large and robust? The answer may lie in the structure of the plant's vascular tissue. Now consider differences in the structure and function of plants with flowers and plants without flowers. Of animals with backbones and animals without backbones. Of eukaryote cells (with nuclei) and prokaryote cells (without nuclei). Of organisms with chloroplasts and without chloroplasts. What other key structures in biology do you know? The origin of different structures in different groups is explained, in turn, by differences in their environments and evolutionary history.

Figure 14.13 How diversity originates

SECTION REVIEW

1. **K/U** What is the main difference between a gymnosperm and an angiosperm? List five examples of each type of plant.

2. **K/U** An onion seed germinates and a single leaf emerges from the soil. Is the onion a monocot or a dicot? What evidence did you use to make your classification?

3. **C** What are some of the differences between monocots and dicots? List them and give examples of plants that show these differences.

4. **K/U** A shopper notices that alfalfa sprouts have two leaves each. Classify alfalfa as either monocot or dicot. What evidence did you use?

5. **I** You are given seeds from an unidentified plant. Outline a procedure that you could use to help you classify the seeds to a major plant group.

UNIT ISSUE PREP

Many industries in Canada are based on resources from various species of gymnosperm and angiosperm. What are some of these industries and what is their value to the Canadian economy? How would you summarize this information for a brief presentation? Who would you be addressing? Would this affect how you present your data? Prepare an outline of your ideas in preparation for your Unit 5 Project.

Vascular Systems

- Understand the basic vascular systems in plants.

- Describe the differences and similarities between xylem and phloem.

Figure 14.14 Vascular tissue makes it possible for water to travel up the 40 m trunk of this tall conifer and for food to travel down to the roots.

Vascular plants have specialized tissue for transporting material from one location to another within the plant, as in the tall tree in Figure 14.14. This vascular tissue consists of an internal system of tubes that transport water and dissolved food throughout the plant.

Humans and all other mammals also possess a "vascular system," which consists of tubes that transport water, dissolved food, and oxygen throughout their bodies. In animals, this mixture is pushed around in the blood by a pump called the heart. How can material move throughout a plant with no heart to pump it? Look for the answer in the following sections.

Vascular Bundles

If you have ever had a "string" of celery stuck in your teeth, you have encountered a **vascular bundle**. These bundles transport material within the plant. In dicot stems, the bundles form a discontinuous ring of vascular bundles. In monocot stems, the vascular bundles are scattered throughout the stem of the plant in no discernible pattern. These patterns are shown in Figure 14.15.

◄◄ REWIND

To review transport tissues and vascular bundles, turn to Chapter 9, Section 9.5.

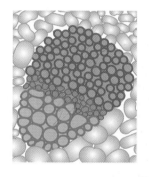
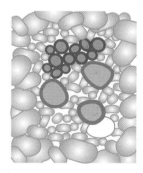

vascular bundles

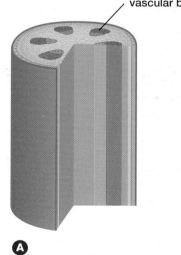
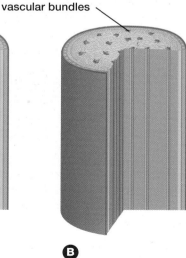

A **B**

Figure 14.15 Locate the vascular bundles in the stem cross-sections of a typical dicot (A) and a typical monocot (B).

The vascular bundles in a stem are continuous, tube-like strands connecting the vascular tissue of the root to the vascular tissue in the leaves. In the root, the vascular tissue forms a central cylinder, or core. In the stem, this cylinder branches out to form several separate bundles. These bundles form a continuous connection through the stem, running up and down between the roots and the leaves.

Xylem Transports Water

The transportation of water is carried out by specialized tissue called xylem in the vascular bundles. In angiosperms, xylem consists of long, mainly hollow tubes formed by the nonliving cell walls of **tracheids** or **vessel elements** (see Figure 14.16.) These structures begin as living cells that grow end-to-end in the immature stem. When the cells mature, their living contents die, leaving the non-living cell walls in place. Fluids pass from one tracheid or vessel element to the next.

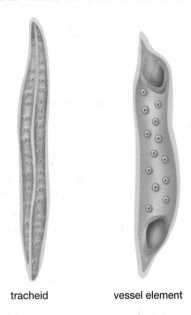

tracheid   vessel element

Figure 14.16 Both tracheids (left) and vessel elements (right) conduct water. The xylem of gymnosperms contains only tracheids, while the xylem of angiosperms contains both tracheids and vessel elements. Water (and anything dissolved in it) passes from one tracheid to the next through "pits," which are thin regions in the adjacent end walls.

◄◄ REWIND

To find out more about xylem and phloem, turn back to Chapter 9, Section 9.5.

Translocation and Phloem

The term **translocation** can mean different things. A few authors use this term as a synonym for transportation. Others use it only for the transport of organic molecules. A few reserve it for the transport of food (specifically sugar) from one plant part to another. The greater precision of this third definition allows us to give the transport of food its own dedicated name. This textbook defines translocation as the transportation of food from one region in a plant part to another region. Translocation is carried out within the specialized tissue called phloem.

The process of translocation is still poorly understood. Several main points concerning how translocation occurs are summarized here:

- Sugary tree sap rises in the spring when there are no leaves from which transpiration can occur. So transpiration-tension cannot be responsible for the movement of dissolved food through phloem.

- Phloem moves food from regions of low concentration to regions of high concentration. Therefore, translocation cannot be explained by simple diffusion, which can only move solutes from regions of high concentration to regions of low concentration.

- Phloem is made of living cells, which use oxygen while they are moving food (see Figure 14.17).

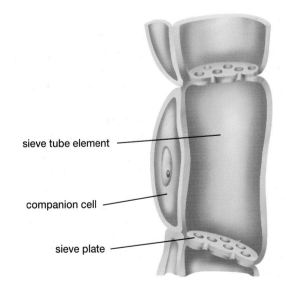

sieve tube element

companion cell

sieve plate

Figure 14.17 The phloem is made up of a companion cell, sieve-tube element, and sieve plate.

Researchers have concluded that translocation is an active process. That is, the living cells of the phloem somehow provide the energy for translocation through their own cellular respiration. Exactly how the phloem moves the dissolved sugars around the plant is not yet understood, and is an ongoing topic of investigation by scientists.

Figure 14.18 illustrates how the structure of phloem differs from that of xylem. Note especially that phloem consists of *living* cells.

You may recall from Chapter 1 that glucose is produced by photosynthesis and is immediately converted to starch and stored in tiny grains within the cell's chloroplasts. You have also learned that starch grains are stored in the cortex cells of the root, and that the phloem transports dissolved food between the leaf and the root. However, starch is insoluble in water, which raises an unavoidable question: what "dissolved food" is being transported by the phloem? The answer: sucrose.

⏸ PAUSE	⏺ RECORD

Recall from Chapter 1 that the structure of sucrose differs from the structure of glucose, even though both are classified as sugars. Glucose is a single sugar or monosaccharide. Why is sucrose often called a double sugar or disaccharide? Why is starch called a polysaccharide?

Glucose, Sucrose, or Starch

The food stored in a tree's roots is starch, but this food cannot be transported through the stem in the form of starch. It must be broken down chemically into sucrose so it can dissolve in water. The sap that floods upward through the phloem of maple trees in spring contains large amounts of sucrose. It also contains small amounts of the organic molecules that give maple syrup its distinctive flavour. Once the maple sap is delivered to the immature buds, the sucrose is further broken down into glucose. The cells in the buds need this glucose to provide the energy they need to divide and grow in order to produce full-grown leaves. The growing leaves then begin to make their own glucose by photosynthesis.

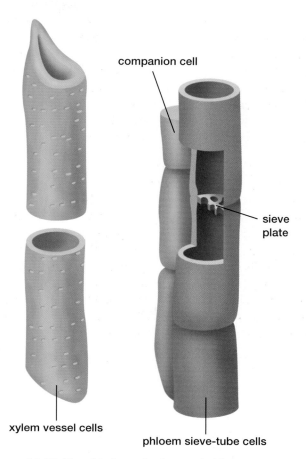

Figure 14.18 The structure of xylem and phloem.

Once the leaves are producing more glucose than they require, the excess glucose is converted into starch grains in the chloroplasts. Then the starch is broken down to form sucrose. Dissolved sucrose will travel from the leaves to the root by way of the phloem tissue in the stem. It is converted to starch in the root and stored mainly in the root cortex.

Most plants, large or small, handle the translocation of food in the same way as the maple tree, as shown in Figure 14.19 on the next page. That is, the food is transported up and down the stem in the form of dissolved sucrose molecules.

⏵ PLAY

Go to your Electronic Learning Partner to enhance your learning about plant transport systems.

BIO FACT

What makes honey sweet? Bees make honey from flower nectars that consist mainly of dissolved sucrose.

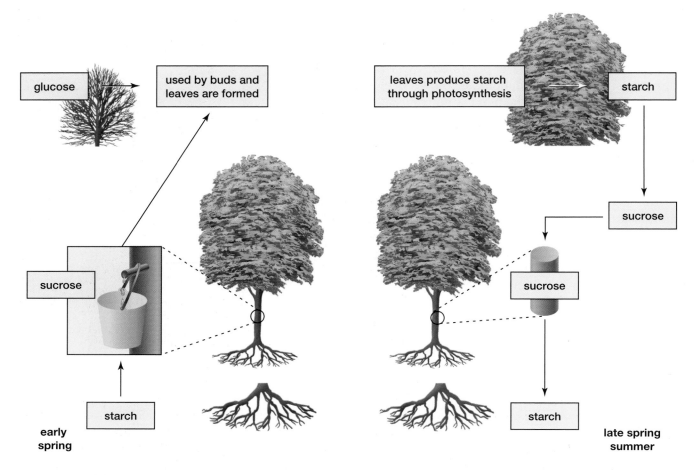

Figure 14.19 The formation and use of maple sap in a maple tree.

⏸ **PAUSE** ⏺ **RECORD**

Use the information presented on the previous page, along with the diagram shown here in Figure 14.19, to summarize how food is transported through a tree. You may use diagrams, a flow chart, or a written description for your summary. Keep this information in your notebook.

SECTION REVIEW

1. **K/U** Compare and contrast the function of the phloem and xylem in vascular plants.

2. **K/U** What are the structural differences between the phloem and xylem?

3. **K/U** If you analyzed the liquid that is found in the xylem, what would be its largest component?

4. **C** If the xylem or phloem of a plant were damaged, what would happen to the plant? Give explanations for your answer.

5. **MC** Would the rate of maple sap retrieved from the trees be greater during the day or during the night? Why?

6. **I** In an experiment, a researcher interrupted the flow of materials through a tree by placing a metal plate part of the way through the trunk. One day later, a chemical analysis revealed that the sugar concentration in the tree tissue was higher above the plate than below the plate. As well, the concentration of minerals and water was greater below the plate than above the plate. Explain the results.

7. **I** Maple syrup consists mainly of sucrose and water. Could the procedures for making this sweet treat be used with other tree saps, such as oak sap, willow sap, or birch sap? What types of information would you need to test this hypothesis?

Structure and Function

- Describe the structure and function of leaves, stems, and roots.

- Analyze the leaf, stem, and root in cross section.

- Examine growth rings to determine the age of a tree.

- Analyze the role of root hairs.

Figure 14.20 The major structures of a vascular plant are the leaves, the stem, and the roots.

As you have discovered, vascular tissue is found in the structures shown in Figure 14.20 — the leaf, the stem and the root. Water and nutrients travel from the soil into the root through root hairs, and then into the vascular tissue of the root, the stem, and the leaves. How does the material move from the soil to the root hairs and from the root hairs to the vascular tissue of the root? How does the material get to the leaves? How does material move from the leaves to the stems and the roots?

Figure 14.21 The forest floor is covered with a variety of leaves.

The Leaf

Even though leaves of vascular plants come in many shapes, sizes, patterns, and arrangements

(see Figure 14.21), all leaves play the same basic role in the life of plants, whether gymnosperm or angiosperm, monocot or dicot. The primary role of leaves is to convert the Sun's energy into food for the plant through photosynthesis. Quite apart from contributing oxygen and food to the biosphere, leaves also provide shade and camouflage for other organisms. Some insects are coloured or shaped like the leaves in their usual habitat, which allows the insects to evade predators. Fallen leaves on the forest floor provide habitat and food for decomposers, such as fungi and bacteria. Besides all that, leaves add great beauty to the world. We in Canada are especially fortunate. Many of us live where we can appreciate the changing colours of autumn and the green renewal of spring.

The underlying structures that enable all leaves to perform their functions are similar. These structures will be discussed in the following section.

BIO FACT

Bright autumn colours are produced by photosynthetic yellow pigments (carotenoids) and red pigments (anthocyanins) in leaves. During autumn, the green pigments (chlorphylls) fade more quickly as the leaves die, revealing the underlying yellow and red colours. The intensity of the colour depends on the plant's genetics and local environmental conditions.

Leaf: Epidermis

Most multicellular organisms have an external layer of living tissue, the **epidermis**, to protect their interior tissues. The human epidermis consists of thin, flat cells that fit together like tiles to form a germ-proof barrier. Leaf epidermis is similar. The cell margins fit tightly against their neighbours. As long as the epidermis is unbroken, it can repel many invaders such as fungi and bacteria. However, leaf epidermis is not completely waterproof.

You have probably seen water droplets resting on leaves like those in Figure 14.22. The waterproofing function of the leaf is performed by the **cuticle**. This waxy, non-living exterior layer is exuded by the cells of the epidermis, and it forms a continuous covering around the body of the leaf. The cuticle even blocks the passage of gases through the cells of the epidermis.

Both the cuticle and most epidermis cells are transparent, which allows light to penetrate through to the leaf's interior. So how do the CO_2 and H_2O molecules needed for photosynthesis enter the leaf if they cannot pass through the double barrier of cuticle and epidermis?

Word LINK

The word epidermis comes from two Greek roots: *epi*, meaning "above" or "upon," and *derma*, meaning "skin."

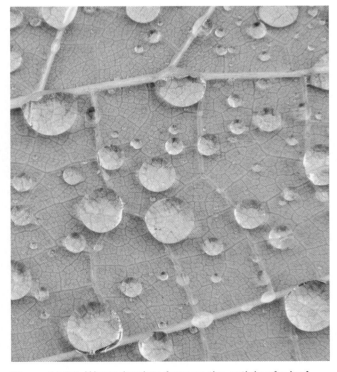

Figure 14.22 Water droplets form on the cuticle of a leaf.

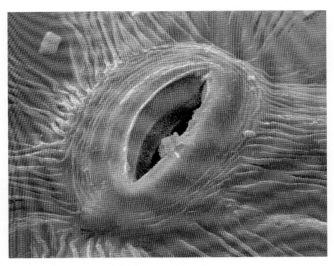

Figure 14.23 An electron micrograph of a stoma

Leaf: Stoma

A **stoma** (plural, stomata) is a pore-like opening in the plant's epidermis, usually in a leaf. Stomata are especially numerous on the underside of the leaf. Their function is to permit gas exchange between the leaf's interior and the external environment.

Each stoma is bordered by two guard cells that act together as a pair. These non-transparent cells regulate the rate of gas exchange by controlling the size of the stomata. The larger the openings, the faster the leaf can exchange gaseous oxygen (O_2) and carbon dioxide (CO_2) with the surrounding air. How might the rate of exchange increase? Decrease? Under what conditions? How would this be advantageous or disadvantageous? No two-dimensional diagram can fully convey the stoma's three-dimensional structure as well as an electron micrograph shown in Figure 14.23.

Guard cells are firmly linked to form a permanent pair. Each cell is girdled by several non-stretchy microscopic rings. The guard cells have thickened inner walls. To open the stoma, water flows into the guard cells from the surrounding cells. The resulting rise in water pressure pushes out on the cell membranes. However, since the rings prevent the cells from increasing in diameter, they expand in length instead. Even though each cell increases in length, their fastened ends prevent the two-cell pair from increasing in length. The pressurized cells curve outward and the space between them gets larger. To close the stoma, water flows out of the guard cells. The resulting drop in water pressure allows the individual cells to return to their original length, lose their curve, and close up the previously opened space.

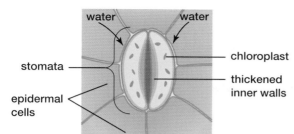

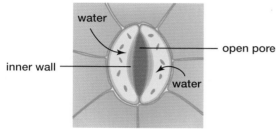

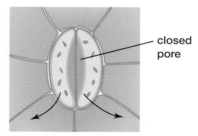

A Structure of a pair of guard cells

water

stomata

epidermal
cells

chloroplast

thickened
inner walls

water

inner wall

open pore

water

B Water flows into guard cells

closed
pore

C Water flows out of guard cells

Figure 14.24 The structure and function of guard cells

Leaf: Spongy Layer

Recall the word equation for photosynthesis from Chapter 3. Based on the equation for photosynthesis, you might expect the spongy spaces inside the leaf (shown in Figure 14.25) to contain gaseous carbon dioxide and oxygen (as well as gaseous nitrogen,

which makes up about 80% of the air around us). Water vapour is also present. Every cell inside the leaf is full of water, and cells give off or release H_2O molecules all the time. Therefore, water vapour molecules move into the spaces between the spongy cells.

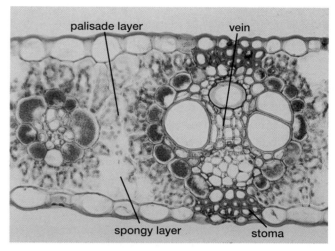

palisade layer

vein

spongy layer

stoma

Figure 14.25 Cross section of a leaf

Inevitably, many of the water molecules in the spongy spaces between cells escape as water vapour through the stomata in a process called transpiration. The following MiniLab will help you to understand just how much water is likely to be involved.

◀◀ REWIND

To review the process of photosythesis, turn to Chapter 3, Section 3.2.

 MINI LAB

Plant Transpiration

Weigh a transparent plastic bag and record this weight. Then, put the bag over a potted plant. Secure the bag's open end to the pot by pulling a large elastic band up from the bottom. Expose the bagged plant to sunlight for one hour. Then, to estimate the volume of water transpired by the plant during that time, count the drops of water on the bag. (It takes about 20 drops to add up to 1 mL.) Carefully remove the bag, making sure you keep all the water droplets in the bag. Now weigh the bag again. The difference in weight is the weight of the water. (1 mL of water has a mass of 1 g.)

Analyze

1. Compare the results you obtained from these two different methods of estimating transpiration. Do the results differ? What might be the reasons for the difference?

2. Using one of your estimates, calculate how much water would be transpired by the plant in 12 h, in a day, and in a year. How do you expect the following factors to affect the transpiration rate of the plant: night versus day, cloudy versus sunny, cold versus warm?

Leaf: Vascular Tissue

The **veins** in a leaf are made up of xylem and phloem, which are bundled together in long thin strands. The veins in a dicot leaf are arranged in a net-like pattern, whereas the veins in a monocot leaf are arranged in a parallel pattern. These patterns are shown in the Investigation 14-A on page 526. Regardless of the pattern, the veins conduct water and dissolved minerals into and out of the leaf. Once the leaf cells have produced food by photosynthesis, any dissolved carbohydrates must exit the leaf so food can be delivered to the non-photosynthesizing parts of the plant. Thus, the veins in a leaf perform three fluid-conducting functions.

1. They conduct water into the leaf.
2. They conduct dissolved minerals into the leaf.
3. They conduct dissolved carbohydrates (nutrients) out of the leaf.

Figure 14.26 The arrangement of palisade cells in a leaf is not unlike a solar panel.

Investigation   14 • B

Observing Stomatal Action

In this investigation, you will observe the function of guard cells and their effect on size of stomata.

Pre-lab Questions

- What leaf tissue contains the stomata?
- Would you expect to see more stomata on the leaf's upper surface or on its lower surface?
- What colour would you expect to see in the stomata? in the guard cells?

Problem

How does the leaf's external environment affect the size of the stomatal openings and the action of the guard cells?

Prediction

Predict what you would expect to observe if you treated part of a leaf's stoma-containing surface with pure water, and another part with salty water.

CAUTION: Water on electrical connectors is a hazard. Use care unplugging the microscope. Wash your hands thoroughly after the investigation.

Materials

compound light microscope	5 mL measuring spoon
2 microscope slides and cover slips	shallow dish (a petri dish or a clear plastic sour cream container)
2 beakers, cups, or jars	lettuce or geranium leaf
labels and markers	dropper
water	paper towel (for cleanup)
salt	

Procedure

1. Label the slides 1 and 2. Repeat with the beakers.

2. Add water to Beaker 1 so it is half full. Add water to Beaker 2 until it is half full, and then add 5 mL of salt.

3. Place a small piece of a fresh lettuce leaf in the shallow dish. If you are using a geranium leaf, try to get only the *thin bottom layer*. Add sufficient water from Beaker 1 to half fill the dish. Let stand for 5 min so the leaf cells become turgid (swollen with water).

Leaf: Palisade Cells

The solar panels in Figure 14.26 transform light into electricity. Some people use similar-looking panels to heat swimming pools. Whatever their purpose, such structures are always broad and flat to maximize the collection of solar energy. This pattern might lead us to expect that something similar would be found under the transparent epidermis of a leaf.

Figure 14.27, however, shows a different pattern. The principal light-collecting layer of a dicot leaf is composed of tall, thin cells that stand upright. These are called **palisade cells**, after the long thin poles once used to create a fence or palisade around a fort.

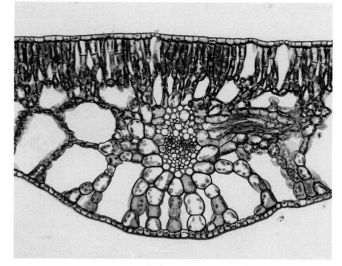

Figure 14.27 Find the palisade cells in this photomicrograph.

4. Follow your teacher's instructions for how to tear a thin section of the leaf *sideways* so you get a small portion of the lower epidermis *only* (it should be transparent). Divide this portion of lower epidermis into two pieces.

5. Mount one piece of lower epidermis on Slide 1 with a drop of plain water from Beaker 1. Add a cover slip. Mount the other piece of lower epidermis on Slide 2 with a drop of salty solution from Beaker 2. Add a cover slip. For care and use of a microscope and how to prepare a wet mount, turn to *Appendices 3* and *4*.

6. Place Slide 1 under the microscope and locate a stoma and the surrounding guard cells. Note whether the stomata are open or closed. Now look for chloroplasts. Sketch what you see and label your sketch.

7. Repeat step 6 with slide 2. Record your observations and conclusions.

Post-lab Questions

1. Compare the appearance of lower epidermis treated with plain water to the epidermis treated with the salt solution. Which has larger stomatal openings? Suggest why.

2. Compare the appearance of a closed (or nearly closed) stoma to that of an open stoma. How have the guard cells changed shape?

3. Explain how the stomata are related to the guard cells. Do you think the stomata could exist without guard cells?

4. Compare the size of a guard cell to the size of a chloroplast (for example, 1   1; 1   1; 1   1). Does the guard cell have room for more chloroplasts? Explain how you know.

Conclude and Apply

5. Write a conclusion for this Investigation.

6. You immersed the leaves of terrestrial plants in a liquid. This seldom happens in nature. What state of matter usually makes up a leaf's external environment?

7. You "polluted" the liquid experimental environment. Identify the pollutant.

8. Identify some pollutants that might affect the size of a leaf's stomata and the action of its guard cells in nature. Give reasons for your answers.

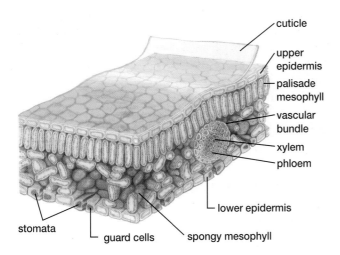

Figure 14.28 The palisade cells viewed from the top

Only a small part of each palisade cell's surface area — its top end — is exposed to the incoming light (see Figure 14.28). The cell's bottom end is exposed to the gases in the spongy layer. As a result, plenty of energy and raw materials are available to each cell. This arrangement maximizes light collection to make photosynthesis efficient.

> ◄◄ REWIND
>
> To review the process of photosynthesis, turn to Chapter 3, Section 3.2.

Figure 14.29 Water from this willow's roots must travel upward, sideways, and downward through its stems to reach the most distant leaves. Equally, food produced by the outermost leaves must travel up, across, and down to reach the roots.

The Stem

The most noticeable part of a plant stem is its outer covering. Plants that have green, flexible, herbaceous stems must be replanted from seed every growing season. Those with brown, rigid stems often have a longer life span. For example, petunias, which have herbaceous stems, must be replanted from seed every growing season. In contrast, maple trees, which have woody stems, may live for over 100 years.

The inner tissues of a stem may also show significant contrasts. Figure 14.7 on page 525

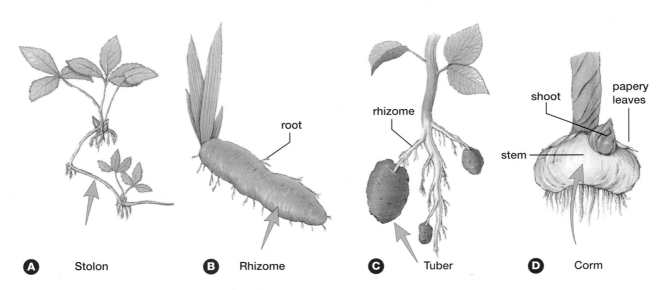

Figure 14.30 Modified stems of (A) a strawberry plant, (B) an iris, (C) a potato plant, (D) a gladiolus

shows how the internal structure of a dicot stem differs from the internal structure of a monocot stem. Note that the vascular bundles in monocots are distributed randomly throughout the stem cross section, while the vascular bundles in dicots are gathered together in orderly rings.

The growth pattern of stems can vary greatly, as shown in Figure 14.30. Above-ground horizontal stems called **stolons**, or **runners**, produce new plants where the nodes in the stem touch the ground. This type of stem is seen in strawberry plants, for example. Other vertical stems can also be modified in various ways. For example, the stems of cacti are modified for water storage, and the tendrils of grape plants are modified to wrap around a support structure.

Rhizomes are underground, horizontal stems. They may be long and thin, as seen in grasses that form sod, or they can be thick and fleshy as seen in an iris plant. Rhizomes are able to reproduce asexually because each node of the stem bears a bud. Some rhizomes have enlarged sections called **tubers**. For example, potatoes are tubers.

Some stems are bulbous underground structures called **corms**. These stems are covered by papery leaves, and lie dormant underground during the winter months. Gladiolus plants, well known for their beauty, grow from corms.

Nearly all stems share similar functions and or internal structures. Most of these are comparable to those of the root. Like the root, the stem plays both a supporting and a nutritional role in the life of a plant (see Figure 14.30). The stem's support role involves holding the plant's leaves up to the light. The stem's nutrient transport role involves three functions:

1. Water and dissolved mineral nutrients are transported from the roots to the leaves. (This function is performed by the xylem.)

2. Newly manufactured food molecules are transported from the leaves to the roots for storage. (This function is performed by the phloem.)

3. Food stored in the root is transported to any plant part that needs it. (This function is also performed by the phloem.)

Stem: Epidermis

Figure 14.31 on the following page shows the cross section of a typical young dicot stem. As you might expect, the epidermis of a stem is a layer of cells that protects the inner tissues. Like leaf epidermis, the epidermis of a young green stem is covered by cuticle and perforated by stomata, which allow gases to enter and exit. The epidermis cells of young stems contain chloroplasts and can perform photosynthesis.

 THINKING LAB

Counting Growth Rings

Background

Foresters and biologists determine the age of trees by counting growth rings. To do this without chopping trees down, they use a technique called core sampling. A core sample is a pencil-like cross section of a tree stem that is cut out by a special drill and used for study.

You Try It

1. Examine some sample stem cross sections from trees or shrubs (and photocopies of core samples taken from the stems of large trees) with a magnifying lens.

2. With a partner, work out a way to determine the age of the stem samples when they were cut from the plant. Use the magnifying lens to take a closer look at the growth rings of each stem sample. If sample stems are used, do not forget to wash your hands at the end of the Thinking Lab.

3. Now study the photocopied core samples. Determine the probable age of the trees from which the photocopied core samples were taken.

4. What visible features helped you to detect the growth rings? How do the growth rings differ in size? What do you think caused these differences?

5. Do the growth rings appear to be made of a different kind of cell than the rest of the stem? Explain.

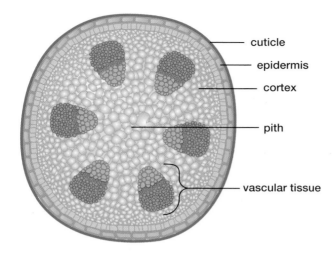

Figure 14.31 A cross section of the stem of a young dicot

Stem: Cortex and Pith

The **cortex** of a dicot stem contains cells that are irregular in shape and arrangement. There is also a **pith** in the stem. Pith is similar to cortex tissue, but it is usually spongier because the cell walls of pith are thinner and there are more air spaces among the cells. (Note the relative location of cortex and pith in Figure 14.32.)

The high water pressure inside the pith and cortex cells keeps them fully expanded. This condition, called **turgor**, helps to keep the young stems upright. The stem's cortex stores food in the form of starch. The pith is thought to store water and perhaps small amounts of food. Neither of these storage tissues plays a role in the transportation of food and water.

Web **LINK**

Do an Internet search to identify some practical uses for pith. Go to **Science Resources**, then to **BIOLOGY 11** to find out where to go next. From what plant species is the pith most likely to be useful? Do any of these species grow in Canada? in your region?

www.school.mcgrawhill.ca/resources/

The Root

One of the major roles of the root is to anchor the plant in the soil and to hold the stem in place. Roots also play a vital role in the biosphere by anchoring the soil and preventing erosion.

Landscape architects advise city planners on planting and cutting trees to avoid serious problems with erosion. Plants chosen to stabilize steep highway embankments through plantings must have the right type of roots and must grow quickly. Two general types of roots are shown in Figure 14.33. Many plants have a fibrous root system, which consists of a large number of slender roots. Other plants grow one large root, or taproot. This root is dominant, fleshy, and usually stores food. Many commonly consumed vegetables, such as carrots, beets, turnips, and radishes, are actually taproots. Which type of root do you think would be more effective in preventing erosion?

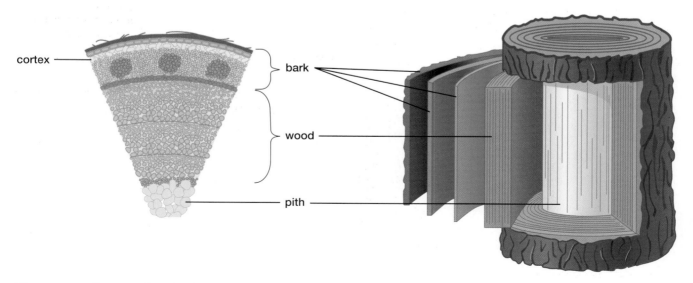

Figure 14.32 Cross section of a three-year-old woody dicot stem

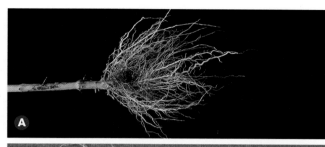

Figure 14.33 The two main types of roots are (A) fibrous root and (B) taproot.

The Nutrient Transport Functions of Roots

The second major role of the root is nutrient transport within the plant. To do this, roots perform three functions:

1. Roots absorb water needed by the leaves for photosynthesis and replace water lost during transpiration.

2. Roots absorb dissolved minerals and regulate the quantity of these minerals entering the rest of the plant.

3. Roots store starch made from the food produced by the leaves. Some of this stored food is used by the cells of the root itself, and some is transported to other plant parts that require it.

The absorption functions of the root are performed by the outer surface of the root cells. Many root systems are divided and subdivided into networks of roots to increase surface area, as shown in Figure 14.34. Roots can absorb the most when their external surface area is at a maximum. Figure 14.35 shows the structure of a typical root.

Figure 14.34 Some roots grow extensive branching underground networks.

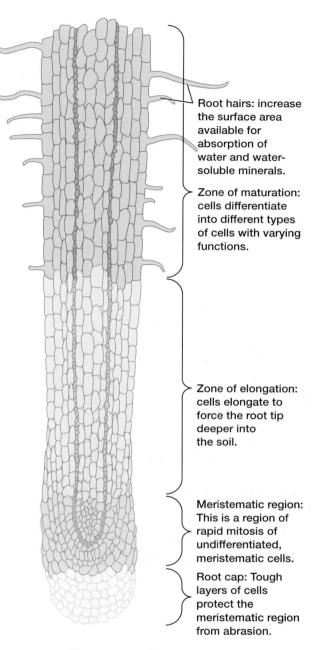

Root hairs: increase the surface area available for absorption of water and water-soluble minerals.

Zone of maturation: cells differentiate into different types of cells with varying functions.

Zone of elongation: cells elongate to force the root tip deeper into the soil.

Meristematic region: This is a region of rapid mitosis of undifferentiated, meristematic cells.

Root cap: Tough layers of cells protect the meristematic region from abrasion.

Figure 14.35 The structure of a root

⋙ FAST FORWARD

Turn to Chapter 15, Section 15.1, to learn more about meristem tissues.

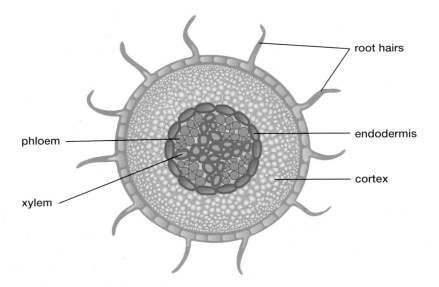

Figure 14.36 A cross section of a typical dicot root

Labels: root hairs, endodermis, cortex, phloem, xylem

Root: Epidermis

Figure 14.36 shows a cross section of the most common type of root — a dicot root. You can see that the root hairs are simply extensions of the close-fitting cells that make up a continuous cover around the root's exterior. As in the leaf, this outer layer is known as the epidermis. Its function is twofold: to protect and enclose the interior root structures, and to absorb water and dissolved minerals from the surrounding soil. The root hairs greatly increase the surface area available for the absorption function.

In the next MiniLab, you will observe these structures and estimate the numerical advantage they provide in terms of increasing the surface area of the roots.

MINI LAB

Viewing Root Hairs and Estimating Their Area

The tiny root hairs that you can see in this photograph play an important role for the plant. Note that each "hair" is actually an extension of a single cell. Examine the photograph and answer the following questions.

Analyze

1. Working with a partner, develop a method for estimating the number of root hairs extending from the germinated seed. Then develop a method for estimating the length and diameter of an average root hair.

2. Calculate the surface area of an average root hair. Then, multiply to estimate the total surface area of all the root hairs, convert the units to cm^2, and cut out a piece of paper with equivalent area.

3. What features of a root hair suit it for its role in absorbing water and dissolved minerals?

4. Write one or two sentences describing the extent and importance of the plant's root hairs. Use evidence from this MiniLab to support your statements.

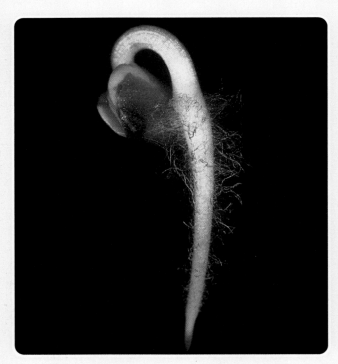

Germinated radish seeds under a microscope at low power

Root epidermis cells have no chloroplasts, and consequently they cannot manufacture food. Yet, these cells must perform cellular respiration to obtain the energy they need to stay alive. The glucose required for cellular respiration comes from the breakdown of starch stored in the cortex layer of the root.

Root: Cortex

The root's cortex layer lies just inside its epidermis. In young dicots, the cortex occupies the bulk of the root's volume (see Figure 14.37).

Note the numerous air spaces created by the irregular shape and arrangement of the cortex cells. The cells themselves contain large vacuoles for food storage. The purple grains you see inside these vacuoles are composed of starch, which is formed from carbohydrate molecules manufactured by the leaves. Note that starch is actually white; the grains in the photomicrograph are purple because the slide was treated with iodine to make the starch easier to see.

BIO FACT

Not all plants grow in soil. Some types of orchids are epiphytes, or plants that grow on other plants. Many orchids grow on the branches of trees, with their roots exposed to warm humid air. The epidermis of these exposed roots is covered with a cork-like layer that absorbs and retains the air-borne moisture.

Root: Endodermis

The **endodermis** lies just inside the cortex. At first glance, its structure seems similar to that of the epidermis, because the endodermis cells fit closely together like tiles to form a thin, continuous, sleeve-like layer. However, special cells in the endodermis act to ensure that materials travelling into the centre of the root are carefully filtered before moving on. This filtering keeps many harmful substances out, while permitting needed nutrients and water to pass through into the root's vascular tissue. From there, the nutrients and water can be carried up to the rest of the plant's cells. As Figure 14.38 on the following pages shows, the only pathway into the root's vascular tissue involves passing through the selectively permeable membrane of an endodermis cell. The membrane cannot block the diffusion of small molecules such as water or oxygen. However, it can block the passage of large particles such as dissolved minerals, which get through the endodermis only if the cell membrane selects them. This gives the endodermis complete control over which minerals get through to the vascular tissue at the centre of the root, and in what quantities.

The vascular tissue of the root is continuous with that in the stem and leaf. Thus, the root endodermis determines what enters the entire vascular system for transport to the rest of the plant.

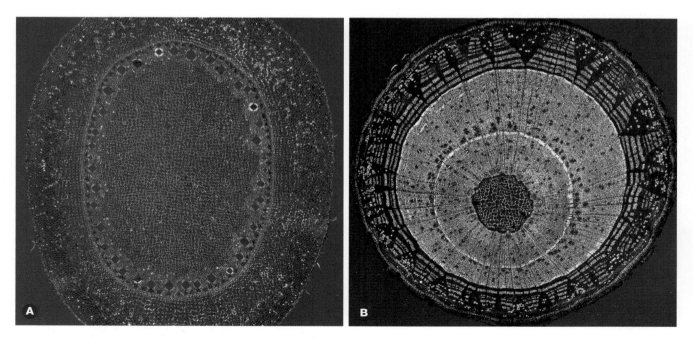

Figure 14.37 Monocot roots have alternating strands of xylem and phloem surrounding the central tissues (A). The xylem in a dicot root is located in the centre of the root and is in the shape of a star (B).

Root: Vascular Tissue

In most young plants, the vascular tissue of the root is clumped together in a single **vascular cylinder**, which contains both phloem and xylem. The xylem's function is to transport water, minerals, and any other dissolved materials absorbed by the root to the upper parts of the plant. The function of phloem is to conduct dissolved food. When the leaves are manufacturing extra glucose, the phloem will conduct dissolved food into the root. When there is a food shortage, the phloem will conduct dissolved food out of the root and upward into the plant's stem and other structures.

Figure 14.38 See the illustration on the right. Water and dissolved minerals enter the root, by osmosis through the root hairs. Substances then move into or between the cortex cells, to the single layer of endodermal cells. There is a waterproof seal around each endodermal cell, ensuring that all substances pass through the endodermis before they reach the vascular tissue of the plant.

Investigation 14 • C

SKILL FOCUS

Performing and recording

Analyzing and interpreting

Communicating results

Viewing Structures, Inferring Functions

In Investigation 14-B on page 538, you viewed the cellular structures on the outer surface of an unstained leaf. In this Investigation, you will use a microscope to view a cross section of a leaf, stem, and root. Each specimen consists of a thin slice that has been stained to provide better visibility of the specimen's features.

Any drawing done to look as much like the original subject as possible is said to be realistic. Flip back and find three examples of realistic drawings in this textbook. In a stylized drawing, the shapes have been simplified so you can see the underlying structural pattern more easily. Flip back and find three examples of stylized drawings in this textbook.

Pre-lab Question

■ How do biological drawings help to convey information about structure and function?

Problem

By examining the structures of the leaf, stem, and root, can you identify the parts that make it function?

Prediction

Predict how a stylized drawing can be used to simplify a process.

CAUTION: Handle your microscope carefully and safely.

Materials

compound light microscope
prepared slide of leaf cross section (for example, the common sunflower *Helianthus annuus*)
prepared slide of stem cross section
prepared slide of root cross section
sketching materials

Procedure

1. View and sketch the cross section of a leaf as you see it under the microscope.

2. Is your drawing of the slide an example of a realistic drawing? Give reasons for your answer. (Note: your drawing need not be a great work of art to be realistic.)

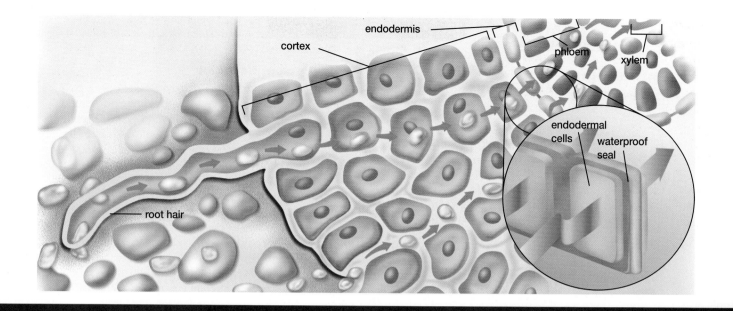

cortex

endodermis

phloem

xylem

endodermal
cells

waterproof
seal

root hair

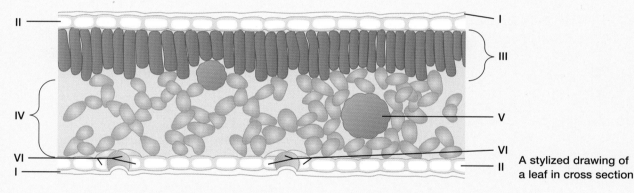

A stylized drawing of
a leaf in cross section

3. Contrast your realistic drawing with this stylized drawing of the leaf cross section. The main structural parts in the stylized diagram have been labelled with Roman numerals. Use these numerals to label the matching parts on your realistic drawing.

4. Sketch an example of each cross section of the stem and root, and label as many structural parts in the samples as you can.

Post-lab Questions

1. Which numbered leaf part probably performs each of the following functions? Explain your reasoning in each case.

   (a) lets gases into and out of the leaf

   (b) holds or stores gases inside the leaf

   (c) conducts water and dissolved matter

   (d) performs most of the photosynthesis

   (e) protects the interior tissues of the leaf

Conclude and Apply

2. What evidence do you see in the cross-section that the vascular tissue is continuous?

Exploring Further

3. Can you infer what the longitudinal section of the vascular tissue would look like from this cross section? Draw a sketch of what you expect the longitudinal section to look like.

4. The stylized drawing of the leaf gives no clue to the technical names of the labelled parts. List the Roman numerals on separate lines, and assign your own descriptive name to each part.

Immunologist

Dr. Julia Levy

Success in science, according to Dr. Julia Levy, depends on a passion for research, a keen eye for scientific problems, and an ability to seize opportunities. Julia Levy's story began when her children found a humble cow parsley plant (*Athriscus sylvestris*). It ends, for now, with the recent launch of Dr. Levy's new "blockbuster" drug — a photo-dynamic treatment that promises to restore the vision of thousands of people who are blinded by macular degeneration.

Harnessing the Power of Photosynthesis

Photosynthesis depends on chlorophyll, which is a light-sensitive pigment that absorbs the photons in sunlight to generate a plant's food energy. Chlorins (some of these pigments) are structurally similar to porphyrins in animals. When activated by light, both catalyse the conversion of oxygen into a short-lived, high-energy form of oxygen, known as singlet oxygen, which is very damaging to cells.

When Dr. Levy's children brushed up against cow parsley plants, they were burned by singlet oxygen because the photosensitive chlorins in the plant had been activated in the sunlight. Later, she wondered whether light-sensitive compounds could help doctors pinpoint treatment for cancerous cells without damaging nearby healthy cells.

Self-sufficient Scientist

Born in Singapore in 1934, Dr. Levy grew up in Vancouver with a strong interest in biology. She learned the value of self-sufficiency during World War II, while her father was away and her mother was left to support the family. Inspired by a female biology teacher in Grade 11, Dr. Levy was driven by a desire to contribute to useful scientific discoveries. After graduating from the University of British Columbia (UBC) in 1955 and getting a PhD in England in 1958, Dr. Levy returned to UBC. There, she focussed on immunochemistry and on developing genetically engineered antibodies for cancer treatment. In 1980, Dr. Levy and several colleagues created a company now known as QLT Phototherapeutics Inc., to advance this work. Later, they began to focus on harnessing photosensitizer molecules that target abnormal tumour cells.

At that time, few were interested in photo-dynamic therapy, which gave Dr. Levy and her new biotechnology venture a significant advantage. In 1984, Dr. Levy's laboratory identified BPD-MA, a lipophilic photosensitizer molecule (activated by red light) that seemed to deliver itself to abnormal cells. Dr. Levy discovered this molecule was useful for treating blindness caused by macular degeneration.

Career Tips

Dr. Levy's advice to students is, "You never know what the next year is going to bring, especially when you're growing up. To cut off your options — in terms of your education, where you want to go, what you want to do, or how you want to do it — is the worst mistake anyone can make."

SECTION REVIEW

1. **K/U** Do both leaf types perform the same functions? Explain.

2. **K/U** Is the leaf a tissue, organ, or organ system? Support your answer.

3. **K/U** In looking at the stem, what evidence do you see that trees grow continuously? What factors might make a tree grow faster? grow slower? stop growing?

4. **C** Draw a simple sketch to show the functions in a stem.

5. **K/U** How does the branching structure of a root suit it for performing its structural functions? Its nutrient transport functions?

6. **K/U** Explain why roots need structures to store air and water. Which root structures store air? which store water?

7. **I** Leaves of the desert plant Aloe are adapted to store water. Make a hypothesis about the structure of these leaves that would enhance their ability to store water.

 UNIT PROJECT PREP

Which plant industries make use of the processes used by leaves, stems, and roots to transport materials? Where do these industries exist and where are they most common? Start collecting answers for these questions in preparation for your Unit 5 Project.

Chapter Expectations

Briefly explain each of the following points:

- Plants can be classified as either vascular or non-vascular depending on how water and nutrients are transported through the plant tissue. (14.1)
- Biologists group angiosperms as either moncots or dicots. (14.1)
- Vascular bundles, which transport materials within the plant, consist of xylem and phloem. (14.2)
- Gas exchange in a leaf occurs through small openings in the epidermis called stomata. (14.3)
- Photosynthesis occurs in a layer of tall, thin palisade cells that collect light energy. (14.3)
- In addition to supporting the leaves, the stem of the plant has three main functions in transporting nutrients. (14.3)
- The roots of a plant absorb and store nutrients. (14.3)
- Roots branch into a series of fine hairs that greatly maximize the surface area of the root system. (14.3)
- The endodermis of the root regulates the kinds of materials that are absorbed by a plant. (14.3)

Language of Biology

Write a sentence using each of the following words or terms. Use any six terms in a concept map to show your understanding of how they are related.

- vascular tissue
- woody
- herbaceous
- vascular bundle
- tracheid
- vessel element
- translocation
- epidermis
- cuticle
- stoma
- vein
- palisade cell
- stolons
- runners
- tubers
- corms
- cortex
- pith
- turgor
- endodermis
- vascular cylinder

UNDERSTANDING CONCEPTS

1. In which of the following environments would you be most likely to find non-vascular plants: in desert soil, near the snow line on a mountain, on a sandy ocean beach, or on the forest floor? Give reasons for your answer.

2. Which plants do you think were the first to adapt to life on land, vascular plants or non-vascular plants? Give reasons for your answer.

3. List three ways that vascular plants differ from non-vascular plants. Give an example of each type of plant.

4. Centuries ago, dried mosses were used to fill in the cracks between timbers in log buildings. Explain why mosses would work well for this purpose.

5. What part of the plant is shown in this cross section? Is it a monocot or a dicot? What characteristics provide you with clues to your answer?

6. Where is vascular tissue located in a growing plant? Explain what role vascular tissue plays in the plant's continuing growth.

7. Leaf epidermis is covered with cuticle for protection. Root epidermis is not. Explain why.

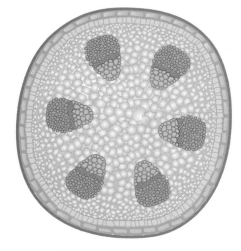

8. What structure provides some protection for the growing root? Describe where this structure is located, and explain why it is needed.

9. The Singh family is looking for land on which to build a house. They are shown a beautiful plot of land that is lush with ferns and mosses. Do you think it would be wise to build a house on this land? Why or why not?

10. Describe how biologists differentiate between monocots and dicots. What was the original purpose of creating these two categories? Do they reflect significant differences in structure? in function?

11. Design a field trip in your local area to map the various types of plants (vascular and nonvascular, gymnosperms and angiosperms, monocots and dicots). Outline all the steps, procedures, materials, safety concerns, and questions that would apply for the field trip plan.

12. A researcher was interested in determining if environmental conditions have an effect on plant water loss. She set up an experiment using three potted geranium plants as follows: plant one was placed in a clear plastic bag; plant two was placed in front of a fan; plant three served as a control. The results of the experiment are shown in the graph above right. Which line best represents the control? Which line best represents the plant in the bag? Which line best represents the plant placed in front of the fan? Do environmental conditions influence the rate of plant water loss? Write a conclusion for the experiment.

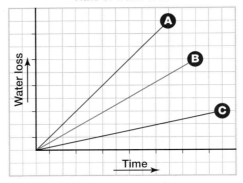

Rate of water loss

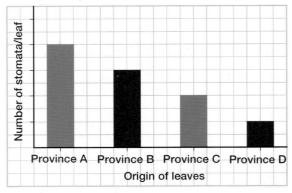

Comparison of numbers of stomata

13. The graph above shows data on daisies collected in four different provinces. Study the graph and answer the following questions. In which province might there be least rainfall? In which province might there be most rainfall? Suggest a relationship between rainfall and number of stomata per leaf. Explain your answer.

14. Prepare a concept diagram showing the relationships between the following groups of plants: dicots, vascular plants, gymnosperms, monocots, non-vascular plants, angiosperms. Then expand your diagram by including examples of each group.

15. Develop a chart to communicate the structural relationships among the root, the stem, and the leaf of a vascular plant.

16. What factors might make a tree grow faster? grow slower? stop growing entirely?

17. Some plants transpire at a more rapid rate than others. Assume that you are a farmer in an area with little precipitation. Finding a plant variety that has a low transpiration rate is, therefore, critical to you. Design an experiment to compare two different varieties of a plant species to determine which would be better to plant as a crop.

18. Sketch a diagram or diagrams to show how water and nutrients enter a vascular plant, and how the material is transported from the roots to the leaves. Describe the process using your diagram(s).

19. How does the amount of water in seeds affect how long they can be stored? Design an experiment to find out. Include a way of measuring the amount of water in seeds as a part of your experimental design.

20. In an experiment, a plant in a clear, sealed container was exposed to radioactive carbon dioxide $^{14}CO_2$ for one hour. Following this, a thin cross-section of the stem of the plant was made and placed against photographic film. The radioactive carbon, which exposed the film (visible as black grains), occurred only in the phloem sieve tubes of the stem. Explain these results, using your knowledge of photosynthesis and how gases enter and exit plants.

21. One group of students did an investigation to estimate the total surface area of the roots in a geranium plant growing in a pot about the size of your two fists cupped together. They found the plant's roots provided it with an absorptive surface the size of the gym floor in their school. Does their finding seem realistic? Explain.

22. Your grandfather has more time for the garden now that he has retired. In spring, just after the tulips finished blooming, he decided to tidy up the garden by cutting off all of the tulip leaves. Your grandmother was dismayed. She said she'd be surprised if any tulips would bloom the next spring. What do you think will happen, and why?

23. Figure 14.8, on page 525, shows a giant panda eating bamboo. This is the only food plant the pandas eat. The once extensive bamboo forests of China now occupy only about one percent of their former area. What do you think caused this reduction in the bamboo population? What do you think has happened to the giant panda population as a result?

24. What roles do root hairs play for a plant? In your explanation, include your answer to this question, which was asked in Chapter 8: What role do root hairs play in plant respiration? Do roots help absorb oxygen for use by other parts of the plant?

25. For most of the nineteenth and twentieth centuries, cut flowers or potted plants were removed from the rooms of hospital patients at night and returned the next morning. Explain why this was done. Why is this practice no longer prevalent?

26. One source of new pharmaceuticals is the tropical rain forests. Currently, these forests are being cleared for agriculture at an alarming rate. What long-term effects will this create?

27. Are you in favour of preserving the habitat of a rare plant? What if this meant that some people that earned their living from this land might lose their jobs? Explain your answer.

28. Describe how angiosperms differ from gymnosperms. Which group is more important to the biosphere? to humans? to certain animals? Give reasons for your answers.

29. Root epidermis admits both the water surrounding the root as well as any and all substances dissolved in the water. How does the root control which substances actually enter the main body of the plant? Explain why control is important.

30. Describe the structure and function of the root's vascular cylinder. Name the two types of tissue it contains, and suggest why the term "cylinder" is used.

31. Using information from Chapter 3 and from this chapter, describe the role of leaves in a plant.

32. Farmers dry grain before storing it. Why is this done?

CHAPTER 15

Using Plants

Reflecting Questions

- What factors affect plant growth?
- How do people use plants?
- What plant-related technologies are you familiar with?

Herbivores, such as this giraffe, need to eat plant material every day to survive. When the giraffe has eaten all the acacia leaves within reach, it will move on to another tree to find more food. In a few months, the acacia tree will have produced new branches and leaves. If the same giraffe should return, it will find an abundance of freshly grown food.

Unlike the giraffe, the acacia cannot change its location. As well, its does not survive by consuming other organisms. All plants have the ability to manufacture their own food from materials in the environment. The acacia and all other plants continue to grow throughout their lives. Plants can also grow new tissues or replace lost parts. In fact, an injury often triggers a cascade of chemical events within a plant that stimulates new growth.

For centuries, people have collected observations about the lives of plants. We have amassed considerable scientific knowledge about the daily processes of plants, such as their growth, development, and how plants respond to their environment. This knowledge has provided the basis for a wide variety of technologies that take advantage of these processes. Selected plant species, such as cotton plants, have been cultured and used for a variety of purposes, including the manufacture of fabrics for the many clothes we wear.

In this chapter, you will learn how different plant parts develop from the same type of plant cells and how this ability can be used in cloning plant tissues. You will also discover how various plant hormones regulate plant growth and development. Plants produce a huge assortment of compounds that people and other organisms cannot make for themselves. These compounds play an important role in supplying our nutritional and other needs.

Finally, you will discover how plant-breeding technologies can be used to produce hybrids and maintain certain traits in cultivated plants. Through genetic engineering, researchers are investigating the possibility of producing edible vaccines in tomatoes or potatoes that could grant immunity to various diseases.

Plants are able to provide food for other animals and continue to live and grow. The same is not true of most animals.

Chapter
Contents

Plant Responses to Stimuli

EXPECTATIONS

- Describe the effects of growth regulators.

- Design and carry out experiments to study factors that affect the growth of plants.

- Describe the structure and function of a vascular plant.

- Describe some of the industrial processes that use plants.

Figure 15.1 Some plants can propogate, or grow new individuals, from a leaf.

Plants as living organisms have the ability to:

- use energy to obtain materials from the external environment, and

- use energy to rearrange those materials into new plant substances.

With very few exceptions, plants acquire all the matter and energy they need:

- without changing location (as must most animals, protists, and bacteria),

- without preying on other living organisms (as animals do), and

- without relying on matter assembled by other organisms (as fungi do).

Some plants, such as the *Bryophyllum* shown in Figure 15.1 can grow new individuals from a leaf. Some trees, such as sumac and poplar, grow new individuals, called suckers, from the roots. Spider plants and strawberries grow stems from which new individuals can become established at some distance from the original plant. This is shown in Figure 15.2. Many grasses grow from nodes in their roots. A field that has been ploughed or overgrazed will be covered by a new blanket of grasses that grew from the roots of the old plants.

Word LINK

The term "plant" comes from the Latin word *planta* which means sprout, slip, or cutting. Today we apply the term "plant" to entire organisms, not just slips or cuttings.

Figure 15.2 Plants such as this spider plant are able to grow new individuals from stems from the plant.

Herbivorous animals eat and gain nutrients from plants. Most plants however, obtain their nutrients from the air and the soil. Some plant species however, are able to "prey", or eat and gain nutrients from animals. Figure 15.3 on the next page shows the pitcher plant (the provincial flower

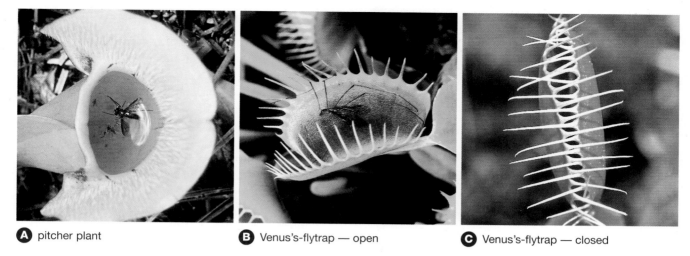

(A) pitcher plant   (B) Venus's-flytrap — open   (C) Venus's-flytrap — closed

Figure 15.3 Plants such as the pitcher plant and the Venus's-flytrap are consumers. They are not able to meet their nutritional requirements from the air and the soil.

of Newfoundland and Labrador) and the Venus's-flytrap, both of which are consumers. They trap and digest insects in order to obtain nutrients that are not available in the nutrient-poor soil they grow in. These plants are also producers because they photosynthesize, as well.

Development in the Meristem

What gives plants their amazing ability to grow throughout their lives? Although mitosis and cell division occurs throughout a plant as it grows, eventually new growth is restricted to small regions of unspecialized tissue collectively called the **meristems** shown in Figure 15.4. Growth in meristem tissue results from the accumulation of rapidly dividing cells. When a cell in the meristem divides, one of the two resulting cells remains in the meristem. The other cell becomes part of the plant body. Initially, all meristem cells are identical in structure, and they have no specialized function. As they divide

repeatedly, they begin to differ in shape, in the relative proportions of their various organelles, and in the functions they can perform. These changes result in the cells becoming specialized for particular functions, such as photosynthesis, storage, and support.

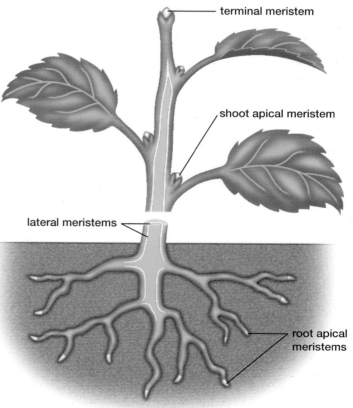

terminal meristem

shoot apical meristem

lateral meristems

root apical meristems

Figure 15.4 At first, the small, actively dividing cells of meristem tissue are identical. With repeated division, they "differentiate." That is, they become specialized for different plant functions.

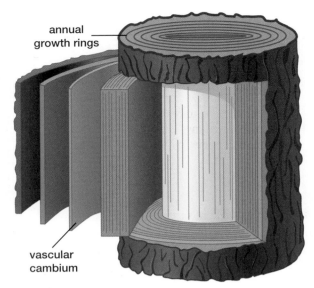

annual growth rings

vascular cambium

Figure 15.5 The meristem in a tree stem is located in the vascular cambium.

Types of Meristem Tissue

There are two main types of meristem tissue. The first type is called **apical meristem** tissue. It is located in the root and shoot tips of plants. Division of apical meristem cells results in growth of roots, leaves, and flowers. In the root, the apical meristem is protected by a root cap. In the stem it is protected within a terminal bud. In colder climates, the terminal buds stop growing in the winter and resume growing in the spring. These buds are protected by bud scales, which fall off when growth begins in the spring.

Lateral meristem results in the growth of tissue beneath the bark of tree stems, as shown in Figure 15.5. The division of cells in the lateral meristems results in the thickening of cylinders of tissue. Most woody plants have two kinds of lateral meristems: a vascular cambium and a cork cambium.

DESIGN YOUR OWN
Investigation

15 • A

SKILL FOCUS

Hypothesizing

Identifying variables

Performing and recording

Analyzing and interpreting

Factors Affecting Plant Growth

There are many different factors that will determine how well a plant will grow. What external factors affect plant growth? The list includes: the amount of light; the type of soil; the amount of water; the amount of minerals and other nutrients; and temperature. Which of these factors can be explored in an experimental setting? In this investigation, you will design an experiment to identify and investigate one external factor affecting plant growth.

Problem

What is the effect of an external factor on the growth of plants?

Hypothesis

Make a hypothesis about the effect of an external factor (of your choice) on plant growth.

CAUTION: Wash your hands thoroughly after working with soil.

Materials

bean seeds (or other easy to grow seeds)
labels
plant pots or planting trays
water
ruler
potting soil (or other types of potting material)
factors that you will be testing such as different fertilizers, water, or salt

Experimental Plan

1. Decide which condition you are going to vary in your experiment. Prepare a list of possible ways you might test your hypothesis.

2. Decide on one approach for your experiment that could be conducted in the classroom.

3. Your design should test one variable at a time. Plan to collect quantitative data.

4. Outline a procedure for your experiment listing each step.

The lateral meristem, called the **vascular cambium** produces xylem and phloem cells in the stems and roots. The other lateral meristem, called the **cork cambium**, produces a tough covering for the surface of stems and roots. The outer bark of a tree is produced by the cork cambium.

Meristem tissue enables plants to grow from cuttings. Growing plants from cuttings is the basis of plant cloning. Cloning technology, especially relevant to agriculture, is the process of growing genetically identical copies of an organism from a single cell or part of an organism. For some species, growing plants from cuttings can be much faster than growing them from seed.

◀◀ REWIND

Turn to Chapter 6, Section 6.2, to review cloning techniques and the results of cloning experiments.

‖ PAUSE ● RECORD

Make a chart with two columns headed "now" and "later." In the "now" column, record a definition of plant as you understand the term today, using your knowledge from Chapters 13 and 14. Your personal definition will grow and develop as you progress through this chapter. Use the "later" column to record your new understandings. On a separate page, write your ideas of why plants are important to Earth, the weather, animals, and other plants.

Internal Regulation of Plant Growth and Development

Plants can grow to their maximum height when environmental conditions are optimal. Optimal conditions include adequate moisture, warmth, light, and nutrients. Fertilizers promote plant growth and development by providing additional nutrition. Pesticides and fungicides promote plant

5. Show an outline of your plan to your teacher. Get your teacher's approval before continuing.

Checking the Plan

1. What will be your independent variable? What will be your dependent variable(s)? What will be your control variable(s)?

2. What will your experimental steps be? How would you apply the different treatments to the plants in the appropriate labelled pots?

3. What will you measure or count? How will you determine if your variable has had an effect on plant growth?

4. Design a table to record your data.

Data and Observations

Conduct your experiment and make your measurements. Enter the data into your table. Make a graph of your results. **CAUTION:** Make sure you are wearing all the appropriate safety equipment while you perform your experiment.

Analyze

1. At what level of the variable you were testing did your plant grow best?

2. Suggest reasons why your plant may not have grown as well in the other conditions.

3. Do your results support your hypothesis? Give reasons for your answer.

4. If the results were different than what you expected, what might be the reasons for these results?

5. Determine which treatment was the most beneficial and which treatments were the least beneficial. Look at other factors that may have affected your experiment. Were there any that you did not control?

Conclude and Apply

6. Based on your results, what recommendations would you make to farmers growing crops of your plant?

Exploring Further

7. What would happen if you varied two of the treatments at one time? Would you be able to tell which treatment affected the plants?

8. How do scientists determine what factors affect plant growth under field conditions when there are many variables (or treatments) that are affecting growth?

growth by controlling numbers of insects and fungi that feed on plants. However, plant growth and development are also controlled by the plant's own hormones.

From your previous studies, you learned that a hormone is a chemical compound manufactured by specialized tissue in one body part of an organism but that governs or regulates the activity of another body part or parts. Even though a hormone may circulate throughout an organism, it will act only on specific "target" tissues or organs.

Hormonal Control of Plant Growth

In the early 1800s, experiments undertaken by Charles Darwin and his son Francis described the effects of a mysterious "influence" that affected the growth of grass seedlings. The seedlings normally grew toward a light source, however this behaviour was not seen if the tips of the grass seedlings were covered with an opaque capsule that did not let light through. The remainder of the plant, where the growth actually occurs, was still exposed to light. If the tip of the seedling were covered with a gelatin capsule, which allowed light to pass through, then the seedling would grow towards the light as expected. For many years, researchers

Investigation 15 • B

SKILL FOCUS

Predicting

Performing and recording

Analyzing and interpreting

Conducting research

How Gibberellic Acid Affects Plant Growth and Development

Many garden centres stock chemicals that promote growth. Brand names differ, but the labels reveal that many contain the same main ingredient: gibberellic acid. What does this compound do for plants?

Pre-lab Questions

- What are the classes of plant hormone growth promoters?
- What are the effects of these different classes of hormones?

Problem

How does gibberellic acid affect the growth of bean plants?

Prediction

Predict what will happen to the rate of growth as plants absorb gibberellic acid.

CAUTION: Wash your hands thoroughly after handling seeds, seedlings, soil, or gibberellic acid.

Materials

recycled 6-compartment
  planting tray
labels and marking pens
soil or potting mixture
water

pre-soaked bean seeds,
  6 per group
ruler
gibberellic acid
graph paper

Procedure

1. Label the tray with your group's name. Fill each compartment with soil or potting mixture.

2. Plant one pre-soaked bean seed in each compartment. Place the tray in a brightly lit location that is warm enough for plant growth but not too hot.

3. Every day, add enough water to keep the potting mixture moist, using equal amounts of water in each compartment.

4. When most seedlings are over 10 cm tall, select three seedlings that are equivalent in height. Mark them and leave them in the tray. Remove the other three. This is Day 1 of your investigation.

5. Join another group so that two trays are available. Prepare two labels, one for each tray: "GA YES" (meaning treat with gibberellic acid) and "GA NO" (meaning do not treat with gibberellic acid). Prepare an observation chart in your notebook like the one shown on the next page.

conducted experiments to try to explain the nature of this observation. In 1926, Frits Went performed a series of experiments that showed there was a chemical messenger in the grass seedlings. This chemical could enhance plant growth. He named the substance **auxin**, from the Greek work *auxein*, which means "to increase".

Other discoveries about plant hormones came as a result of people noticing unusual growth in plants. For example, observers noticed that a rice plant infected with the fungus *Gibberella fujikoroi* grew abnormally tall. In 1935, researchers were finally able to isolate the chemical compound that caused the accelerated growth, and named it

gibberellic acid. They discovered that applying artificially-manufactured gibberellic acid to a plant not infected by the fungus caused the plant to grow abnormally tall.

Scientists and researchers continued to search for other plant hormones that might affect growth and development. They discovered two types of plant growth hormones: promoter hormones, which are hormones that cause growth, and inhibitor hormones, which are hormones that block growth.

Average height of seedlings in cm over several days

Tray	Day 1	Day 2	Day 3	Day 4	Day 5
GA No					
GA Yes					

6. Measure the height of each individual seedling. Calculate the average height for the seedlings in each tray and record your results in the Day 1 column.

7. Treat the plants in the "GA YES" tray by placing one drop of gibberellic acid on the shoot tip of each seedling.

8. Repeat Steps 6 and 7 for up to 5 days, recording your results in the appropriate column. Be sure all seedlings receive the same amount of light, warmth, and water each day.

9. Watch for any obvious difference in growth between the two trays. Note when this difference becomes apparent.

10. Use the data in your observation chart to create a graph. Plot height vs. time for both trays on the same piece of graph paper. Label the curves appropriately.

Post-lab Questions

1. What variable were you testing? Which tray was the experimental group? Which tray was the control group? What variables were you controlling in both trays?

2. Based on your observations, how does gibberellic acid affect the growth of the bean seedlings? How soon after the first application can this effect be observed?

3. What would you expect to observe if the gibberellic acid were applied to the base of the stem rather than to the tip of the shoot?

Conclude and Apply

4. What medium did your plants grow in? Where did you place the drops of gibberellic acid? Do you think gibberellic acid would make a good additive for impoverished soil? Explain why or why not.

5. Look at this sketch of a normal rice plant. Sketch the probable appearance of a rice plant infected with the fungus *Gibberella fujikuroi*. How would you know the infection is present?

Figure 15.6 As auxin concentrations decrease, the deciduous trees begin to shed their leaves.

The Classes of Hormones

The different classes of plant hormones and their molecular structure are summarized in Table 15.1. A full summary of the type and function of all of the plant hormones is given in Table 15.2 on the next page. Auxins are a class of hormone that is produced in the apical meristem of shoots. There are both natural and synthetic auxins that promote cell elongation, the development of vascular tissue, and trigger the development of above-ground stems, which help support the plant. These hormones also cause leaves to drop after they are no longer needed. The stimulation of cell elongation occurs because auxin increases the plasticity of the plant cell wall. The more plastic the cell wall is, the more it can stretch during active cell growth. This process is shown in Figure 15.7.

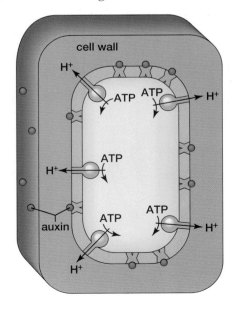

Table 15.1
Naturally occurring plant growth hormones

I Class	II Example	III Molecular structure
Auxins	β-indoleacetic acid	
Cytokinins	6-furfurylaminopurine	
Gibberellins	Gibberellic acid (GA_3)	
Abscisic acid	Abscisic acid (ABA)	
Ethylene	Ethylene gas	

Note: Three of the hormone classes listed in column I are shown as plurals. Each of these classes includes two or more chemical compounds with similar functions but different structures or formulas. Only the most common example of each is shown in column II.

Figure 15.7 Auxin stimulates an H^+ pump so that hydrogen ions (H^+) are transported out of the cytoplasm of the cell. The resulting acidity causes the cell wall to weaken, and solutes enter the cell. Water follows by osmosis and the cell elongates.

Gibberellins are also produced in the apical meristem and act to increase stem length. As well, gibberellins increase the uptake of starch in the embryo of germinating seeds and stimulate the development of vascular tissue. The effects of gibberellins include taller and stronger plants, plants that flower early, or genetically dwarf plants that grow to normal heights. Gibberellins are used in commercial crops to increase fruit size, and cluster size in grapes. As well, they can delay the ripening of citrus fruits and speed up the flowering of strawberries.

Cytokinins promote cell division and cell differentiation. Cell differentiation occurs when specialized cells are needed to perform certain functions. They also delay the aging of leaves and fruit. Cytokinins work by influencing the synthesis and activation of proteins that are required for mitosis.

Oligosaccharins are a recently discovered class of growth promoters. They stimulate plants to manufacture antibiotics in response to attack by fungi or bacteria. This allows the plant to grow to its full potential because the negative influences of pests are diminished.

In addition to hormones that promote plant growth, plants produce hormones that inhibit growth. There are two classes of hormone growth inhibitors. The first is **abscisic acid (ABA)**, which is synthesized mainly in mature green leaves, fruits, and root caps. This hormone inhibits the germination of seeds, inhibits the growth of buds in plant stems, and blocks the intake of carbon dioxide by controlling the opening and closing of leaf stomata. Abscisic acid also blocks the action of growth promoting hormones.

Ethylene, the second inhibitor, is a gaseous hydrocarbon. It occurs as a natural plant hormone. It stimulates the aging of plant tissues, the ripening and sweetening of fruit, and can also speed up the dropping of leaves from trees. The production of ethylene gas by plants can stimulate other plants to ripen. This was initially noted when bananas ripened quickly if they were left near oranges. The ripening action of ethylene has led to its use in agriculture. For example, tomatoes may be picked while green and then ripened artifically by the application of ethylene.

Table 15.2

Summary of plant growth hormones and their actions

Growth promoters

Auxins act to

- promote cell elongation
- suppress the growth of lateral branches
- trigger the growth of prop roots that grow from aboveground stems
- suppress leaf drop before leaf ages; promote leaf drop afterward
- stimulate the vascular cambium to produce secondary phloem in woody plants
- promote "bolting," the rapid elongation of the flower stem in plants such as cabbage

Gibberellins act to

- promote cell enlargement
- promote uptake of starch tissue by the embryos in germinating seeds
- reverse genetic dwarfism

Cytokinins act to

- promote cell division (recall that cytokinesis is the process of cell division after mitosis)
- stimulate formation of adventitious buds
- delay senescence (ageing) of leaves by maintaining chlorophyll content
- reverse suppression by auxin

Growth inhibitors

Abscisic acid (ABA) acts to

- block intake of carbon dioxide by causing the closure of leaf stomata
- inhibit seed germination
- inhibit active growth of axillary lateral buds
- block the action of growth-promoting hormones
- promote abscission of leaves and fruits

Ethylene acts to

- stimulate fruits to ripen
- stimulate other effects associated with tissue ageing
- trigger its own production through positive feedback (its presence promotes the production of still more ethylene, so ethylene levels build up rapidly)

Plant Tropisms

Plants exhibit the ability to orient themselves in response to external stimuli such as light. A directional growth response to unequal stimulation from the external environment is called a **tropism**, and it controls the growth pattern of the plant. Various external stimuli affect the production of plant hormones. This results in the directional growth of a plant. In tropism, the plant may grow either toward or away from the stimulus. Growth toward the stimulus is a positive tropism. Growth away from the stimulus is a negative tropism. There are three major kinds of plant tropisms that are affected by light, gravity, and touch.

Phototropism occurs when the growth of a plant is affected by light. In general, plants are positively phototropic, that is, they grow toward light. Roots are negatively phototropic and grow away from light. The growth is caused by differing amounts of auxin produced on the light and dark sides of the stem. Auxin accumulates on the shaded side of the stem, which causes the cells there to elongate. This causes the stem bend toward the light, as shown in Figure 15.8. Turning the plant around will cause the stem to bend in the other direction however, it will not change the original curve in the stem because it is the result of growth. Figure 15.9 demonstrates the experimental procedure that led to the discovery of phototropism.

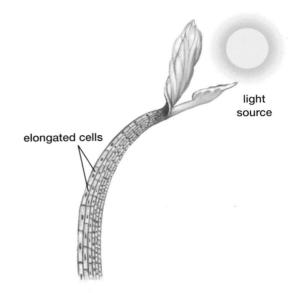

Figure 15.8 Tropisms result when external stimulation is unequal. For example, the stem of this plant is receiving much more light on its right surface than on its left surface.

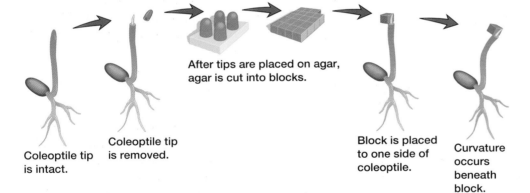

After tips are placed on agar, agar is cut into blocks.

Coleoptile tip is intact.

Coleoptile tip is removed.

Block is placed to one side of coleoptile.

Curvature occurs beneath block.

Figure 15.9 Oat seedlings, shown here, are protected by a hollow sheath called a coleoptile. After a tip is removed and placed on a block of agar, a block of that agar placed on one side of the coleoptile can cause it to curve even in the absence of light. The agar blocks contain the hormone produced by the original coleoptile.

 MINI LAB

How Plants Respond to Light

The flowering heads of sunflowers can be seen to turn in response to the movement of the Sun as it moves across the sky. This is one example of phototropism.

Plant some bean, tomato, or other vegetable seeds or acquire some seedlings. When the plants are a few inches high, place them in a room where the only light comes from one light source. (For example, place them on a window ledge with a cardboard box blocking out the light from the classroom.) Examine the plants daily and record what you see.

Analyze

1. How long does it take to see any bending of the stems?

2. How could you get the plant to straighten out?

3. Where would you expect the auxin to be produced in these plants?

Gravitropism is a plant's response to gravity. This tropism causes roots to grow downwards (positive gravitropism) and shoots and stems to grow upward (negative gravitropism). This benefits the plant, because shoots that grow upward will receive light and roots that grow downward will receive nutrients from the soil.

Thigmotropism is the response of plants to touch. This behaviour is a caused by specialized cells in the epidermis of the plant. Vining plants demonstrate a strong positive thigmatropism, as shown in Figure 15.10. The vines grow toward the object touching them causing them to coil around the object. Other plants demonstrate a negative thigmotropism.

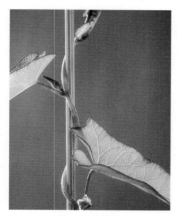

Figure 15.10 Vining plants such as bindweed demonstrate thigmotropism.

Figure 15.11 *Mimosa* is sometimes called the sensitive plant. When it is touched, it folds its leaves in less than one-tenth of a second.

⏸ PAUSE   ⏺ RECORD

Record how you would expect the primary root of a germinating seed to respond to light and to gravity. Name these tropisms. Repeat for the stem of a germinating seed. Write a brief explanation of why you would expect these responses.

Nastic Responses in Plants

Another type of response, called **nastic movements**, are caused by a stimulus that is not directional. For example, the leaves on a mimosa plant fold up when the plant is touched, as shown in Figure 15.11. This response might seem to illustrate a negative thigmotropism, however, it is neither directional nor permanent. The leaflets fold downward in the same way regardless of the direction of the stimulus. These movements are not a result of growth, but rather a change in turgor pressure in the cells at the base of each leaflet. A sudden drop in pressure causes the cells to become limp and the leaflets fold down. Once the stimulus has ceased, the turgor pressure in the cells rises once again and the leaflets open. Another example of a nastic response is shown in Figure 15.3 on page 555, where you can see the hinged leaf of a Venus's-flytrap. The movement of an insect on the leaf triggers the hinged leaf to close, trapping the insect between the leaves.

Commercial Use of Growth Regulators

Over the past century, scientists have learned much about plant growth hormones. Horticulturists and other agricultural scientists use this knowledge of plant growth regulators to influence the growth and development of crops and ornamental plants. Most growth regulating hormones used for commercial purposes are synthetically produced rather than extracted from plants. For example, there appears to be only one naturally occuring auxin, but many more synthetic auxin-like growth regulators exist. Although these synthetically produced hormones are not identical to natural auxins, their chemical action is similar, and the plants respond as they would to naturally occurring auxin. Commercial uses of several types of plant growth regulators are listed in Table 15.3 on the next page.

Table 15.3
Some uses for commercial plant growth regulators

Plant growth regulators	Commercial uses	
Auxin-like growth regulators	▪ stimulate rooting ▪ act as a herbicide for dicots ▪ prevent sprouts in pruned trees ▪ prevent fruit from dropping too soon	
Cytokinin-like regulators	▪ promote axillary bud growth in orchids and daylilies (results in more flowers) ▪ prevent browning in cut salads ▪ increase fruit size	
Gibberellic acid-like regulators	▪ increase flower size (for example, camellias) ▪ increase grape size ▪ stimulate separation of berries from stalks ▪ stimulate seed germination	
Gibberellic acid-like inhibitors	▪ control (restrict) height in flowerpot plants (lilies, orchids) ▪ control height of bedding plants	
Ethylene-like regulators	▪ stimulate flowering ▪ stimulate ripening (bananas, tomatoes) ▪ accelerate colour development in tomatoes and citrus fruits ▪ stimulate separation of cherry stems from branches (for mechanical harvesting machines)	
Ethylene inhibitors	▪ allow long-term, controlled storage of apples ▪ allow hypobaric (low-pressure) storage of many fruits, vegetables, and flowers	

A large industry is based on the manufacture of artificial plant growth regulating hormones. Some of the growth regulating hormones that are produced can be very specialized For example, a chemical treatment can be applied to ornamental trees to prevent them from growing too tall and interfering with utility lines. From the ground, the trees look normal, but the tops look as if they have been pruned flat. Table 15.3 outlines more of the commercial uses of plant growth regulators.

Chemical Look-alikes: Commercial Growth Regulators

Over the past century, scientists have built up an impressive body of knowledge about plant growth hormones. As in any branch of science, there is more to be learned and research is ongoing. However, horticulturists are already taking advantage of our present knowledge by applying plant growth regulators to influence the growth and development of crops and ornamental plants.

❚❚PAUSE	●RECORD

What have you learned about growth regulators? Do you think there should be more public awareness of these chemicals? Suggest how public awareness of plant growth technology could be improved. List two reasons to support your position.

SECTION REVIEW

1. **K/U** Both plants and animals depend on hormones to regulate growth and development. Name three of these hormones and describe their effects.

2. **K/U** Which plant growth hormone is gaseous? What is its function?

3. **C** How does a plant growth regulator differ from a plant growth hormone? Explain what the two have in common.

4. **I** Your uncle buys two unripe pears. He puts the first in a plastic bag by itself and puts the second in a plastic bag with a ripe banana. The second pear becomes edible much faster than the first. Develop a hypothesis to explain why this happens. Give reasons for your answer.

5. **K/U** Which of the following effects would you expect to observe if the tip of a shoot is cut off? Support your answer.

   - The plant will become taller because the production of gibberellins will be increased.

   - The leaves will fall off because the tip will release ethylene.

6. **C** Where is meristem tissue located? Explain how meristem tissue works. Draw a labelled diagram of apical or lateral meristem tissue to support your answer.

7. **MC** Plant growth regulators are involved in the cultivation, processing, and storage of many commercially grown fruits and vegetables. Yet, few shoppers are aware of this. Should supermarkets post signs identifying produce treated with plant growth regulators? Give reasons for your answer.

8. **I** A researcher is investigating how an auxin-cytokinin mixture affects the development of meristematic tissue. When the mixture contains a higher concentration of auxin, the meristematic tissue develops into organized root tissue. When the cytokinen is more concentrated, the meristematic tissue develops buds. What would you expect to observe if the mixture contained equal mixtures of the two hormones? Explain your reasoning.

Practical Knowledge of Plants

- Explain some of the uses of plant extracts in food and therapeutic products.

- Explain ways in which society influences plant science and technology.

Figure 15.12 The knowledge related to plants for food and medicine is a valid example of technology.

The plant expert in Figure 15.12 categorizes plants entirely according to their usefulness. She knows which plant can relieve headaches when heated and ingested, which one has roots that can be ground into a paste for leg ulcers, and which one has twigs that can be brewed into a tea that prevents scurvy.

This knowledge represents a huge data base of information that has been passed on by oral history to generation after generation of her ancestors. Such hunter-gatherer societies value only the most practical knowledge. Their languages reveal that plants with no known therapeutic or nutritional benefit are not considered important, because such plants either have no name at all or they have a vague name such as "one of those yellow-flowered plants".

The principal question asked in a hunter-gatherer society would be, "*What* is this plant good for?" The more technologically advanced societies of ancient Egypt (around 2500 B.C.E.) also valued only practical knowledge about plants. The principal questions about plants would also have been *how* — how to manage the land for maximum crop yield, or how to make plant extracts used for beautification or mummification.

Exploring Plants for Knowledge

As far as we know, the earliest culture to look at plants and ask *why* arose in ancient Greece. The scholar Aristotle (384–322 B.C.E.) wrote, taught, and asked questions about the fundamental nature and structure of plants without referring to their utility. Scholarly interest in plants began to flourish during the Age of Exploration (1450–1650), when ships such as *Endeavour* similar to the one shown in Figure 15.13 returned with thousands of previously unknown plant species. As European botanists collected, described, named, catalogued, and classified the new plants, they began asking *what* and *where*.

Figure 15.13 Ships, like the one shown here, ventured to unexplored lands bringing back unique specimens of plants and animals.

Then, around 1800, advances in glass manufacture dramatically improved the quality of microscopes. Suddenly, nearly every botanist was looking through a microscope and discovering that the myriad of plants they had been examining had both enormous differences and enormous similarities. Once again, the questions started with *why*. The pursuit of answers to these questions continues to drive present-day research. However, the study of plants has now come full circle. Scientists are combing rain forests for plants that might be useful for therapy.

Using Plant Products

Plants such as tea, coffee, and cocoa make caffeine or similar chemicals so they can cope with their natural environment. Such plants typically grow in high-altitude locations where the range between hot daytime temperatures and cold nighttime temperatures is as much as 30°C. To survive the night, the plants must enter a nearly dormant state. The caffeine-like chemicals give the plants a "jump start" in the morning. They do much the same for yawning people all over the world.

Whether the product is caffeine, cotton, or carrots, humans take advantage of properties that the plant needs for its own functions (see Figure 15.14). Whatever the desired product, we want useful plants to grow as fast as possible and as big as possible. Applying scientific knowledge enables plant industries to meet these goals.

Web LINK

Jan Baptista van Helmont (1577–1644) conducted the first controlled experiment designed to determine what kind of matter plants use to grow. To find out more about the work of van Helmont, go to the web site shown below. Go to **Science Resources**, then to **BIOLOGY 11** to find out where to go next. What assumptions did van Helmont make in designing his experiment? What conclusion did he reach? How do van Helmont's results compare with your current understanding of plant growth? How would you revise the experiment? **www.school.mcgrawhill/resources/**

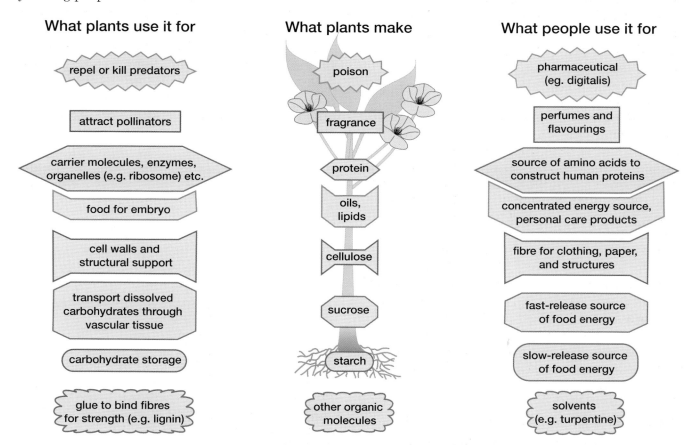

Figure 15.14 Plants organize (produce or manufacture) molecules for their own use and humans are able to take advantage of these properties.

Museum Technician

How many species of plants and animals are there in the world? How are they related to one another? How do they interact? In what habitats are they found? Why is biodiversity important? Is there a fossil record? Identifying and cataloguing all the living species in the world is an ongoing process carried out by scientists, curators, and museum technicians.

The Challenge of Biodiversity

The job of identifying and cataloguing all living things is complicated. To date, scientists have identified about one million animal species and about one half million plant species. But scientists think there are from three to ten million animal and plant species that have not yet been identified. Life science collections in museums play an important role in providing historical information about species diversity. Museum curators interpret these collections and their relevance to current biodiversity studies.

Museum Technicians

Museum technicians assist curators in a variety of ways. They participate in expeditions to study and collect specimens and in other kinds of field work. The "field" might be a rain forest in British Columbia, a desolate seashore in Brazil, or a jungle in Vietnam. They prepare, preserve, and catalogue newly acquired specimens, and install them in the collections. In the laboratory, they conduct DNA analyses that are instrumental in determining species relationships and evolutionary history. Technicians also assist in maintaining collections

to ensure their long-term preservation. It is especially important for technicians to prevent infestation by insect pests that feed on specimens.

The work of a life science technician is varied and challenging. Good communication skills are important for this job because the job includes participation in public programs and giving educational talks within or outside of the museum. The ability to work as part of a team is also important. Museum technicians often interact with scientists from other disciplines and other museums.

Educational Qualifications

Currently, the minimum requirement is a B.Sc. in Zoology or Botany, although many technicians have an M.Sc. Computer skills, including familiarity with data base and word processing applications and with the Internet, are also important. Familiarity with techniques in DNA analysis may also be required.

 MINI LAB

Grow Your Own Vitamin C

Grow some watercress in your class or at home. To do this, start by placing a few sprigs of watercress in a glass or jar containing water. After two weeks, add some soil to the bottom of jar. What does this do for the plant?

Analyze

1. Design a controlled experiment to study how watercress grows. Write a hypothesis that addresses an interesting question about watercress growth. For example, can you increase the rate of growth of watercress, or can you increase the crop size? State your predictions and the variables you would have in your study.

2. Conduct research on the Internet or in your resource centre to find out how much vitamin C is present in watercress by weight. Calculate how much vitamin C

is present in your crop of watercress. Compare this amount to the amount found in vitamin C tablets available in drug stores. How much watercress would a person need to eat per day to meet their daily requirement for vitamin C?

Watercress contains vitamin C.

Meeting our Nutritional Needs

Imagine living in a world only 30 m long. This is what sailors who set to sea during the Age of Exploration from late fifteenth century to the mid-eighteenth century experienced for months at a time. The ships that went off to sea needed to carry all the provisions that would be required on the voyage. Figure 15.13 on page 566 shows a ship like the HMS *Endeavour*. Like other ships of its era, *Endeavour* carried barrels of pickled meat, as well as domestic animals such as cows and hens. Meat, milk, and eggs are a good source of concentrated protein, and they contain fat, as well. Other barrels held carbohydrate-rich potatoes and hard-tack (a type of dried bread that keeps for months without spoiling).

Unfortunately this sort of diet caused many long-distance sailors to die of scurvy, which is caused by vitamin C deficiency. Scurvy is associated with inadequate supplies of fresh fruits and vegetables. The first obvious symptom is swollen, spongy, bleeding gums, but these symptoms may not show for three or more months after the deficiency begins (see Figure 15.15). Surprisingly, the *Endeavour*'s crew was never affected by scurvy. The reason? Unlike other ships of its time, *Endeavour* had a "garden". This was actually a barrel of water used to grow watercress. The captain, James Cook, insisted that the sailors eat its salad-like leaves. Other barrels contained sauerkraut (fermented cabbage) and orange extract.

Today we know that watercress, cabbage, and oranges are rich in ascorbic acid, a chemical compound better known as vitamin C. This nutrient is essential in preventing scurvy. Most animals can make their own vitamin C from glucose in their food. The exceptions include certain fish, certain birds, guinea pigs, and all primates. These animals must obtain this nutrient by eating foods that already contain vitamin C.

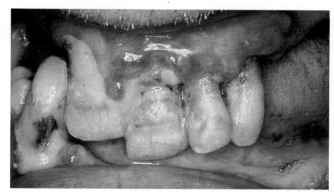

Figure 15.15 Many of Hudson's men died of scurvy while exploring the Arctic.

SECTION REVIEW

1. **K/U** List several kinds of plant-based products and give one familiar example of each.

2. **K/U** What part or parts of a carrot plant do humans use for food? What function does this part or parts perform for the carrot plant? What part or parts of a carrot plant do rabbits eat? What function does this part or parts perform for the carrot plant?

3. **MC** Give examples of plants that people use for each of the following:

   (a) forestry   (b) spices

   (c) chemicals   (d) lumber

   (e) fuel   (f) food

   (g) medicine   (h) horticulture

4. **K/U** Wild roses produce numerous pink petals and smell sweet.

   (a) How do the petals help the plant perform its life functions?

   (b) How does the fragrance help the plant perform its life functions?

   (c) How do people use the fragrance and the petals?

5. **C** Refer to Figure 15.14 on page 567. Use this information to create a concept organizer about plants, their functions, and ways that humans use plants.

UNIT PROJECT PREP

For your Unit Project you will be preparing an executive brief about one aspect of a plant-based industry. This section has discussed the many ways that humans take advantage of plants' natural processes and functions, and use plant products to suit our own needs. This is the foundation of plant-based industries. If you have chosen the industry that you will be studying, think about what the plant is being used for. Make notes about the different uses humans have for these plant products.

Plant Technologies

- Describe some of the uses of plant extracts in food products.

- Identify factors that result in trade-offs in the development of food technologies.

- Explain ways in which society influences plant science and technology.

Figure 15.16 Few Canadians would recognize a cassava plant, but anyone who has eaten tapioca pudding has tasted a cassava product.

In this chapter, you have explored some technologies that allow selected plant species to be used for human benefit. This section will consider the technology used to introduce new features or new combinations of features into those selected species.

Much of this technology is aimed at improving the world's carbohydrate crops, the starch-rich staple foods that Earth's people depend on for the bulk of their energy intake. Worldwide, the top three carbohydrate crops are rice, corn, and cassava.

Most of us have eaten, or at least seen, rice and corn. Both are cereal crops; their edible seeds are rich in carbohydrate and protein. Other examples of cereal crops are wheat, millet, and oats.

In contrast, cassava is a root crop. Its wild ancestor was originally found in Central America, but domesticated cassava is now grown in tropical regions all over the world. Dried and ground, the roots are used to make flour and bread. Other important root crops are potatoes and yams. Like cereals, root crops are high in carbohydrates, but most root crops have a lower protein content (and therefore less nutritive value) than cereals. However, root crops are easily cultivated, and thus they provide a low-cost source of food energy in many poor countries. Improving the yield and quality of these root crops will help provide nourishment in areas where there is not presently enough food.

Web LINK

Root crops with a higher protein content could save many children in the developing world from a particularly insidious form of malnutrition. Do some research on kwashiorkor. What are its symptoms? Why is it considered a major health problem? Go to the web site below. Go to **Science Resources**, then to **BIOLOGY 11**, to find out where to go next.
www.school.mcgrawhill.ca/resources/

Artificial Selection

Bananas and plantains are dietary staples in some parts of the world. In the recent past, most of the world's cultivated bananas were in danger of being killed by a fungal infection. These crops, however, were saved by researchers using techniques of selective breeding. The scientists were able to produce strains of bananas and plantains that were resistant to the fungus. Recall that in selective breeding, only individuals with certain desired traits are allowed to reproduce. Eventually, this results in an increase in the percentage of offspring that possess the desired traits. Selective breeding is a form of artificial selection. There are three main forms of artificial selection, mass selection, pure line selection, and crossbreeding.

◄◄ REWIND

Turn to Chapter 4, Section 4.1 to review information in artifical selection and selective breeding.

(A) wild wheat   **(B)** modern wheat

Figure 15.17 Selecting the most productive plants to reproduce changes the characteristics of the plant over time, as shown here.

Mass Selection

Mass selection involves gathering the seeds of the biggest, strongest, and most productive plants. These seeds are then set aside to be planted the next season. The crop from these seeds will likely contain a higher percentage of plants demonstrating the desired traits. When mass selection is repeated over many generations, it results in more productive strains of cereal crops, such as wheat, rice, and corn.

Pure Line Selection

Pure line selection involves only mating plants with certain desired traits. Examples of desired traits might include seed size or root mass in the case of carbohydrate crops, or flower colour in the case of blooming shrubs. Only offspring that express the desired trait are allowed to reproduce. Offspring are mated for several generations until every generation expresses only the desired traits. At that point, a purebred line has been established. Recall that Mendel used this technique to produce purebred or true-breeding pea plants.

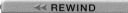

◄◄ REWIND

The production of pure lineages is covered in Chapter 4, Section 4.2. Turn to this section to review this information.

Crossbreeding

The goal of crossbreeding is to combine two or more desirable features in one offspring. For example, some years ago, commercial tomato growers wanted to reduce damage and spoilage during storage and long-distance transportation. They appealed to scientists in the seed-growing companies for help.

The scientists targeted two features of the ripened fruit: shape and firmness. They reasoned that very firm tomatoes would be better able to withstand handling. They also thought that fruit with a boxy, almost cubical shape would pack more closely, with less likelihood of crushing, than spherical fruit. So, they scanned tomato fields for plants with even the slightest sign of the desired features, harvested their seeds, and crossbred their offspring in a controlled environment. Their methods were successful: the result was a boxy, firm tomato that was easier to pack and sustained fewer losses during shipping.

The Benefits of Artificial Selection

Is it beneficial to crossbreed food plants for market appeal and storage characteristics, rather than for yield and nutritional value? The answer to this question depends on your perspective. The tomato growers, who got just the features they wanted, would likely say yes. The seed growers, who sold lots of seed, would likely agree. The desires of consumers, however, were not taken into account — they found themselves trying to eat well-preserved but hard and nearly tasteless fruit.

Whether beneficial or not, each feature (boxy shape, firmer flesh, tomato taste) is the consequence of instructions contained in the tomato's DNA. In other words, each outward feature arises from one or more genes inherited from a parent plant. Crossbreeding simply assembles new gene combinations that would not occur often enough by chance to be of commercial benefit. The advantage of crossbreeding is that it works on nearly any crop plant grown from seed. The disadvantage is that it may take many trials and a lot of time.

Producing Hybrids

Heritage roses like those in Burlington's Royal Botanical Gardens are seldom seen in home gardens and never in florist shops. Though wonderfully fragrant, the blossoms are short-lived and frail. They fall apart at a touch and come only in various shades of pink.

The well-formed blossoms of today's best-known and most popular roses come in a wide variety of colours and last for days. Although they are descended from the same ancestors as the earlier heritage varieties, they look (and often smell) quite different, because they are hybrids. This term refers to the offspring of parents with differing genotypes.

Hybrids occur in nature, but humans can produce made-to-order hybrids through controlled pollination. Regardless of species or whether used as decoration or food, hybrid offspring are often more vigorous than either parent. For example, they may flower earlier, they may give a greater yield or they may have a higher protein content.

Figure 15.19 Hybrid roses come in a variety of colours and shapes.

Figure 15.18 Heritage roses are spectacular, but their fragility make them unsuitable for mass production and sale.

The hybridization of corn has had an enormous impact on world food supplies. Hybridization makes it possible to propagate, or reproduce, the genes responsible for inherited variations in new combinations of corn. Corn is well-suited for this procedure because the male and female reproductive organs are separate. In uncontrolled cornfields, the wind blows pollen from the male

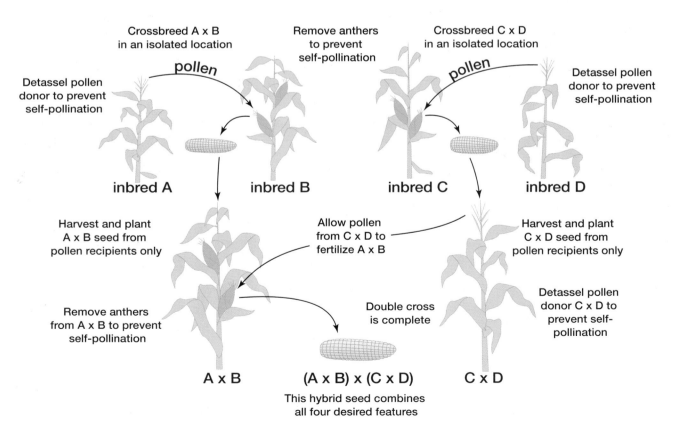

Figure 15.20 The process of developing purebred lines for four desired features

tassels that sway at the tops of the plants to the female silks that spill out of the immature ears.

The hybridization technique illustrated in Figure 15.20 allows seed growers to combine four desirable features. For example, purebred line A may contain genes for appealing colour; line B may have genes for good taste; line C may have genes for big ears; and line D may have genes for high yield.

The resulting "double cross" A × B × C × D hybrid seeds will grow into offspring plants with all four desired features. The ears of corn from these offspring plants will grow large, look appealing, taste good, and produce lots of edible kernels. However, if the seeds from these ears are planted, *their* offspring will express an unpredictable combination of colour, taste, size, and yield. Often during hybridization seed growers may suppress the genes that control fertility, so the hybrid seed may not reproduce at all.

BIO FACT

One of the greatest achievements of Canadian hybridization programs in the twentieth century was the development of pest-resistant wheat. Some wild wheat species naturally manufacture and release chemicals that either repel the pest directly or attract the pest's predators and parasites. Hybridization transferred the genes that coded for these chemicals to wheat species that did not originally possess them.

Once a successful hybrid has been developed, it would be good to maintain the same combination of desirable properties in successive generations. As mentioned above, the hybrid offspring produce unpredictable variations. The only way for wheat and corn farmers to prevent unwanted variation is to buy new hybrid seed each year from seed growers who go through the entire hybridization process that is illustrated in Figure 15.20. Naturally, this means that hybrid seed is a major annual expense for cereal farmers. Root-crop farmers, however, have another option. They prevent unwanted variation by cutting up roots from last year's crop and using the pieces to plant next year's crop.

PAUSE ● **RECORD**

Which form of cell division — mitotic or meiotic — is involved in developing hybrid seed for growing wheat and corn? Which form is involved in reproducing root crops by cutting up last year's roots? Write your ideas in your notebook.

Preventing Unwanted Variation

You have learned that plants have a remarkable ability to produce genetically identical offspring by asexual methods of reproduction. These methods, which involve mitotic cell division allow plants to increase their populations much faster than would be possible through sexual reproduction, which involves meiotic cell division and produces non-identical offspring.

Horticulturists mimic nature by using asexual methods of reproduction to propagate desirable house plants and flowering shrubs with no unwanted variations. Agriculturists also use asexual methods to propagate genetically identical crops such as potatoes and strawberries. Actual growth and development will, of course, depend on the availability of light, water, warmth, and nutrients. But all offspring created in this way will carry the same genetic instructions, because asexual reproduction propagates the same genes without unwanted mixing. The offspring of asexual reproduction are clones of each other and of the original plant. A cloned plant is shown in Figure 15.21.

Figure 15.21 A new geranium plant grown from a leaf cutting is a clone of the plant from which the leaf was taken.

◄◄ **REWIND**

To review information about cloning technology and related issues, turn to Chapter 6, Section 6.2.

Tissue Culture Technology

Horticulturist are able to speed up cloning by using a technology called **tissue culturing**. This technique has several steps. First, meristem cells taken from one plant are grown to produce a mass of unspecialized cells called a **callus**. Then fragments of the callus are treated with a carefully balanced mixture of auxin and cytokinin. These hormones cause shoots and roots to develop, and each plant would be potted separately. Once mature, the plants will express the same traits as the original plant from which the meristem cells were obtained. This happens because the new cells are produced through mitotic cell division. Each plant is a clone because it has exactly the same genetic makeup.

Large numbers of hybrids can be reproduced after the first hybrid has been developed. By definition, tissue culture and other cloning technologies prevent natural variation from occurring.

Biology Magazine   TECHNOLOGY • SOCIETY • ENVIRONMENT

Issues on Genetically Modified Plants

The public debate over genetically modified crops has created a fear among Canadian consumers that the food they eat may harm them. At the same time, Canadian farmers are concerned that their crops may not be saleable. Newspaper headlines and magazine covers are beginning to highlight the issue of genetically modified crops. Questions include: Should farmers plant seeds that have been genetically manipulated? Will consumers buy these products? Are consumers entitled to explicit labelling on products that contain genetically modified organisms? Do consumers have enough knowledge to make an informed decision? What are the consequences to human health and to the environment? Are there genuine food safety and ecological issues? By examining the risks and benefits of this new technology, you will be able to decide for yourself.

genetically manipulated to produce a product that grows faster, grows larger, and requires less fertilizer than in the past.

In contrast to the large factory farm, the organic farm is certified to use only natural products to grow food crops. Organic farms are usually smaller in size and sell their produce locally, not globally. They are also labour-intensive and have lower yields, and as a result their produce is more expensive. Consumers frequently believe that organic produce is safer and higher in nutritive value.

Consumers decide which products to purchase, but their decisions may not be based on accurate scientific information. To date, there have been no large-scale studies into the effects of the genetically modified plants that are frequently contained in foods on the market shelf. Many consumers are now confused about what products are safe for them to eat.

Genetically Modified vs Organic Crops

The typical farm in Canada is rapidly changing from the traditional family farm to a large commercial farming operation. Agribusinesses are buying vast tracts of land and, with new technology and economies of scale, producing large crop yields at a lower price. To maximize production, crops such as soy and corn are being

Arguments in Favour of Genetically Modified Crops

Contrary to popular belief, genetically modified plants are not artificially cloned to create fields of identical plants. Instead, new genes are inserted and used to generate desirable characteristics. The effects include:

Gene Transfer Technology

In the past, introducing a desirable new feature such as rust resistance into an existing plant species such as high-yield wheat through hybridization meant devoting years or even decades to crossbreeding trials. Now, there is a faster and more reliable way to incorporate change into a plant's genome called **gene transfer technology**.

- reduced demand for fertilizers for certain plants
- delayed ripening, to allow time for delivery to supermarkets
- coloured fibres, to eliminate the need for artificial dyes
- increased resistance to insect pests, fungi, or disease
- delayed rotting, to promote longer shelf-life
- increased yields per acre at a reduced cost
- increased resistance to drought or frost
- resistance to herbicides
- reduction of soil erosion

Arguments Against Genetically Modified Crops

These desirable characteristics do have possible negative side effects. Some potential risks that scientists have identified include:

- allergies
- poor nutrition
- toxic health risks
- antibiotic resistance
- harm to non-target species, such as insect pollinators
- kill-genes, or new genes that render the seeds of traditional plants infertile
- super-weeds, or weeds that adapt to compete with the engineered plant species
- crop pests that develop resistance and require more, instead of less, chemical control

These complex concepts lead to difficult questions. Are consumers aware that the produce is genetically modified? Should labelling be required by the federal and provincial governments?

Are there enough data to decide for or against genetically modified crops? Will there be a loss of genetic diversity? Is there a correlation between human disease and genetically modified plants? Perhaps it is time to devote our research into the long-term and short-term effects of this new technology. As a society, we must use any technology responsibly. Greater public disclosure (in the form of labelling) and tighter regulation through more testing (both before and after the release of new plants) are of prime importance.

Other Issues

Few would dispute that the need to improve Third World agriculture must be a primary goal. There are over 800 million people worldwide who are either hungry or chronically undernourished, the majority of whom are women and young children. Every year, diseases related to malnutrition account for more than five million deaths of children under age five. As the populations of most Third World countries rapidly grow, the demand for the world's supply of food continues to escalate. To meet future needs, a Green Revolution must be achieved. What, then, is the alternative to farming with genetically modified crops?

Follow-up

1. What has caused the general concern about genetically modified crops?

2. In your opinion, what are the risks and the benefits of genetically modified crops?

3. What responsibilities do developed countries have to develop technology that will benefit Third World countries?

4. Is it possible that the public reaction to the potential hazards of this technology could affect sources of research funding?

5. How might Canadian farmers react if consumers respond negatively or positively to genetically engineered crops? What crops might they cultivate?

When gene transfer technology was first developed, many people found it mind-boggling; it seemed almost magical. Now, it has become routine. This technology is possible because, despite the outward differences among species and kingdoms, there are also strong similarities. First, nearly every living thing on Earth is made of cells and run by instructions coded in DNA. Second, regardless of variations in specialized function, cell structure and cell organelles in all the kingdoms are so similar that a gene can be snipped out of one species (the host) and spliced into the genome of another (the recipient). The cells of the recipient organism will follow the new instructions. For example, bacteria can now produce human insulin.

Web LINK

To find out more information on how transgenic plants are produced, go to the web site shown below. Go to **Science Resources**, then to **BIOLOGY 11**, to find out where to go next. Summarize the steps for this technology in a list or make a diagram of the procedure.

www.school.mcgrawhill.ca/resources/

The gene transfer process from plant to plant occurs as follows:

1. The target gene (a DNA sequence that codes for the desired feature) is identified. This initial phase could take years.

2. The target gene is isolated from nuclei of the host and tagged with an extra DNA sequence.

3. Multiple copies of the tagged target gene are made and suspended in a liquid.

4. Recipient plant cells, which have had their cellulose walls removed, are added to the liquid containing the mass-produced target genes.

5. An electric current opens tiny, temporary holes in the cell membranes of the protoplasts. The target genes enter the protoplasts through the holes.

6. The protoplasts are collected, cultured, and tested for the tag target gene. If the tag is present, they are grown in a hormone-treated environment so that roots and shoots will develop.

7. The resulting plants have the spliced gene in every cell nucleus.

THINKING LAB

Growing Cuttings

Background

In this lab, you will view the results of a two-week experiment. Both test tubes contain a solution of blue fertilizer in water. To compensate for evaporation, enough water will be added each day to maintain the liquid in both test tubes at the same level. On Day 1 of the experiment, shown in the Figure below left, a cutting is placed in one of the tubes. The Figures in the middle and on the right show the conditions at Day 7 and Day 16.

You Try It

1. Carefully examine the images shown below. Observe and record any changes that have occurred between

Day 1 and Day 7. Observe and record any changes that have occurred between Day 7 and Day 16. What is the purpose of the second test tube shown in all the photos? Why is it needed?

2. The plant material shown is called a cutting because it is not a complete plant. Explain. What evidence do you see that the plant cutting is (a) collecting matter from its environment over time? and (b) rearranging the matter it collects and using it to form new substances?

3. Write a hypothesis that could be tested using this experimental setup. Create a data table, and fill it with appropriate but hypothetical data. Graph your data. Write a summary of the experiment explaining what was done, why, and what the results indicate.

Day 1

Day 7

Day 16

Creating Edible Vaccines

Type I juvenile diabetes, or JD, is an example of an auto-immune disease. Auto-immune diseases occur when the body mounts an immune response to its own tissues. Insulin is produced in the body by pancreas cells. In individuals with JD, these cells have a surface marker called GAD that acts like a flag to the immune system. The immune system attacks the GAD-marked cells and destroys them. As a result, JD patients do not produce insulin naturally, and therefore they must inject it on a daily basis. The drawbacks of this include the fact that insulin, like many drugs that are proteins, is expensive to produce. Furthermore, insulin injection is a treatment for JD, not a cure.

In the future, plants may play a significant role in fighting off juvenile diabetes. Through plant biotechnology, tomatoes and potatoes can be generated that contain genes that can either grant immunity or suppress immunity to a disease. In other words, these are edible vaccines. Think about it — instead of getting a needle, you eat a tomato or potato!

Who Is Developing and Researching Edible Vaccines?

Dr. Shengwu Ma at the London Health Sciences Centre is developing an edible vaccine against juvenile diabetes. He earned a B.Sc. and an M.Sc. in China. He earned a Ph.D. at Carleton University in Ottawa. His Ph.D. focussed on bacterial genetics and plant molecular biology.

Dr. Shengwu Ma

How Are New Genes Introduced into Plants?

New and different genes are introduced into plants through transgenic plant technology. This approach will enable researchers to create plants that produce vast amounts of medicine for an extremely low cost.

Transgenic plants can be generated in the laboratory. The first step is to identify the gene to be transferred into the plant. In the case of Dr. Ma and his team, the gene encodes the GAD protein found in the pancreas cells of those with JD. The DNA encoding this protein is transferred into a bacteria. A scientist then cuts a leaf off of the plant he or she wishes to make transgenic. The cut side of the leaf is inoculated with the bacteria containing the transgene. When the bacteria infect the plant cells, they transfer DNA into plant cells, which is integrated into the plant's own DNA. Using this technology Dr. Ma and his team have generated potatoes that produce high levels of the GAD protein.

How Can the GAD-producing Potatoes Help Those with JD?

Edible vaccination to autoimmune diseases works on the principle of oral tolerance. When we eat, we are taking in many different varieties of food, each made up of cells with many proteins not found in the human body. We do not mount an immune response to these proteins because our immune system mounts an immuno-suppressive response to the proteins we eat. That is, suppressor T cells are produced that tell killer T cells not to go after the food protein. This is called oral tolerance.

Dr. Ma reasoned that if an individual with JD was fed GAD-producing potatoes, that person's immune system might recognize GAD as a food protein instead of a foreign protein. GAD-specific suppressor T cells would then be generated to tell the killer T cells to stop their response to anything bearing the GAD protein. In this way, the autoimmune response against the insulin-producing pancreas cells would be brought to a halt. Since these cells would no longer be destroyed, the patient's insulin-producing cells would regrow and insulin production would resume. This would mean that the JD patient would no longer have to inject insulin.

What Are the Results of Dr. Ma's Study?

Not every protein we eat causes oral tolerance. In fact, some cause an extreme immune response in individuals. Peanut allergy is simply a massive and immediate immune response to a substance in the peanuts. Could GAD-producing potatoes cause such a response? For mice, the answer is no. Dr. Ma has found that feeding mice with GAD-producing potatoes leads to oral tolerance in those mice. The next phase is to move into human trials. If the same results are seen, there is great hope for an effective, inexpensive, and even pleasant treatment for a horrible disease. This approach may also be extended to individuals with other autoimmune diseases, as well as to transplant recipients.

The Results of Gene Transfer Technology

This method has already been used to add new features to more than 50 crop plants, including soy, cotton, alfalfa, rice, and wheat. Gene transfer technology is currently making the greatest strides with cassava. Researchers had successfully used selective breeding to increase the size and number of edible roots. However, cassava is very vulnerable to invasion by bacterial, fungal, and viral parasites. Traditional technologies such as hybridization were ineffective against these pests. Progress in combatting the parasites is now being made through gene transfer technology.

Gene transfer technology is as revolutionary as the development of agriculture was, and the development of computer technology was. Not surprisingly, it is also controversial, especially as applied to food plants.

Plant technologists are continually developing new techniques for introducing foreign or modified DNA sequences into plant genomes. They are also developing more efficient ways to regenerate whole plants from the clones of lab-cultured cells. In fact, this whole area of study is moving so quickly that it is impossible to predict today what techniques or issues will be making the headlines a few weeks or months from now.

BIO FACT

Gene transfer technology includes methods to transfer genes not only from one variety of the same species to another, but also from one species to another in an entirely different kingdom. For example, the gene that makes certain bacteria frost-resistant has been successfully transferred to certain strawberry varieties.

SECTION REVIEW

1. **K/U** What is the purpose of artificial selection? List three forms of artificial selection and briefly describe how each one works.

2. **K/U** What is a clone? Describe two methods of cloning plants.

3. **K/U** Define gene transfer technology and give an example involving the plant kingdom. What makes gene transfer between kingdoms possible?

4. **C** What is a hybrid? Draw a diagram to show how hybrids are produced. Explain why so many vegetables are grown from hybrid seeds.

5. **K/U** Explain why wheat and corn farmers must buy new hybrid seed each year. Why can't they simply save the best seeds from this fall's crop and plant them next spring?

6. **K/U** Explain why potato farmers do not always have to buy new hybrid seed each year. What circumstances would require them to buy new hybrid seed?

7. **MC** What advantage does cloning plants have compared to growing plants from seed? Write a short essay explaining why this technology is so important to our society. Considering the food shortages in parts of the world, is it possible that cloning plants can have an impact on world hunger? Explain your answer.

8. **C** The figure shown here outlines the process of developing purebred lines for four desired features. Copy the figure into your notebook. Create a list

showing the steps of this procedure, in order. Describe a situation when this process would be used. Describe a situation when you would not use this process. What alternate procedures could you use?

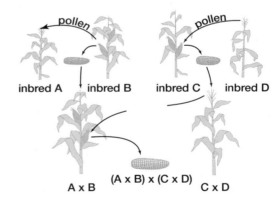

UNIT PROJECT PREP

This section has discussed many different technologies that are used in plant-based industries. Some of them are modified from technologies that have been in use, in one form or another, for centuries. Other technologies are very new. The plant-based industry that you are going to examine for your Unit 5 Project probably involves more than one type of technology. While you study your industry, note how many different technologies are present in your industry. Does the aspect of the industry that you are examining involve old or new technologies? Remember to comment on this in your executive brief.

Chapter Expectations

Briefly explain each of the following points.

- Plants have specialized tissue that continue to grow throughout life. These regions are collectively called meristem. (15.1)
- There are two types of meristem tissue, apical and lateral meristem. (15.1)
- The growth and development of all plants are regulated by hormones. (15.1)
- There are two classes of plant hormones, promoters and inhibitors. Promoters include auxins, gibberellins, cytokinins, and oligosaccharins. Inhibitors include abscisic acid (ABA) and ethylene. (15.1)
- Commercial growth regulators are hormone-like chemicals used by agriculturists and horticulturists. (15.1)
- Plants respond to external stimuli by showing directional growth called tropisms. The three main tropisms are in response to light (phototropism), gravity (gravitropism), and touch (thigmotropism). (15.1)
- Plants also exhibit nastic responses, which are responses to stimuli in a non-directional and non-permanent way. Nastic movements are a result of changes in turgor pressure in the cells at the base of the leaf. (15.1)

- Humans influence the growth and development of plants by using plant growth regulators, which are synthetic plant hormones. (15.1)
- Plants are adapted to survive in their environments and humans are able to take advantage of these traits for our own use. (15.2)
- Recent technologies, such as artificial selection, hybridization, cloning, and gene transfer technology are used to improve the yield and quality of crop plants. (15.3)

Language of Biology

Write a sentence using each of the following words or terms. Use any six terms in a concept map to show your understanding of how they are related.

- meristem
- apical meristem
- lateral meristem
- vascular cambium
- cork cambium
- auxin
- gibberellic acid
- gibberellins
- cytokinins
- oligosaccharins

- abscisic acid (ABA)
- ethylene
- tropism
- phototropism
- gravitropism
- thigmotropism
- nastic movement
- tissue culturing
- callus
- gene transfer technology

UNDERSTANDING CONCEPTS

1. Describe an example of a modern plant-based technology and an example of an ancient plant based technology.

2. Decide if the following statement is correct and support your answer. If the statement is inaccurate, correct it. Plants manufacture products such as fragrance molecules for use in perfumes.

3. Potatoes grown today make crisper potato chips than potatoes grown a century ago. What technology is probably responsible? Give reasons for your answer.

4. What is the goal of cross-breeding? What is an organism produced by cross-breeding commonly called?

5. Define tropism in plants. Give an example of a positive tropism and a negative tropism.

6. A tulip blossom opens wide in the sunshine but shuts when skies are cloudy or rain begins to fall. Explain why this action is NOT an example of a tropism.

7. How do plants control their own growth and development?

8. Classify each of the following as either a growth promoter or a growth inhibitor. Explain your answer.
   (a) Hormones that trigger the ripening of fruit
   (b) Hormones that cause tropisms

9. Where is the meristem located in a young, immature plant? In an older, mature plant?

10. Explain why a mature plant can never be regarded as "fully grown."

11. Choose one modern plant technology and describe how it imitates nature's own methods and how it differs from what happens in nature.

12. Some people think that "artificial selection" is a modern plant technology. Is it? Support your answer.

13. Sunflowers are so named because the flower heads rotate throughout the day to face the Sun. As the sky darkens at sunset, the heads droop. Next morning at sunrise, they spring up to face the light again. Is this an example of positive phototropism? Give reasons for your answer.

14. Why do orchard keepers spray developing fruits with auxin? What other hormones might they use during a growing season? Explain your answers.

15. A plant is placed on its side in the dark. Explain the growth of the plant's stem and roots in terms of stimuli and the action of hormones.

INQUIRY

16. You have been invited to listen to a seminar given by Dr. Shengwu Ma on creating edible vaccines. Your colleagues do not understand his research. Write a hypothesis concerning his research. What are the predictions of Dr. Ma and his team with regards to the hypothesis?

17. The list below describes different stages of a naturally ripening pear. The terms are not in order. Organize the terms into their proper sequence. At what stage would you expect the ethylene levels in the plant to be highest and at what stage would you expect the ethylene levels to be lowest:
    (a) Pale yellow, firm, slight breakdown in cell structure
    (b) Deep yellow, soft, further breakdown in cell structure
    (c) Yellow-green, hard, cell structure intact
    (d) Bright green, hard, cell structure intact
    (e) Deep yellow, very soft, extensive breakdown in cell structure

18. Design an experiment to test the effect of different colours of light on phototropism in one plant. What would be your control situation? What variables would you use? Write out an hypothesis you could test with your experimental procedure. Describe hypothetical data that you would collect if your data supported your hypothesis. Describe hypothetical data that you would collect if your data did not support your hypothesis.

19. Explain the difference between nastic movements and tropic movements. If you observed movement in a plant, how could you experimentally test whether it was a tropic or a nastic movement?

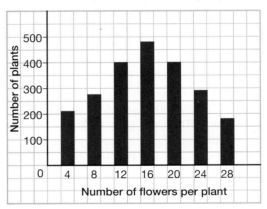

Number of Flowers Produced by Plants

20. A horticultural researcher who is attempting to develop drought-tolerant garden plants has identified a population of wild daisies of an unusual and desirable colour. The graph shown above illustrates the number of flowers produced per plant by this population.
    (a) How many total plants are there in this population?
    (b) Suppose the researcher hopes to reproduce the daisies by asexual methods, such as digging up and dividing root clumps. Which plants will probably yield the most flowers next season? Explain your answer.
    (c) Suppose the researcher hopes to reproduce the daisies by sexual methods, that is, by planting seeds. Collecting seeds is easier than digging roots. Should the researcher collect seeds from all of the plants, or just from the plants you identified in (b)? Explain your answer.

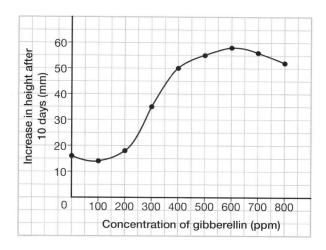

Increase in height after 10 days (mm) — vertical axis
Concentration of gibberellin (ppm) — horizontal axis

21. A researcher has been studying the effects of gibberellin placed on the roots of bean plants. The results of placing different concentrations of gibberellin on the roots are presented in the graph shown here.
(a) Given these data write a conclusion to the experiment.
(b) After the experiment is over, what steps would need to be taken to return the plant stems back to their original vertical position. Support your answer.

COMMUNICATING

22. What are the main goals of plant technologies? Describe the impact of these technologies on the biosphere.

23. Give one example of a cereal crop and one example of a root crop. Which crop always involves meiotic cell division. Write an explanation of why the other crop type can be raised without involving meiotic cell division.

24. What is the goal of gene transfer technology? Briefly describe the process that must be carried out. Support your description with drawings.

25. Experts recommend that those with small yards plant corn in blocks of at least 12 plants, spaced about 15 cm apart. If the blocks contain fewer plants, the ears of corn do not develop full sets of kernels. What do you think is the cause of this failure to develop? Would this knowledge influence how you would sow seed on a larger farm?

26. Compile a table of the plant products that people use. Divide your list into the following categories: (a) forestry, (b) spices, (c) chemicals, (d) lumber, (e) fuel, (f) food, (g) medicine, and (h) horticulture. Give at least two examples for each category. Draw a chart showing the categories, the list of the plant or plants, and the use people make of the plant or plants. Display this information using at least one other method such as a graph, a chart, a diagram, a flowchart, or a concept diagram.

27. Raspberries sold in a plastic-wrapped basket usually ripen, and then spoil, sooner than fruit that is not wrapped. Write a short paragraph to account for this observation.

MAKING CONNECTIONS

28. Gene transfer technology is a promising technology. Possible benefits include creating and improving resistance to disease-causing viruses, to insect predators, or to herbicides so the herbicides can be used to control weeds without killing crop plants. However, like all technologies, gene transfer technology could be used unethically or inappropriately. Give examples of how gene transfer technology can be used for potential benefits and how it may also be used inappropriately. Provide a brief discussion for each example.

29. What are the ecological consequences of altering genetic material? For example, what might happen if altered plant or animal species without natural predators were introduced into a new environment?

Plants and Their Environment

Reflecting Questions

■ What foods would you choose as a source of the mineral calcium? Trace the calcium in that food back to its original source.

■ What foods would you choose as a source of energy? Trace the energy in that food back to its original source.

■ How are plants involved in the production of the foods you listed in the questions above?

The images you see here illustrate two aspects of plants in the modern world. The large photograph shows a natural ecosystem apparently unaffected by human development or agriculture. Plant populations live together in ecosystems like these, and interact with other organisms. These organisms include animals, fungi, protists, and other micro-organisms. Although some of these organisms may not be visible in the photograph, they are surely present in this ecosystem. All of these organisms, regardless of their size or way of life, depend on plants to survive.

The small photograph is an example of one of the many plant species cultivated to serve the needs of people. The crop shown here is corn. Even in this monoculture there are other populations, such as mice, insects, and fungi. These organisms, although unwanted by those who planted the corn seeds, are a perfectly natural addition to the huge population of a single plant species in one field.

The corn being grown here may be intended as food for people: corn on the cob, canned corn, corn flour, corn starch, or corn syrup are just a few of the ways we eat this crop. Perhaps the corn is being raised as feed for domestic animals, such as cattle. It may even be fermented to produce ethanol, which can be mixed with gasoline and sold as fuel for automobiles. Farmed crops are not the only plants humans use. Wild plants are also harvested and used for food, feed, fuel, and fibre products such as paper, fragrances, flavourings, or pharmaceuticals. Many of today's medicines were obtained from plants.

In this chapter you will learn what all plants, both wild and domestic, need to grow. As well, you will learn how plant populations and species change through time, and what people do to enhance and maintain the growth of certain plants.

People have created fields of a single crop where communities made up of dozens of species once lived.

Chapter Contents

What Plants Need

- Identify nutrients required for the growth of plants.

- Describe how nutrients cycle in the environment.

- Explain the vital role of plants in recycling matter.

Figure 16.1 The roots of a soybean plant have nodules containing nitrogen-fixing bacteria.

To survive, plants require an environment that provides nutrients, soil, and light. Essential nutrients include the materials that a living thing needs to make its own structures and obtain energy for survival. For example, vitamin C and glucose are essential nutrients for you because you cannot manufacture them in your body.

Plants need nutrients, too, but vitamin C and glucose are not essential plant nutrients because plants can make these substances for themselves. In contrast, carbon dioxide is an essential plant nutrient because plants cannot make it from simpler materials. Water is also an essential plant nutrient, and like carbon dioxide, it is needed in very large amounts. Land plants get carbon dioxide from the air, and water from the soil in which they grow.

The other essential nutrients that plants require, especially minerals, also come from soil. Plants require large amounts of nitrogen-containing compounds. These are produced through the action of micro-organisms in the soil. You may recall from earlier studies that members of the legume family, such as peas and clover, play host to nitrogen-fixing bacteria that live in nodules on the roots, as shown in Figure 16.1.

Plants also require elements such as phosphorus, calcium, potassium, and small amounts of copper, zinc, and iron. Compounds containing these mineral elements dissolve in water in the soil and enter the plant through its roots. Only dissolved minerals can be absorbed by plants. Table 16.1 lists some of the different soil elements involved in plant growth. Figure 16.2 shows how a lack of essential nutrients can affect plant health.

Table 16.1
The function of soil elements in plant growth

Element	Function or effect	If deficient
Nitrogen	■ gives plants their dark green colour	■ plants have yellowing leaves and stunted growth
Potassium	■ builds strength and disease resistance, improves quality of plant seeds	■ plants are stunted, the edges of older leaves turn brown and die
Magnesium	■ needed for photosynthesis	■ leaves are yellow with green veins
Sulfur	■ helps plants grow new cells	■ leaves have yellow veins and stunted growth
Phosphorous	■ helps develop roots, buds, and seeds	■ plants grow slowly; young leaves may be greyish, older leaves may be reddish
Calcium	■ helps develop healthy cell walls	■ may be unable to grow new leaves, stems, and roots

A Nitrogen deficiency

C Magnesium deficiency

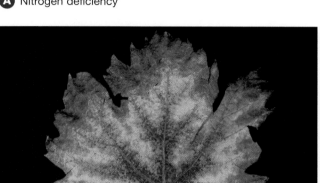

B Potassium deficiency

D Sulfur deficiency

Figure 16.2 The effects of different nutritional deficiencies on plants

THINKING LAB

Interpreting Nutrient Cycles

Background

In this activity, you will analyze four nutrient cycles that circulate matter through the biosphere. Study Figures 16.3 to 16.6 on the next page. Follow the arrows until you are sure why each figure represents a cycle. Note if the substance that is cycling ever seems to stop circulating for a prolonged period.

You Try It

1. What two elements are circulated through the environment by the water cycle? What process or processes makes these elements available to living things?

2. Both plants and animals require nitrogen. What percentage of the air is composed of nitrogen? Check Table 16.2 on page 591. Do animals obtain the nitrogen they need from the air? do plants? Explain.

3. Nitrogen atoms anchor the protein molecules in your body. These atoms have been in many other bodies before they entered yours. State some examples of other bodies they may have been in.

4. What two major processes make the carbon cycle possible? What organisms play the most important role in the carbon cycle? Could one organism play its role without the other? Explain.

5. Calcium and phosphorus atoms are essential for strong bones.

   (a) Milk from a cow is a good source of calcium, but where does the cow get the calcium?

   (b) Phosphorus atoms in your bones may have come from guano (bird droppings) used as fertilizer. What organism absorbed the phosphorus before you? Explain how it got into your diet.

6. Name three plant nutrients that circulate through the environment in complete cycles. Name three nutrients that follow an incomplete cycle. Distinguish between a complete cycle and an incomplete cycle.

7. **(a)** Which of the plant nutrients shown in these cycles would you classify as minerals? Explain.

   (b) Which of the plant nutrients in these cycles do you think are also human nutrients? Give reasons for your answer.

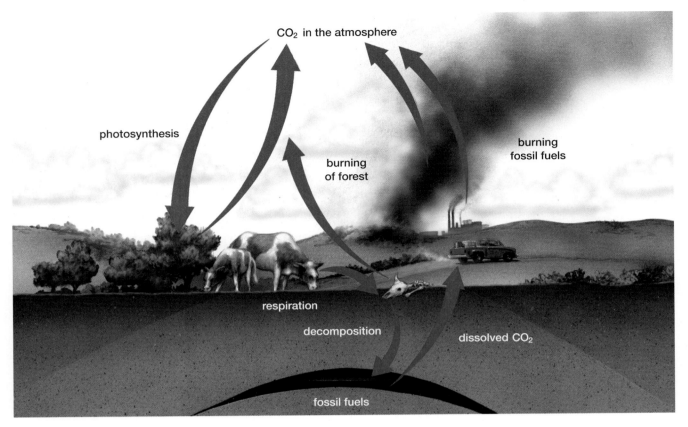

Figure 16.3 The carbon cycle.

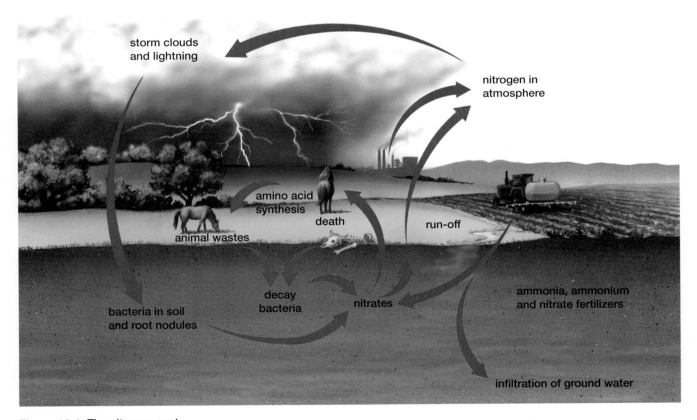

Figure 16.4 The nitrogen cycle.

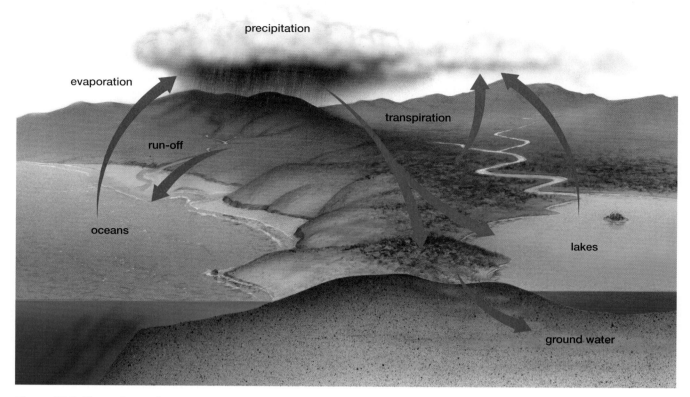

Figure 16.5 The water cycle.

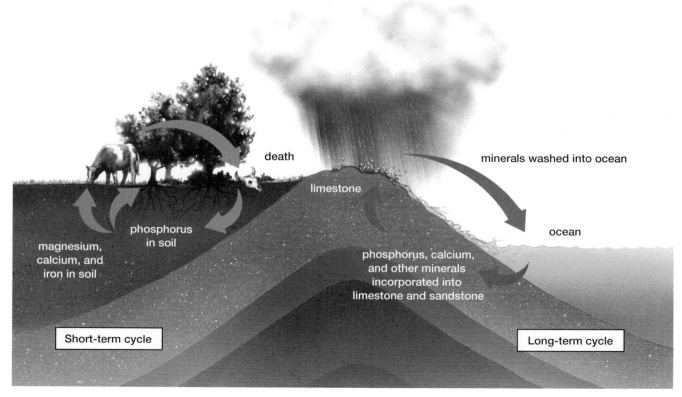

Figure 16.6 Other nutrients also cycle.

Soil: An Essential Resource

Soil is a substance composed of broken rock, decomposed organic matter, and an active community of living organisms. Also present are variable amounts of air and water. The rock particles are derived from a parent rock. This once-intact rock layer was broken by natural forces, such as erosion, into small pieces.

The decomposing organic matter, called **humus**, comes from dead organisms and it acts to bind mineral particles together and retain water. As humus breaks down into smaller and smaller pieces, it also provides some nutrients for plants. Without humus, soil loses its capacity to retain the water and atmospheric gases that the living community requires. The living community includes plants, animals, fungi, and micro-organisms.

Soil draws most of its minerals from the underlying parent rock. The minerals dissolve and are released into the soil and thus are made available to the organisms living there. Soil also contains a network of air spaces, created by the plants themselves through the continual growth of their roots, and the movement of animals such as earthworms.

The Role of Plants in Maintaining Soil

Forests and grasslands are complex and important to the natural environment. They provide homes for a wide variety of animal life, and they stabilize soils by controlling the rate of run-off from rain and melting snow.

BIO FACT

Soil scientists estimate that the earthworm has done more to change the face of our planet than any other organism, including ourselves. Soil is much more than just dirt. The total mass of organisms living in the soil under a natural meadow is much greater than the total mass of the rabbits, deer, and mice grazing on the surface of the meadow.

◀◀ REWIND

To learn more about micro-organisms and other organisms that live in the soil, turn to Chapters 12 and 13.

❚❚ PAUSE ● RECORD

It takes thousands of years for nature to convert rock into soil, but some farming practices can destroy this soil in an alarmingly short time. For example, in some developing countries, large tracts of rain forest have been burned to provide farmland to feed growing human populations. Once the trees have been burnt to stumps, the minerals from their ashes permit food crops to grow for only two or three years. So the farms are soon abandoned, after which nothing much will grow on the nearly sterile soil. This form of agriculture is clearly unsustainable. It degrades a natural resource so that it cannot be used for the same purpose in the foreseeable future, yet governments allow this practice to continue. Suggest reasons why, and suggest possible ways to reduce this damaging practice.

Figure 16.7 Both forests and grasslands help to improve the quality of the soil where they grow by breaking rock into smaller grains, by contributing to the formation of humus, and by maintaining airspaces in the soil. Some prairie grasses have roots 2 m deep.

Sunshine: The Ultimate Resource

Background

Even with the highest quality soil, rich in humus and minerals, and unlimited access to non-mineral nutrients such as carbon dioxide and water, a plant cannot survive without light. For plants in the wild, there is just one source of light energy: the Sun.

On average, solar energy reaches Earth's upper atmosphere at the rate of 42.7 MJ/m^2. Only a fraction of that reaches Earth's surface, and less than 1% of that fraction is used for photosynthesis. Yet, just 1 m^2 of forest may produce several kilograms of organic compounds in a single growing season.

The actual amount of sunlight that shines on a given location is affected by factors such as the season, the local climate, and distance from the equator. This map shows the amount of solar radiation that reaches different areas of Canada in a year.

You Try It

1. Examine the map shown on this page. Which part of Canada gets the most solar energy per year? The least? How does the location of your home compare?

2. Locations A and B get about 1800 h of bright sunlight per year.

   (a) From the map, read the annual solar radiation at each location.

(b) In your opinion, which location is more likely to support a diverse forest ecosystem? Give reasons for your answer.

3. Thunder Bay and Winnipeg get about 2100 h of bright sunlight per year.

   (a) From the map, read the annual solar radiation at each location.

   (b) Winnipeg is surrounded by rich grassland, much of it now used for farming. Thunder Bay is surrounded by sparse coniferous forest. What factor(s) other than amount of sunlight might account for this difference? Explain your answer.

4. Halifax and Vancouver get about 1700 h of bright sunlight per year.

   (a) From the map, read the annual solar radiation at each location.

   (b) The natural habitat in the area surrounding Vancouver consists of towering trees. Around Halifax, the trees are much smaller even when fully grown. What factor(s) other than amount of sunlight might account for this difference?

5. Three factors, season, climate, and distance from the equator, might affect the amount of sunlight that shines on a particular location. Based on the map, which of the three do you think has the greatest influence on the locations and habitats in questions 3 and 4 above? Give reasons for your answer.

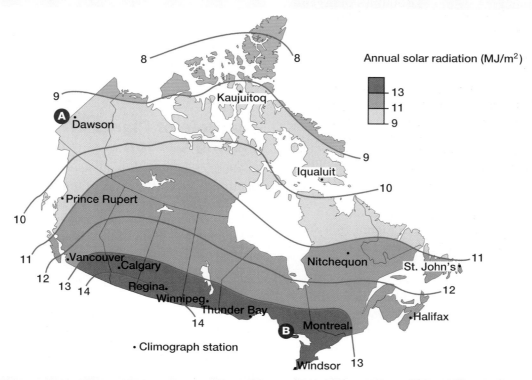

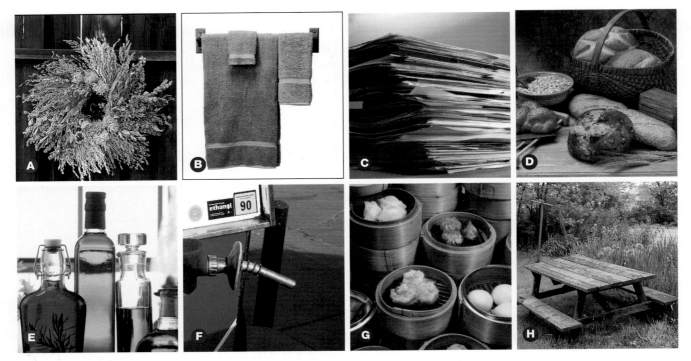

Figure 16.8 Many Canadians use various types of organic material such as:
(A) dried flower arrangement, (B) cotton towels, (C) paper, (D) wheat, (E) cooking oil,
(F) ethanol, (G) bamboo products, and (H) wooden furniture.

What are Plants Made Of?

The different objects shown in Figure 16.8 are no longer able to synthesize food, collect matter and reorganize it, so they are not living. However, these objects were initially organized as components of living things and are therefore examples of **organic matter**. Food is an example of organic matter too. So are straw hats and leather boots. Can you think of some other examples of organic matter?

Plants produce the food they need by means of photosynthesis. The reactants and products of this process appear in the following word equation. Only one of these, glucose, can be classed as food.

$$\text{carbon dioxide} + \text{water} \xrightarrow{\text{light energy}} \text{glucose} + \text{oxygen}$$

The glucose molecule is rich in stored chemical energy, whereas the reactants (CO_2 and H_2O) contain only a little energy. However, there is more to the structure of plants than just glucose. For example, the dead tree stumps in Figure 16.9 on the next page probably contain very few individual glucose molecules. However, the wood does contain many molecules of cellulose, a large and complex carbohydrate. Each cellulose molecule contains several strands of carbohydrate, and each strand contains many thousands of linked glucose units. The strands themselves are cross-linked. In wood, the cellulose molecules are stuck together by

lignin, a glue-like substance. Many other compounds are present in the bark, twigs, leaves, and flowers of trees.

The Role of Plants in Storing Carbon

In 1900, carbon dioxide made up 0.003% of air in the troposphere (the layer of the atmosphere next to the Earth's surface). By the year 2000, the carbon dioxide concentration had increased almost 25% to nearly 0.004%. Both of these values appear to be very small. However, the amount of carbon dioxide in the atmosphere is rising by about 5% per decade. In 2010, the level will be about 0.0042%. Studies of tree growth rings reveal that in the past several thousand years, this increase is by far the greatest. How is it possible to track these changes using trees? Carbon is fixed, or incorporated, in organic tissue. This is called carbon storage. Many trees are very long-lived, and the amount of carbon that has been stored in their tissues at different times can be assessed.

Trees and vegetation can store excess carbon in their tissues for as long as they are alive. A **carbon sink** is an area, such as a forest, where there is a lot of carbon stored in organic tissue. Several countries have announced plans to plant billions of trees to help remove excess carbon dioxide from the atmosphere. This is only a short-term solution for carbon storage, because eventually, the trees will die and the carbon will be released when they decay.

The Role of Plants in Making Oxygen

Today, the air in the troposphere is a mixture of several gases. Earth's early atmosphere held no oxygen at all but now oxygen molecules make up about 21% of the total volume (see Table 16.2).

Plants release far more oxygen than they ever use and this excess is released into the biosphere. Even though plants were not the first organisms to produce oxygen by photosynthesis, today they play a major role in producing the oxygen used in cellular respiration by almost all organisms.

Math LINK

Earth's diameter is roughly 13 000 km. The troposphere is about 10 km deep. Estimate the volume of the troposphere in cubic centimetres. Assume that there are about 3×10^9 gas molecules in each cubic centimetre of air. Use this information to determine the number of oxygen molecules in the troposphere.

Table 16.2
Composition of air in the troposphere

Gas	% by volume
N_2 (nitrogen)	78
O_2 (oxygen	21
Ar (argon)	1
CO_2 (carbon dioxide)	0.004
Other gases	traces

≪ REWIND

Turn to Chapter 3, Section 3.2 to review the process of photosynthesis and how plants are involved in carbon and oxygen cycling.

Figure 16.9 The rest of these trees were sawn into lumber. The bark and other scraps were burned as fuel to help run the sawmill.

SECTION REVIEW

1. **K/U** What form of energy do plants use for manufacturing food? What is the usual source of this energy for plants? Is there any alternative to the source you identified?

2. **K/U** What nutrients do plants obtain from the atmosphere? from the soil?

3. **K/U** In the following list, which are examples of organic matter? Explain why the others are not. Wool sweater, straw mat, silk shirt, penicillin pill, aluminum rowboat, birchbark canoe, diamond ring, rubber boot, fingernail clippings.

4. **K/U** Explain what is essential about an essential nutrient. Give an example of an essential nutrient for plants and for humans. Give an example of a non-essential nutrient for plants and for humans.

5. **MC** Name and describe some human activities that may disrupt each of these cycles: carbon cycle, nitrogen cycle, water cycle.

6. **K/U** List the main components of soil. Identify the origin of each component and describe its function.

7. **C** Prepare a flowchart or concept map to show the relationships among (a) the role of humus in soil, (b) the role of soil in plant growth, and (c) the role of plants in producing humus.

The Process of Succession

Figure 16.10 Severe soil erosion has changed the growing conditions for this tree.

From Fort Severn south through Algonquin Park and all the way to Point Pelee, the plant ecosystems of southern Ontario, like other provinces, are diverse. In each ecosystem, the native plants are adapted to the local growing conditions. Local growing conditions are the physical conditions of a particular location, including such factors as light, rainfall, temperature, and type of soil.

What if those growing conditions are altered abruptly, as shown in Figure 16.10? In some cases, the plants would not be able to survive, and would die. This might allow other species to grow there. In other cases, the plants might be able to tolerate the new growing conditions. In the same way that growing conditions affect the species living in them, the species living in an area can affect the growing conditions.

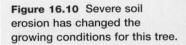

Web LINK

Go to the web site shown below to research one specific adaptation that suits each of these plants to its usual environment: mayflower in Nova Scotia, cactus in British Columbia, Manitoba maple in Manitoba, black walnut in southern Ontario, pitch pine in eastern Ontario. Go to **Science Resources**, then to **BIOLOGY 11** to find out where to go next. **www.school.mcgrawhill.ca/resources/**

The Effects of Glaciation

Imagine the Canadian landscape about 8000 B.C.E. Great mounds of boulders, pebbles, gravel, and dust are accumulating as the last glacier melts. These ground-up remains of rocks were transported from northern Canada. No plants grow here. Previous glaciers have pushed farther south, but this one will not. A narrow margin of soil-covered land, between the hills of rubble and Lake Ontario, is warm enough to support vegetation. South of the lake, where the climate is warmer, a broad band of deciduous forest stretches from the East coast to the Midwest. The drier western climate cannot support many trees, and the forest gives way to extensive grasslands that stretch westward to the Rocky Mountains.

If you could see a time-lapse aerial view of the northern hemisphere as the glaciers receded, you would get the impression that areas of forests and other vegetation were migrating toward the North Pole. However, the trees are not actually travelling. What you are seeing is the natural process of succession. A sequence of change in a community that starts with bare rock and ends with a stable ecosystem is called **primary succession**. A similar sequence of change in a community that begins with a previously existing but disturbed community is called **secondary succession**. Figures 16.11 and 16.12 show these two types of succession.

Figure 16.11 Primary succession from bare rock to deciduous forest.

living trees → charred stumps → fire weed → aspen, beeches and other plants (for example: blueberries) → return to same climax forest

Figure 16.12 Secondary succession following a forest fire.

THINKING LAB

Tracing Succession

Background

In this lab, you will interpret and compare the two main forms of natural succession. Figure 16.11 shows a typical example of primary succession, the orderly sequence of changes that occurs as a rocky region is colonized by plants. Figure 16.12 shows an example of secondary succession, which usually follows a significant disruption to an existing plant community.

You Try It

1. Study the labels and captions in Figures 16.11 and 16.12 carefully. Working with a partner, compare the two figures and create a chart with the headings shown here. Complete your chart.

	Primary succession	Secondary succession
Where?		
When?		
Starts with?		
Sequence?		
How fast?		
Leads to?		

2. Based on what you see in Figure 16.11 and 16.12, and your own research, describe the final stage of succession. This can be your preliminary definition of "climax community." Keep your definition handy as you read on.

Climax Communities

Large stretches of the northern Canadian landscape, stripped bare by the glaciers, can still be seen as glacial pavement. Here the rocks, cracked and grooved by the action of the ice, support first lichens and then mosses. Eventually, during the process of primary succession, these rocks will be broken down and converted to fertile soil.

The final stage of succession is a **climax community**. Depending upon the environment, the climax community will be different. The soil, water, temperature, and other factors will influence the final result. Table 16.3 on page 596 lists some examples of climax communities.

Figure 16.13 Glacial pavement supports lichens and mosses.

Biology *Magazine*   TECHNOLOGY • SOCIETY • ENVIRONMENT

Purple Plague

If you have driven along any of the highways in Canada, you may have seen what many are calling the "purple plague." Purple loosestrife (*Lythrum salicaria*) is wreaking havoc on our environment. It is just one of many exotic (non-native) species that have started to make up a large portion of the landscape in southern Canada's heavily populated areas. These uninvited guests take over wetlands and choke out native plants (such as cattails, sedges, and bulrushes) that are necessary parts of our natural ecosystems. Their rampant growth has greatly reduced the ecological variety of marshes and other wetlands. Purple loosestrife has interfered with the succession patterns of native wetland species because it takes over the areas that native plants need to reproduce. The competition between native and non-native plants results in a loss of biodiversity — unique plants disappear and the ecosystem becomes less complex. These introduced species do not necessarily have the same benefits to the ecosystem as the native plants they replace. In an ecologically fragile area, these invasive plants can increase soil erosion, create fire hazards, destroy streams and wetlands, decrease forage for animals, and negatively affect recreation, fisheries, and public water supplies.

How Did Purple Loosestrife Become Such a Nuisance?

The purple loosestrife plant arrived from Europe about 200 years ago, as an ornamental species for gardeners. However, the early gardeners failed to recognize that it would spread easily beyond the boundaries of their small plots. Since pollination patterns and winds expand a flora's territory far beyond one individual garden, an invasive species such as purple loosestrife can easily find its way into the native ecosystem where it did not evolve. Purple loosestrife was able to compete with and outgrow the surrounding plants — both above and below the ground. Unlike its European ancestors, the plant became a vigorous competitor in our ecosystem because it had no natural predators in Canada.

On a mountainside any particular climax community will be very small because the same growing conditions persist over only a small area. This is because elevation above sea level determines not only temperature, but rainfall. The mountain tops are cooler (about 9°C for every 1000 m increase in elevation) and, usually, wetter. There are two reasons for the increased moisture: water vapour condenses more readily at cool temperatures, and the mountain peaks disrupt clouds and "catch" more rain. Where similar growing conditions persist over a large region, as is the case in most parts of Canada, a climax community may cover thousands of square kilometres. The type of climax community produced by primary succession depends on climate.

Climax communities are often named for their dominant vegetation, for example, the boreal forest climax community. Any climax community consists of plants, animals, fungi, and micro-organisms — a whole complex world living together in a dynamic balance. Such a balance may take thousands of years to develop but, once established, may persist for several centuries.

The key word is "dynamic." Although stable, a climax community is not static: things do change. As long as the climate remains stable, individuals that die will be replaced by new individuals of the same species. However, the composition of the climax community will change if growing conditions do. Growing conditions can change even though the climate remains stable.

Insect Controls

In its native Eurasia, there are more than 100 different insects that consume loosestrife. Loosestrife cannot become an invasive species there because it has natural predators. However, this is not the case in Canada. In an attempt to find a way to control the spread of loosestrife, researchers have identified four possible candidates among the European predator insects — two leaf feeders, a flower feeder, and a root feeder. All have been deemed unlikely to harm a new environment. In one test conducted, the insects starved to death when offered any plant but loosestrife to eat. The major question is whether these insects would be the entire answer to loosestrife management, or whether introducing them would just create another pest problem (since they are also non-native species).

Other Possible Solutions

In 1993, the World Conservation Congress declared invasive species second only to habitat loss as a threat to global biodiversity. Invasive plants vary by region, with rainfall, climate, soil type, and other cultural conditions all playing a role in determining if a plant will become invasive. Uprooting plants such as loosestrife is only partially effective because their seeds can remain dormant for a long time. Adding a herbicide to loosestrife's watery environment pollutes the water table.

The loosestrife problem is most severe in areas that have been disturbed by tilling and grazing. Any disturbed soil allows new plant life to take hold. Because disturbed soil contains no plants, aggressive plants can gain a foothold before the native species. Thus, loosestrife often becomes dominant in ecologically abused areas for which the previous flora and fauna are largely unknown.

Before an eradication program is launched, we need to know more about the local ecology.

Can Gardeners Play a Role in the Control of Loosestrife?

Loosestrife is still considered an ornamental species by some gardeners. Nurseries sell sterile cultivars of this plant, but the seeds that are produced may be viable if they are grown in close proximity to the wild species. This is because the bees carrying the pollen may inadvertently pollinate the garden plant, thereby allowing the formation of seeds that can germinate. Gardeners must take some responsibility for the plants they choose to grow. If a plant is considered invasive in your area, caution must be exercised. Growth and seed development must be monitored. Gardeners must be diligent in reading plant labels and staying informed about the possibility of new plants becoming invasive.

Follow-up

1. Why are some plants only considered invasive in some areas of Canada?

2. Would you consider the Norway maple to be invasive? Explain.

3. Identify other invasive plants in your community.

4. Would a program to pull out loosestrife plants help to eradicate them?

5. Could garden mint become an invasive species in your area?

Table 16.3

Examples of some climax communities in Canada

Climax community	Climate	Example
Tundra	■ long cold winters ■ short cool summers ■ low precipitation (<25 cm/year)	Baker Lake, Nunavut Fort Severn, Ontario
Boreal forest	■ long cold winters ■ short warm summers ■ more precipitation (25–50 cm/year)	Timmins, Ontario Yellowknife, Northwest Territories
Mixed forest (deciduous and coniferous)	■ shorter winters ■ warmer summers ■ still more precipitation (50–75 cm/year)	Fredericton, New Brunswick Muskoka, Ontario
Deciduous forest	■ milder winters ■ hotter summers ■ precipitation (>75 cm/year)	Montréal, Québec Toronto, Ontario

Word LINK

"Boreal" comes from the Greek *Boreas*, god of the north wind. Another term for this is *taiga*, a Russian word for the environment between tundra to the north and the steppes to the south. Sometimes this biome is called "transitional forest" instead.

Canada's Biomes

The 34-million-year-old tree trunk in Figure 16.14 is part of several found in a fossil forest on Axel Heiberg Island in Nunavut, in the eastern Arctic. When this trunk was part of a living tree, the climate around the North Pole was warm enough to support a coniferous forest and wet enough to support organisms resembling today's alligators. Today, Axel Heiberg Island is barren land and snow — the boreal forest biome no longer exists there.

Today, nearly half of Canada's land area is covered in forest. Figure 16.15 shows some of Canada's dominant biomes. The northern coniferous forest of spruce, fir, and pine is one of the largest in the world, sweeping across the country in a broad band. The eastern forests are a mixture of conifers and deciduous trees, such as maple, beech, pine, and hemlock. The Pacific coast rainforest includes dense stands of immense trees such as western red cedar, yellow cedar, and Douglas fir.

Figure 16.14 Large trees once grew just 700 km south of the North Pole.

Climax communities such as Saskatchewan's grasslands or British Columbia's temperate rainforest may persist for hundreds of years, if nothing disrupts them. However, disruptions are common, and were occurring even before humans appeared. Natural disruptions include floods, earthquakes, tornadoes, volcanic eruptions, and wildfires.

Human activities that disrupt biomes or interrupt natural successions are becoming increasingly frequent. Regular harvesting of trees for pulpwood or lumber occurs in about two-thirds of Canada's forested land. Secondary succession can replace these forests, and many forestry companies operate extensive tree-planting programs so that the forests become a renewable resource. Regrowth does not occur, however, when forests have been cleared and used for farmland, because repeated ploughing prevents trees from developing. When farmland is converted to suburbs, industrial parks, and highways, the human-built structures prevent natural succession from taking place.

The destruction of forests through the processes of clear cutting, forest fires, flooding, diseases, or acid rain leads directly to a loss of habitat for many animals. Loss of forested land can also affect the climate by altering the water cycle and this, in turn, can lead to soil erosion. Changes in carbon dioxide levels as a result of cutting and burning trees (and thus losing carbon sinks and increasing greenhouse gases) also affect climate change.

A The temperate deciduous forest spans southern Ontario.

C Boreal forest spans northern Europe, Asia, and North America.

B A mixed forest of conifers and deciduous trees covers parts of southern Ontario and eastern Canada.

D Tundra is the biome nearest to the polar region.

Figure 16.15 The dominant biomes of Canada.

SECTION REVIEW

1. **K/U** Describe what growing conditions would favour a plant with the adaptations described below.

   ▪ thick, succulent stems
   ▪ deep tap roots
   ▪ large lacy leaves
   ▪ rapid life cycle

2. **K/U** Define the term "climax community." Give one example from Ontario and one from outside Ontario.

3. **K/U** Some of Canada's most striking twentieth-century artworks were landscapes painted in Ontario's Muskoka area. If the artists of these landscapes could travel in time, what features would a painting done 10 000 years ago show? What features would a painting done today show? What happened to change the landscape so dramatically?

4. **K/U** Climax communities may include desert, forest, grassland, or tundra.

   (a) Which is most common in Canada?

   (b) What human activities may disrupt the climax community named in (a)?

5. **C** Most native plants are well adapted to the growing conditions in their environment. What adaptations do you think allow the poplar (a deciduous tree) to thrive in so many parts of Canada, despite the cold winters? What adaptations allow the white spruce (an evergreen tree) to thrive throughout the same range? Sketch the adaptations of both trees to compare them.

6. **MC** Explain the term "ecologically successful." Do you think plants are ecologically successful? Do you think humans are ecologically successful? State your reasoning.

7. **MC** Long-term climate change can cause succession to occur. Predict the effect of an increase in rainfall on the grassland of the prairie. Predict the effect of an increase in temperature on the coniferous forests of northern Ontario. Explain the significance of this to the biosphere.

Technology and Plant Growth

- Briefly review the history of agriculture.

- Evaluate the use of technology to fertilize land and to reduce the number of crop pests and weeds.

- Describe and evaluate different technologies used in agriculture.

Figure 16.16 Early technology for living off the land. Similar tools are still used today by less industrialized agricultural societies around the globe.

Technology refers to more than just tools or mechanical devices. It also refers to any knowledge, systems, procedures, or techniques that can be used to solve practical problems. Early agricultural technologies for example, are shown in Figure 16.16.

The earliest humans were nomadic hunter-gatherers. They had a very practical problem to solve: how to get enough food for survival. You and everyone around you are descendants of people who invented technology to help them survive. Others who tried to hunt or harvest with ineffective technology left no descendants.

Regular harvesting of wild roots led to the development of specialized digging tools. By today's standards for technology, such tools seem simple and crude. However, they were sophisticated enough to launch an agricultural revolution.

Table 16.4
Emergence of agriculture around the globe

Location of early agricultural site	Emergence of agriculture
Middle East	10 000 B.C.E. (12 000 years ago)
Eastern Europe	6 100 B.C.E. (8 100 years ago)
Western Mediterranean; central Europe	5 000 B.C.E. (7 000 years ago)
Central and South America	5 000 B.C.E. (7 000 years ago)
Yellow River valley of China	4 000 B.C.E. (6 000 years ago)

The Emergence of Agriculture

The term **agricultural revolution** refers to a fundamental change in people's way of life. The ability to control the growth of plants for food contrasted sharply with the nomadic lifestyle of hunter-gatherers who had to search for food. Table 16.4 shows that agriculture emerged at different times in different locations.

Nomadic hunter-gatherers already had two-thirds of the technology needed to make the transition to an agricultural way of life. First, they had the *knowledge*: a vast memory bank of data enabling them to recognize which plants were edible, what parts were edible, where these plants grew, and at what time of year they could be harvested. Second, the nomads had already invented and manufactured tools for digging up edible roots, for harvesting seeds, and for grinding the seeds into an edible form. Then, around 10 000 B.C.E., the third component was developed: a new technique for tilling the soil and deliberately planting wild grass seeds and pieces of roots or tubers.

This practice increased the quantity and quality of food that a given plot of land could produce. Development of the plough 6000 years ago increased the productivity of the land a thousandfold. The result was a food-producing revolution that enabled the human population to increase dramatically.

Monocultures

The corn field shown in the small photograph at the beginning of this chapter is an example of a **monoculture**. This practice substitutes hundreds of hectares of one type of plant for the original, natural ecosystem. The intended effect of any monoculture is to maximize the amount of feed, food, or other plant product that can be obtained from a given area of land. However, monocultures also cause unintended effects.

In particular, soil nutrients will be depleted. The composition of soil changes over time because its mineral content is reduced by high levels of rainfall and by agricultural use. If the same plot is used repeatedly for the same crop, the same minerals will be absorbed by the plants repeatedly, and the site will eventually become unusable. Along some rivers, such as the lower Nile, fresh supplies of mineral-rich rock particles are delivered annually by natural flooding. Elsewhere, farmers must find some means for replenishing the lost minerals.

Another effect of monoculture is that crop-specific pests are inevitable. By selecting one particular crop species for preferable treatment, farmers are also attracting the pests that are associated with that crop. Pests may include animals, such as insects or rodents. As well, disease-causing micro-organisms (fungi, protists, bacteria, or viruses) and unwanted plants (weeds) may be attracted. Decreased plant diversity leads to increased vulnerability to disease. Pest control technology is discussed in greater detail on page 601.

 MINI LAB

Modern Farm Math: A Case Study

In this lab, you will compare two technologies (farm manure and commercial chemical fertilizer) used to restore depleted soil.

Suppose you are the manager of a modern factory farm owned by a large corporate grain producer. Your farm raises corn exclusively. Corn requires large amounts of replacement nutrients if repeat crops are to be grown on the same fields. The modern farm manager must balance the cost of supplying these nutrients against the expected increase in crop value.

Your farm is about 10 km away from another factory farm. It is not very large, but its buildings house thousands of pigs. Environmental authorities are threatening to close this operation because the pig manure drains through the soil into local waterways, where it accelerates the growth of water plants that choke out other aquatic organisms. As well micro-organisms in the manure may contaminate the human water supply.

Analyze

1. Calculate the mass of N, P, and K provided by a 50 kg bag of 20-10-20 fertilizer. (20-10-20 means 20% N, 10% P, and 20% K). Calculate how many kilograms of manure are required to provide equivalent nutrients. A typical analysis of manure is 0.5% N, 0.25% P, and 0.5% K.

2. How many kilograms of N, P, and K does a typical hectare of corn absorb in one growing season?

3. Assume that all the corn is carried away for sale, so the N, P, and K it contains are lost to the soil. Calculate the cost of replacing the lost nutrients with commercial fertilizers. Include the cost of purchasing, delivering, handling, and storing the fertilizer, and the cost of labour, fuel, and leasing the machines.

4. Calculate the cost of replacing the lost nutrients with farm manure. Assume that the manure could be obtained free of charge from the pig farm, but your corn farm would be responsible for transportation costs.

5. Why might environmental authorities prefer the use of manure rather than fertilizer, even though the same quantity of nutrients would enter the soil in either case?

6. Based on your analysis, would you use the free manure or place an order for fertilizer? Is there a third way?

II PAUSE ● **RECORD**

Even the most fertile soil cannot support plant life unless the required light, moisture, and temperature for growth are also present. For example, desert soil may be rich in nutrients but unable to support crops because it is too dry. Think about the practicality of using technologies such as irrigation, greenhouses, or grow-lights to grow plants in an environment that is too dry, too cool, or too dark. Write your thoughts in your notebook.

Technology for Improving Soil Fertility

As discussed earlier in this chapter, plants need several essential nutrients for normal growth and development. Obtaining enough carbon, hydrogen, and oxygen does not depend on the quality of the soil. However, plants also require nitrogen, phosphorus, potassium, sulfur, calcium, and magnesium, and small amounts of other elements. Soil that contains these elements in a form that plants can use is said to be fertile. Soil is made up of sand, silt, or clay that is derived from rocks, so **soil fertility** often depends on the mineral content of the parent rock.

However, the mineral content of soil may be reduced by heavy rainfall or by agriculture. Technology for restoring soil fertility may be grouped into four classes:

- *Crop rotation* Crops are rotated or fields are allowed to lie fallow (rest) as shown in Figure 16.17 for a period of time.

- *Green manure* Crops such as fall rye are planted but ploughed under (rather than harvested) when mature.

- *Farm manure* Animal wastes are spread on the soil before cultivation.

- *Fertilizers* Inorganic chemicals that contain the missing minerals are added to the soil.

Figure 16.17 Some fields are allowed to lie fallow for a season of growth.

Crop Rotation

Fresh supplies of potassium and phosphorus (but not nitrogen) enter the soil through the continued weathering of rocks. You may recall from studying the nitrogen cycle, shown in Figure 16.4 on page 586, that plants cannot use gaseous nitrogen; they require soluble nitrogen compounds. In part, these compounds are supplied through the natural breakdown of dead plants and the wastes of plant-eating animals. When crop plants are harvested, the nitrogen they contain is not recycled into the field where the crop grew.

As you have learned, certain soil bacteria have the ability to take in atmospheric N_2 and convert it to soluble compounds. This process is called nitrogen fixation. Legume plants, such as peas and beans, harbour nitrogen-fixing bacteria in their roots. Carefully planned **crop rotation**, in which legumes are grown in alternate seasons with crops that use large amounts of nitrogen will restore some of the nitrogen. A field undergoing this process is shown in Figure 16.18. However, nitrogen fixation is too gradual to prevent the rapid depletion of nitrogen when the same crop is grown on the same soil season after season.

Figure 16.18 Legume crops can restore some of the nitrogen that is taken out of the soil when other crops that use up the nitrogen are harvested.

Web LINK

To learn more about soil fertility and the addition of nutrients to facilitate crop growth, go to the web site shown below. Go to **Science Resources**, then to **BIOLOGY 11** to find out where to go next. Find out what the optimum fertilizer additions are to enhance the flowering of one crop species (vegetable or fruit) or one horticultural species.
www.school.mcgrawhill.ca/resources/

Farm Manure Technology

In the past, farmers restored nutrients to depleted soil by applying farm manure. This term refers to refuse from farm animals, including urine, feces, and straw or sawdust used to absorb these substances. In addition to its moisture-absorbing components, manure is rich in the three important mineral nutrients: nitrogen (N), phosphorus (P), and potassium (K). Some of the benefits of farm manure technology include:

■ Manure is natural and easily obtained and the nitrogen is in a natural, slow-release form;

■ Manure needs to be disposed of anyway, whether or not it is used to fertilize crops; and

■ Manure will decompose and form humus, which increases the soil's ability to absorb and retain water

There are some drawbacks to this technology. The main ones include:

■ It requires careful, time-consuming management and it is difficult to control application so that nutrients are evenly distributed;

■ Manure must be stored so as to prevent depletion of nutrients by rain. A large volume of manure is needed, and its aroma is strong;

■ Manure with high levels of bacteria (for example, *E. coli*) may compromise water safety; and

■ The cost of labour to apply manure may exceed the cost of fertilizer with equivalent nutrients.

Commercial Chemical Fertilizers

Modern farmers often choose to supply nitrogen, phosporus and potassium by applying commercial chemical fertilizers instead of manure. Fertilizers for the agricultural industry are usually manufactured in the form of dry granules.

Such fertilizers are convenient to store, handle, and apply. However, care must be taken not to use too much fertilizer, as excess concentrations can actually kill the crop plants. As well, fertilizer runoff can promote the growth of aquatic plants and algae, disrupting aquatic ecosystems.

Technology for Controlling Pests

There are always many interacting organisms associated within natural systems. A pest is an organism that is not wanted by humans. In agriculture, pests are organisms that cause damage to human crops. They can either cause disease and ruin the crop as shown in Figure 16.19 below, or they can eat or spoil an already harvested crop.

Controlling pests associated with agricultural crops on a large scale usually involves the application of pesticides. By definition, all pesticides are toxic to some living thing. This raises some strong concerns which need to be addressed. For example, the pesticide may also be toxic to non-target organisms. Rodenticides kill mice on wheat farms, but they may also reduce soil fertility by killing off beneficial soil organisms, such as earthworms.

Other problems include the fact that some pesticides may cause health problems in people either working on farms, as shown in Figure 16.20, or eating produce. Newer pesticides are designed to break down rapidly so that they cannot affect non-target organisms for very long. However, the cost of these pesticides is high, and the time that they are effective is still too long and may cause damage.

Figure 16.20 Farm workers may be at risk from exposure to pesticides.

Figure 16.19 Locusts invading a field in Africa.

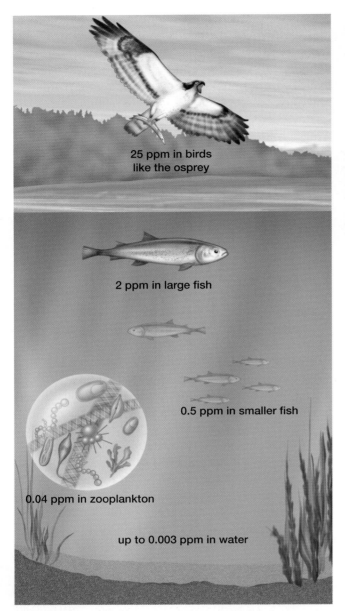

25 ppm in birds
like the osprey

2 ppm in large fish

0.5 ppm in smaller fish

0.04 ppm in zooplankton

up to 0.003 ppm in water

Figure 16.21 Pesticides like DDT pass through the food chain. Levels of DDT are shown in parts per million (ppm).

Pesticides can travel along a food chain, in a process called **biomagnification**. Pesticides are applied to the producers in a food chain, and then ingested by herbivores. Those herbivores are then eaten by other higher level consumers. At each stage, the pesticides are passed along from organism to organism. The pesticides become concentrated in the tissues of the top predators in the system. This process is shown in Figure 16.21.

Figure 16.22 Cargo ships can harbour small pests, so many regulations are imposed on incoming cargo.

Through natural selection the target pest population may become resistant to the pesticide. For example, the first year a new insecticide is introduced, it will kill nearly all of the pest insects exposed to it. This outcome may seem like a huge success, but unfortunately it is not. The insects that were able to survive already possessed some genetic ability to survive the presence of the insecticide. Only the surviving pests can reproduce so their resistant genes are passed onto their offspring. As the pest population continues to reproduce, each generation will be more and more able to survive the insecticide, and the insecticide will no longer be effective.

In addition to controlling pests through the use of pesticides, it is important to keep new pests from arriving and associating with Canadian crops. Figure 16.22 shows a cargo ship loading cargo at a port. Many pests, including insects and rodents, can arrive in imported cargo.

Web LINK

During the twentieth century, *P. infestans* (the micro-organism responsible for the Irish potato famine) was kept under control by the use of pesticides. Now, over 160 years after the Irish potato famine, *P. infestans* is once again threatening potato crops in Mexico and elsewhere. Find out why pesticides are no longer fully effective by going to the web site shown below. Go to **Science Resources**, then to **BIOLOGY 11** to find out where to go next. Is there a risk to Canada's potato crops? What measures need to be taken now? Why were these measures not taken earlier?
www.school.mcgrawhill.ca/resources/

Alternative Pest Control Technology

When first developed, pesticides seem like a perfect solution to the problem of crop losses due to pests. There are, however, alternatives to the intensive use of pesticides on agricultural crops.

- *Mechanical control* involves trapping, catching, picking off, or pulling up the unwanted pests. Once pulled up, plant pests such as weeds can be left to die.

- *Cultural control* refers to cultivation methods that discourage pests. In the past, farmers left bare soil between rows of crop plants. Now most farmers cover this bare soil with plants that attract the pest insect's predators. Another form of cultural control is crop rotation — fields are planted with alternating crops every other year. This technique is effective against pests that attack the crop's roots.

- *Sex attractant control* involves sterilizing male insects in the laboratory using radiation. The sterile males are released in large numbers during the mating season for that particular species. Wild females that mate with the plentiful, but sterile, males will lay infertile eggs. Another variation of this method involves the use of lab-produced sex attractants (pheromones) to disrupt the mating patterns of insects.

- *Biological control* involves using a pest's natural enemies to reduce its population. One version involves the release of predators, parasites, or pathogens that will eat, disable, or infect the pest. Figure 16.23 shows a ladybug feeding on aphids, which are a common pest. Another method involves co-planting with selected non-crop species that manufacture their own natural pesticides. For example, many home gardeners plant marigolds, like the ones shown in Figure 16.24, among their vegetables because some pests are repelled by the strong scent emitted by the marigold flowers.

Even though these methods act more slowly than many chemical pesticides, they are widely regarded as a safer alternative. The alternatives are also capable of becoming problems. For example, in 1932 the Australian sugar industry imported 101 cane toads (*Bufo marinus*) from Hawaii. The toads were supposed to feed on the grubs of two beetle species that were damaging sugar cane plants. These toads reproduced quickly, and within six months there were 60 000 young toads. Unfortunately, the toads had little effect on the cane beetles because the toads did not stay in the cane fields. They moved out into the surrounding ecosystems and competed with the native insect-eaters for food. The imported toads were much bigger than the native species and were also poisonous to predators that might ordinarily eat toads. Today, millions of cane toads are spread over a quarter of Australia and are still expanding the borders of their territory at about 30 km per year.

Figure 16.23 Ladybugs are used as biological control of some pests.

Figure 16.24 Marigolds can be used to repel some pests of garden vegetables.

Methods of pest control vary in their reliability and effectiveness. A recent strategy is called **integrated pest management** or **IPM**. Knowledge of pests and the environment is combined with proven control methods (both chemical and non-chemical) to prevent unacceptable levels of pest damage. Although IPM has many benefits, and is likely the most effective strategy for long-term pest control, it is costly in terms of time, labour, and ongoing management.

An alternative way to grow plants in a pest-free environment is **soil-free horticulture**. This method involves using a covered, controlled environment. **Hydroponic culturing** involves growing plants with their roots immersed in water that contains dissolved nutrients, as shown in Figure 16.25. Fairly high concentrations of fertilizer must be provided to supply the roots with adequate nutrition. Once the crop is harvested, growers recycle the leftover fertilizer and water for use on the next crop. In some cases, the leftover water and fertilizer must be changed. For example, cucumber roots exude their own defence chemicals that would affect the growth of other vegetables, such as tomatoes. If the two crops are to be cultivated the cucumber defence chemicals must be removed or neutralized before a healthy tomato crop can be grown.

Aeroponic culturing involves raising plants with their roots enclosed in containers. The containers are fitted with spray nozzles that dispense just the right mix and quantity of water and nutrients to the roots. This method is even more costly than hydroponic culture. It is used only for growing plants that will yield high prices (such as winter tomatoes) or plants whose crop value depends on the quality of the roots (such as *Echinacea*).

Figure 16.25 Hydroponic culture involves the growth of plants without soil.

SECTION REVIEW

1. **K/U** What three technological factors combined to make the agricultural revolution possible?

2. **K/U** Name three elemental nutrients that become depleted when fertile soil is used to grow a crop. What technologies can be used to restore soil fertility?

3. **K/U** What types of crop pests can be controlled by pesticides? Give three reasons why the use of pesticides is controversial. List some alternatives to the use of pesticides. For each alternative, state one advantage and one disadvantage.

4. **C** Explain how growing the same crop repeatedly on the same field can deplete the soil. What is it that becomes depleted? What steps can be taken to replenish the soil?

5. **C** Define monoculture and give an example. Explain the advantages and disadvantages of monoculture technology.

6. **MC** How might you expect agricultural workers to be affected by air and water pollution in the long term? How might the field mice and the birds that feed on them be affected? What would happen to the ecosystem in that region?

7. **MC** In India, about one third of formerly arable land is now sterile. Some is contaminated, some is exhausted or impoverished as a result of repeated agriculture without mineral replacement, and some is so compacted that any future use for agriculture seems highly unlikely. Suggest a technological fix that might restore the land in each case. Is your solution practical?

UNIT PROJECT PREP

You have probably already chosen the plant-based industry that you will be investigating for your Unit 5 Project. This section has given you information about different types of technologies and their effects on agricultural practices. Ensure that you are keeping ongoing notes about how your new learnings can be applied to your project and the industry you have chosen.

Plant Technology and the Biosphere

- Appreciate that Earth's human population is supported by agricultural technology.

- Describe the energy and water costs of intensive agriculture.

- Evaluate the interactions among society, plant technology, and the environment.

Figure 16.26 A very large amount of energy is used by giant combines to harvest crops from the fields.

It is estimated that Earth's natural resources could have supported a maximum of 10 million humans before the agricultural revolution. By 1750, our planet was supporting 800 million humans — many more than would have been possible without agricultural technology. Abundant food has provided many opportunities for growth and development, but they have created an entirely new lifestyle that has shaped human society in many ways. They effects include:

- *A new vulnerability.* People became more vulnerable to bad weather. As well, investing heavily in non-portable technology means people can not easily abandon their fields and permanent dwellings.

- *A new work ethic.* In order to produce adequate amounts of food, humans have had to work very hard in certain seasons. In earlier agricultural societies, there was little leisure time for most individuals.

- *A new awareness of time.* People have had to become very time-conscious to maximize the time for planting and harvesting.

- *A new definition of group.* As large families became both possible and practical, family interests came to predominate over the welfare of the group. Children became a valuable resource.

- *A new need for sanitation.* Areas of permanent settlement needed to develop sanitary systems for disposing of waste products.

- *A new need for disease resistance.* Large numbers of people in close proximity to each other for extended periods of time provided breeding ground for disease. Epidemics became common.

Energy Cost of Modern Food Production

For early hunter-gatherers, the energy costs of food gathering were low: they obtained about 5–10 J of energy for each joule of energy they spent gathering food. Most members of the population took part in food gathering. The earliest form of agriculture — rotational cropping — yielded about 20 J of energy for each joule of energy "spent". This greater efficiency freed some individuals to specialize in other non-food collecting activities such as tool-making.

Modern agricultural technology is far less efficient: it yields only 0.1 J of food energy for every joule of energy invested. In the developed world, only 2% of the population actually work on farms. Another 18% do the related work of food processing, transportation, and marketing. The remaining 80% of the population are free to do other work. However, the energy required to liberate 80% of the population is enormous.

Modern humans use far more energy per person than any earlier society. Each new technology is followed by a sharp surge in energy consumption. Where does that energy come from? For early

Figure 16.27 In the long term, family advantage was not always equal to good public policy. Dividing properties into smaller and smaller parcels yielded farms incapable of supporting all of the subsequent generations.

farmers it came from their own muscles; that is, from their food, whose energy can be traced back to the Sun. For modern farm operations, most of the energy used comes from the burning of fossil fuels, whose energy can also be traced back to the Sun. However, the energy we are using now when we burn petroleum fuels first reached the Earth millions of years ago. We are withdrawing this energy from ancient reserves that are not being replenished.

The Water Cost

Unlike many of the world's countries, Canada contains extensive natural water resources. Modern societies have numerous uses for fresh water, using it for drinking, sanitation, and industry, as well as for growing crops. In many of the sunniest parts of North America, rainfall is inadequate for intensive crop production, so water from rivers, lakes and underground rivers called aquifers is used to irrigate the land. For example, river water is sometimes redirected and used for irrigation. However, when the used water returns to the river it contains a heavy concentration of mineral compounds that it picked up from fertilizers in the ground. About 40% of the water we use for irrigation is taken from aquifers, often at a rate many times faster than nature can replace it.

Table 16.5
Costs and benefits of some agricultural practices

Practices	Benefits	Costs
Fertilizers	Fertilizers can enhance the quality and quantity of produce while preventing impoverishment of the soil.	Fertilizers can be harmful to other parts of the biosphere.
Pesticides	Pesticides can reduce crop loss and increase yield.	Bioconcentration of pesticides can cause harm to entire food chains.
High-yield hybrid seed	High-yield hybrid seed can generate a profitable crop.	Farm managers must buy new high-yield hybrid seed every year. They cannot save some seeds from the crop for use the next season. Either the seeds will not grow true, or they will not grow at all.
Gene transfer	Seed containing genes transferred from other species can generate crops with a better yield and special features.	Farmers must pay a royalty to seed growers for the seed containing genes transferred from other species.
New crop plant varieties	New crop plant varieties may have a longer shelf life.	New crop varieties may have a different flavour or nutritional value than previous varieties.

Groundwater pollution — from industry, from farming, and from sewage disposal — is contaminating many aquifers. From all this, you can infer that a water crisis is possible. So far, the cost of fresh water has remained low considering its true value. This means that plant foods cost less than perhaps they should. Another problem with irrigation practices is that they may be contaminating the soil itself. You will explore this idea in the following Minilab.

The Impact of Plant Technologies on the Biosphere

The hunter-gatherer societies that preceded the agricultural revolution had a much smaller impact on the biosphere than our present societies have. They did not modify the environment to the extent that is common today. The agricultural revolution altered this pattern by applying technology and increasing certain plant populations for human use. This has affected our biosphere in several ways:

- *Loss of diversity.* As agriculture displaced natural ecosystems with plant monocultures, many wild species (both plants and animals) have declined or died out entirely.

- *Loss of forests.* Forests have been cut down for farmland, fuel, and development.

- *Contaminated soil and water.* Many of the earliest agricultural sites that depended on irrigation no longer support agriculture because mineral salts have migrated to the upper levels of the soil as a result of irrigation. The main impacts that agriculture has had on the biosphere are summarized in Figure 16.28 on the next page.

Who Is Defending the Biosphere?

Some people worry that our interactions with the global ecosystem have placed the entire biosphere at risk. In fact, we see and hear so many negative statistics about issues such as diminishing forests and farmland, increasing pollution, and ozone depletion that it can lead to despair and a discouraging sense of hopelessness.

So, can *you* do anything to defend the biosphere? The answer is yes — here are some suggestions.

- *Continue to educate yourself.* You do not need an advanced degree to stay informed about issues relating to biology and technology.

- *What does media communicate?* Are issues chosen based on their "shock value"? Think about whether these media companies are in business to disseminate accurate information and well-considered opinion, or whether they just want to sell more advertising space or commercial time.

 MINI LAB

Modelling Irrigation

To model the contaminating effect that irrigation can have on agricultural soil, hang a strip of soaking wet filter paper — representing healthy, irrigated soil — in a jar containing dry crystals of a soluble, coloured mineral compound such as hydrated copper sulfate. When the paper dries out, irrigate it (wet it and hang it) again.

Analyze

1. Describe the appearance of the strip of filter paper after several cycles of "irrigation". If you "irrigated" the paper 10 more times, what would you predict about its appearance?

2. What does the hydrated copper sulfate represent in your "soil"? Based on this information what can you infer is happening to the mineral content of the upper layers of soil in an irrigated field? Evaluate the mineral content of the upper layers of soil after 10 irrigation cycles. 100 cycles? 1000 cycles?

- *Develop a healthy skepticism.* Beware of easy answers to your questions. Consider whether the data you access so easily on the Internet are the products of research or opinion. Try to find information about the the author.

- *Recognize the limitations of science.* Scientific knowledge can help us solve problems such as

the ones discussed in this chapter, but science cannot always give a definitive answer.

- *Take action.* Decide what issue is most important to you and pursue it. Write to politicians and corporations expressing your opinion.

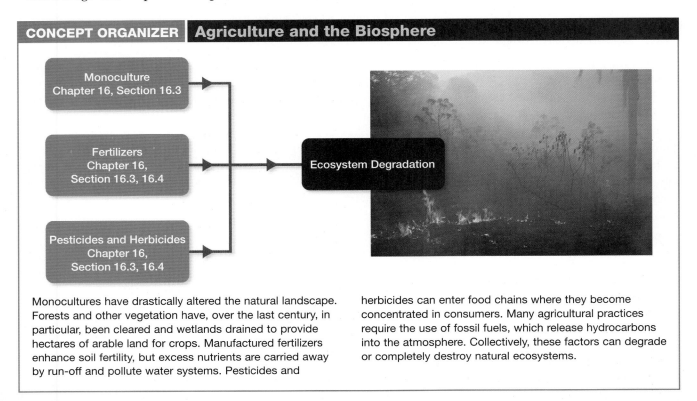

CONCEPT ORGANIZER | **Agriculture and the Biosphere**

Monoculture
Chapter 16, Section 16.3

Fertilizers
Chapter 16,
Section 16.3, 16.4

Pesticides and Herbicides
Chapter 16,
Section 16.3, 16.4

Ecosystem Degradation

Monocultures have drastically altered the natural landscape. Forests and other vegetation have, over the last century, in particular, been cleared and wetlands drained to provide hectares of arable land for crops. Manufactured fertilizers enhance soil fertility, but excess nutrients are carried away by run-off and pollute water systems. Pesticides and

herbicides can enter food chains where they become concentrated in consumers. Many agricultural practices require the use of fossil fuels, which release hydrocarbons into the atmosphere. Collectively, these factors can degrade or completely destroy natural ecosystems.

Figure 16.28 Modern agricultural practices degrade natural ecosystems.

SECTION REVIEW

1. **K/U** What societal factors drive the development of new technologies?

2. **K/U** List three ways that the development of agricultural altered human societies.

3. **K/U** How can the storage of food consume energy? What energy resources supply the energy that is consumed?

4. **MC** The impact of habitat loss on vulnerable and endangered species is not always a direct result of reducing the amount of food available. Many previously natural habitats are being destroyed for the purposes of agriculture. List two different ways, other than loss of food, that the loss of habitat can affect wild animals.

5. **MC** If the agricultural revolution had never reached this country, how do you think you would you be living today? Where would you likely be living?

6. **MC** Does modern agriculture represent an "advance" for humans? Does it represent an "advance" for the biosphere? Explain your answer.

7. **MC** The concept organizer shown in Figure 16.28 illustrates agricultural practices that can have a negative impact on ecosystems. Select one of these practices and suggest ways in which its impact on the environment can be reduced.

UNIT PROJECT PREP

This section has looked at the effects of modern agricultural technologies on the biosphere. You will be preparing an executive brief for your Unit 5 Project and the purpose of this brief is to summarize information about a plant-based industry. Think about the ways in which the plant-based industry you are investigating will influence the biosphere. Keep an ongoing file of your thoughts so you can add this information to your brief.

Overall Expectations

Briefly explain each of the following points.

- Plants obtain nutrients from their environment and provide energy and nutrition to other organisms. (16.1)
- Soil is composed of broken rock, humus, and living organisms, and it provides the essential nutrients needed by plants. (16.1)
- Plants are made of organic matter and they store carbon in their tissues. (16.1)
- Primary succession is a sequence of changes in a community that starts with bare rock and ends with a stable ecosystem. (16.2)
- Secondary succession is a sequence of changes in a community that begins with a previously existing but disturbed community and ends with a stable ecosystem. (16.2)
- The final stage of succession is called a climax community. (16.2)
- The agricultural revolution refers to the change from a nomadic lifestyle of hunter-gatherers to a lifestyle where humans are able to control the growth of plants for food. (16.3)
- Monoculture is the practice of farming large plots of land with a single crop plant. (16.3)
- Many farming practices deplete minerals in the soil, so various methods are used to replenish those nutrients, including crop rotation, and farm manure technology. (16.3)
- There are many different technologies for controlling pest organisms. Each method has advantages and disadvantages. (16.3)
- Some plants can be grown without soil using soil-free hydroponics. (16.3)
- Abundance of food resulting from advanced agricultural processes has shaped our current society. (16.4)
- Modern agricultural technology is not very energy efficient. (16.4)
- The use of water for irrigation can have negative consequences on both the water and the irrigated soil. (16.4)

Language of Biology

Write a sentence using each of the following words or terms. Use any six terms in a concept map to show your understanding of how they are related.

- soil
- humus
- organic matter
- carbon sink
- primary succession
- secondary succession
- climax community
- agricultural revolution
- monoculture
- soil fertility
- crop rotation
- biomagnification
- integrated pest management (IPM)
- soil-free horticulture
- hydroponic culture
- aeroponic culture

UNDERSTANDING CONCEPTS

1. What role does the plant kingdom play in the biosphere?

2. Write one or two sentences to answer each of the following questions.
   (a) What do plants need for growth?
   (b) What do plants do for the biosphere?
   (c) What do plants do for us?
   (d) What do we have to do to support the needs of plants?

3. Define "technology." Give two examples of plant-based technology, one ancient and one modern.

4. In your notebook, state whether each of the following statements is true. Rewrite any false statement to make it true.
   (a) Agricultural technology has caused the productivity of the land to decline.
   (b) Nomadic hunter-gatherers invented agriculture.

5. List the nutrients that plants must obtain from the soil in which they grow. What soil nutrient cannot be obtained from rock particles? What nutrient is most likely to be depleted by the growing of crops?

6. List some methods of restoring the fertility of depleted soil. What method is most commonly used by large factory farms?

7. Define "pesticide." Compare the value of pesticide use to its drawbacks. List some alternatives to the intensive use of pesticides.

8. For each of the following pairs of terms, state what the terms have in common and explain how they differ.
   (a) hydroponic, aeroponic
   (b) commercial chemical fertilizer, farm manure
   (c) pesticide, fertilizer
   (d) pesticide, integrated pest management

9. Why do most farmers use fertilizers either after harvesting a crop or just before planting a new one?

10. What is the main goal of all plant technologies? Describe the impact of these technologies on the biosphere.

11. In integrated pest management, what is integrated? Give some specific examples to support your answer.

12. According to scholars, when did agriculture first emerge? Explain why they cannot be absolutely sure.

13. List the main components of soil. What role do plants play in making soil?

14. What is the goal of monoculture? List the main advantages and disadvantages of this technology.

15. Explain how the following statements might contradict each other, even though both are true.
   • Farmland is much more productive than at any time in the past.
   • We are growing more food on less land and feeding more people yet more people are going hungry.

16. Modern farming technology is often described as highly efficient compared to the technology used 100, 1000, or 10 000 years ago. This claim is only half true. What aspect of modern farming is genuinely more efficient? What aspect is much less efficient?

INQUIRY

17. Find out the price per kilogram of fresh pineapple flown from Hawaii. Using this rate, calculate how much it would cost for you to take a return trip to Hawaii. Compare this calculated rate to advertised return-trip fares. How can growers afford to transport pineapples by air?

18. A sign about 30 km from the outskirts of a large city says "Experimental poplar plantation planted and raised using reclaimed water and biosolids."
   (a) Interpret the term "reclaimed water." What do you think is the source of the reclaimed water?
   (b) Interpret the term "biosolids." What do you think is the source of the biosolids?
   (c) In your opinion, what is the point of this experiment? Give reasons to support your opinion.
   (d) Poplar trees grow quickly, but their wood is not very strong. What is a possible use for these trees when they are mature enough to be harvested?

19. Some flowers were planted outside in spring in southern Ontario. Each plant was measured weekly, and the average growth per week and the average total growth per week were recorded in the table shown here. When was the growth of the plants the greatest? Now create a graph that shows the new growth and the total growth of the plants. Can you see on your graph where the growth of the plants was greatest? where it was the smallest? What might explain the lack of growth in Week 3?

Time	New growth each week (in centimetres)	Total growth (in centimetres)
Week 1	1	1
Week 2	3	4
Week 3	0	4
Week 4	3	7
Week 5	2	9
Week 6	4	13
Week 7	5	18
Week 8	5	23
Week 9	6	29
Week 10	4	33

20. Soil has been described as "the ultimate resource." Develop an argument to support this statement. Develop a counter-argument in favour of some other resource that could reasonably be regarded as the "ultimate" one.

21. Describe the possible places where the calcium found in your bones may have been. Draw a nutrient cycle to help explain your answer.

MAKING CONNECTIONS

22. Sketch a diagram of secondary and primary succession. Use these diagrams to compare the two processes of succession. What does the final ecosystem resemble in both of these successional areas? Explain your answer.

23. Create a flowchart that describes the steps a farmer might take to increase the yield of her crops if (a) her yield is low because of poor soil fertility, and (b) her yield is low because of a pest problem. Be sure to include the steps that help decide either why the soil is not fertile, or the steps to determine which pests are present.

24.

25 ppm in birds like the osprey

2 ppm in large fish

0.5 ppm in smaller fish

0.04 ppm in zooplankton

up to 0.003 ppm in water

Refer to this figure and write an explanation of what is happening. How could this affect human populations? Create a diagram of the process of biomagnification that could occur in a terrestrial environment.

25. An ever-increasing human population size is a threat to the continued existence of the human species, *Homo sapiens*.
(a) Under what conditions is this statement likely to be true?
(b) What could be done to ensure that this statement proves to be untrue?

26. Identify trade-offs in the development of food technologies and explain the motivation behind the trade-offs. For example, explain why vegetable growers might prefer varieties that travel well over those with more flavour or nutritional value.

27. What trade-off in the development of food technologies do you find most alarming? State your reasons. How did the decision to make this trade-off get made? by whom? Must we keep on making this trade-off? Could the original decision be reversed or modified?

28. What unique problems make plant technologies more difficult to influence or control than other technologies, such as computer or communications technologies?

29. Noted environmentalist and broadcaster David Suzuki has said that human biology is an integral part of the global ecosystem. Do you agree?

30. Imagine it is 2042 and you have just retired. Your grandchildren want to know what the biosphere was like when you were growing up. What will you tell them? What would you expect to hear if you asked people of your grandparents' age that question today?

31. Consumers want fresh produce of consistent quality at low prices. The agricultural industry wants crop plants to generate a high yield at the lowest possible cost. Are these goals compatible? Or are we making trade-offs that will eventually prove unfavourable to the biosphere and our own health for the sake of low prices and convenient technology? Think about this issue, and write down your opinion about it.

After you complete this project,

- Assess your executive brief based on the feedback from your classmates;
- Assess your research skills during the course of this project. How have your skills improved?
- Use the rubrics you developed as a class to assess both the executive brief presentation and your information sheet.

An Executive Brief on Plant-based Industries

Background

Imagine having the chance to invest in a new product. It's a syrup made with extracts from some leaves and a nut.

Are you interested?

What if you knew that, by chance, someone mixed the syrup with soda water, and found the concoction refreshing and great-tasting? Are you interested now? This, "in a nutshell," is how Coca-Cola™ was born.

Plants and plant parts are the foundation for an astounding number and variety of industries. The food industry, for example, is a plant-based industry. It includes industries that provide fresh produce and grains, industries that manufacture processed and refined food products, and industries that supply feed for livestock.

Other important industries take advantage of the structural properties of plant tissues. The cell walls that provide vascular plants with structural support also provide fibres and other materials. The fabric industry uses natural plant fibres such as those from flax plants (linen) and cotton seeds. The lumber industry exists because of lignin. This glue-like substance gives wood rigidity and the structural strength that makes it a useful building material. The paper industry depends on wood fibres. These fibres are obtained by using chemicals to remove the lignin that holds the tree's xylem and phloem tubes together. The resulting mushy mixture is called pulp. It is used to produce a vast array of paper products.

Plants are also the basis of many chemical products, including pharmaceuticals, fragrances, and flavourings. They have evolved unique chemical defences against pests and diseases. These chemicals are also helpful to us. For example, early physicians and healers often prescribed plant products for pain relief and healing properties. Today, plant chemicals are the source of many modern medicines produced by the pharmaceutical industry.

Many flowering plants produce strong fragrance molecules to attract pollinators such as insects. We use these molecules in perfumes, cosmetics, and many deodorizing products. As well, many plant parts are used to flavour food. For example, vanilla comes from seeds, cinnamon from bark, and ginger from a root.

Challenge

The term "executive brief" is often used in the business world. It refers to a summary document and a presentation that provides information in a concise, compact form. A brief is prepared by researching and extracting the most relevant information about a topic or issue.

In this project, you will play the role of an executive assistant working for Megalith Media. Megalith wants to diversify its investments. The board chairperson wants to investigate plant-based industries, reasoning that "everybody needs food to eat, a place to live, furniture to sit on, sheets for the bed, and towels to dry off with after a shower." Your boss has asked your team to prepare a presentation and an executive brief on one aspect of a plant-based industry. Your presentation may include a variety of media.

Materials

Print resources and/or the Internet, appropriate materials to present your brief, such as video equipment, computer presentation software, etc.

Design Criteria

A. Work in groups of three or four and use the guidelines in the Action Plan below to choose a topic and produce an executive brief. Decide how you wish to present your brief. You will need to provide summary information sheets to the class to support your brief. Each information sheet should be no more than two or three pages long.

B. A spreadsheet, diagram, flowchart, map, graph, may be appropriate to include in your information sheet to support your brief.

C. However your team decides to present its brief, prepare a written introduction to your project. This should include:
- the names of your group members;
- what topic your group chose to research and why you chose it;
- the role of each team member; and
- a log or memo describing your efforts to complete the project.

D. Your brief should outline different facets of a plant-based industry. You will be focussing most of your brief on one aspect of an industry. However, you must set this one aspect in the context of the industry's impact on society and the environment.

E. As a class, develop two rubrics: one for your executive brief presentation, and one for your summary information sheets.

Action Plan

1. Collect information, such as newspaper or magazine articles, on issues related to plant-based industries. Post this information on your classroom bulletin board. With your team, choose one plant-based industry for further investigation.

2. Brainstorm possible resources. For example, publicly traded corporations issue annual reports to shareholders. These reports often contain technical information in addition to financial records.

3. Prepare a research plan that lists all the sources you expect to use in your research.

4. Keep a log in which you detail the research process, including successes and difficulties encountered. Include a description of how you decided what to include in your brief and what to leave out. A copy of the log should be provided for everyone who will view or read your presentation.

5. Prepare a presentation plan. Decide on a format for your executive brief. Consider what medium will best convey the information you have uncovered. Have your plan approved by your teacher.

6. Make your presentation. Be prepared to field questions from the audience if they ask for more details.

Evaluate

1. Assess your team's brief according to its information content. Is the information in your brief taken mainly from one source? Did you research several different sources? Did you allow for bias among the sources?

2. What were some of the challenges and successes of your action plan? How would you improve your research plan if you were to do the project again?

3. As a class, rate how well each executive brief conveyed essential information.

4. Is the brief easy to understand for a person who has not done the actual research? How could the brief be made clearer and/or simpler?

UNIT 5 REVIEW

UNDERSTANDING CONCEPTS

True-False

In your notebook, indicate whether each statement is true or false. Correct each false statement.

1. Vascular plants must live where there is a steady supply of water.

2. Mosses and their relatives live where there is a steady supply of water.

3. Mosses have stems, leaves, and roots.

4. Xylem moves water and minerals up the stem of a plant.

5. Phloem moves minerals up the stem of the plant.

6. Plants produce food, fuel, flavourings, fragrances, and pharmaceuticals for humans to use.

7. Food produced in the leaves is transported through the stem in the form of glucose.

8. All plant tissues originate from one type of tissue called meristem.

9. The constant loss of water from a plant's leaves is called respiration.

10. The root hair is a specialized epidermal cell.

11. The root hair is covered with a waxy cuticle for protection.

12. The growth and development of a plant is controlled by self-produced enzymes.

13. The main function of any root system is support for the plant.

14. Vitamin C is an essential nutrient for plants.

15. Vitamin C is an essential nutrient for humans.

16. Plants help to cycle energy through the biosphere.

17. The lateral meristem is an adaptation to life as a plant.

18. A climax community is characterized by its stability.

19. A boreal forest climax community is usually associated with annual precipitation greater than 75 cm/year.

Multiple Choice

In your notebook, write the letter of the best answer for each of the following questions.

20. Which of these are seedless vascular plants?
    - (a) green algae
    - (b) purple algae
    - (c) sphagnum moss
    - (d) princess pine
    - (e) whisk fern

21. The phloem is vascular tissue that
    - (a) consists of dead tubular cells
    - (b) transports sugar from the leaves to all parts of the plant
    - (c) is present only in the stems
    - (d) transports water from the roots to the leaves
    - (e) has no specialized function

22. The leaves of most angiosperms are thin yet flat, and have a large surface area. This structure enhances the plant's ability to
    - (a) take in water
    - (b) balance and stay upright
    - (c) store food
    - (d) perform cellular respiration
    - (e) perform photosynthesis

23. Parallel veins in a leaf would indicate that the plant is
    - (a) nonvascular
    - (b) herbaceous
    - (c) woody
    - (d) dicot
    - (e) monocot

24. Which of the following is not a dicot?
    - (a) lettuce
    - (b) maple
    - (c) moss
    - (d) dandelion
    - (e) grass

25. The primary function of plant leaves is to
    - (a) support the plant
    - (b) produce flowers
    - (c) take in water
    - (d) shade the roots
    - (e) trap sunlight for photosynthesis

26. The veins of a leaf contain the
    - (a) cuticle
    - (b) epidermis
    - (c) endodermis
    - (d) vascular tissue
    - (e) meristem

27. Cells in the apical meristem that cause a root to grow longer are found
    - (a) just behind the root cap
    - (b) along the side of the root
    - (c) in the centre of the root
    - (d) at the top of the root where it joins the stem
    - (e) in the stem itself

28. Most photosynthesis takes place in
    - (a) the cells of the cortex
    - (b) the cells of the spongy layer
    - (c) the cells of the palisade layer
    - (d) the cells of the vascular tissue
    - (e) the guard cells around the stomata

29. To control water loss from a plant, the size of the stomata is reduced by
   (a) xylem tissue   (d) guard cells
   (b) phloem tissue   (e) palisade cells
   (c) spongy tissue

30. Which of the following statements comparing fibrous and taproot systems is incorrect?
   (a) Fibrous root systems are common in grasses.
   (b) Dandelions have taproots.
   (c) Taproots store food more efficiently than fibrous roots.
   (d) Plants with taproots prevent erosion more efficiently than plants with fibrous roots.
   (e) Taproots are able to reach deep into the soil for water.

31. Touching the leaves of *Mimosa piduca* causes them to fold up rapidly. After a short time, the leaves begin to unfold. This is an example of
   (a) phototropism   (d) gravitropism
   (b) geotropism   (e) nastic movement
   (c) thigmotropism

Short Answers

In your notebook, write a sentence or a short paragraph to answer each of the following questions.

32. Describe some plant adaptations that allow plants to live in terrestrial environments.

33. Define "stomata."

34. Define "nonvascular plant."

35. If you examine fossils that are 500 million years old, could you find evidence of plants? Explain why or why not. What about fossils that are one billion years old?

36. Describe the earliest plants to appear in the fossil record.

37. How do the stomata regulate the amount of water that escapes from a plant?

38. How does the cuticle prevent water loss?

39. Describe the adaptive advantage of vascular tissue.

40. Some mosses that live in deserts dry out, and all their metabolic activities cease during a dry spell. At the next rainfall, however, they revive, grow, and reproduce. Explain why this ability is adaptive.

41. What are the differences between phototropism, gravitropism, and thigmotropism?

42. Why can plants with xylem and phloem grow larger than plants without vascular tissue?

43. How do the stems of dicots differ from the stems of monocots?

44. How do the leaves and flowers of dicots differ from the leaves and flowers of monocots?

45. List the structural functions of a root. What other functions does the root perform?

46. Fossil fuels (such as coal, oil, and natural gas) are being produced naturally right now in rock layers, and oceans all around the planet. Yet, fossil fuels are considered to be non-renewable. Explain.

47. What is the primary function of the leaf of a plant? What are some other functions?

48. What are the functions of the root and the stem?

49. Where is meristem tissue located in a mature plant? in a developing plant?

50. Plants play many vital roles in our environment. List three of these and briefly note the importance of each.

51. What is the role of energy in plant growth and development? State the form(s) of energy involved.

52. List the three principal goals of agricultural and other plant-based industries.

53. List four essential nutrients required by plants, and state where each nutrient comes from and how it enters the plant.

54. What environmental factors hinder the growth and development of plants?

55. Explain how plants survive the negative effects of the factors you identified in question 54.

56. Explain how plants survive at night when they cannot perform photosynthesis to make glucose.

57. Name a plant that is a consumer rather than a producer and explain how it gets its food.

58. Name a plant that is a parasite and explain how it gets much of its food.

59. Contrast the use of land by nomadic hunter-gatherers with that of early agriculturists. Refer to area and time in your answer.

60. By 10 000 B.C.E., nomadic hunter-gatherers in the near east already had two of the three technologies needed to become agriculturists. Name these two forms of technology. What third technology did they then develop?

61. State the intended effect of a monoculture. What unintended effects often follow?

62. Define the term "soil fertility," and list four classes of technology for improving soil fertility.

63. What essential mineral nutrients may be added to soil by using farm manure technology? What about commercial chemical fertilizers? List at least one benefit and one objection for each technology.

64. What options do modern farm managers have for eliminating crop pests such as insects and fungi? List at least one benefit and one objection for each technology.

65. The agricultural revolution arose through the use of technology to increase selected plant populations for human use. How has this affected Earth's biosphere? How has it affected Earth's human population?

66. What chemical growth regulator or inhibitors would you use
 (a) if you were trying to delay the ripening of a fruit?
 (b) if you wanted to stimulate the ripening of a fruit?
 (c) if you wanted to stimulate seed germination?
 (d) if you wanted to promote bud growth in some flowers?

67. What is artificial selection? Give examples of how people have modified plants through artificial selection.

INQUIRY

68. Design an experiment that NASA could use to determine the difference between how gravitropism affects one species of plant on Earth and how gravitropism affects the same species on a space flight. What factors may be hard to keep the same in both environments?

69. Obtain an enlarged photocopy of the tree rings shown in this photograph. Measure the width of each ring by determining the distance from one edge of the dark part of the ring to the edge of the light part of the ring. Each increment is related to one year's growth. Design a table to record your results. What information can you obtain from the tree rings?

70. Design a plan to landscape the lawn around a public fountain. The lawn is 10 m by 30 m. At the side farthest from the fountain, there is a low-lying wet area. Right beside the fountain there is rock with a shallow layer of soil. In the middle of the lawn, the soil is deep. Draw a sketch of your design, putting in some of the following plants: mosses, a tall tree with a tap root, horsetail, some grass with fibrous roots, ferns, a small gymnosperm, a vegetable garden.

71. Design an investigation to determine whether the stem, leaf, or root is the first to emerge from a germinating seed. What is your hypothesis? How will you test it?

COMMUNICATING

72. Explain how nonvascular plants like mosses function without a specialized vascular system.

73. Explain the functions of the xylem and phloem in a vascular plant. Use diagrams to help explain the functions.

74. Summarize how phloem transports food within a plant. Trace the movement of excess glucose from where it is produced in a leaf to the area where it is stored.

75. Develop a flowchart to illustrate how water moves into a vascular plant from the soil, up through the plant, and out the leaves. Label your flowchart.

76. Debate the benefits and drawbacks of genetically modifying plants. Prepare a summary for one side of the debate and defend your answers with examples. Use this summary as your introduction to the debate.

77. Describe how stomata open and close in a leaf.

78. Describe how commercially produced plant hormones such as auxin-like growth regulators, cytokinin-like regulators, and gibberellic acid-like regulators, are similar to hormones produced in the plant. Why are commercial growth regulators produced? Give examples of the responses promoted by each of the commercial growth regulators named above.

79. In your notebook, copy the concept map shown here and complete it by using the following groups of plants: monocots, vascular plants, non-seed bearing plants, nonvascular plants, angiosperms, dicots, gymnosperms, seed bearing plants.

80. Under each of the groups named in your concept map, add some more examples of the group.

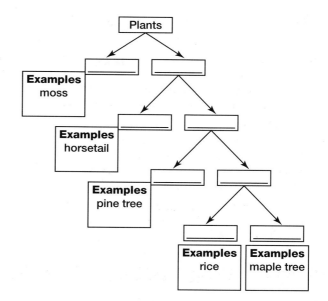

MAKING CONNECTIONS

81. An old, run-down farm is sold. The new owners decide to use fertilizer to add nutrients to the depleted soil. A lake near the farm is a healthy ecosystem where floating algae and aquatic plants are growing in balance with the animals and other organisms that live in the lake. Aerobic (oxygen-dependent) bacteria are the major decomposers. How might the fertilizer reach this ecosystem? How might the fertilizer affect species composition in the ecosystem?

82. Suppose a particular herbicide is designed to kill wild oats, which is a monocot. Evaluate the advantages and disadvantages of genetically modifying wheat or corn to make it resistant to this herbicide.

83. You are a specialist in soil science and you must communicate the latest information about increasing the fertility of farm soil in your area. You decide to write a series of articles called "Improving Soil Fertility" for your local newspaper. Your articles will be on green manure, crop rotation, animal manure, and chemical fertilizers. Choose one of these topics and write your first article for the newspaper. In your article, be sure to outline the advantages and disadvantages of this topic.

84. If you were planting a large garden to feed yourself and your family, which monocots and which dicots would you choose to plant? Give reasons for your choices.

85. Summarize the use of five plants that have been or are currently used in medicines.

COURSE CHALLENGE

Consider the following points as you continue to prepare for your Biology Course Challenge.

- Parts of plants can often be used to identify the species of plant (or at least to which group the plant belongs).

- Species or groups of plants can be used to identify environments. As people walk through an environment, they often collect parts of plants (such as pieces of leaves, mosses, seeds, and spines). How could you use this information?

- What a person eats can sometimes give some indication of where the person lives. Rice, wheat, corn, and cassava are staple foods in various parts of the world. Perhaps analysis of stomach contents could assist you in your Biology Course Challenge.

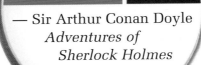

Using Forensic Science

"Whenever you have excluded the impossible, whatever remains, however improbable, must be the truth."

— Sir Arthur Conan Doyle
Adventures of Sherlock Holmes

Many people enjoy a good mystery, such as a Sherlock Holmes short story. Although we enjoy the "chase," we also need to learn the truth in order to satisfy our natural curiosity. A forensic investigation, above all, is a search for the truth. Forensics is the application of science, particularly medical knowledge, to matters of the law. This often involves the investigation of a crime.

Forensic science can be used to solve crimes in a wide variety of settings. There are many disciplines within the field of forensics, each with its unique specialty. Many of these disciplines require knowledge in one or more areas of biology.

An investigator at a crime scene.

Challenge

In a small group, research, design, and present a mystery that can be solved using forensic science. The mystery may involve a crime or other scenario, such as an archeological investigation. Prepare a portfolio of forensic clues, which correspond to the case. Describe the evidence and lab results that may be detectable in your situation. The presentation may be one of the following:

■ a diorama with accompanying files,

■ a virtual mystery on a web site,

■ a docudrama, which you write and perform.

Remember, it is not the crime that is to be depicted but the analysis of the evidence.

Materials

The diorama scene should be accompanied with a portfolio of forensic clues. The portfolio must be contained in a one-inch (2.5 cm) binder. The diorama may be constructed using a variety of materials and art supplies. A virtual mystery should be able to be viewed on available computers or audio-visual equipment. A docudrama should be presented in class with suitable props.

Design Criteria

A. Prepare a solvable mystery using forensics.

B. As a class, decide on the following: If your presentation is a diorama, what will be the maximum dimensions? The size should be small enough to transport easily, yet contain all the evidence you wish to present. If you intend to develop a web site for your presentation, how much memory will it require? How many links will you use and how will you prompt users as they explore your site? If your presentation will be a docudrama, decide on the length of the presentation. Who will perform each role in the docudrama?

C. Your mystery should contain forensic evidence based on information you have learned in each unit of the Biology 11 course.

D. The method chosen to present the drama must provide enough forensic evidence for a third party to solve the crime.

Action Plan

1. As a class, design a rubric(s) for assessing this task.

2. Decide on the groupings, or assessment categories, for this task.

3. Brainstorm a location and/or situation in which forensic science would play a vital role.

4. Develop a plan to find, collect, and organize the information that is vital to your project. Some of the techniques used in forensic science have been profiled in this section. However, you should investigate other techniques, such as blood typing, hair analysis, toxicology, foot print analysis, finger print or bite mark analysis, and forensic botany. A good place to begin would be the McGraw-Hill Ryerson web site: www.school.mcgrawhill.ca/resources/

5. Carry out your plan and make modifications as necessary.

6. Present your case to the class. Review each presentation and try to solve each case based on the information available.

Evaluate Your Project

1. Using the rubric you have prepared, evaluate your work and presentation. How effective do you think they were? Were the other groups able to solve the mystery you presented? If not, how would you revise your presentation.

2. Evaluate projects presented by the other groups.

3. After seeing the projects produced by your classmates, what changes would you make to your own project? Provide reasons for your changes.

4. How did the organization of information for this project help you to think about what you have learned in this course?

Background Information

To carry out this project, the following information may give you ideas for how to proceed.

Introducing Forensic Science

In the field of forensic science, a variety of techniques are used in order to help solve crimes. Each technique may help to narrow the

search for a suspect, determine the cause and/or location of an injury, or estimate the time of death. This is possible because all living things, whether they are animals, plants, fungi, protists, or micro-organisms, exhibit unique characteristics. As you learned in Unit 4, it is possible to make use of these characteristics to distinguish among various organisms. Forensic techniques may also be used to determine relatedness among individuals, as you will recall from Chapter 6, Section 6.1, when you conducted a DNA fingerprint analysis.

Throughout this course you have examined basic concepts that form the foundation of certain important forensic techniques. Thus, you are in a position to explore a variety of intriguing questions such as: How much information can a human leg bone yield? How can insects be used to establish a time of death? What types of information can body fluids provide?

By studying the remains of ancient peoples, forensic methods may also help us to determine how these people lived, their diet, and diseases they may have had.

Although "forensics" may be considered a field of science, it is actually comprised of many diverse sciences. For example, the work of a forensic pathologist is different from the work of a forensic anthropologist or a forensic entomologist. Each has detailed knowledge within their own field. This knowledge is gained through years of experience, study, and investigation.

It's in the Bones and Teeth

Because teeth and bones are among the hardest substances in an organism, they may be found when all other physical structures of an organism have decomposed. Consider the following example: In 1849, John Webster was convicted of murdering George Parkman in Boston, Massachusetts. To obtain the conviction, though, police first had to identify the victim. The only evidence found was the victim's skeletal remains and a set of dentures. A team of scientists was organized to reconstruct the skeleton from more than 150 bones and bone fragments, and the victim's dentures. Based on this information, they determined the approximate height, build, and age of the person and, in turn, were able to identify the victim. This case was the first conviction of a murderer in North America, based on skeletal evidence alone.

Although the passage of time can make gathering evidence more difficult at a crime scene, bones can yield a wealth of information to a skilled professional.

Teeth are perhaps the most useful method of identification when little other evidence is available. If a person has been dead a long time or if the body has sustained severe trauma (for example, in a fire), teeth may be the only part of the body that remains. Each person has teeth that are slightly different. For example, teeth have sizes and shapes that are unique. The pattern of wear on the molars varies from person to person. As well, dental work can provide vital information. As a result, dental records have played an important part in helping to identify many people.

Bones can also play an important part in identification. Certain bones, such as the pelvis, can yield information about the sex of an individual, while the shape of a person's skull can provide clues about geographic origins. Also, by taking detailed measurements of certain bones, and comparing them to known ranges, estimates of a person's height and build can be made. If a body has sustained some type of trauma, traces of this often can be found on the bones.

Math LINK

Scientists can use various formulas to determine the approximate height of a person based on the length of one of their bones. For example,

Average male height = (length of femur in cm) × (2.38) + 61.41 cm

Using this formula, determine the length of your femur. How accurate do you think this is for you? Why? When might this type of information be helpful to law enforcement officials? Describe an instance when using this type of information would be misleading to law enforcement officials.

Time Passages

Establishing a time of death is usually important in solving a death-related crime. In the absence of an eyewitness, it may be necessary to use other sources of evidence to determine the timing of events. Again, the body may provide important clues. Some techniques used to examine a body may include taking internal temperature. The body cools at a known rate after death. However, this can vary greatly based on surrounding conditions and the build of the victim. Thus, other evidence must be considered. For example, an examiner can determine if *rigor mortis* has set in. This condition — the gradual stiffening of the muscles after death — becomes fully established twelve hours after death. Alternatively, *livor mortis*, or "bruising" of the body after death, may be found. In other cases, forensic scientists may use insects to determine the time of death. Flies and other insects are attracted to bodies soon after death. They lay their eggs within wounds or other available cavities. If a body is found with an insect at a certain stage of development, entomologists can estimate a time of death for the individual.

The life cycle of certain insects has been used as evidence in forensic investigations.

Forensic entomology can sometimes be used to prove a person's innocence. For example, one case involved a Hungarian ferry skipper who was convicted and jailed for a murder. Eight years later, an entomologist was able to use the information from the original autopsy to prove that it was not possible for the ferry skipper to have murdered the victim. The original autopsy had reported numerous fly eggs and newly hatched larvae on the victim. The entomologist determined that the flies could not have hatched if the murder had occurred on the date the investigators claimed. Based on the life cycle of the fly, the entomologist testified that the victim must have perished the day before officials had claimed — a time when the skipper had an alibi.

Dael Morris, forensic entomologist, at a crime scene

Web LINK

To find out more about forensic entomology and how insects can be used to solve crimes, go to the web site shown below. Go to **Science Resources**, then to **BIOLOGY 11** to find out where to go next. Research the reproductive cycle of an insect, such as the carrion beetle, blow fly, or flesh fly, that may spend part of its time on a deceased person. Prepare a timeline that would be helpful in determining the date of death by studying the insects found on a corpse.

www.school.mcgrawhill.ca/resources/

Back at the Lab

Blood, hair, bones, and even the vitreous fluid of the eye can provide valuable clues in a forensic examination. One technique that has gained increasing attention is DNA fingerprinting. Because a person receives DNA from both parents, a family lineage can be traced by comparing DNA fingerprints. The method can also identify people that are not related.

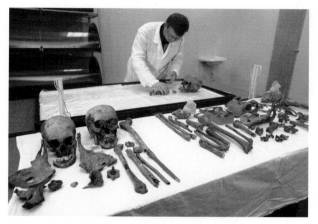

Some of the most exciting advances in forensic investigation have involved the use of DNA as evidence.

A Case Study

A famous mystery, which was partially solved using DNA evidence, was the case of Tsar Nicholas II and his family. After the Russian Revolution, the Tsar, his wife, Tsarina Alexandra, and their children were imprisoned and eventually executed by the Communist government of Russia. The family was then buried in a secret location. In 1991, Gely Ryabov, a Russian interior ministry official, announced that he had found the burial site. Because so much time had elapsed, there were few human remains at the site. In order to prove that these were indeed the remains of the Imperial Family, a special type of analysis using mitochondrial DNA was carried out. Using this technique, DNA can be extracted from small pieces of bone or other tissues. A DNA fingerprint was prepared and then compared to a DNA fingerprint of Prince Phillip, Duke of Edinburgh (Queen Elizabeth's husband). Prince Phillip was a descendant of the Tsarina's sister. The DNA profiles indicated that the two people were, in fact, related, and one mystery was solved. However, the remains of one of the children, Anastasia, were not found at the burial site. It had been rumoured that she had escaped execution. In the 1920s, a woman named Anna Anderson claimed to be Anastasia, but this claim was not verified. In 1964, Anna Anderson died. However, some of her tissue was preserved in a hospital where she had undergone an operation before her death. DNA extracted from the tissue proved that she could not have been related to the Imperial Family. Later, Anna Anderson's true family came forward and identified her as Franzisca Schankowska. The disappearance of Anastasia remains a mystery.

The missing remains of Tsar Nicholas II and his family were identified using DNA evidence.

Interview with an Expert

Each of us receives information from people every day. We correspond through e-mail, exchange documents and files, or talk directly to each other over the phone or in person. Since victims of fatal accidents or crimes are no longer able to communicate, their death may remain a mystery unless we are able to learn what happened to them. This is the job of Dr. Jacqueline Parai. She is a forensic pathologist at the Forensic Pathology Unit of the Office of the Chief Coroner of Ontario. Dr. Parai uses her medical knowledge and experience to solve mysteries every day — she learns how and why people lost their lives.

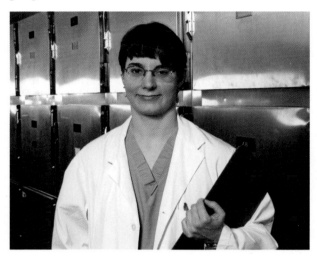
Dr. Jacqueline Parai, forensic pathologist

Q: How would you define forensic science?

A: The simplest definition of forensic science is the application of science to the law. Just like the sciences there are many disciplines within forensic science, including (but not limited to): pathology, toxicology, biology, chemistry, odontology, physical anthropology, ballistics, latent print examinations, document examination, and engineering. Forensic pathology is the branch of pathology that specializes in the recognition, documentation, and interpretation of body injuries in order to arrive at a cause of death. The forensic pathologist also aids in determining whether other factors may have contributed to death, collects trace evidence, and assists in how the manner of death should be classified.

Q: What is the most interesting part of your job?

A: Each autopsy is unique, and you never know what to expect.

Q: Is there a case that stands out in your mind?

A: No single case stands out. However, I do encounter situations where there is a combination of different types of injuries to a body. Also, deaths that involve a combination of injury and natural disease are among the most challenging to solve.

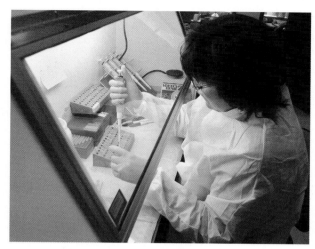

A forensic pathologist uses techniques such as a forensic autopsy to distinguish death from natural and unnatural causes.

Q: How has the field of forensic science evolved over its history?

A: The field of forensic pathology has not evolved too much over the years. There have been only slight modifications in different techniques of dissection. However, other fields, such as toxicology, chemistry and biology (especially with the introduction of DNA analysis) have evolved significantly.

Q: How do you see the field changing in the future?

A: Right now, many of the fields in forensics are rather labour intensive. I believe with time, new techniques will allow for more automation. With this automation, results from laboratory tests will be available more rapidly. I still believe, despite any automation, however, that there will always be a need for people to interpret the meaning of these results.

Q: What type of training did you have to become a forensic pathologist?

A: As an undergraduate student at university, I earned a Bachelor of Science degree in chemistry. I continued my studies in medical school, completed my degree in medicine and finished my residency training in Anatomical Pathology. I then did further training as a Fellow in Forensic Pathology at the Office of the Chief Medical Examiner in Baltimore, Maryland.

Q: How did high school science influence your career choice?

A: Everyone in high school has different strengths. I was good at math and science. In high school I didn't know I was going to become a forensic pathologist, but I did learn basic science. I then built upon my basic training during university and medical school.

Q: What type of person would be interested in this field of science?

A: Because there are so many different disciplines within forensic sciences, I think many types of people could be interested in this area. I believe strengths that would be of value to someone pursuing forensics would include good communication skills (you are usually working in a group), enjoying details, and a strong background in math and science.

Wrapping Up

Today's forensic scientists use a wide range of equipment and techniques to help them recreate events and solve crimes. However, all the technology in the world is no substitute for keen observations, sound logical reasoning, and a healthy dose of intuition. If Sherlock Holmes were alive today, he undoubtedly would be thrilled by the possibilities offered by modern technologies. However, like any modern investigator, he would use ingenuity and creativity to help him interpret the evidence he gathered. Remember to draw upon these qualities, as well as the knowledge and skills you have developed, when you plan your Course Challenge.

BIO FACT

Sir Arthur Conan Doyle (1859–1930) was greatly influenced as a writer by his mother, Mary, who had a love of books and was a wonderful story teller. In school he, like his mother, fascinated others with tales he made up. His family all thought he would choose a career in the arts but he became fascinated by medicine, and thus became a physician. He was first a surgeon on a whaling ship, then was a physician in the Bohr War (1899–1902). Never losing his love of writing and story telling, his medical background made possible many of the interesting deductions in his mystery novels.

The Cell Theory

The following four points will re-acquaint you with the fundamental principles of the cell theory:

1. The cell is the basic structural unit of living things. This means that every living thing, no matter how large, is composed of cells.

2. The cell is the basic functional unit of living things. This means that the life functions of an organism are carried out at the cellular level.

3. All cells are derived from pre-existing cells. This means that life does not arise spontaneously; it arises from pre-existing cells.

4. In a multicellular organism, the activity of the entire organism depends on the total activity of its independent cells.

Background

The cell theory developed in a climate of great scientific activity during the 1800s. Improved glass-making technology had made it possible to manufacture reliable compound microscopes on a large scale and at a reasonable price. As a result, hundreds of curious naturalists began peering into the microscopic world. The development of stains for specimens improved the ability of scientists to make observations, and the theories and discoveries made in other scientific disciplines spurred on the quest to learn more about cells. In 1808, John Dalton (1766–1844) published his atomic theory, which described matter as being made up of numerous, tiny units called atoms. This idea suggested a new line of investigation. What if living things were also made of small units?

Investigating this question revealed that plants and animals are made of cells and that these cells have many features in common. This is why biologists say that the cell is the unifying structure that links all life — despite the cell's great diversity of form.

The first two points of the cell theory were well accepted by 1840. The third, which was first stated by 1858, was not fully understood or accepted until 1864. That was when Louis Pasteur demonstrated in a series of experiments that living organisms only arise from living organisms. Since the time of Greek philosopher and scientist Aristotle (384–322 B.C.E.), it had been commonly believed that living things could arise spontaneously from non-living matter.

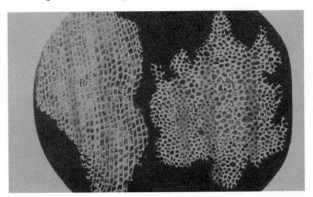

The first recorded cell observations (shown here) were reported in 1665 by Robert Hooke (1635–1703). To obtain them, Hooke used a double-lens compound light microscope. Its optical design was similar to the optical design of the microscopes in your school laboratory. The dead cork cells that Hooke observed were hollow, and the rectangular shape of their walls reminded him of the small cells (sleeping rooms) in a monastery. Biologists have used the word "cell" ever since.

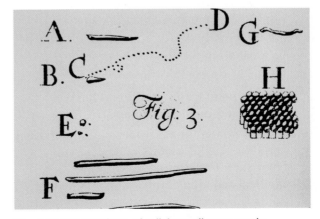

The first observations of a *living* cell were made sometime before 1674. In that year, Anton von Leeuwenhoek (1632–1723) accurately drew and described such organisms as bacteria for the first time.

Chemical Bonding:
A Quick Reference for the Biology Student

The Nature of Matter

Matter is anything that takes up space and has mass. Overwhelming evidence shows that the matter in living organisms is made up of atoms and that changes in the organic matter in living systems take place at the atomic level. An ordinary chemical or biochemical reaction cannot destroy, create, or split an atom. Current research also reveals a remarkable array of subatomic particles — particles smaller than an atom.

The Structure of Atoms

To understand and explain chemical reactions, you need to know about the subatomic particles called *protons*, *neutrons*, and *electrons*. Their properties are summarized in the following table.

Table A2.1
Protons, neutrons, and electrons

Subatomic particle	Symbol	Charge	Amount of charge	Relative mass (in atomic mass units)
proton	p^+	positive	+1	1
neutron	n^0	neutral	0	1
electron	e^-	negative	−1	$\frac{1}{2000}$

In atoms, these subatomic particles are arranged in a characteristic structure (Figure A2.1). The protons and neutrons are clustered together in the nucleus, which contains over 99% of an atom's mass but makes up less than 1% of its volume. The electrons surround the nucleus in regions called shells. Electrons make up less than 1% of an atom's mass, although the shells they occupy make up over 99% of its volume.

Different elements, such as hydrogen and oxygen, are distinguished from one another by the number of protons their atoms contain. All atoms of the same element contain the same number of protons. The number of electrons in an atom always equals the number of protons it contains. This means that, overall, an atom has a neutral charge. The periodic table lists and provides information about all the known elements. For a given element, the number of neutrons may vary from one atom to another.

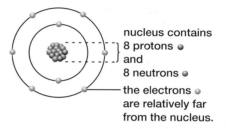

nucleus contains
8 protons
and
8 neutrons
the electrons
are relatively far
from the nucleus.

Figure A2.1 This model of oxygen shows the arrangement of subatomic particles in the atom. Fixed numbers of electrons occupy regions called shells. The outermost shell is called the valence shell.

The Covalent Bond

Atoms group together, often forming very strong bonds. The following example will help you understand how and why one type of bond, the *covalent bond*, forms.

Figure A2.2 illustrates the forces that come into play as two hydrogen atoms approach each other. Four interactions develop between the two atoms, as follows:

1. a force of repulsion between the two electrons;

2. a force of repulsion between the two protons;

3. a force of attraction between the electron of hydrogen atom A and the proton of hydrogen atom B; and

4. a force of attraction between the electron of hydrogen atom B and the proton of hydrogen atom A.

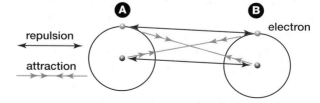

repulsion

attraction

electron

Figure A2.2 The forces between two hydrogen atoms.

As the atoms continue to approach each other, the forces of both repulsion and attraction increase, but the force of attraction increases at a faster rate. The maximum force of attraction occurs when the nuclei of the two atoms are about 1.05×10^{-4} µm apart. At this point, the electron shells of the two atoms merge. Now each nucleus has access to both of the electrons. The two positive hydrogen nuclei share the same electron shell and are held together (bonded) by the shell's negative charge. The type of chemical bond that involves shared electrons is called a covalent bond.

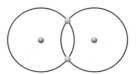

Figure A2.3 Two hydrogen atoms that share a pair of electrons have formed a molecule (H_2) with a single covalent bond. The structural formula to show the single covalent bond between the hydrogen atoms is H — H.

Tendency Toward Stability

The noble gases (Group 18 on the periodic table) are known to be so chemically stable that they are unlikely to take part in chemical reactions. When atoms bond, they share, give up, or gain electrons to achieve the same arrangement of valence electrons as that of the noble gas to which they are closest in the periodic table.

You may recall from previous studies that the maximum number of electrons that can occupy the first valence shell outside a nucleus is two (the valence shell arrangement of the noble gas helium). By sharing a valence electron with another hydrogen atom, each of

the hydrogen atoms in the new H_2 molecule achieves a stable valence shell arrangement. This is shown in Figure A2.3.

Double and Triple Bonds

Atoms can also share two pairs of electrons or three pairs of electrons in a covalent bond. In a double covalent bond, two atoms share two pairs of electrons. This is illustrated using two oxygen atoms in Figure A2.4.

The electron-dot diagram of carbon dioxide (Figure A2.5) shows an example of a three-atom molecule held together by double covalent bonds. The maximum number of electrons that can occupy the valence shell of elements with atomic numbers 3 to 20 is eight. This is a stable electron shell configuration. Examine the CO_2 molecule in Figure A2.5. Look for evidence that each atom in the molecule has access to a stable valence shell arrangement. In a triple covalent bond, two atoms share three pairs of electrons.

$$:\ddot{O}:\ :C:\ :\ddot{O}:$$

Figure A2.5 An electron-dot diagram of carbon dioxide. Its structural formula is, thus, O = C = O.

> ➤➤ **FAST FORWARD**
>
> To review the periodic table, turn to *Appendix 11*.

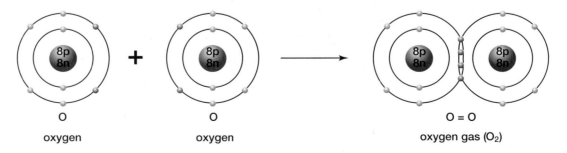

Figure A2.4 Notice that by sharing two pairs of electrons (in a double bond), each of the oxygen atoms has access to eight electrons in its valence shell. This gives it the same stable valence-shell arrangement as the noble gas closest to it in the periodic table, neon.

The Polar Covalent Bond

Most of the biochemical reactions in a living cell take place in a water solution. The chemical bonds binding together the atoms in a water molecule have to be strong enough to keep the molecule intact even when heat added to the water makes it evaporate.

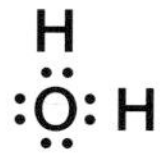

$$\begin{array}{c} H \\ :\ddot{O}:H \end{array}$$

Figure A2.6 An electron-dot model of a water molecule

The electron-dot diagram in Figure A2.6 suggests that a water molecule is held together by ordinary covalent bonds. What this type of diagram cannot show is the relative importance of the protons in the nuclei of the three atoms. The O nucleus has eight positive protons to attract the shared electrons, while the hydrogen nuclei have only one proton each. As a result, the shared valence electrons spend more of their time around the O nucleus than they do around the H nuclei. This gives the O end, or pole, of a water molecule a partially negative charge. The H ends, or poles, have partial positive charges. The model in Figure A2.7 provides a useful representation of the polarity in a water molecule.

To reflect the unequal sharing of electrons within a water molecule, the special type of covalent bond holding it together is called a *polar covalent bond*. In a polar covalent bond, the valence electrons of the atoms are tightly bound, and no electrons are available to carry an electric current.

The Hydrogen Bond

When two water molecules collide, the polar nature of each molecule has an effect on what happens. If the two negative poles (O) meet "head to head," the molecules will repel each other because like charges repel. The two molecules will also repel each other if their positive poles (H) collide. However, in most collisions the negative pole of one molecule will be attracted by a positive pole of the other, and the two molecules will attract each other strongly enough to remain close together. Other water molecules in the vicinity will be attracted to each other in the same way. This type of electrostatic attraction between polar molecules containing a positive hydrogen pole is called a *hydrogen bond*. Figure A2.8 shows the pattern of attractions that forms between liquid water molecules as a result of hydrogen bonding.

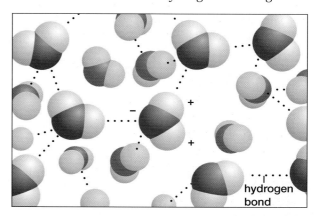

Figure A2.8 The polarity of water molecules allows attractions called hydrogen bonds to form between the water molecules. A dotted line is used to represent a hydrogen bond; it indicates the hydrogen bond's weakness relative to covalent or ionic bonds.

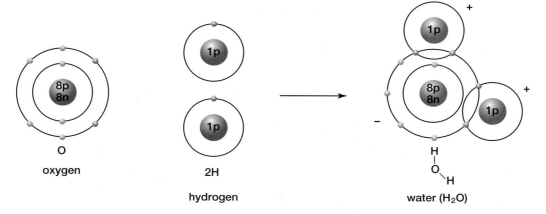

Figure A2.7 Even though a water molecule is polar, it is electrically neutral overall.

The Ionic Bond

Atoms can also form ionic bonds. From earlier studies, you may recall that when an atom or group of atoms gains or loses electrons, it acquires an electric charge and becomes an *ion*. The ions formed in this kind of electron transfer are chemically stable because each ion has a valence shell arrangement like that of a noble gas. When the number of electrons is less than the number of protons, the ion is positive (a cation). When the number of electrons exceeds the number of protons, the ion is negative (an anion). Ions can be composed of only one element, such as the hydrogen ion (H^+), or of several elements, such as the bicarbonate ion (HCO_3^-). The attraction between oppositely charged ions is called an *ionic bond*.

Forming Ionic Compounds

If a large number of chlorine atoms are brought together, they pair up to form covalently bonded Cl_2 molecules. The shared electrons are strongly attracted by the two nuclei. In contrast, a sodium atom's single valence electron is only weakly attracted to its nucleus. If a large number of sodium atoms are brought together, a solid does form, but the valence electrons in the solid are so loosely attached to each nucleus that they can easily flow to conduct an electrical current.

However, if a piece of solid sodium is exposed to chlorine gas (Cl_2) there is an explosive reaction that releases both heat and light. In this reaction, electrons are actually transferred from the sodium atoms to the chlorine atoms. Thus, two ions are formed simultaneously: Na^+ and Cl^-. You can follow what happens in Figure A2.9.

All that remains after the reaction are tiny cubic crystals of sodium chloride (table salt). The ions have aligned themselves in a pattern that reduces repulsion and maximizes attraction. For the ionic compound NaCl, the cubical ion arrangement shown in Figure A2.10 is most stable. Ionic compounds bond into regular, repeating patterns that are determined by the size of the individual ions, the amount of charge they carry, and the kind of charge they carry.

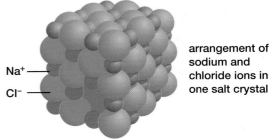

many salt crystals

1 mm

Na^+

Cl^-

arrangement of sodium and chloride ions in one salt crystal

Figure A2.10 An ionic compound such as NaCl (salt) has a characteristic crystalline shape. Like sodium chloride, most ionic compounds involve bonds between metal cations and non-metal anions.

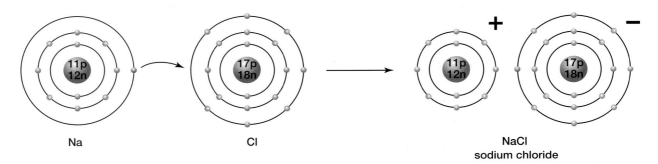

Na   Cl   NaCl
                        sodium chloride

Figure A2.9 The formation of NaCl

Ionic Solids

The hundreds of different ionic compounds all have these two things in common:

1. They are solids at room temperature.
2. The total charge on the positive ions equals the total charge on the negative ions. Therefore, every ionic solid is electrically neutral even though it is composed of strongly charged particles.

The ionic bonds holding ionic solids (salts) together are extremely strong and stable. For example, sodium chloride melts only at a very high temperature (801°C) and can safely be kept in a cupboard for years with no danger of decomposition.

Even though it contains millions of charged particles (ions), a crystal of sodium chloride cannot conduct an electrical current. Immobilized by their close-packed solid state, the ions cannot carry a current from one side of a crystal to the other.

Ionic Compounds in Solution

You know that table salt dissolves in water. Many other ionic compounds are also water soluble. What happens to the ions in sodium chloride when it dissolves in water? Attraction by the charged poles of the surrounding water molecules pulls the ions away from the crystal and into solution. Figure A2.11 shows how the polar water molecules interact with and surround the sodium and chloride ions.

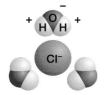 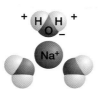

Figure A2.11 Notice the orientation of the water molecules around the sodium ion and the chloride ion.

Once dissolved in water, the sodium and chloride ions are free to move about and collide with other particles. This makes the ions mobile enough to carry an electric current from one location to another. It also allows chemical reactions to occur. So, like many ionic compounds, sodium chloride is an electrolyte. An *electrolyte* is a substance that, when dissolved in water, enables water to carry an electric current.

The Biological Significance of Ions

Ions play a vital role in the chemistry of living cells and body systems. For example, modern athletes pay close attention to the level of electrolytes in their body. Intense physical activity causes the loss of NaCl (in sweat). If the lost sodium ions are not replaced, nerve cells cannot send signals to the muscles. Table A2.2 identifies the significance of the important ions in your body.

Table A2.2
Significant ions in the body

Name	Symbol	Special significance
sodium	Na^+	found in body fluids; important in muscle contraction and nerve conduction
chloride	Cl^-	found in body fluids
potassium	K^+	found primarily inside cells; important in muscle contraction and nerve conduction
phosphate	PO_4^{3-}	found in bones, teeth, and the high-energy molecule ATP
calcium	Ca^{2+}	found in bones and teeth; important in muscle contraction
bicarbonate	HCO_3^-	important in acid-base balance
hydrogen	H^+	important in acid-base balance
hydroxide	OH^-	important in acid-base balance

Care and Use of a Microscope

Part 1: Care of a Microscope

A *light microscope* is an optical instrument that greatly magnifies objects too small to be seen with the unaided eye. The figure on the next page shows a compound light microscope. This kind of microscope has a series of lenses (rather than only one, as in a hand lens) and requires a light source to view an object. Study the compound light microscope shown in Figure A3.1 and review the major parts and their functions.

To keep your microscope in good operating condition, the following points should be observed.

1. To carry a microscope, always use one hand to hold the arm and your other hand to support the base.

2. Do not touch the lens surfaces with your fingers.

3. Use only lens tissue to clean the lens surfaces.

4. Do not adjust any of the focussing knobs until you are ready to use the microscope.

5. Always focus first using the coarse adjustment knob, with the low-power objective lens in position.

6. Do not use the coarse adjustment knob when either the medium-power or high-power objective lens is in position.

7. Cover the microscope when it is not in use.

Part 2: Using a Microscope

Here, you will use the microscope to view a prepared slide. You will determine the area that can be seen through the eyepiece, called the *field of view*, and calculate the magnification. Finally, you will make a scale drawing, and estimate the actual size of the object you are viewing.

CAUTION: Be sure your hands are dry when handling electrical equipment. Handle microscope slides carefully, since they can break easily and cause cuts.

Materials

microscope
prepared microscope
  slide
mathematical compass

clear plastic ruler
blank sheet of paper
pencil

Procedure

1. Place the microscope on a flat surface.

2. The microscope should always be stored with the low-power objective in position. If your microscope has not been stored that way, look from the side and rotate the revolving nosepiece until the low-power objective clicks into place.

3. Use the coarse-adjustment knob to lower the low-power objective until the lens is about 1 cm above the stage.

4. Look through the eyepiece and adjust the diaphragm until the view is as bright as possible.

Total Magnification and Field of View

5. To calculate the total magnification of an object, multiply the power of the eyepiece by the power of the objective. For example, if the eyepiece magnification is 10×, the low-power objective is 4×, and the high-power objective is 40×, then:

   (a) The total magnification using the low-power objective is 10 × 4 = 40×.

   (b) The total magnification using the high-power objective is 10 × 40 = 400×.

6. To determine the field of view, place the clear plastic ruler on the stage.

7. Using the coarse-adjustment knob, focus on the ruler. Position the ruler so that one of the millimetre markings is at the left edge of the field of view, as shown in Figure A3.2.

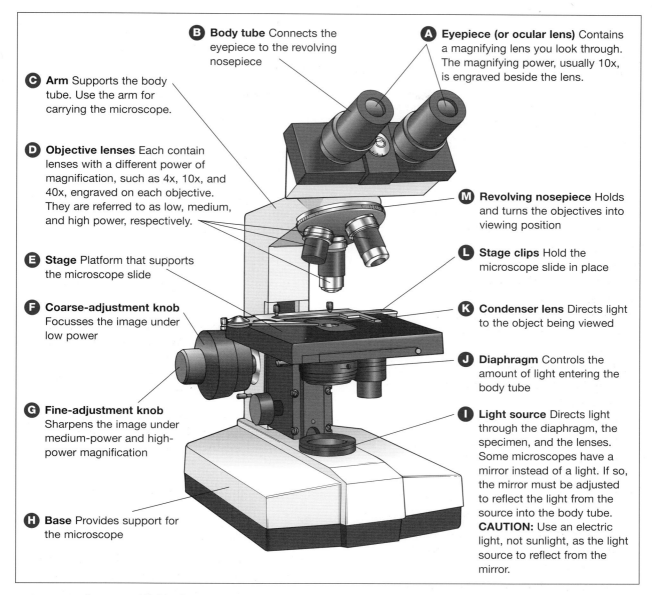

B Body tube Connects the eyepiece to the revolving nosepiece

A Eyepiece (or ocular lens) Contains a magnifying lens you look through. The magnifying power, usually 10x, is engraved beside the lens.

C Arm Supports the body tube. Use the arm for carrying the microscope.

D Objective lenses Each contain lenses with a different power of magnification, such as 4x, 10x, and 40x, engraved on each objective. They are referred to as low, medium, and high power, respectively.

M Revolving nosepiece Holds and turns the objectives into viewing position

E Stage Platform that supports the microscope slide

L Stage clips Hold the microscope slide in place

F Coarse-adjustment knob Focusses the image under low power

K Condenser lens Directs light to the object being viewed

J Diaphragm Controls the amount of light entering the body tube

G Fine-adjustment knob Sharpens the image under medium-power and high-power magnification

I Light source Directs light through the diaphragm, the specimen, and the lenses. Some microscopes have a mirror instead of a light. If so, the mirror must be adjusted to reflect the light from the source into the body tube. **CAUTION:** Use an electric light, not sunlight, as the light source to reflect from the mirror.

H Base Provides support for the microscope

Figure A3.1 Compound light microscope

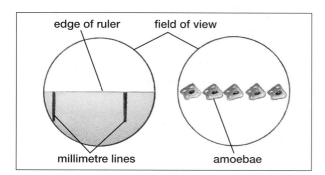

edge of ruler   field of view

millimetre lines   amoebae

Figure A3.2 The diameter of the field of view under low power illustrated here is about 1.5 mm.

8. Measure and record the diameter of the field of view in millimetres (mm) for the low-power objective.

9. Use the following formula to calculate the field of view for the medium-power objective:

Medium-power field of view

$= $ Low-power field of view $\times \dfrac{\text{Magnification of low-power objective}}{\text{Magnification of medium-power objective}}$

For example, if the low-power objective is 4× with a field of view of 2 mm, and the medium-power objective is 10×, then:

Medium-power field of view $= 2$ mm $\times \dfrac{4}{10}$

$= 2$ mm $\times 0.4$

$= 0.8$ mm

Similarly, calculate the field of view for the high-power objective and record the value.

10. Objects in the field of view of a microscope are usually measured in micrometres (μm). One micrometre equals 0.001 mm; or 1000 μm equals one millimetre.

(a) In the example in step 9, the field of view under the medium-power objective would be 0.8 mm × 1000 = 800 μm.

(b) Calculate the field of view in μm under the high-power objective.

11. You can determine the size of a specimen (such as an amoeba) by estimating how many could fit end to end across the field of view. See Figure A3.2 on the previous page. To do this, divide the field of view by the number of specimens. If the field of view in the illustration is 1500 μm, what is the diameter of each amoeba?

Viewing a Prepared Slide

12. Place a prepared slide on the stage and secure it in place with the stage clips. The low-power objective should be in position. Make sure the object you intend to view is centred over the opening in the stage.

(a) Look through the eyepiece. Slowly turn the coarse-adjustment knob until the object is in focus.

(b) Use the fine-adjustment knob to sharpen the focus.

13. Once the object is in focus using low power, carefully rotate the revolving nosepiece to the medium-power objective. Look at the side of the objective as you rotate the nosepiece to be sure the objective lens does not strike the surface of the slide.

(a) Adjust the focus using *only* the fine-adjustment knob.

(b) Next, view the object using the high-power objective. Carefully rotate the nosepiece until the high-power objective clicks into position. Again, be sure the objective does not strike the surface of the slide as you rotate the nosepiece. Adjust the focus using *only* the fine-adjustment knob.

14. Once you have finished viewing the slide, carefully rotate the nosepiece until the low-power objective is in position. If you do not proceed to step 15, making a scale drawing, remove the slide from the stage and return

it to its proper container. Unplug the light source and return the microscope to its cabinet. **CAUTION:** Never tug on the electrical cord to unplug it.

Making a Scale Drawing

15. With a mathematical compass, draw a circle (the size does not matter) on blank paper. The circle represents the microscope's field of view.

16. Use the ruler and pencil to divide the circle into four equal sections, as shown in the illustration.

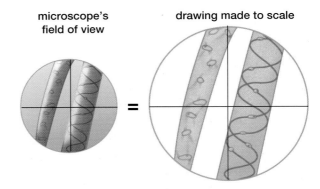

microscope's field of view   drawing made to scale

17. Using the low or medium-power objective, find an area of interest on the prepared slide. Imagine that the field of view is also divided into four equal sections.

18. Notice how much space each part of the object occupies in the field of view.

19. Draw the object to scale in the circle. Draw each part of the object so it is in the same part of the circle as it appears in the field of view. This means the object should occupy the same proportion of space in the circle as it does in the field of view. Label your drawing. Indicate the total magnification and calculate the actual size of the object.

Preparing a Wet Mount

Now prepare and view slides of a variety of specimens.

CAUTION: Be careful when using sharp objects such as tweezers. Handle microscope slides and cover slips carefully, since they can break easily.

Materials

microscope
cover slips
tweezers
cotton fibres
tap water

microscope slides
medicine dropper
small piece of newspaper
  and other samples
lens paper

Procedure

1. To prepare a wet mount, begin with a clean slide and cover slip. Hold the slide and cover slip by their edges to avoid getting your fingerprints on their surfaces.

2. Tear out a small piece of newspaper containing a single letter. Use an *e, f, g,* or *h.* Using the tweezers, position the letter in the centre of the slide.

3. Using the medicine dropper, place one drop of water on the sample. Hold a cover slip over the sample at a 45° angle. One edge of the cover slip should touch the surface of the slide near the newspaper letter sample.

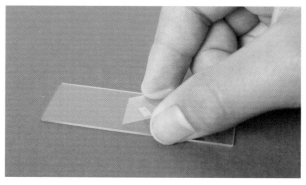

4. Slowly lower the opposite edge of the cover slip over the sample. Be sure no bubbles form beneath the cover slip. This type of sample preparation is called a *wet mount.*

5. With the low-power objective of the microscope in position, place the slide on the stage and secure it with the stage clips. Centre the sample over the opening in the stage.

   (a) Look though the eyepiece. Reposition the slide, if necessary, until you can see the letter. Using the coarse-adjustment knob, focus on the letter. Then, adjust the focus with the fine-adjustment knob.

   (b) Examine the letter using the medium-power objective. Notice that it is composed of many small dots.

6. To reveal the structure of small objects, the microscope must do more than magnify — it must also reveal detail. The capacity to distinguish detail is call *resolution*, and the measure of resolution is known as *resolving power*. The resolving power of a microscope is defined as the minimum distance that two objects can be apart and still be seen as separate objects.

Instant Practice

1. While looking through the eyepiece, move the slide slowly from right to left. In what direction does the specimen move as seen through the microscope?

2. Prepare another wet mount using several fibres from a cotton ball. Using the low-power objective, locate a part of the slide where two fibres cross each other. Change to the high-power objective. Use the fine-adjustment knob to focus on the fibres. Can both strands of cotton be seen clearly at the same time under high power? How might you explain this result?

3. Prepare a wet mount using a drop of pond water. Scan the slide with the low-power objective. What organisms do you see? Select one and prepare a scale drawing of it. Indicate the total magnification and estimate the actual size of the organism.

Safety in your Laboratory

Safety Symbols

The following safety symbols are used in this *Biology 11* textbook to alert you to possible dangers. Make sure that you understand each symbol in a lab or investigation before you begin.

	Disposal Alert This symbol appears when care must be taken to dispose of materials properly.
	Biological Hazard This symbol appears when there is danger involving bacteria, fungi, or protists.
	Thermal Safety This symbol appears as a reminder to be careful when handling hot objects.
	Sharp Object Safety This symbol appears when there is danger of cuts or punctures caused by the use of sharp objects.
	Fume Safety This symbol appears when chemicals or chemical reactions could cause dangerous fumes.
	Electrical Safety This symbol appears as a reminder to be careful when using electrical equipment.
	Skin Protection Safety This symbol appears when the use of caustic chemicals might irritate the skin or when contact with micro-organisms might transmit infection.
	Clothing Protection Safety A lab apron should be worn when this symbol appears.
	Fire Safety This symbol appears as a reminder to be careful around open flames.
	Eye Safety This symbol appears when there is danger to the eyes and safety glasses should be worn.
	Poison Safety This symbol appears when poisonous substances are used.
	Chemical Safety This symbol appears when chemicals could cause burns or are poisonous if absorbed through the skin.
	Animal Safety This symbol appears when live animals are studied and the safety of the animals and the students must be ensured.

WHMIS Symbols

Look carefully at the WHMIS (Workplace Hazardous Materials Information System) safety symbols shown below. These symbols are used throughout Canada to identify dangerous materials in all workplaces, including schools. Make sure that you understand what these symbols mean. When you see these symbols on containers in your classroom, at home, or in a workplace, use safety precautions.

Compressed Gas	Flammable and Combustible Material
Oxidizing Material	Corrosive Material
Poisonous and Infectious Material Causing Immediate and Serious Toxic Effects	Poisonous and Infectious Material Causing Other Toxic Effects
Biohazardous Infectious Material	Dangerously Reactive Material

Units of Measurement

When you take measurements in science, you use the International System of Measurement (commonly known as SI, from the French for *Système international d'unités*). SI includes the metric system and other standard units. It is accepted as the standard for measurement throughout most of the world. This appendix provides you with a review of SI metric symbols and prefixes.

In SI, the base units include the metre, the kilogram, and the second. The size of any particular unit can be determined by the prefix used with the base unit. Larger and smaller units of measurement can be obtained by either dividing or multiplying the base unit by a multiple of 10.

For example, the prefix *kilo-* means multiplied by 1000. So, one kilogram is equivalent to 1000 grams:

$$1 \text{ kg} = 1000 \text{ g}$$

The prefix *milli-* means divided by 1000. So, one milligram is equivalent to one thousandth of a gram:

$$1 \text{ mg} = \frac{1}{1000} \text{ g}$$

The following table shows the most commonly used metric prefixes. Adding metric prefixes to a base unit is a way of expressing powers of 10.

Metric Prefixes

Prefix	Symbol	Relationship to the base unit
giga-	G	$10^9 = 1\ 000\ 000\ 000$
mega-	M	$10^6 = 1\ 000\ 000$
kilo-	k	$10^3 = 1\ 000$
hecto-	h	$10^2 = 100$
deca-	da	$10^1 = 10$
–	–	$10^0 = 1$
deci-	d	$10^{-1} = 0.1$
centi-	c	$10^{-2} = 0.01$
milli-	m	$10^{-3} = 0.001$
micro-	μ	$10^{-6} = 0.000\ 001$
nano-	n	$10^{-9} = 0.000\ 000\ 001$

Commonly Used Metric Quantities, Units, and Symbols

Quantity	Unit	Symbol
length	nanometre	nm
	micrometre	μm
	millimetre	mm
	centimetre	cm
	metre	m
	kilometre	km
mass	gram	g
	kilogram	kg
	tonne	t
area	square metre	m^2
	square centimetre	cm^2
	hectare	ha ($10\ 000$ m^2)
volume	cubic centimetre	cm^3
	cubic metre	m^3
	millilitre	mL
	litre	L
time	second	s
temperature	degree Celsius	°C
force	newton	N
energy	joule	J
	kilojoule *	kJ
pressure	pascal	Pa
	kilopascal **	kPa
electric current	ampere	A
quantity of electric charge	coulomb	C
frequency	hertz	Hz
power	watt	W

* Many dieticians in North America continue to measure nutritional energy in Calories, also known as kilocalories or dietetic Calories. In SI units, 1 Calorie = 4.186 kJ.

** In current North American medical practice, blood pressure is measured in millimetres of mercury, symbol mm Hg. In SI units, 1 mm Hg = 0.133 kPa.

Scientific Notation

Scientific notation is a method of expressing numbers that are very large or very small as exponents of the power 10. An *exponent* is the symbol or number denoting the power to which another number or symbol is to be raised. The exponent shows the number of repeated multiplications of the base. In 10^2, the exponent is 2 and the base is 10. The table below shows the powers of 10 as numbers in standard form and in exponential form.

	Standard form	Exponential form
ten thousands	10 000	10^4
thousands	1000	10^3
hundreds	100	10^2
tens	10	10^1
ones	1	10^0
tenths	0.1	$\frac{1}{10^1} = 10^{-1}$
hundredths	0.01	$\frac{1}{10^2} = 10^{-2}$
thousandths	0.001	$\frac{1}{10^3} = 10^{-3}$
ten thousandths	0.0001	$\frac{1}{10^4} = 10^{-4}$

Why use exponents? Consider a very large number, such as the distance between Mercury and the Sun (which is 58 000 000 km). If a zero were accidentally added to or left off this number, the distance would appear to be either 10 times larger or smaller than it really is. To avoid making these kinds of mistakes, scientists express numbers in scientific notation.

Example 1

Express the distance between Mercury and the Sun in scientific notation.

Solution

In scientific notation, a number has the form $x \times 10^n$, where x is greater than or equal to 1 but less than 10, and 10^n is a power of 10.

58 000 000. ← The decimal point starts here. Move the decimal point 7 places to the left.

$= 5.8 \times 10\ 000\ 000$
$= 5.8 \times 10^7$

Example 2

The electron in a hydrogen atom is, on average, 0.000 000 000 053 m from the nucleus. Write 0.000 000 000 053 in scientific notation.

Solution

To write the number in the form $x \times 10^n$, move the decimal point to the right until there is one, non-zero number to the left of the decimal point.

The decimal point starts here. Move the decimal point 11 places to the right. 0.000 000 000 053

$= 5.3 \times 0.000\ 000\ 000\ 01$
$= 5.3 \times 10^{-11}$

Notice that, when you move the decimal point to the left, the exponent of ten is positive. When you move the decimal point to the right, the exponent of ten is negative. The number of places you move the decimal point is the number in the exponent.

Instant Practice

1. Express each of the following in scientific notation.

   (a) Fossil algae have been found from the Precambrian period, which was 600 000 000 years before present (B.P.).

   (b) The distance across the universe is estimated to be 800 000 000 000 000 000 000 000 km.

   (c) The mass of a proton is approximately 0.000 000 000 000 000 000 000 0017 g.

2. Change the following numbers to standard notation.
   (a) 2.4×10^{10} g   (b) 5.1×10^6 m
   (c) 9.5×10^{-8} L   (d) 4.4×10^{-5} s

Significant Digits

In order to conduct experiments in biology and other sciences, you need to make measurements and manipulate numbers. However, there is always some degree of uncertainty in each measured value that you record. Scientists around the world have agreed that a measurement should include the number of digits that reasonably indicate its precision. Such digits are called *significant digits*.

For example, imagine that you measured 16 mL of a solution using a cylinder that has millilitres as its smallest gradation. In reality, you can only be certain that the volume measured lies somewhere between 15 and 17 mL — the final digit of "6" in the value 16 mL is uncertain. Figure A8.1 shows an example of different levels of precision.

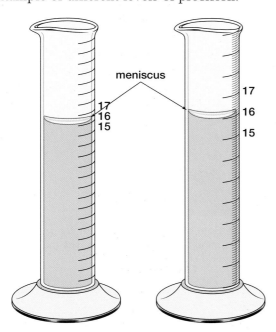

Figure A8.1 The measurement to the right can be stated with greater precision.

Zeros to the right of the decimal marker in measured quantities are considered significant. For example, in the expression 21.00 mL, both zeros are significant. They indicate a precision to one hundredth of a millilitre. Zeros may or may not be significant depending on where they are located. The rules used to determine whether zeros in a quantity are significant are as follows.

1. Zeros at the end of a quantity that includes a decimal marker are significant. Therefore, 7.50 mg has three significant digits.

2. Zeros that are used exclusively to locate the decimal marker in a quantity are not significant. Therefore, 0.000 1 mm has only one significant digit.

3. Zeros located between digits 1 and 9 are significant. Therefore, 909 g has three significant digits.

4. Zeros at the end of a whole number may be ambiguous and require interpretation on the part of the reader. For example, $1000 would be considered to be exact; however, 5 000 000 bacteria is probably not exact.

One way to avoid ambiguity is to express numbers using scientific notation. Thus, in 5×10^6 bacteria, there is one significant digit.

Mathematical Operations

The answer for any calculation involving measurements cannot be expressed with more significant digits than contained in the measurements being used to perform the calculation. Rounding off must often be used to bring the answer to the proper number of significant digits. Round your answer to the number of significant digits contained in the least precise number used in the calculation.

Instant Practice

1. How many significant digits are there in the following measurements?

   (a) 17.60 mL   (b) 37.8°C

   (c) 0.009 V   (d) 1006 cm

2. Calculate the following and round to the correct number of significant digits:

   (a) 104 cm × 0.62 cm   (b) 2.15 g/2 L

   (c) 505 mL + 0.9 mL   (d) 5.05 s − 1.7 s

Understanding pH

Biological processes take place within specific limits of acidity and alkalinity. If an environment becomes too acidic or too alkaline for a process to continue at optimum levels, the organism that depends on that process may suffer and die. Fresh-water fish, for example, cannot survive in water that is too acid. Pitcher plants, sundews, and many other plants that grow in acidic soils cannot tolerate alkaline conditions.

Whether an environment is acidic or alkaline depends on the concentration of hydrogen ions ($H^+(aq)$) found in solution. Pure water at 25°C ionizes very slightly to produce an equal number of hydrogen and hydroxide ions:

$$H_2O(l) \leftrightarrow H^+(aq) + OH^-(aq)$$

Because the hydrogen and hydroxide ions are in balance (that is, equal in number), pure water is said to be neutral.

This neutral point is used as a reference in understanding how acidic or alkaline other solutions are. As solutions become increasingly acid from this point, the concentration of hydrogen ions in them increases. As they become increasingly alkaline, the concentration of hydrogen ions in them decreases. These relationships are summed up very neatly on the pH scale shown in Figure A9.1. Each change in number up or down the scale represents a tenfold increase or decrease in the concentration of hydrogen ions.

Measuring pH

For a relative indication of the pH level, a sample can be tested with litmus paper. This simple test will determine whether a solution is either acidic or alkaline. It can also be tested by adding an acid-base indicator such as bromothymol blue. The resulting colour is then compared to a colour chart that indicates relative pH. More precise readings can be determined using a pH meter or probe, such as the one shown in Figure A9.2. pH meters and probes use a pair of electrodes to measure the electrical potential of the solution being tested. When used to test a solution whose pH is unknown, the difference in potential between the two electrodes is measured and displayed as a pH value.

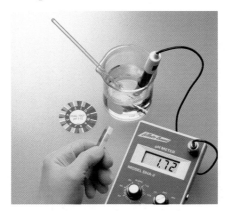

Figure A9.2 Both pH paper and a pH meter can be used to determine the pH of a solution. The meter will give the more precise reading.

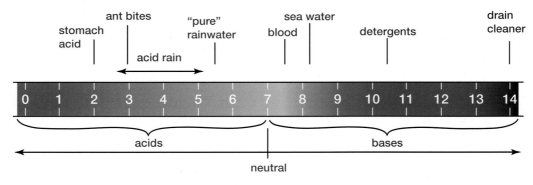

Figure A9.1 The average pH values for various substances are indicated on this pH scale.

The Dissection of a Fetal Pig

Expectations

By the end of this investigation, you should be able to:

- Dissect a fetal pig, exposing the organs of the body cavity.
- Draw and label the following organs and organ systems:
  - **(a)** the organs of the digestive system and the abdominal cavity;
  - **(b)** the organs of the respiratory system and thoracic cavity; and
  - **(c)** the heart and associated vessels of the circulatory system.
- Discuss how the structure of the major organs relates to their function.
- Compare the structure and function of organs in the fetal pig to human organs.

Figure A10.1 The internal systems of a pig are representative of those of all placental mammals.

Pigs are members of the class mammalia. Before birth, the young are nourished by the placenta in the mother's womb. For this reason, pigs (like humans) are known as placental mammals. The structure and organization of the internal organs of the pig are representative of those of all placental mammals. Although the fetal pig is not yet born, its internal systems are complete. In this investigation you will dissect a fetal pig to study its internal organs. This dissection will give you a sense of how internal systems are arranged within your own body.

Dissection involves the careful and systematic examination of the internal structures of an organism. A good dissection will reveal not only the location and structure of individual organs, but also how different organs relate to one another in the various systems of the body. To carry out a successful dissection, you should be familiar with the terms listed in Table A10.1. These are the terms used to describe the location of the various features of the animal and to direct incisions.

This dissection is divided into four parts. In the first part, you will investigate the external anatomy of your specimen and identify its age and sex. In the second part, you will examine the organs of the digestive system. In the third part, you will examine the organs of the circulatory system. Finally, in the fourth part, you will examine the organs of the respiratory system. In between each investigation you will store your specimen. Remember to wrap and store your specimen properly, and to label it so you can identify it again.

Term	Meaning
Dorsal	Upper or back surface
Ventral	Under or belly surface
Lateral	Side
Anterior	Toward the front (head) end
Posterior	Toward the back end
Superficial	Near the surface
Proximal	Close to
Distal	Far from

Table A10.1 The anatomical terms used to locate organs or incisions during this dissection.

> **PLAY**

Illustrations used in this dissection are also available electronically. If you do not dissect a fetal pig or some other organism in your course, many virtual dissections are available to enhance your learning.

CAUTION: **Extreme care must be taken when using dissecting instruments, particularly scalpels. To the extent possible, make cuts away from your body. The pigs are preserved in a chemical solution. Wear plastic gloves, goggles and an apron at all times, and work in a well-ventilated area. If some of the chemical comes into contact with your skin, wash it off immediately. At the end of each lesson, wash your hands thoroughly. Dispose of all materials as instructed by your teacher, and clean your work area.**

Materials

preserved fetal pig	dissecting tray
dissecting instruments	string or strong thread
plastic bag and tie (to store your specimen)	water-proof tags (to identify your specimen)
disposable plastic gloves	apron
large tongs	newspapers and/or paper towelling
T pins	

Procedure

Part 1. External Anatomy

1. Rinse your specimen and place it on its side in the dissecting tray.

2. Measure your specimen from the snout to the base of the tail. Use Figure A10.2 to estimate the gestational age of your specimen.

3. Identify the external features of your specimen using Figure A10.3. Make your own drawing of the lateral view of your specimen, labelling the features. Record the age of your specimen with this drawing.

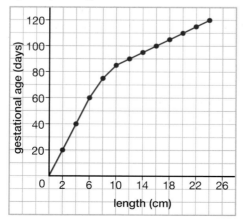

Figure A10.2 The gestation period of the pig is about 115 days. About how old is your specimen?

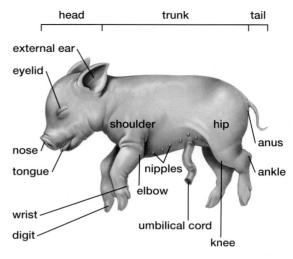

Figure A10.3 A lateral view of a fetal pig.

4. Turn your specimen onto its back. Using Figures A10.4 and A10.5, determine the sex of your specimen. Examine a specimen of each sex.

5. Make your own drawing of the external reproductive organs of specimens of both sexes. Label the structures.

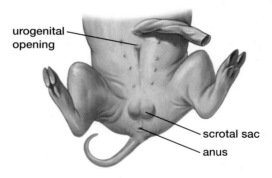

Figure A10.4 The external reproductive organs of a male fetal pig.

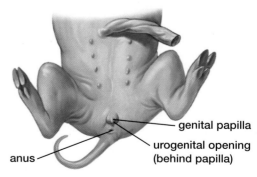

Figure A10.5 The external reproductive organs of a female fetal pig.

Part 2. The Digestive System

A. The mouth

1. Using a strong pair of dissecting scissors, make a cut in the corner of the mouth, cutting toward the posterior of the specimen. Repeat on the other side.

2. Pry the mouth open. Using Figure A10.6, locate and identify the features of the oral cavity.

3. Make your own drawing of the mouth of your specimen, labelling the features.

Analyze

1. Explain how the appearance of the following structures relates to their function as part of the digestive system. Give as much detail as possible, including size, texture, external structure, and internal structure.

   (a) the teeth
   (b) the hard palate
   (c) the tongue
   (d) the epiglottis

2. What differences can you see between the pig's mouth structures and your own? How can you explain these differences?

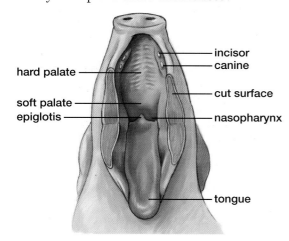

Figure A10.6 The oral cavity of the fetal pig.

B. Exposing the abdominal organs

1. Place the pig in the dissecting tray with its ventral surface uppermost. Spread out the limbs. Tie a piece of string to one of the forelimbs near the ankle. Pass the string under the tray and securely tie the other forelimb. Repeat the process with the hind limbs.

2. Select a point just anterior to the umbilical cord on the specimen's ventral surface. Using forceps, pinch the skin of the abdomen along the midventral line and draw it slightly away from the animal. With your scissors, make an incision in the skin. The incision should be just large enough to pass the point of your scissors through. Now make a midventral cut ending just posterior to the midline of the animal (shown as #1 in Figure A10.7 on the next page). To avoid damaging the organs as you cut, keep the tips of the scissors pointing up. Be careful not to damage the umbilical cord.

3. From the same starting point, make a second incision around the base of the umbilical cord extending back to just anterior to the anus (shown as #2 on Figure A10.7). You may wish to turn your specimen around so you can cut away from you. Repeat on the other side.

4. Locate the base of the sternum (breast bone), situated in the centre of the chest. The ribs are attached to the sternum. Select a point slightly posterior to the sternum and cut across the ventral surface (shown as #3 in Figure A10.7). The incision should be posterior to the diaphragm, which you will be able to see as a dome-shaped layer of muscle separating the abdominal and thoracic cavities.

5. Make two final incisions, one on each side of the cuts bordering the umbilical cord and just anterior to the hind limbs (shown as #4 in Figure A10.7). Use T pins to pin back the skins to expose the internal organs of the abdominal cavity. The T pins should point away from the specimen so they will not interfere with your work.

6. The organs of the abdomen are covered and protected by a membrane called peritoneum. The double-layered sheets of peritoneum are called mesenteries. Using forceps or a dissecting probe, gently move the mesenteries aside to reveal the underlying organs.

7. Using Figure A10.8 below and Figure A10.9 on the next page, locate and identify the organs of the abdominal cavity. Make a drawing of your specimen showing the location of the internal organs and labelling them.

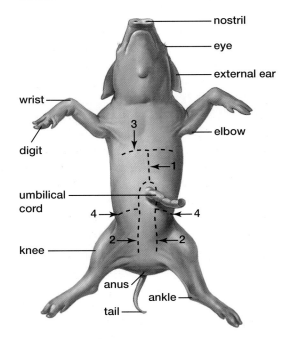

Figure A10.7 A ventral view of a fetal pig showing the pattern of incisions that expose the internal organs.

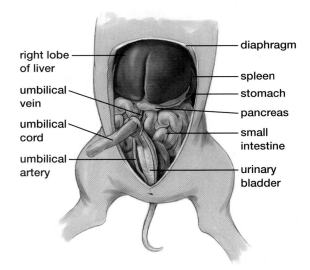

Figure A10.8 The major organs found in the abdominal cavity of the fetal pig.

C. Examining the abdominal organs

1. Locate the liver, the largest organ of the abdominal cavity. Describe its appearance in your own words. Identify its different lobes.

2. Locate and describe the esophagus. Note how it passes through the diaphragm just before it enters the stomach.

3. Locate and describe the stomach. Carefully cut open the stomach and describe the inner surface.

4. Locate and describe the pancreas, situated below the stomach and between the stomach and the small intestine. It is usually lighter in colour than the surrounding organs.

5. Locate and describe the small intestine. See if you can identify the separate portions of the duodenum, ileum, and jejunum.

6. Using forceps or a probe, gently lift the connective tissue that links the liver and the duodenum. Locate the bile duct in this mesentery and trace it back to its source at the gall bladder. The gall bladder is embedded on the surface of the liver.

7. Move to the distal end of the small intestine and locate the point on the left side of the abdominal cavity where the large intestine begins. A blind pouch called the caecum is found here.

8. The main part of the large intestine is called the colon. Identify the path the colon takes in the abdomen.

9. Toward the end of the large intestine is the rectum. Note where the tract terminates at the anus.

10. Cut the esophagus as close to the top of the abdominal cavity as you can. Make a second cut as close as you can to the end of the digestive tract near the anus. Carefully remove the entire digestive tract, in one piece, from the specimen.

11. Carefully cut away the connective tissue around the digestive tract. Unravel the tract and make a drawing of it, identifying the different portions of the digestive tract. Measure each section of the digestive tract.

12. Remove a portion of the stomach tissue and examine it under a microscope. Make a drawing of the unravelled digestive tract and describe the appearance of this tissue in your own words.

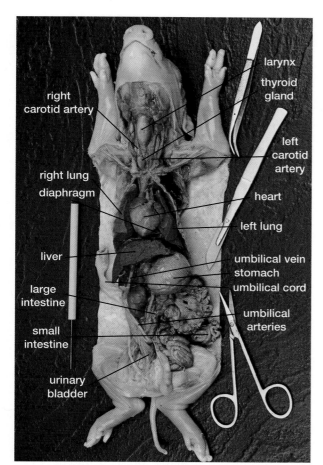

right carotid artery

larynx
thyroid gland

right lung
diaphragm

left carotid artery

heart

left lung

liver

umbilical vein
stomach
umbilical cord

large intestine

umbilical arteries

small intestine

urinary bladder

Figure A10.9 The internal abdominal and thoracic organs of the fetal pig. (Note: the pancreas is not visible in this photograph.)

Analyze

1. Explain how the appearance of the following structures relates to their function as part of the digestive system. Give as much detail as possible, including size, texture, external structure, and internal structure.

   (a) liver
   (b) pancreas
   (c) esophagus
   (d) stomach
   (e) small intestine
   (f) large intestine
   (g) gall bladder
   (h) mesentery

2. Using your own drawings of the abdominal organs, trace the path of food from the mouth to the rectum. Identify the major steps in the digestive process that take place along the way.

◀◀ REWIND

To review the organs and processes involved in digestion, turn to Chapter 10.

Part 3. The Circulatory System

A. Exposing the organs of the thoracic cavity

1. Locate the base of the sternum (breast bone), situated in the centre of the chest. The ribs are attached to the sternum. Use this as the starting point for your incision. With forceps, pinch the skin of the abdomen along the midventral line and draw it slightly away from the animal. With your scissors, make an incision in the skin. The incision should be just large enough to pass the point of your scissors through. Now make a midventral cut (shown as #1 in Figure A10.10 on the next page.). This cut should extend as far forward as the hairs near the base of the throat. Be careful not to damage the underlying body wall as you cut. Remember to keep the tips of your scissors pointing up, not down, to avoid damaging the internal organs.

2. Next, make two cuts (shown as cuts #2 and #3 in Figure A10.10) from the midventral line in the region of the thoracic cavity. Carefully lift the skin and pin it to the sides of the specimen using T pins. The T pins should point away from the specimen so they will not interfere with your work.

3. Using a sturdy pair of dissecting scissors, cut the ribs along the sternum, and pry them apart to reveal the organs of the thoracic cavity.

4. Using forceps or a dissecting probe, remove the connective tissues and membranes that surround the lungs and heart.

5. Using Figure A10.9 and Figure A10.11 on the next page, identify the internal organs of the thoracic cavity. Make a drawing of your specimen.

BIO FACT

The same pattern of incisions you have performed exposing the organs in the thoracic cavity (including the separation of the rib cage) is used by surgeons performing heart or lung surgery on a human patient.

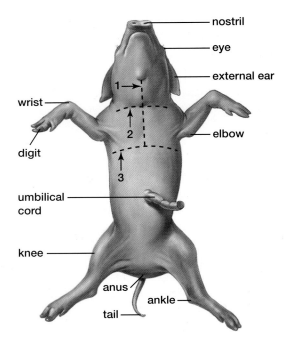

Figure A10.10 A ventral view of a fetal pig showing the pattern of incisions that will expose the organs of the thoracic cavity.

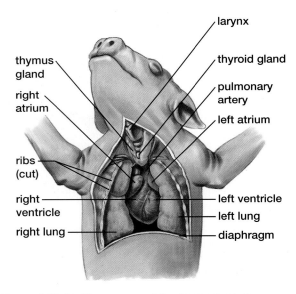

Figure A10.11 The organs of the thoracic cavity.

B. Examining the organs of the circulatory system

1. Using Figure A10.11 and A10.13 on the next page for reference, identify and compare the sizes of the following major blood vessels.

   (a) the aorta, including the aortic arch;

   (b) the superior vena cava;

   (c) the pulmonary artery;

   (d) the pulmonary vein;

   (e) the inferior vena cava;

   (f) the carotid arteries.

2. Your specimen may have a small blood vessel connecting the pulmonary artery to the aorta. This vessel is called the ductus arteriosis. Try to locate this vessel on your own specimen. If you cannot find it, examine another specimen in which this vessel is visible.

3. Locate and describe the heart.

4. Make a drawing of your specimen showing the location of the circulatory organs.

5. Carefully cut through the blood vessels a short distance from the heart. Remove the heart. Make an incision in the ventral surface of the heart as shown in Figure A10.12. Your incision should expose all four chambers of the heart.

6. Using Figure A10.13 for reference, identify the internal features of the heart. Try to locate and identify the heart valves at the opening to the blood vessels.

7. Compare the structure of the different chambers of the heart. Make a labelled drawing and describe the structures in your own words.

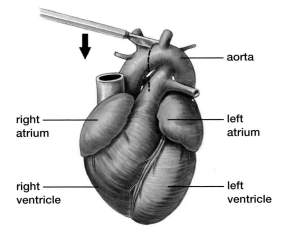

Figure A10.12 With the heart on its dorsal surface, make your incision beginning at the aortic arch and continuing straight to the base of the ventricles.

Analyze

1. Explain how the appearance of the following structures relates to their function as part of

the circulatory system. Give as much detail as possible, including size, texture, external structure, and internal structure.

(a) right atrium (b) left atrium

(c) right ventricle (d) left ventricle

(e) arteries (f) veins

(g) ductus arteriosis (h) heart valves

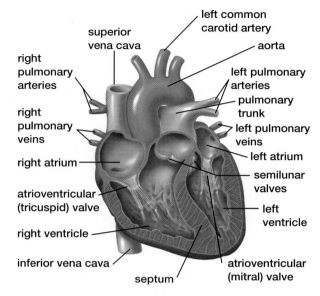

Figure A10.13 A ventral cross section of the heart.

2. Using your own drawings, trace the passage of blood from the body through the heart and back to the body.

◄◄ REWIND

To review the organs and processes involved in circulation, turn to Chapter 9.

Part 4. The Respiratory System
Examining the respiratory organs

1. Using Figure A10.11 on the previous page for reference, identify the major organs of the respiratory system.

2. Note the difference in structure between the right and left lung. In your own words, describe the structure and texture of the lungs.

3. Locate and describe the pleural membranes encasing each lung.

4. Using a probe, move aside the layers of muscle to work deeper into the neck. If necessary, carefully cut the muscle tissue.

Locate the larynx, trachea, and esophagus. Describe the difference in structure between the trachea and esophagus.

5. Examine the rib cage and try to identify the external and internal intercostal muscles.

6. Open the mouth and describe the relationship between the glottis, esophagus, and pharynx.

7. Trace the passage of the trachea through the throat. Try to identify the two branches of the bronchi.

8. Make a drawing of your specimen showing the location of the organs of the respiratory system.

9. Using a small syringe or dropper, blow a small amount of air into the trachea. Note the inflation of the lungs.

10. Remove a portion of lung tissue and examine it under a microscope. Make a drawing and describe the internal structure of the lung in your own words.

Analyze

1. Explain how the appearance of the following structures relates to their function as part of the circulatory system. Give as much detail as possible, including size, texture, external structure, and internal structure.

(a) trachea (b) right lung

(c) left lung (d) pleural membrane

(e) larynx (f) glottis

(g) diaphragm (h) rib cage

2. Using your own drawings, trace the path of air from the mouth to the lungs.

◄◄ REWIND

To review the organs and processes involved in gas exchange, turn to Chapter 8.

Periodic Table and List of Elements

MAIN-GROUP ELEMENTS

MAIN-GROUP ELEMENTS

Period

atomic number
atomic mass

Metals
Metalloids
Nonmetals

TRANSITION ELEMENTS

1A (1)	2A (2)	3B (3)	4B (4)	5B (5)	6B (6)	7B (7)	8B (8)	8B (9)	8B (10)	1B (11)	2B (12)	3A (13)	4A (14)	5A (15)	6A (16)	7A (17)	8A (18)
1 **H** 1.008																	2 **He** 4.003
3 **Li** 6.941	4 **Be** 9.012											5 **B** 10.81	6 **C** 12.01	7 **N** 14.01	8 **O** 16.00	9 **F** 19.00	10 **Ne** 20.18
11 **Na** 22.99	12 **Mg** 24.31											13 **Al** 26.98	14 **Si** 28.09	15 **P** 30.97	16 **S** 32.07	17 **Cl** 35.45	18 **Ar** 39.95
19 **K** 39.10	20 **Ca** 40.08	21 **Sc** 44.96	22 **Ti** 47.88	23 **V** 50.94	24 **Cr** 52.00	25 **Mn** 54.94	26 **Fe** 55.85	27 **Co** 58.93	28 **Ni** 58.69	29 **Cu** 63.55	30 **Zn** 65.39	31 **Ga** 69.72	32 **Ge** 72.61	33 **As** 74.92	34 **Se** 78.96	35 **Br** 79.90	36 **Kr** 83.80
37 **Rb** 85.47	38 **Sr** 87.62	39 **Y** 88.91	40 **Zr** 91.22	41 **Nb** 92.91	42 **Mo** 95.94	43 **Tc** (98)	44 **Ru** 101.1	45 **Rh** 102.9	46 **Pd** 106.4	47 **Ag** 107.9	48 **Cd** 112.4	49 **In** 114.8	50 **Sn** 118.7	51 **Sb** 121.8	52 **Te** 127.6	53 **I** 126.9	54 **Xe** 131.3
55 **Cs** 132.9	56 **Ba** 137.3	57 **La** 138.9	72 **Hf** 178.5	73 **Ta** 180.9	74 **W** 183.9	75 **Re** 186.2	76 **Os** 190.2	77 **Ir** 192.2	78 **Pt** 195.1	79 **Au** 197.0	80 **Hg** 200.6	81 **Tl** 204.4	82 **Pb** 207.2	83 **Bi** 209.0	84 **Po** (209)	85 **At** (210)	86 **Rn** (222)
87 **Fr** (223)	88 **Ra** (226)	89 **Ac** (227)	104 **Rf** (261)	105 **Db** (262)	106 **Sg** (266)	107 **Bh** (262)	108 **Hs** (265)	109 **Mt** (266)	110 **Uun** (269)	111 **Uuu** (272)	112 **Uub** (277)		114 **Uuq** 285		116 **Uuh** 289		118 **Uuo** 293

INNER TRANSITION ELEMENTS

6 Lanthanoids	58 **Ce** 140.1	59 **Pr** 140.9	60 **Nd** 144.2	61 **Pm** (145)	62 **Sm** 150.4	63 **Eu** 152.0	64 **Gd** 157.3	65 **Tb** 158.9	66 **Dy** 162.5	67 **Ho** 164.9	68 **Er** 167.3	69 **Tm** 168.9	70 **Yb** 173.0	71 **Lu** 175.0
7 Actinoids	90 **Th** 232.0	91 **Pa** (231)	92 **U** 238.0	93 **Np** (237)	94 **Pu** (242)	95 **Am** (243)	96 **Cm** (247)	97 **Bk** (247)	98 **Cf** (251)	99 **Es** (252)	100 **Fm** (257)	101 **Md** (258)	102 **No** (259)	103 **Lr** (260)

List of Elements

Element	Symbol	Atomic Number	Atomic Mass*	Element	Symbol	Atomic Number	Atomic Mass*
Actinium	Ac	89	(227)	Mercury	Hg	80	200.6
Aluminum	Al	13	26.98	Molybdenum	Mo	42	95.94
Americium	Am	95	(243)	Neodymium	Nd	60	144.2
Antimony	Sb	51	121.8	Neon	Ne	10	20.18
Argon	Ar	18	39.95	Neptunium	Np	93	(244)
Arsenic	As	33	74.92	Nickel	Ni	28	58.70
Astatine	At	85	(210)	Niobium	Nb	41	92.91
Barium	Ba	56	137.3	Nitrogen	N	7	14.01
Berkelium	Bk	97	(247)	Nobelium	No	102	(253)
Beryllium	Be	4	9.012	Osmium	Os	76	190.2
Bismuth	Bi	83	209.0	Oxygen	O	8	16.00
Bohrium	Bh	107	(262)	Palladium	Pd	46	106.4
Boron	B	5	10.81	Phosphorus	P	15	30.97
Bromine	Br	35	79.90	Platinum	Pt	78	195.1
Cadmium	Cd	48	112.4	Plutonium	Pu	94	(242)
Calcium	Ca	20	40.08	Polonium	Po	84	(209)
Californium	Cf	98	(249)	Potassium	K	19	39.10
Carbon	C	6	12.01	Praseodymium	Pr	59	140.9
Cerium	Ce	58	140.1	Promethium	Pm	61	(145)
Cesium	Cs	55	132.9	Protactinium	Pa	91	(231)
Chlorine	Cl	17	35.45	Radium	Ra	88	(226)
Chromium	Cr	24	52.00	Radon	Rn	86	(222)
Cobalt	Co	27	58.93	Rhenium	Re	75	186.2
Copper	Cu	29	63.55	Rhodium	Rh	45	102.9
Curium	Cm	96	(247)	Rubidium	Rb	37	85.47
Dubnium	Db	105	(262)	Ruthenium	Ru	44	101.1
Dysprosium	Dy	66	162.5	Rutherfordium	Rf	104	(261)
Einsteinium	Es	99	(254)	Samarium	Sm	62	150.4
Erbium	Er	68	167.3	Scandium	Sc	21	44.96
Europium	Eu	63	152.0	Seaborgium	Sg	106	(266)
Fermium	Fm	100	(253)	Selenium	Se	34	78.96
Fluorine	F	9	19.00	Silicon	Si	14	28.09
Francium	Fr	87	(223)	Silver	Ag	47	107.9
Gadolinium	Gd	64	157.3	Sodium	Na	11	22.99
Gallium	Ga	31	69.72	Strontium	Sr	38	87.62
Germanium	Ge	32	72.61	Sulfur	S	16	32.07
Gold	Au	79	197.0	Tantalum	Ta	73	180.9
Hafnium	Hf	72	178.5	Technetium	Tc	43	(98)
Hassium	Hs	108	(265)	Tellurium	Te	52	127.6
Helium	He	2	4.003	Terbium	Tb	65	158.9
Holmium	Ho	67	164.9	Thallium	Tl	81	204.4
Hydrogen	H	1	1.008	Thorium	Th	90	232.0
Indium	In	49	114.8	Thulium	Tm	69	168.9
Iodine	I	53	126.9	Tin	Sn	50	118.7
Iridium	Ir	77	192.2	Titanium	Ti	22	47.88
Iron	Fe	26	55.85	Tungsten	W	74	183.9
Krypton	Kr	36	83.80	Ununbium	Uub	112	(277)
Lanthanum	La	57	138.9	Ununhexium	Uuh	116	289
Lawrencium	Lr	103	(257)	Ununnilium	Uun	110	(269)
Lead	Pb	82	207.2	Ununoctium	Uuo	118	293
Lithium	Li	3	6.941	Ununquadium	Uuq	114	285
Lutetium	Lu	71	175.0	Unununium	Uuu	111	(272)
Magnesium	Mg	12	24.31	Uranium	U	92	238.0
Manganese	Mn	25	54.94	Vanadium	V	23	50.94
Meitnerium	Mt	109	(266)	Xenon	Xe	54	131.3
Mendelevium	Md	101	(256)	Ytterbium	Yb	70	173.0
				Yttrium	Y	39	88.91
				Zinc	Zn	30	65.39
				Zirconium	Zr	40	91.22

*All atomic masses are given to four significant figures. Values in parentheses represent the mass number of the most stable form of the atom.

Glossary

abscisic acid   plant hormone (growth inhibitor) which inhibits the germination of seeds, inhibits the growth of buds in the axils of plant stems, and blocks the intake of carbon dioxide by causing leaf stomata to close. Abscisic acid also blocks the action of growth promoting hormones. (15.1)

acetylcholine   a chemical that slows the heart rate by inhibiting the firing of the sinoatrial node. (9.3)

acoelomates   animals with three cell layers (ectoderm, endoderm, and mesoderm), but no body cavities such as cnidaria and flatworms. (13.3)

acquired immune response   a response through which the body's resistance to a specific pathogen is built up over time. (9.2)

actin filaments   long, thin, flexible protein cables that can contract; part of the cytoskeleton and a major component of muscle fibres. (2.1)

active transport   cellular process of moving substances across a living membrane *against* their concentration gradients. (1.2)

adenine   one of four nitrogen-containing bases in nucleotides which make up DNA and RNA. (6.2)

aerobic   requiring molecular oxygen (O_2) to maintain cellular functions. (3.3, 8.1)

aeroponic   having a type of soil-free horticulture where plants' source of nutrients is the "air". The plant roots are enclosed in containers which are fitted with spray nozzles that dispense water and nutrients to the roots. (16.3)

agglutination   clumping of red blood cells in response to antibodies fending off foreign materials, such as the material found in incompatible blood groups. The antibodies recognize and bind to the markers on the incompatible donor blood, causing them to clump together. (9.2)

agricultural revolution   period which contrasted sharply with that of the nomadic hunter-gatheres, namely people stayed in one place, planted seeds, built dwellings, and made use of one plot of land for a long period of time. (16.3)

air sacs   in birds, pockets within the respiratory tract that collect air on inspiration and expiration. The arrangement of air sacs helps to increase the respiratory efficiency of the bird. (8.2)

albinism   a genetic abnormality in animals where the eyes, skin, and hair have no pigment. (6.1)

algae   plant-like autotrophic protists that carry out photosynthesis. (12.3)

alkaptonuria   hereditary condition where an individual lacks an enzyme that converts urine to its usual colour. (6.1)

allele   alternate form of a gene located at a particular place on a chromosome. (4.2)

alveoli   (singular alveolus) the gas exchange structures within mammalian lungs. Alveoli are tiny air pockets with walls made of a membrane a single cell thick. Respiratory gases are exchanged across these membrane walls. (8.2)

amylase   an enzyme that breaks down starch and is produced by the salivary glands and by the pancreas. Salivary amylase is called ptyalin and pancreatic amylase is called amylopsin. (10.3)

amniocentesis   a medical procedure in which a sample of cells from the amniotic fluid is tested for abnormalities in a fetus. (7.4)

amniotic fluid   the fluid that surrounds the fetus during its development. (7.4)

amniotic sac   the fluid-filled membrane inside the uterus in which a growing fetus is suspended. (7.4)

amoebae   blob-like protists of the phylum Sarcodina. (12.3)

anabolic steroids   synthetic derivatives of the male hormone testosterone. (10.5)

anaerobic   performing processes or reactions in the absence of molecular oxygen (O_2). (3.3)

anal canal   the last portion of the large intestine opening to the anus. (10.2)

anaphase   a phase of mitosis in which the centromere splits apart and the chromatids are pulled to opposite poles of the cell by the spindle fibres (5.1)

anemia   a condition where the overall red blood cell count is too low to support the body's oxygen requirements. (7.1)

angioplasty   medical procedure in which a cardiologist inserts a fine plastic tube into a clogged artery and then inflates part of the tube, opening the artery. (9.3)

angiosperms   plants that protect their seeds within the body of a fruit, also known as flowering plants. (13.2)

animal manure   refuse from farm animals, including urine, feces, and straw or sawdust used to absorb these. (16.3)

Annelida   a phylum contained in the Kingdom Animalia. Commonly known as segmented worms, such as earthworms, marine bristleworms, featherworms, and leeches. (13.3)

antheridium a structure in seedless plants that produces sperm. (13.2)

Anthoceraphytes members of the division Anthoceraphyta, Kingdom Plantae, commonly known as hornworts. They are nonvascular plants with small flat gametophyte and a horn-like sporophyte. (13.2)

antibiotics antibacterial agents that work to stop bacteria growing by interfering with the specific processes that are essential for bacterial growth and reproduction. (12.2)

antibody Y-shaped protein molecule in the blood plasma that is made up of two heavy polypeptide chains bound to two light polypeptide chains. Antibodies are produced by the body in response to antigens. (9.2)

antigen a foreign substance that triggers immune responses, such as the production of antibodies. (9.2)

anus the opening of the digestion system through which waste is eliminated from the body. (10.2)

aorta the main blood vessel that carries blood from the heart into the systemic circulation. (9.3)

aortic arches heart-like pumps that drive the circulation of blood in some animals, such as annelids. More than one aortic arch may be linked in a series; for example, the earthworm has a series of five aortic arches. (9.1)

apoptosis a process in the development and maintenance of all tissues in which some cells turn on an orderly self-destruct process (programmed cell death). (2.3)

appendix appendage that comes off the caecum portion of the large intestine. It has no role in digestion but it may have a role in fighting infections. (10.2)

archegonium (plural archegonia) a structure in seedless plants that produces eggs. (13.2)

arteriole small artery that takes blood from the arteries to the capillaries. (9.2)

arteriosclerosis a condition in which cholesterol or other fatty material becomes deposited under the inner lining of arteries. (9.3)

artery blood vessel that carries blood away from the heart. (9.1)

Arthropoda a phylum contained in the Kingdom Animalia, which includes lobsters, crabs, shrimp, barnacles, sow bugs, scorpions, spiders, mites, millipedes, and insects. (13.3)

artificial selection a process of selective breeding in plants where the percentage of offspring that possess desirable traits is increased by selecting plants with the desirable traits through mass selection, pure-line selection and cross-breeding. (15.3)

asci small fingerlike sac structures in which sac fungi develop spores. (12.4)

ascomycotes a division of the Kingdom Fungi commonly called sac fungi, which includes powdery mildews, yeasts, morels, and truffles. (12.4)

asymmetrical having an irregular shape, as applied to an organism. (13.3)

atom smallest particle of a chemical element that has the properties of that element; a basic unit of all materials. (Appendix 2)

ATP adenosine triphosphate; carries packages of chemical energy between reactions in the cell. (3.2)

atrioventricular node (A-V node) node, located near the atria on the partition between the two ventricles, that transmits an electrical impulse over the walls of ventricles to start their contraction. The A-V node fires in response to the impulse produced by the contraction of the atria. (9.3)

atrium (plural atria) chamber of the heart that collects blood flowing into the heart. In the mammalian heart, the right atrium receives blood from the systemic circulation while the left atrium receives blood from the pulmonary circulation. (9.1)

autosomes chromosomes that are not directly involved in determining the sex of an individual. (5.3)

autotroph an organism that can produce organic molecules from simple inorganic molecules and thus make its own food. (10.1)

auxins group of plant hormones that promote cell elongation and trigger the development of prop roots from above ground stems. They also promote the dropping of leaves after the leaves have reached a certain stage. (15.1)

B

B cell type of lymphocyte that arises from the bone marrow and plays a role in the body's acquired immune response. (9.2)

bacilli (singular bacillus) rod-shaped bacterial cells; one of the three main shapes of bacterial cells. (12.2)

bacteriophages viruses that attack and kill a bacterium. The virus uses the cell's ability to make copies of viral DNA. (6.1)

balanced diet a healthy diet containing six essential nutrients (carbohydrates, fats, proteins, minerals, vitamins, and water) in the amounts that keep body and mind functioning at their best. (10.5)

Barr body the inactivated X chromosome, one of two X chromosomes found in every cell in females. (5.3)

basidia club-shaped hyphae found in members of the Basidiomycotes that bear spores call basidiospores. (12.4)

basidiocarps short-lived reproductive structures called fruiting bodies characteristic of Basidiomycotes. (12.4)

Basidiomycotes a division of the Kingdom Fungi, which include mushrooms, bracket fungi, shelf fungi, puffballs, and stinkhorns. (12.4)

basidiospores spores that are borne on club-shaped hyphae called basidia found in members of the Basidiomycotes. (12.4)

bilateral symmetry one of two types of symmetry among organisms. The organism can be cut into two equal, mirror-image halves through only one vertical plane. (13.3)

binary fission the asexually reproductive process of cell division in bacteria. (12.2)

binomial nomenclature system of using a two-word name for each species. (11.3)

biochemistry study of the chemistry of living things including the chemical substances and processes involved. (1.1)

bioremediation a technology that uses micro-organisms to break complex toxic compounds down into simpler, non-toxic substances. (3.4)

biotechnology use of living organisms to manufacture products or provide services for humans; application of technology to life sciences. (2.4)

blood vascular tissue specially adapted to carry particular substances. (9.1)

blood group system of classification of blood according to the presence or absence of particular protein markers on the walls of the red blood cells. The main human blood groups are A, B, AB, and O. (9.2)

breathing act of ventilating a respiratory surface with air. Breathing is usually accomplished through muscular movements that can be divided into inspiration and expiration. (8.3)

bronchi (singular bronchus) in a mammal, the passageways that branch from the trachea into the lungs. One bronchus carries air into each lung. (8.2)

bronchioles in a mammal, the passageways that branch from the bronchi into the separate lobes of the lungs. The bronchioles divide into smaller and smaller passageways that carry air into all portions of the lungs. (8.2)

brown algae phaeophytes, a type of algae made up of nearly all multicellular marine organisms, commonly called seaweeds. They have cell walls made of cellulose and alginic acid. (12.3)

Bryophytes members of the division Bryophyta of the Kingdom Plantae, commonly known as mosses. They are nonvascular plants. (13.2)

caecum sac-like portion of the large intestine near the small intestine that has a blind end. (10.2)

caffeine type of drug that acts on the hypothalamus at the base of the brain to inhibit the production of ADH and that also causes blood vessels to constrict. (10.5)

Calvin cycle the main pathway of the light-independent synthesis reactions in photosynthesis; converts carbon dioxide to carbohydrate. (3.2)

capillary tiny blood vessel with a wall only a single cell thick. Gases and other substances are exchanged between the circulatory system and the tissues of the body across the capillary walls. (9.2)

capillary action one mechanism for the translocation of water in plants. Capillary action relies on the adhesive properties of water. In a small tube, the polarity of the walls of the tube will attract water molecules, which will climb up and cling to the sides of the tube. (9.5)

capsid protective protein coat that surrounds strands of DNA or RNA in viruses. (11.2)

capsule a sticky gelatinous shell around the cell wall of some bacteria. (2.1)

carbohydrate organic compound that contains CH_2O groups, such as monosaccharides, disaccharides, and polysaccharides. (1.1)

cardiac circulation a route taken by the blood within the heart. Cardiac circulation is one of three primary cycles in the mammalian circulatory system. (9.2)

cardiac output amount of blood pumped by the heart, usually measured in mL per min. (9.3)

cardiovascular system circulatory system in which the vascular fluid is pumped around the body by the action of a specialized organ, the heart. (9.1)

carrier an organism that is heterozygous for the given trait but does not show the recessive trait. (4.2)

carrier protein membrane protein that facilitates the movement of a substance through the cell membrane. (1.3)

cassava plants of the genus *Manihot* with starch tuberous roots, which is made into tapioca. (15.3)

cell cycle a continuous sequence of cell growth and division. (5.1)

cell membrane a fluid mosaic membrane that separates the cell interior from its exterior environment and controls the movement of materials into and out of the cell. (2.1)

cell wall a rigid structure surrounding the cell membrane that protects and supports the cell and allows materials to pass to and from the cell membrane through pores. (2.1)

cellular respiration all of the chemical reactions needed to break down (metabolize) carbohydrates and other molecules to transfer chemical energy to ATP. (3.3, 8.2)

cellular slime moulds Acrasiomycotes, one of two types of slime moulds contained in the fungus-like protists, which exist as individual amoeboid cells with one nucleus each. (12.3)

cellulose polysaccharide composed of glucose subunits that forms the main component of plant cell walls. (1.1)

central vacuole a very large, membrane-bound, fluid-filled storage sac that gives added internal support to a plant cell. (2.1)

centriole a short, cylindrical organelle found in animal cells and made up of microtubules. (2.1)

centromere the region where two sister chromatids are held together in a chromosome. (5.2)

centrosome an organelle located near the nucleus that organizes the cell's microtubules and helps to organize the even distribution of cell components when cells divide; in animal cells, contains a pair of centrioles. (2.1)

Cephalochordata a subphylum of the phylum Chordata, commonly known as lancelets. (13.3)

channel protein membrane protein with a tunnel-like shape that creates a channel through a membrane that allows charged particles (ions) to pass through. (1.3)

chemical energy the energy stored in the bonds between atoms in molecules. (3.1)

chemoautotrophs organisms that obtain energy by breaking apart chemical bonds in inorganic compounds. (12.2)

chemoheterotrophs organisms that obtain both their carbon and energy from organic compounds. (12.2)

chlorophyll green pigment that absorbs the light energy necessary for photosynthesis. (3.2)

chloroplast a plastid that gives green plants their colour and transfers the energy in sunlight into stored energy in carbohydrates during photosynthesis. (2.1)

cholesterol soft, waxy substance found among the lipids (fats) in arteries, veins and body cells. It is used to form cell membranes, insulate nerves, and produce vitamin D and bile acids, as well as some hormones. (7.4, 10.5)

Chordata a phylum of the Kingdom Animalia, commonly known as chordates. Most chordates are vertebrates, with bony skeletons and backbones. (13.3)

chorion tissue that surrounds the amniotic sac housing the fetus. (7.4)

chorionic villi sampling sampling of cells of the chorion to test for genetic conditions in a fetus. (7.4)

chromosomes structures within the nucleus that contain the cell's genetic information (5.1)

chromosome theory of inheritance theory that states genes are located on chromosomes, and chromosomes provide the basis for the process of segregation and independent assortment of these genes. (5.3)

chyme thick liquid mixture of partially broken down food and gastric juice that passes from the stomach into the first part of the small intestine, the duodenum. (10.2)

cilia hairlike structures extending from the cell membrane that beat in a co-ordinated rhythm to produce movement. (2.1)

circulatory system vascular system in which the progress of fluid is controlled by muscle movements so that it follows a specific pattern. (9.1)

cladistics classification scheme that is based on phylogeny. (11.4)

cladogram branching diagram that resembles a phylogenetic tree, but that can be used to test alternative hypotheses. (11.4)

cleft palate physical development that results in a groove in the upper lip and roof of the mouth. (7.3)

climax community mature, stable ecosystem or ecological community that results from succession and remains the same until disturbed. (16.2)

clones identical copies of an organism or part of an organism that have the same genetic makeup such as the offspring of asexual reproduction. (6.2, 15.3)

cloning process of creating identical copies of molecules, genes, cells, or organisms. (6.2, 15.1)

closed transport system a transport system in which the blood is pumped around the body within a closed network of vessels. (9.1)

Cnidaria a phylum of the Kingdom Animalia, commonly called cnidarians, including jellyfish, corals, and anemones. (13.3)

cocci (singular coccus) round bacterial cells; one of the three main shapes of bacterial cells. (12.4)

co-dominant the case when both alleles for a trait are dominant. (4.4)

codon set of three bases in mRNA that directs or codes amino acid placement on polypeptides. (6.1)

coelom   fluid-filled body cavity completely surrounded by mesoderm. Provides space for the development and suspension of organs and organ systems. (13.3)

coelomates   organisms with a coelom, such as annelids, molluscs, joint-legged animals, sea stars, and chordates. (13.3)

colon   main part of the large intestine that extends from the caecum to the rectum. (10.2)

commercial chemical fertilizers   fertilizers sold commercially for the agricultural industry that are usually manufactured from chemicals in the form of dry granules and rated according to the quantities of N, P, and K they contain. (16.3)

complementary base pairs   pairs of nitrogen bases in DNA; adenine pairs with thymine and guanine pairs with cytosine. (6.1)

complete protein   protein that contains all eight of the essential amino acids. It can be found in meat, legumes, eggs, cheese, milk, and whole grain products. (10.5)

concentration gradient   the difference in concentrations of a substance between two regions. (1.3)

conidia   type of spore that produces mycelia in the deutermycotes, basidiomycotes and ascomycotes. (12.4)

conjugation   a process whereby some bacteria are able to reproduce sexually. (12.2)

continuous variation   a range of variation in one trait resulting from the protein products produced by many genes. (5.3)

coronary bypass   medical procedure that involves removing a segment of healthy blood vessel from another part of the body and using it to create a new pathway around a blockage in a blood vessel near the heart. (9.3)

cortex   layer of tissue between the epidermis or corky layer and the vascular tissue of a plant; usually irregular in shape and arrangement. (14.3)

cotyledons   structure of a seed plant embryo that provides nutrients to the seed. May become the plant's first leaves. (13.2)

counter-current flow   or counter-current exchange: an arrangement in which two fluids exchange substances or heat with one another as they flow in opposite directions. This arrangement maximizes the concentration or heat gradient between the vessels containing the fluids. (8.4)

covalent bond   bond between atoms where they share a pair of electrons. (Appendix 2)

cristae   the folds of the inner membrane of mitochondria, which provide a large surface area for the enzyme complexes involved in transforming the energy stored in macromolecules into ATP. (2.1)

crossing over   the process where non-sister chromatids exchange genes during prophase I of meiosis allowing for the recombination of genes. (5.2)

cuticle   protective, waxy coating on the epidermis of plants, reducing water loss. (14.3)

cyanobacteria   photoautotrophs in the Kingdom Bacteria that are major producers of oxygen through the process of photosynthesis; commonly called blue-green algae. (12.2)

cytogenetics   study of the chromosomes in cells. (7.3)

cytokinesis   separation of the cytoplasm and the formation of two new daughter cells. (5.1)

cytokinins   hormones in plants that promote cell division; they delay the aging of leaves and fruit. (15.1)

cytosine   one of four nitrogen-containing bases in a nucleotide which make up DNA and RNA. (6.1)

cytoskeleton   a network of three kinds of interconnected fibres that maintains cell shape and allows for movement of its parts: actin filaments, intermediate filaments, and microtubules. (2.1)

daughter cells   one of two cells produced during mitosis of the parent cell. (5.1)

deletion   change in the physical structure of a chromosome where a portion of the chromosome is lost. (7.3)

denatured   a protein that has lost its normal shape because of extreme temperature or pH so that it can no longer perform its normal function. (1.1)

Deuteromycota   a subgroup of the Kingdom Fungi, commonly known as the imperfect fungi because they reproduce only asexually. Includes *Pencillium* and fungi found in some blue cheese. (12.4)

diaphragm   in mammals, a muscle layer that forms the floor of the thoracic cavity. The contraction of the diaphragm contributes to inspiration by increasing the volume of the thoracic cavity. (8.2)

diastolic pressure   pressure in the circulatory system when it reaches its lowest point immediately before another contraction of the ventricles. (9.3)

diatoms   members of the phylum Chrysophyta, a group of plant-like protists. The most abundant unicellular algae in the oceans, these golden-brown algae make up a large proportion of plankton. (12.3)

dicots   short form of dicotyledons, a class of angiosperms that has two cotyledons within the seed. (13.2, 14.2)

diffusion movement of molecules from a region of high concentration to one of low concentration. (1.3)

digestion process of chemical breakdown of food. (10.3)

digestive system system inside animals in which food is taken in and broken down to the point where useful substances can be absorbed into and transported by the circulatory system to individual cells. (10.1)

dihybrid cross a cross of two heterozygous individuals that differ in two traits, e.g., AaBb × AaBb (4.2)

dinoflagellates members of the phylum Zoomastiginia, a group of animal-like protists, which are unicellular, photosynthetic, and mostly marine. (12.3)

diplo- prefix describing a characteristic paired arrangement of bacterial cells. (12.2)

diploid cells that contain two copies of every chromosome, designated as 2n. (5.1)

disaccharide sugar that contains two monosaccharide subunits, for example, maltose and sucrose.

dissociation curve graphic representation of how much oxygen is bound to hemoglobin at different partial pressures of oxygen in the body. (9.2)

DNA deoxyribonucleic acid, a nucleic acid that contains genetic material used to construct an organism. It specifies protein synthesis in cells. (6.1)

DNA fingerprinting a process of using DNA or fragments of DNA to identify a person, or other organism. The DNA fragments have distinct bands separated by spaces and these band patterns are so distinct that they can be used like fingerprints. (6.2)

DNA replication copying process of DNA where two DNA molecules are formed from one. (6.2)

domain a level of classification above kingdoms. (11.1)

dominant type of trait, where the characteristic is always expressed, or appears, in an individual. (4.2)

double circulation circulatory system in blood is pumped through the heart twice during every complete cycle. (9.1)

double helix double spiral that describes the shape of the DNA molecule. (6.1)

Down syndrome a genetic disorder resulting from nondisjunction during gamete formation. During fertilization an individual receives three rather than two copies of chromosome 21 (also called trisomy 21). (7.3)

Duchenne muscular dystrophy form of muscular dystrophy caused by X-linked recessive inheritance resulting in muscle cells becoming engorged with fat and connective tissue deposits, and then eventually wasting away. (7.2)

ducts tubular canals that carry glandular secretions from one part of the body to another. (10.2)

duodenum shortest, widest, and first section of the small intestine following the stomach; bile and pancreatic juice enter the small intestine here, making the duodenum an important site for chemical digestion. (10.2)

duplication a change in the physical structure of a chromosome where a gene sequence is repeated one or more times within one or several chromosomes. (7.3)

Echinodermata a phylum contained in the Kingdom Animalia composed of marine animals that have an endoskeleton, a unique water vascular system, and are radially symmetrical, including animals such as sea cucumbers, starfish and sea urchins. (13.3)

ectoderm layer of cells on the outer layer of the gastrula, which eventually develop into the skin and nervous tissue of an animal. (13.3)

electrolyte chemical compound that forms ions in solution, producing a medium that can conduct an electric current. (Appendix 2)

electromagnetic spectrum the entire range of radiation produced by natural or human-made sources. (3.2)

electron a negatively charged particle found around the nucleus of an atom. (Appendix 2)

electron microscope microscope that uses beams of electrons instead of light to produce an image; capable of a magnification greater than one million times. (1.2)

element a substance composed of only one type of atom that cannot be broken down into other substances with different properties. (Appendix 2)

endocytosis process of the cell membrane folding in on itself to form a vesicle that brings a substance into the cell. (1.4)

endoderm layer of cells on the inner surface of the gastrula, which eventually develop into the lining of the animal's digestive tract and organs associated with digestion. (13.3)

endodermis layer of cells just inside the cortex of a plant root where the cells fit closely together like tiles to form a thin, continuous sleeve-like layer; it functions to filter all material coming into the root of the plant. (14.3)

endoplasmic reticulum a system of flattened membrane-bound sacs and tubes continuous with the outer membrane of the nuclear envelope that has two types of membrane: rough ER, which is studded with ribosomes and synthesizes proteins, and smooth ER, which synthesizes phospholipids and packages macromolecules in vesicles for transport to other parts of the cell. (2.1)

endoscope long tube with a camera on one end; inserted into a small incision made in the mother's abdomen to observe the fetus. (7.4)

endospore small seedlike structure that contains bacterial DNA and a small amount of cytoplasm surrounded by a protective outer covering. Germinates during favourable conditions. (12.2)

energy the capacity to do work. (3.1)

enzyme protein in living organisms that acts as a biological catalyst to increase the rate of and facilitate biochemical reactions without being used up. (2.2, 7.1)

epidermis outermost layer of cells that covers and protects a plant. (14.3)

epiglottis in mammals, a flap located over the entrance to the trachea. The epiglottis closes during swallowing to prevent food from entering the respiratory tract. (8.2)

equistophytes members of the division Equistophyta of the Kingdom Plantae, seedless vascular plants commonly known as horsetails. (13.2)

erythrocytes also known as red blood cells. Blood cells that are specialized for oxygen transport. (9.2)

esophagus tube that connects the mouth to the stomach, lined with both circular and longitudinal muscles. (10.2)

essential amino acids amino acids required by humans because the body cannot manufacture them itself. (1.1)

essential nutrient chemical substance taken in or derived from food that can be used by an organism to sustain its life processes. (10.1)

ethylene plant hormone that stimulates the aging of plant tissues and the ripening and sweetening of fruit. It also stimulates the plant to produce more ethylene and, where fruit is stored together, levels can build up rapidly. (15.1)

euglenoids small unicellular freshwater organisms that have characteristics of both plants and animals. They have chloroplasts, which enable them to photosynthesize, and they are motile. (12.3)

eukaryote organism with cells containing nuclei and other types of membrane-bound organelles; protists, fungi, plants, and animals. (2.1, 11.1)

exocytosis process used in the secretion of cell products where a vesicle from inside the cell moves to the cell surface and fuses with the cell membrane, releasing its contents outside the cell. (1.4)

expiratory reserve volume volume of additional air that can be forcibly expired from the lungs following a regular exhalation. (8.3)

external respiration process of exchanging respiratory gases with the external environment. In all aerobic animals, external respiration involves absorbing oxygen and releasing carbon dioxide. (8.2)

extracellular digestion digestion of food occurring outside the body. (10.1, 12.4)

extracellular fluid fluid bathing cells that consists of a variable mixture of water and dissolved materials. (1.3)

F_1 **generation** offspring from the cross of the P generation, the first filial generation. (4.2)

F_2 **generation** offspring from the cross of the F_1 generation, the second filial generation. (4.2)

facilitated diffusion passive movement of a substance into or out of the cell along a concentration gradient through a carrier protein molecule. (1.3)

fatty acid molecule that contains a hydrocarbon chain with a COOH (acid) group at one end. (1.1)

feces mass of damp undigestible material eliminated from the body through the anus. (10.2)

fermentation breakdown of carbohydrates that releases energy in the absence of oxygen. It includes glycolysis followed by the breakdown pyruvate to become either lactate or alcohol, depending on the organism. (3.3)

fetoscopy a medical procedure that involves direct observation of the fetus with an endoscope. (7.4)

fibrin insoluble material that forms a mesh of strands around the area of an injury to prevent the loss of blood from damaged blood vessels. (9.2)

fibrinogen plasma protein in the blood. (9.2)

filial generation offspring of a cross of parent organisms; the F_1 generation or subsequent generations. (4.2)

flagella (singular flagellum) long, hairlike projections extending from the cell membrane that propel the cell using a whiplike motion. (2.1)

fluid-mosaic model of membrane structure description of cell membrane structure where phospholipids form a bilayer that has a fluid consistency and is studded with protein molecules. (1.2)

fragile X syndrome   a weak segment in the X chromosome caused by a duplication. (7.3)

fragmentation   simple asexual method of reproduction in fungi, in which pieces of hyphae are broken off and grow into new mycelia. (12.4)

frameshift mutation   mutation that occurs when one or more nitrogen base pairs are added or deleted from a DNA strand causing the polypeptide chain to be affected from the point of mutation. (6.2)

frequency   the number of wave crests that pass a point during one second; measured in hertz (Hz). (3.2)

fronds   leaves of ferns, which grow up from a thick, underground rhizome. (13.2)

G

gall bladder   organ that stores bile produced in the liver. (10.4)

gametes   reproductive cells, either eggs or sperm, produced during meiosis. (5.2)

gametocytes   spores in a plant that develop into male or female gametes. (12.3)

gametogenesis   gamete formation when daughter cells, or gametes, are produced at the end of meiosis II resulting in the production of sperm and eggs. (5.2)

gametophyte   haploid generation of a plant that produces male and female gametes. (13.1)

gas exchange   process of exchanging respiratory gases. Gas exchange is the fundamental objective of all respiratory systems. See also external respiration and internal respiration. (8.1)

gastrin   hormone secreted by glands in the stomach which stimulates individual glands to secrete mucin (which both lubricates food and protects the walls of the stomach), pepsin, hydrochloric acid, and lipases. (10.2)

gastrula   developmental stage in the animal embryo where cells on one side of the blastula fold inward forming a cavity of two or three layers of cells with an opening at one end. (13.3)

gel electrophoresis   a procedure in which molecules travel though a gel subjected to an electrical current. The distance a molecule travels depends on its size. (7.1)

gene   a part of a chromosome that governs the expression of a particular trait and can be passed on to offspring. (4.2)

gene therapy   medical procedure in which normal or modified genes are transferred into the cells of an individual. (7.4)

gene transfer technology   technology where a gene is snipped out of one species (the host) and spliced into the genome of another (the recipient), after which the recipient organism will follow the new instruction of the host's gene. (15.3)

general adaptations   modifications that are common to many plants that enable them to live the life of a plant. For example, all plant roots share a common cellular structure. (16.2)

genetic code   various codons in RNA that provide the information for building proteins. (6.1)

genetic recombination   re-assortment of the chromosomes and the genes they carry through crossing over and random segregation. (5.2)

genetics   the study of heredity and variation in organisms; how traits are passed from generation to generation. (4.1)

genotype   genetic make-up of an organism, usually indicated by the combination of letters in a Punnett Square. (4.2)

gibberellins   group of plant hormones that promote cell enlargement, with the effect of increasing stem height and girth by promoting the uptake of starch in the embryo of germinating seeds and by stimulating the vascular tissue. (15.1)

gills   respiratory structures found in many aquatic animals. Gills are feathery structures made up of many fine filaments lined with capillaries. (8.1)

glottis   in mammals, the opening through which air enters the larynx. (8.2)

glucagon   a hormone produced by the pancreas that acts in the liver to raise the level of glucose in the blood (opposite of insulin action). (10.5)

glycogen   polysaccharide composed of glucose subunits that is used for energy storage in animals. (1.1)

glycolysis   first step in aerobic or anaerobic cellular respiration; one glucose molecule (with six carbons) is broken down to form two pyruvate molecules (with three carbons each), producing two molecules of ATP. (3.3)

Golgi apparatus   a stack of flattened membrane-bound sacs that receive vesicles from the ER, contain enzymes for modifying proteins and lipids, and package finished products into vesicles for transport to the cell membrane (for secretion through exocytosis) and within the cell as lysosomes. (2.1)

Gram-negative bacteria   bacteria with a thin protein layer on their cell wall, which stain pink when using Gram stain. (12.2)

Gram-positive bacteria   bacteria with a thick single protein layer on their cell wall, which stain purple when using Gram stain. (12.2)

gravitropism   plant's response to gravity. (15.1)

green algae members of the phylum Chlorophyta, a unicellular or multicellular algae that have the same types of chlorophyll and the same colour as most land plants, that have cell walls containing cellulose, and that store food reserves as starch. (12.3)

guanine one of four nitrogen-containing bases in nucleotides which make up DNA and RNA. (6.1)

gymnosperms plants that have seeds which are often exposed, or naked. Includes the cone-bearing trees, such as pines, firs, yew, spruce, cedars, redwood, and many other large trees. (13.2)

haploid cells containing half the number of chromosomes (n) the diploid (2n) parent cell has; as in gametes, either egg or sperm. (5.2)

haustoria specialized hyphae found in parasitic fungi, which can penetrate host cells without immediately killing them. (12.4)

heart attack condition in which the heart beats irregularly and may stop functioning altogether. (9.3)

heart murmur common congenital condition that occurs when one or more of the heart valves does not open or close properly. (9.3)

heme group part of the hemoglobin molecule that contains an iron molecule that can bind with oxygen. Each hemoglobin molecule contains four heme groups. (9.2)

hemoglobin respiratory pigment found in the red blood cell. It is an iron-containing molecule that binds with oxygen, allowing the oxygen to be transported in the blood. (7.1, 9.2)

Hepatophytes members of the division Hepatophyta of the Kingdom Plantae, nonvascular plants commonly known as liverworts. There are two types, the leafy liverworts and the thallose liverworts. (13.2)

herbaceous non-woody. (14.1)

heterotroph an organism that must derive some of its nutrients from organic molecules formed by autotrophs. (10.1)

heterozygotes individuals who have inherited two different alleles for a particular trait. (7.1)

heterozygous having two alleles for a trait that are different. (4.2)

heterozygous advantage a survival benefit for those individuals who inherit two different alleles for the same trait. (7.1)

homeostasis maintenance of the internal environment at a steady state, regardless of external changes, to ensure survival of a living organism. (1.3)

homeotherms animals that keep their body temperature relatively constant such as birds and mammals. (9.3)

homologous having biological features of a common evolutionary origin. (11.4)

homologous chromosomes chromosomes containing the same gene sequences, but they may not be made up of the same alleles. (5.2)

homozygous having two alleles for a trait that are the same, as is the result of pure breeding. (4.2)

hormone chemical compound that is manufactured in very small quantities by specialized tissue in one body part of an organism but governs or regulates the activity of a distant body part. (10.1, 15.1)

human genome all the genes that code for a human being. (7.5)

Huntington disease an autosomal dominant condition, which is a lethal disorder in which the brain progressively deteriorates over a period of about 15 years. (7.1)

hybrid an organism heterozygous for a trait. (4.2)

hydrogen bond weak bond between molecules where a hydrogen atom, which has a weak positive charge, on one molecule bonds with an atom with a strongly negative charge on another molecule. (Appendix 2)

hydroponic having a type of soil-free horticulture where plants are grown with their roots immersed in water in a solution containing dissolved nutrients. (16.3)

hypertension chronically elevated blood pressure, often associated with health problems such as a greatly increased risk of stroke and heart disease. (9.3)

hypertonic containing a higher concentration of solute and a lower concentration of water than that found in a cell. (1.3)

hyphae (singular hypha) a network of fine filaments found in fungi. (12.4)

hypotonic containing a lower concentration of solute and a higher concentration of water than that found in a cell. (1.3)

hypoxia condition in which insufficient oxygen is delivered to the body tissues to meet metabolic requirements. Initial symptoms include headaches, fatigue, dizziness and nausea. (8.4)

ileum portion of the small intestine, about 3 m long, attached to the large intestine; contains fewer and smaller villi. Its function is to absorb more nutrients as well as to push remaining undigested material into the large intestine. (10.2)

incomplete dominance   an inheritance pattern where the heterozygote exhibits an intermediate phenotype between the two homologous phenotypes; neither allele for the trait is completely dominant. (4.4)

independent assortment   the random positioning of tetrads along the cell's equator in which some sister chromatids of one parent face one pole of the cell while other sister chromatids of the same parent face the other pole of the cell. (5.2)

inherited   having certain physical traits that are transmitted from one generation to the next. (4.1)

innate immune response   a generalized response through which the body's resistance to a pathogen is inborn. (9.2)

inspiratory reserve volume   volume of additional air that can be forcibly inspired into the lungs following a normal inhalation. (8.3)

insulin   hormone produced by the pancreas that acts in the liver to lower the level of glucose in our blood. (10.5)

integrated pest management   coordinated use of pest and environmental knowledge along with proven control methods (both chemical and nonchemical) to prevent unacceptable levels of pest damage by the most economical means, with the least possible hazard to people, property, and the environment. (16.3)

intercostal muscles   muscles of the rib cage. In mammals, these muscles help to expand and contract the rib cage and play an important role in breathing. (8.2)

intermediate filaments   protein cables that anchor organelles into regions in the cell, as well as support the nuclear envelope and cell membrane; part of the cytoskeleton. (2.1)

internal respiration   exchange of gases with the cells of the body tissues. In all aerobic animals, internal respiration involves the uptake of oxygen and the release of carbon dioxide by the tissue cells. (8.2)

interphase   growth phase when a cell makes new molecules, increasing the cell's volume and mass. DNA replication occurs during this growth phase. (5.1)

interstitial fluid   fluid that constantly bathes all of the cells of the body. (9.2)

intracellular digestion   type of digestion in which food particles are taken within cells and subjected to the action of enzymes there. (10.1)

inversion   change in the physical structure of a chromosome when a certain gene segment becomes free from its chromosome momentarily before being reinserted in the reverse order. (7.3)

ion   an atom or a group of atoms that has a positive or negative electric charge. (Appendix 2)

ionic bond   bond between two oppositely charged ions. (Appendix 2)

isotonic   containing the same concentration of solute and of water as that found in a cell. (1.3)

jejunum   part of the small intestine following the duodenum. (10.2)

karyotype   illustration or photograph of the chromosomes in the nucleus of a somatic cell in an organism. (7.2)

kinetic energy   the energy of motion. (3.1)

kingdom   the highest classification of all living things first applied to the Kingdom Plantae and Animalia by Aristotle and now comprising six groups. (13.1)

Kingdom Animalia   one of six kingdoms used to classify living things consisting of animals that are motile and ingest the food they have obtained. (13.3)

Kingdom Archaea   one of six kingdoms used to classify living things consisting of certain types of bacteria found in extreme environments (such as salt lakes or hot, acid springs), which have unique structures and mechanisms. (12.1)

Kingdom Bacteria   one of six kingdoms used to classify living things consisting of bacteria which have DNA not organized into a nucleus or chromosomes and which also lack other organelles. (12.2)

Kingdom Fungi   one of six kingdoms used to classify living things consisting of fungi which do not carry out photosynthesis and obtain food by absorbing materials into their bodies. (12.4)

Kingdom Plantae   one of six kingdoms used to classify living things consisting of plants which are non-motile and obtain their food through photosynthesis. (13.2)

Kingdom Protista   one of six kingdoms used to classify living things consisting of all micro-organisms that do not belong in the other kingdoms. (12.3)

lacteal   minute lymph vessel contained within each villus, which serves to absorb digested lipids into the lymphatic circulatory system. (10.2)

large intestine   final portion of the digestive system, about 1.5 m long, consisting of the caecum, colon, rectum, and anal canal. Undigested food from the small intestine enters the large intestine through a valve. Some undigested food is digested and then, water and dissolved minerals are absorbed from the remaining undigested food, which is eliminated from the body. (10.2)

laryngospasm   reflex closing of the larynx. Many drowning victims actually die as a result of asphyxiation due to laryngospasm, rather than because of water entering the lungs. (8.4)

larynx   in mammals, a structure within the upper respiratory tract that contains the vocal cords. Also commonly known as the "voice box." As air passes through the larynx, the vibration of the vocal cords can produce sounds. (8.2)

law of independent assortment   Mendel's second law of inheritance, stating that the inheritance of alleles for one trait does not affect the inheritance of alleles for another trait. (4.3)

law of segregation   Mendel's law of segregation where the hereditary traits are determined by pairs of alleles from each parent. These alleles separate during gamete formation giving each offspring only one allele from each parent. (4.2)

lenticels   loose arrangements of cells in the outer bark of a woody plant. The arrangement results in pores in the bark through which gases can be exchanged with the environment. (8.5)

leucocytes   white blood cells that protect the body from invasion of foreign substances such as bacteria. (9.2)

lipid   organic compound that does not dissolve in water, such as fats, oils, and steroids (e.g., cholesterol and testosterone). (1.1)

liver   organ that has many roles in the body. It makes bile salts from parts of the decomposed hemoglobin molecules, stores some excess chemicals collected from the bloodstream, breaks down old red blood cells, and has many roles in digestion such as stimulating duct cells there to release an alkaline fluid containing sodium carbonate and sodium bicarbonate. (10.4)

lung   respiratory structure contained entirely within the body of an animal, and connected to the outside air by means of passageways. Characteristic of all mammals as well as some other species including birds and spiders. (8.1)

lycopodophytes   members of the division Lycopodophyta of the Kingdom Plantae, seedless vascular plants known as club mosses. (13.2)

lymph   the colourless or pale yellow fluid that flows through the lymphatic system. Lymph is much like the plasma of blood in composition. (9.4)

lymph nodes   glands within the lymphatic system that contain lymphocytes and macrophages. Lymph glands are found in a number of areas in the mammalian body. (9.4)

lymphatic circulatory system   network of glands and vessels that carry lymph throughout the mammalian body. (9.4)

lymphocyte   type of white blood cell that plays a role in the body's acquired immune response, enabling the body to recognize and fend off specific pathogens. Two main types are T cells and B cells. (9.2)

lysis   bursting of the cell membrane, causing destruction of the cell. (1.3)

lysosomal digestion   step-by-step process of breaking down macromolecules within lysosomes; intracellular digestion. (2.2)

lysosome   a membrane-bound vesicle filled with digestive enzymes that can break down worn-out cell components or materials brought into the cell through phagocytosis. (2.1)

lytic cycle   a cycle of viral replication where the virus depends entirely on the metabolism of a eukaryotic or prokaryotic cell to replicate their DNA or RNA, and to make protein coats for each newly formed virus particle. (11.2)

macromolecule   very large molecule composed of smaller subunits linked together, such as polysaccharides, lipids, proteins, and nucleic acids. (1.1)

macrophages   phagocytic cells that can pass through the walls of the capillaries to engulf and digest pathogens such as bacteria circulating within the body. (9.2)

mantle   fleshy covering common to all molluscs that wraps around the body like a cloak and secretes the shell on the organism's outer surface. (13.3)

mass-flow   theory to explain the transport of organic materials in phloem. The theory is based on a combination of osmosis and pressure dynamics in the phloem. (9.5)

matter   a physical substance that has mass and takes up space. (Appendix 2)

medulla oblongata   portion of the brain located at the junction between the spinal cord and the brain. The medulla oblongata controls many automatic functions such as heart rate, respiratory rate, vasoconstriction, and swallowing. (8.4)

medusa   umbrella-shaped body form stage of cnidarians. Medusas float with their mouths pointing downward, like a jellyfish. (13.3)

meiosis type of cell division that occurs only in reproductive organs producing reproductive cells called gametes. (5.2)

melanin a brown pigment produced in special pigment cells responsible, in varying amounts, for the colour of an organism's hair, skin, and eyes. (7.1)

membrane receptor specific membrane protein with a uniquely shaped projection or cavity that fits (receives) the shape of only one specific molecule. (1.4)

Mendelian ratio ratio of dominant phenotype (homozygous dominant genotype and heterozygous genotypes) to recessive phenotype (homozygous recessive genotype). (4.2)

Mendelian ratio for genotype ratio of homozygous dominant genotype to heterozygous genotypes to homozygous recessive genotype. (4.2)

meristem regions of active growth in plants where undifferentiated cells divide to develop new structures throughout the life of the plant. (15.1)

mesoderm middle cell layer in the gastrula between the ectoderm and the endoderm. Develops into the muscles, circulatory system, excretory system, and in some animals, the respiratory system. (13.3)

metabolism the total of all of the chemical reactions that occur within a cell to keep it alive. (3.1)

metaphase phase of mitosis in which the chromosomes are aligned at the cell's equator. (5.1)

microtubules rod-like, hollow protein tubes that act like tracks along which other organelles, such as vesicles and mitochondria, can move; part of the cytoskeleton. (2.1)

microvilli very small extensions of cell membrane that increase the surface area available for absorption and secretion. (2.1)

minerals inorganic compounds that the body needs in small amounts to enable certain chemical reactions and the building of bones and cartilage. (10.5)

mitochondria organelles with a double membrane where organic molecules, usually carbohydrates, are broken down to release energy. (2.1)

mitosis division of the cell's nucleus where the daughter cells receive the exact number of chromosomes and genetic makeup as the parent cell. (5.1)

modifier genes genes that work along with other genes to control the expression of a trait. (5.3)

Mollusca a phylum in the Kingdom Animalia, commonly known as molluscs. These are soft-bodied animals such as slugs, snails, clams, oysters and squid. Most species are marine and most protect themselves with a hard external shell. (13.3)

monocots short form of monocotyledons, a class of angiosperms that has one cotyledon within the seed. (13.2)

monoculture culture of one group of species such as a field of rice, a field of corn or a grove of orange trees. (16.3)

monohybrid a cross of two heterozygous individuals that differ in one trait; e.g. Aa × Aa. (4.2)

monosaccharide a simple sugar such as glucose, fructose, or galactose. (1.1)

mRNA messenger ribonucleic acid (RNA); carries a copy of the coded message from the DNA to ribosomes. (2.2)

multiple alleles pattern of inheritance when a gene may have more than two alleles for any given trait. (4.4)

mutation an error in the DNA sequence that can be caused by various mutagens, such as toxic compounds, radiation, or viruses. (5.1)

mutualism relationship between two species that is of a type that benefits both species. (14.1)

mycelium loose, branching network of hyphae under the soil making up the main bulk of a fungus. (12.4)

mycorrhizae symbiotic relationships that are mutually beneficial between fungi and roots of plants. (12.4)

nastic movement plant's response to touch; a result of a change in turgor in the cells at the base of the leaves, not a result of growth such as a vine growing up a fence. (15.1)

negative mutation mutation that is harmful to the organism or cell in which it occurs. (6.2)

neutral mutation mutation that has no effect on an organism or cell in which it occurs. (6.2)

neutron a particle in the nucleus of an atom that has no charge, similar in mass to a proton. (Appendix 2)

nicotine type of drug made from a very poisonous substance found in tobacco that is used in tobacco products. (10.5)

nitrogen base pair substitutions type of mutation where one base pair is replaced by another base pair in a DNA strand. (6.2)

nondisjunction failure of chromosomes to separate properly during meiosis resulting in the addition or deletion of one or more chromosomes from a gamete. (5.2)

nonpolar equal sharing of electrons in the (covalent) bonds of a molecule; molecule with even charge distribution. (1.1)

non-sister chromatids   in a tetrad, chromatids that do not belong to the same chromosome and undergo crossing over during prophase I of meiosis. (5.2)

noradrenaline   chemical that increases the heart rate by causing the S-A node to fire more rapidly. It is released when the medulla oblongata sends impulses along the nervous system. (9.3)

notochord   rod of cartilage that runs along the dorsal length of the body of chordates. In most vertebrates, the notochord occurs only in the embryo, and is later replaced by a cartilage or bone structure. (13.3)

nucleic acids   complex organic compounds that carry the hereditary information in cells; DNA and RNA. (1.1)

nucleoid   an area within prokaryotic cells where the DNA is found. (2.1)

nucleolus   a specialized area of chromatin (uncoiled DNA) inside the nucleus where ribosomal RNA is produced to make ribosomes. (2.1)

nucleotide   a molecule composed of a sugar, called deoxyribose, a phosphate group (also called phosphoric acid), and a nitrogen base. (1.1, 6.1)

nucleus   organelle with a double membrane that contains the DNA instructions for making proteins. (2.1)

oligosaccharins   group of plant hormones that have been most recently discovered; a class of growth promoters that stimulate plants to manufacture antibiotics in response to attack by fungi or bacteria. (15.1)

oncogenes   genes that can be switched "on" by a mutation causing the cell to divide, which can transform a normal cell into a cancerous cell. (5.1)

oogenesis   a process of female gamete production in animals. (5.2)

oogonium   the diploid germ cell from which eggs are produced in the ovaries. (5.2)

open transport system   transport system in which the blood does not always stay contained within blood vessels but rather bathes the cells directly. (9.1)

organ   a group of two or more different tissues working together to perform a common function, such as the leaf of a plant. (2.3)

organelle   a specialized structure within a cell with a specific function, such as nuclei and chloroplasts. (2.2)

organic compound   compound that contains both carbon and hydrogen. (1.1)

organic matter   material that is derived from once-living organisms, such as animals and plants. (16.1)

osmosis   diffusion of water across a semi-permeable membrane from a region of higher water concentration to a region of lower water concentration. (1.3)

oxygen debt   the oxygen needed to break down lactate that has accumulated from anaerobic cellular respiration, such as the lactate that builds up in muscle cells after vigorous exercise. (3.3)

P generation   the designation for the parent generation. (4.2)

pancreas   organ important in digestion that is the source of several enzymes that act on carbohydrates, fats, and peptides, which are subunits of proteins. (10.4)

papillae   tiny pimple-like structures on the upper surface of mammalian tongues that house taste buds. (10.2)

parent cell   the original cell that divides to produce two new daughter cells during cell division. (5.1)

partial pressure   measurement of the pressure exerted by a single gas within a mixture of gases. Partial pressure is calculated by multiplying the fraction of the mixture accounted for by the gas in question, by the total pressure of the mixture. (9.2)

pathogens   disease-causing agents such as some bacteria. (9.2)

pedigree   diagram that illustrates the genetic relationships among a group of individuals. (4.2)

peptide bond   chemical linkage that joins two amino acids together. (1.1)

peristalsis   movement of food through the digestive tract, accomplished by a series of wavelike contractions and relaxations of the circular and longitudinal muscles that surround the various parts of the digestive tract. (10.2)

peroxisome   a membrane-bound vesicle containing enzymes that break down lipids and toxic waste products, such as alcohol. (2.1)

pesticides   broad class of crop-protection chemicals, including rodenticides (to kill mice and rats), herbicides (to kill weeds), insecticides (to kill insects), and fungicides (to kill moulds and fungi). (16.3)

phagocytosis   taking in of bacteria or chunks of organic matter by endocytosis. (1.4))

pharynx   structure located just behind the mouth that connects the esophagus and the trachea. (8.2)

phenotype   the appearance of a trait in an organism. (4.2)

phenylalanine   an amino acid essential for regular growth and development, and for protein metabolism. (7.1)

phenylketonuria   autosomal recessive disorder that affects young children where an enzyme that converts phenylalanine to tyrosine is either deficient or defective. (7.1)

phloem   vascular tissue that transports organic material in plants. (9.5, 14.2)

phospholipid   lipid with a phosphate group. (1.2)

phospholipid bilayer   two layers of phospholipid molecules arranged with their phosphate-containing (polar) ends facing a water solution and their fatty-acid (nonpolar) ends facing each other. (1.2)

photoautotrophs   organisms that use light energy to carry out photosynthesis and obtain carbon from carbon dioxide, such as the cyanobacteria and most plants. (12.2)

photoheterotrophs   organisms that carry out photosynthesis and obtain carbon from organic compounds rather than carbon dioxide. (12.2)

photon model of light   a model proposed by Albert Einstein to explain how light travels in individual "packets," or photons. (3.2)

photons   individual "packets" of light energy. (3.2)

photosystem   cluster of a few hundred pigment molecules (mostly chlorophylls) within the thylakoid membrane that act together during photosynthesis. (3.2)

phototropism   directional growth in plants in response to light, usually toward a light source. (15.1)

phylogeny   hypothesis about the evolutionary history of groups of organisms. (11.4)

pigment   substance that absorbs specific wavelengths of visible light. (3.2)

pili   a hollow, hairlike structure on the surface of prokaryotic cells that allows them to attach to each other or to a surface. (2.1)

pinnae   small leaflets making up a fern frond. (13.2)

pinocytosis   taking in of fluid and dissolved substances by endocytosis. (1.4)

pith   spongy tissue in the centre of stems and roots of most flowering plants. (14.3)

placenta   a structure that forms the chorion and uterine wall and allows the fetus to obtain nutrients from the mother and discharge wastes. (7.4)

plant growth regulators   substances, which can be plant hormones or chemicals, that influence the growth and development of plants; most commercial plant growth regulators are chemical look-alikes rather than actual hormones extracted from plants. (15.1)

plasma   fluid portion of the blood. Plasma is made up of water plus dissolved gases, proteins, sugars, vitamins, minerals, and waste products. (9.2)

plasmid   small, self-duplicating loop of DNA in a bacterial cell that is separate from the main chromosome and contains from one to a few genes. (2.1)

plasmodial slime moulds   members of the phylum Myxomycota, one of two types of slime moulds in the fungus-like protists, which look like tiny slug-like organisms that creep over damp, decaying plant material in forests and fields. (12.3)

plasmodium   part of the life cycle of a plasmodial slime mould, cytoplasm that resembles a slimy mass and contains many nuclei. (12.4)

plasmolysis   contraction of cell contents due to the loss of water. (1.3)

plastid   an organelle in plant cells that contains a series of stacked internal membrane sacs and vesicles enclosed within a double membrane, has the ability to perform photosynthesis, and can store starches, lipids, and proteins. (2.1)

platelets   component of the formed portion of the blood. Platelets are fragments of cells that play an important role in the formation of blood clots. (9.2)

Platyhelminthes   a phylum of the Kingdom Animalia, commonly known as flatworms. (13.3)

pleura   (singular pleuron) the membranes that envelop the lungs. Each lung is encased in two separate pleural membranes separated by a thin layer of fluid. (8.2)

poikilotherm   animals which have a body temperature that fluctuates depending on the temperature of the animal's environment. (9.3)

polar   unequal sharing of electrons in the (covalent) bonds of a molecule; molecule with uneven charge distribution. (1.1)

polar covalent bond   type of covalent bond between atoms where they share a pair of electrons but the electrons spend more time around the atom with the larger number of (positive) protons in its nucleus. (Appendix 2)

pollen tube   specialized tube produced when a pollen grain lands next to an archegonium that grows into the tissue of the female gametophyte. Sperm pass along this tube to the egg. (13.2)

pollen-tube competition   competition among pollen tubes where the sperm contained in the fastest growing pollen tube is able to fertilize the egg. (13.2)

pollination   transferring pollen from the male to the female of the same species in plants. (13.2)

polygenic inheritance   a pattern of inheritance where a trait is controlled by more than one gene. (5.3)

polymerase chain reaction (PCR) a type of gene cloning which can copy a DNA sequence or portion of that sequence. Can be used to amplify, or generate multiple copies of DNA for analyses. (6.2)

polyp one of two body forms of cnidarians that is cylindrical and is usually attached to a rock with its mouth directed upwards, like a sea anemone or freshwater hydra. (13.3)

polypeptide chain of amino acids linked by peptide bonds. (1.1, 6.1)

polyploid organism that has more than two (2n) sets of chromosomes. It may have 3n, 4n or more. (5.2, 13.3)

polysaccharide complex carbohydrate consisting of many simple sugars linked together, including starch, cellulose, and glycogen. (1.1)

Porifera a phylum contained in the Kingdom Animalia, commonly known as sponges. These organisms are the only animals where digestion occurs within cells. (13.3)

positive mutation mutation that is useful to the organism or cell in which it occurs. (6.2)

primary succession the process of successive changes that take place as an area of bare rock is colonized and develops into a climax community. (16.2)

principle of dominance when individuals with contrasting traits are crossed, the offspring will express only the dominant trait, first described by Gregor Mendel. (4.2)

prion an infectious particle that causes damage to neurons (nerve cells) in the brain, and that appears to consist mostly or entirely of a single protein. It may replicate by causing one of the normal neuron proteins to change shape, and that is believed to be linked to several diseases of the nervous system, including Creutzfelt-Jakob disease in humans. (1.3)

probability the chance, or likelihood, of a particular outcome usually expressed as a ratio. (4.2)

Progeria rare disorder that causes a child to age rapidly. (7.1)

prokaryote organism with cells lacking a true nucleus and most other types of organelles; bacteria and archaea. (2.1, 11.1)

prophase a phase of mitosis where the chromatin condenses and chromosomes appear. (5.1)

protein organic compound made of one or more polypeptides. (1.1)

protein synthesis the process of making proteins, which involves transcription (of DNA) and translation (of mRNA). (2.2)

prothallus tiny, independent gametophyte developing from a lycopodophyte spore. (13.2)

prothrombin serum protein in blood that is involved in the formation of blood clots. (9.2)

proton a particle in the nucleus of an atom that has a positive charge, similar in mass to a neutron. (Appendix 2)

Protozoa animal-like protists that are heterotrophs that ingest or absorb their food. (12.3)

provirus virus that undergoes a replication cycle in which its DNA becomes integrated with the host cell chromosomes; the virus can invade the cell but does not kill it. (11.2)

pseudoplasmodium group of joined amoeboid cells resembling a jelly-like mass, which is part of the life cycle of a cellular slime mould; individual cells join together when food becomes scarce. (12.4)

pseudopodia limb-like extensions of an amoebae's cytoplasm that move and engulf prey. (12.3)

psilotophytes members of the division Psilotophyta of the Kingdom Plantae, seedless vascular plants commonly known as whisk ferns. (13.2)

psychoactive drugs chemicals that affect the central nervous system and interfere with the normal functioning of the brain; include stimulants, depressants, narcotics, and hallucinogens. (10.5)

pteridophytes members of the division Pteridophyta of the Kingdom Plantae, seedless vascular plants commonly known as ferns. (13.2)

pulmonary artery the artery that carries blood from the right ventricle of the heart to the lungs. (9.3)

pulmonary circulation the pathway of blood from the heart to the lungs and back. The pulmonary circulation is one of three primary cycles in the mammalian circulatory system. (9.2)

pulmonary vein the vein that carries oxygenated blood from the lungs back to the left atrium of the heart. (9.3)

Punnett Square a simple grid used to illustrate all possible combinations of gametes from a given set of parents. (4.2)

purebred having descended from common ancestors of a distinct type, or breed, where all share similar traits. (4.2)

purines double-ring structure nucleotides such as adenine and guanine. (6.1)

pyloric sphincter the circular muscle layer that acts as a valve between the stomach and the duodenum, controlling the passage of food out of the stomach. (10.2)

pyrimidines single-ring nucleotides such as thymine and cytosine. (6.1)

radial symmetry   one of two types of symmetry among animals when their bodies are organized equally around a central vertical axis like a wheel around its axle. (13.3)

radioactive   capable of producing radiant energy by disintegration of atomic nuclei. (3.3)

reaction centre   a special pair of chlorophylls that function as target or funnel for incoming light energy relayed from the other pigment molecules in a photosystem. (3.2)

receptor-assisted endocytosis   taking in by endocytosis of specific molecules that bind to a membrane receptor. (1.4)

recessive   having an allele that is latent (present but inactive) and is therefore not usually expressed unless there is no dominant allele present. (4.2)

rectum   last 20 cm of the large intestine. (10.2)

red algae   members of the phylum Rhodophyta, multicellular seaweeds (algae), which have chlorophyll *a*, carotenoids, and yellow-brown pigments. (12.3)

reduction division   division of cells that reduces the chromosome number. For example, in meiosis the chromosome number is reduced from diploid (2n) to haploid (n). (5.2)

regurgitation   movement of food from the stomach up through the esophagus and out of the mouth; in humans it is often a reaction to bad food or illness. (10.2)

residual volume   volume of air that remains in the respiratory tract following a forced exhalation. (8.3)

respiratory efficiency   rate at which oxygen can be transferred from the respiratory surface to the internal transport system or tissues of an animal. (8.3)

respiratory pigment   molecule that binds to oxygen, which allows the blood to pick up and transport more oxygen than would otherwise be possible. (9.1)

respiratory surface   any surface across which gases are exchanged for the purpose of respiration. (8.1)

retrovirus   type of viral replication where a virus uses reverse transcriptase to copy the viral RNA into DNA. The retroviral DNA is than integrated into the host cell's chromosome. An example is the human immunodeficiency virus. (11.2)

Rhesus factor   protein marker in human blood. The Rhesus factor affects the compatibility of human blood. People who do not carry the Rh protein are called Rh negative, while people who do have this protein are called Rh-positive. (9.2)

rhizoids   in fungi, a downward growing hyphae present in the mycelium of a bread mould. (12.4) In non-vascular plants, small root-like structures, which develop from the lower surfaces of the plants. (13.2)

rhizomes   small horizontal underground stems that take the place of leaves or roots in some vascular plants. (13.2)

ribosome   tiny two-part structure found in the cytoplasm and attached to the rough endoplasmic reticulum that helps put together proteins. (2.1)

root hairs   fine hair-like structures that cover the surface of the root of a plant. Root hairs serve to increase the surface area available for gas exchange or the absorption of water and nutrients. (8.5)

root pressure   one mechanism for the translocation of water in plants. The accumulation of water in the xylem of roots results in a pressure gradient that forces water upward in the plant. Root pressure can account for the translocation of water in certain plants under specific conditions. (9.5)

saliva   watery secretion of the salivary glands; in addition to containing a starch-digesting enzyme, saliva helps to lubricate food so it may be swallowed more easily. (10.2)

salivary glands   three pairs of glands, the parotid, sublingual, and submaxillary, that secrete saliva into the mouth. (10.2)

saprotrophs   organisms that break down and live off dead organic matter. (12.3)

saturated   type of fatty acid where each of the carbon atoms beyond the one bonded to oxygen is bonded to four other atoms. (1.1)

secondary succession   a process of successive changes that take place as an area disrupted by natural disaster or human intervention develops into a climax community. (16.2)

secretin   hormone which is released from ductless glands in the walls of the duodenum in response to the presence of chyme in the duodenum. The hormone is released into the bloodstream and it goes to the pancreas where it stimulates duct cells there to release an alkaline fluid containing sodium carbonate and sodium bicarbonate, which increase the pH of the chyme. (10.3)

seed   reproductive structure of plants made up of an embryo, stored food, and a tough waterproof coat. (13.2)

selectively permeable membrane   membrane that is permeable to some substances, such as water, but not to others. (1.3)

septa   cross walls found in some fungal hyphae that divide the hyphae into cells. Each individual cell has one or more nuclei. (12.4)

septum   wall that separates the right and left ventricles of the heart. (9.3)

serum   the straw-coloured liquid produced by removing fibrinogen and other clotting agents from blood plasma. Serum contains cellular nutrients, hormones, electrolytes, enzymes, hormones, antibodies, and waste materials. (9.2)

seta   stalk on a moss sporophyte that carries a spore-producing capsule. (13.2)

sex chromosome   X or Y chromosome that carries the genes involved in determining an individual's sex. (5.2)

sex-linked inheritance   the transfer of genes on the X or Y chromosome from one generation to the next. (5.3)

sickle cell anemia   an autosomal disorder where a defect in the hemoglobin in red blood cells leads to sickle-shaped blood cells that can clog arteries and reduce blood flow to vital organs. (7.1)

simple dominant trait   trait that has only two possible alleles (dominant or recessive) and is not influenced by the inheritance of other simple dominant traits. (4.2)

single circulation   type of circulation in which the blood travels through the heart only once during each complete circuit around the body. (9.1)

sinoatrial node   (S-A node) bundle of specialized muscle tissue (also known as the pacemaker), located in the wall of the right atrium of the mammalian heart. The S-A node stimulates the muscle fibres to contract and relax rhythmically, producing a regular heart beat. (9.3)

sister chromatids   two structures in a chromosome that are genetically identical, which are held together by a centromere. (5.1)

skin respiration   respiratory process in which the entire body surface is used as a respiratory surface. Characteristic of some animals including annelids and, to some extent, amphibians. (8.1)

slime moulds   fungus-like protists, having some characteristics similar to fungi, protozoa, and plants, made up of two groups: plasmodial slime moulds and cellular slime moulds. (12.3)

small intestine   narrow diameter length of the digestive tract between the stomach and the large intestine, comprised of the duodenum, jejunum, and ileum; most products of digestion are reduced to nutrients and absorbed along its length. (10.2)

soil   surface layer of Earth that is made up of broken-up rock, humus (partly decomposed organic matter), and an active community of living organisms. (16.1)

soil fertility   ability of the soil to grow plants, which depends on the mineral content of the original "parent" rock and is based on the presence of mineral compounds that plants require, specifically significant amounts of nitrogen, phosphorus, potassium, sulfur, calcium, and magnesium, as well as minuscule amounts of certain trace elements. (16.3)

soil-free horticulture   using either hydroponic or aeroponic methods to grow plants in a covered, controlled environment. (16.3)

solute   substance that dissolves in a solvent to form a uniform mixture, or solution. (1.3)

solvent   fluid, such as water, that can dissolve other substances. (1.3)

sori   small, brown spore-producing structures clustered on the underside of the pinnae of the fern plant. (13.2)

specific adaptations   modifications that suit each type or species of plant for its own local growing conditions. (16.2)

spermatogenesis   a process of male gamete production in animals. (5.2)

spermatogonium   the diploid germ cell from which sperm are produced in the testes. (5.2)

spicules   needle-like fibres that help strengthen the body of the sponge. (13.3)

spiracles   pores in the skin of an insect that can be opened to admit air into the insect trachea for respiration. Controlled opening and closing of the spiracles contribute to the insect's breathing movement. (8.1)

spirilli   spiral-shaped bacterial cells; one of the three main shapes of bacterial cells. (12.2)

sporangia   spore-bearing structures developing from a plasmodium during sexual reproduction of a plasmodial slime mould. (12.4)

sporangiophores   form of hyphae that project up above the mycelium of a bread mould. Used during asexual reproduction. (12.4)

spores   windblown reproductive cells that help fungi disperse to new locations. (12.4)

sporophyte   diploid generation of a plant that produces haploid spores through the process of meiosis, which can develop without fertilization. (13.1)

Sporozoa   a phylum in the Kingdom Protista, named for the spores that they form during their parasitic life cycle. (12.3)

sporozoites   spore cells of Sporozoa. (12.3)

Staphylo-   prefix describing a characteristic clustered arrangement of bacterial cells resembling grapes. (12.2)

starch   polysaccharide that is used for energy storage in plants. (1.1)

stolons horizontal hyphae present in the mycelium of a bread mould. (12.4)

stomach a "J"-shaped sac lying between the esophagus and small intestine whose muscles work to physically break down food; its inner lining also contains millions of gastric glands that release gastric juice which begins the chemical breakdown of proteins. (10.2)

stomata small openings in the epidermis of a plant leaf, which allow gases to enter and leave for the processes of photosynthesis and cellular respiration. (8.5, 13.2, 14.3)

stop codons triplets on RNA that indicate that no more amino acids should be added to particular protein. (6.1)

Strepto- prefix describing a characteristic chain arrangement of bacterial cells. (12.2)

strobili (singular strobilus) specialized spore-bearing leaves present in lycopodophytes, which form compact clusters that protect the reproductive cells. (13.2)

stroke condition in which a blood clot blocks a blood vessel in the brain, causing a portion of the brain to be starved of oxygen. (9.3)

stroke volume amount of blood forced out of the heart with each heartbeat. (9.3)

substrate molecule on which an enzyme acts. Examples are starch, protein, fat, and peptides. (10.3)

superior vena cava the main blood vessel that collects blood from the systemic circulation of the body and returns it to the right ventricle of the heart. (9.3)

symmetrical body shape that is regular and balanced either radially or bilaterally. (13.3)

syndrome group of disorders that occur together. (7.3)

system a group of organs working together, such as the circulatory system or nervous system. (2.3)

systemic circulation the path taken by blood as it flows from the heart to the rest of the body and back. The pulmonary circulation is one of three primary cycles in the mammalian circulatory system. (9.2)

systolic pressure the pressure in the cardiac cycle generated by the contraction of the left ventricle as it forces blood out of the heart. (9.3)

T cell type of lymphocyte which is processed in the thymus gland and plays a role in the body's acquired immune response. (9.2)

taxon (plural taxa) one of a series of progressively smaller groups made when subdividing the three domains and the six kingdoms. (11.3)

taxonomy practice of classifying organisms. (11.3)

Tay-Sachs disease autosomal recessive condition in children who appear normal at birth but their brains and spinal cords begin to deteriorate at about eight months. (7.1)

telophase a phase of mitosis where two daughter nuclei are formed. (5.1)

test cross cross of an individual of unknown genotype with a homozygous recessive individual, used as a method to determine the unknown genotype. (4.2)

tetrad a homologous pair formed during prophase of meiosis containing four chromatids. (5.2)

thalli (singular thallus) flattened lobed bodies found on thallose liverworts. (13.2)

thigmotropism response in plants in which they grow toward what is touching them, and tend to coil around a support; e.g., vining plants. (15.1)

thrombin enzyme produced when thromboplastin reacts with prothrombin. It is involved in the formation of blood clots. (9.2)

thromboplastin enzyme produced when certain chemicals in the blood combine with other clotting agents. It is involved in the formation of blood clots. (9.2)

thylakoids a membrane system consisting of interconnected flattened sacs containing chlorophyll, other pigments, and enzymes necessary for the light-dependent part of photosynthesis. (2.1)

thymine one of four nitrogen-containing bases in nucleotides which make up DNA. (6.1)

tidal volume volume of air that is moved out of the lungs in a regular, unforced exhalation. (8.3)

tissue a group of specialized cells that have the same structure and perform the same function, such as muscle tissue. (2.3)

tissue culture method to grow plants by cloning using advanced technology. (15.3)

tracheae in insects, the tubes that carry respiratory gases between the internal tissues of the animal and the external environment. (8.1) In vertebrates, the tube that carries air from the nasal passages or mouth to the lungs (also known as the windpipe). (8.2)

tracheid type of xylem cell in vascular plants that transports water and minerals and is made up of cells with tapered ends that contain piths. (14.2)

traits distinguishing characteristics or phenotypic features of an individual. (4.2)

transcription the process of making a copy of the information along one strand of DNA to produce a strand of mRNA. (2.2)

translation the process of using the coded mRNA instructions for a sequence of amino acids to produce a polypeptide. (2.2)

translocation changes in the physical structure of chromosomes where a part of one chromosome changes places with part of the same chromosome or with part of another, nonhomologous chromosome. (7.3) Also, in plants, the movement of water or organic materials from one region to another. (9.5)

transpiration pull or cohesion-tension one mechanism for the translocation of water in plants where transpiration loss in the leaves above may act to pull water up the plant. Transpiration pull is the most widely accepted mechanism to account for the movement of water from the roots to the top of a tall tree. (9.5)

tricuspid valves heart valves located between the atria and ventricles. Tricuspid valves ensure that blood flows only one way through the cardiac cycle. (9.3)

triglyceride nonpolar fat molecule composed of one molecule of glycerol and three molecules of fatty acid. (1.1)

triploidy a condition where an organism has three (3n) sets of chromosomes. (5.2)

trisomy having an extra chromosome usually produced when a gamete with an extra chromosome is fertilized by a normal gamete. (5.2)

tRNA transfer ribonucleic acid (RNA); carries an amino acid to a ribosome and attaches to the mRNA there to allow the amino acid to be added to a polypeptide. (2.2)

tropism plant response to different stimuli including a negative response by growing away from the stimulus or a positive response by growing towards the stimulus. (15.1)

true breeding organisms that are homozygous for a particular trait or sets of traits and produce like offspring. (4.2)

turbinates fine bone structures that project into the nasal chambers. The turbinates increase the surface area available to warm and moisten incoming air. (8.2)

turgor tension produced by the fluid content of plant cells. (14.3)

tyrosine amino acid used by the body to make melanin and certain hormones. (7.1)

ultrasound a medical procedure where sound waves beyond the limit of human hearing are sent through the body to produce an image of internal organs or of a fetus. (7.4)

unsaturated type of fatty acid that has double bonds between carbon atoms where more hydrogen atoms could be attached. (1.1)

Urochordata a non-vertebrate subphylum in Chordata commonly called tunicates, or sea squirts. These are squat, thick-walled organisms that live on the ocean floor and have a protective layer called a tunic that covers their bodies. (13.3)

vascular bundle in plants, the longitudinal cylinder of xylem and phloem that connect the vascular tissue of the root to that in the leaves. (14.2)

vascular cylinder cylinder of vascular tissue of the root which is clumped together, and contains both phloem and xylem. (14.2)

vascular system system of fluid tissue found in almost all multicellular organisms that plays a role in transporting nutrients and other materials from the external environment to the cells of the organism. (9.1)

vascular tissue tissue that transports materials in plants and is made up of xylem and phloem. (14.2)

vasoconstriction constriction of blood vessels. (9.3)

vasodilation dilation of blood vessels. (9.3)

vegans vegetarians who rely strictly on foods derived from plants and who use substitutes for even dairy products and eggs. (10.5)

vegetarians people who rely strictly on foods derived from plants and avoid meat and fish altogether, but may consume dairy products and eggs. (10.5)

vein in animals, a blood vessel that carries blood to the heart. (9.1) In plants, the vascular bundles in the leaf. (14.3)

ventilate to forcibly move a respiratory medium across a respiratory surface. (8.1)

ventricle chamber of the heart that collects blood to be pumped away from the heart. In mammals, the right ventricle pumps blood to the pulmonary circulation while the left ventricle pumps blood into the systemic circulation. (9.1)

venule small vein that carries blood from the capillaries to the veins. (9.2)

vesicle a small membrane sac for transport or storage of material within a cell. (1.4)

vessel elements type of xylem cell in angiosperms, which when joined with others form a major tube to conduct water. (14.2)

villi finger-like projections that line the folds of the small intestine and serve greatly to increase its absorptive surface area. (10.2)

virus particulate that contains strands of DNA or RNA surrounded by a protective protein coat and that act as mobile genes that parasitize cells. (11.2)

vital capacity total volume of air that can be moved in or out of the lung. The vital capacity is the sum of the tidal volume, inspiratory reserve volume, and expiratory reserve volume. (8.3)

vitamin essential requirement of a healthy diet; required in the body in relatively small amounts, but act as coenzymes and are involved in tissue development and growth and in helping the body to fight and resist disease. (10.5)

water moulds members of the phylum Oomycota, fungus-like protists that are heterotrophs. They extend fungus-like threads into their host's tissues, where they release digestive enzymes and absorb the resulting nutrients. Most of them live as saprotrophs but some species are parasites on fish, insects, and plants. (12.3)

wave model of light a model used to explain how radiation such as light consists of energy waves with both electrical and magnetic properties. (3.2)

wavelength the distance between identical points on two adjacent waves. In the electromagnetic spectrum, wavelength decreases as frequency increases. (3.2)

woody plants that have xylem and lignin, such as trees and shrubs. (14.1)

xylem vascular tissue that carries water and minerals from the roots of the plant to the stem and leaves. Made up of tracheids and, in angiosperms, vessel elements. (9.5, 14.2)

zygomycotes zygospore fungi include bread moulds and other saprotrophs. (12.4)

zygospores diploid structures that develop after two haploid hyphae of opposite types (called mating strains + and –) combine and fuse their nuclei together. Characteristic to the zygospora, a group of fungi that keep sexual reproduction in reserve for unfavourable times. (12.4)

Index

The page numbers in **boldface** type indicate the pages where the terms are defined. Terms that occur in Investigations (*inv*), Thinking Labs (*TL*), and MiniLabs (*ML*) are also indicated.

other functions of, 299–300
oxygen pick-up and release, 293–294
Rh factors, 301
types, *300TL*
Blood groups, **300**
Blood pressure, 316–319
risks, 317
stress, *316–317inv*
Blood types, *144SP*
Bohr-Rutherford model, 637
Bones, *506TL*
Boreal forest, 524
Boveri, Theodor, 175
Bovine spongiform encephalopathy (BSE), 388
Breathing, **254**, 256
control of, 268–270
high altitude, 268
mechanics of, 260–266
Bronchi, **258**
Bronchioles, **258**
Brown algae, 444
Brown, Dr. Moira, 507
Bryophytes, 470, 471
Burst swimming, 314
Butany, Dr. Jagdish, 310

Caecum, **341**
Caffeine, **364**
Callus, **574**
Calvin cycle, **90**
Calvin, Melvin, 90
Cambium, 556, 557
Canada Food Guide, 358
pizza, *360ML*
Cancer, 69, 74, 172, 196
Capillary, **291**
Capillary action, **322**
Capsid, **385**
Capsule, **54**
Carbohydrases, 343
Carbohydrates, **10**, 354
function/structure, 10–11
Carbon dioxide, 99
Carbon monoxide, 99
Carbon monoxide poisoning, 271
Carbon sink, **591**
Cardiac circulation, **288**
Cardiac output, **306**
Cardiovascular fitness, 359–360
Cardiovascular system, **282**
Carnivores, 80
Carrier, **131**
Carrier protein, **28**
Cassava, 570
Catalase, 60
Cell cycle, **152**
timing of, 153
Cell division, 153
Cell membrane, 7, **46**
diffusion, 25–26

structure, 21–24
Cell size and diffusion, 25–26
Cell theory, 636
Cell wall, **52**, **53**, **54**
Cells
chemical reactions, 8
division, 150, 152
energy, 80
function, 2
matter, 80
mitosis, 155
modelling specialized, *64–65inv*
molecules, 6
organic compounds, 10
parietal, 64
polar molecules, 9
prokaryotes, 54
reproductive, 160
specialized, 63–66
squamous epithelial, 66
staining, 45
stem, 67
theory, 624
water, 8
Cellular processes, environment, 102
Cellular respiration, **92**, 256
gas exchange, 250
Cellular slime mould, 448
Cellulose, **12**, 355
plant, 590
Central vacuole, **52**, **53**
Centrioles, **51**, 157
Centromere, **154**, 157, 163
Centrosome, **47**, **51**
Channel protein, **30**
Characteristic, 116, 118, 120
Chargaff, Erwin, 188, 189
Chase, Martha, 186, 187
Chemical bonding, 637
Chemical energy, **81**
Chemical reactions in cells, 8
Chemoheterotrophs, 430
Chlorophyll, 54, **87**, 88
Chlorophytes, 442
Chloroplast, **52**, **53**, 58
photosynthesis, 88
Cholecystokinin, 347
Cholesterol, 14, 23, **233**, **355**, 356
Chordata, 489, 504–506
Chorion, **232**
Chorionic villi sampling (CVS), **232**
Chromatids, 157, 161
Chromatin, **46**, 48, **53**
Chromosome theory of inheritance, **175**
Chromosomes, **154**, 186, 210
changes in, 226–230
changes in structure, 229
deletion, 229
duplication, 229
genes, 177
heredity, 175–180

inversion, 230
translocation, 230
Chrysophytes, 445
Chyme, **339**, 346
Cilia, **51**, **52**, **439**
Ciliates, 439
Circulatory system, **282**
amphibians, 286
annelids, 285
birds, 287
fish, 286
mammals, 287–301
Civil engineer, 31
Cladistics, **404**
Cladogram, **405**
Class, 391
Cleft palates, **233**
Climax community, **594**, 595
Cloning, **203**, **557**, 573
gene, 204
Closed transport system, **284**
Closed, complete, double circulatory system, 287, 288
Club fungi, 454
Club mosses, 475
Cnidaria, 490
diversity of, *491TL*
extracellular digestion, 491
transport, 282
Co-dominant, **143**
Cocci, **420**
Codominant genetic disorder, 212–214
Codon, **194**
Coelom, **497**
Coelomates, **497**
Coenzymes, **357**
Cohesion-tension, **322**, 323
Collip, J.B., 70
Colon, **341**
Colon cancer, 236
Colour blindness, 175, 222–223
Complementary base pairs, **189**
Complete protein, **356**
Compounds, inorganic/organic, 9
Compound light microscopes, 7
Concentration gradient, **26**
Conidia, **458**
Conifers, 477, 479
identifying, *480–481inv*
Conjugation, **425**
Continuous variation, **178**
Corals, 490
Cork cambium, **557**
Corms, **540**
Coronary bypass, **319**
Cortex, **542**
Cortisol, 314
Côté, Dr. Pierre, 31
Cotyledon, **481**, 524
Counter-current flow, **264**, 265
Covalent bond, 637

Photo Credits

x (top), © Will & Deni McIntyre/Photo Researchers, Inc.; **x** (top right), © E. Webber/Visuals Unlimited, Inc; **x** (top right), © Tom Walker/SI/Take Stock Inc.; **x** (top right), © M. Abbey/Visuals Unlimited, Inc.; **xi** (top), From p. 7 *Inquiry Into Life 9th ed.* © 2000, 1997 by McGraw-Hill Companies, Inc. All rights reserved.; **xii** (top), From p. 48, *Inquiry Into Life 9th ed.* © 2000, 1997 by McGraw-Hill Companies, Inc.; **ii** (bottom left), Astrid & Hanns-Frieder Michler/Science Photo Library; **iii** (top right), © David M. Phillips/Visuals Unlimited, Inc.; **iv** (top right), © 2001 James Gritz/PhotoDisc #WL003492; **v** (bottom right), Charles Gupton/Stone; **vi** (bottom right), © Bill Kamin/Visuals Unlimited Inc.; **vii** (top right), © Digital Stock Four Seasons Vol. 101.; **2** (bottom centre), © Gordon Garradd/Science Photo Library; **3** (centre), Courtesy Michael W. Davidson/National High Magnetic Field Laboratory; **4** (bottom right), © A.M. Siegelman/Visuals Unlimited, Inc.; **5** (centre), © Meckes/Ottawa/Eye of Science/Photo Researchers, Inc.; **6** (top right), Reuters NewsMedia Inc./CORBIS/Magma; **7** (top right), LSHTM/Stone; **8** (bottom right), © Artville; **10** (bottom centre), © Dwight Kuhn; **11** (centre), From p. 32 *Inquiry Into Life 9th ed.* © 2000, 1997 by McGraw-Hill Companies, Inc.; **12** (bottom left), Figure 1.10 photos: top Corel Corporation #757009, middle © L.S. Stepanowicz/Visuals Unlimited, Inc., bottom © Digital Stock, Business & Agriculture Vol. 102. Figure 1.10 Illustration: Tom Kennedy/Romark Illustrations from p. 163 *Biology: The Dynamics of Life* © 2000 by McGraw-Hill Companies, Inc.; **12** (bottom right), © Brian Milne/Animals Animals; **13** (top centre), From p. 34 *Inquiry Into Life 9th ed.* © 2000, 1997 by McGraw-Hill Companies, Inc.; **13** (bottom right), Adapted from p. 34 Figure 2.22, *Inquiry Into Life 9th ed.* © 2000, 1997 by the McGraw-Hill Companies, Inc.; **14** (top right), © Burns-Jansen/Valan Photos; **14** (top right), From p. 75 *Biology: Living Systems* © 1998 by McGraw-Hill Companies, Inc.; **14** (bottom centre), From p. 37 *Inquiry Into Life 9th ed.* © 2000, 1997 by McGraw-Hill Companies, Inc.; **15** (top centre), From p. 38 *Inquiry Into Life 9th ed.* © 2000, 1997 by McGraw-Hill Companies, Inc. All rights reserved.; **15** (centre right), © Jean Claude Revy/Phototake Inc.; **18** (centre), From p. 39 *Inquiry Into Life 9th ed.* © 2000, 1997 by McGraw-Hill Companies, Inc.; **19** (top left), From p. 40, *Inquiry Into Life 9th ed.* © 2000, 1997 by McGraw-Hill Companies, Inc.; **19** (centre right), © Lawrence Livermore Laboratory/Science Photo Library/Photo Researchers, Inc.; **20** (top centre), From p. 40, *Inquiry Into Life 9th ed.* © 2000, 1997 by McGraw-Hill Companies, Inc.; **21** (top right), Eugene Kedl/Quebec Tourism; **21** (bottom left), © Michel Julien/Valan Photos; **22** (top left), University of Toronto Archives#A78-0050/001; **22** (bottom left), © D.E. Akin/Visuals Unlimited, Inc.; **22** (bottom right), © Don W. Fawcett/Visuals Unlimited, Inc.; **23** (top left), From p. 35 *Inquiry Into Life 9th ed.* © 2000, 1997 by McGraw-Hill Companies, Inc.; **24** (top centre), From p. 68 *Inquiry Into Life 9th ed.* © 2000, 1997 by McGraw-Hill Companies, Inc.; **25** (top right), © Jeannie R. Kemp/Valan Photos; **25** (centre right), © Astrid & Hanns-Frieder Michler/Science Photo Library; **27** (centre right), Adapted from Tom Kennedy/Romark Illustrations p. 203 *Biology: The Dynamics of Life* © 2000 by McGraw-Hill Companies, Inc.; **28** (bottom right), Design Your Own Investigation (Osmosis in a Model Cell) was adapted from pp. 104–105 *Biology: Living Systems* © 1998 by McGraw-Hill Companies, Inc.; **29 & 30**, adapted from Tom Kennedy/Romark Illustrations p. 204 *Biology: The Dynamics of Life* © 2000 by McGraw-Hill Companies, Inc.; **30** (bottom right), © John P. Kelly/The Image Bank; **31** (top left), Courtesy Pierre Cote/©2000 Craig Minielly MPA/Aura; **32** (top right), © Gregg Otto/Visuals Unlimited, Inc.; **32** BIOLOGY by Helena Curtis and N. Sue Barnes © 1968, 1975, 1983, 1989 by Worth Publishers. Used with the permission of W. H. Freeman and Company.; **35** (centre right), From p. 78 *Inquiry Into Life 9th ed.* © 2000, 1997 by McGraw-Hill Companies, Inc.; **35** (bottom right), From p. 78, *Inquiry Into Life 9th ed.* © 2000, 1997 by McGraw-Hill Companies, Inc.; **35** (top right), ©Hans Gelberblom/Visuals Unlimited, Inc; **36** (top left), Courtesy Kenneth Storey © J.M. Storey, Carleton University; **38** (centre left), Courtesy Mark Bretscher; **38** (centre right), © Fred Hossler/Visuals Unlimited, Inc.; **41** (centre and centre right), adapted from Tom Kennedy/Romark Illustrations p. 203, *Biology: The Dynamics of Life* © 2000 by McGraw-Hill Companies, Inc.; **42** (bottom right), © Newcomb/Wergin/BPS/Stone; **43** (centre), © Kevin Fleming/CORBIS/Magma; **44** (top right), © Dr. Linda Stannard, UCT/Science Photo Library; **45** (top right), © Alfred Pasieka/Science Photo Library; **46** (top centre), From p. 50 *Inquiry Into Life 9th ed.* © 2000, 1997 by McGraw-Hill Companies, Inc.; **47** (top right), © D.W. Fawcett/Photo Researchers, Inc.; **47** (top centre), © Professors P. Motta & T. Naguro/Science Photo Library; **47** (bottom right), From p. 52 *Inquiry Into Life 9th ed.* © 2000, 1997 by McGraw-Hill Companies, Inc.; **48** (top right), from p. 53 *Inquiry Into Life 9th ed.* © 2000, 1997 by the McGraw-Hill Companies, Inc.; **48** (centre right), R. Bolender/Visuals Unlimited Inc; **48** (bottom right), from p. 53 *Inquiry Into Life 9th ed.* © 2000, 1997 by McGraw-Hill Companies, Inc.; **49** (centre left), © Don W. Fawcett/Visuals Unlimited, Inc.; **49** (centre right), Professors P. Motta & T. Naguro/science Photo Library; **49** (bottom right), From p. 57 *Inquiry Into Life 9th ed.* © 2000, 1997 by McGraw-Hill Companies, Inc.; **50** (top left), © M. Schliwa/Visuals Unlimited, Inc.; **50** (centre left), © Dr. Gerald Schatten/Science Photo Library/Photo Researchers, Inc.; **50** (centre left), © Don W. Fawcett/Visuals Unlimited; **51** (bottom left), From p. 60 *Inquiry Into Life 9th ed.* © 2000, 1997 by McGraw-Hill Companies, Inc.; **51** (bottom right), © Don W. Fawcett/Visuals Unlimited, Inc.; **52** (top left), © I. Gibbons, D. Fawcett/Visuals Unlimited, Inc.; **52** (top centre), © Dr. G. Moscoso/Science Photo Library; **52** (top right), Dr. Tony Brain/Science Photo Library; **52** (centre right), © J. Litvay/Visuals Unlimited, Inc.; **53** (centre), From p. 51 *Inquiry Into Life 9th ed.* © 2000, 1997 by McGraw-Hill Companies, Inc.; **54** (top left), © Dr. Jeremy Burgess/Science Photo Library/Photo Researchers, Inc.; **54** (top right), From p. 56 *Inquiry Into Life 9th ed.* © 2000, 1997 by McGraw-Hill Companies, Inc.; **55** (top left), From p. 62 *Inquiry Into Life 9th ed.* © 2000, 1997 by McGraw-Hill Companies, Inc.; **55** (top right), © Barry Dowsett Camr/Science Photo Library; **55** (centre left), From p. 62 *Inquiry Into Life 9th ed.* © 2000, 1997 by McGraw-Hill Companies, Inc.; **55** (centre right), © Elizabeth Gentt/Visuals Unlimited, Inc.; **56** (top right), © Mark Schneider/Visuals Unlimited, Inc.; **56** (bottom left), © Professor Oscar Miller/Science Photo

Mark Newman/Weststock; **146** (centre right), Rick Strange/Weststock; **148** (bottom right), © Jerome Wexler/Visuals Unlimited, Inc.; **149** (centre right), From p 265 *Biology: The Dynamics of Life* © 2000 by McGraw-Hill Companies, Inc.; **150** (bottom right), © K.G. Murti/Visuals Unlimited, Inc.; **151** (background), © Randy Wells/CORBIS/Magma; **152** (top right), © Gary Retherford/Photo Researchers, Inc.; **152** (bottom right), From p. 212 *Biology: The Dynamics of Life* © 2000 by McGraw-Hill Companies, Inc.; **153** (centre left), From p. 210 Lab 8.2 *Biology: The Dynamics of Life* © 2000 by McGraw-Hill Companies, Inc.; **153** (centre right), Paul Vathis/Associated Press/Canadian Press Picture Archive; **153** (bottom right), © 1990 Andrew J. Martinez/Photo Researchers, Inc.; **154** (centre left), From p. 212 *Biology: The Dynamics of Life* © 2000 by McGraw-Hill Companies, Inc.; **154** (centre left), © Science VU/Visuals Unlimited, Inc.; **156** (background), From p. 213 *Biology: The Dynamics of Life* © 2000 by McGraw-Hill Companies, Inc.; **156** (centre), From p. 213 *Biology: The Dynamics of Life* © 2000 by McGraw-Hill Companies, Inc.; **156** © Kent Wood/Photo Researchers Inc.; **157** (top right), © David M. Phillips/Visuals Unlimited, Inc.; **157** (bottom right), © R. Calentine/Visuals Unlimited, Inc.; **158** (top right), © David M. Phillips/Visuals Unlimited, Inc.; **158** (bottom right), © 2001 Jim Wehtje/PhotoDisc #AB0046722; **159** (bottom left), © Ken Greer/Visuals Unlimited, Inc.; **160** (top right), Frederick Schussler/Weststock; **160** (bottom left), From p. 272 *Biology: The Dynamics of Life* © 2000 by McGraw-Hill Companies, Inc.; **162** (top) Illustration from page 273 *Biology: The Dynamics of Life* © 2000 by McGraw-Hill Companies, Inc.; **162** (top centre and top right), A-D) © John Cunningham/Visuals Unlimited Inc.; **162** (bottom right and bottom left), E-F) CBS/Phototake, Inc.; **162** (centre left and top left), G) © John Cunningham/Visuals Unlimited Inc.; **162** (centre left), H) CBS/Phototake Inc.; **163** (bottom), From p. 275 *Biology: The Dynamics of Life* © 2000 by McGraw-Hill Companies, Inc.; **164** (top left), © John B. Cabisco/Visuals Unlimited, Inc.; **165** (top), From p.97 *Inquiry Into Life 9th ed.* © 2000, 1997 by McGraw-Hill Companies, Inc.; **166** (centre left), © Biophoto Associates/Photo Researchers, Inc.; **166** (centre), © Biophoto Associates/Photo Researchers, Inc.; **167** (centre right), © E. R. Degginger/Photo Researchers, Inc.; **167** (top right), © David M. Phillips/Visuals Unlimited, Inc.; **168** (centre left), From p. 614 *Inquiry Into Life 9th ed.* © 2000, 1997 by McGraw-Hill Companies, Inc.; **170** (bottom), From p. 187 *Biology: Living Systems* © 1998 by McGraw-Hill Companies, Inc.; **171** (top right), © 2001 Siede Preis/PhotoDisc #WSl002772; **171** (bottom), From p. 276 *Biology: The Dynamics of Life* © 2000 by McGraw-Hill Companies, Inc.; **172** (centre right), Courtesy Dr. Corrinne Lobe; **173** (top right), Corel Corporation #586042; **173**, Figure 5.22 from p. 489 *Inquiry Into Life 9th ed.* © 2000, 1997 by McGraw-Hill Companies, Inc.; **174** (top right), © D. Cavagnaro/Visuals Unlimited Inc.; **175** (top right), © Biophoto Associates/Photo Researchers, Inc.; **176** (bottom left), © Dr. Jeremy Burgess/Science Photo Library/Photo Researchers, Inc.; **177** (top left), From page 214, *Biology: Living Systems* © 1998 by McGraw-Hill Companies, Inc.; **177** (centre left), From p. 214 *Biology: Living Systems* © 1998 by McGraw-Hill Companies, Inc.; **177** (bottom left), From p. 213 *Biology: Living Systems* © 1998 by McGraw-Hill Companies, Inc.; **177** (bottom right), © 2001 Santokh Kocharwz/PhotoDisc #WL004308; **179** (top), From p. 215 Figure 8-22 *Biology: Living Systems* © 1998 by McGraw-Hill Companies, Inc.; **180** (top left), © Victor De Schwanberg/ Science Photo Library/Photo Researchers, Inc.; **180** (top centre), © Rory McClenaghan/Science Photo Library/Photo Researchers, Inc.; **180** (top right), © Eyewire Photography #e121301-1; **180** (centre left), © SIU/Visuals Unlimited, Inc.; **180** (centre), © Steve Percival/Science Photo Library/Photo Researchers, Inc.; **181** (bottom left), From p. 270 Lab 10.2 *Biology: The Dynamics of Life* © 2000 by McGraw-Hill Companies, Inc.; **182** (bottom right), © John B. Cabisco/Visuals Unlimited Inc.; **184** (bottom right), © Will & Deni McIntyre/Photo Researchers, Inc.; **185** (background), © Artbase, Inc.; **186** (top right), © Biophoto Associates/Photo Researchers, Inc.; **186** (bottom right), © R. Bhatnagar/Visuals Unlimited, Inc.; **187** (bottom), From p. 228 *Biology: Living Systems* © 1998 by McGraw-Hill Companies, Inc.; **188** (top left), From p. 288 *Biology: The Dynamics of Life* © 2000 by McGraw-Hill Companies, Inc.; **188** (bottom left), From p. 508 *Inquiry Into Life 9th ed.* © 2000, 1997 by McGraw-Hill Companies, Inc.; **188** (bottom right), College Archives, King's College, London; **189** (top left), College Archives, King's College, London; **189** (bottom), From p. 233 *Biology: Living Systems* © 1998 by McGraw-Hill Companies, Inc.; **191** (bottom right), © A. Barrington Brown/Science Source/Photo Researchers, Inc.; **191** (top left), From p. 294 *Biology: The Dynamics of Life* © 2000 by McGraw-Hill Companies, Inc.; **193** (top), From p. 237 *Biology: Living Systems* © 1998 by McGraw-Hill Companies, Inc.; **194** (top), From p. 239 *Biology: Living Systems* © 1998 by McGraw-Hill Companies, Inc.; **195** (top right), Mark Humphey/Associated Press AP/Canadian Press Picture Archives; **196** (top left), © 2001 PhotoDisc Professional Science Vol. 72; **197** (top right), Adapted from p. 361 Lab 13.3 *Biology: The Dynamics of Life* © 2000 by McGraw-Hill Companies, Inc.; **198** (top right), © Eyewire Photography #e000498m; **198** (bottom right), From p. 16-8, question #8 *Biology: The Dynamics of Life, Computer Test Bank Question Manual,* © 1998 by McGraw-Hill Companies, Inc.; **199** (top right), Corel Corporation #720099; **199** (bottom centre), From p. 291 *Biology: The Dynamics of Life* © 2000 by McGraw-Hill Companies, Inc.; **199** (centre right), © K.G. Murti/Visuals Unlimited, Inc.; **200** (bottom right), © 2001 PhotoDisc Professional Science Vol. 72; **200–201** (top), From p. 234 *Biology: Living Systems* © 1998 by McGraw-Hill Companies, Inc.; **201** (centre right), Frederick Schussler/Weststock; **202** (centre left), Courtesy of University of British Columbia; **203** (centre right), Associated Press AP/Canadian Press Picture Archive; **204**, Text excerpt from p. 204 *Biology: Living Systems* © 1998 by McGraw-Hill Companies, Inc.; **205** (bottom right), © 2001 PhotoDisc Professional Science Vol. 72; **206** (centre left), © K.G. Murti/Visuals Unlimited Inc.; **207** (centre right and centre), From p. 228 *Biology: Living Systems* © 1998 by McGraw-Hill Companies, Inc.; **207** (bottom right), © Eyewire Photography #e000498m; **208** (bottom right), © Dan McCoy/Rainbow/PictureQuest; **209** (background), © Bettman/CORBIS/Magma; **210** (top right), © John Sann/Stone; **211** (bottom left), ©1992 IMS Creative/Custom Medical Stock Photo; **212** (bottom), Figure 7.3: Photo © R. Kessel/Visuals Unlimited, Inc.; Art: From p. 250 *Inquiry Into Life 9th ed.* © 2000, 1997 by McGraw-Hill Companies, Inc.; **213** (top), From p. 483 *Inquiry Into Life 9th ed.* © 2000, 1997 by McGraw-Hill Companies, Inc; **213** (bottom left), © Stanley

Flegler/Visuals Unlimited, Inc.; **215** (background), From p. 352 *Biology: The Dynamics of Life* © 2000 by McGraw-Hill Companies, Inc.; **215** (centre left), © Michael G. Gabridge/Visuals Unlimited, Inc.; **216** (centre left), © 1987 Rod Planck/ Photo Researchers, Inc.; **219** (top right), © Custom Medical Stock Photo; **220** (top), Photo: CNRI/Science Photo Library/ Photo Researchers Art: From p. 488 *Inquiry Into Life 9th ed.* © 2000, 1997 by McGraw-Hill Companies, Inc.; **220** (top left), © Mark Gibson/Visuals Unlimited, Inc.; **221** (bottom), From p. 498 *Inquiry Into Life 9th ed.* © 2000, 1997 by McGraw-Hill Companies, Inc.; **221** (bottom right), © Bettman/CORBIS/Magma; **222** (top left), Ishihara's Test for Colour Blindness, published by KANEHARA & CO., LTD, Tokyo, Japan. For accurate testing the original plate should be used. From p. 499 *Inquiry Into Life 9th ed.* © 2000, 1997 by McGraw-Hill Companies, Inc.; **223** (top), From p. 332 *Biology: The Dynamics of Life* © 2000 by McGraw-Hill Companies, Inc.; **225** (top right), From p. 332 Lab 12.3 *Biology: The Dynamics of Life* © 2000 by McGraw-Hill Companies, Inc.; **226** (top), © L. Willatt, East Anglian Regional Genetics Service/Science Photo Library; **227** (bottom right), John Gibson/ Canadian Press Picture Archives; **227** (bottom centre), © CNRI/Science Photo Library; **228** (top left), © Christopher Rutty/Courtesy of Irene Uchida; **229** (left), From p. 491 *Inquiry Into Life 9th ed.* © 2000, 1997 by McGraw-Hill Companies, Inc.; **229** (centre right), © 1990 Custom Medical Stock Photo; **230** (top left), Science Vu/Visuals Unlimited Inc.; **231** (top right), © Dr. Yorgos Nikas/Science Photo Library; **232** (bottom left), From p. 291 *Biology: Living Systems* © 1998 by the McGraw-Hill Companies, Inc.; **232** (bottom right), © St. Bartholomew's Hospital/Science Photo Library; **232** (centre right), © Petit Format/Nestle/Science Photo Library/Photo Researchers, Inc.; **233** (bottom left), © Cabisco/Visuals Unlimited, Inc.; **233** (bottom right), © W. Ober/Visuals Unlimited, Inc.; **234** (bottom), From p. 539, *Inquiry Into Life 9th ed.* © 2000, 1997 by McGraw-Hill Companies, Inc.; **236** (centre left), © Rob Teteruk/The Hospital For Sick Children; **240** (centre left), © Sinclair Stammers/Science Photo Library/Photo Researchers, Inc.; **243** From p. 273 *Inquiry Into Life 9th ed.* © 2000, 1997 by McGraw-Hill Companies, Inc.; **244** (bottom left), From p. 187 *Biology: Living Systems* © 1998 by McGraw-Hill Companies, Inc.; **246** (bottom), Artbase, Inc.; **246–247** (background), © David Young Wolff/Stone; **248** (bottom right), Doug Mills/Associated Press AP/Canadian Press Picture Archive; **249** (background), © David M. Phillips/Science Source/Photo Researchers, Inc.; **250** (top right), © Eric Grave/Science Source/Photo Researchers, Inc.; **251** (centre left), © Roland Birke/Photo Researchers, Inc.; **251** (centre right), © Michael Abbey/Photo Researchers, Inc.; **251** (top right), © John D. Cunningham/Visuals Unlimited, Inc.; **251** (bottom right), © Digital Stock, Four Seasons Vol. 101; **252** (centre right), © 2001 Frank & Joyce Barek/PhotoDisc #AA035478; **253** (top left), From p. 618 *Biology: Living Systems* © 1998 by McGraw-Hill Companies, Inc.; **253** (bottom right), © The Cousteau Society/The Image Bank; **256** (top right), © 2001 James Gritz/PhotoDisc #WL003442; **257** (bottom), From p. 285 *Inquiry Into Life 9th ed.* © 2000, 1997 by McGraw-Hill Companies, Inc.; **257** (top right), From p. 286 *Inquiry Into Life 9th ed.* © 2000, 1997 by McGraw-Hill Companies, Inc.; **258** (top left), © Veronika Burmeister/Visuals Unlimited, Inc.; **258** (top right), © Fred Hossler/Visuals Unlimited, Inc.; **259** (top), From p. 1004 *Biology: The Dynamics of Life* © 2000 by McGraw-Hill Companies, Inc.; **260** (bottom), From p. 291 *Inquiry Into Life 9th ed.* © 2000, 1997 by McGraw-Hill Companies, Inc.; **260** (top right), © 2001 Doug Menuez/ PhotoDisc #LS011154; **263** (centre left), ©1986 SIU/Photo Researchers, Inc.; **263** (top), From p. 288 *Inquiry Into Life 9th ed.* © 2000, 1997 by McGraw-Hill Companies, Inc.; **264** (top right), Corel Corporation #424073; **264** (centre right), Adapted from p. 618 *Biology: Living Systems* © 1998 by McGraw-Hill Companies, Inc.; **266** (centre left), © Owen Franken/CORBIS/Magma; **268** (top right), Associated Press AP/Canadian Press Picture Archive; **269** (bottom centre), William Plowman/Associated Press AP/Canadian Press Picture Archive; **273** (top), Frank Gunn/Canadian Press Picture Archive; **274** (top right), Corel Corporation #131082; **274** (bottom right), © Cabisco/Visuals Unlimited, Inc.; **275** (bottom left), From p. 163 *Inquiry Into Life 9th ed.* © 2000, 1997 by McGraw-Hill Companies, Inc.; **275** (bottom right), © John D. Cunningham/Visuals Unlimited, Inc.; **276** (top left), © Biodisc #3184/Visuals Unlimited, Inc.; **280** (bottom right), © 2001 Russel Illiq/PhotoDisc #NA002638; **281** (centre), © Vince Michaels/Stone; **282** (top right), © Scott Leslie/Valan Photos; **285** (top centre), From p. 589 *Biology: Living Systems* © 1998 by McGraw-Hill Companies, Inc.; **285** (centre right), Corel Corporation #707072; **287** (top left), © 2001 James Gritz/PhotoDisc #WL003487; **288** (top left), © Mehau Kulyk/Science Photo Library/Photo Researchers, Inc.; **289** (top left), From p. 246 *Inquiry Into Life 9th ed.* © 2000, 1997 by McGraw-Hill Companies, Inc.; **290** (bottom centre), From p. 240 *Inquiry Into Life 9th ed.* © 2000, 1997 by McGraw-Hill Companies, Inc.; **292** Adapted from p. 249 *Inquiry Into Life 9th ed.* © 2000, 1997 by McGraw-Hill Companies, Inc.; **293** (top left), From p. 1008 *Biology: The Dynamics of Life* © 2000 by McGraw-Hill Companies, Inc.; **293** (centre left), © Andrew Syred/Science Photo Library; **294** (centre left), © Larry Hobbs/Weststock; **296** (top right), From p. 648 *Biology: Living Systems* © 1998 by McGraw-Hill Companies, Inc.; **297** (centre left), From p. 657 *Biology: Living Systems* © 1998 by McGraw-Hill Companies, Inc.; **297** (bottom right), © David M. Phillips/Visuals Unlimited, Inc.; **298** (centre left), © St. Bartholomew's Hospital/Science Photo Library; **298** (bottom left), Frank Gunn/Canadian Press Picture Archive; **301** (bottom left), © George J. Wilder/Visuals Unlimited, Inc.; **303** (top right), © Klaus Guldbrandsen/Science Photo Library/ Photo Researchers, Inc.; **303** (bottom), From p. 242–243 *Inquiry Into Life 9th ed.* © 2000, 1997 by McGraw-Hill Companies, Inc.; **304** (centre left), From p. 243. *Inquiry Into Life 9th ed.* © 2000, 1997 by McGraw-Hill Companies, Inc.; **305** (top centre), From p. 1015 *Biology: The Dynamics of Life* © 2000 by McGraw-Hill Companies, Inc.; **309** (centre left), © M. I. Walker/Photo Researchers, Inc.; **310** (centre left), Courtesy Dr. Jagdish Butany; **312** (top left), Corel Corporation #541056; **313** (top left), From p. 1068 *Biology: The Dynamics of Life* © 2000 by McGraw-Hill Companies, Inc.; **313** (bottom left), From p. 255 *Inquiry Into Life 9th ed.* © 2000, 1997 by McGraw-Hill Companies, Inc.; **314** (top left), Dr. Louise Milligan, photo by Chris Schramek; **315** (top left), © J. R. Page/Valan Photos; **315** (centre left), Renee DeMartin/WestStock; **317** (bottom left), © 2001 Photo Link/PhotoDisc #MD000535; **318** (centre left), From p. 257 *Inquiry Into Life 9th ed.* © 2000, 1997 by McGraw-Hill Companies, Inc.; **318** (bottom right), From p. 258 *Inquiry Into*

Life 9ᵗʰ ed. © 2000, 1997 by McGraw-Hill Companies, Inc.; **319** (top left), From p. 258, *Inquiry Into Life 9ᵗʰ ed.* © 2000, 1997 by MGraw-Hill Companies, Inc.; **320** (top left), © Bill Banaszewski/Visuals Unlimited, Inc.; **322** (centre left), © David Sieren/Visuals Unlimited, Inc.; **330** (bottom right), © CHRIS JOHNS/National Geographic/First Light; **331** (background), © David B. Fleetham/Tom Stack & Associates; **332** (top), From p. 545 *Biology: Living Systems* © 1998 by McGraw-Hill Companies, Inc.; **332** (centre right), From p. 544, *Biology: Living Systems* © 1998 by McGraw-Hill Companies, Inc.; **333** (bottom), © Richard Sears/Valan Photos; **333** (centre left), © Digital Stock; **334** (top left), From p. 556 *Biology: Living Systems* © 1998 by McGraw-Hill Companies, Inc.; **334** Cath Ellis, Dept. of Zoology, University of Hull/Science Photo Library/Photo Researchers Inc.; **335** (bottom left), Hawk: © Mark K. Peck/Valan Photos; **335** (bottom left), Bat: © Rexford Lord/Photo Researchers, Inc.; **335** (bottom left), Sponge: © Marty Snyderman/Visuals Unlimited, Inc.; **335** (bottom left), Butterfly: © 2001 Jess Alford/PhotoDisc #WL003712; **335** (bottom left), Deer Fly: © Darwin Dale/Photo Researchers, Inc.; **335** (bottom left), Bat: © Wayne Lankinen/Valan Photos; **335** (centre right), Bee: © Dr. Jeremy Burgess/Science Photo Library/Photo Researchers, Inc.; **335** (centre right), Goose: © Arthur Morris/Visuals Unlimited, Inc.; **335** (centre right), Lamprey: © Paul L. Janosi/Valan Photos; **336** (bottom left), From p. 553 *Biology: Living Systems* © 1998 by McGraw-Hill Companies, Inc.; **336** (bottom right), From p. 550 *Biology: Living Systems* © 1998 by McGraw-Hill Companies, Inc.; **337** (top right and centre right), From p. 546–547 *Biology: Living Systems* © 1998 by McGraw-Hill Companies, Inc.; **338** (top and centre right), From p. 214–215 *Inquiry Into Life 9ᵗʰ ed.* © 2000, 1997 by McGraw-Hill Companies, Inc.; **339** (bottom left), From p. 216, Figure 12.3 *Inquiry Into Life 9ᵗʰ ed.* by Sylvia Mader © 2000, 1997 by the McGraw-Hill Companies, Inc. All rights Reserved.; **340** (top), From p. 219 *Inquiry Into Life 9ᵗʰ ed.* © 2000, 1997 by McGraw-Hill Companies, Inc.; **340** (top right), © Quest/Science Photo Library/Photo Researchers Inc.; **341** (top right), From p. 950 *Biology: The Dynamics of Life,* © 2000 by McGraw-Hill Companies, Inc.; **351** (top), From p. 567 *Biology: Living Systems* © 1998 by McGraw-Hill Companies, Inc.; **353** (top right), Sandwich: © 2001 David Buffington/PhotoDisc #FD002818, Hamburger: Carin Krasner/Stone; **354** (top left), From p. 958 *Biology: The Dynamics of Life* © 2000 by McGraw-Hill Companies, Inc.; **358 & 359**, Health Canada; **359** (top right), Nathan Bilow/Associated Press/Canadian Press Picture Archive; **362** (centre right), © Digital Vision; **364** (bottom left), Charles Bennett/Associated Press AP/Canadian Press Picture Archive; **365** (centre right), Mike Ridewood/Canadian Press Picture Archive; **368** (bottom left), From p. 225 *Inquiry Into Life 9ᵗʰ ed.* © 2000, 1997 by McGraw-Hill Companies, Inc.; **370** (centre left), © Bettman/CORBIS/Magma; **377** (background), Inga Spence/Tom Stack & Associates; **378** (bottom right), © Digital Stock Animals and Wildlife.; **379** (background), © Digital Stock; **380** (top centre), © 2001 James Gritz /PhotoDisc; **380** (bottom right), Gregory Ochocki/Weststock; **382** (top), From p. 469 *Biology: The Dynamics of Life* © 2000 by McGraw-Hill Companies, Inc.; **383** (bottom right & left), From p. 180 *Biology: The Dynamics of Life* © 2000 by McGraw-Hill Companies, Inc.; **385** (top right), NIBSC/Science Photo Library/Photo Researchers Inc; **385** (bottom right), From p. 390 *Biology: Living Systems* © 1998 by McGraw-Hill Companies, Inc.; **386** (bottom), From p. 492. *Biology: The Dynamics of Life* © 2000 by McGraw-Hill Companies, Inc.; **387** (bottom left), From p. 495 *Biology: The Dynamics of Life* © 2000 by McGraw-Hill Companies, Inc.; **390** (top right), © Eyewire Photography #ffc_031-1; **391** (top left), Bee: Corel Corporation #240065; **391** (top left), Shark: Zephyr Images/Weststock; **391** (top centre), Horse: Corel Corporation #648000; **391** (top right), Dog: Rick Morley/Weststock; **391** (top right), Oyster: Corel Corporation #355020; **392** (centre right), Corel Corporation #35136;#35137; **393** (bottom), From p. 475 *Biology: The Dynamics of Life* © 2000 by McGraw-Hill Companies, Inc.; **395** (centre left), B) Neil G. McDaniel, 1989/Photo Researchers; **395** (centre right), A) Corel Corporation #828034; **395** (centre left), C) © Tom W. Parkin/Valan Photos; **395** (centre right), D) © Digital Stock; **395** (bottom left), E) © Tom McHugh/Photo Researchers; **396** (top left), Curt & Cary Given/Weststock; **396** (top right), © Laurie Campbell/Stone; **397** (top right), From p. 566 *Inquiry Into Life 9ᵗʰ ed.* © 2000, 1997 by McGraw-Hill Companies, Inc.; **397** (bottom right), From p. 566 *Inquiry Into Life 9ᵗʰ ed.* © 2000, 1997 by McGraw-Hill Companies, Inc.; **400** (bottom left), © James L. Amos/Photo Researchers; **400** (centre right), From p. 555 *Inquiry Into Life 9ᵗʰ ed.* © 2000, 1997 by McGraw-Hill Companies, Inc.; **401** Corel Corporation #35164; #827052; **401** (bottom left), © Stan Elems/Visuals Unlimited; **401** (bottom right), © Wm. C. Jorgensen/Visuals Unlimited; **402** (centre left), © Herman H. Giethoorn/Valan Photos; **402** (centre right), © Robert C. Simpson/Valan Photos; **402** (bottom left), © Francois Gohier/Photo Researchers Inc.; **402** (bottom right), © James L. Amos/Photo Researchers Inc; **403** (centre left), © 2001 Allan and Sandy Carr/ PhotoDisc; **403** (centre right), © Eyewire Photography; **403** (centre), © Rubberball Productions; **405** (centre left), Steve Solum/Weststock; **405** (centre), Red panda: Tom & Pat Leeson/Weststock; **405** (centre), Bear: John Luke/Weststock; **405** (centre right), Mark Newman/Weststock; **405** (bottom), From p. 375 *Biology: Living Systems* © 1998 by McGraw-Hill Companies, Inc.; **407** (centre left), Corel Corporation #714024; **411** (top), From p. 375 *Biology: Living Systems* © 1998 by McGraw-Hill Companies, Inc.; **412** (bottom right), © Mark Wagner/Stone; **413** (background), © Tim Flach/Stone; **414** (top right), © 2001 Emanuele Taroni/PhotoDisc #AA019666; **415** (top left), Corel Corporation #632091; **415** (centre right), Kaj R. Svensson/Science Photo Library/Photo Researchers Inc.; **415** (centre left), © 2001 John Wang/PhotoDisc #NA009114; **416** (bottom left), Courtesy Verena Tunnicliffe; **417** (bottom left), Courtesy Keith Shepherd/Canadian Scientific Submersible Facility; **418** (top right), From p. 390 *Biology: The Dynamics of Life* © 2000 by McGraw-Hill Companies, Inc.; **419** (top right), Dr. Tony Brain/Science Photo Library; **420** (top left), Dr. Kari Lounatmaa/Science Photo Library; **420** (top centre), Alfred Pasieka/Science Photo Library/Photo Researchers, Inc.; **420** (top right), A.B. Dowsett/Science Photo Library/Photo Researchers Inc; **420** (bottom left, centre, right), David M. Phillips/Visuals Unlimited Inc.; **421** (top right), © Jack M. Bostrack/Visuals Unlimited Inc.; **423** (bottom right), Charles Gupton/Stone; **424** (bottom right), A.B. Dowsett/Science Photo Library/Photo Researchers Inc; **424** (bottom left), From P. 581 *Inquiry Into Life 9ᵗʰ ed.* © 2000, 1997 by McGraw-Hill Companies, Inc.; **425** (centre), Dr. Linda Stannard/UCT/Science Photo

Library/Photo Researchers Inc; **425** (bottom), From p. 372 *Biology: The Dynamics of Life* © 2000 by McGraw-Hill Companies, Inc.; **426** (centre left), George B. Chapman/Visuals Unlimited; **427** (top left), © 2001 Photolink/PhotoDisc #FD001363; **430** (bottom left), Sherman Thompson/Visuals Unlimited; **431** (top left), Hugh Spencer/Photo Researchers Inc.; **431** (top centre), Dr. Jeremy Burgess/Science Photo Library/Photo Researchers; **431** (centre right), From p. 581 *Inquiry Into Life 9th ed.* © 2000, 1997 by McGraw-Hill Companies, Inc.; **432** (top right), © Oliver Meckes/Photo Researchers, Inc.; **432** (bottom centre), © Cabisco/Visuals Unlimited Inc.; **432** (bottom right), Corel Corporation #158015; **437** (top right), Eric Gravel/Science Source/Photo Researchers; **437** (centre right), C.P. Hickman/Visuals Unlimited; **437** (bottom right), © M.B. Fenton; **438** (bottom right), Eric V. Grave/Photo Researchers Inc.; **438** (centre left), Professor P.M. Motta, F. M. Magliocca/Science Photo Library; **439** (top left), M. Abbey/Photo Researchers Inc.; **439** (top right), From p. 521 *Biology: The Dynamics of Life* © 2000 by McGraw-Hill Companies, Inc.; **439** (bottom), From p. 523 *Biology: The Dynamics of Life* © 2000 by McGraw-Hill Companies, Inc.; **440** (bottom), From p. 525 *Biology: The Dynamics of Life* © 2000 by McGraw-Hill Companies, Inc.; **443** (top left), Arthur Strange/Valan Photos; **443** (top centre), Roger Klocek/Visuals Unlimited Inc.; **443** (top centre), M. Abbey/Visuals Unlimited Inc.; **443** (top right), M. Abbey/Visuals Unlimited Inc.; **444** (top right), Kevin & Betty Collins/Visuals Unlimited; **444** (bottom left), © Dan Gotshall/Visuals Unlimited Inc.; **445** (top right), Jan Hinsch/Science Photo Library/Photo Researchers Inc.; **445** (bottom), From p. 528 *Biology: The Dynamics of Life* © 2000 by McGraw-Hill Companies, Inc.; **446** (bottom left), E.R. Degginger/Photo Researchers Inc.; **446** (top right), Tom Adams/Visuals Unlimited, Inc.; **446** (bottom right), Courtesy Jennifer Martin/Fisheries and Oceans Canada Photo by Rick Doucet; **447** (centre right), James W. Richardson/Visuals Unlimited; **448** (bottom left), Text and art from p. 534 Lab 19.3 *Biology: The Dynamics of Life* © 2000 by McGraw-Hill Companies, Inc.; **448** © Cabisco/Visuals Unlimited, Inc.; **449** (top), From p. 535 *Biology: The Dynamics of Life* © 2000 by McGraw-Hill Companies, Inc.; **450** (bottom right), From p. 547 *Biology: The Dynamics of Life* © 2000 by McGraw-Hill Companies, Inc.; **450** (top right), Corel Corporation #758044; **451** (top), From p. 559 *Biology: The Dynamics of Life* © 2000 by McGraw-Hill Companies, Inc.; **451** (bottom left), Corel Corporation #158088; **451** (bottom right), Greg G. Dimijian/Photo Researchers; **452** (bottom left), VU/©Science VU/Visuals Unlimited Inc.; **452** (centre right), Bill Keogh/Visuals Unlimited; **453** (bottom), From p. 552 *Biology: The Dynamics of Life* © 2000 by McGraw-Hill Companies, Inc.; **453** (centre right), David Phillips/Visuals Unlimited Inc.; **453** (centre left), From *Sciencepower 9* © 1999 McGraw-Hill Ryerson Ltd.; **454** (top right), U.S. Department of Agriculture; **454** (centre right), Corel Corporation #0216-001; **454** (bottom right), Rob Simpson/Visuals Unlimited Inc.; **455** (bottom right), Corel Corporation #754058; **455** (top), From *Biology: The Dynamics of Life* © 1998 by McGraw-Hill Companies, Inc.; **457** (top left), J. Forsdyke/Gene Cox/Photo Researchers Inc.; **458** (top centre), Jack Bostrack/Visuals Unlimited Inc; **458** (top right), V. Wilkinson/Valan Photos; **462** (bottom right), Curt & Cary Given/Weststock; **463** (background), Corel Corporation #827074; **464** (top right), Corel Corporation #9010; **467** (top left), © Jeremy Burgess/Science Source/Photo Researchers, Inc.; **468** (top left), From p. 578 *Biology: The Dynamics of Life* © 2000 by McGraw-Hill Companies, Inc.; **469** (bottom left), Dinodia Picture Agency/Weststock; **469** (bottom centre), Fern: Corel Corporation #236050; Pine: #757021; **469** (top right), Fritz Polking/Frank Lane Picture Agency/CORBIS/Magma; **470** (bottom), From p. 597 *Biology: The Dynamics of Life* © 2000 by McGraw-Hill Companies, Inc.; **471** (bottom left), Harold V. Green/Valan Photos; **471** (bottom right), David Sieren/Visuals Unlimited Inc.; **471** (bottom right), Ken Wagner/Visuals Unlimited Inc.; **473** (top right), © Robert & Linda Mitchell Photography; **473** (top right), From p. 600 *Biology: The Dynamics of Life* © 2000 by McGraw-Hill Companies, Inc.; **474** (bottom left), Tom & Vicky Kirkendall-Spring/Weststock; **474** (centre right), Biophoto Associates/Photo Researchers; **475** (top right), Michael P. Gadomski/Photo Researchers Inc.; **476** (top left), John Kaprielian/Photo Researchers Inc.; **476** (centre right), © Digital Stock #CB035037; **476** (centre right), Jerome Wexler/Visuals Unlimited Inc.; **477** (centre right), Hans Wiesenhofer/Weststock; **478** (top), From p. 611 *Biology: The Dynamics of Life* © 1998 by McGraw-Hill Companies, Inc.; **479** (centre left), John D. Cunningham/Visuals Unlimited Inc.; **479** (centre right), John N. Tager/Visuals Unlimited Inc.; **479** (bottom left), Biophoto Associates/Photo Researchers; **479** (bottom right), E. Webber/Visuals Unlimited Inc.; **480** (top left), From p. 619 *Biology: The Dynamics of Life* © 1998 by McGraw-Hill Companies, Inc.; **480** (top right), © 2001 Photolink/PhotoDisc #ab000809; **482** (top left), Corel Corporation #514024; **482** (top centre), Ralph Hunt Williams/Weststock; **482** (top centre), Daisies: Hans Wiesenhofer/Weststock; **482** (top right), © 2001 Andrew Ward/Life File/PhotoDisc; **482** (bottom left), Corel Corporation #740058; **483** (bottom right), From p. 667 *Biology: The Dynamics of Life* © 1998 by McGraw-Hill Companies, Inc.; **483** (bottom left), Merlin D. Tuttle/ Bat Conservation International/Photo Researchers, Inc.; **483** (top right), Dr. Jeremy Burgess/Science Photo Library; **484** (background), From p. 668 *Biology: The Dynamics of Life* © 2000 by McGraw-Hill Companies, Inc.; **485** (bottom left), ©2000 Fritz Pölking/Visuals Unlimited, Inc.; **487** (top right), Gregory Ochocki/Weststock; **487** (centre left), Jeff Lepore/Photo Researchers Inc.; **487** (centre right), Noah Poritz/Photo Researchers Inc.; **487** (bottom right), Corel Corporation #163063; **487** (bottom left), K.G. Vock/Okopia/Photo Researchers; **488** (top left), Eyewire Photography #e001231-1; **488** (top right), Renee DeMartin/Weststock; **488** (centre left), Corel Corporation #718097; **488** (centre right), Nigel J. Dennis/Photo Researchers Inc.; **489** (bottom), Andrew Syred/Science Photo Library/Photo Researchers Inc.; **489** (centre), Corel Corporation; **489** (centre right), © Digital Stock Animals and Wildlife; **489** (centre left, centre), Corel Corporation #35052; #757048; **489** (centre right), © 2001 E. Pollard/PhotoDisc #ST00011; **489** (bottom left, bottom centre, bottom right), Corel Corporation #35175; #240086; #35115; **490** (top left), Corel Corporation #164029; **490** (top left), © 2001 PhotoDisc #WL003941; **490** (centre left), Mary Beth Angelo/Photo Researchers Inc.; **490** (top right), From p. 713 *Biology: The Dynamics of Life* © 1998 by McGraw-Hill Companies, Inc.; **491** (centre left), From p. 716 *Biology: The Dynamics of Life* © 1998 by McGraw-Hill Companies, Inc.; **491** (centre) From p. 622 *Inquiry Into Life 9th ed.* ©

2000, 1997 by McGraw-Hill Companies, Inc.; **491** (bottom right), Dave B. Fleetham/Visual Unlimited Inc.; **492** (top right), Kjell B. Sandved/Visuals Unlimited; **492** (centre right), From p. 728 *Biology: The Dynamics of Life* © 2000 by McGraw-Hill Companies, Inc.; **492** (bottom left), © Michael Abbey/Photo Researchers Inc.; **493** (centre), From p. 748 *Biology: The Dynamics of Life* © 1998 by McGraw-Hill Companies, Inc.; **495** (top), From pp. 698–699. *Biology: The Dynamics of Life* © 1998 by McGraw-Hill Companies, Inc.; **496** (centre left), © Digital Stock #CB045529; **496** (centre right), From p. 619 *Inquiry Into Life 9ᵗʰ ed.* © 2000, 1997 by McGraw-Hill Companies, Inc.; **497** (bottom right), From p. 700 *Biology: The Dynamics of Life* © 1998 by McGraw-Hill Companies, Inc.; **497** (centre), From pp. 704–705. *Biology: The Dynamics of Life* © 1998 by McGraw-Hill Companies, Inc.; **498** (top left), From p. 628 *Inquiry Into Life 9ᵗʰ ed.* © 2000, 1997 by McGraw-Hill Companies, Inc.; **498** (top right), Milton Rand/Tom Stack & Associates; **499** (top left), Corel Corporation #427027; #427061; **499** (centre left), Mike Severns/Tom Stack & Associates; **499** (bottom right), From p. 630 *Inquiry Into Life 9ᵗʰ ed.* © 2000, 1997 by the McGraw-Hill Companies, Inc.; **500** (bottom right), From *Biology: The Dynamics of Life*: Laboratory Manual © 2000 by McGraw-Hill Companies, Inc.; **501** (top left), © Bill Beatty/Visuals Unlimited; **502** (centre left), © Digital Stock # CB036231; **502** (centre right), Corel Corporation #141062; **502** (bottom left), Herman H. Giethoorn/Valan Photos; **502** (bottom right), John Mitchell/Valan Photos; **502** (top right), USDA/ Science Source/Photo Researchers Inc.; **503** (centre left), Corel Corporation #452001; **503** (centre right), © Digital Stock #UST052; **503** (bottom left), © Digital Stock #CB021679; **503** (bottom right), Frederick Schussler/Weststock; **503** (top right), From p. 790 *Biology: The Dynamics of Life* © 2000 by McGraw-Hill Companies, Inc.; **504** (centre left, centre), Corel Corporation #210067; #484089; **504** (centre right, bottom left, bottom right), © Digital Stock © 1996 Animals and Wildlife #AW080; #AW069; #AW027; **505** (centre left), © Digital Stock #CB043283; **505** (centre left), John D. Cunningham/Visuals Unlimited Inc.; **505** (top right), From p. 793 *Biology: The Dynamics of Life* © 1998 by McGraw-Hill Companies, Inc.; **506** (centre), Tom Stack/Tom Stack & Associates; **506** (top centre), Tom McHugh/Photo Researchers Inc.; **508** (top), Adapted from p. 647 Figure 31.3 *Inquiry Into Life 9ᵗʰ ed.* © 2000, 1997 by McGraw-Hill Companies, Inc.; **511** (top right), Adapted from p. 578 Figure 21.5 *Biology: The Dynamics of Life* © 2000 by McGraw-Hill Companies, Inc.; **516** (bottom left), From p. 470 Lab 17.2 *Biology: The Dynamics of Life* © 2000 by McGraw-Hill Companies, Inc.; **517** (centre right), © James Richardson/Visuals Unlimited, Inc.; **518** (bottom left), Artbase, Inc.; **519** (background), © James H. Robinson/Earth Scenes; **520** (bottom right), © Dale Jackson/Visuals Unlimited, Inc.; **521** (background), © Stephen J. Krasemann/Photo Researchers, Inc.; **522** (top right), © Andrew J. Martinez/Photo Researchers, Inc.; **523** (top left), Fotopic International/Weststock; **523** (centre left), © J. W. Richardson/Visuals Unlimited, Inc.; **523** (centre left), © Robert & Linda Mitchell Photography; **524** (top left), Ron Mellott/Weststock; **524** (centre left), From p. 578 *Biology: The Dynamics of Life* © 2000 by McGraw-Hill Companies, Inc.; **525** (bottom), From p. 641 *Biology: The Dynamics of Life* © 2000 by McGraw-Hill Companies, Inc.; **525** (centre right), © Bill Kamin/Visuals Unlimited, Inc.; **526** (centre left), © 2001 Sue Sarkis/PhotoDisc #AB001446; **526** (centre), © Jeff Daly/Visuals Unlimited, Inc.; **527** (centre left), Trillium: © Wayne Lankinen/Valan Photos; **527** (centre left), Wild rose: © Clara Parsons/Valan Photos; **527** (centre), Pasque flower: ©1997 Jana R. Jirak/Visuals Unlimited, Inc.; **527** (centre), Violet: © John Mitchell/Valan Photos; **527** (centre right), Dogwood: © Mildred McPhee/Valan Photos; **527** (centre right), Lily: Halle Flygare/Valan Photos; **527** (bottom left), Flag: © John Fowler/Valan Photos; **527** (bottom left), Pitcher: © Jim Merli/Valan Photos; **527** (bottom centre), Slipper: Steve Solum/Weststock; **527** (bottom centre), Saxifrage: © Hugh Rose/Visuals Unlimited, Inc.; **527** (bottom centre), Fireweed: Larry Hobbs/Weststock; **527** (bottom right), Avens: © Wayne Lankinen/Valan Photos; **527** (bottom right), Mayflower: © Michel Bourque/Valan Photos; **528** (top left, top centre), Corel Corporation #802023; #28027; **528** (top right), © 2001 James Gritz/PhotoDisc #AG001549; **529** (top left), © Rob Simpson/Visuals Unlimited, Inc.; **529** (top right), © Digital Vision #342097-1; **529** (centre left), "Saw Whet Owl" by Robert Bateman, © Robert Bateman. By arrangement with Mill Pond Press, Inc. Venice, Fl. 34292. For information on the limited editions prints by Robert Bateman contact Mill Pond Press 1-800-535-0331.; **530** (centre right), © Digital Stock Four Seasons Vol. 101; **531** (top right), Photo by Caulfield; **532** (centre left), From p. 629 *Biology: The Dynamics of Life* © 1998 by McGraw-Hill Companies, Inc.; **532** (bottom right), From p. 630, *Biology: The Dynamics of Life* © 1998 by McGraw-Hill Companies, Inc.; **535** (top right), Steve Alden/Weststock; **535** (bottom left), ©1999 Paul A. Grecian/ Visuals Unlimited, Inc.; **536** (bottom left), Ron Mellott/Weststock; **536** (top right), © Alfred Pasieka/Science Photo Library/Photo Researchers, Inc.; **537** (top right), © Ken Wagner/Visuals Unlimited, Inc.; **538** (top right), © Steve McCutcheon/Visuals Unlimited, Inc.; **539** (top right), © John D. Cunningham/Visuals Unlimited, Inc.; **540** (top left), From p. 638 *Biology: The Dynamics of Life* © 1998 by McGraw-Hill Companies, Inc.; **540** (top right), © 2001 Bruce Heinemann/PhotoDisc #NA003086; **541** (bottom), From p. 164 *Inquiry Into Life 9ᵗʰ ed.* © 2000, 1997 by the McGraw-Hill Companies, Inc.; **541** (bottom left), © Dale Jackson/Visuals Unlimited, Inc.; **543** (bottom left), © Kenneth Murray/Photo Researchers, Inc.; **543** (top left), © Michael P. Gadomski/Photo Researchers, Inc.; **543** (top left), © Jack M. Bostrack/Visuals Unlimited, Inc.; **544** (bottom right), © John D. Cunningham/Visuals Unlimited, Inc.; **545** (bottom left), © Alfred Pasieka/Peter Arnold, Inc.; **545** (bottom right), © Andrew Syred/Science Photo Library/Photo Researchers, Inc.; **548** (top left), Courtesy Dr. Julia Levy; **550** (top right), Question and chart from p. 639, *Biology: The Dynamics of Life* © 2000 by McGraw-Hill Companies, Inc.; **550** (bottom left), Question and chart adapted from p. 651 *Biology: The Dynamics of Life* © 2000 by McGraw-Hill Companies, Inc.; **550** (bottom right), Photo by Caulfield; **552** (bottom right), © Digital Stock Business and Agriculture Vol. 102; **553** (background), © Walt Anderson/Visuals Unlimited, Inc.; **554** (top right), © Walter H. Hodge/Peter Arnold, Inc.; **554** (centre right), Artbase, Inc.; **555** (top left), © David Sieren/Visuals Unlimited, Inc.; **555** (top centre), © Cabisco/Visuals Unlimited, Inc.; **555** (top right), © Ed Reschke/Peter Arnold, Inc.; **555** (bottom), From p. 631 *Biology: The Dynamics of Life* © 2000 by McGraw-Hill Companies, Inc.; **560** (top left),

© Wally Eberhart/Visuals Unlimited, Inc.; **561** (bottom left), Tom & Pat Leeson/Weststock; **562** (top right), © Jerome Wexler/Photo Researchers, Inc.; **562** (top centre), © Nuridsany et Perennou/Photo Researchers, Inc.; **562** (centre right), © David Sieren/Visuals Unlimited, Inc.; **563** (top left), Glencoe *Biology of Life* p. 644; **564** (top right), Purple Grapes: © Dane S. Johnson/Visuals Unlimited, Inc.; **564** (top right), Orchid: © Dick Keen/Visuals Unlimited, Inc.; **564** (top right), Lily: © Dick Keen/Visuals Unlimited, Inc.; **564** (centre right), Green grapes: Corel Corporation #25021; **564** (centre right), Greenhouse: © 2001 David Buffington/PhotoDisc #AG00137; **564** (bottom right), Ripe tomato: © 2001 Skip/ PhotoDisc #AG001415; **564** (bottom right), Green Tomato: © John D. Cunningham/Visuals Unlimited, Inc.; **564** (bottom right), Apples: ©LINK/Visuals Unlimited, Inc.; **566** (top right), © Denis Roy/Valan Photos; **568** (bottom right), © Bill Beatty/Visuals Unlimited, Inc.; **568** (centre right), © Grapes. Michaud/Photo Researchers Inc; **569** (centre right), © Biophoto Associates/Science Source/Photo Researchers, Inc.; **570** (top right), Corel Corporation #750097; **571** (top left), © Harold V. Green/Valan Photos; **571** (top centre), © Ken Patterson/Valan Photos; **572** (top left), Courtesy Jean Bullard/photographer Derek Bullard; **572** (top centre, top right, top centre), Corel Corporation #476028; #476045; #84095; **573** (bottom right), ©1978 Jerome Wexler/Photo Researchers, Inc.; **574** (centre left), ©William J. Weber/Visuals Unlimited Inc.; **575** (bottom right), Corel Corporation #616072(1); **577** (centre left), Courtesy Dr. Shengwu Ma; **580** (centre right), From p. 341 *Biology: The Dynamics of Life* © 1998 by McGraw-Hill Companies, Inc.; **581** (top left), From p. 697 *Biology: Living Systems* © 1998 by McGraw-Hill Companies, Inc.; **582** (bottom left), © Digital Stock; **583** (centre), Artbase, Inc.; **584** (top right), © E. Webber/Visuals Unlimited, Inc.; **585** (top left), © E. Webber/Visuals Unlimited, Inc.; **585** (centre left), © Nigel Cattlin/Holt Studios International/Photo Researchers, Inc.; **585** (top right), © Nigel Cattlin/ Holt Studios International/Photo Researchers, Inc.; **585** (top centre), © Nigel Cattlin/Holt Studios International/Photo Researchers, Inc.; **586** (top, bottom), From pp. 57–58 *Biology: The Dynamics of Life* © 1998 by McGraw-Hill Companies, Inc.; **587** (top, bottom), From p. 55 *Biology: The Dynamics of Life* © 1998 by McGraw-Hill Companies, Inc.; **588** (centre right bottom centre) Artbase, Inc.; **590** (top left), A) © Alan & Sandy Carey/Photo Researchers, Inc.; **590** (top centre), B) © 2001 C Squared Studios/PhotoDisc #LS012474; **590** (top centre), C) Tom & Vicky Kirkendall-Spring/ Weststock; **590** (top right), D) © 2001 Izzy Schwartz/PhotoDisc #FD000339; **590** (centre left), E) © 2001 Frank Wing/ PhotoDisc #FD003709; **590** (centre), F) © Roy David Farris/Visuals Unlimited, Inc.; **590** (centre), G) © 2001 Tim Hall/ PhotoDisc #FD004924; **590** (centre right), H) © William G. Johnson/Visuals Unlimited, Inc.; **591** (centre right), Corel Corporation #539034; **592** (top right), © 1984 Guy Gillette/Photo Researchers, Inc.; **593** (top), From p. 70 *Biology: The Dynamics of Life* © 1998 by McGraw-Hill Companies, Inc.; **594** (top right), © 2001 PhotoDisc #NA005385; **594** (bottom right), © Steve Callahan/Visuals Unlimited, Inc.; **594** (centre left), © Kennon Cooke/Valan Photos; **596** (top right), © Ed Struzik/07-11-99; **597** (top left, centre left), Corel Corporation #423035; #341009; **597** (top right), © 2001 Patrick Clark/ PhotoDisc #NA007621; **597** (centre right), © William J. Weber/Visuals Unlimited, Inc.; **598** (top right), Jonothan Blair/ CORBIS/Magma; **599** (centre left), © Digital Stock; **599** (bottom centre), Ken Mantyla MBR/Associated Press AP/ Canadian Press Picture Archive; **600** (bottom left), © Digital Stock #CB007331(1); **600** (centre right), © Digital Stock Business and Agriculture, Vol. 102; **601** (bottom right), © Sylvan H. Wittwer/Visuals Unlimited, Inc.; **601** (bottom left), © Digital Stock Business and Agriculture, Vol. 102; **602** (top right), Paul A. Souders/CORBIS/Magma; **603** (centre right), © Nigel Cattlin/Holt Studios International/Photo Researchers, Inc.; **603** (bottom right), © 2001 PhotoDisc #LS004442; **604** (centre right), Carol Lee/Weststock; **605** (top right), © Digital Stock Business and Agriculture, Vol. 102; **606** (top), © Phillip Norton/Valan Photos; **607** (bottom right), © Digital Stock Business and Agriculture, Vol. 102; **608** (centre right), Corel Corporation #854026(1); **612** (bottom left), © 2001 Kim Steele/PhotoDisc #LS015133; **612** (centre right), © Digital Stock; **618** (centre left), Chuck Stoody/Canadian Press Picture Archive; **619** (bottom right), © Charles & Josette Lenars/ CORBIS/Magma; **620** (bottom left), Victor R. Caivano/Associated Press AP/Canadian Press Picture Archive; **621** (top left), © C.P. Hickman/Visuals Unlimited Inc.; **621** (centre right), Alexander Zemlianichenko/Associated Press AP/ Canadian Press Picture Archive; **621** (bottom left), Courtesy John Skeaff; **622** (centre left), © Bettman/CORBIS/Magma; **622** (top right), Dr. Jacqueline Parai; **623** (top left), Ed Andrieski/Associated Press AP/Canadian Press Picture Archive; **624** (centre right), Visuals Unlimited, Inc.; **624** (bottom right), Science VU/Visuals Unlimited Inc.; **625** (top right), From p. 139, *Sciencepower 10*, © 2000 McGraw-Hill Ryerson Ltd.; **627** (bottom), Adapted from p. 24 *Inquiry Into Life 9th ed.* © 2000, 1997 by McGraw-Hill Companies, Inc.; **627** (centre right), Adapted from p. 26, Figure 2.8 *Inquiry Into Life 9th ed.* © 2000, 1997 by McGraw-Hill Companies, Inc.; **628** (bottom), Adapted from p. 22, Figure 2. *Inquiry Into Life 9th ed.* © 2000, 1997 by McGraw-Hill Companies, Inc.; **628** (centre right), Larry Stepanowicz/Visuals Unlimited Inc.; **628** (centre right), From p. 22 *Inquiry Into Life 9th ed.* © 2000, 1997 by McGraw-Hill Companies, Inc.; 629 (centre left), From p. 22 *Inquiry Into Life 9th ed.* © 2000, 1997 by McGraw-Hill Companies, Inc.; **629** (centre right), From p. 23 *Inquiry Into Life 9th ed.* © 2000, 1997 by McGraw-Hill Companies, Inc; **631** (top), From p. SH1 *Biology: The Dynamics of Life* © 1998 by McGraw-Hill Companies, Inc.; **631** (bottom left), From p. SH5 *Biology: The Dynamics of Life* © 1998 by McGraw-Hill Companies, Inc.; **632** (centre right), From p. 591 *Sciencepower 10*, © 2000 McGraw-Hill Ryerson Ltd.; **633** (bottom left), From p. 592 *Sciencepower 10*, © 2000 McGraw-Hill Ryerson Ltd.; **636** (centre left), From p. 587 *Sciencepower 10*, © 2000 McGraw-Hill Ryerson Ltd.; **636** (centre right), From p. 576. *Sciencepower 9*, © 1999 McGraw-Hill Ryerson Ltd.; **638** (bottom), Adapted from p. 338. See additions referred to below. *Sciencepower 8*, © 1999 McGraw-Hill Ryerson Ltd.; **638** (centre right), Richard Megna/Fundamental Photos; **639** (centre left), © Digital Vision; **643** (top left), Courtesy Science Kit and Boreal Laboratory 800-828-7777; **645** (top left), From p. 243 *Inquiry Into Life 9th ed.* © 2000, 1997 by McGraw-Hill Companies, Inc.; **646** (centre), Periodic Table from *Silberberg, Chemistry 2nd edition* © 2000 by the McGraw-Hill Companies, Inc.

Illustration Credits

xii (top right) Imagineering, 8 (bottom left) Imagineering, 9 (top centre) Imagineering, 17 (top left) Imagineering, 18 Imagineering, 19 Imagineering, 22 Imagineering, 23 (top right) Imagineering, 26 (centre right) Imagineering, 33 (top right) Imagineering, 37 (top centre) Imagineering, 41 Imagineering, 57 (top centre) Imagineering, 59 (bottom centre) Imagineering, 76 (top right) From p. 51 Figure 3.3 *Inquiry Into Life 9th ed.* by Sylvia Mader ©2000, 1997 by the McGraw-Hill Companies, Inc. All rights reserved., 86 (top left) Imagineering, 88 (top left) Imagineering, 89 (bottom) Imagineering, 93 (top) Imagineering, 113 (top right) From p. 50 Figure 3.2 *Inquiry Into Life 9th ed.* by Sylvia Mader ©2000, 1997 by the McGraw-Hill Companies, Inc. All rights reserved., 128 (centre left) Imagineering, 155 (bottom) Imagineering, 164 (bottom left) Imagineering, 166 (centre right) Imagineering, 176 (top) Imagineering, 177 (top left) From page 214, Figure 8-18 *Biology: Living Systems* by R.F Oram. Glencoe/McGraw-Hill, ©1998 by McGraw-Hill Companies, Inc., 187 (top) Imagineering, 196 (centre right) Imagineering, 197 (centre right) Imagineering, 218 (top left) Imagineering, 220 (bottom left) Imagineering, 252 (top right) Imagineering, 253 (top left) From p. 618 *Biology: Living Systems* by R.F Oram Glencoe/McGraw-Hill, ©1998 by McGraw-Hill Companies, Inc., 254 (bottom left) Imagineering, 254 (bottom right) Imagineering, 255 (top right) Imagineering, 261 (centre) Imagineering, 265 (centre left) Imagineering, 267 (top) Imagineering, 267 (bottom left) Imagineering, 269 (top right) Imagineering, 276 (top right) Imagineering, 278 (top right) Imagineering, 279 (top right) Imagineering, 283 (centre) Imagineering, 283 (top right) Imagineering, 284 (bottom centre) Imagineering, 285 (top centre) From p. 589 *Biology: Living Systems* by R.F Oram Glencoe/McGraw-Hill, ©1998 by McGraw-Hill Companies, Inc., 286 (bottom centre) Imagineering, 289 (top left) From p. 246 Fig. 13.7 *Inquiry Into Life 9th ed.* by Sylvia Mader ©2000, 1997 by the McGraw-Hill Companies, Inc. All rights Reserved., 291 (bottom centre) Imagineering, 292 (bottom right) Imagineering, 293 (bottom left) Imagineering, 296 (bottom) Imagineering, 297 (centre right) Imagineering, 301 (top left) Imagineering, 306 (top left) Imagineering, 306 (centre) Imagineering, 310 (top left) Imagineering, 313 (top right) Imagineering, 315 (bottom) Imagineering, 321 (top left) Imagineering, 322 (top left) Imagineering, 322 (centre right) Imagineering, 323 (top) Imagineering, 324 (bottom) Imagineering, 325 (top left) Imagineering, 329 (top) Imagineering, 334 (bottom left) Brett Clayton, 334 (bottom right) Brett Clayton, 335 (top left) Brett Clayton, 335 (top left) Brett Clayton, 335 (top right) Brett Clayton, 339 (centre right) Brett Clayton, 341 (bottom right) Brett Clayton, 343 (top right) Brett Clayton, 345 (centre left) Imagineering, 347 (top) Brett Clayton, 347 (centre right) Brett Clayton, 348 (centre right) Imagineering, 355 (centre right) Imagineering, 388 (centre) Imagineering, 394 (bottom left) Imagineering, 398 (bottom right) Imagineering, 404 (bottom) Imagineering, 410 (top right) Imagineering, 410 (top right) Imagineering, 411 (centre right) Imagineering, 427 (bottom) Imagineering, 433 (background) Imagineering, 435 (bottom) Imagineering, 436 (bottom) Imagineering, 441 (bottom) Imagineering, 447 (centre left) Imagineering, 449 (bottom left) Imagineering, 457 (bottom left) Imagineering, 465 (top) Imagineering, 465 (bottom right) Imagineering, 512 (centre left) Deborah Crowle, 515 (centre right) Deborah Crowle, 516 (top left) Deborah Crowle, 523 (bottom left) Imagineering, 523 (bottom centre) Imagineering, 523 (bottom centre) Imagineering, 523 (bottom right) Imagineering, 524 (top right) Imagineering, 528 (bottom right) Imagineering, 531 (bottom right) Imagineering, 533 (top right) Imagineering, 534 (top) Imagineering, 537 (top left) Imagineering, 542 (top left) Imagineering, 542 (bottom) Imagineering, 543 (right) Imagineering, 544 (top) Imagineering, 547 (centre) Imagineering, 549 (centre right), Imagineering 556 (top left), Imagineering 559 (bottom right) Imagineering, 566 (bottom right) Imagineering, 567 (bottom) Imagineering, 572 (bottom) Imagineering, 576 (bottom left), 576 (bottom centre) Imagineering, 576 (bottom right) Imagineering, 589 (bottom) Imagineering, 593 (centre) Imagineering, 602 (top left) Imagineering, 637 (centre left) Jun Park, 640 (top right) Bart Vallecoccia, 640 (bottom right) Bart Vallecoccia, 640 (centre right) Bart Vallecoccia, 641 (centre left) Bart Vallecoccia, 642 (top left) Bart Vallecoccia, 642 (centre left) Bart Vallecoccia, 644 (top left) Bart Vallecoccia, 644 (bottom right) Bart Vallecoccia

Answers to Practice Problems

Student Textbook p. 128

1. $\frac{1}{2}$; probability = desired outcome divided by total possible outcomes.

2. $1/6 \times 1/6 = 1/36$

3. 2 boys and 2 girls: 1/5; all girls: 1/5; 3 boys: 2/5

4. $\frac{1}{4}$

Student Textbook p. 130

1. All offspring are heterozygous and round.

2. (a) $\frac{1}{2}$ red, $\frac{1}{2}$ yellow

   (b) Rr × Rr: RR, Rr, rr
   Rr × rr: Rr, rr
   rr × rr: rr

   (c) Rr × Rr: red and yellow
   Rr × rr: red and yellow
   rr × rr: yellow

3. Hh and hornless

Student Textbook p. 140

1. Let: W represent curly hair
   w represent straight hair
   F represent tongue curler
   f represent tongue non-curler

For the following possible cross:
WwFf × Wwff

Female

		Wf	wf
	WF	WWFf	WwFf
Male	Wf	WWff	Wwff
	wF	wWFf	wwFf
	wf	wWff	wwff

Genotypes:
WWFf:1/8; WWff:1/8; WwFf:1/4; Wwff:1/4; wwFf:1/8; wwff:1/8

Phenotypes:
curly hair, tongue rollers: 3/8; curly hair, tongue non-rollers: 3/8; straight hair, tongue rollers: 1/8; straight hair, tongue non-rollers: 1/8

Solutions to Sample Problems

Student Textbook p. 144

1. Yes, if both parents are heterozygous ($I^A i$ or $I^B i$) for their blood type.

2. If the man is homozygous for his blood type, the expected blood types among the children are AB and B. However, if the man is heterozygous for his blood type, then the expected blood types among the children are AB, A, and B.

3. No, because a cross of heterozygotes (Pp × Pp) will always produce one silver and one lethal phenotype.

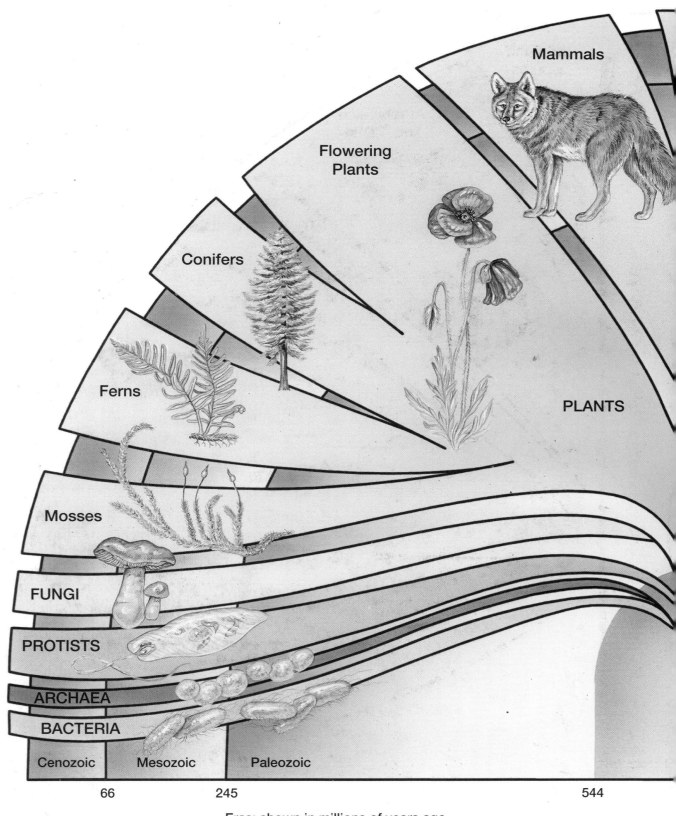

Mammals

Flowering
Plants

Conifers

Ferns

PLANTS

Mosses

FUNGI

PROTISTS

ARCHAEA

BACTERIA

Cenozoic	Mesozoic	Paleozoic	

66   245   544

Eras: shown in millions of years ago